Lectures on Ordinary Differential Equations

EINAR HILLE

Professor Emeritus
Yale University

ADDISON-WESLEY PUBLISHING COMPANY

Reading, Massachusetts · Menlo Park, California · London · Don Mills, Ontario

 Library of Congress Catalog Card No. 69-14427.

HELGE von KOCH

In memoriam

PREFACE

On revient toujours à son premier amour

When starting to study at the University of Stockholm in 1911, I was torn between concentrating in organic chemistry and mathematics. Lack of manual skill proved a handicap in the former field and teachers like Bendixson, Fredholm, von Koch, and Marcel Riesz tipped the balance in favor of mathematics. Helge von Koch's elegant lectures on ordinary differential equations in the complex domain created my interest in this field. I wrote my dissertation on such a topic, my early work at Harvard and Princeton was devoted to differential equations, and I have often returned to the field in later years.

The word "lectures" in the title of this book is not a misnomer, for practically all the topics treated in it have figured in lectures given over a period of forty-five years at Harvard, Princeton, Yale, Mainz, Uppsala, Tata Institute in Bombay, University of California, Irvine (U.C.I.), the Australian National University (A.N.U.), the University of Oregon, and the University of New Mexico.

Friends and students have often suggested that my lectures be published. This became feasible in 1964 because of the generosity of the Office of Scientific Research of the United States Air Force through its book-writing grant AFOSR 776–65. The work was started at A.N.U., Canberra, in January, 1965, was continued at Stanford and U.C.I., and finally finished at A.N.U. almost two and a half years later. Both U.C.I. and A.N.U. gave generous financial and practical help, and in 1966, at U.C.I., the National Science Foundation gave added support.

The present treatise is not a compendium on the theory of ordinary differential equations. Many important topics have been omitted: topics outside my range of interest or knowledge, topics that have recently been treated adequately elsewhere—more adequately than I could ever hope to do were I to try. Among the most noteworthy omissions are the Poincaré-Bendixson theory of characteristics and the Lyapunov stability theory of which at least the latter is now very much in the center of attention.

After this admission, let me mention some aspects of the theory which are stressed. In Chapter 1, attention is focused on fixed point theorems, functional inequalities, and their interrelations. These notions occur again and again in later chapters, and form the basis for existence and uniqueness theorems, for variation of solutions with equation and initial conditions, and for the *a priori* estimates for approach to a singular point.

Chapters 6, 7, 11, and 12 and all four Appendixes are concerned with differential equations in the complex domain and, even in the treatment of boundary value problems, complex variable methods play a basic role. On the other hand, there is no sharp division between real and complex variables, and much attention is devoted to extending classical results to equations where the dependent variable takes values in a Banach algebra or, more specially, in a star algebra. Chapter 4 gives the necessary functional analytical background for such extensions.

The book is divided into three parts: Part I gives the general theory, Part II is devoted to linear second order equations, and the brief Part III deals with some non-linear problems in the complex domain.

The prospective reader should have had an introductory course in differential equations as well as a good grounding in linear algebra and real and complex analysis.

The author gratefully acknowledges much and generous help from many colleagues. H. Komatsu and G. Latta at Stanford read part of the manuscript and made helpful suggestions. Many seeming paradoxes were ironed out in discussion with G. K. Kalisch at U.C.I. The early part of the manuscript was read critically by J. B. Miller while he was still at A.N.U., and during my second stay at A.N.U. comments, references, and suggestions were received from W. A. Coppel, whose help was most valuable. Fred Brauer, University of Wisconsin, who acted as referee, carefully read the whole manuscript, and his many suggestions have added much to the value of the book. J. E. N. Lilleyman of A.N.U. prepared the original sketches for the figures. At the University of Oregon, the running comments of R. M. Koch, F. Lowenthal and W. E. Pfaffenberger removed many errors and led to a clarification of my ideas. To them all I express my heartfelt thanks.

Finally I wish to thank the staff of Addison-Wesley Publishing Company for the thoughtful care devoted to presenting the book to the reader in the most attractive and efficient form.

EINAR HILLE

Albuquerque, N.M.
August, 1968

CONTENTS

Part I GENERAL THEORY

Chapter 1 Preliminaries

1.1 Vector spaces . . . 3
1.2 Metric spaces . . . 4
1.3 Mappings . . . 6
1.4 Fixed point theorems . . . 10
1.5 Functional inequalities . . . 15
1.6 Compactness . . . 20

Chapter 2 Existence and Uniqueness Theorems

2.1 Ordinary differential equations . . . 25
2.2 The fixed point method . . . 27
2.3 The method of successive approximations . . . 32
2.4 The Cauchy-Lipschitz-Peano method . . . 42
2.5 The Cauchy-Lindelöf method . . . 48
2.6 Other uniqueness theorems . . . 58

Appendix A Some Differential Equations of Function-Theoretical Significance

A.1 The circular functions . . . 63
A.2 The Jacobi elliptic functions . . . 66

Chapter 3 Variation of Data

3.1 Variation of the initial vector . . . 76
3.2 Variation of the initial point . . . 81
3.3 Variation of the equation . . . 85
3.4 Dependence on parameters . . . 90

Chapter 4 Abstract Spaces

4.1 Some concepts of functional analysis . . . 99
4.2 Banach algebras . . . 105
4.3 The resolvent . . . 112
4.4 Gelfand's representation theorem . . . 119
4.5 Operational calculus . . . 125
4.6 The commutator operator . . . 129

Chapter 5 Linear Differential Equations with Almost Constant Coefficients

5.1 Constant coefficients . . . 139
5.2 The matrix case . . . 147
5.3 Infinite matrices . . . 157
5.4 Asymptotically constant coefficients . . . 164

Appendix B Linear Differential Equations in the Complex Domain

B.1 Existence and independence . . . 176
B.2 Regular singular points . . . 182
B.3 The method of H. Kneser . . . 192
B.4 Irregular singular points . . . 198

Chapter 6 Linear Differential Equations in Banach Algebras

6.1 Fundamental solutions . . . 210
6.2 Analytic continuation. The monodromy group . . . 217
6.3 Approach to a singular point . . . 223
6.4 The integrable case . . . 226
6.5 Regular singular points . . . 229
6.6 The method of Frobenius . . . 234
6.7 The Fuchsian class . . . 239
6.8 Irregular singular points, $p = 1$ . . . 250
6.9 Irregular singular points, $p > 1$ . . . 257

Appendix C Riccati's Equation

C.1 The classical Riccati equation . . . 273
C.2 Second order linear matrix equations . . . 278
C.3 Matrix Riccati equations . . . 283

Part II LINEAR SECOND ORDER DIFFERENTIAL EQUATIONS

Chapter 7 Special Linear Second Order Differential Equations

7.1 The hypergeometric equation . . . 291
7.2 Legendre's equation . . . 307
7.3 Bessel's equation . . . 319
7.4 Asymptotic integration . . . 330
7.5 On the confluent hypergeometric equation . . . 344
7.6 Mathieu's equation . . . 358

Chapter 8 Sturm-Liouville Theory

8.1 Oscillation theory . . . 373
8.2 Regular boundary value problems . . . 384
8.3 Prüfer's method . . . 394
8.4 Another variant of Prüfer's method . . . 402
8.5 Expansion problems . . . 407

Chapter 9 Solutions on the Real Line

9.1 Almost uniform motion 428
9.2 Growth properties 437
9.3 Spiral motion 447
9.4 Non-oscillation and the Riccati equation 456
9.5 The oscillatory case 472
9.6 Abstract oscillation theory 479

Chapter 10 Singular Boundary Value Problems

10.1 Limit-circle or limit-point? 494
10.2 The $m(\lambda)$ functions 505
10.3 On the nature of the spectrum 518
10.4 Unitary transformations 532
10.5 Representation theorems 540
10.6 The resolvent 556
10.7 Remarks on generalizations. 565

Chapter 11 Complex Oscillation Theory

11.1 Oscillatory behavior 576
11.2 Some comparison theorems 587
11.3 Use of the Green's transform 598
11.4 Applications to special equations 609
11.5 Asymptotic integration and the indicatrices 624
11.6 Variation of parameters 638

Part III NON-LINEAR EQUATIONS

Appendix D The Schwarzian

D.1 The Schwarzian derivative 647
D.2 Applications to conformal mapping 650
D.3 The Schwarzian and univalence 654
D.4 Univalent solutions of $y'' + Py = 0$ 659

Chapter 12 Non-linear Differential Equations in the Complex Domain

12.1 Equations of the first order and the first degree 662
12.2 Binomial equations 675
12.3 The equations of Briot and Bouquet 684
12.4 The transcendents of Painlevé 693

Bibliography 711

Index 715

PART I

General Theory

1 PRELIMINARIES

This introductory chapter contains a medley of notions that will be used extensively in the following chapters. There are six sections: Vector Spaces; Metric Spaces; Mappings; Fixed Point Theorems; Functional Inequalities; Compactness.

1.1 VECTOR SPACES

In mathematical analysis a set $\mathfrak{X}$ of elements $\mathbf{x}, \mathbf{y}, \ldots$ is often called an *abstract space*. The elements are then referred to as *points*. To be of interest to the analyst it is desirable that the space should have some *structure*, algebraic or geometric, or both. We say that the space has an algebraic structure if one or more algebraic operations can be performed on the elements, or if the notion of order is meaningful.

The set $\mathfrak{X}$ is a *linear vector space* if the operations of *addition* and *scalar multiplication* can be performed. We demand that the set be an Abelian group under addition, that is $\mathbf{x} + \mathbf{y}$ is defined as an element of $\mathfrak{X}$, addition is commutative and associative, there is a unique *neutral element* $\mathbf{0}$ such that $\mathbf{x} + \mathbf{0} = \mathbf{x}$ for all $\mathbf{x}$ and every $\mathbf{x}$ has a unique *negative*, $-\mathbf{x}$ with $\mathbf{x} + (-\mathbf{x}) = \mathbf{0}$.

Scalar multiplication presupposes a field of scalars which is almost always taken to be the real field R or the complex field C. For any scalar α and any element $\mathbf{x}$ there is a unique element $\alpha\mathbf{x}$; scalar multiplication is distributive, with respect to addition, and associative and $1 \cdot \mathbf{x} = \mathbf{x}$, where "1" is the unit element of the scalars.

We speak of a *real* or a *complex vector space* according as the field is R or C. The elements $\mathbf{x}$ are referred to as *vectors* in this connection. This is an obvious extension of customary terminology in the plane and in three space which form the simplest examples of linear vector spaces. We add: a linear vector space which also contains the product of any two elements is called an *algebra*.

Let $\mathbf{x}_j \in \mathfrak{X}, j = 1, 2, \ldots, n$, be n vectors in $\mathfrak{X}$ and let the underlying scalar field be denoted by F. We say that they are *linearly independent* over F, if

$$\alpha_1\mathbf{x}_1 + \alpha_2\mathbf{x}_2 + \cdots + \alpha_n\mathbf{x}_n = \mathbf{0}, \quad \alpha_j \in F \tag{1.1.1}$$

implies $\alpha_1 = \alpha_2 = \cdots = \alpha_n = 0$. They are *linearly dependent* if α's can be found satisfying this relation with $|\alpha_1| + |\alpha_2| + \cdots + |a_n| > 0$. The space

$\mathfrak{X}$ is said to be of *dimension n*, if n linearly independent vectors can be found in $\mathfrak{X}$ but any set of $n + 1$ vectors is linearly dependent. The space is of infinite dimension if n linearly independent vectors can be found for any n.

Another type of algebraic structure is implied by a *partial ordering* of $\mathfrak{X}$. We say that $\mathfrak{X}$ is *partially ordered* if for some pairs of elements $\mathbf{x}$, $\mathbf{y}$ there is an ordering relation $\mathbf{x} < \mathbf{y}$ (equivalently $\mathbf{y} > \mathbf{x}$) which is *reflexive*, *proper*, and *transitive*. The simplest case and the only one of importance for us, is that in which the space is linear as well as partially ordered. Here it is postulated that

$$\mathbf{x} < \mathbf{y} \quad \text{implies} \quad \mathbf{x} + \mathbf{a} < \mathbf{y} + \mathbf{a}, \qquad \alpha\mathbf{x} < \alpha\mathbf{y} \quad (\alpha > 0). \tag{1.1.2}$$

In this case the space has a *positive cone* $\mathfrak{X}^+$ consisting of all elements such that $\mathbf{0} < \mathbf{x}$. The positive cone contains $\mathbf{0}$ and is invariant under addition and multiplication by positive scalars.

EXERCISE 1.1

1. Verify that the polynomials of degree $\leq n$ in a variable t form a linear vector space. Is it an algebra?
2. Prove that $1, t, t^2, \ldots, t^n$ are linearly independent. What is the dimension of the space?

1.2 METRIC SPACES

The analyst works with limits and limiting processes and from his point of view an abstract space having a geometric structure in which such concepts become meaningful is to be preferred. A *metric space* has the desirable properties. A metric space is one in which a *distance* is defined with the following properties:

D1. *For any two points P and Q of $\mathfrak{X}$ a number $d(P, Q) \geq 0$ is defined, called the distance from P to Q, and $d(P, Q) = 0$ iff $P = Q$.*

D2. $d(P, Q) = d(Q, P)$.

D3. $d(P, Q) \leq d(P, R) + d(R, Q)$ (*the triangle axiom*).

As an example of a metric space we can take R^n or C^n with the Euclidean distance

$$d(\mathbf{x}, \mathbf{y}) = \|\mathbf{x} - \mathbf{y}\| = \left\{\sum_{j=1}^{n} |x_j - y_j|^2\right\}^{1/2}. \tag{1.2.1}$$

This is also an example of a *normed linear vector space*. In such a space we say that a *norm* is defined if the following conditions hold:

N_1. *For every $\mathbf{x} \in \mathfrak{X}$ there is a number $\|\mathbf{x}\| \geq 0$ with "=" iff $\mathbf{x} = \mathbf{0}$.*

N_2. $\|\alpha \mathbf{x}\| = |\alpha| \, \|\mathbf{x}\|, \forall \mathbf{x} \in \mathfrak{X}, \forall \alpha \in F \; (C \text{ or } R)$.

N_3. $\|\mathbf{x} + \mathbf{y}\| \leq \|\mathbf{x}\| + \|\mathbf{y}\|$.

We then define

$$d(\mathbf{x}, \mathbf{y}) = \|\mathbf{x} - \mathbf{y}\|. \tag{1.2.2}$$

As another example we may take the space $C[a, b]$ of functions $f(t)$ continuous in $[a, b]$. The expression

$$\sup_t |f(t)| = \|f\| \tag{1.2.3}$$

is known as the *sup norm* of f. It obviously satisfies N_1 to N_3.

Once a distance has been defined in a space, the concepts of real analysis can be carried over. *A sequence of points $\{P_n\} \subset \mathfrak{X}$ converges to a point $P_0 \in \mathfrak{X}$ if*

$$\lim_{n \to \infty} d(P_n, P_0) = 0. \tag{1.2.4}$$

Cauchy's convergence principle gives a necessary condition for this to hold: For any given $\varepsilon > 0$ there is an N such that

$$d(P_m, P_n) < \varepsilon \qquad \text{if } m, n > N. \tag{1.2.5}$$

If this is true, $\{P_n\}$ is called a *Cauchy sequence.* The condition is only necessary and not sufficient. A metric space $\mathfrak{X}$ is said to be *complete,* if every Cauchy sequence converges to an element of the space.

We recall briefly some classical concepts which extend to complete metric spaces. A point $P_0 \in \mathfrak{X}$ is a *cluster point* of a set S of points in $\mathfrak{X}$, if there exists a sequence $\{P_n\} \subset S$ such that $\lim_{n\to\infty} d(P_n, P_0) = 0$. In general the Bolzano-Weierstrass theorem is not valid, i.e. a bounded infinite set need not have a cluster point. The union of a set S with its cluster points is called the *closure* of S and written $\bar{S}$. A set S is *dense* in $\mathfrak{X}$ if $\bar{S} = \mathfrak{X}$. The set $[P \mid d(P, P_0) < \varepsilon]$ is an *ε-neighborhood* of P_0. It is also an *open sphere* with center at P_0 and radius ε. A set S in $\mathfrak{X}$ is *open,* if $P_0 \in S$ implies that some ε-neighborhood of P_0 is also in S.

Finally, the *topological diameter* $d(S)$ of S is the least upper bound of the distances $\{d(P, Q) \mid P \in S, Q \in S\}$.

EXERCISE 1.2

1. Show that $\|\mathbf{x}\|_1 = \sum_1^n |x_j|$ and $\|\mathbf{x}\|_s = \sup_j |x_j|$ are admissible norms in C^n. If the Euclidean norm of $\mathbf{x}$ is unity, between what limits can the other norms vary?
2. Show that if a set S in C^n is open in terms of one of the three norms, it is open with respect to the other norms.

3. Verify that C^n is complete with respect to anyone of the three normed metrics defined above.
4. What does it mean that $\{f_n\}$ is a Cauchy sequence in $C[0, 1]$ under the sup norm? Prove that the space is complete.
5. The space (l) or l_1 is defined as the set of all sequences $\{\alpha_j\}$ such that $\sum_1^\infty |\alpha_j| = \|\{\alpha_j\}\| < \infty$. Prove the space is complete.

1.3 MAPPINGS

We shall be concerned with mappings of a metric space $\mathfrak{X}$ into a metric space $\mathfrak{Y}$ where often $\mathfrak{Y} = \mathfrak{X}$.

To every $x \in \mathfrak{X}$ corresponds a unique $y \in \mathfrak{Y}$, the *image* of x under T. We write

$$y = T[x]. \tag{1.3.1}$$

The mapping is said to be *bounded* if there is a finite M such that

$$d[T(x_1), T(x_2)] \leq Md(x_1, x_2). \tag{1.3.2}$$

Note that d stands merely for distance and may mean one thing on one side of the inequality and something else on the other if $\mathfrak{Y} \neq \mathfrak{X}$.

A bounded transformation is necessarily *continuous* since (1.3.2) is simply a general type of a *Lipschitz condition.*

A mapping is *onto* if every point of $\mathfrak{Y}$ is the image of at least one point of $\mathfrak{X}$. It is (1, 1) (read one-to-one) if

$$x_1 \neq x_2 \qquad \text{implies} \qquad T(x_1) \neq T(x_2). \tag{1.3.3}$$

If $\mathfrak{X}$ and $\mathfrak{Y}$ are linear spaces over the same field and if

$$T(\alpha_1 x_1 + \alpha_2 x_2) = \alpha_1 T(x_1) + \alpha_2 T(x_2), \tag{1.3.4}$$

then T is called a *linear transformation*. It is bounded iff

$$d[T(x), 0] \leq Md(x, 0).$$

If $\mathfrak{X}$ and $\mathfrak{Y}$ are normed linear spaces this takes the form

$$\|T[x]\| \leq M\|x\|. \tag{1.3.5}$$

If T is a linear transformation, then $T(0) = 0$ and the transformation is (1, 1) iff

$$T(x) = 0 \qquad \text{implies} \qquad x = 0.$$

If $\mathfrak{X}$ and $\mathfrak{Y}$ are both normed linear vector spaces, then the set $\mathfrak{E}(\mathfrak{X}, \mathfrak{Y})$ of all linear bounded transformations of $\mathfrak{X}$ into $\mathfrak{Y}$ is also a normed linear vector space under suitable definitions of the algebraic operations and of the norm. We define

$$(T_1 + T_2)[x] = T_1[x] + T_2[x], \qquad (\alpha T)[x] = \alpha T[x], \tag{1.3.6}$$

$$\|T\| = \sup_{\|x\|=1} \|T[x]\|. \tag{1.3.7}$$

If $\mathfrak{Y} = \mathfrak{X}$ we write $\mathfrak{E}(\mathfrak{X}, \mathfrak{X}) = \mathfrak{E}(\mathfrak{X})$ and note that products can also be defined by setting

$$(T_1T_2)[x] = T_1[T_2[x]]. \tag{1.3.8}$$

This gives

$$\|T_1T_2\| \le \|T_1\|\,\|T_2\|. \tag{1.3.9}$$

This relation makes $\mathfrak{E}(\mathfrak{X})$ into a normed algebra. If $T \in \mathfrak{E}(\mathfrak{X})$ and is (1, 1) there is an *inverse transformation* T^{-1} such that

$$T^{-1}[T[x]] = x, \qquad \forall x, \qquad T[T^{-1}[y]] = y \qquad \text{if } y = T[x]. \tag{1.3.10}$$

The rest of this section will be devoted to the very special case $\mathfrak{X} = \mathfrak{Y} = C^n$ and the prototype of all linear mappings. The elements of C^n are the vectors or ordered n tuples

$$\mathbf{x} = (x_1, x_2, \ldots, x_n), \tag{1.3.11}$$

where the x_j's are complex numbers. Let us introduce the n unit vectors

$$\mathbf{e}_j = (\delta_{jk}), \qquad j = 1, 2, \ldots, n,$$

where δ_{jk} is the Kronecker delta, that is, 1 if $k = j$, otherwise 0. We have then the unique representation

$$\mathbf{x} = x_1\mathbf{e}_1 + x_2\mathbf{e}_2 + \cdots + x_n\mathbf{e}_n. \tag{1.3.12}$$

We say that the $\mathbf{e}_j$'s form a *basis* of C^n.

Suppose now that T is a linear transformation of C^n into C^n. There will then exist n^2 complex numbers a_{jk} such that for each k

$$T[\mathbf{e}_k] = a_{1k}\mathbf{e}_1 + a_{2k}\mathbf{e}_2 + \cdots + a_{nk}\mathbf{e}_n. \tag{1.3.13}$$

This simply says that $T[\mathbf{e}_k]$ is a vector in C^n and as such is expressed linearly and uniquely in terms of the basis vectors. By the linearity T is uniquely determined by its action on the unit vectors. Hence

$$T[\mathbf{x}] = T\left[\sum_{k=1}^{n} x_k\mathbf{e}_k\right] = \sum_{k=1}^{n} x_k T[\mathbf{e}_k]$$

or

$$T[\mathbf{x}] = \sum_{j=1}^{n}\left(\sum_{k=1}^{n} a_{jk}x_k\right)\mathbf{e}_j \equiv \mathbf{y} \tag{1.3.14}$$

so that the components of $\mathbf{y}$ are

$$\sum_{k=1}^{n} a_{jk}x_k \equiv y_j, \qquad j = 1, 2, \ldots, n. \tag{1.3.15}$$

We write

$$\mathcal{A} = \begin{bmatrix} a_{11} & a_{12} & \cdots & a_{1n} \\ a_{21} & a_{22} & \cdots & a_{2n} \\ \cdot & \cdot & \cdot & \cdot \\ a_{n1} & a_{n2} & \cdots & a_{nn} \end{bmatrix} \tag{1.3.16}$$

or simply $\mathcal{A} = (a_{jk})$ and refer to $\mathcal{A}$ as the *matrix of the transformation T with respect to the chosen basis.* We also write

$$\mathbf{y} = T[\mathbf{x}] \equiv \mathcal{A} \cdot \mathbf{x}. \tag{1.3.17}$$

The last member is thought of as the product of the matrix $\mathcal{A}$ with the column vector $\mathbf{x}$, the result being the column vector $\mathbf{y}$.

The mapping is (1, 1) iff $T[\mathbf{x}] = \mathbf{0}$ implies $\mathbf{x} = \mathbf{0}$ or iff the homogeneous system of linear equations

$$\sum_{k=1}^{n} a_{jk}x_k = 0, \qquad j = 1, 2, \ldots, n, \tag{1.3.18}$$

has the unique solution

$$x_1 = x_2 = \cdots = x_n = 0.$$

We recall that this is the case if

$$\det(\mathcal{A}) \neq 0. \tag{1.3.19}$$

If this holds, then T is also *onto* for (1.3.15) has then for given $\mathbf{y}$ a unique solution $\mathbf{x}$. This means that T has a unique inverse T^{-1} which is an element of $\mathfrak{E}(C^n)$ since it is a linear bounded transformation defined everywhere in C^n. As such, T^{-1} has a corresponding matrix which we denote by $\mathcal{A}^{-1}$ and refer to as the *inverse* of $\mathcal{A}$. We have then

$$\mathbf{x} = T^{-1}[\mathbf{y}] = \mathcal{A}^{-1} \cdot \mathbf{y}, \forall \mathbf{y}. \tag{1.3.20}$$

We get the elements of the inverse matrix by solving the system (1.3.15) for the x_j's, say, by Cramer's rule. The element in the place (j, k) is

$$A_{kj}/\Delta \tag{1.3.21}$$

where $\Delta = \det(\mathcal{A})$ and A_{jk} is the cofactor of a_{jk} in the determinant.

Let $\mathfrak{M}_n$ be the set of all n by n matrices with complex elements. We have seen that there is a (1, 1) correspondence between matrices and linear transformations belonging to $\mathfrak{E}(C^n)$. We recall that the latter set is an algebra with operations and norm defined by (1.3.6) to (1.3.8). If to T_1 and T_2 correspond the matrices $\mathcal{A}$ and $\mathcal{B}$, respectively, then the matrices corresponding to $T_1 + T_2$, αT_1, and T_1T_2 are, respectively,

$$(a_{jk} + b_{jk}) \equiv \mathcal{A} + \mathcal{B}, \tag{1.3.22}$$

$$(\alpha a_{jk}) \equiv \alpha \mathcal{A}, \tag{1.3.23}$$

$$\left(\sum_{m=1}^{n} a_{jm} b_{mk}\right) \equiv \mathcal{A}\mathcal{B}. \tag{1.3.24}$$

These relations serve as definitions of sum, scalar product, and product for matrices. With these conventions $\mathfrak{M}_n$ becomes an algebra. We have now a so-called *isomorphism* between the two algebras $\mathfrak{M}_n$ and $\mathfrak{E}(C^n)$, i.e. a (1, 1) correspondence which is preserved under the admissible algebraic operations. The algebra $\mathfrak{E}(C^n)$ is normed by (1.3.7). It is natural that we should also introduce a norm in $\mathfrak{M}_n$. We can take the operator norm, i.e.

$$\|\mathcal{A}\|_0 = \|T\|. \tag{1.3.25}$$

In the following we shall make frequent use of the norm

$$\|\mathcal{A}\| = \max_j \sum_{k=1}^{n} |a_{jk}| \tag{1.3.26}$$

which is easier to handle.

A matrix $\mathcal{A}$ is said to be *regular* or *singular* according as det $(\mathcal{A}) \neq 0$ or $= 0$. For certain values of the complex number λ the equation

$$\mathcal{A}\mathbf{x} = \lambda \mathbf{x} \tag{1.3.27}$$

has a non-trivial solution. It is clear that this requires that $\lambda\mathcal{E} - \mathcal{A}$ is singular, $\mathcal{E}$ the unit matrix, and thus λ is a root of the equation

$$\det(\lambda\mathcal{E} - \mathcal{A}) = 0. \tag{1.3.28}$$

This is known as the *characteristic equation* of $\mathcal{A}$, the roots are called *characteristic values* or *eigen values* or *latent roots.* The corresponding solutions of (1.3.27) are known as *characteristic vectors* or *eigen vectors.*

If $\mathcal{A}$ is real and symmetric, that is $a_{jk} = a_{kj}$ real, then the roots are real and vectors corresponding to distinct roots are *orthogonal* in the sense that the *inner product* $(\mathbf{x}, \mathbf{y}) = 0$ where

$$(\mathbf{x}, \mathbf{y}) = \sum_{j=1}^{n} x_j \bar{y}_j. \tag{1.3.29}$$

For, suppose that λ were complex and $\mathbf{x}$ with $\|\mathbf{x}\| = 1$ a corresponding characteristic vector. Then

$$\lambda(\mathbf{x}, \mathbf{x}) = (\lambda\mathbf{x}, \mathbf{x}) = (\mathcal{A}\mathbf{x}, \mathbf{x}) = (\mathbf{x}, \mathcal{A}\mathbf{x}) = (\mathbf{x}, \lambda\mathbf{x}) = \bar{\lambda}(\mathbf{x}, \mathbf{x})$$

so that λ is real. Similarly, from

$$\mathcal{A}\mathbf{x} = \lambda_1\mathbf{x}, \quad \mathcal{A}\mathbf{y} = \lambda_2\mathbf{y}, \quad (\mathbf{x}, \mathbf{x}) = (\mathbf{y}, \mathbf{y}) = 1, \quad \lambda_1 \neq \lambda_2,$$

we get

$$\lambda_1(\mathbf{x}, \mathbf{y}) = (\lambda_1\mathbf{x}, \mathbf{y}) = (\mathcal{A}\mathbf{x}, \mathbf{y}) = (\mathbf{x}, \mathcal{A}\mathbf{y}) = (\mathbf{x}, \lambda_2\mathbf{y}) = \lambda_2(\mathbf{x}, \mathbf{y}) \quad \text{and } (\mathbf{x}, \mathbf{y}) = 0.$$

In the general case, suppose that the roots of (1.3.28) are $\lambda_1, \lambda_2, \ldots, \lambda_n$, not necessarily distinct. We can then find n linearly independent vectors $\mathbf{x}_1, \mathbf{x}_2, \ldots, \mathbf{x}_n$ such that

$$\mathcal{A}\mathbf{x}_j = \lambda_j\mathbf{x}_j, \qquad j = 1, 2, \ldots, n. \tag{1.3.30}$$

In C^n any $n + 1$ vectors are linearly dependent. Hence, for each $\mathbf{x} \in C^n$ there exists n uniquely determined numbers $\alpha_1, \alpha_2, \ldots, \alpha_n$ such that

$$\mathbf{x} = \alpha_1\mathbf{x}_1 + \alpha_2\mathbf{x}_2 + \cdots + \alpha_n\mathbf{x}_n. \tag{1.3.31}$$

We note that the characteristic vectors of $\mathcal{A}$ form a basis of C^n.

EXERCISE 1.3

1. For a fixed j the elements in the jth row form the components of a vector, the jth *row vector*. *Column vectors* are defined in a similar manner. Show that the matrix is singular if the row vectors (column vectors) are linearly dependent.
2. A matrix $\mathcal{U} = (a_{jk})$ with real elements is *unitary* if the row vectors form an *orthonormal system*, that is $(\mathbf{r}_j, \mathbf{r}_k) = \delta_{jk}$ with obvious notation. Prove that the column vectors also form an orthonormal system.
3. Prove that $\mathcal{U}$ is its own inverse.
4. Prove that the characteristic roots of $\mathcal{U}$ have absolute value 1.
5. Verify that $\|\mathcal{A}\mathcal{B}\| \leq \|\mathcal{A}\|\,\|\mathcal{B}\|$ if the norm is defined by (1.3.26).
6. A complex valued function of matrices satisfies the functional equation $f(\mathcal{A}\mathcal{B}) = f(\mathcal{A})f(\mathcal{B})$. Show that $\det(\mathcal{A})$ is a solution. Any others?
7. Form the matrix polynomial $\prod_{j=1}^{n} (\lambda_j\mathcal{E} - \mathcal{A}) \equiv \mathcal{H}(\mathcal{A})$ and show that $\mathcal{H}(\mathcal{A})\mathbf{x} = 0, \forall\mathbf{x}$. It follows that $\mathcal{H}(\mathcal{A}) = 0$, i.e., $\mathcal{A}$ *satisfies its own characteristic equation* (*Cayley-Hamilton theorem*).
8. Show that $\mathfrak{E}(C^n)$ and $\mathfrak{M}_n$ are complete metric spaces.

1.4 FIXED POINT THEOREMS

Let $\mathfrak{X}$ be a complete metric space, T a mapping of $\mathfrak{X}$ into $\mathfrak{X}$ which is bounded in the sense of (1.3.2). We shall often encounter such mappings and a basic problem is to decide if T leaves any point of $\mathfrak{X}$ invariant, i.e. does the equation

$$T(x) = x \tag{1.4.1}$$

have a solution, preferably a unique solution? A statement about such matters is called a *fixed point theorem*, x being the *fixed point*. We shall present two such results.

The simplest deals with so-called *contractions.* We say that T is a contraction if the constant M entering in (1.3.2) is <1. Hence there exists a k, $0 < k < 1$, such that

$$d[T(x_1), T(x_2)] \leq kd(x_1, x_2) \tag{1.4.2}$$

for all x_1 and x_2 in $\mathfrak{X}$. For such transformations we have the following fixed point theorem which goes back to the 1922 dissertation of Stefan Banach (1892–1945).

Theorem 1.4.1. *If T is a contraction on a complete metric space, then there is one and only one fixed point.*

Proof. We start with an arbitrary element x_1 in $\mathfrak{X}$ and form its successive transforms:

$$x_{n+1} = T(x_n), \qquad n = 1, 2, \ldots \tag{1.4.3}$$

It is claimed that this is a Cauchy sequence and this is proved if we show the existence of an N such that for a given $\varepsilon > 0$

$$d(x_n, x_{n+p}) < \varepsilon, \qquad n > N, p = 1, 2, \ldots$$

Here the left member does not exceed

$$d(x_n, x_{n+1}) + d(x_{n+1}, x_{n+2}) + \cdots + d(x_{n+p-1}, x_{n+p})$$

by the triangle inequality. On the other hand,

$$d(x_m, x_{m+1}) \leq kd(x_{m-1}, x_m) \leq \cdots \leq k^{m-1}d(x_1, x_2),$$

so that

$$d(x_n, x_{n+p}) \leq (k^{n-1} + k^n + \cdots + k^{n+p-1})d(x_1, x_2)$$
$$< \frac{k^{n-1}}{1-k} d(x_1, x_2).$$

The last member is clearly as small as we please for large n and all p.

Hence $\{x_n\}$ is a Cauchy sequence and since $\mathfrak{X}$ is complete

$$\lim x_n \equiv x_0$$

exists. Since

$$x_{n+1} = T(x_n)$$

we have

$$x_0 = \lim x_{n+1} = \lim T(x_n) = T(\lim x_n) = T(x_0)$$

by the continuity of T which is a consequence of the Lipschitz condition (1.4.2). Hence

$$T(x_0) = x_0 \tag{1.4.4}$$

and x_0 is a fixed point.

Suppose that z_0 is a fixed point. Then

$$d(x_0, z_0) = d[T(x_0), T(z_0)] \leq kd(x_0, z_0).$$

This is impossible since $k < 1$ unless $d(x_0, z_0) = 0$ or $z_0 = x_0$. Thus there is one and only one fixed point. ∎

Corollary. *There is a unique fixed point, if there exists some power of T, say T^m, which is a contraction.*

Proof. Since T^m is a contraction

$$\lim_{n\to\infty} (T^m)^n[x_1] \equiv x_0$$

exists for an arbitrary choice of x_1 and is independent of x_1. Here we set $x_1 = T(x_0)$ and note that $T^m(x_0) = x_0$. Hence

$$(T^m)^n[T(x_0)] = T[(T^m)^n(x_0)] = T(x_0)$$

and when $n \to \infty$ the first member tends to x_0. It follows that

$$T(x_0) = x_0$$

and T admits x_0 as a fixed point. The latter must be unique, for any fixed point of T is also a fixed point of T^m and the latter transformation has only one fixed point. ∎

As an illustration, let us consider the space $C[a, b]$ of continuous functions on the finite interval $[a, b]$ with the sup norm metric so that

$$d(f, g) = \|f - g\| = \sup_{a \le t \le b} |f(t) - g(t)|.$$

We take the transformation T which takes f into

$$T[f](t) = K\int_a^t f(s)\, ds, \qquad a \le t \le b. \tag{1.4.5}$$

Here the norm of T is $K(b - a)$, so that T is a contraction if $K(b - a) < 1$. On the other hand,

$$T^m[f](t) = \frac{K^m}{(m-1)!}\int_a^t (t - s)^{m-1} f(s)\, ds$$

and here

$$\|T^m\| = \frac{1}{m!}[K(b - a)]^m \tag{1.4.6}$$

which is as small as we please if m is large. It follows that T has a unique fixed point. Since the zero element, $f(t) \equiv 0$, is obviously invariant, this must be the fixed point.

We shall now prove a theorem which is implicit in the work of Vito Volterra (1860–1940) on linear integral equations in the 1890's.

Theorem 1.4.2. Let $\mathfrak{X}$ be a normed linear complete vector space (= B-space). Let z_0 be a given element in $\mathfrak{X}$ and let $S \in \mathfrak{E}(\mathfrak{X})$ and such that

$$\sum_{n=1}^{\infty} \|S^n\| < \infty. \tag{1.4.7}$$

Then the transformation

$$T[x] = z_0 + S[x] \tag{1.4.8}$$

has a unique fixed point.

Proof. Here we start again with an arbitrary element x_1 of $\mathfrak{X}$ and form its successive transforms under T so that

$$x_{n+1} = T[x_n], \qquad n = 1, 2, \ldots$$

Hence

$$x_n = z_0 + S[z_0] + S^2[z_0] + \cdots + S^{n-1}[z_0] + S^n[x_1]$$

and this gives

$$\|x_{n+p} - x_n\| = \|-S^n[x_1] + S^n[z_0] + S^{n+1}[z_0] + \cdots + S^{n+p-1}[z_0] + S^{n+p}[x_1]\|.$$

By assumption this does not exceed

$$2 \max (\|z_0\|, \|x_1\|) \sum_{k=n}^{n+p} \|S^k\|$$

which goes to 0 as $n \to \infty$. It follows that

$$\lim_{n\to\infty} x_n = x_0$$

exists and $T[x_0] = x_0$. Here

$$x_0 = z_0 + \sum_{n=1}^{\infty} S^n[z_0] \tag{1.4.9}$$

and the series converges in norm as just shown.

Since $\mathfrak{X}$ is complete, $x_0 \in \mathfrak{X}$. Suppose that there were a fixed point y_0, possibly distinct from x_0. Then

$$x_0 - y_0 = T[x_0] - T[y_0] = S[x_0 - y_0] = S^2[x_0 - y_0] = \cdots = S^n[x_0 - y_0]$$

and this goes to 0 as $n \to \infty$. Hence $y_0 = x_0$ and the fixed point is unique. ▮

This is the fixed point theorem which underlies the proof of the uniqueness of the solution of Volterra's equation

$$f(t) = g(t) + \int_0^t K(s, t)f(s)\, ds, \tag{1.4.10}$$

special cases of which will figure prominently in the following. Here $g(t)$ and the kernel $K(s, t)$ are known functions and $f(t)$ is the unknown. The following special case will be particularly useful.

Theorem 1.4.3. *Suppose that* $g(t) \in C[0, a]$ *and* $K(t) \in L(0, a)$. *Then the equation*

$$f(t) = g(t) + \int_0^t K(s)f(s)\,ds \tag{1.4.11}$$

has in $C[0, a]$ *the unique solution*

$$f(t) = g(t) + \int_0^t K(s) \exp\left[\int_s^t K(u)\,du\right] g(s)\,ds. \tag{1.4.12}$$

Proof. Here $\mathfrak{X} = C[0, a]$, $z_0 = g(t)$, and

$$S[x](t) = \int_0^t K(s)x(s)\,ds$$

which is clearly a linear bounded transformation on $C[0, a]$. A simple calculation shows that

$$S^n[x](t) = \frac{1}{(n-1)!}\int_0^t K(u)\left[\int_u^t K(s)\,ds\right]^{n-1} x(u)\,du. \tag{1.4.13}$$

This gives

$$\|S^n\| \le \frac{1}{n!}\left[\int_0^a |K(s)|\,ds\right]^n.$$

Hence condition (1.4.7) is satisfied and replacing x by g and summing for n we obtain (1.4.12) as the unique solution. ∎

Corollary. *For* $K(t) \equiv K$ *the equation*

$$f(t) = g(t) + K\int_0^t f(s)\,ds \tag{1.4.14}$$

has the unique solution

$$f(t) = g(t) + K\int_0^t \exp[K(t-s)]g(s)\,ds. \tag{1.4.15}$$

EXERCISE 1.4

1. Use Theorem 1.4.1 to give a proof of the *Implicit Function Theorem* in the following version: For $|x| \le r$, $|y| \le b$, let $F(x, y)$ be continuous, $F(0, 0) = 0$, $|F(x, y)| \le M$, and let $|F(x, y_1) - F(x, y_2)| \le k\,|y_1 - y_2|$, $0 < k < 1$. Let $b > M$ and $b - M \ge |a|r$. Then the equation $y = ax + F(x, y)$ has a unique solution $y = f(x)$ with $f(0) = 0$, $|f(x)| \le b$ and $f \in C[-r, r]$. [*Hint:*

Take $\mathfrak{X}$ as the subspace of $C[-r, r]$ whose elements satisfy $g(0) = 0$ and $\|g\| \leq b$, and take the mapping T which carries $g(t)$ into $at + F(t, g(t))$. Show that this is a contraction under the stated conditions on a, b, r, M.]

2. The equation $y^3 - y + x = 0$ has a unique continuous solution $y = f(x)$ which tends to 0 with x. Use the preceding theorem to find an interval $(-r, r)$ in which $f(x)$ exists. Show that $r = \frac{2}{9}\sqrt{3}$ is the maximal choice.
3. If $\mathcal{A}$ is a real 2 by 2 matrix (a_{jk}) and the norm in R^2 is taken to be $\|(x_1, x_2)\| = \max(|x_1|, |x_2|)$, find sufficient conditions on a_{jk} so that $y = \mathcal{A}x$ be a contraction.
4. If $\mathfrak{X} = C(-\infty, \infty]$, for what values of μ is

$$P[f, \mu](t) \equiv \tfrac{1}{2}\mu \int_{-\infty}^{\infty} \exp[-|t - s|]f(s)\, ds$$

a contraction? What is then the fixed point? Show that there are infinitely many fixed points if $\mu = 1$.

1.5 FUNCTIONAL INEQUALITIES

In the theory of differential equations, functional inequalities frequently occur and have to be discussed with a view to determine what restrictions they impose on the functions involved.

A typical situation is the following. We have a class F of real valued functions f defined in some set S, a mapping T on F into itself, and the inequality

$$f \leq T[f], \tag{1.5.1}$$

valid everywhere in S. Such an inequality may be *trivial* in the sense that it is satisfied by all f in F, it may be *absurd* in that it holds for no $f \in F$. If it holds for any f in a proper subset F_0 of F, we say that the inequality is *restrictive*. It becomes *determinative* if F_0 reduces to a single element.

The four cases are illustrated by

$$\begin{aligned} &f(t) \leq \tfrac{1}{4}\{3 + [f(t)]^4\}, && f(t) \leq [f(t)]^2, \\ &f(t) \leq K\int_0^t f(s)\, ds, && f(t) \leq -1, \end{aligned} \tag{1.5.2}$$

F being the positive cone of $C[0, a]$.

We shall prove that the third inequality is determinative. This is the inequality which underlies uniqueness proofs based on an ordinary Lipschitz condition.

Theorem 1.5.1. *If $f \in C^+[0, a]$ and $K > 0$ and if*

$$f(t) \leq K\int_0^t f(s)\, ds, \tag{1.5.3}$$

then $f(t) \equiv 0$.

Proof. We shall indicate several proofs of this important result. The most direct argument is based on iteration. From (1.5.3) we conclude that

$$f(t) \leq \frac{1}{(n-1)!} K^n \int_0^t (t-s)^{n-1} f(s)\, ds, \tag{1.5.4}$$

say by induction. Since f is continuous in $[0, a]$, the right member tends to 0, uniformly in t, when $n \to \infty$.

The following argument is more sophisticated and uses a device which is useful in similar situations. We set

$$F(t) = K \int_0^t f(s)\, ds.$$

Then $F(0) = 0$ and

$$F'(t) = Kf(t) \leq KF(t)$$

so that

$$\frac{d}{dt} [\exp(-Kt)F(t)] \leq 0.$$

Hence the function inside the brackets is non-increasing in $[0, a]$. Since $F(0) = 0$, this implies that $F(t) \leq 0$. But $F(t) \geq 0$ since $f(t) \geq 0$. Hence $F(t) \equiv 0$ and thus also $f(t) \equiv 0$. ▮

Other arguments will be given below. The corresponding transformation T was shown to have a unique fixed point, namely the zero element. See (1.4.5) to (1.4.7). We shall return to this observation below.

A more general type of Lipschitz condition leads to:

Theorem 1.5.2. *Let $K(t) > 0$ and $K(t) \in L(0, a) \cap C(0, a]$. If $f(t) \in C^+[0, a]$ and satisfies*

$$f(t) \leq \int_0^t K(s) f(s)\, ds, \tag{1.5.5}$$

then $f(t) \equiv 0$.

We omit a proof. Either of the methods used above applies.

A more special result, not implied by Theorem 1.5.2, is the inequality underlying the uniqueness theorem of M. Nagumo (see Theorem 2.6.1).

Theorem 1.5.3. *Let $f \in C^+[0, a]$, $f(0) = 0$, and let f have a right-hand derivative at $t = 0$ with $f'(0) = 0$. Then $f(t) \equiv 0$, if*

$$f(t) \leq \int_0^t f(s) \frac{ds}{s}. \tag{1.5.6}$$

Proof. We use the integration method and set

$$F(t) = \int_0^t f(s) \frac{ds}{s}.$$

The integral exists since $\lim_{s\to 0}[f(s)/s] = f'(0) = 0$. Further

$$F'(t) = \frac{f(t)}{t} \le \frac{F(t)}{t}$$

so that

$$\frac{d}{dt}\frac{F(t)}{t} \le 0$$

and $F(t)/t$ is non-increasing. Since $F(0) = 0$, this gives $F(t) \le 0$. But $F(t) \ge 0$ so we must have $F(t) \equiv 0$ and hence also $f(t) \equiv 0$. ▮

A more complicated inequality underlies the uniqueness theorem of W. F. Osgood (see Theorem 2.6.2).

Theorem 1.5.4. *Let $\omega(t)$ be an increasing function belonging to $C^+[0, a]$ such that $\omega(0) = 0$ and $\omega(t) > 0$ for $t > 0$ while*

$$\lim_{\delta \downarrow 0} \int_\delta^a [\omega(s)]^{-1}\, ds = +\infty. \tag{1.5.7}$$

Let $f \in C^+[0, a]$. Then $f(t) \equiv 0$ is implied by

$$f(t) \le \int_0^t \omega[f(s)]\, ds, \qquad 0 < x \le a. \tag{1.5.8}$$

Proof. We set $g(t) = \max_{0 < s \le t} f(s)$ and assume that $g(t) > 0$ for $0 < t \le a$. Then $f(t) \le g(t)$ and for each t there is a t_1, $t_1 \le t$, such that $f(t_1) = g(t)$. We have then

$$g(t) = f(t_1) \le \int_0^{t_1} \omega[f(s)]\, ds$$

$$\le \int_0^{t_1} \omega[g(s)]\, ds \le \int_0^t \omega[g(s)]\, ds,$$

i.e. the increasing function $g(t)$ satisfies the same inequality as $f(t)$ does. Set

$$G(t) = \int_0^t \omega[g(s)]\, ds.$$

Then $G(0) = 0$, $g(t) \le G(t)$, $G'(t) = \omega[g(t)]$. It follows that

$$G'(t) \le \omega[G(t)].$$

Hence, on the one hand

$$\int_\delta^a \frac{G'(t)}{\omega[G(t)]}\, dt < a,$$

on the other

$$\int_\delta^a \frac{G'(t)}{\omega[G(t)]}\, dt = \int_\Delta^A \frac{du}{\omega(u)}, \qquad G(a) = A, \qquad G(\delta) = \Delta,$$

and the last integral becomes infinite when $\delta \downarrow 0$ by assumption. This contradiction shows that $g(t)$ cannot be positive. Hence $f(t) \equiv 0$. ▮

Theorems 1.5.1 to 1.5.4 all involve determinative inequalities. Proofs have been given in detail since the results are basic for the theory of differential equations. We proceed now to some restrictive inequalities which also play an important role for differential equations. Here partial ordering of the space is essential.

Theorem 1.5.5. *Let F be a complete metric space and partially ordered in such a manner that, if an increasing sequence $\{x_n\}$ has the limit x_0, then $x_n < x_0$ for all n. Let T be an order-preserving contraction on F. Let f_0 be the unique fixed point of T. Then*

$$f < T[f] \quad \textit{implies} \quad f < f_0. \tag{1.5.9}$$

Proof. Here the statement that T is *order-preserving* means that $f_1 < f_2$ implies $T[f_1] < T[f_2]$. Suppose now that $f \in F_0 \subset F$, that is $f < T[f]$. Then

$$f < T[f] < T^2[f] < \cdots < T^n[f] \quad \text{and} \quad \lim T^n[f] = f_0$$

by the proof of Theorem 1.4.1. By the assumption on the partial ordering, this implies (1.5.9). ▮

Corollary. *The same conclusion is valid if a power of the order-preserving transformation T is a contraction.*

For we have still a unique fixed point.

This result is a consequence of Theorem 1.4.1, the Banach fixed point theorem. We can draw a similar conclusion from the Volterra fixed point Theorem 1.4.2.

Theorem 1.5.6. *Let F be the positive cone of a partially ordered normed complete linear vector space $\mathfrak{X}$ where F is supposed to be closed in the norm topology. Let $S \in \mathfrak{E}(\mathfrak{X})$ be a positive transformation which satisfies* (1.4.7). *Let g be a given element of F and let f_0 be the unique fixed point of the mapping $T[f] = g + S[f]$. Then $f_0 \in F$ and for $f \in F$*

$$f < g + S[f] \quad \textit{implies} \quad f < f_0. \tag{1.5.10}$$

Proof. S is a *positive transformation* on $\mathfrak{X}$ into $\mathfrak{X}$ if it maps the positive cone into itself. Thus F is mapped into itself by S. A positive linear transformation is order-preserving for $f_1 - f_2 > 0$ implies $S[f_1 - f_2] = S[f_1] - S[f_2] > 0$. Theorem 1.4.2 gives

$$f_0 = g + \sum_{n=1}^{\infty} S^n[g] \in F$$

since f_0 is the fixed point of T which maps F into F. Suppose now that $f \in F$ and $f < g + S[f]$. Since S is order-preserving

$$S[f] < S[g] + S^2[f]$$

or

$$f < g + S[f] < g + S[g] + S^2[f]$$

and by complete induction, for all n,

$$f < g + S[g] + S^2[g] + \cdots + S^{n-1}[g] + S^n[f] \equiv g_n + S^n[f].$$

Hence $g_n + S^n[f] - f > 0$. Here the limit of the left member is $f_0 - f$ and, since F is closed, $f_0 - f > 0$. ∎

In particular, we obtain from Theorem 1.4.3 the following:

Theorem 1.5.7. *Suppose that* $g(t) \in C^+[0, a]$, $K(t) > 0$, *and* $K(t) \in L(0, a)$. *If* $f(t) \in C^+[0, a]$ *and*

$$f(t) \leq g(t) + \int_0^t K(s)f(s)\, ds, \tag{1.5.11}$$

then

$$f(t) \leq g(t) + \int_0^t K(s) \exp\left[\int_s^t K(u)\, du\right] g(s)\, ds. \tag{1.5.12}$$

Proof. We have

$$S[f](t) = \int_0^t K(s)f(s)\, ds$$

which shows that S is linear bounded and positive. Condition (1.4.7) is satisfied and by Theorem 1.4.3 the right member of (1.5.12) is the invariant element under the transformation $T[f] = g + S[f]$. ∎

Corollary 1. *If* $K(t) \equiv K$, *then*

$$f(t) \leq g(t) + K\int_0^t f(s)\, ds \tag{1.5.13}$$

implies

$$f(t) \leq g(t) + K\int_0^t \exp\,[K(t - s)]g(s)\, ds. \tag{1.5.14}$$

Corollary 2. *If both* $K(t)$ *and* $g(t)$ *are constants, then*

$$f(t) \leq c + K\int_0^t f(s)\, ds \tag{1.5.15}$$

implies

$$f(t) \leq c \exp\,(Kt). \tag{1.5.16}$$

We shall refer to Theorem 1.5.7 and its corollaries as *Gronwall's lemma.* T. H. Gronwall (1877–1932) considered in 1918 the special case $K(t) = K$, $g(t) = at$.

We note that Theorems 1.5.1 and 1.5.2 are special cases obtained by setting $g(t) \equiv 0$ in (1.5.12). This gives $f(t) \leq 0$, while $f(t) \geq 0$ by assumption.

EXERCISE 1.5

1. If $0 < t$ and $0 < f(t) < t + f(t)[1 + f(t)]^{-1}$, find sharper bounds for f.
2. The inequality $0 \leq f(t) \leq \int_0^t [f(s)]^2\,ds$ falls under Theorem 1.5.4 if f is continuous. Find a simpler proof, assuming $\sup f = M$ and using iteration.
3. If $f \in C^+[0, a]$ and $f(t) \leq \exp\,[\int_0^t f(s)\,ds] - 1$, prove that $f = 0$.
4. If $f \in C^+[0, a]$ and $f(t) \leq [\int_0^t f(s)\,ds]^2$, what conclusion can be drawn?
5. If the exponent "2" in the preceding problem is replaced by "$\frac{1}{2}$", does the same conclusion hold?
6. Verify the following trivial modification of Theorem 1.5.7. If the conditions on f, g, and K hold in $[a, b]$ instead of in $[0, a]$ and if the lower limit of integration in (1.5.11) is a instead of 0, then (1.5.12) holds with a instead of 0. Same for the corollaries.
7. Prove the following companion to Theorem 1.5.7. *Let* $K(t) > 0$ *and belong to* $L(a, \infty)$. *Let* $g(t) \in C^+[a, \infty]$. *If* $f(t) \in C^+[a, \infty]$ *and if*

$$f(t) \leq g(t) + \int_t^\infty K(s)f(s)\,ds$$

then

$$f(t) \leq g(t) + \int_t^\infty K(s) \exp\left[\int_t^s K(u)\,du\right] g(s)\,ds.$$

8. An alternate proof of Theorem 1.5.1 is to use a step-by-step argument. Consider the interval $[0, \delta]$ where $K\delta < 1$ and show that $\sup f(t) = 0$ in $[0, \delta]$. Next take $[\delta, 2\delta]$ and so on. Details?
9. A direct proof of Theorem 1.5.7 can be given using the integration method (see second proof of Theorem 1.5.1). Set $F(t) = \int_0^t K(s)f(s)\,ds$ and discuss the resulting differential inequality $F'(t) - K(t)F(t) \leq K(t)g(t)$.

1.6 COMPACTNESS

The *Heine-Borel theorem* plays an important role in real analysis. In general it is not valid in abstract spaces. We proceed to a discussion of some aspects of this question.

Let $\mathfrak{X}$ be a complete metric space and $S \subset \mathfrak{X}$. A system of sets $\{A_\alpha\}$ is a *covering* of S if each point of S is interior point of at least one of the sets A_α. The set S is said to have the *Borel property* if every system of open sets $\{G_\alpha\}$ which covers S contains a finite subsystem which also covers S. Such a set is also said to be *compact*; in particular, $\mathfrak{X}$ is compact if it has the Borel property.

A set is *conditionally compact* if its closure is compact. It is *sequentially compact* if every sequence of points in S contains a subsequence which converges to a point in S. The set S is *totally bounded*, if, for every $\varepsilon > 0$, there is a finite covering of S by ε-spheres. We state without proof:

Theorem 1.6.1. *In a complete metric space a set S is sequentially compact if it is compact. It is conditionally compact if it is totally bounded.*

Compactness properties of continuous functions will play an important role in this treatise. Consider a family F of functions f_α defined and continuous in a closed rectangular parallelepiped in R^n

$$\Pi: a_j \le x_j \le b_j, \qquad j = 1, 2, \ldots, n,$$

and make F into a metric space by introducing the sup norm

$$\|f_\alpha\| = \sup |f_\alpha|.$$

If the closure of F is to be compact, then F must be totally bounded, in particular, bounded.

Definition 1.6.1. *The family F is said to be uniformly bounded in Π, if there exists a finite M such that for all α*

$$\|f_\alpha\| \le M. \tag{1.6.1}$$

This condition is not sufficient for conditional compactness, however, as is shown by the family $\{\sin nx\}$ which is uniformly bounded on $[0, \pi]$ but contains no convergent subsequence. Some additional property is needed, and in 1895 Cesare Arzelà showed that *equicontinuity* is such a property. This notion had been introduced by Guilio Ascoli in 1884.

Definition 1.6.2. *The family F is equicontinuous in Π, if, given any $\varepsilon > 0$, there exists a $\delta(\varepsilon)$ such that, for all α,*

$$|f_\alpha(x_1) - f_\alpha(x_2)| < \varepsilon \tag{1.6.2}$$

provided x_1 and x_2 are any points in Π with $d(x_1, x_2) < \delta(\varepsilon)$.

We now state and prove the theorem of Arzelà.

Theorem 1.6.2. *A family F of equicontinuous uniformly bounded functions in Π is conditionally compact.*

Proof. We shall suppose that F is complete under the sup norm and prove that F is sequentially compact. Let $\{f_m\}$ be an infinite sequence of distinct elements of F and let Q be a countable set of points dense in Π, say the points with rational co-ordinates. We arrange these points in a sequence $\{x_m\}$. Consider now the values taken on by the functions f_m at the point

$x = x_1$. By assumption this is a bounded set of real or complex numbers and has at least one cluster point y_1. We can then find a subsequence $\{f_{m1}\}$ such that $\lim f_{m1}(x_1) = y_1$. We consider this subsequence at $x = x_2$ and by the same argument there is a subsequence $\{f_{m2}\} \subset \{f_{m1}\} \subset \{f_m\}$ such that $\lim f_{m2}(x_1)$ and $\lim f_{m2}(x_2)$ exist. In this manner we proceed. After k steps we have a subsequence $\{f_{mk}\}$ such that

$$\lim f_{mk}(x_j) \text{ exists}, \qquad j = 1, 2, \ldots, k.$$

Next we form the so-called *diagonal sequence* $\{f_{mm}\}$. Here $\{f_{mm}\} \subset \{f_{mk}\}$ for $k \leq m$. It follows that

$$\lim f_{mm}(x_j) \quad \text{exists for every} \quad x_j \in Q.$$

Thus there is a subsequence $\{f_{mm}\}$ convergent in the dense set Q.

So far only uniform boundedness has been used. The equicontinuity plays a decisive role in proving the convergence of f_{mm} everywhere in Π. For a pre-assigned $\varepsilon > 0$, let $\delta(\varepsilon)$ be the corresponding number furnished by Definition 1.6.2. We can then find an integer N such that each $x \in \Pi$ is at a distance $< \delta(\varepsilon)$ from at least one point in the set $x_1, x_2, \ldots, x_N$. Now take an $x \in \Pi$ distinct from this finite subset and suppose that x_j is the point nearest to x. Then

$$|f_{mm}(x) - f_{pp}(x)| \leq |f_{mm}(x) - f_{mm}(x_j)| + |f_{mm}(x_j) - f_{pp}(x_j)| + |f_{pp}(x_j) - f_{pp}(x)|.$$

For all m and p, the first and third expressions on the right are $< \varepsilon$ by the equicontinuity. The second term is also $< \varepsilon$ for any j from the set $1, 2, \ldots, N$ provided m and p exceed some integer $k(\varepsilon)$. For such values of m and p and for all x

$$|f_{mm}(x) - f_{pp}(x)| < 3\varepsilon.$$

This shows that the diagonal sequence converges uniformly in Π to a function $f(x)$ which belongs to F since F was supposed to be complete under the sup norm. ∎

The theorem admits of a converse.

Theorem 1.6.3. *If a family F of functions f_α continuous in Π is sequentially compact, then the functions are equicontinuous.*

Proof. By assumption F is totally bounded. Hence, given any $\varepsilon > 0$, there exists a finite number N of functions in F, say $f_1, f_2, \ldots, f_N$, such that for every α there is at least one integer j, $1 \leq j \leq N$, with

$$\|f_\alpha - f_j\| < \varepsilon.$$

The functions $f_1, \ldots, f_N$ are continuous in Π. Hence there exists a $\delta(\varepsilon)$ such that $|f_j(x_1) - f_j(x_2)| < \varepsilon$ if $d(x_1, x_2) < \delta(\varepsilon)$ and $j = 1, 2, \ldots, N$. This gives

$$|f_\alpha(x_1) - f_\alpha(x_2)| \le |f_\alpha(x_1) - f_j(x_1)| + |f_j(x_1) - f_j(x_2)| + |f_j(x_2) - f_\alpha(x_2)| < 3\varepsilon$$

for the appropriate choice of j. This implies equicontinuity in Π. ∎

EXERCISE 1.6

1. The sequence $\{1/n \sin n^2x\}$ obviously converges to 0 in $[0, \pi]$. Is the convergence uniform? Are the functions equicontinuous?
2. The sequence of polynomials $\{1 - [(1 - x)/2]^n\}^{2^n}$ converges in $[-1, 1]$. Find the limit. Are the functions equicontinuous?
3. If $f_\alpha(x)$ is continuous and differentiable in $[a, b]$ and if $|f_\alpha(x)| \le M$, $|f'_\alpha(x)| \le M$, show that the family $\{f_\alpha\}$ is equicontinuous.
4. If $\{f_\alpha\}$ is a family of uniformly bounded equicontinuous functions, show the existence of a common modulus of continuity $\mu(\delta)$, i.e. a continuous nondecreasing function with $\mu(0) = 0$ such that for every α we have
$$|f_\alpha(x_1) - f_\alpha(x_2)| < \mu(\delta) \quad \text{if} \quad d(x_1, x_2) < \delta.$$
5. Show that in C^n every bounded set is totally bounded.
6. Consider the set of all n by n matrices $\mathcal{A} = (a_{jk})$ with $|a_{jk}| \le M$. Show that this set is sequentially compact.
7. A sequence of functions on $(0, 1)$ is defined by $f_0(x) \equiv 1$,
$$f_n(x) = 1 + \int_0^x f_{n-1}(s)\, ds.$$
Does $\lim f_n(x)$ exist?
8. Prove Theorem 1.6.1.

COLLATERAL READING

A reader who wants to review the subject matter of Chapter 1 may find the following references useful.

BARTLE, R. G., *The Elements of Real Analysis.* Wiley, New York (1964).

HILLE, E., *Analysis*, Vol. II, Blaisdell, New York (1965).

Compactness and Arzelà's theorem are discussed in Bartle's book, linear algebra in that of the author; metrics, vector spaces, and the contraction fixed point theorem are featured in both.

For functional inequalities, the reader can start with Chapter 1 of the author's article

SAATY, T. L. (ed.), "Topics in Classical Analysis," *Lectures on Modern Mathematics*, Vol. III, Wiley, New York (1965).

For a more detailed account, the outstanding monograph in the field is

WALTER, W., *Differential- und Integralungleichungen*, Springer Tracts on Natural Philosophy, Vol. 2, Berlin (1964).

Further references:

BELLMAN, R., *A survey of the Theory of the Boundedness, Stability, and Asymptotic Behavior of Solutions of Linear and Non-linear Differential and Difference Equations*, Office of Naval Research, Navexos P-596. Washington, D.C. (1949).

GRONWALL, T. H., "Note on the derivative with respect to a parameter of the solutions of a system of differential equations," *Annals of Math.*, (2) **20**, 292–296 (1918).

2 EXISTENCE AND UNIQUENESS THEOREMS

We shall now start the theory of ordinary differential equations with a discussion of existence and uniqueness theorems covering various types of equations and using various modes of approach.

There are six sections: Ordinary Differential Equations, The Fixed Point Method, The Method of Successive Approximations, The Cauchy-Lipschitz Method, The Cauchy-Lindelöf Method, Other Uniqueness Theorems.

2.1 ORDINARY DIFFERENTIAL EQUATIONS

What is a differential equation is a moot question. Obviously it should be a functional equation where the unknown function or functions are present as derivatives with respect to a single variable in the case of an ordinary differential equation. The order of the highest derivative is called the *order* of the equation. Now derivatives can occur in various ways and we do not admit equations where the unknown is subjected to other operations than algebraic and differential operations. The following list of six examples of functional equations involving derivatives contains some bona fide differential equations and also some which are not.

Example 1. $f'(x) = f(x)$.

Example 2. $f'(x) = f(x + 1)$.

Example 3. $f'(x) = a_0(x) + a_1(x)f(x) + a_2(x)[f(x)]^2$.

Example 4. $f''(x) = 6x + [f(x)]^2$.

Example 5. $f'(x) = \int_0^x \{1 + [f(s)]^2\}^{1/2}\, ds$.

Example 6. $f(x) = \int_0^1 \{[f'(s)]^2 + [f(x)]^2\}^{1/2}\, ds$.

Here Nos. 1 and 3 are ordinary first order differential equations, while No. 2 is a difference differential equation and not a differential equation in the usual sense. No. 4 is a second order differential equation. No. 5 is not a differential equation as it stands but differentiation yields

$$f''(x) = \{1 + [f(x)]^2\}^{1/2}$$

which is a second order differential equation equivalent to No. 5. Finally, No. 6 is not a differential equation and is not reducible to such an equation by elementary means.

The normal form of a first order differential equation is

$$y' = F(x, y) \tag{2.1.1}$$

or, equivalently,

$$f'(x) = F[x, f(x)].$$

In the simplest case x and y are real variables and $F(x, y)$ is a function on R^2 to R^1. We can also allow x and y to be complex variables and F to be a function on C^2 to C^1.

But there is nothing to prevent us from letting $\mathbf{y}$ and $\mathbf{F}$ be vector valued (vectors are indicated by bold face in the following). Here the first step in the generalizations is to assume

$$\mathbf{y} = (y_1, y_2, \ldots, y_n), \qquad \mathbf{F} = (F_1, F_2, \ldots, F_n) \tag{2.1.2}$$

where

$$F_j = F_j(x, y_1, y_2, \ldots, y_n) \tag{2.1.3}$$

are functions on R^{n+1} to R^1 or on C^{n+1} to C^1. *We then define the derivative of a vector as the vector of the derivatives*:

$$\mathbf{y}' = (y_1', y_2', \ldots, y_n'). \tag{2.1.4}$$

With this notation Eq. (2.1.1) becomes a condensed convenient way of writing a *system of first order differential equations*:

$$y_j'(x) = F_j(x, y_1, y_2, \ldots, y_n), \qquad j = 1, 2, \ldots, n. \tag{2.1.5}$$

Conversely, *every such system can be written as a first order vector differential equation.*

This generalization has the advantage of covering n^{th} order equations. We simply set

$$\mathbf{y} = (y, y', y'', \ldots, y^{(n-1)})$$

to convert an nth order ordinary differential equation in y to a first order vector differential equation in $\mathbf{y}$.

As a further generalization we can consider differential equations in more general spaces than the Euclidean. Here the interpretation of the derivative becomes a matter of concern, and convergence questions also arise if the space is of infinite dimension.

Differential equations normally have an infinite number of solutions and in order to find a particular one we have to impose some special condition on the solution, usually an *initial condition.* The object of an *existence theorem* is to show that there exists a function which satisfies the equation in some neighborhood of a point (x_0, y_0) or $(x_0, \mathbf{y}_0)$ and which at $x = x_0$ takes the value $y = y_0(\mathbf{y} = \mathbf{y}_0)$. A *uniqueness theorem* asserts that there is only one such function. We can, however, assert the existence of solutions under much more general conditions than those which guarantee uniqueness. As we shall see, this lies in the nature of things and is not due to our lack of knowledge.

EXERCISE 2.1

1. Example 6 is satisfied by $f(x) \equiv C$, $C \geq 0$. Show that this is the only real solution.
2. If $f(x)$ satisfies the integral equation

$$f(x) = y_0 + \int_{x_0}^{x} F[s, f(s)]\, ds,$$

find a differential equation satisfied by $f(x)$. What initial condition does $f(x)$ satisfy?
3. Show that $[f'(x)]^2 + [f(x)]^2 = 0$ has no real solution except $f(x) \equiv 0$. Are there complex solutions?
4. Transform $f(x) = \int_0^x [f(s)]^2\, ds$ into a differential equation. Here $f(x) \equiv 0$ is obviously a solution. Are there other solutions of the functional equation?
5. Show that the difference differential equation

$$f'(x) = af\left(x + \frac{1}{ae}\right), \qquad a > 0,$$

has a solution of the form $f(x) = Ce^{\alpha x}$ where C is arbitrary and α is real.
6. The functional equation $f(x) = 1 + \int_0^x f(s)\, ds$ implies that f satisfies a differential equation. Find the latter and find the common solution.

2.2 THE FIXED POINT METHOD

We start with a topological method based on the contraction fixed point theorem of Section 1.4.

In order to apply this theorem we have to replace the differential equation by an equivalent integral equation that can be used to define a contraction operator on a suitably chosen metric space.

Let us start with the equation

$$\mathbf{f}'(x) = \mathbf{F}[x, \mathbf{f}(x)], \qquad \mathbf{f}(x_0) = \mathbf{y}_0. \tag{2.2.1}$$

Here $\mathbf{F} = (F_1, F_2, \ldots, F_n)$ is a vector valued function defined and continuous in

$$B\colon |x - x_0| < a, \qquad \|\mathbf{y} - \mathbf{y}_0\| < b. \tag{2.2.2}$$

As norm in R^n we can use any of the three obvious possibilities

$$\left[\sum_1^n (y_j - y_{j0})^2\right]^{1/2}, \quad \sum_1^n |y_j - y_{j0}| \quad \text{or} \quad \max |y_j - y_{j0}|. \qquad (2.2.3)$$

For the general theory it makes no difference which norm is used, though in specific cases one norm may be handier than another.

We impose two further conditions on $\mathbf{F}$:

$$\|\mathbf{F}(x, \mathbf{y})\| \leq M, \qquad (2.2.4)$$

$$\|\mathbf{F}(x, \mathbf{y}_1) - \mathbf{F}(x, \mathbf{y}_2)\| \leq K\|\mathbf{y}_1 - \mathbf{y}_2\|, \qquad (2.2.5)$$

i.e. a boundedness and a Lipschitz condition.

We now replace the vector differential equation by a vector integral equation

$$\mathbf{f}(x) = \mathbf{y}_0 + \int_{x_0}^{x} \mathbf{F}[s, \mathbf{f}(s)]\, ds. \qquad (2.2.6)$$

Here *the integral of a vector valued function is defined as the vector the components of which are the integrals of the components of the integrand*:

$$\int_{x_0}^{x} (F_1, F_2, \ldots, F_n)\, ds = \left(\int_{x_0}^{x} F_1\, ds, \int_{x_0}^{x} F_2\, ds, \ldots, \int_{x_0}^{x} F_n\, ds\right). \qquad (2.2.7)$$

An important property of this integral which will be used repeatedly in the following is that the norm of the integral does not exceed the integral of the norm of the integrand:

$$\left\|\int_{x_0}^{x} \mathbf{F}\, ds\right\| \leq \int_{x_0}^{x} \|\mathbf{F}\|\, ds, \qquad x_0 < x. \qquad (2.2.8)$$

This follows from the definition of the integrals by Riemann sums. We recall that, for the time being, we are concerned only with integrals of continuous functions.

We note that if (2.2.1) has a solution $\mathbf{f}(x)$ with $\mathbf{f}(x_0) = \mathbf{y}_0$, then $\mathbf{f}(x)$ necessarily satisfies (2.2.6) and vice versa. We can now state and prove

Theorem 2.2.1. *Under the stated assumptions on* $\mathbf{F}$, *the equation* (2.2.1) *has a unique solution defined in an interval* $(x_0 - r, x_0 + r)$ *where*

$$r < \min\left(a, \frac{b}{M}, \frac{1}{K}\right). \qquad (2.2.9)$$

Proof. We consider the space $\mathfrak{X}$ of all functions $\mathbf{g}(x)$ on R^1 to R^n continuous in $(x_0 - r, x_0 + r)$, such that $\mathbf{g}(x_0) = \mathbf{y}_0$ and $\|\mathbf{g} - \mathbf{y}_0\|_{\mathfrak{X}} \leq b$ where $\|\mathbf{g} - \mathbf{y}_0\|_{\mathfrak{X}} = \sup_x \|\mathbf{g}(x) - \mathbf{y}_0\|$. For such a $\mathbf{g}(x)$ the function $\mathbf{F}[x, \mathbf{g}(x)]$ exists and is continuous. Further its $\mathfrak{X}$-norm does not exceed M. We then define the transformation

$$T: \mathbf{g}(x) \to \mathbf{y}_0 + \int_{x_0}^{x} \mathbf{F}[s, \mathbf{g}(s)]\, ds, \qquad -r < x - x_0 < r. \tag{2.2.10}$$

Here $T[\mathbf{g}](x)$ is continuous, $T[\mathbf{g}](x_0) = \mathbf{y}_0$, and

$$\|T[\mathbf{g}](x) - \mathbf{y}_0\| < Mr < b$$

by the choice of r. It follows that $T[\mathbf{g}] \in \mathfrak{X}$. Next observe that

$$\|T[\mathbf{g}_1](x) - T[\mathbf{g}_2](x)\| = \left\| \int_{x_0}^{x} \{\mathbf{F}[s, \mathbf{g}_1(s)] - \mathbf{F}[s, \mathbf{g}_2(s)]\}\, ds \right\|$$
$$< K \left| \int_{x_0}^{x} \|\mathbf{g}_1(s) - \mathbf{g}_2(s)\|\, ds \right|$$

by (2.2.5). This shows that

$$\|T[\mathbf{g}_1] - T[\mathbf{g}_2]\|_{\mathfrak{X}} \leq Kr\|\mathbf{g}_1 - \mathbf{g}_2\|_{\mathfrak{X}} = k\|\mathbf{g}_1 - \mathbf{g}_2\|_{\mathfrak{X}},$$

where $Kr = k < 1$ by the choice of r. Hence T is a contraction and Theorem 1.4.1 applies. Hence there exists one and only one function $\mathbf{f}(x) \in \mathfrak{X}$ such that

$$\mathbf{f}(x) = \mathbf{y}_0 + \int_{x_0}^{x} \mathbf{F}[s, \mathbf{f}(s)]\, ds, \qquad \mathbf{f}(x_0) = \mathbf{y}_0,$$

and this also is the unique solution of the differential equation (2.2.1) with the stated initial condition. ∎

This is an existence and uniqueness theorem. Actually it is a little more than that. We recall that the invariant element $\mathbf{f}$ can be obtained from any element $\mathbf{g}$ of $\mathfrak{X}$ by repeated application of the transformation T, i.e.

$$\mathbf{f} = \lim_{n \to \infty} T^n[\mathbf{g}]. \tag{2.2.11}$$

We can start, e.g. with $\mathbf{g}(x) \equiv \mathbf{y}_0$. We even know something about the speed with which $T^n[\mathbf{g}]$ approaches $\mathbf{f}$, since the series

$$\mathbf{f} = \mathbf{g} + \sum_{1}^{\infty} \{T^n[\mathbf{g}] - T^{n-1}[\mathbf{g}]\} \tag{2.2.12}$$

converges as the geometric series $\sum k^n$. This is much less favorable, however, than the estimates obtainable from the method of successive approximations where the corresponding series converges as an exponential series.

Before passing over to that method let us first examine the possibility of extending the work to spaces of infinitely many dimensions. Here the question of the meaning of the vector equation

$$\mathbf{y}' = \mathbf{F}(x, \mathbf{y}) \tag{2.2.13}$$

becomes pertinent. We have now an abstract space $\mathfrak{Y}$ to which $\mathbf{y}(x)$ is to belong while $\mathbf{F}(x, \mathbf{y})$ is a function on $R \times \mathfrak{Y}$ to $\mathfrak{Y}$. But what is $\mathbf{y}'$? There are at least two possible interpretations.

If we prefer to stay entirely within the framework of abstract spaces, we have to introduce a metric in $\mathfrak{Y}$ and let $\mathbf{y}'(x)$ be the so-called *strong derivative*, i.e. we require that

$$\mathbf{y}'(x) = \lim_{h\to 0} \frac{1}{h} [\mathbf{y}(x + h) - \mathbf{y}(x)] \tag{2.2.14}$$

in the sense of the metric. For this concept to be meaningful, $\mathfrak{Y}$ must be a linear vector space. Further we should require that $\mathbf{F}(x, \mathbf{y})$ be continuous and satisfy a Lipschitz condition, both in the sense of the metric. Theorem 2.2.1 then carries over to the new situation with no essential changes.

The requirement that $\mathbf{y}'(x)$ be the strong derivative is unnecesssarily restrictive and may be replaced by weaker assumptions. To fix the ideas, suppose that $\mathfrak{Y}$ is a sequence space, say (l). Here $\mathbf{y} = (y_1, y_2, \ldots, y_n, \ldots)$ and we have a norm

$$\|\mathbf{y}\| = \sum_1^\infty |y_n|.$$

Now $\mathbf{F}(x, \mathbf{y})$ is a function on $R \times (l)$ to (l) and $\mathbf{F} = (F_1, F_2, \ldots, F_n, \ldots)$. We interpret (2.2.13) as a condensed way of writing

$$y_k'(x) = F_k[x, y_1(x), y_2(x), \ldots, y_n(x), \ldots], \qquad k = 1, 2, \ldots \tag{2.2.15}$$

Here $y_k'(x)$ is simply the ordinary derivative of a function of a real variable. Equivalently, we have

$$y_k(x) = y_{k0} + \int_{x_0}^x F_k[s, y_1(s), \ldots, y_k(s), \ldots]\, ds \tag{2.2.16}$$

where $\mathbf{y}_0 = (y_{10}, y_{20}, \ldots, y_{n0}, \ldots) \in (l)$. We ask for a solution $\mathbf{y}(x) = (y_1(x), y_2(x), \ldots, y_n(x), \ldots)$ in (l).

Now we may very well be able to solve the infinite systems (2.2.15) or (2.2.16) but this is no guarantee that the solutions belong to the space under consideration. The following trivial example exhibits some of the difficulties that may arise.

We take

$$y_n'(x) = n y_n(x), \qquad y_n(0) = \frac{1}{n^3}, \qquad n = 1, 2, 3, \ldots \tag{2.2.17}$$

The solution is

$$y_n(x) = \frac{1}{n^3} e^{nx}. \tag{2.2.18}$$

These functions are defined and satisfy the system for all x. The initial values are given at $x = 0$ and they belong to (l). The solution, on the other hand, does not belong to (l) on any interval $(0, \omega)$. It belongs to (l) in $(-\infty, 0)$. Thus the equation makes a distinction between left and right. It admits a solution in (l) for any choice of $\mathbf{y}_0 \in (l)$ to the left of the initial point, to the right only for very special choices of $\mathbf{y}_0$. This is a new and, at first sight, puzzling phenomenon.

For us right now the important fact is that the continuity of F_k for all k and the choice of $\mathbf{y}_0 \in \mathfrak{Y}$ does not suffice to guarantee the existence of a solution in $\mathfrak{Y}$. It may be objected (and with justice) that in (2.2.17) $\mathbf{F}(x, \mathbf{y})$ is neither a function on $R \times \mathfrak{Y}$ to $\mathfrak{Y}$ nor does it satisfy a boundedness or a Lipschitz condition. Note that

$$\mathbf{F}(x, \mathbf{y}) = (y_1, 2y_2, \ldots, ny_n, \ldots) \tag{2.2.19}$$

which is normally not in (l). This example shows that we cannot get too far away from the assumptions of Theorem 2.2.1 without jeopardizing even the existence of the solution.

On the other hand, if we do impose proper restrictions on $\mathbf{F}(x, \mathbf{y})$, Theorem 2.2.1 carries over to (l) as well as to other sequence spaces such as (m).

We suppose that $\mathbf{F}(x, \mathbf{y})$ is a function on $R \times (l)$ to (l) defined and continuous in

$$B\colon |x - x_0| < a, \qquad \|\mathbf{y} - \mathbf{y}_0\| < b, \qquad \mathbf{y}_0 \in (l), \tag{2.2.20}$$

in terms of the (l)-norm. Continuity now means that

$$\|\mathbf{F}(x_2, \mathbf{y}_2) - \mathbf{F}(x_1, \mathbf{y}_1)\| \leq \varepsilon \quad \text{if} \quad |x_1 - x_2| + \|\mathbf{y}_1 - \mathbf{y}_2\| \leq \delta(\varepsilon).$$

We also assume for $(x, \mathbf{y})$, $(x, \mathbf{y}_1)$, $(x, \mathbf{y}_2)$ in B:

$$\|\mathbf{F}(x, \mathbf{y})\| \leq M, \tag{2.2.21}$$

$$\|\mathbf{F}(x, \mathbf{y}_1) - \mathbf{F}(x, \mathbf{y}_2)\| \leq K\|\mathbf{y}_1 - \mathbf{y}_2\|. \tag{2.2.22}$$

We have then

Theorem 2.2.2. *Under the stated conditions on* $\mathbf{F}$, *the system* (2.2.15) *with* $\mathbf{y}_0 \in (l)$ *has a unique solution in* (l) *defined in the interval* $(x_0 - r, x_0 + r)$, *where*

$$r < \min\left(a, \frac{b}{M}, \frac{1}{K}\right). \tag{2.2.23}$$

Proof. The proof of Theorem 2.2.1 carries over step by step. The space $\mathfrak{X}$ is the set of all functions $\mathbf{g}$ on R to (l) with the following properties: (i) $\|\mathbf{g}\|_{\mathfrak{X}} = \sup \|\mathbf{g}(x)\| < \infty$, (ii) $\|\mathbf{g} - \mathbf{y}_0\|_{\mathfrak{X}} < b$, (iii) $\mathbf{g}(x_0) = \mathbf{y}_0$, (iv) $\mathbf{g}(x)$ is continuous in $(x_0 - r, x_0 + r)$. For functions **g** satisfying conditions (i) and (iv), the integral is defined by

$$\int_{x_0}^{x} (g_1, g_2, \ldots, g_n, \ldots)\, ds = \left(\int_{x_0}^{x} g_1\, ds, \int_{x_0}^{x} g_2\, ds, \ldots, \int_{x_0}^{x} g_n\, ds, \ldots \right) \qquad (2.2.24)$$

that exists and is an element of (l). We note that $F[x, \mathbf{g}(x)]$ exists and is continuous and integrable over $(x_0 - r, x_0 + r)$ so that $T[\mathbf{g}]$ can be defined by (2.2.10). That it is a contraction is shown as above. ▮

The idea of using topological fixed point theorems to prove the existence and uniqueness of solutions of ordinary differential equations goes back to G. D. Birkhoff and O. D. Kellogg (1922). The use of the contraction fixed point theorem for this purpose is due to R. Cacciopoli (1930).

EXERCISE 2.2

For the following differential equations determine an interval $(x_0 - r, x_0 + r)$ where Theorem 2.2.1 ensures the existence of a solution satisfying the stated initial condition.

1. $y' = y,\ y(0) = 1.$
2. $y' = y^3,\ y(0) = 2.$
3. $y' = x + y^2,\ y(0) = 0.$
4. $y' = xy + y^2,\ y(0) = 0.$
5. $y_1' = y_1 + y_2,\ y_1(0) = -1,\ y_2(0) = 1.$
   $y_2' = y_1 - y_2$. Use the maximum co-ordinate norm.
6. Write out a complete proof of Theorem 2.2.2.
7. Let $\{r_n\}$ be an enumeration of the rationals in [0, 1]. Does the system
   $$y_n'(x) = r_n y_n(x), \qquad y_n(0) = 1/n^2, \qquad n = 1, 2, \ldots$$
   have a solution in (l)? If so, in what interval does it exist?
8. The system (2.2.17) favors the interval to the left of the initial point. Find a similar system which favors the interval to the right.
9. In system (2.2.17) replace n in the right member by $(-1)^n n$ and show that the resulting system in general has no solution in (l) for any $x \neq 0$.
10. Find the explicit solution in No. 4.

2.3 THE METHOD OF SUCCESSIVE APPROXIMATIONS

This method is a refinement of the old device of trial and error. What has been added is control of the limiting process. We know how often the process must be repeated to bring the result within the desired limits of tolerance.

We can trace the method of trial and error back to Sir Isaac Newton who was the first to be concerned with approximate solutions of algebraic equations. An infinite iteration process for the positive solution of the transcendental equation

$$x = \alpha \arctan x, \qquad 1 < \alpha, \tag{2.3.1}$$

was given by J. Fourier in his *Théorie Analytique de la Chaleur* of 1822. Fourier's argument is geometrical and highly intuitive. It is not difficult to give a strict analytic convergence proof.

The method of successive approximations was given by Émile Picard for differential equations in 1891. It very soon became the standard method for proving existence and uniqueness theorems for all sorts of functional equations.

Let us consider a vector differential equation

$$\mathbf{y}' = \mathbf{F}(x, \mathbf{y}), \qquad \mathbf{y}(x_0) = \mathbf{y}_0, \tag{2.3.2}$$

with the same assumptions as in the preceding section, i.e. $\mathbf{F}(x, \mathbf{y})$ is defined and continuous in

$$B: |x - x_0| < a, \qquad \|\mathbf{y} - \mathbf{y}_0\| < b,$$

$$\|\mathbf{F}(x, \mathbf{y})\| \le M, \tag{2.3.3}$$

$$\|\mathbf{F}(x, \mathbf{y}_1) - \mathbf{F}(x, \mathbf{y}_2)\| \le K\|\mathbf{y}_1 - \mathbf{y}_2\|. \tag{2.3.4}$$

We have then:

Theorem 2.3.1. *There exists a unique function* $\mathbf{f}(x)$ *on* R^1 *to* R^n *defined for* $|x - x_0| < r$ *where*

$$r < \min\left(a, \frac{b}{M}\right), \tag{2.3.5}$$

such that

$$\mathbf{f}'(x) = \mathbf{F}[x, \mathbf{f}(x)], \qquad \mathbf{f}(x_0) = \mathbf{y}_0. \tag{2.3.6}$$

Remark. This is, of course, the same function as that given by Theorem 2.2.1, but the interval where it is defined is likely to be longer since we do not now have the restriction $rK < 1$.

Proof. We replace the differential equation with the initial condition by the equivalent integral equation

$$\mathbf{f}(x) = \mathbf{y}_0 + \int_{x_0}^{x} \mathbf{F}[s, \mathbf{f}(s)]\, ds, \tag{2.3.7}$$

and define

$$\mathbf{f}_0(x) = \mathbf{y}_0,$$

$$\mathbf{f}_m(x) = \mathbf{y}_0 + \int_{x_0}^{x} \mathbf{F}[s, \mathbf{f}_{m-1}(s)]\, ds, \qquad m = 1, 2, 3, \ldots \tag{2.3.8}$$

For these functions to be well defined we restrict x to the interval $(x_0 - r, x_0 + r)$. Suppose it is known that, for some value of m, the function $\mathbf{f}_{m-1}(x)$ is well defined in this interval. It is obvious that $\mathbf{f}_{m-1}(x_0) = \mathbf{y}_0$, but the induction hypothesis must also include that $\mathbf{f}_{m-1}(x)$ is continuous and $\|\mathbf{f}_{m-1}(s) - \mathbf{y}_0\| < b$. We then see that $\mathbf{F}[s, \mathbf{f}_{m-1}(s)]$ is well defined and continuous. Further

$$\|\mathbf{F}[s, \mathbf{f}_{m-1}(s)]\| \leq M.$$

Hence

$$\int_{x_0}^{x} \mathbf{F}[s, \mathbf{f}_{m-1}(s)]\, ds$$

exists as a continuous function of x and its norm does not exceed

$$M|x - x_0| < Mr < b,$$

by the choice of r. This implies that $\mathbf{f}_m(x)$ is also continuous, and satisfies $\mathbf{f}_m(x_0) = \mathbf{y}_0$, $\|\mathbf{f}_m(x) - \mathbf{y}_0\| < b$. It follows that the approximations are well defined for all m.

To prove the existence of $\lim \mathbf{f}_m(x)$, we resort to the Lipschitz condition. We have

$$\|\mathbf{f}_m(x) - \mathbf{f}_{m-1}(x)\| = \left\| \int_{x_0}^{x} \{\mathbf{F}[s, \mathbf{f}_{m-1}(s)] - \mathbf{F}[s, \mathbf{f}_{m-2}(s)]\}\, ds \right\|$$

$$\leq K \left| \int_{x_0}^{x} \|\mathbf{f}_{m-1}(s) - \mathbf{f}_{m-2}(s)\|\, ds \right| .$$

Suppose that for some m we have the estimate

$$\|\mathbf{f}_{m-1}(s) - \mathbf{f}_{m-2}(s)\| \leq \frac{K^{m-2}}{(m-1)!} M|s - x_0|^{m-1}, \qquad |s - x_0| < r. \tag{2.3.9}$$

This is certainly true for $m = 2$. We then get

$$\|\mathbf{f}_m(x) - \mathbf{f}_{m-1}(x)\| \leq \frac{K^{m-1}}{(m-1)!} M \left| \int_{x_0}^{x} |s - x_0|^{m-1}\, ds \right|$$

$$= \frac{K^{m-1}}{m!} M|x - x_0|^m$$

so the estimate is true for all m.

This shows that the series

$$\mathbf{f}_0(x) + \sum_{k=1}^{\infty} [\mathbf{f}_k(x) - \mathbf{f}_{k-1}(x)] \tag{2.3.10}$$

whose m^{th} partial sum is $\mathbf{f}_m(x)$, converges in norm for $|x - x_0| < r$ uniformly in x. Hence its sum $\mathbf{f}(x)$ is a continuous function on R^1 to R^n. The strong uniform convergence of the vector series (2.3.10) obviously implies the absolute and uniform convergence of the n component series to continuous functions on R^1 to R^1.

The estimate (2.3.9) obviously implies that

$$\|\mathbf{f}(x) - \mathbf{f}_m(x)\| \le \frac{K^m}{m!} M \exp(K|x - x_0|)|x - x_0|^m. \tag{2.3.11}$$

We see that if $|x - x_0|$ is not large, $\mathbf{f}_m(x)$ converges rapidly to its limit $\mathbf{f}(x)$. This is a much more rapid convergence than that guaranteed by Theorem 2.2.1 when they both apply.

From the uniform convergence of $\mathbf{f}_m(x)$ to $\mathbf{f}(x)$ it follows that $\mathbf{F}[s, \mathbf{f}_{m-1}(s)]$ converges uniformly to $\mathbf{F}[s, \mathbf{f}(s)]$ and

$$\int_{x_0}^{x} \mathbf{F}[s, \mathbf{f}_{m-1}(s)]\, ds \to \int_{x_0}^{x} \mathbf{F}[s, \mathbf{f}(s)]\, ds$$

uniformly in x. From (2.3.8) it then follows that $\mathbf{f}(x)$ satisfies (2.3.7) and consequently also the differential equation and the initial condition.

That this is the only solution also follows from the Lipschitz condition via Theorem 1.5.1. For suppose that $\mathbf{g}(x)$ is also a solution defined in some interval $(x_0 - r_1, x_0 + r_1)$. Then

$$\mathbf{g}(x) = \mathbf{y}_0 + \int_{x_0}^{x} \mathbf{F}[s, \mathbf{g}(s)]\, ds$$

and if $|x - x_0| < \min(r, r_1)$ we have

$$\|\mathbf{f}(x) - \mathbf{g}(x)\| = \left\| \int_{x_0}^{x} \{\mathbf{F}[s, \mathbf{f}(s)] - \mathbf{F}[s, \mathbf{g}(s)]\}\, ds \right\|$$

$$\le K \left| \int_{x_0}^{x} \|\mathbf{f}(s) - \mathbf{g}(s)\|\, ds \right| .$$

Now

$$h(x) \equiv \|\mathbf{f}(x) - \mathbf{g}(x)\|$$

is a continuous non-negative function that satisfies

$$0 \le h(x) \le K \left| \int_{x_0}^{x} h(s)\, ds \right| \tag{2.3.12}$$

and by Theorem 1.5.1 such a function is identically 0. Hence $\mathbf{f}(x)$ is the only solution of (2.3.2) with $\mathbf{f}(x_0) = \mathbf{y}_0$. ∎

Various questions arise when Theorem 2.3.1 is to be used. The first of these concerns the effective determination of a, b, and M and the verification of the Lipschitz condition. This usually has to be done in several steps. We start by choosing some admissible values of a and b. Here "admissible" means that $\mathbf{F}(x, \mathbf{y})$ should be continuous and bounded in the corresponding domain B. Again "bounded" means with respect to some one of the norms that can be used in R^n. Actually, if $\|\mathbf{F}(x, \mathbf{y})\|$ is bounded with respect to one norm, it is bounded with respect to all, but the numerical value of the supremum depends upon the choice of norm. The maximum co-ordinate norm gives the least value of the supremum and is usually also easier to handle numerically than the other norms. After the norm has been chosen and we have got at least an upper bound for $\|\mathbf{F}(x, \mathbf{y})\|$ in terms of a and b, say $M(a, b)$, the question of *optimization* becomes pertinent. We have

$$r < \min\left(a, \frac{b}{M(a, b)}\right)$$

and here the minimum is really a function of a and b. We want to choose a and b so that the minimum becomes as large as possible. Sometimes we can do this by a simple argument and sometimes not. Quite often the best we can do is to make a and $b/M(a, b)$ equal. This enables us to express b in terms of a and then find the best choice of a. The following examples will illustrate these aspects of the problem.

Example 1. Take the system

$$\begin{aligned} y_1' &= y_2 + xy_1^2, \\ y_2' &= y_1 + xy_2^2. \end{aligned} \qquad y_1(0) = y_2(0) = 0. \tag{2.3.13}$$

Here a and b are completely arbitrary positive numbers. With the maximum co-ordinate norm we get $M(a, b) = b + ab^2$ and we have the problem of maximizing

$$\min\left(a, \frac{1}{1 + ab}\right).$$

Equating a and $(1 + ab)^{-1}$ we get $b = (1 - a)/a^2$. Since b cannot be negative, this requires $a < 1$, but we can clearly take any $r < 1$ and obtain existence in the interval $(-r, r)$. Moreover, in this interval the norm of the solution does not exceed $(1 - r)/r^2$. This is arbitrarily small, if r is close to 1, so we conclude that the solution must be identically 0 in $(-r, r)$. This is confirmed by computing the successive approximations $f_m(x)$. They are identically 0 for all m and all x. This is evidently an exceptional situation.

Example 2. We take the same system but change the initial conditions to $y_1(0) = y_2(0) = 1$. The new value of $M(a, b)$ is

$$M(a, b) = (b + 1)(ab + a + 1).$$

Equating a and $b/M(a, b)$ we get the quadratic relation

$$a^2(b + 1)^2 + a(b + 1) - b = 0.$$

Solving for a this time we get

$$a = \tfrac{1}{2}[(1 + 4b)^{1/2} - 1](b + 1)^{-1},$$

the maximum of which equals $\frac{1}{3}$, its value for $b = 2$. Hence the solution exists for $|x| < \frac{1}{3}$ and $\|(y_1, y_2) - (1, 1)\| < 2$ in this interval.

So far we have neglected the Lipschitz condition. In particular, we have tacitly assumed that $\mathbf{F}(x, \mathbf{y})$ in the preceding examples does satisfy a Lipschitz condition. This is not difficult to verify, in fact the estimate

$$\|\mathbf{F}(x, \mathbf{y}_1) - \mathbf{F}(x, \mathbf{y}_2)\| \leq [1 + 2a(b + 1)]\|\mathbf{y}_1 - \mathbf{y}_2\| \tag{2.3.14}$$

holds in both cases. Unless we are interested in getting sharp estimates for the degree of approximation, the best value of K is of little importance as long as we can verify that a K can be found.

In most applications $\mathbf{F}(x, \mathbf{y})$ has first order partials with respect to the components of $\mathbf{y}$ and if these turn out to be uniformly bounded in B then a Lipschitz condition holds in B. This follows from a variant of the mean value theorem which shows that

$$F_j(x, \mathbf{y}_1) - F_j(x, \mathbf{y}_2) = (\nabla F_j, \mathbf{y}_1 - \mathbf{y}_2). \tag{2.3.15}$$

Here the right member is an inner product,

$$\nabla F_j = \left(\frac{\partial F_j}{\partial y_1}, \frac{\partial F_j}{\partial y_2}, \ldots, \frac{\partial F_j}{\partial y_n}\right),$$

and the partials are evaluated at some point $(x, \mathbf{y}_3)$ on the line segment joining $(x, \mathbf{y}_1)$ with $(x, \mathbf{y}_2)$. Suppose that

$$\max_{j,k} \max_{B} \left|\frac{\partial F_j}{\partial y_k}\right| = P.$$

Then, for any j,

$$|F_j(x, \mathbf{y}_1) - F_j(x, \mathbf{y}_2)| \leq nP\,\|\mathbf{y}_1 - \mathbf{y}_2\|$$

for the maximum co-ordinate norm. We have then also

$$\|\mathbf{F}(x, \mathbf{y}_1) - \mathbf{F}(x, \mathbf{y}_2)\| \leq nP\,\|\mathbf{y}_1 - \mathbf{y}_2\|, \tag{2.3.16}$$

so we have a Lipschitz condition with $K = nP$.

Let us remark in passing that it is not necessary in (2.3.8) to choose $\mathbf{f}_0(x) \equiv \mathbf{y}_0$. We can start with any continuous function $\mathbf{f}_0(x)$ such that $\mathbf{f}_0(x_0) = \mathbf{y}_0$ and $\|\mathbf{f}_0(x) - \mathbf{y}_0\| < b$. The proof is unchanged.

The role of the Lipschitz condition in Theorem 2.3.1 is twofold. It ensures convergence of the successive approximations and it guarantees uniqueness of the solution. It is not a necessary condition, however, and may be replaced by weaker assumptions without loss. We shall consider such an assumption, but let us first look at an example where the absence of a Lipschitz condition plays havoc with the solutions.

Example 3. Take

$$y' = |y|^{1/3}, \qquad y(x_0) = 0. \tag{2.3.17}$$

A relation

$$\big||y_1|^{1/3} - |y_2|^{1/3}\big| < K|y_1 - y_2|$$

cannot hold in any interval containing $y = 0$. It does hold if y is bounded away from 0 and then we can take for K the maximum value of $\frac{1}{3}y^{-2/3}$ in the interval. A simple calculation shows that

$$y_1(x) = (\tfrac{2}{3})^{3/2} \operatorname{sgn}(x - x_0)|x - x_0|^{3/2}$$

is a solution, and it is obvious that

$$y_2(x) \equiv 0$$

is also a solution. But this does not exhaust the possibilities. Take any two numbers x_1 and x_2, such that $x_1 < x_0 < x_2$ and define

$$f(x) = \begin{cases} -(\frac{2}{3})^{3/2}|x - x_1|^{3/2}, & x < x_1, \\ 0, & x_1 \le x \le x_2. \\ (\frac{2}{3})^{3/2}(x - x_2)^{3/2}, & x_2 < x. \end{cases} \tag{2.3.18}$$

This function is continuous together with its first derivative for all x, including the points $x = x_1$ and x_2, and it satisfies equation (2.3.17) for all x as well as the initial condition. Here x_1 and x_2 are completely arbitrary so we have an infinite number of solutions passing through $(x_0, 0)$.

All these solutions lie between two extremal solutions

$$f_l(x) = \begin{cases} -(\frac{2}{3})^{3/2}|x - x_0|^{3/2}, & x < x_0, \\ 0, & x_0 < x, \end{cases} \qquad f_u(x) = \begin{cases} 0, & x < x_0, \\ (\frac{2}{3})^{3/2}(x - x_0)^{3/2}, & x_0 < x. \end{cases}$$

These extremal solutions bound two curvilinear sectors, one S^- to the left of x_0 below the x-axis, the other S^+ to the right of x_0 above the x-axis. Through each interior point of one of these sectors passes one—and only one—integral curve which goes to the boundary of the sector, more precisely to the x-axis. From the point of tangency to the axis its continuation as an integral curve is ambiguous. If it comes from S^+, it may continue to the left an arbitrary distance along the x-axis and then branch off along a semi-cubical parabola into the lower half-plane. Some of these extensions pass through $x = x_0$ and are members of the family of solutions through $(x_0, 0)$. (See Figure 2.1.)

Thus we see that the absence of a Lipschitz condition may cause lack of uniqueness. It is natural to ask if the convergence of the successive approximations is also affected. Let us examine Example 3 from this point of view. It is easily seen that, if we take $f_0(x) \equiv 0$, then every $f_n(x) \equiv 0$ and the limit is the solution $y_2(x) \equiv 0$. A more interesting choice is

$$f_0(x) = (x - x_0)^\alpha, \qquad x_0 < x, \quad 0 < \alpha.$$

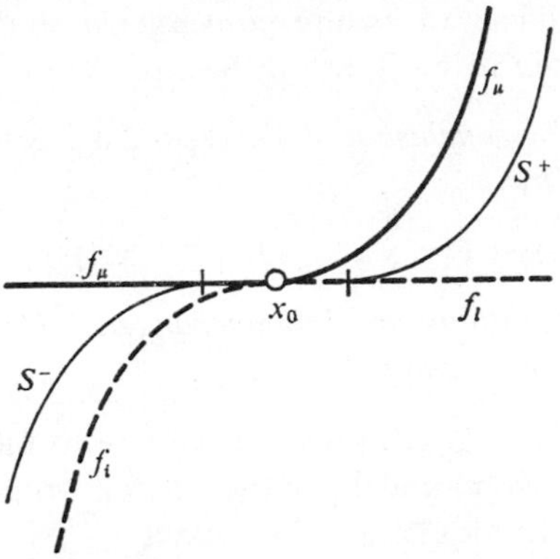

Figure 2.1

Then

$$f_n(x) = C_n(\alpha)(x - x_0)^{e_n(\alpha)},$$

where

$$e_n(\alpha) = 1 + \frac{1}{3} + \frac{1}{3^2} + \cdots + \frac{1}{3^{n-1}} + \frac{\alpha}{3^n} \to \frac{3}{2}. \tag{2.3.19}$$

Further, if we set

$$\frac{3}{3 + e_n(\alpha)} \equiv q_n(\alpha),$$

then

$$\begin{aligned} \log C_n(\alpha) &= \log q_n(\alpha) + \frac{1}{3}\log C_{n-1}(\alpha) \\ &= \log q_n(\alpha) + \frac{1}{3}\log q_{n-1}(\alpha) + \frac{1}{3^2}\log C_{n-2}(\alpha) \\ &\quad \cdot \quad \cdot \quad \cdot \quad \cdot \quad \cdot \quad \cdot \quad \cdot \quad \cdot \quad \cdot \quad \cdot \quad \cdot \quad \cdot \\ &= \log q_n(\alpha) + \frac{1}{3}\log q_{n-1}(\alpha) + \frac{1}{3^2}\log q_{n-2}(\alpha) \\ &\quad + \cdots + \frac{1}{3^{n-1}}\log q_1(\alpha) + \frac{1}{3^n}\log C_0(\alpha) \to \frac{3}{2}\log\frac{2}{3}, \end{aligned} \tag{2.3.20}$$

since $q_n(\alpha) \to \frac{2}{3}$. It follows that for every choice of $\alpha > 0$, the sequence $\{f_n(x)\}$ converges to the solution $y_1(x) = (\frac{2}{3})^{3/2}(x - x_0)^{3/2}$. Thus the lack of a Lipschitz condition need not impede the convergence of the successive approximations. We note, however, that the choice of the initial approximation may affect the final outcome. We got one solution for $f_0(x) \equiv 0$, another for $f_0(x) = (x - x_0)^\alpha$.

We return to the question of relaxing the Lipschitz condition. The following theorem (due to C. Carathéodory (1918)) involves a weaker condition that still suffices to ensure convergence and uniqueness. Other uniqueness theorems are to be found in Section 2.6.

Theorem 2.3.2. *The conclusion of Theorem* 2.3.1 *is unchanged if condition* (2.3.4) *is replaced by*

$$\|\mathbf{F}(x, \mathbf{y}_1) - \mathbf{F}(x, \mathbf{y}_2)\| \le K(|x - x_0|)\|\mathbf{y}_1 - \mathbf{y}_2\|, \tag{2.3.21}$$

while the other conditions are left unchanged. Here $K(u)$ is a positive function in $L(0, a)$, continuous for $u > 0$.

Proof. Since (2.3.3) is unaltered, the approximations $\mathbf{f}_m(x)$ can be defined by (2.3.8) for $x - x_0$ in $(-r, r)$ and have the desired properties. It remains to prove convergence and uniqueness. Let us set

$$J(x) = \int_0^x K(u)\, du. \tag{2.3.22}$$

This is an absolutely continuous function which tends to 0 with x. We have now

$$\begin{aligned}\|\mathbf{f}_2(x) - \mathbf{f}_1(x)\| &\le \left| \int_{x_0}^x K(|s - x_0|)\|\mathbf{f}_1(s) - \mathbf{f}_0(s)\|\, ds \right| \\ &\le MrJ(|x - x_0|).\end{aligned}$$

Suppose that for some m we have

$$\|\mathbf{f}_{m-1}(s) - \mathbf{f}_{m-2}(s)\| \le \frac{Mr}{(m-2)!}[J(|s - x_0|)]^{m-2}.$$

Then we obtain

$$\begin{aligned}\|\mathbf{f}_m(x) - \mathbf{f}_{m-1}(x)\| &\le \left| \int_{x_0}^x K(|s - x_0|)\|\mathbf{f}_{m-1}(s) - \mathbf{f}_{m-2}(s)\|\, ds \right| \\ &\le \frac{Mr}{(m-2)!} \left| \int_{x_0}^x K(|s - x_0|)[J(|s - x_0|)]^{m-2}\, ds \right| \\ &= \frac{Mr}{(m-2)!} \int_0^{|x-x_0|} [J(u)]^{m-2} J'(u)\, du \\ &= \frac{Mr}{(m-1)!}[J(|x - x_0|)]^{m-1},\end{aligned}$$

and the estimate is true for all m since it obviously holds for $m = 2$. It follows that

$$\lim_{m\to\infty} \mathbf{f}_m(x) \equiv \mathbf{f}(x)$$

exists and

$$\|\mathbf{f}(x) - \mathbf{f}_m(x)\| \le \frac{Mr}{m!}[J(|x - x_0|)]^m \exp[J(|x - x_0|)]. \tag{2.3.23}$$

That $\mathbf{f}(x)$ satisfies the differential equation and the initial condition follows from the uniform convergence of $\mathbf{f}_m(x)$ to $\mathbf{f}(x)$.

The uniqueness of the solution follows this time from Theorem 1.5.2. For if we have two solutions $\mathbf{f}(x)$ and $\mathbf{g}(x)$, then

$$h(x) = \|\mathbf{f}(x) - \mathbf{g}(x)\|$$

is a continuous non-negative function that satisfies

$$0 \leq h(x) \leq \left| \int_{x_0}^{x} K(|s - x_0|)h(s)\, ds \right| \tag{2.3.24}$$

and, by Theorem 1.5.2, this implies $h(x) \equiv 0$. Hence the solution is unique. ∎

So far we have restricted ourselves to differential equations of finite order. We can however apply the method of successive approximations to certain types of infinite systems. In particular, this method can be used to give another proof for Theorem 2.2.2 where we can dispense with the condition $rK < 1$.

EXERCISE 2.3

1. If $\alpha > 1$ and $x_1 = x$, $x_n = \alpha \arctan x_{n-1}$, $n > 1$, prove the existence of $\lim x_n$.
2. In (2.3.20) we have made use of the following lemma. If $\sum_0^\infty a_n = S$ is absolutely convergent and if $\lim b_n = b$, then
$$\lim\,(a_0b_n + a_1b_{n-1} + \cdots + a_nb_0) = Sb.$$
Prove this!
3. Solve $y' = 2|y|^{1/2}$ for $x > 0$ using the method of successive approximations and taking $f_0(x) = x^\alpha$, $\alpha > 0$.
4. Solve $y' = y + x$, $y(0) = C$, by the method of successive approximations.
5. If $y(x)$ is a solution of
$$y'' - x^2y = 0, \qquad y(0) = y_{01}, \qquad y'(0) = y_{02},$$
show that
$$y(x) = y_{01} + y_{02}x + \int_0^x (x - s)s^2y(s)\, ds.$$
Use the method of successive approximations to find $y(s)$ in the special case $y_{01} = 1$, $y_{02} = 0$. Take $f_0(x) \equiv 1$.
6. Given $y' = y^2$, $y(0) = 1$. Find r and find the third approximation if $f_0(x) \equiv 1$.
7. Given $y' = 1 + y^2$, $y(0) = 0$. If $f_0(x) \equiv 0$, the nth approximation $f_n(x)$ is a polynomial in x. Find its degree. How large must n be taken in order that the first three terms of lowest degree of $f_n(x)$ agree with the first three non-zero terms of the tangent series?

8. If $y' = 1 + y^4$, $y(0) = 0$ and we take $f_0(x) = x$, prove that $f_n(x)$ is of the form x times a polynomial in x^4 with positive coefficients. What is the degree of $f_n(x)$?
9. Find the solution of the system
$$y_n'(x) = \frac{1}{n}[y_1(x) + y_2(x) + \cdots + y_n(x)], \qquad n = 1, 2, 3, \ldots,$$
if $y_1(0) = 1$, $y_k(0) = 0$, $k > 1$. Does the solution belong to (l)?
10. In the preceding problem, replace the multipliers $1/n$ by $1/n^2$. Prove that the resulting system satisfies the conditions of Theorem 2.2.2.
11. The *Thomas-Fermi equation*
$$x^{1/2}y'' = y^{3/2}$$
arises in nuclear physics. Show that it has a solution of the form Cx^α. Show also that it can be transformed into a system to which Theorem 2.3.2 applies so that there are solutions in some interval $[0, r]$ satisfying an initial condition of the form $y(0) = a > 0$, $y'(0) = b$.
12. By the Corollary of Theorem 1.4.1 it is known that a transformation T has a unique fixed point if some power of T is a contraction. Prove that this holds for the transformation defined by (2.2.10). Use this to give an alternate proof of the existence theorem. This device eliminates the condition $rK < 1$. [*Hint*: The calculations involve some of the estimates used in the proof of Theorem 2.3.1.]

2.4 THE CAUCHY-LIPSCHITZ-PEANO METHOD

We proceed to a more general existence theorem where there is no claim of uniqueness. The method goes back to Cauchy in the 1820's, refinements were added by R. Lipschitz (1876) and the modern version of the method, based on considerations of compactness, i.e. the theorem of Arzelà, is due to G. Peano in 1890.

In the plane a useful method of constructing approximate solutions is based on the vector field defined by the equation
$$y' = F(x, y). \tag{2.4.1}$$
If $F(x, y)$ is continuous in a domain
$$D: |x - x_0| < a, \qquad |y - y_0| < b,$$
we mark at each point $(x_1, y_1) \in D$ the local unit vector of slope $F(x_1, y_1) \equiv \tan \alpha_1$, $-\frac{1}{2}\pi < \alpha_1 < \frac{1}{2}\pi$. This is the vector $(\cos \alpha_1, \sin \alpha_1)$ with initial point at (x_1, y_1). See Figure 2.2, where $F(x, y) = x + y$ and vectors are marked at points (m, n). In this connection, the vectors are often referred to as *lineal elements* of the equation. The integration problem calls for the determination

of a system of curves, the *integral curves* of (2.4.1), such that at each point (x_1, y_1) the curve is tangent to the lineal element, i.e. its tangent vector has the same direction as the local vector of the field.

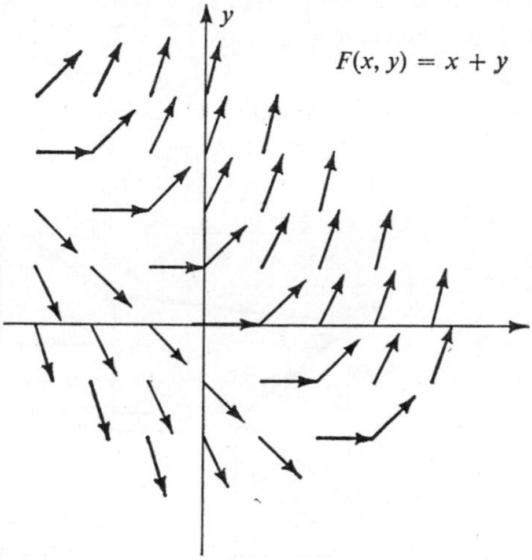

Figure 2.2

We can get some idea of the integral curves by approximating them by polygonal lines made up of short line segments, each line segment having the direction of the local vector at, for example its left end-point. This procedure can be extended in principle to n dimensions and can be developed into an existence proof by combining it with a limiting process. This we proceed to do.

Consider

$$\mathbf{y}' = \mathbf{F}(x, \mathbf{y}), \qquad \mathbf{y}(x_0) = \mathbf{y}_0. \tag{2.4.2}$$

Suppose that $\mathbf{F}(x, \mathbf{y})$ is continuous in

$$D: |x - x_0| < a, \qquad \|\mathbf{y} - \mathbf{y}_0\| < b \tag{2.4.3}$$

where D lies in $R^1 \times R^n$ and suppose that

$$\|\mathbf{F}(x, \mathbf{y})\| \leq M \tag{2.4.4}$$

in D. We choose

$$r < \min\left(a, \frac{b}{M}\right). \tag{2.4.5}$$

We shall give the existence proof for the interval $[x_0, x_0 + r]$ rather than $[x_0 - r, x_0 + r]$, the extension to $[x_0 - r, x_0]$ is immediate. We divide the interval $[x_0, x_0 + r]$ into 2^m equal parts and set

$$x_{jm} = x_0 + j2^{-m}r.$$

We shall now define a sequence of piecewise linear functions $\{\mathbf{f}_m(x)\}$. The general idea is the following. From the point $(x_0, \mathbf{y}_0)$ we proceed to the point $(x_{1m}, \mathbf{y}_{1m})$ along a straight line in the direction given by $\mathbf{F}(x_0, \mathbf{y}_0)$. From $(x_{1m}, \mathbf{y}_{1m})$ we go to $(x_{2m}, \mathbf{y}_{2m})$ in the direction given by $\mathbf{F}(x_{1m}, \mathbf{y}_{1m})$ and so on. See Figure 2.3, where an attempt has been made to represent such a broken line in three space. Here $n = 2$ and $m = 2$. If $(x, \mathbf{y})$ is a point on the polygonal line, then

$$\mathbf{f}_m(x) = \mathbf{y}.$$

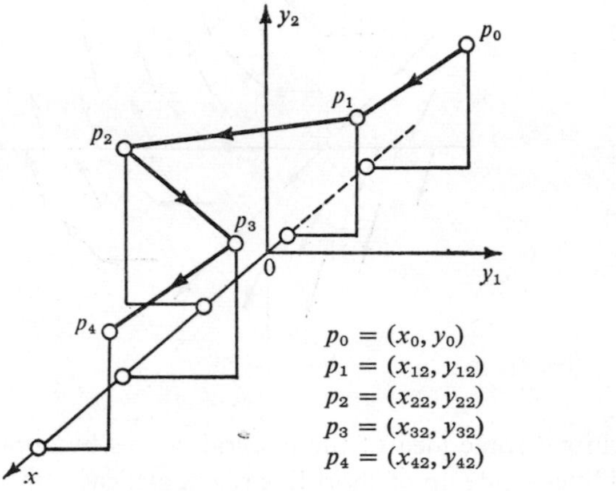

Figure 2.3

This amounts to defining $\mathbf{f}_m(x)$ by the following formulas:

$$\begin{aligned} \mathbf{f}_m(x) &= \mathbf{y}_0 + \mathbf{F}(x_0, \mathbf{y}_0)(x - x_0), & x_0 \le x \le x_{1m}, \\ \mathbf{f}_m(x) &= \mathbf{y}_{jm} + \mathbf{F}(x_{jm}, \mathbf{y}_{jm})(x - x_{jm}), & x_{jm} \le x \le x_{j+1,m} \end{aligned} \tag{2.4.6}$$

where $j = 1, 2, 3, \ldots, 2^m - 1$ and

$$\mathbf{y}_{jm} = \mathbf{f}_m(x_{jm}).$$

Lemma 2.4.1. *The functions* $\mathbf{f}_m(x)$ *are uniformly bounded and equicontinuous in* $[x_0, x_0 + r]$.

Proof. In the jth interval

$$\|\mathbf{f}_m(x) - \mathbf{y}_{jm}\| \le \|\mathbf{F}(x_{jm}, \mathbf{y}_{jm})\| 2^{-m} r \le M 2^{-m} r.$$

This gives

$$\begin{aligned} \|\mathbf{f}_m(x) - \mathbf{y}_0\| &\le \|\mathbf{f}_m(x) - \mathbf{y}_{jm}\| + \|\mathbf{y}_{jm} - \mathbf{y}_{j-1,m}\| \\ &\quad + \|\mathbf{y}_{j-1,m} - \mathbf{y}_{j-2,m}\| + \cdots + \|\mathbf{y}_{1m} - \mathbf{y}_0\| \\ &\le (j + 1) M 2^{-m} r \le Mr < b \end{aligned}$$

by the choice of r. This shows that the $\mathbf{f}_m(x)$ are uniformly bounded in $[x_0, x_0 + r]$.

Let ξ_1 and ξ_2 be two points in $[x_0, x_0 + r]$ with $|\xi_1 - \xi_2| \leq 2^{-m}r$. They are then either in the same subinterval or in adjacent ones. In either case

$$\|\mathbf{f}_m(\xi_1) - \mathbf{f}_m(\xi_2)\| \leq M|\xi_1 - \xi_2|. \tag{2.4.7}$$

Here we can obviously dispense with the restriction $|\xi_1 - \xi_2| \leq 2^{-m}r$. For if $|\xi_1 - \xi_2| > 2^{-m}r$, we can break up the interval $[\xi_1, \xi_2]$ into subintervals of length $<2^{-m}r$ and use (2.4.7) for each subinterval. Adding the resulting inequalities we get on the left a sum $\geq \|\mathbf{f}_m(\xi_1) - \mathbf{f}_m(\xi_2)\|$, while on the right we get $M|\xi_1 - \xi_2|$. This shows that (2.4.7) holds for any choice of ξ_1, ξ_2 in $[x_0, x_0 + r]$ and for any choice of m. Hence the functions $\mathbf{f}_m(x)$ satisfy a fixed Lipschitz condition and form an equicontinuous family. ∎

By Theorem 1.6.2 we can find a subsequence $\{\mathbf{f}_{m_k}(x)\}$ which converges uniformly in $[x_0, x_0 + r]$ to a continuous function $\mathbf{f}(x)$. We shall examine the differentiability of $\mathbf{f}(x)$.

Each function $\mathbf{f}_m(x)$ is piecewise linear and hence piecewise differentiable. At the partition points x_{jm} the derivative does not exist but we have left- and right-hand derivatives and for large values of m these derivatives differ very little.

Take a value ξ, $x_0 \leq \xi < x_0 + r$. If $\xi = x_0$, every $\mathbf{f}_m'(x_0) = \mathbf{F}(x_0, \mathbf{y}_0)$ so we have also $f'(x_0) = \mathbf{F}(x_0, \mathbf{y}_0)$. This is actually the right-hand derivative but a discussion of the interval $[x_0 - r, x_0]$ shows that the left-hand derivative has the same value. Suppose now that $x_0 < \xi$ and determine for each k the corresponding j such that

$$x_{j-1,m_k} < \xi \leq x_{j,m_k}.$$

Then for the left-hand derivative we have

$$D^-\mathbf{f}_{m_k}(\xi) = \mathbf{F}\big(x_{j-1,m_k}, \mathbf{f}_{m_k}(x_{j-1,m_k})\big),$$

while the right-hand derivative $D^+\mathbf{f}_{m_k}(\xi)$ either has the same value or equals

$$\mathbf{F}\big(\xi, \mathbf{f}_{m_k}(\xi)\big) \qquad \text{if} \qquad \xi = x_{j,m_k}.$$

Now $x_{j-1,m_k} \to \xi$ and

$$\begin{aligned}\|\mathbf{f}_{m_k}(x_{j-1,m_k}) - \mathbf{f}(\xi)\| &\leq \|\mathbf{f}_{m_k}(x_{j-1,m_k}) - \mathbf{f}_{m_k}(\xi)\| + \|\mathbf{f}_{m_k}(\xi) - \mathbf{f}(\xi)\| \\ &\leq M2^{-m_k}r + \|\mathbf{f}_{m_k}(\xi) - \mathbf{f}(\xi)\| \to 0\end{aligned}$$

as $k \to \infty$ and this implies that

$$\mathbf{F}\big(x_{j-1,m_k}, \mathbf{f}_{m_k}(x_{j-1,m_k})\big) \to \mathbf{F}\big(\xi, \mathbf{f}(\xi)\big)$$

since $\mathbf{F}$ is continuous in both arguments simultaneously. Thus $\mathbf{f}'(x)$ exists for all x in $[x_0, x_0 + r]$ and

$$\mathbf{f}'(x) = \mathbf{F}[x, \mathbf{f}(x)]. \tag{2.4.8}$$

This proves

Theorem 2.4.1. *Suppose that* $\mathbf{F}(x, \mathbf{y})$ *is defined and continuous in* $D: |x - x_0| < a$, $\|y - y_0\| < b$ *where* D *lies in* $R^1 \times R^n$, *and suppose that* $\|\mathbf{F}(x, \mathbf{y})\| \leq M$ *in* D. *Then the differential equation*

$$\mathbf{y}' = \mathbf{F}(x, \mathbf{y})$$

with the initial condition $\mathbf{y}(x_0) = \mathbf{y}_0$, *has at least one solution* $\mathbf{f}(x)$ *defined in the interval* $[x_0 - r, x_0 + r]$ *where*

$$r < \min\left(a, \frac{b}{M}\right).$$

We note that any limit function of the sequence $\{\mathbf{f}_m(x)\}$ is a solution of the differential equation. Thus if the sequence does not have a unique limit, the solution of the differential equation passing through the point $(x_0, \mathbf{y}_0)$ is not unique.

That non-uniqueness can arise in the absence of a Lipschitz condition or similar restriction was shown in the preceding section. Thus, in the case of equation (2.3.17), there is an infinite number of solutions passing through an arbitrary point $(x_0, 0)$ on the x-axis. We found a *maximal solution* $y^+(x)$ and a *minimal solution* $y^-(x)$ such that every solution through $(x_0, 0)$ satisfies

$$y^-(x) \leq y(x) \leq y^+(x).$$

Actually this is a general phenomenon.

We shall prove this for the plane case

$$y' = F(x, y), \qquad y(x_0) = y_0, \tag{2.4.9}$$

where F is continuous and bounded in some domain D, say a rectangle containing (x_0, y_0). We know the existence of an r such that in the interval $[x_0 - r, x_0 + r]$ there is at least one solution of (2.4.9). Let S be the family of solutions passing through (x_0, y_0). Let us set

$$f^-(x) = \inf_{f \in S} f(x), \qquad f^+(x) = \sup_{f \in S} f(x). \tag{2.4.10}$$

If S reduces to a single element, then $f^- = f^+ = f$. Suppose this is not the case. We then note that f^+ and f^- are continuous functions of x in $[x_0 - r, x_0 + r]$, which in fact satisfy the same Lipschitz condition as all the functions of S. For if $f_\alpha \in S$ and x_1 lies in the interval under consideration, then

$$f_\alpha(x_1 + h) \leq f_\alpha(x_1) + M|h| \leq f^+(x_1) + M|h|,$$

and this is true for all α. Hence

$$f^+(x_1 + h) \leq f^+(x_1) + M|h|.$$

On the other hand,

$$f^+(x_1 + h) \geq f_\alpha(x_1 + h) \geq f_\alpha(x_1) - M|h|,$$

and this holds for all α, hence also for the supremum so that

$$f^+(x_1 + h) \geq f^+(x_1) - M|h|.$$

Combining, we see that

$$|f^+(x_1 + h) - f^+(x_1)| \leq M|h|.$$

Similarly we prove that

$$|f^-(x + h) - f^-(x)| \leq M|h|.$$

Actually f^+ and f^- are elements of S. To show this, we prove first that they can be approximated uniformly by elements of S. Given any $\varepsilon > 0$, we can find an integer m, a partition of $[x_0, x_0 + r]$ into m subintervals, and m elements f_j of S, such that in the jth subinterval

$$f^+(x) - f_j(x) < \varepsilon.$$

Next we set

$$f^*(x) = \sup_j f_j(x), \qquad x_0 \leq x \leq x_0 + r.$$

This function is piecewise differentiable since each $f_j \in S$. Moreover, at a transition point where the supremum passes from an f_j to an f_k, the derivative of f^* changes continuously. For at such a point, f_j and f_k are solutions of (2.4.9), having the same slope, and this is also the slope of f^*. Thus $f^* \in S$ and f^* is within an ε-distance from f^+ throughout the interval $[x_0, x_0 + r]$.

Here ε is arbitrary. It follows that we can find a sequence $\{f_p\} \subset S$ such that $f_p(x) \to f^+(x)$ uniformly in x. Since

$$f_p(x) = y_0 + \int_{x_0}^{x} F[s, f_p(s)]\, ds,$$

it follows that

$$f^+(x) = y_0 + \int_{x_0}^{x} F[s, f^+(s)]\, ds,$$

i.e. $f^+ \in S$. In the same way we show that $f^- \in S$. This implies that every solution $f(x)$ of (2.4.9) lies between the two extremal solutions

$$f^-(x) \leq f(x) \leq f^+(x), \qquad x_0 - r \leq x \leq x_0 + r, \qquad (2.4.11)$$

since obviously the argument extends to the interval $[x_0 - r, x_0]$.

EXERCISE 2.4

Determine f^- and f^+ for the following equations at the points indicated

1. $y' = (1 - y^2)^{1/2}$, $y(0) = 1$, $|x| < \frac{1}{2}\pi$.

2. $y' = |y|^\alpha$, $y(0) = 0$, $0 < \alpha < 1$.
3. Find constant solutions of the equation

$$y' = \prod_{k=0}^{n} \left| y - \frac{k}{n} \right|^{1/2}.$$

Are there other solutions having the same initial values (as the constant solutions) for $x = 0$? Find the solutions explicitly for $n = 1$.

2.5 THE CAUCHY-LINDELÖF METHOD

In 1671 Sir Isaac Newton wrote a treatise on what he called *fluxional equations.* It was published in 1736 after his death. Here he developed a method of solving differential equations by power series with undetermined coefficients, and he claimed that all such equations could be solved by this method.

The first real examination of the scope of this method is due to Cauchy (1842) who supplied convergence proofs based on what he called a *Calcul des limites* (calculus of bounds rather than limits). This is a method of *majorants* (see below). A majorant for the equation provides a majorant for the solution and, if the second majorant converges, so does the solution. Cauchy used a particular majorant furnished by the theory of functions of two complex variables. In 1896 Ernst Lindelöf observed that a better majorant could be found and that the whole discussion could be given in the real domain, using rather elementary means. This method will be given in what follows.

We shall be concerned with the equation

$$w' = F(z, w), \qquad w(0) = 0, \tag{2.5.1}$$

where $F(z, w)$ is given by a convergent double series

$$F(z, w) \equiv \sum_{j=0}^{\infty} \sum_{k=0}^{\infty} a_{jk} z^j w^k. \tag{2.5.2}$$

The assumption on $F(z, w)$ implies the existence of two positive numbers, s and t, such that

$$\sum_{j=0}^{\infty} \sum_{k=0}^{\infty} |a_{jk}| s^j t^k \equiv M(s, t) < \infty. \tag{2.5.3}$$

We write $M(s, t)$ to recall that the bound is a function of s and t, which numbers can be chosen in infinitely many different ways. It may happen that there are two fixed numbers, R_1 and R_2, such that the double series is absolutely convergent for all z and w with $|z| < R_1$, $|w| < R_2$. It is more common, however, that R_1 and R_2 are variable so that we can consider R_2 as a function of R_1. Thus, for the three power series

$$\sum_{j=0}^{\infty}\sum_{k=0}^{\infty} z^j w^k, \qquad \sum_{j=1}^{\infty} z^j w^j, \qquad \text{and} \qquad \sum_{j=0}^{\infty}\sum_{k=0}^{\infty}\binom{j+k}{j} z^j w^k,$$

we have

$$R_1 = R_2 = 1, \qquad R_1R_2 = 1, \qquad \text{and} \qquad R_1 + R_2 = 1,$$

respectively.

We shall have to use various properties of power series in one variable. We list these as lemmas for reference.

Lemma 2.5.1. *A power series*

$$\sum_0^{\infty} c_n z^n \equiv f(z)$$

has a radius of convergence R such that the series is absolutely convergent for $|z| < R$ *and diverges for* $|z| > R$ *because the terms are unbounded. We may have* $R = 0$ *or* $0 < R < \infty$ *or* $R = \infty$.

Lemma 2.5.2. *A power series can be differentiated termwise as often as we please, the derived series having the same radius of convergence R. If the sum of the given series is* $f(z)$, *the sum of the* k^{th} *derived series is* $f^{(k)}(z)$.

Lemma 2.5.3. *Two power series*

$$\sum_0^{\infty} a_n z^n \equiv f(z), \qquad \sum_0^{\infty} b_n z^n \equiv g(z),$$

convergent for $|z| < R$, *have a Cauchy product series*

$$\sum_{n=0}^{\infty} (a_0b_n + a_1b_{n-1} + \cdots + a_nb_0)z^n$$

which is absolutely convergent for $|z| < R$ *and the sum of the series is then* $f(z)g(z)$. *This extends to any number of factors.*

Lemma 2.5.4. *If* $\sum c_n z^n$ *converges for* $|z| < R$, *then so does its* k^{th} *power*

$$\left[\sum_0^{\infty} c_n z^n\right]^k \equiv \sum_0^{\infty} c_n^{(k)} z^n.$$

The coefficients $c_n^{(k)}$ *are multinomials in* $c_0, c_1, \ldots, c_n$ *with coefficients that are positive integers.*

Lemma 2.5.5. *Let s and t be two positive numbers for which the series* (2.5.2) *satisfies* (2.5.3). *If r is chosen so that $r \leq s$ and*

$$\sum_{1}^{\infty} |c_n| r^n \leq t,$$

then the multiple series

$$\sum_{j=0}^{\infty} \sum_{k=0}^{\infty} a_{jk} z^j \left[\sum_{1}^{\infty} c_n z^n \right]^k$$

is absolutely convergent for $|z| \leq r$ and can be rearranged as a power series in z.

For

$$\sum_{j=0}^{\infty} \sum_{k=0}^{\infty} |a_{jk}| r^j \left[\sum_{1}^{\infty} |c_n| r^n \right]^k \leq \sum_{0}^{\infty} \sum_{0}^{\infty} |a_{jk}| s^j t^k = M(s, t),$$

and an absolutely convergent multiple series can be rearranged and summed in any manner we please.

Lemma 2.5.6. *Two power series represent the same function iff their coefficients are identical.*

Returning to the problem described in (2.5.1), (2.5.2), and (2.5.3), we can now state and prove the main result.

Theorem 2.5.1. *There exists a uniquely determined power series*

$$\sum_{n=1}^{\infty} c_n z^n, \tag{2.5.4}$$

absolutely convergent for $|z| \leq r$ where

$$r = \min \left[s, \frac{t}{M(s, t)} \right]. \tag{2.5.5}$$

such that

$$\frac{d}{dz} \left\{ \sum_{n=1}^{\infty} c_n z^n \right\} = \sum_{j=0}^{\infty} \sum_{k=0}^{\infty} a_{jk} z^j \left[\sum_{n=1}^{\infty} c_n z^n \right]^k, \tag{2.5.6}$$

where all the series are absolutely convergent for $|z| \leq r$. Thus the series (2.5.4) *is a solution of the differential equation* (2.5.1).

Remarks. The proof involves a number of steps. First we show how to determine the coefficients c_n to find the formal series (2.5.4). Then we observe that the majorant equation

$$W' = \sum_{j=0}^{\infty} \sum_{k=0}^{\infty} |a_{jk}| z^j W^k \tag{2.5.7}$$

has a formal solution

$$W = \sum_{n=1}^{\infty} C_n z^n, \tag{2.5.8}$$

where $C_n \geq 0$ and $|c_n| \leq C_n$ for all n. Next, using an induction argument on the partial sums of (2.5.8) we show that this series is absolutely convergent for $|z| \leq r$ and satisfies (2.5.7) for such values of z. The final conclusion is then immediate.

Proof. The first step is based on Lemma 2.5.5. We substitute into the differential equation the series (2.5.4), whose coefficients are to be determined, obtaining the formal relation (2.5.6). Now if the series (2.5.4) has a positive radius of convergence, then we can find an $r \leq s$ such that

$$\sum_{n=1}^{\infty} |c_n| r^n \leq t;$$

for, since the series on the left has no constant term, its sum is arbitrarily small for sufficiently small values of r: in particular, we can make the sum $\leq t$. In these circumstances, Lemma 2.5.5 applies and shows that the right member of (2.5.6) can be rewritten as a convergent power series in z. It now becomes a question of determining the coefficients of the various powers of z.

When we expand

$$\sum_{j=0}^{\infty} \sum_{k=0}^{\infty} a_{jk} z^j \left[\sum_{n=1}^{\infty} c_n z^n \right]^k$$

and collect terms, a given power of z, say z^p, can occur only in a finite number of places. For

$$\left[\sum_{n=1}^{\infty} c_n z^n \right]^k = \sum_{n=k}^{\infty} c_n^{(k)} z^n$$

starts with a term in z^k and will contain z^p only if $k \leq p$. But we have also to take into account the multipliers z^j. Again we must have $j \leq p$. Taking these facts into account, we see that the coefficient of z^p is

$$\sum a_{jk} c_n^{(k)},$$

where the summation extends over those values of j and k for which $0 \leq j$, $0 \leq k$, $j + k \leq p$. We now recall that

$$c_n^{(k)} = M_k(c_1, c_2, \ldots, c_n)$$

is a multinomial in the arguments shown. Hence in the right member of (2.5.6) the coefficient of z^p equals

$$\sum a_{jk} M_k(c_1, c_2, \ldots, c_{p-j}) \tag{2.5.9}$$

with j and k restricted as stated.

On the other hand, the coefficient of z^p in the left member of (2.5.6) is simply

$$(p + 1)c_{p+1}.$$

By Lemma 2.5.6 we have then for all $p \geq 1$

$$(p + 1)c_{p+1} = \sum_{j+k \leq p} a_{jk}M_k(c_1, c_2, \ldots, c_{p-j}). \tag{2.5.10}$$

For $p = 0$ we get simply

$$c_1 = a_{00}. \tag{2.5.11}$$

With the aid of these formulas we can compute $c_1, c_2, \ldots, c_p, \ldots$ consecutively. The formulas for c_2 to c_4 read

$$2c_2 = a_{10} + a_{01}c_1,$$

$$3c_3 = a_{20} + a_{11}c_1 + a_{02}c_1^2 + a_{01}c_2,$$

$$4c_4 = a_{30} + a_{21}c_1 + a_{12}c_1^2 + a_{03}c_1^3 + 2a_{02}c_1c_2 + a_{11}c_2 + a_{01}c_3.$$

For larger values of p, the formulas become increasingly more complicated, but the general structure is clear and in principle we can determine all coefficients uniquely. This is the first step.

For the second step we replace Eq. (2.5.1) by (2.5.7) and compute the formal solution (2.5.8). Here

$$\begin{aligned} C_1 &= |a_{00}| = |c_1|, \\ (p + 1)C_{p+1} &= \sum |a_{jk}|M_k(C_1, C_2, \ldots, C_{p-j}). \end{aligned} \tag{2.5.12}$$

On the other hand

$$\begin{aligned} (p + 1)|c_{p+1}| &\leq \sum |a_{jk}|\,|M_k(c_1, c_2, \ldots, c_{p-j})| \\ &\leq \sum |a_{jk}|M_k(|c_1|, |c_2|, \ldots, |c_{p-j}|), \end{aligned}$$

since the multinomials have positive coefficients. Suppose it be known that

$$|c_j| \leq C_j \quad \text{for} \quad j = 1, 2, \ldots, p.$$

We have then

$$(p + 1)|c_{p+1}| \leq \sum |a_{jk}|M_k(C_1, C_2, \ldots, C_{p-j}) = (p + 1)C_{p+1}$$

or

$$|c_{p+1}| \leq C_{p+1}. \tag{2.5.13}$$

Since the induction hypothesis is valid for $p = 1$, this holds for all p. This is the second step.

We have now to prove that the formal solution (2.5.8) of (2.5.7) is an actual solution by proving the convergence of the series. Let x be a real positive number and set

$$P_n(x) \equiv \sum_{p=0}^{n} C_p x^p. \tag{2.5.14}$$

We have now to consider the two polynomials

$$P'_{n+1}(x) \quad \text{and} \quad \sum_{j=0}^{n} \sum_{k=0}^{n} |a_{jk}| x^j [P_n(x)]^k.$$

The first is of degree n, the second of degree $n(n+1)$. All coefficients are positive. Since in formula (2.5.12) figure only the coefficients a_{jk} with $j \le p$, $k \le p$ and only C_m's with $m \le p$, it follows the terms of degree $\le n$ are the same for both polynomials. Hence

$$P'_{n+1}(x) \le \sum_{j=0}^{n} \sum_{k=0}^{n} |a_{jk}| x^j [P_n(x)]^k.$$

Suppose it be known that

$$P_n(x) \le t \quad \text{for} \quad 0 \le x \le r, \tag{2.5.15}$$

where r is chosen subject to (2.5.5). Then

$$\begin{aligned} P'_{n+1}(x) &\le \sum_{j=0}^{n} \sum_{k=0}^{n} |a_{jk}| r^j [P_n(r)]^k \\ &\le \sum_{j=0}^{n} \sum_{k=0}^{n} |a_{jk}| s^j t^k \le M(s, t). \end{aligned}$$

For $0 \le x \le r$, this gives

$$P_{n+1}(x) \le xM(s, t) \le rM(s, t) \le t$$

by the choice of r. Now

$$P_1(x) = |a_{00}| x \le rM(s, t) \le t,$$

so that (2.5.15) holds for $n = 1$. Hence it holds for all n.

But if (2.5.15) holds for all n, then

$$\sum_{p=1}^{\infty} C_p x^p \le t \quad \text{for} \quad 0 \le x \le r,$$

i.e. the formal solution (2.5.8) of (2.5.7) is actually absolutely convergent for $|z| \le r$. By virtue of Lemma 2.5.5 the formal solution is then an actual solution of (2.5.7) for $|z| \le r$. This is the third step.

Finally we observe that (2.5.13) implies that

$$\sum_{p=1}^{\infty} c_p z^p$$

is absolutely convergent for $|z| \leq r$. This means that the substitution of the series (2.5.4) into the differential equation, the expansion of powers and the rearrangement of the resulting series into a single power series are legitimate operations. Since the coefficients are determined by the condition that the two sides of (2.5.6) are identical power series, we see that the formal solution (2.5.4) of (2.5.1) is an actual solution. It is clearly uniquely determined. ▮

The choice of r given by (2.5.5) is evidently highly flexible and it is in general difficult to make an optimum choice of s and t, i.e. a choice which gives the largest possible value for r that this method can furnish. In the following special case such a choice can be made. Take

$$w' = z^3 + w^3, \qquad w(0) = 0. \tag{2.5.16}$$

Here s and t are arbitrary positive numbers and

$$M(s, t) = s^3 + t^3.$$

For a fixed $s > 0$ the maximum of

$$\frac{t}{M(s, t)} \quad \text{is} \quad \tfrac{1}{3}2^{2/3}s^{-2}.$$

This is a decreasing function of s so the optimal choice of s is that for which

$$\tfrac{1}{3}2^{2/3}s^{-2} = s \quad \text{or} \quad s = 2^{2/9}3^{-1/3}.$$

This gives

$$r < 2^{2/9}3^{-1/3}.$$

This is the best that the method can give. It is fairly poor since actually the radius of convergence of the series is >1. For this assertion and some further properties of the solution of (2.5.16), see Problems 4 to 9 in the exercise below.

Given two power series

$$\sum_{n=0}^{\infty} a_n z^n \quad \text{and} \quad \sum_{n=0}^{\infty} b_n z^n$$

we say that the second series is a *majorant* of the first if

$$|a_n| \leq b_n$$

for all n and we express the relationship by the symbol

$$\sum_{n=0}^{\infty} a_n z^n \ll \sum_{n=0}^{\infty} b_n z^n. \tag{2.5.17}$$

The relationship and the symbolism is used for power series in several variables in an obvious manner.

If the power series for $F(z, w)$ converges for non-trivial values of z and w, we must be able to find values z_0, w_0 with $z_0 \neq 0$, $w_0 \neq 0$, such that the terms of the series are bounded, say

$$|a_{jk}|\,|z_0|^j|w_0|^k \leq B \tag{2.5.18}$$

for all j and k. We have then for $|z| < |z_0|$, $|w| < |w_0|$,

$$|a_{jk}|\,|z|^j|w|^k \leq B\left|\frac{z}{z_0}\right|^j\left|\frac{w}{w_0}\right|^k,$$

so that

$$\sum_0^\infty\sum_0^\infty a_{jk}z^jw^k \ll B\sum_0^\infty\sum_0^\infty\left(\frac{z}{|z_0|}\right)^j\left(\frac{w}{|w_0|}\right)^k$$

$$= B\left(1 - \frac{z}{|z_0|}\right)^{-1}\left(1 - \frac{w}{|w_0|}\right)^{-1}.$$

This is the majorant of Cauchy.

Now in the equation

$$W' = B\left(1 - \frac{z}{|z_0|}\right)^{-1}\left(1 - \frac{W}{|w_0|}\right)^{-1}, \tag{2.5.19}$$

the variables can be separated and the solution with $W(0) = 0$ satisfies

$$W - \frac{W^2}{2|w_0|} = -B|z_0|\log\left(1 - \frac{z}{|z_0|}\right),$$

whence

$$W(z) = |w_0| - \left\{|w_0|^2 + 2|z_0|\,|w_0|B\log\left(1 - \frac{z}{|z_0|}\right)\right\}^{1/2}. \tag{2.5.20}$$

The singular point of $W(z)$ nearest to the origin is

$$z_1 = |z_0|\left\{1 - \exp\left(-\frac{|w_0|}{2B|z_0|}\right)\right\}, \tag{2.5.21}$$

where the expression under the square root becomes 0.

It follows that the power series for $W(z)$ converges for $|z| < |z_1|$. Since this is a majorant series for $w(z)$, it follows that the power series (2.5.4) is also absolutely convergent for $|z| < |z_1|$. This lower bound for the radius of convergence looks simpler than the Lindelöf bound (2.5.5). Actually there is not much difference in practice. We still have the problem of finding the most favorable values of z_0 and w_0.

The results of Theorem 2.5.1 can be extended to systems.

Theorem 2.5.2. In the system

$$w'_m = F_m(z, w_1, w_2, \ldots, w_n), \qquad m = 1, 2, \ldots, n, \tag{2.5.22}$$

let

$$F_m = \sum \cdots \sum a^{(m)}_{jk_1k_2\cdots k_n} z^j w_1^{k_1} w_2^{k_2} \cdots w_n^{k_n}. \tag{2.5.23}$$

Let s and t be so chosen that

$$M_m(s, t) = \sum \cdots \sum |a^{(m)}_{jk_1k_2\cdots k_n}| s^j t^{k_1+k_2+\cdots+k_n} < \infty \tag{2.5.24}$$

and set

$$M(s, t) = \max_m M_m(s, t). \tag{2.5.25}$$

Then there exist n power series

$$\sum_{p=1}^{\infty} c_p^{(m)} z^p \equiv w_m(z) \tag{2.5.26}$$

which satisfy the system. Here all series involved converge absolutely for $|z| \le r$ where

$$r < \min\left(s, \frac{t}{M(s, t)}\right). \tag{2.5.27}$$

We omit the proof, which follows the lines of the proof of Theorem 2.5.1.

In these two theorems the right-hand sides are given as power series in z, w, and $z, w_1, w_2, \ldots, w_n$, respectively. We can, of course, handle the case where $F(z, w)$ is a power series in $z - z_0$, $w - w_0$ simply by setting

$$z = z_0 + Z, \qquad w = w_0 + W.$$

The power series may not be given in advance. If we want to discuss the solution of

$$w' = F(z, w)$$

with the initial value $w(z_0) = w_0$, then we should first expand $F(z, w)$ in ascending powers of $z - z_0$ and $w - w_0$. Assuming this to be possible, the methods developed above apply.

EXERCISE 2.5

1. Show that $M_1(c_1, c_2, \ldots, c_n) = c_n$ for all n and determine $M_2(c_1, c_2, \ldots, c_n)$.
2. Show that

$$M_3(c_1, c_2, \ldots, c_n) = \sum c_j c_k c_l,$$

where the summation extends over the partitions of n into three summands, $n = j + k + l$, where j, k, l are positive integers and attention is paid to order. This means, e.g. that, if j, k, l are distinct then this partition gives rise to six equal terms in the sum.

3. The algebraic equation

$$w = z^3 + w^3$$

is satisfied by a power series which is 0 for $z = 0$. Give the recurrence relations for the coefficients. Show that the series is of the form z^3 times a power series in z^6 and compute the first three terms of the series.

4. Show that the solution of (2.5.16) is of the form z^4 times a power series in z^9 with positive coefficients. Determine c_p for $p = 4$, 13, and 22.

5. Suppose that the solution of the preceding problem is continuous in $(0, \omega)$. From $w'(x) > [w(x)]^3$ deduce that for $0 < x_1 < x_2 < \omega$

$$[w(x_1)]^{-2} - [w(x_2)]^{-2} \geq 2(x_2 - x_1)$$

and use this to show that ω must be finite.

6. If x_1 is so chosen that $w(x_1) = 1$, show that $\omega \leq x_1 + \frac{1}{2}$.

7. Show that $w(x)$ cannot stay bounded as x increases to ω. Use one of the existence theorems.

8. Use No. 5 to show that $(\omega - x)[w(x)]^2 \leq \frac{1}{2}$ for $0 < x < \omega$. What does this imply concerning the rate of growth of $w(x)$ as $x \to \omega$?

9. Use $w'(x) < \omega^3 + [w(x)]^3$ for $0 < x < \omega$ to show that

$$\int_0^{w(x)} \frac{du}{\omega^3 + u^3} < x < \omega$$

and derive from this that

$$\omega^3 \geq \int_0^{\infty} \frac{dv}{1 + v^3} = \tfrac{2}{9}\sqrt{3}\,\pi > 1.$$

Show that the radius of convergence of the series for $w(z)$ is >1.

Determine an admissible r for each of the following systems:

10. $w_1' = -w_2,\ w_2' = w_1,\ w_1(0) = 1,\ w_2(0) = 0.$

11. $w_1' = w_2 w_3,\ w_2' = -w_1 w_3,\ w_3' = -k^2 w_1 w_2,\ w_1(0) = 0,\ w_2(0) = w_3(0) = 1.$ Here $0 < k < 1$.

12. Determine the solution of No. 10.

13. In No. 11 show that

$$[w_1(z)]^2 + [w_2(z)]^2 \equiv 1, \qquad [w_3(z)]^2 + k^2[w_1(z)]^2 \equiv 1.$$

14. What differential equation is satisfied by e^z? Use a uniqueness theorem to show that $e^z \neq 0$ everywhere.

15. What differential equation is satisfied by $\tan z$? Use a uniqueness theorem to show that $\tan z$ can nowhere take on the value $+i$ or $-i$.

2.6 OTHER UNIQUENESS THEOREMS

In this brief section we shall discuss some further uniqueness theorems which are implied by the determinative functional inequalities of Section 1.5. We start with the theorem of M. Nagumo (1926).

Theorem 2.6.1. *Suppose that* $\mathbf{F}(x, \mathbf{y})$ *is continuous and bounded in a domain* D *of* $R^1 \times R^m$, *say*

$$D: |x - x_0| < a, \qquad \|\mathbf{y} - \mathbf{y}_0\| < b,$$

and satisfies the condition

$$\|\mathbf{F}(x, \mathbf{y}_1) - \mathbf{F}(x, \mathbf{y}_2)\| \leq |x - x_0|^{-1}\|\mathbf{y}_1 - \mathbf{y}_2\|. \tag{2.6.1}$$

Then there is an interval $[x_0 - r, x_0 + r]$ *in which there is one and only one solution of*

$$\mathbf{y}' = \mathbf{F}(x, \mathbf{y}) \tag{2.6.2}$$

passing through $(x_0, \mathbf{y}_0)$.

Proof. Theorem 2.4.1 applies and shows the existence of a solution $\mathbf{f}(x)$ in the interval $[x_0 - r, x_0 + r]$ where

$$r < \min\left(a, \frac{b}{M}\right).$$

Suppose there were another solution $\mathbf{g}(x)$ in this interval. Then

$$\mathbf{f}(x) = \mathbf{y}_0 + \int_{x_0}^{x} \mathbf{F}[s, \mathbf{f}(s)]\, ds, \qquad \mathbf{g}(x) = \mathbf{y}_0 + \int_{x_0}^{x} \mathbf{F}[s, \mathbf{g}(s)]\, ds$$

and in the usual manner we conclude that

$$\|\mathbf{f}(x) - \mathbf{g}(x)\| \leq \left| \int_{x_0}^{x} |s - x_0|^{-1}\|\mathbf{f}(s) - \mathbf{g}(s)\|\, ds \right|.$$

Let us set

$$h(t) = \|\mathbf{f}(x_0 + t) - \mathbf{g}(x_0 + t)\|.$$

Then $h(t)$ satisfies the inequality

$$h(t) \leq \left| \int_0^t h(s) \frac{ds}{s} \right|. \tag{2.6.3}$$

Here $h(t)$ is continuous and $h(0) = 0$. Moreover, $h'(t)$ exists for $t = 0$ since

$$\frac{1}{t}[\mathbf{f}(x_0 + t) - \mathbf{g}(x_0 + t)] \to \mathbf{f}'(x_0) - \mathbf{g}'(x_0) = 0.$$

This shows that the derivative also goes to 0, i.e.

$$\frac{h(t)}{t} \to 0.$$

Hence the conditions of Theorem 1.5.4 are satisfied and $h(t) \equiv 0$. This shows that the solution is unique. ▮

Next we take up the uniqueness theorem of W. F. Osgood (1898).

Theorem 2.6.2. *Suppose that* $\mathbf{F}(x, \mathbf{y})$ *is continuous and bounded in the domain D as above and there satisfies the condition*

$$\|\mathbf{F}(x, \mathbf{y}_1) - \mathbf{F}(x, \mathbf{y}_2)\| \leq \omega[\|\mathbf{y}_1 - \mathbf{y}_2\|], \tag{2.6.4}$$

where $\omega(s)$ *is a continuous strictly increasing function with* $\omega(0) = 0$ *and*

$$\lim_{\delta \downarrow 0} \int_\delta^b \frac{ds}{\omega(s)} = \infty. \tag{2.6.5}$$

Then, in some interval $[x_0 - r, x_0 + r]$ *the equation* (2.6.2) *has a unique solution passing through* (x_0, y_0).

Proof. The existence of at least one solution, $\mathbf{f}(x)$ say, is known. If there were a second solution $\mathbf{g}(x)$, then by the usual argument

$$h(t) \equiv \|\mathbf{f}(x_0 + t) - \mathbf{g}(x_0 + t)\|$$

would satisfy

$$h(t) \leq \int_0^t \omega[h(s)]\, ds. \tag{2.6.6}$$

Here $h(t) \geq 0$ and is continuous. By Theorem 1.5.4 the inequality implies $h(t) \equiv 0$ or $\mathbf{g}(x) = \mathbf{f}(x)$ and the solution is unique. ▮

Generalizations of these uniqueness theorems have been given by various authors. We shall prove a theorem suggested by results due to E. Kamke (1930) and E. A. Coddington and N. Levinson (1955). Though we impose more restrictive conditions than do these authors, we still get a result which essentially contains our previous uniqueness theorems as special cases. We introduce some notation and conventions.

Let $H(r)$ be the class of functions $h(t)$ belonging to $C^+[0, r]$ with the side conditions $h(0) = 0$, $\lim_{t \downarrow 0} h(t)/t = 0$. Further, let $\omega(x, y)$ be defined for $0 < x \leq a$, $0 \leq y \leq b$ and have the following properties:

i) ω is continuous and ≥ 0.

ii) $\omega(x, y)$ is a non-decreasing function of y for fixed x.

iii) There exists a constant $c > 0$ such that

$$\omega(x, cx) \leq c, \qquad 0 < x \leq a. \tag{2.6.7}$$

iv) If $h \in H(a)$, then

$$\lim_{t \downarrow 0} \omega(t, h(t)) = 0. \tag{2.6.8}$$

We have now

Theorem 2.6.3. *Let* $\mathbf{F}(x, \mathbf{y})$ *be continuous in* $|x - x_0| \le a$, $\|\mathbf{y} - \mathbf{y}_0\| \le b$ *and satisfy*

$$\|\mathbf{F}(x, \mathbf{y}_1) - \mathbf{F}(x, \mathbf{y}_2)\| \le \omega(|x - x_0|, \|\mathbf{y}_1 - \mathbf{y}_2\|) \tag{2.6.9}$$

where ω *satisfies the conditions listed above. If the only solution in* $H(a)$ *of*

$$z'(t) = \omega[t, z(t)] \tag{2.6.10}$$

is $z(t) \equiv 0$, *then Eq.* (2.6.2) *has a unique solution passing through* $(x_0, \mathbf{y}_0)$.

Proof. There is certainly one solution; if there were two, $\mathbf{f}$ and $\mathbf{g}$, we set

$$h_0(t) = \|\mathbf{f}(x_0 + t) - \mathbf{g}(x_0 + t)\|$$

and conclude that

$$h_0(t) \le \int_0^t \omega[s, h_0(s)]\, ds, \qquad 0 < t \le r \le a, \tag{2.6.11}$$

provided the integral exists. Now $h_0(t) \in C^+[0, r]$, $h_0(0) = 0$, and, as in the proof of Theorem 2.6.2, $\lim_{t \downarrow 0} h_0(t)/t = 0$. This shows that $h_0 \in H(r)$ for some $r > 0$ and also, by conditions (i) and (iv), that the integral in (2.6.11) exists. Set

$$h_1(t) = \int_0^t \omega[s, h_0(s)]\, ds$$

and note that

$$h_0(t) \le h_1(t) \le \int_0^t \omega[s, h_1(s)]\, ds$$

since $\omega(s, t)$ is non-decreasing in t for fixed s.

Here $h_1 \in H(r)$, for $h_1(t)$ is continuous, $h_1(0) = 0$, and

$$\frac{1}{t} h_1(t) = \frac{1}{t} \int_0^t \omega[s, h_0(s)]\, ds \to 0 \qquad \text{as} \quad t \to 0.$$

Since $h_0(s) = o(s)$ as $s \to 0$, the inequality

$$0 \le h_0(s) \le cs$$

will hold for small values of s. Without restricting the generality we may suppose that the inequality holds in $[0, r]$. Here c is the constant entering in (2.6.7). This gives

$$0 \le h_1(t) = \int_0^t \omega[s, h_0(s)]\, ds \le \int_0^t \omega(s, cs)\, ds \le ct.$$

We now define

$$h_n(t) = \int_0^t \omega[s, h_{n-1}(s)]\, ds, \qquad n = 1, 2, \ldots \tag{2.6.12}$$

and note that $h_n \in H(r)$ for all n,

$$h_n(t) \le ct, \qquad 0 < t \le r, \\ h_n(t) \le h_{n+1}(t), \tag{2.6.13}$$

for all n. It follows that $\lim h_n(t) \equiv h(t)$ exists, is an element of $H(r)$ and satisfies

$$h(t) = \int_0^t \omega[s, h(s)]\, ds.$$

This says that $h(t)$ is a solution of (2.6.10). By assumption the only solution of this equation in $H(r)$ is $z(t) \equiv 0$. Hence $h(t) \equiv 0$ and this implies $h_n(t) \equiv 0$ for all n. In particular, $h_0(t) \equiv 0$ so that $\mathrm{g}(x) \equiv \mathrm{f}(x)$ and the solution of (2.6.2) is unique. ∎

Our previous uniqueness theorems correspond to the following specializations:

$\omega(x, y)$	Theorem
Ky	2.3.1
$K(x)y$	2.3.2
y/x	2.6.1
$\omega(y)$	2.6.2.

In the second case $K(x) \in L(0, a)$ and (2.6.7) will be satisfied if, e.g. $K(x)$ is non-increasing. In the fourth case, $\omega(x)$ should satisfy the conditions of Theorem 2.6.2. Here condition (2.6.7) is trivially satisfied for $c = 1$ in a sufficiently short interval. Another possible choice of $\omega(x, y)$ is

$$\frac{y + y^2}{x + x^2} \quad \text{with} \quad c = 1. \tag{2.6.14}$$

EXERCISE 2.6

1. Show that $z(t) \equiv 0$ is the only solution in $H(r)$ of
$$(t + t^2)z'(t) = z(t) + [z(t)]^2.$$
2. Prove the same result for the other equations $z' = \omega(t, z)$ which figure in the uniqueness theorems listed above.
3. Give examples of functions $\omega(s)$ which satisfy the conditions of Theorem 2.6.2 and do not satisfy a Lipschitz condition.
4. Suppose that in equation (2.6.10) the variables can be separated, i.e. $\omega(t, z) = A(t)B(z)$. Formulate some sufficient conditions on A and B for small values of the variables so that $z(t) \equiv 0$ is the only solution in any $H(r)$.
5. The following obseɹvation is due to E. Picard (1890). Let $F(x, y)$ be continuous and strictly increasing in y for (x, y) in some domain of the plane.

Consider two solutions $y_1(x)$ and $y_2(x)$ of the equation $y'' = F(x, y)$ defined in some interval (a, b). Then, if $y_1(a) = y_2(a)$ we must have $y_1(b) \neq y_2(b)$. In other words, there is at most one solution taking on prescribed values at the end-points of the interval. Prove!

COLLATERAL READING

Going back to the sources can be both inspiring and useful in mathematics as well as in other fields of learning. Some of the investigations referred to in Chapter 2 are listed below.

BANACH, S., "Sur les opérations dans les ensembles abstraits et leur application aux équations intégrales," *Fundamenta Mathematicae*, **3**, 133–181 (1922).

BIRKHOFF, G. D., and O. D. KELLOGG, "Invariant points in function space," *Trans. Amer. Math. Soc.*, **23**, 96–115 (1922).

CACCIOPPOLI, R., "Un teorema generale sull'esistenza di elemente uniti in una trasformazione funzionali," *Rendiconti Accad. dei Lincei*, Roma, (6) **11**, 794–799 (1930).

CAUCHY, A., "Mémoire sur l'emploi du nouveau calcul, appelé calcul des limites, dans l'intégration d'un système d'équations différentielles," *Comptes Rendus*, **15** (1842); *Œuvres* (1) **7**, 5–17 (1898).

LINDELÖF, E., "Démonstration élémentaire de l'existence des intégrales d'un système d'équations différentielles ordinaries," *Acta Soc. Scientiarum Fennicae*, **21**, No. 7, 13 pp. (1897).

LIPSCHITZ, R., "Sur la possibilité d'intégrer completement un système donné d'équations différentielles," *Bulletin des sciences math. et astron.*, **10**, 149–159 (1876).

NAGUMO, M., "Eine hinreichende Bedingung für die Unität der Lösung der Differentialgleichung erster Ordnung," *Japanese Journal of Math.*, **3**, 107–112 (1926).

OSGOOD, W. F., "Beweis der Existenz einer Lösung der Differentialgleichung $dy/dx = f(x, y)$ ohne Hinzunahme der Cauchy-Lipschitzschen Bedingung," *Monatshefte der Math.*, **7**, 331–345 (1898).

PEANO, G., "Démonstration de l'intégrabilité des équations différentielles ordinaries," *Math. Annalen*, **37**, 182–228 (1890).

PICARD, E., "Mémoire sur la théorie des équations aux dérivées partielles et la méthode des approximations successives," *Journal de Math. pures et appliquées*, (4) **6**, 145–210 (1890).

Appendix A

SOME DIFFERENTIAL EQUATIONS OF FUNCTION-THEORETICAL SIGNIFICANCE

The object of this appendix is to demonstrate how differential equations can be used for a study of the properties of certain classes of functions. At the present time we restrict ourselves to the *circular functions* and to the *elliptic functions of Jacobi.*

A.1 THE CIRCULAR FUNCTIONS

We start with the system

$$\begin{aligned} w_1'(z) &= -w_2(z), \qquad & w_1(0) &= 1, \\ w_2'(z) &= w_1(z), \qquad & w_2(0) &= 0. \end{aligned} \tag{A.1.1}$$

The reader will recognize that $w_1(z) = \cos z$ and $w_2(z) = \sin z$. We shall not use this fact at all; on the contrary we try to find the properties of these two functions from the differential equations.

Theorem 2.5.2 applies and shows that there are two power series

$$w_1(z) = \sum_0^\infty c_n z^n, \qquad w_2(z) = \sum_0^\infty s_n z^n \tag{A.1.2}$$

with real coefficients which converge in some disk $|z| \leq r$ where they satisfy the differential equations. Since

$$-w_2 = -w_2, \qquad w_1 = 1 + (w_1 - 1)$$

are the expansions of the right members in the neighborhood of the initial values we can take

$$M(s, t) = 1 + t$$

and note that $t/(1 + t)$ is as close to 1 as we please. It follows that any value of $r < 1$ will do. Since the solutions are actually entire functions of z, this is a very conservative estimate of the radius of convergence.

Multiplying the first equation by $w_1(z)$, the second by $w_2(z)$, and adding we get

$$w_1(z)w_1'(z) + w_2(z)w_2'(z) = \frac{1}{2}\frac{d}{dz}\{[w_1(z)]^2 + [w_2(z)]^2\} = 0.$$

Hence

$$[w_1(z)]^2 + [w_2(z)]^2 \equiv 1 \tag{A.1.3}$$

where the value of the constant is given by the initial conditions.

For real values of x this implies that

$$-1 \leq w_1(x) \leq 1, \qquad -1 \leq w_2(x) \leq 1. \tag{A.1.4}$$

To start with we know only that $w_1(x)$ and $w_2(x)$ are defined in some interval $[-r, r]$, but by appealing repeatedly to Theorem 2.5.2 we can show that the functions exist for all real values of x. If following the real axis we arrive at a point $x = x_0$ with values $w_1(x_0) = u$, $w_2(x_0) = v$, $u^2 + v^2 = 1$, we see that the differential equations give us functions $w_1(z)$, $w_2(z)$ which are holomorphic at least in the disk $|z - x_0| < 1$. It follows that in a finite number of steps we can include any point $z = x + iy$ in the domain of existence of $w_1(z)$ and $w_2(z)$ provided $-1 < y < 1$.

Let us return to (A.1.4). There exists an interval $[0, a]$ in which $w_1(x) > 0$ since $w_1(0) = 1$. Here we cannot have $a = \infty$. For if this were the case, then $w_2'(x) > 0$ for all $x > 0$ and this would imply that $w_2(x)$ were positive and increasing for such values. Then $\lim w_2(x) \equiv \lambda$ exists and $0 < \lambda \leq 1$. On the other hand, by (A.1.1), $w_1'(x) \to -\lambda < 0$ and this requires that

$$\frac{w_1(x)}{x} \to -\lambda,$$

so $w_1(x)$ would be negative and unbounded. This is clearly impossible so we conclude that $a < \infty$.

Thus we have shown that the equation

$$w_1(x) = 0$$

has a least positive root a so that

$$w_1(a) = 0, \qquad w_2(a) = 1.$$

It should be noted that $w_2(x)$ is positive and increasing in $(0, a)$. By (A.1.1) and (A.1.3)

$$w_2'(x) = +\{1 - [w_2(x)]^2\}^{1/2}. \tag{A.1.5}$$

Since $w_2(x)$ is continuous, increasing and differentiable in $(0, a)$, there is a unique inverse $x = x(w_2)$, also continuous, increasing and differentiable for $0 < w_2 < 1$, and

$$x'(w_2) = [1 - (w_2)^2]^{-1/2}.$$

We integrate this relation with respect to w_2 from 0 to 1 and obtain

$$a = \int_0^1 (1 - s^2)^{-1/2}\, ds.$$

From our present point of view we can say that this integral defines $\frac{1}{2}\pi$.

Let us now return to (A.1.1). Since the equations do not involve z explicitly, they are invariant under any transformation $z \to z + \alpha$ where α is an arbitrary complex number. This implies that $w_1(z + \alpha)$ and $w_2(z + \alpha)$ are also solutions of the differential equations. In particular, we can take $\alpha = a$. Let us set

$$w_1(z + a) = -u_2(z), \qquad w_2(z + a) = u_1(z).$$

We have then

$$u_1'(z) = -u_2(z), \qquad u_1(0) = 1,$$
$$u_2'(z) = u_1(z), \qquad u_2(0) = 0,$$

i.e. the original system and initial conditions only with w replaced by u. Since the initial conditions determine the solutions uniquely, we have

$$u_1(z) = w_1(z), \qquad u_2(z) = w_2(z), \tag{A.1.6}$$

so that

$$w_1(z + a) = -w_2(z), \qquad w_2(z + a) = w_1(z). \tag{A.1.7}$$

Replacing z by $z + a$ we get, after simplification,

$$w_1(z + 2a) = -w_1(z), \qquad w_2(z + 2a) = -w_2(z), \tag{A.1.8}$$

and finally

$$w_1(z + 4a) = w_1(z), \qquad w_2(z + 4a) = w_2(z), \tag{A.1.9}$$

i.e. $w_1(z)$ and $w_2(z)$ are periodic with period $4a$. It follows that any integral multiple of $4a$ is also a period.

Further we see that the odd multiples of a are zeros of $w_1(z)$ and the even ones of $w_2(z)$.

Actually this enumeration of zeros and periods of $w_1(z)$ and $w_2(z)$ is exhaustive. We shall not prove this but we remark that, without using any analytic properties of w_1 and w_2, we can read off from the differential equations that all their zeros are real. This excludes the existence of complex periods as well. (See Chapter 11.)

Just as we derived the periodicity from the equations, we can also derive the addition theorems. Let α be an arbitrary complex number and observe that $w_1(z + \alpha)$ and $w_2(z + \alpha)$ satisfy the differential equation. We now introduce two functions $v_1(z)$ and $v_2(z)$ such that

$$\begin{aligned} w_1(z + \alpha) &= w_1(\alpha)v_1(z) - w_2(\alpha)v_2(z), \\ w_2(z + \alpha) &= w_2(\alpha)v_1(z) + w_1(\alpha)v_2(z). \end{aligned} \tag{A.1.10}$$

Since the determinant of this system is identically 1, $v_1(z)$ and $v_2(z)$ are uniquely determined. They satisfy the following system of differential equations:

$$\begin{aligned} w_1(\alpha)v_1'(z) - w_2(\alpha)v_2'(z) &= -w_2(\alpha)v_1(z) - w_1(\alpha)v_2(z), \\ w_2(\alpha)v_1'(z) + w_1(\alpha)v_2'(z) &= w_1(\alpha)v_1(z) - w_2(\alpha)v_2(z), \end{aligned} \tag{A.1.11}$$

with the initial values $v_1(0) = 1$, $v_2(0) = 0$. Solving these equations for v_1' and v_2' we get

$$v_1'(z) = -v_2(z), \qquad v_2'(z) = v_1(z), \tag{A.1.12}$$

i.e. the original system with the original initial conditions. Hence $v_1(z) = w_1(z)$, $v_2(z) = w_2(z)$ and finally we have the addition theorems

$$\begin{aligned} w_1(z + \alpha) &= w_1(\alpha)w_1(z) - w_2(\alpha)w_2(z), \\ w_2(z + \alpha) &= w_2(\alpha)w_1(z) + w_2(\alpha)w_2(z). \end{aligned} \tag{A.1.13}$$

With this we end the discussion of the circular functions $w_1(z) = \cos z$, $w_2(z) = \sin z$.

EXERCISE A.1

1. Express the higher derivatives of w_1 and w_2 in terms of w_1 and w_2 and use this to compute the power series (A.1.2).
2. In (A.1.13) take $z = x$, $\alpha = iy$ and express $w_1(iy)$ and $w_2(iy)$ as power series in y. Show that $w_1(iy) \geq 1$ and that $w_2(iy) = 0$ if and only if $y = 0$.
3. Use the preceding results to prove that all zeros of w_1 and w_2 are real.
4. Suppose that $w_1(b) = 0$ where b is real but not an odd multiple of a. Show that this implies the existence of a zero of $w_1(x)$ in the interval $(0, a)$ contrary to the definition of a.
5. Use the power series of $\cos x$ to show that the least positive root lies between 1 and 2.

A.2 THE JACOBI ELLIPTIC FUNCTIONS

A more sophisticated illustration of differential equation technique is furnished by the equations which lead to the *elliptic functions* of C. G. J. Jacobi (1804–51). We have

$$\begin{aligned} w_1'(z) &= w_2(z)w_3(z), & w_1(0) &= 0, \\ w_2'(z) &= -w_3(z)w_1(z), & w_2(0) &= 1, \\ w_3'(z) &= -k^2w_1(z)w_2(z), & w_3(0) &= 1. \end{aligned} \tag{A.2.1}$$

Here k is a parameter, known as the *modulus*, and we assume k real, $0 < k < 1$. We set

$$k' = +(1 - k^2)^{1/2}. \tag{A.2.2}$$

It is known as the *complementary modulus*.

Theorem 2.5.2 shows the existence of power series solutions with the given initial values. A computation shows that these series start as follows:

$$w_1(z) = z - (1 + k^2)\frac{z^3}{3!} + (1 + 14k^2 + k^4)\frac{z^5}{5!} - \cdots,$$

$$w_2(z) = 1 - \frac{z^2}{2!} + (1 + 4k^2)\frac{z^4}{4!} - (1 + 44k^2 + 16k^4)\frac{z^6}{6!} - \cdots, \quad \text{(A.2.3)}$$

$$w_3(z) = 1 - k^2\frac{z^2}{2!} + k^2(4 + k^2)\frac{z^4}{4!} - \cdots$$

The functions defined by the series are known as *sine*, *cosine*, and *delta amplitude*, respectively. Jacobi denoted them by

$$\sin \text{am}\, z, \qquad \cos \text{am}\, z, \qquad \Delta\, \text{am}\, z.$$

We shall use the more condensed notation of C. Gudermann (1798–1851)

$$\text{sn}\, z, \qquad \text{cn}\, z, \qquad \text{dn}\, z. \qquad \text{(A.2.4)}$$

The series suggest that sn z is an odd function of z while cn z and dn z are even. Further, it looks as if the signs of the coefficients alternate. Both observations are correct and can be verified by complete induction, using the formula of Leibniz which gives

$$w_1^{(n+1)}(0) = \sum_{k=0}^{n} \binom{n}{k} w_2^{(k)}(0) w_3^{(n-k)}(0)$$

and similar expressions for the higher derivatives at $z = 0$ of w_2 and w_3. These formulas give

$$w_1^{(2m)}(0) = w_2^{(2m+1)}(0) = w_3^{(2m+1)}(0) = 0, \qquad \text{(A.2.5)}$$

$$\text{sgn}\, w_1^{(2m+1)}(0) = \text{sgn}\, w_2^{(2m)}(0) = \text{sgn}\, w_3^{(2m)}(0) = (-1)^m, \qquad \text{(A.2.6)}$$

from which the assertions follow.

As we shall see later, the series (A.2.3) have the same finite radius of convergence. Let us find what can be obtained from Theorem 2.5.2. With a view to further applications, we generalize the problem slightly and consider initial conditions

$$w_1(z_0) = a, \qquad w_2(z_0) = b, \qquad w_3(z_0) = c. \qquad \text{(A.2.7)}$$

The right-hand sides of the Eqs. (A.2.1), F_1, F_2, F_3 in our previous notation, are quadratic polynomials in the variables w_1, w_2, w_3. At the initial values we have

$$F_1 = bc + c(w_2 - b) + b(w_3 - c) + (w_2 - b)(w_3 - c)$$

and similar expressions for F_2 and F_3. This gives, in the notation of Theorem 2.5.2,

$$M_1(s, t) = (t + |b|)(t + |c|),$$
$$M_2(s, t) = (t + |c|)(t + |a|),$$
$$M_3(s, t) = k^2(t + |a|)(t + |b|).$$

The maxima of $t/M_j(s, t)$, $j = 1, 2, 3$, are, respectively,

$$[|b|^{1/2} + |c|^{1/2}]^{-2}, \quad [|c|^{1/2} + |a|^{1/2}]^{-2}, \quad k^{-2}[|a|^{1/2} + |b|^{1/2}]^{-2} \tag{A.2.8}$$

and the smallest of these numbers is a permissible upper bound for r. In particular, for the given initial data $a = 0$, $b = c = 1$ we have $r < \frac{1}{4}$. Thus the series (A.2.3) are certainly absolutely convergent for $|z| < \frac{1}{4}$.

Before going any further with this type of argument, let us return to (A.2.1). Proceeding as in the case of the circular functions, we obtain the two identities

$$\mathrm{sn}^2 z + \mathrm{cn}^2 z \equiv 1, \qquad k^2 \,\mathrm{sn}^2 z + \mathrm{dn}^2 z \equiv 1. \tag{A.2.9}$$

For real values of z this gives

$$-1 \le \mathrm{sn}\, x \le 1, \qquad -1 \le \mathrm{cn}\, x \le 1, \qquad k' \le \mathrm{dn}\, x \le 1. \tag{A.2.10}$$

To start with, our functions are defined merely in a disk $|z| < \frac{1}{4}$. But we can extend the definition by analytic continuation using the differential equations. If the functions are already defined at a point $z = z_0$ where

$$\mathrm{sn}\, z_0 = a, \quad \mathrm{cn}\, z_0 = b, \quad \mathrm{dn}\, z_0 = c, \quad a^2 + b^2 = 1, \quad k^2a^2 + c^2 = 1,$$

then Theorem 2.5.2 asserts that the system (A.2.1) has unique solutions w_1, w_2, w_3 taking on the initial values a, b, c at $z = z_0$. The corresponding series in $z - z_0$ converge for $|z - z_0| \le r$, where r is any number less than the smallest of the three numbers in (A.2.8). Since the solution is unique, these three series represent $\mathrm{sn}\, z$, $\mathrm{cn}\, z$, and $\mathrm{dn}\, z$ in their circle of convergence.

If $\max(|a|, |b|, |c|) = M$, then r is at least $(4M)^{-1}$. In particular, if $z_0 = x_0$ is real, then $M \le 1$ and we see that the three functions can be continued along the real axis and $\mathrm{sn}\, z$, $\mathrm{cn}\, z$, $\mathrm{dn}\, z$ are certainly holomorphic functions of $z = x + iy$ in the strip $-\frac{1}{4} < y < \frac{1}{4}$. More generally, we can continue the functions from the origin along any path in the complex plane on which the functions remain bounded. Incidentally, (A.2.9) shows that the functions are simultaneously bounded or unbounded. This shows that the only possible singularities of the functions of Jacobi are points where the functions become infinite. We can be more precise:

The only finite singularities of the Jacobi functions are simple poles.

We shall work with $w_1(z)$ which satisfies the equation

$$w' = (1 - w^2)^{1/2}(1 - k^2w^2)^{1/2}, \tag{A.2.11}$$

where the square roots have the value $+1$ at $w = 0$. This equation is found from the first equation under (A.2.1) eliminating w_2 and w_3 with the aid of (A.2.9). By assumption the equation has a solution that becomes infinite as $z \to z_0$ along some path. We set $w = 1/v$ and find that v satisfies the equation

$$v' = -(v^2 - 1)^{1/2}(v^2 - k^2)^{1/2}. \tag{A.2.12}$$

Here we are interested in a solution $v(z)$ that tends to 0 when $z \to z_0$ along the path in question. Now the right member of (A.2.12) is a holomorphic function of v in $|v| < k$ which at the origin takes the value $+k$ or $-k$. By Theorem 2.5.2 the equation has a unique solution $v(z)$ that vanishes at $z = z_0$. This must coincide with the solution that tends to 0 along the path since the solution is unique. The latter is of the form

$$v(z) = \pm k(z - z_0) + c_2(z - z_0)^2 + \cdots$$

and has a simple zero at $z = z_0$. It follows that

$$w_1(z) = \frac{1}{v(z)} = \pm\frac{1}{k}\frac{1}{z - z_0} + \sum_0^\infty b_n(z - z_0)^n \tag{A.2.13}$$

has a simple pole at $z = z_0$ with residue $\pm 1/k$.

In the same manner we show that $w_2(z)$ and $w_3(z)$ have simple poles at $z = z_0$ with residues $\mp i/k$ and $\mp i$, respectively. For the time being, we do not know if there are any poles or where they are located.

Let us return to the real axis. We know that the elliptic functions are defined for all real x and satisfy (A.2.10), just as in the circular case we observe that the function $\operatorname{cn} x$ cannot be positive for all x. Note that $\operatorname{dn} x$ has this property since $\operatorname{dn}^2 x \geq 1 - k^2$, $\operatorname{dn}(0) = 1$, and $\operatorname{dn} x$ is continuous. If $\operatorname{cn} x > 0$ for all x, then

$$d/dx \operatorname{sn} x = \operatorname{cn} x \operatorname{dn} x > 0$$

and $\operatorname{sn} x$ would be strictly increasing. It would then tend to a limit λ, $0 < \lambda \leq 1$, when $x \to +\infty$. Then $\operatorname{cn} x$ and $\operatorname{dn} x$ would also have limits and

$$d/dx \operatorname{cn} x \to -\lambda(1 - k^2\lambda^2)^{1/2}.$$

This implies that

$$\operatorname{cn} x/x \to -\lambda(1 - k^2\lambda^2)^{1/2}$$

or $\operatorname{cn} x$ would become infinite with x, and this is absurd.

Thus $\operatorname{cn} x$ must change its sign. We denote the least positive zero of $\operatorname{cn} x$ by K. Then $\operatorname{cn} x > 0$ for $-K < x < K$ and $\operatorname{sn} x$ is increasing in this interval. Hence

$$\operatorname{sn}(\pm K) = \pm 1, \qquad \operatorname{cn}(\pm K) = 0, \qquad \operatorname{dn}(\pm K) = k'. \tag{A.2.14}$$

We can express K as a definite integral. For this purpose we go back to Eq. (A.2.11). We have seen that $\operatorname{sn} x$ is a positive increasing differentiable function of x for $0 < x < K$. It then possesses a unique inverse $x(w)$ which is positive, continuous and differentiable for $0 < w < 1$. By (A.2.11)

$$x'(w) = (1 - w^2)^{-1/2}(1 - k^2w^2)^{-1/2},$$

so that integrating with respect to w from 0 to 1 we get

$$K = \int_0^1 (1 - w^2)^{-1/2}(1 - k^2w^2)^{-1/2}\, dw. \tag{A.2.15}$$

Here K is a function of k^2. It will be shown later (Chapter 7) that K is a *hypergeometric function* of k^2.

The circular functions correspond to letting $k \to 0$ in (A.2.1). In the circular case, four times the least positive zero of $\cos x$ is a period of $\sin z$ and $\cos z$. Here we shall show that $4K$, that is four times the least positive zero of $\operatorname{cn} z$, is a period of $\operatorname{sn} z$ and $\operatorname{cn} z$. In the circular case this was proved by observing that the differential equations are invariant under a translation of z where $z \to z + a$ combined with a linear transformation on the vector (w_1, w_2) so that

$$[w_1(z + a), w_2(z + a)] = [-u_2(z), u_1(z)].$$

In the elliptic case we also know that

$$w_1(z + K), \qquad w_2(z + K), \qquad w_3(z + K)$$

are solutions of (A.2.1). However, a linear transformation on (w_1, w_2, w_3) will not suffice, we need a fractional linear transformation. We set

$$\begin{aligned} w_1(z + K) &= \frac{u_2(z)}{u_3(z)}, \\ w_2(z + K) &= -k'\,\frac{u_1(z)}{u_3(z)}, \\ w_3(z + K) &= \frac{k'}{u_3(z)}. \end{aligned} \tag{A.2.16}$$

It is easy to show that

$$u_1^2(z) + u_2^2(z) \equiv 1, \qquad k^2u_1^2(z) + u_3^2(z) \equiv 1.$$

We leave the verification to the reader. Since

$$w_3'(z + K) = -k^2w_1(z + K)w_2(z + K),$$

we get

$$-k'\,\frac{u_3'(z)}{u_3^2(z)} = k^2k'\,\frac{u_1(z)u_2(z)}{u_3^2(z)}$$

or

$$u_3'(z) = -k^2u_1(z)u_2(z).$$

In the same manner we prove that

$$u_1'(z) = u_2(z)u_3(z), \qquad u_2'(z) = -u_3(z)u_1(z).$$

Setting $z = 0$ and using (A.2.14) we get

$$k' = \operatorname{dn} K = \frac{k'}{u_3(0)} \quad \text{or} \quad u_3(0) = 1.$$

This gives $u_1(0) = 0$ and $u_2(0) = 1$.

It follows that u_1, u_2, u_3 satisfy the same differential equations and the same initial conditions as w_1, w_2, w_3. Since the initial conditions determine the solutions uniquely we must have

$$u_1(z) \equiv w_1(z), \qquad u_2(z) \equiv w_2(z), \qquad u_3(z) \equiv w_3(z).$$

Formulas (A.2.16) thus become

$$\begin{aligned} \operatorname{sn}(z + K) &= \frac{\operatorname{cn} z}{\operatorname{dn} z}, \\ \operatorname{cn}(z + K) &= -k' \frac{\operatorname{sn} z}{\operatorname{dn} z}, \\ \operatorname{dn}(z + K) &= \frac{k'}{\operatorname{dn} z}. \end{aligned} \tag{A.2.17}$$

The transformation $z \to z + K$ gives

$$\operatorname{sn}(z + 2K) = -\operatorname{sn} z, \qquad \operatorname{cn}(z + 2K) = -\operatorname{cn} z, \qquad \operatorname{dn}(z + 2K) = \operatorname{dn} z.$$

Further

$$\operatorname{sn}(z + 4K) = \operatorname{sn} z, \quad \operatorname{cn}(z + 4K) = \operatorname{cn} z, \quad \operatorname{dn}(z + 2K) = \operatorname{dn} z. \tag{A.2.18}$$

Thus $2K$ is a period of dn z while $4K$ is a period of sn z and cn z.

We see also that the odd multiples of K are zeros of cn z while the even ones are zeros of sn z. The function dn z has no real zeros.

The elliptic functions also have complex periods, complex poles and complex zeros. This is a novel feature not present in the degenerate case of the circular functions. If $0 < k < 1$, as we assume, there are purely imaginary periods, poles, and zeros. These we proceed to find.

Since sn z is odd while cn z and dn z are even and since the coefficients have alternating signs,

$$\operatorname{sn}(iy) = iv_1(y), \qquad \operatorname{cn}(iy) = v_2(y), \qquad \operatorname{dn}(iy) = v_3(y), \tag{A.2.19}$$

where $v_1(y)$, $v_2(y)$, $v_3(y)$ are positive increasing functions of y in some interval $(0, R)$. These functions satisfy the differential equations

$$\begin{aligned} v_1'(y) &= v_2(y)v_3(y), & v_1(0) &= 0, \\ v_2'(y) &= v_3(y)v_1(y), & v_2(0) &= 1, \\ v_3'(y) &= k^2 v_1(y)v_2(y), & v_3(0) &= 1. \end{aligned} \tag{A.2.20}$$

For the moment, let R denote the radius of convergence of the series (A.2.3). As we shall see below, R is finite. Since the coefficients of the power series for v_1, v_2, v_3 in terms of y are non-negative, we can apply a theorem of A. Pringsheim that asserts that $y = R$ is a singular point of such functions. For a proof of this theorem we refer to, e.g. E. Hille, *Analytic Function Theory*, **I**, 133, Ginn, Boston (1959). This implies that the point $z = iR$ is a singularity of sn z, cn z, dn z. We saw above that the only finite singularities of these functions are simple poles. Thus, if R is finite then $z = iR$ is a simple pole of each of these functions. This implies that $v_1(y)$, $v_2(y)$, and $v_3(y)$ become infinite as y increases to R.

Let us now prove that R is really finite. By (A.2.9) with $z = iy$ we have

$$v_2^2(y) = 1 + v_1^2(y), \qquad v_3^2(y) = 1 + k^2v_1^2(y). \tag{A.2.21}$$

Hence

$$v_2(y) > v_1(y), \qquad v_3(y) > kv_1(y), \qquad \text{and} \qquad v_1'(y) > kv_1^2(y).$$

For $0 < y < y_1 < R$ this gives

$$\int_y^{y_1} \frac{dv_1(t)}{[v_1(t)]^2} > k(y_1 - y),$$

and, *a fortiori*,

$$\frac{1}{v_1(y)} > k(y_1 - y).$$

This cannot be true for arbitrarily large values of y_1. Hence R must be finite. We also see that

$$v_1(y) < \frac{1}{k(R - y)}. \tag{A.2.22}$$

Knowing that R is finite and that $v_1(y) \to \infty$ as $y \uparrow R$, we can proceed to compute R which in this connection is denoted by K' in elliptic function theory. By (A.2.20) and (A.2.21)

$$v'(y) = (1 + v^2)^{1/2}(1 + k^2v^2)^{1/2}, \qquad v = v_1. \tag{A.2.23}$$

Here $v(y)$ is positive, continuous, strictly increasing, and differentiable for $0 < y < K'$. It then has a unique inverse with the same properties for $0 < v < \infty$. We have

$$y'(v) = (1 + v^2)^{-1/2}(1 + k^2v^2)^{-1/2}.$$

Integration with respect to v from 0 to ∞ gives

$$K' = \int_0^\infty (1 + v^2)^{-1/2}(1 + k^2v^2)^{-1/2}\, dv. \tag{A.2.24}$$

This is also a hypergeometric function of k^2.

We proceed to a closer study of the differential equations in the neighborhood of the point iK'. Again we have a fractional linear transformation which leaves (A.2.1) invariant. We now set

$$\begin{aligned} w_1(z+iK') &= \frac{1}{kU_1(z)}, \\ w_2(z+iK') &= -\frac{i}{k}\frac{U_3(z)}{U_1(z)}, \\ w_3(z+iK') &= -i\frac{U_2(z)}{U_1(z)}. \end{aligned} \tag{A.2.25}$$

The equation

$$w_1'(z+iK') = w_2(z+iK')w_3(z+iK')$$

gives

$$-\frac{1}{k}\frac{U_1'(z)}{[U_1(z)]^2} = -\frac{1}{k}\frac{U_2(z)U_3(z)}{[U_1(z)]^2},$$

so that

$$U_1'(z) = U_2(z)U_3(z).$$

In the same manner we prove that

$$U_2'(z) = -U_3(z)U_1(z), \qquad U_3'(z) = -k^2U_1(z)U_2(z),$$

as well as the relations

$$U_1^2(z) + U_2^2(z) \equiv 1, \qquad k^2U_1^2(z) + U_3^2(z) \equiv 1.$$

Since $|w_1(z+iK')| \to \infty$ as $z \to 0$, we have $U_1(z) \to 0$. This shows that $U_1(0) = 0$ and $U_2(0) = \pm 1$, $U_3(0) = \pm 1$. Here we must take $+1$ in both cases as is shown by examining $w_j(-iy+iK')$ for small positive values of y. Thus U_1, U_2, U_3 satisfy the same differential equations as w_1, w_2, w_3 with the same initial conditions so that

$$U_1(z) \equiv w_1(z), \qquad U_2(z) \equiv w_2(z), \qquad U_3(z) \equiv w_3(z).$$

Formulas (A.2.25) now take the form

$$\begin{aligned} \operatorname{sn}(z+iK') &= \frac{1}{k \operatorname{sn} z}, \\ \operatorname{cn}(z+iK') &= -\frac{i}{k}\frac{\operatorname{dn} z}{\operatorname{sn} z}, \\ \operatorname{dn}(z+iK') &= -i\frac{\operatorname{cn} z}{\operatorname{sn} z}. \end{aligned} \tag{A.2.26}$$

We now obtain

$$\operatorname{sn}(z + 2iK') = \operatorname{sn} z, \qquad \operatorname{cn}(z + 2iK') = -\operatorname{cn} z, \tag{A.2.27}$$

$$\operatorname{dn}(z + 4iK') = \operatorname{dn} z. \tag{A.2.28}$$

From these results we can obtain a complete list of periods, poles, and zeros of our functions:

	sn z	cn z	dn z
periods	$4mK + 2niK'$	$4mK + 2n(K + iK')$	$2mK + 4niK'$
poles	$4mK + (2n + 1)iK'$	$4mK + (2n + 1)iK'$	$2mK + (2n + 1)iK'$
zeros	$2mK + 2niK'$	$(2m + 1)K + 2niK'$	$(2m + 1)K + (2n + 1)iK'$

Here m and n are arbitrary integers. We shall not prove that the list is really exhaustive. The contrary assumption would lead to various absurd results: infinitesimal periods, or poles and zeros in any neighborhood of the origin. etc.

This completes our discussion of the elliptic functions of Jacobi. See also Section 12.3

EXERCISE A.2

1. Prove formulas (A.2.5) and (A.2.6).
2. Show that
$$K(k) = \int_0^{\pi/2} (1 - k^2 \sin^2 \theta)^{-1/2}\, d\theta$$
and use this to expand $K(k)$ in powers of k.
3. Show that $K'(k) = K(k')$.
4. Find the residues of cn z and dn z at $z = K'i$.
5. Show that all the roots of the equations
$$\operatorname{sn} z = \pm 1, \qquad \operatorname{sn} z = \pm\frac{1}{k}$$
are double roots.
6. If the square roots are $+1$ at $z = 0$, prove that the functions
$$[1 - \operatorname{sn}^2 z]^{1/2} \qquad \text{and} \qquad [1 - k^2 \operatorname{sn}^2 z]^{1/2}$$
are single valued. In other words, it is not possible for the roots to represent $-\operatorname{cn} z$ and $-\operatorname{dn} z$, only cn z and dn z.

7. Consider the system*

$$\begin{aligned} w_1' &= w_2 w_3 w_4, & w_1(0) &= 0, & & \\ w_2' &= -w_2 w_4 w_1, & w_2(0) &= 1, & & \\ w_3' &= -\alpha^2 w_4 w_1 w_2, & w_3(0) &= 1, & & 0 < \alpha < 1, \\ w_4' &= -\beta^2 w_1 w_2 w_3, & w_4(0) &= 1, & & 0 < \beta < 1. \end{aligned}$$

Obtain the quadratic relations between the functions and express $(w_j')^2$ as a polynomial in w_j.

8. Show that the power series solutions converge in a circle of finite radius R and express R as a definite integral.

9. Show that $w_1(iy)$ becomes infinite as $y \uparrow R$ in such a manner that there are two positive numbers γ and a such that $\lim_{y \uparrow R} (R - y)^\gamma w_1(iy) = ai$. Find γ and a.

COLLATERAL READING

The discussion in Appendix A is patterned on that of

Tricomi, F., *Equazioni Differenziale*, Einaudi, Torino (1965).

See pages 32–49. We have extended Tricomi's discussion to the complex plane. In the elliptic case, this is necessary to bring out the doubly-periodic character of the solutions and to show their singularities.

The reader will find a discussion of the functions of Jacobi in the author's treatise

Analytic Function Theory, Vol. II, Ginn, Boston (1962).

See pages 144–156. This is largely based on a discussion of the solutions of the differential equation (A.2.11) in the notation used above but does not employ the transformation theory which is the characteristic feature of Tricomi's procedure.

---

* This example was suggested by Professor Kurt Mahler, A.N.U., Canberra, Australia. The solutions are *hyperelliptic functions of genus* 2, infinitely many valued functions with infinitely many algebraic branch points. The example can be generalized in an obvious manner. A system of n equations in n unknowns leads to hyperelliptic functions of genus $n - 2$.

3 VARIATION OF DATA

This chapter is devoted to a study of the dependence of the solution upon the initial data in a wide sense. Here "initial data" is taken to cover initial point, initial vector, and the right member of the equation. Changes in these data will cause corresponding changes in the solution which can be estimated with the aid of Theorem 1.5.7. In addition we shall consider the dependence upon parameters. Here, series expansions often lead to the desired results.

There are four rather brief sections: Variation of the Initial Vector, Variation of the Initial Point, Variation of the Equation, and Dependence upon Parameters.

3.1 VARIATION OF THE INITIAL VECTOR

Let the differential equation

$$\mathbf{y}' = \mathbf{F}(x, \mathbf{y}) \tag{3.1.1}$$

be given, where $\mathbf{F}$ is a function on $R^1 \times R^m$ to R^m, continuous and bounded in a domain

$$D: |x - x_0| < a, \qquad \|\mathbf{y} - \mathbf{y}_0\| \le b, \tag{3.1.2}$$

such that

$$\|\mathbf{F}(x, \mathbf{y})\| \le M \qquad \text{in } D, \tag{3.1.3}$$

$$\|\mathbf{F}(x, \mathbf{y}_1) - \mathbf{F}(x, \mathbf{y}_2)\| \le K\|\mathbf{y}_1 - \mathbf{y}_2\|. \tag{3.1.4}$$

In these circumstances we know the existence of a unique solution $\mathbf{y}(x; x_0, \mathbf{y}_0)$ which at $x = x_0$ takes on the value $\mathbf{y}_0$. Our present problem is the dependence of the solution upon the initial vector $\mathbf{y}_0$. Here we have the following result.

Theorem 3.1.1. *Let* $\mathbf{y}_{10}$ *and* $\mathbf{y}_{20}$ *be two vectors in* R^m *such that* $\|\mathbf{y}_0 - \mathbf{y}_{j,0}\| \le \frac{1}{2}b, j = 1, 2$. *Then for*

$$|x - x_0| < \min\left(a, \frac{b}{2M}\right) \tag{3.1.5}$$

we have

$$\|\mathbf{y}(x; x_0, \mathbf{y}_{10}) - \mathbf{y}(x; x_0, \mathbf{y}_{20})\| \le \|\mathbf{y}_{10} - \mathbf{y}_{20}\| \exp(K|x - x_0|). \tag{3.1.6}$$

Proof. The existence and uniqueness of the two solutions follows, e.g. from Theorem 2.3.1. The restriction to the interval (3.1.5) is dictated by the fact that the distances of the vectors $\mathbf{y}_{10}$ and $\mathbf{y}_{20}$ from the boundary of the sphere $\|\mathbf{y} - \mathbf{y}_0\| < b$ may be arbitrarily close to $\frac{1}{2}b$ so that b should be replaced by $\frac{1}{2}b$ in (2.3.5). To estimate the distance between the solutions we note that for admissible values of x

$$\mathbf{y}_1(x) - \mathbf{y}_2(x) = \mathbf{y}_{10} - \mathbf{y}_{20} + \int_{x_0}^{x} \{\mathbf{F}[s, \mathbf{y}_1(s)] - \mathbf{F}[s, \mathbf{y}_2(s)]\}\, ds,$$

where $\mathbf{y}_j(x)$ is used as an abbreviation of $\mathbf{y}(x; x_0, \mathbf{y}_{j0})$. By the Lipschitz condition this shows that

$$\|\mathbf{y}_1(x) - \mathbf{y}_2(x)\| \le \|\mathbf{y}_{10} - \mathbf{y}_{20}\| + K\left|\int_{x_0}^{x} \|\mathbf{y}_1(s) - \mathbf{y}_2(s)\|\, ds\right|.$$

We can reduce this to an inequality like (1.5.15). If $x_0 < x$ we write

$$\mathbf{y}_j(x) = \mathbf{y}_j(x_0 + t), \qquad j = 1, 2,$$

and set

$$h(t) = \|\mathbf{y}_1(x_0 + t) - \mathbf{y}_2(x_0 + t)\|.$$

We set

$$c = \|\mathbf{y}_{10} - \mathbf{y}_{20}\|, \qquad K(t) = K$$

and obtain

$$h(t) \le c + K\int_0^t h(s)\, ds \tag{3.1.7}$$

and, by Corollary 2 of Theorem 1.5.7, this implies

$$h(t) \le c \exp(Kt). \tag{3.1.8}$$

For $x_0 > x$, we set instead

$$h(t) \equiv \|\mathbf{y}_1(x_0 - t) - \mathbf{y}_2(x_0 - t)\|$$

and leave c and $K(t)$ unchanged. Equation (3.1.7) still holds and gives (3.1.8). Since $t = |x - x_0|$ in either case, (3.1.6) holds. ∎

Formula (3.1.6) states that $\mathbf{y}(x; x_0, y_0)$ satisfies a Lipschitz condition with respect to $\mathbf{y}_0$. To get continuous partials, we sharpen the Lipschitz condition on $\mathbf{F}(x, \mathbf{y})$. We replace (3.1.4) by

The Jacobian matrix $\mathfrak{J}(x, \mathbf{y})$ of $\mathbf{F}$ *with respect to* $\mathbf{y}$ *shall exist, be continuous, and its norm shall not exceed B in D.* (3.1.9)

We recall that the Jacobian matrix is

$$\mathfrak{J}(x, \mathbf{y}) = \left(\frac{\partial F_j}{\partial y_k}\right), \qquad j, k = 1, 2, \ldots, m. \tag{3.1.10}$$

For small values of $\|\mathbf{y} - \mathbf{y}_0\|$ we have

$$\mathbf{F}(x, \mathbf{y}) - \mathbf{F}(x, \mathbf{y}_0) = \mathfrak{J}(x, \mathbf{y}_0)(\mathbf{y} - \mathbf{y}_0) + o(\|\mathbf{y} - \mathbf{y}_0\|). \qquad (3.1.11)$$

We call $\mathfrak{J}(x, \mathbf{y}_0)$ the *partial derivative* of $\mathbf{F}(x, \mathbf{y})$ with respect to $\mathbf{y}$ at $(x, \mathbf{y}_0)$. Similarly, the matrix $\mathfrak{G}$ is the partial derivative of $\mathbf{g}(x, \mathbf{y})$ at $(x_0, \mathbf{y}_0)$ if

$$\mathbf{g}(x_0, \mathbf{y}) - \mathbf{g}(x_0, \mathbf{y}_0) = \mathfrak{G}(\mathbf{y} - \mathbf{y}_0) + o(\|\mathbf{y} - \mathbf{y}_0\|). \qquad (3.1.12)$$

Suppose that in the Jacobian $\mathfrak{J}(x, \mathbf{y})$ we replace $\mathbf{y}$ by $\mathbf{y}(x; x_0, \mathbf{y}_0)$. The resulting matrix $\mathfrak{J}(x, \mathbf{y}(x; x_0, \mathbf{y}_0))$ will be denoted by $\mathfrak{J}(x, \tilde{\mathbf{y}}_0)$, if no confusion is likely to arise.

Consider now the matrix differential equation in $\mathfrak{M}_m$:

$$\mathfrak{Y}'(x) = \mathfrak{J}(x, \mathbf{y}_0)\mathfrak{Y}(x), \qquad \mathfrak{Y}(x_0) = \mathfrak{E}, \qquad (3.1.13)$$

where $\mathfrak{E}$ is the unit matrix in $\mathfrak{M}_m$. This equation is known as the *variational system* corresponding to the solution $\mathbf{y}(x; x_0, \mathbf{y}_0)$. Since the right member satisfies a Lipschitz condition

$$\|\mathfrak{J}(x, \tilde{\mathbf{y}}_0)\mathfrak{Y}_1 - \mathfrak{J}(x, \tilde{\mathbf{y}}_0)\mathfrak{Y}_2\| \le B\|\mathfrak{Y}_1 - \mathfrak{Y}_2\|,$$

the equation has a unique solution $\mathfrak{Y}(x, x_0)$ defined in $|x - x_0| < a$.

We have now

Theorem 3.1.2. *If in the assumptions of Theorem* 3.1.1 *condition* (3.1.4) *is replaced by* (3.1.9), *then* $\mathbf{y}(x; x_0, \mathbf{y}_0)$ *is a differentiable function of* $\mathbf{y}_0$ *and*

$$\mathbf{y}(x; x_0, \mathbf{y}_1) - \mathbf{y}(x; x_0, \mathbf{y}_0) = \mathfrak{Y}(x, x_0)(\mathbf{y}_1 - \mathbf{y}_0) + o(\|\mathbf{y}_1 - \mathbf{y}_0\|) \qquad (3.1.14)$$

for

$$|x - x_0| < \min\left(a, \frac{b}{2M}\right), \qquad \|\mathbf{y}_1 - \mathbf{y}_0\| < \tfrac{1}{2}b.$$

Proof. We have

$$\mathbf{y}(x; x_0, \mathbf{y}_1) = \mathbf{y}_1 + \int_{x_0}^{x} \mathbf{F}[s, \mathbf{y}(s; x_0, \mathbf{y}_1)]\, ds,$$

$$\mathbf{y}(x; x_0, \mathbf{y}_0) = \mathbf{y}_0 + \int_{x_0}^{x} \mathbf{F}[s, \mathbf{y}(s; x_0, \mathbf{y}_0)]\, ds,$$

$$\mathfrak{Y}(x, x_0) = \mathfrak{E} + \int_{x_0}^{x} \mathfrak{J}(s, \tilde{\mathbf{y}}_0)\mathfrak{Y}(s, x_0)\, ds,$$

whence

$$\mathbf{y}(x; x_0, \mathbf{y}_1) - \mathbf{y}(x; x_0, \mathbf{y}_0) - \mathfrak{Y}(x, x_0)(\mathbf{y}_1 - \mathbf{y}_0)$$
$$= \int_{x_0}^{x} \{\mathbf{F}[s, \mathbf{y}(s; x_0, \mathbf{y}_1)] - \mathbf{F}[s, \mathbf{y}(s; x_0, \mathbf{y}_0)] - \mathfrak{J}(s, \tilde{\mathbf{y}}_0)\mathfrak{Y}(s, x_0)(\mathbf{y}_1 - \mathbf{y}_0)\}\, ds.$$

Here we use (3.1.11) with $\mathbf{y}$ and $\mathbf{y}_0$ replaced by $\mathbf{y}(s; x_0, \mathbf{y}_1)$ and $\mathbf{y}(s; x_0, \mathbf{y}_0)$, respectively. This gives

$$\begin{aligned}\mathbf{y}(x; x_0, \mathbf{y}_1) &- \mathbf{y}(x; x_0, \mathbf{y}_0) - \mathfrak{Y}(x, x_0)(\mathbf{y}_1 - \mathbf{y}_0)\\ &= \int_{x_0}^{x} \mathfrak{J}(s, \mathbf{y}_0)[\mathbf{y}(s; x_0, \mathbf{y}_1) - \mathbf{y}(s; x_0, \mathbf{y}_0) - \mathfrak{Y}(s, x_0)(\mathbf{y}_1 - \mathbf{y}_0)]\, ds\\ &\qquad + o\left\{\int_{x_0}^{x} \mathfrak{J}(s, \tilde{\mathbf{y}}_0)[\mathbf{y}(s; x_0, \mathbf{y}_1) - \mathbf{y}(s; x_0, \mathbf{y}_0)]\, ds\right\}.\end{aligned}$$

To estimate the remainder term, we note that (3.1.9) implies a Lipschitz condition for $\mathbf{F}(x, \mathbf{y})$ which may be taken as

$$\|\mathbf{F}(x, \mathbf{y}_2) - \mathbf{F}(x, \mathbf{y}_1)\| \le B\|\mathbf{y}_1 - \mathbf{y}_2\| \tag{3.1.15}$$

if $\|\mathbf{y}\| = \max_j |y_j|$. Hence by (3.1.6)

$$\|\mathbf{y}(s; x_0, \mathbf{y}_1) - \mathbf{y}(s; x_0, \mathbf{y}_0)\| \le \|\mathbf{y}_1 - \mathbf{y}_0\| \exp(B|s - x_0|)$$

and

$$\begin{aligned}\left\|\int_{x_0}^{x} \mathfrak{J}(s, \tilde{\mathbf{y}}_0)[\mathbf{y}(s; x_0, \mathbf{y}_1) - \mathbf{y}(s; x_0, \mathbf{y}_0)]\, ds\right\| &\\ \le B\|\mathbf{y}_1 - \mathbf{y}_0\| &\left|\int_{x_0}^{x} \exp(B|s - x_0|)\, ds\right|\\ = [\exp(B|x - x_0|) &- 1]\|\mathbf{y}_1 - \mathbf{y}_0\|,\end{aligned}$$

so the remainder term is $o(\|\mathbf{y}_1 - \mathbf{y}_0\|)$ uniformly in x. We now set

$$\begin{aligned}f(t) = \|\mathbf{y}(x_0 + t; x_0, \mathbf{y}_1) &- \mathbf{y}(x_0 + t; x_0, \mathbf{y}_0)\\ &- \mathfrak{Y}(x_0 + t, x_0)(\mathbf{y}_1 - \mathbf{y}_0)\|,\end{aligned}$$

for $x > x_0$ and the same expression with t replaced by $-t$ for $x_0 > x$. We then see that

$$\begin{aligned}f(t) &\le o(\|\mathbf{y}_1 - \mathbf{y}_0\|) + \int_0^t \|\mathfrak{J}(x_0 \pm s, \tilde{\mathbf{y}}_0)\| f(s)\, ds\\ &\le o(\|\mathbf{y}_1 - \mathbf{y}_0\|) + B\int_0^t f(s)\, ds.\end{aligned}$$

By Corollary 1 of Theorem 1.5.7 this implies

$$f(t) \le o(\|\mathbf{y}_1 - \mathbf{y}_0\|) \exp(Bt) = o(\|\mathbf{y}_1 - \mathbf{y}_0\|)$$

uniformly in x and (3.1.14) follows. ▮

For $m = 1$, the result is particularly simple. Here

$$Y(x, x_0) = \exp\left\{\int_{x_0}^{x} F_y'[s, y(s, x_0, y_0)]\, ds\right\} \tag{3.1.16}$$

and the right member equals

$$\frac{\partial}{\partial y_0} y(x; x_0, y_0).$$

This was found in 1896 by the Swedish mathematician, Ivar Bendixson (1861–1935). The extension to systems is due to Guiseppe Peano in 1897. The proof given above follows the argument of A. Halanay (1966), which is essentially an adaptation of the proof found by T. H. Gronwall in 1918, based on the original Gronwall inequality.

EXERCISE 3.1

1. How should the conclusion in Theorem 3.1.1 be modified if the Lipschitz condition is replaced by (2.3.21)?
2. Verify (3.1.16).
3. Take the differential equation $y' = 1 + y^2$ and find the solution that takes the value η at $x = 0$. Compute directly the partial of this function with respect to η and compare with (3.1.16).
4. Verify (3.1.15).
5. Justify the use of Corollary 1 of Theorem 1.5.7 to get the final conclusion in the proof Theorem 3.1.2.
6. Take $m = 2$, $F_1 = xy_1 + y_2$, $F_2 = y_1^2$, $\mathbf{y}_0 = (0, 1)$ for $x_0 = 0$. Find $\mathcal{Y}(x, 0)$ explicitly.
7. Take $m = 2$ and suppose that F_1 and F_2 have continuous bounded partials with respect to y_1 and y_2 in D. Let $y_1(x; x_0, \eta_1, \eta_2)$ and $y_2(x; x_0, \eta_1, \eta_2)$ be the components of the solution vector. These functions have continuous partials with respect to η_1 and η_2. Show that the Jacobian determinant

$$J = \begin{vmatrix} \dfrac{\partial y_1}{\partial \eta_1} & \dfrac{\partial y_2}{\partial \eta_1} \\ \dfrac{\partial y_1}{\partial \eta_2} & \dfrac{\partial y_2}{\partial \eta_2} \end{vmatrix}$$

equals

$$\exp\left\{\int_{x_0}^{x} \sum_{\nu=1}^{2} F'_{\nu, y_\nu}\, [s, y_1(s; x_0, \eta_1, \eta_2), y_2(s; x_0, \eta_1, \eta_2)]\, ds\right\}.$$

This is a special case of formula (B.1.20) and generalizes to all m.

8. Suppose that $F(x, y)$ has a continuous second order partial with respect to y. Show that $y(x; x_0, \eta)$ has a continuous second order derivative with respect to η. Find an expression for this derivative.

The following problems concern solutions of the equation

$$y' = 1 - y^3.$$

9. Show that $y(x) \equiv 1$ is a solution and the only real constant solution. Can a solution assume one of the values $1, -\frac{1}{2} \pm i\frac{1}{2}\sqrt{3}$ at a given point without being constant for all x?
10. Let $y(x)$ be a real valued solution defined for all large x and $y(x) \not\equiv 1$. Show (i) $\lim_{x\to\infty} y(x) = 1$, (ii) there exists a number a such that $y(x)$ is defined and continuous on (a, ∞) but becomes infinite as $x \downarrow a$.
11. Show that $(x - a)^{1/2}\, y(x)$ stays bounded.
12. Determine a if $y(0) = 0$.

3.2 VARIATION OF THE INITIAL POINT

Our next problem is to study the result of varying the initial point x_0 leaving the initial vector $\mathbf{y}_0$ unchanged. Here we have to take care that the two solutions have a common interval of existence where a comparison can be made. The following is a sample of what can be attained.

Theorem 3.2.1. *Let* $\mathbf{F}(x, \mathbf{y})$ *satisfy the assumptions of Theorem* 3.1.1. *Let* x_1 *and* x_2 *be two points in* $(x_0 - a, x_0 + a)$ *such that* $0 < x_2 - x_1 < r$ *where*

$$r < b/M. \tag{3.2.1}$$

Let $\mathbf{y}_1(x) = \mathbf{y}(x; x_1, \mathbf{y}_0)$ *and* $\mathbf{y}_2(x) = \mathbf{y}(x; x_2, \mathbf{y}_0)$ *be the solutions of* (3.1.1) *which take the value* $\mathbf{y}_0$ *at* $x = x_1$ *and* $x = x_2$, *respectively. Let* I_j *be the subinterval of* $(x_0 - a, x_0 + a)$ *where* $\mathbf{y}_j(x)$ *is defined,* $j = 1, 2$, *and set* $I = I_1 \cap I_2$. *Then* I *contains* $[x_1, x_2]$ *and in* I

$$\|\mathbf{y}_1(x) - \mathbf{y}_2(x)\| \le M(x_2 - x_1)\exp[K\delta(x)], \tag{3.2.2}$$

where $\delta(x) = \min(|x - x_1|, |x - x_2|)$.

Proof. We know that the $\mathbf{y}_j(x)$ exist and are unique. Further I_1 contains some neighborhood of x_1, and I_2 some neighborhood of x_2. Theorem 2.3.1 is formulated for the case in which the initial point is the mid-point of the interval of continuity. This assumption is, of course, completely unnecessary and the proof shows that the solution exists in that part of the interval of continuity which is at a distance $< b/M$ from the initial point. It follows that x_2 is an interior point of I_1 and x_1 an interior point of I_2. Hence $I = I_1 \cap I_2$ certainly contains $[x_1, x_2]$.

Now for $x \in I$ we have

$$\mathbf{y}_1(x) - \mathbf{y}_2(x) = \int_{x_1}^{x} \mathbf{F}[s, \mathbf{y}_1(s)]\, ds - \int_{x_2}^{x} \mathbf{F}[s, \mathbf{y}_2(s)]\, ds. \tag{3.2.3}$$

Here we have to distinguish between four cases depending upon the position of x with respect to x_1 and x_2. The three points x_1, $\frac{1}{2}(x_1 + x_2)$, x_2 divide I into four subintervals which we number $I^{(1)}, I^{(2)}, I^{(3)}, I^{(4)}$ from left to right. We shall discuss $I^{(2)}$ and $I^{(3)}$, and leave $I^{(1)}$ and $I^{(4)}$ to the reader. In $I^{(2)}$ we have $\delta(x) = x - x_1$. We can rewrite (3.2.3) as

$$\mathbf{y}_1(x) - \mathbf{y}_2(x) = \int_{x_1}^{x_2} \mathbf{F}[s, \mathbf{y}_2(s)]\, ds$$

$$+ \int_{x_1}^{x} \{\mathbf{F}[s, \mathbf{y}_1(s)] - \mathbf{F}[s, \mathbf{y}_2(s)]\}\, ds. \tag{3.2.4}$$

By the Lipschitz condition this gives the inequality

$$\|\mathbf{y}_1(x) - \mathbf{y}_2(x)\| \le M(x_2 - x_1) + K \int_{x_1}^{x} \|\mathbf{y}_1(s) - \mathbf{y}_2(s)\|\, ds.$$

Here we set $x = x_1 + t$, $s = x_1 + \sigma$ and

$$f(t) = \|\mathbf{y}_1(x_1 + t) - \mathbf{y}_2(x_1 + t)\|$$

obtaining

$$f(t) \le M(x_2 - x_1) + K \int_0^t f(\sigma)\, d\sigma. \tag{3.2.5}$$

By Corollary 2 of Theorem 1.5.7 this implies

$$f(t) \le M(x_2 - x_1) \exp(Kt), \tag{3.2.6}$$

in agreement with (3.2.2) since $t = \delta(x)$.

In $I^{(3)}$ we have $\delta(x) = x_2 - x$. Here we rewrite (3.2.3) as

$$\mathbf{y}_1(x) - \mathbf{y}_2(x) = \int_{x_1}^{x_2} \mathbf{F}[s, \mathbf{y}_1(s)]\, ds$$

$$+ \int_{x}^{x_2} \{\mathbf{F}[s, \mathbf{y}_2(s)] - \mathbf{F}[s, \mathbf{y}_1(s)]\}\, ds.$$

This gives the inequality

$$\|\mathbf{y}_1(x) - \mathbf{y}_2(x)\| \le M(x_2 - x_1) + K \int_{x}^{x_2} \|\mathbf{y}_1(s) - \mathbf{y}_2(s)\|\, ds.$$

Here we set $x = x_2 - t$ and

$$f(t) = \|\mathbf{y}_1(x_2 - t) - \mathbf{y}_2(x_2 - t)\|.$$

This function also satisfies (3.2.5) and (3.2.6) follows. Again we have $t = \delta(x)$ so that (3.2.2) holds for $x \in I^{(3)}$. The remaining cases are left to the reader. ▌

We can, of course, combine variation of x_0 with variation of $\mathbf{y}_0$. This leads to the following result, which is stated without a proof.

Theorem 3.2.2. *Let $F(x, y)$ satisfy the assumptions of Theorem* 3.1.1. *Take two points in D, $(x_1, \mathbf{y}_{10})$ and $(x_2, \mathbf{y}_{20})$ where $\|\mathbf{y}_0 - \mathbf{y}_{j0}\| < \frac{1}{2}b$,*

$j = 1, 2$, $0 < x_2 - x_1 < b/(2M)$. Let $\mathbf{y}_j(x) \equiv \mathbf{y}(x; x_j, \mathbf{y}_{j0})$ be defined in I_j and set $I = I_1 \cap I_2$. Then $I \supset [x_1, x_2]$ and for $x \in I$

$$\|\mathbf{y}_1(x) - \mathbf{y}_2(x)\| \leq \|\mathbf{y}_{10} - \mathbf{y}_{20}\| \exp(K|x - x_1|) + M(x_2 - x_1)\exp[K\delta(x)] \tag{3.2.7}$$

where $\delta(x) = \min(|x - x_1|, |x - x_2|)$.

Let us return to Theorem 3.2.1. It asserts that $\mathbf{y}(x; x_0, \mathbf{y}_0)$ satisfies a Lipschitz condition with respect to x_0. Just as in the case of Theorem 3.1.1 we can sharpen the result by imposing slightly heavier restrictions on $\mathbf{F}$.

Theorem 3.2.3. *Let $\mathbf{F}(x, \mathbf{y})$ be continuous and bounded in $D: |x - x_0| < a$, $\|\mathbf{y} - \mathbf{y}_0\| < b$. Let $\mathbf{F}$ have a continuous partial $\mathfrak{J}(x, \mathbf{y})$ with respect to $\mathbf{y}$ in D such that*

$$\|\mathfrak{J}(x, \mathbf{y})\| \leq B. \tag{3.2.8}$$

Set $\mathfrak{J}(x, \mathbf{y}(x; \xi, \mathbf{y}_0)) \equiv \mathfrak{J}^0(x; \xi)$ and let $\mathfrak{Y}^0(x, \xi)$ be the solution of

$$\mathfrak{Y}'(x) = \mathfrak{J}^0(x; \xi)\mathfrak{Y}(x), \qquad \mathfrak{Y}(\xi) = \mathfrak{E}, \tag{3.2.9}$$

where $|\xi - x_0| < \min(a, \frac{1}{2}(b/M))$ and $y(x; \xi, \mathbf{y}_0)$ is the solution of (3.2.1) which has the value $\mathbf{y}_0$ at $x = \xi$. Then $\mathbf{y}(x; \xi, \mathbf{y}_0)$ is a differentiable function of ξ and

$$\frac{\partial}{\partial \xi}\mathbf{y}(x; \xi, \mathbf{y}_0) = -\mathfrak{Y}^0(x, \xi)\mathbf{F}(\xi, \mathbf{y}_0), \tag{3.2.10}$$

i.e. the partial is the solution of the vector differential equation

$$\mathbf{v}'(x) = \mathfrak{J}^0(x; \xi)\mathbf{v}(x), \qquad \mathbf{v}(\xi) = -\mathbf{F}(\xi, \mathbf{y}_0). \tag{3.2.11}$$

The partial is bounded and continuous in

$$D_0: |x - x_0| \quad \text{and} \quad |\xi - x_0| < \min(a, \tfrac{1}{2}(b/M)) \equiv r.$$

Proof. We proceed as in the proof of Theorem 3.1.2. Consider two solutions $\mathbf{y}(x; \xi_1, \mathbf{y}_0)$ and $\mathbf{y}(x; \xi, \mathbf{y}_0)$ where to fix the ideas $x_0 \leq \xi < \xi_1 < x_0 + r$. Then for $\xi_1 < x < x_0 + r$

$$\mathbf{y}(x; \xi_1, \mathbf{y}_0) - \mathbf{y}(x; \xi, \mathbf{y}_0) = \int_{\xi_1}^{x} \{\mathbf{F}[s, \mathbf{y}(s, \xi_1, \mathbf{y}_0)] - \mathbf{F}[s, \mathbf{y}(s; \xi, \mathbf{y}_0)]\}\, ds - \int_{\xi}^{\xi_1} \mathbf{F}[s, \mathbf{y}(s; \xi, \mathbf{y}_0)]\, ds.$$

Now $\mathbf{F}(s, \mathbf{y})$ has a partial derivative with respect to $\mathbf{y}$ which at $\mathbf{y} = \mathbf{y}(s; \xi, \mathbf{y}_0)$ has the value $\mathfrak{J}^0(s; \xi)$. Hence

$$\mathbf{F}[s, \mathbf{y}(s; \xi_1, \mathbf{y}_0)] - \mathbf{F}[s, \mathbf{y}(s; \xi, \mathbf{y}_0)] = \mathfrak{J}^0(s; \xi)[\mathbf{y}(s; \xi_1, \mathbf{y}_0) - \mathbf{y}(s; \xi, \mathbf{y}_0)] + o(\|\mathbf{y}_2 - \mathbf{y}_1\|)$$

with obvious notation. Further

$$\mathcal{Y}(x, \xi) = \mathcal{E} + \int_{\xi}^{x} \mathcal{J}^0(s; \xi)\mathcal{Y}(s, \xi)\, ds.$$

Hence

$$\begin{aligned}
\mathbf{y}(x; \xi_1, \mathbf{y}_0) - \mathbf{y}(x; \xi, \mathbf{y}_0) + \mathcal{Y}(x, \xi)\mathbf{F}(\xi, \mathbf{y}_0)(\xi_1 - \xi) \\
= \int_{\xi_1}^{x} \mathcal{J}^0(s; \xi)[\mathbf{y}(s; \xi_1, \mathbf{y}_0) - \mathbf{y}(s; \xi, \mathbf{y}_0) \\
+ \mathcal{Y}(s, \xi)\mathbf{F}(\xi, \mathbf{y}_0)(\xi_1 - \xi)]\, ds \\
+ \mathbf{F}(\xi, \mathbf{y}_0)(\xi_1 - \xi) - \int_{\xi}^{\xi_1} \mathbf{F}[s, \mathbf{y}(s; \xi, \mathbf{y}_0)]\, ds \\
+ o\left\{\int_{\xi_1}^{x} \mathcal{J}^0(s, \xi)[\mathbf{y}(s; \xi_1, \mathbf{y}_0) - \mathbf{y}(s; \xi, \mathbf{y}_0)]\, ds\right\}. \quad (3.2.12)
\end{aligned}$$

Here by (3.2.2)

$$\|\mathbf{y}(s; \xi_1, \mathbf{y}_0) - \mathbf{y}(s; \xi, \mathbf{y}_0)\| \leq M(\xi_1 - \xi) \exp [B(s - x_0)]$$

since we can replace K by B in the estimate. This shows that the last term on the right in (3.2.12) is $o(\xi_1 - \xi)$. The same estimate holds for the sum of the second and the third terms. With $x = \xi + t$ set

$$f(t) \equiv \|\mathbf{y}(x; \xi_1, \mathbf{y}_0) - \mathbf{y}(x; \xi, \mathbf{y}_0) + \mathcal{Y}(x, \xi)\mathbf{F}(\xi, \mathbf{y}_0)(\xi_1 - \xi)\|.$$

Formula (3.2.12) then gives the estimate

$$\begin{aligned}
f(t) &\leq o(\xi_1 - \xi) + \int_0^t \|\mathcal{J}^0(\xi + s; \xi)\| f(s)\, ds \\
&\leq o(\xi_1 - \xi) + B \int_0^t f(s)\, ds.
\end{aligned}$$

Hence by Corollary 1 of Theorem 1.5.7

$$f(t) \leq o(\xi_1 - \xi) \exp (Bt) = o(\xi_1 - \xi)$$

uniformly in t.

Hence

$$\mathbf{y}(x; \xi_1, \mathbf{y}_0) - \mathbf{y}(x; \xi, \mathbf{y}_0) = -\mathcal{Y}(x, \xi)\mathbf{F}(\xi, \mathbf{y}_0)(\xi_1 - \xi) + o(\xi_1 - \xi)$$

and this implies (3.2.10). The rest is obvious. ∎

For $m = 1$ we obtain

$$\frac{\partial}{\partial \xi} \mathbf{y}(x; \xi, \mathbf{y}_0) = -\exp\left\{\int_{\xi}^{x} \mathbf{F}_y'[s, \mathbf{y}(s; \xi, \mathbf{y}_0)]\, ds\right\}\mathbf{F}(\xi, \mathbf{y}_0). \quad (3.2.13)$$

EXERCISE 3.2

1. How should the conclusion be modified in Theorem 3.2.1 if the Lipschitz condition is replaced by the more general version of formula (2.3.21)?

2. Take the differential equation $y' = 1 + y^2$ and find the solution that takes the value 0 at $x = \xi$. Compute directly the partial of this function with respect to ξ and compare with the result obtainable from formula (3.2.13).

3. Suppose that $F(x, y)$ has a continuous first order partial with respect to x and a continuous second order partial with respect to y. Show that $y(x; \xi, y_0)$ has a continuous second order derivative with respect to ξ. Find an expression for this derivative.

4. Consider the differential equation

$$w' = F(z, w)$$

where $F(z, w)$ is holomorphic in some domain D of $C \times C$. Show that the solution $w(z; z_0, w_0)$ is a holomorphic function of all three variables.

5. Do formulas (3.1.16) and (3.2.13) carry over to the holomorphic case?

6. The equation $w' = (1 - w^2)^{1/2}$ is satisfied by $w(z) \equiv 1$. Why? Is this the only solution which at a given point $z = z_0$ assumes the value $w_0 = 1$? Does this fact contradict the uniqueness theorems?

7. Show that if u is a solution of $y' = 1 + y^2$ and if a is an arbitrary constant, then $(u + a)/(1 - au)$ is also a solution. Use this to derive the addition theorem of the tangent function.

8. Show also that $-1/u$ is a solution. Is this a special case of the preceding problem?

9. Without solving the equation in Problem 7, show that if u becomes infinite as $x \to a$, then u has a simple pole at a with residue -1. Is there a solution which becomes infinite at a preassigned point on the line or in the complex plane?

3.3 VARIATION OF THE EQUATION

We now want to make a comparison between solutions of different differential equations when the solutions are fixed by the same initial condition. This is a problem of considerable practical importance. Often a physical problem leads to an approximate differential equation. Thus the constants entering into the equation may have to be determined experimentally with resulting errors of observation. Another possibility is that theoretical considerations lead to an equation which is difficult to handle in theory or by numerical computation. Neglecting one or more terms may lead to considerable simplification. These errors or omissions naturally affect the solution, and the problem before us is to obtain *a priori* estimates of the error. We list a theorem giving such an estimate for a case in which the true equation has been replaced by an approximate one where the right-hand side satisfies a Lipschitz condition.

Theorem 3.3.1. *Let* $\mathbf{F}(x, \mathbf{y})$ *and* $\mathbf{G}(x, \mathbf{y})$ *be two functions defined and continuous in*

$$D: |x - x_0| < a, \qquad \|\mathbf{y} - \mathbf{y}_0\| < b. \tag{3.3.1}$$

Suppose further that in D

$$\text{(i)} \qquad \|\mathbf{F}(x, \mathbf{y})\| \le M,$$

$$\text{(ii)} \qquad \|\mathbf{F}(x, \mathbf{y}) - \mathbf{G}(x, \mathbf{y})\| < \varepsilon, \qquad \textit{and}$$

$$\text{(iii)} \qquad \|\mathbf{G}(x, \mathbf{y}_1) - \mathbf{G}(x, \mathbf{y}_2)\| < K\|\mathbf{y}_1 - \mathbf{y}_2\|.$$

Let $\mathbf{y}(x) = \mathbf{y}(x; x_0, \mathbf{y}_0)$ *be a solution of*

$$\mathbf{y}' = \mathbf{F}(x, \mathbf{y}), \qquad \mathbf{y}(x_0) = \mathbf{y}_0, \tag{3.3.2}$$

and let $\mathbf{z}(x) = \mathbf{z}(x; x_0, \mathbf{y}_0)$ *be the unique solution of*

$$\mathbf{z}' = \mathbf{G}(x, \mathbf{z}), \qquad \mathbf{z}(x_0) = \mathbf{y}_0. \tag{3.3.3}$$

Let I be a subinterval of $(x_0 - a, x_0 + a)$ *containing* $x = x_0$ *where both* $\mathbf{y}(x)$ *and* $\mathbf{z}(x)$ *are defined. Then for* $x \in I$

$$\|\mathbf{y}(x) - \mathbf{z}(x)\| \le \frac{\varepsilon}{K}\{\exp(K|x - x_0|) - 1\}. \tag{3.3.4}$$

Proof. The differential equations imply that for $x \in I$

$$\mathbf{y}(x) - \mathbf{z}(x) = \int_{x_0}^{x} \{\mathbf{F}[s, \mathbf{y}(s)] - \mathbf{G}[s, \mathbf{z}(s)]\}\, ds.$$

Under the sign of integration we add and subtract $\mathbf{G}[s, \mathbf{y}(s)]$. This function is also well defined and

$$\|\mathbf{F}[s, \mathbf{y}(s)] - \mathbf{G}[s, \mathbf{y}(s)]\| < \varepsilon$$

for the values of s under consideration. We have now

$$\mathbf{y}(x) - \mathbf{z}(x) = \int_{x_0}^{x} \{\mathbf{F}[s, \mathbf{y}(s)] - \mathbf{G}[s, \mathbf{y}(s)]\}\, ds + \int_{x_0}^{x} \{\mathbf{G}[s, \mathbf{y}(s)] - \mathbf{G}[s, \mathbf{z}(s)]\}\, ds. \tag{3.3.5}$$

Using conditions (ii) and (iii) we get the inequality

$$\|\mathbf{y}(x) - \mathbf{z}(x)\| \le \varepsilon|x - x_0| + K\left|\int_{x_0}^{x} \|\mathbf{y}(s) - \mathbf{z}(s)\|\, ds\right|. \tag{3.3.6}$$

This is of the form

$$f(t) \leq g(t) + K\int_0^t f(\sigma)\,d\sigma \tag{3.3.7}$$

if we set $g(t) = \varepsilon t$ and choose $f(t)$ equal to

$$\|\mathbf{y}(x_0 + t) - \mathbf{z}(x_0 + t)\| \quad \text{or} \quad \|\mathbf{y}(x_0 - t) - \mathbf{z}(x_0 - t)\|$$

according as $x > x_0$ or $x < x_0$. The inequality gives

$$f(t) \leq \frac{\varepsilon}{K}\{e^{Kt} - 1\}.$$

This is (3.3.4) since $t = |x - x_0|$. Since $\mathbf{F}(x, \mathbf{y})$ is only supposed to be continuous, $\mathbf{y}(x)$ need not be the only solution of (3.3.2). It is interesting to note that the estimate is not affected by this ambiguity. ∎

The remaining results in this section concern the case $m = 1$, a single differential equation in one unknown. If we increase the right-hand side of such an equation, the slope increases and the integral curves become steeper. This is intuitively obvious. We formalize the assertion as follows.

Theorem 3.3.2. *Let $F(x, y)$ and $G(x, y)$ be continuous in the rectangle*

$$D\colon |x - x_0| < a, \qquad |y - y_0| < b,$$

and suppose that

$$F(x, y) < G(x, y) \tag{3.3.8}$$

everywhere in D. Let $y(x)$ and $z(x)$ be solutions of

$$\begin{aligned} y' &= F(x, y), \qquad y(x_0) = y_0,\\ z' &= G(x, z), \qquad z(x_0) = y_0, \end{aligned} \tag{3.3.9}$$

respectively. Let I be the largest subinterval of $(x_0 - a, x_0 + a)$ where both $y(x)$ and $z(x)$ are defined and continuous. Then for $x \in I$

$$z(x) < y(x), \qquad x < x_0, \tag{3.3.10}$$

$$y(x) < z(x), \qquad x_0 < x. \tag{3.3.11}$$

Proof. Since

$$y'(x_0) = F(x_0, y_0) < G(x_0, y_0) = z'(x_0),$$

the inequalities (3.3.10) and (3.3.11) hold in some neighborhood of $x = x_0$. Let $(x_0 - h_1, x_0 + h_2)$ be the largest interval where the inequalities are valid. If this interval equals I, we are through. If this is not the case, suppose, e.g. that $x_0 + h_2$ is not the right end-point of I. At $x = x_0 + h_2$ we have then

$$y(x_0 + h_2) = z(x_0 + h_2),$$

$$y'(x_0 + h_2) = F[x_0, y(x_0 + h_2)] < G[x_0, z(x_0 + h_2)] = z'(x_0 + h_2).$$

This inequality between the slopes shows that there is an interval

$$(x_0 + h_2 - \delta, x_0 + h_2) \qquad \text{where} \qquad z(x) < y(x).$$

This is impossible, however, for we have $z(x) > y(x)$ in $(x_0, x_0 + h_2)$. This contradiction shows that $x_0 + h_2$ must be the right end-point of I. Similarly we see that $x_0 - h_1$ is the left end-point of I. Thus the inequalities hold everywhere in I. ▌

We note that F and G are assumed merely to be continuous so the solutions $y(x)$ and $z(x)$ need not be uniquely determined. It is remarkable that the inequalities (3.3.10) and (3.3.11) hold for any pair of solutions.

It should also be observed that (3.3.8) is a majorant relation which implies corresponding majorant relations for the solutions. Given an $F(x, y)$ we can always find a majorant of F. Thus if F is bounded in D, we can choose an M such that

$$-M < F(x, y) < M. \tag{3.3.12}$$

This implies that in some neighborhood of $x = x_0$ we have

$$y_0 + M(x - x_0) < y(x) < y_0 - M(x - x_0), \quad x < x_0, \tag{3.3.13}$$

$$y_0 - M(x - x_0) < y(x) < y_0 + M(x - x_0), \quad x_0 < x. \tag{3.3.14}$$

Here the majorants exist for all x but are significant for the differential equation only as long as their graphs stay in D.

This is an important question. The existence theorems usually give an interval of existence for the solution which is far shorter than the maximal one, and we often try to get better information by resorting to a majorant equation. In the holomorphic case this gave us a lower bound for the radius of convergence of the series solution. What can we expect in the real case? The following simple theorem throws some light on this question.

Theorem 3.3.3. *Suppose that $F(x, y)$ and $G(x, y)$ are bounded and continuous in the rectangle D: $|x - x_0| < a$, $|y - y_0| < b$ where also $0 < F(x, y) < G(x, y)$. Let $y(x)$ and $z(x)$ be solutions of the two differential equations* (3.3.9). *Suppose that $z(x)$ exists as a continuous differentiable function whose graph lies in D for $x_0 - r_1 < x < x_0 + r_2$ and in no longer interval. Then $y(x)$ has the same properties in this interval but may conceivably exist in a longer interval.*

Proof. Since the given interval is maximal with respect to $z(x)$ and since $z(x)$ is increasing in this interval, we conclude that $[x, z(x)]$ tends to limit points on the boundary of D as $x \downarrow x_0 - r_1$ or $x \uparrow x_0 + r_2$. Such a limit point can be on the vertical boundary or on the horizontal boundary. In the first case one of the r's equals a. In the second case we have either $z(x_0 - r_1) = y_0 - b$ or $z(x_0 + r_2) = y_0 + b$. In Figure 3.1 we have $r_1 = a$ and $z(x_0 + r_2) = y_0 + b$.

The function $y(x)$ is also increasing in its interval of existence, say $x_0 - \rho_1 < x < x_0 + \rho_2$. We want to show that $\rho_1 \geq r_1$ and $\rho_2 \geq r_2$. To fix the ideas, suppose that $\rho_2 < r_2 \leq a$ and let us consider $\lim_{x \uparrow x_0 + \rho_2} y(x) \equiv y_1$ which exists. Here $0 < y_1 \leq y_0 + b$. Suppose that $y_1 < y_0 + b$. The existence theorems apply at the point $(x_0 + \rho_2, y_1)$ which is interior to D and assert that there is a function $f(x)$ which satisfies the differential equation

$$y' = F(x, y)$$

in some interval $(x_0 + \rho_2 - \delta, x_0 + \rho_2 + \delta)$ and has the property $f(x_0 + \rho_2) = y_1$.
If the solution is unique, it must coincide with $y(x)$ in the left half of this interval. If the solution is not unique, we can choose among the solutions that which coincides with $y(x)$ in the left half. In any case, $f(x)$ will give us a continuous differentiable continuation of $y(x)$ in $(x_0 + \rho_2, x_0 + \rho_2 + \delta)$. Thus the interval cannot be maximal with respect to $y(x)$ and we must have $\rho_2 \geq r_2$.

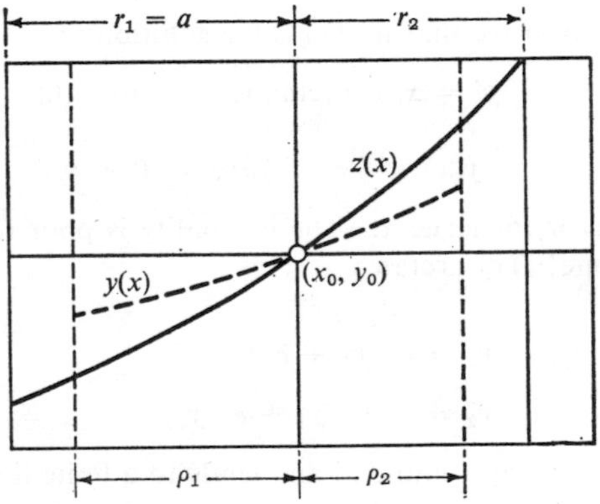

Figure 3.1

If $y_1 = y_0 + b$ we encounter another contradiction. We have now

$$y(x_0 + \rho_2) = y_0 + b,$$

$$z(x_0 + \rho_2) < z(x_0 + r_2) \leq y_0 + b,$$

so that

$$y(x_0 + \rho_2) > z(x_0 + \rho_2).$$

By Theorem 3.3.2 the opposite inequality must hold. This contradiction shows that $y_1 < y_0 + b$ and we are back at the first alternative. It follows that $\rho_2 \geq r_2$ and in the same manner we show that $r_1 \leq \rho_1$. ▌

EXERCISE 3.3

1. Suppose that $F(x, y)$ is bounded and continuous in D and is an increasing function of y for each fixed x, show that the successive approximations with $y_0(x) = y_0$ converge to a solution of $y' = F(x, y)$, $y(x_0) = y_0$.

2. In the equation

$$y' = (1 + \delta)y - (2 + \varepsilon)x, \qquad y(0) = 0,$$

the parameters δ and ε are known to be less than 0.01 in absolute value. If

$$z' = z - 2x, \qquad z(0) = 0,$$

estimate $|z(x) - y(x)|$ for $|x| < 1$.

3. It is desired to find an interval $(0, R)$ in which the solution of

$$y' = x^2 + xy + y^2, \qquad y(0) = 0,$$

is continuous. Use a majorant equation

$$z' = m^2 + mz + z^2, \qquad 0 < x < m,$$

for a suitable choice of m. What is the best choice of m?

4. Use majorants to prove that if $y(x)$ is the solution of

$$y' = x + \arctan y, \qquad y(0) = 0,$$

then

$$y(x) < \tfrac{1}{2}x^2 + \tfrac{1}{2}\pi x, \qquad 0 < x.$$

Estimate the error for large x. The inequality is poor for small positive x. Find a better one! Try $\arctan y < y$.

5. If

$$y_1' = e^{-t}y_1 + e^{-2t}y_2,$$
$$y_2' = -e^{-2t}y_1 + e^{-t}y_2,$$

show that $y_1^2 + y_2^2$ stays bounded and tends to a finite limit as $t \to +\infty$.

6. Show that hypotheses (ii) and (iii) of Theorem 3.3.1 do not imply that the solution $y(x)$ of (3.3.2) is unique.

3.4 DEPENDENCE ON PARAMETERS

A typical problem which leads to variation of the equation is that in which the equation involves one or more parameters. Such cases occur frequently in the applications. Thus the following second order differential equations

$$y'' + \left(1 - \frac{\nu^2 - \frac{1}{4}}{x^2}\right)y = 0, \tag{3.4.1}$$

$$xy'' + (b - x)y' - ay = 0, \tag{3.4.2}$$

$$x(1-x)y'' + [\gamma - (\alpha+\beta+1)x]y - \alpha\beta y = 0 \tag{3.4.3}$$

involve one, two, and three parameters, respectively. The solutions are functions of the parameters as well as of x and the question arises as to what can be said about the dependence on the parameters. We shall consider some aspects of this general question.

Theorem 3.4.1. *Let the equation*

$$\mathbf{y}' = \mathbf{F}(x, \mathbf{y}, \lambda), \qquad \mathbf{y}(x_0) = \mathbf{y}_0, \tag{3.4.4}$$

be given. Here λ is in general a complex number and we assume that $\mathbf{y}_0$ is independent of λ. The function $\mathbf{F}$ shall be bounded and continuous on $R^1 \times C^m \times C^1$ to C^m and defined in

$$D: |x - x_0| < a, \qquad \|\mathbf{y} - \mathbf{y}_0\| < b, \qquad |\lambda - \lambda_0| < \rho,$$

where it satisfies a Lipschitz condition of the form

$$\|\mathbf{F}(x, \mathbf{y}_1, \lambda_1) - \mathbf{F}(x, \mathbf{y}_2, \lambda_2)\| \le K[\|\mathbf{y}_1 - \mathbf{y}_2\| + |\lambda_1 - \lambda_2|]. \tag{3.4.5}$$

Let $\mathbf{y}(x; x_0, \mathbf{y}_0, \lambda)$ be the unique solution. Then for any two values of λ with $|\lambda_0 - \lambda_j| < \rho$, $j = 1, 2$, there exists an interval I containing $x = x_0$ where the solution exists for $\lambda = \lambda_1$ and for $\lambda = \lambda_2$ and for $x \in I$

$$\|\mathbf{y}(x; x_0, \mathbf{y}_0, \lambda_1) - \mathbf{y}(x; x_0, \mathbf{y}_0, \lambda_2)\| \le |\lambda_1 - \lambda_2|\{e^{K|x - x_0|} - 1\}. \tag{3.4.6}$$

Proof. Theorem 3.3.2 applies to this case if we set $\varepsilon = K|\lambda_1 - \lambda_2|$. It should be observed that the assumption that the functions are complex-valued makes no difference, the proof of Theorem 3.3.2 holds also for the complex-valued case. ▮

Thus a Lipschitz condition with respect to $\mathbf{y}$ and λ imposed on $\mathbf{F}(x, \mathbf{y}, \lambda)$ implies a Lipschitz condition with respect to λ for the solution. If we sharpen the assumption to a demand for the existence and continuity of partial derivatives of $\mathbf{F}$ with respect to λ and the components of $\mathbf{y}$, then

$$\frac{\partial}{\partial \lambda} \mathbf{y}(x; x_0, \mathbf{y}_0, \lambda)$$

will exist and be continuous in λ and differentiable in x. In general the more derivatives that $\mathbf{F}$ has, the more derivatives will the solution have.

If the parameters occur in a sufficiently simple manner in the equation, then one can expect the equation to have solutions which are analytic functions of the parameters, often even entire functions. Thus the modified Bessel equation (3.4.1) is satisfied by

$$\left(\frac{x}{2}\right)^{-1/2} J_\nu(x) = \left(\frac{x}{2}\right)^{\nu - 1/2} \sum_{k=0}^{\infty} \frac{(-1)^k}{k!\Gamma(\nu + k + 1)} \left(\frac{x}{2}\right)^{2k} \tag{3.4.7}$$

and for any fixed x, $x \neq 0$ and ∞, this is an entire function of ν. The Pochhammer or confluent hypergeometric equation (3.4.2) is satisfied by

$$F(a, b, x) = 1 + \sum_{k=1}^{\infty} \frac{a(a+1)\cdots(a+k-1)}{b(b+1)\cdots(b+k-1)} \frac{x^k}{k!} \tag{3.4.8}$$

which is an entire function of a but a meromorphic function of b. Similarly the hypergeometric equation (3.4.3) is satisfied by the hypergeometric series

$$F(\alpha, \beta, \gamma; x) = 1 + \sum_{k=1}^{\infty} \frac{\alpha(\alpha+1)\cdots(\alpha+k-1)\beta(\beta+1)\cdots(\beta+k-1)}{1\,2.\ldots.k\;\gamma(\gamma+1)\cdots(\gamma+k-1)} x^k$$

which is an entire function of α and of β and a meromorphic function of γ.

To illustrate this phenomenon we shall discuss a couple of examples which are of some intrinsic importance and where the facts are not obvious by inspection.

Theorem 3.4.2. *Let $q(x) \in C[0, \infty)$. The solution of*

$$y'' + [\lambda - q(x)]y = 0, \qquad y(0) = \alpha, \qquad y'(0) = \beta, \tag{3.4.9}$$

where α and β are independent of λ, is, for any fixed x an entire function of λ of order $\frac{1}{2}$ and normal type.

Remark. We recall that a function $G(z)$ is an *entire function* if it can be expanded in a power series convergent for all finite values. It is of *order* ρ if

$$\limsup_{r\to\infty} \frac{\log\log M(r, G)}{\log r} = \rho, \qquad M(r, G) = \max_{\theta} |G(r\,e^{i\theta})| \cdot \tag{3.4.10}$$

and it is of *normal type of order* ρ if

$$0 < \limsup_{r\to\infty} \frac{\log M(r, G)}{r^\rho} < \infty. \tag{3.4.11}$$

In the theorem, the assertion is to be understood in the sense that the order is at most $\frac{1}{2}$ and, if it is $\frac{1}{2}$, then the type is normal. It should be added: the order is $\frac{1}{2}$ even in the simplest cases.

Proof. It is enough to prove the assertion for the two special cases

$$\alpha = 1, \quad \beta = 0, \quad \text{and} \quad \alpha = 0, \quad \beta = 1. \tag{3.4.12}$$

Denote the corresponding solutions by $y_1(x, \lambda)$ and $y_2(x, \lambda)$, respectively. The solution of (3.4.9) with arbitrary α and β is then given by

$$\alpha y_1(x, \lambda) + \beta y_2(x, \lambda). \tag{3.4.13}$$

For this is a solution and it has the correct initial values.

We replace (3.4.9) by the Volterra integral equations satisfied by y_1 and y_2, namely

$$y_1(x, \lambda) = 1 - \int_0^x (x - s)[\lambda - q(s)]y_1(s, \lambda)\, ds, \tag{3.4.14}$$

$$y_2(x, \lambda) = x - \int_0^x (x - s)[\lambda - q(s)]y_2(s, \lambda)\, ds. \tag{3.4.15}$$

The solutions of these equations obviously give the correct initial values and twofold differentiation shows that y_1 and y_2 are solutions of the differential equation (3.4.9).

We solve the integral equations using the so-called *Neumann series*. We restrict ourselves to a fixed finite interval $[0, \omega]$ and consider the linear operator S on $C[0, \omega]$ to itself defined by

$$S[g](x) = \int_0^x (x - s)[\lambda - q(s)]g(s)\, ds. \tag{3.4.16}$$

The integral equations are of the form

$$y(x) = g(x) - S[y(\cdot)](x), \tag{3.4.17}$$

where $g(x) = 1$ or x. Since

$$[I + S][y] = g,$$

we have symbolically

$$y = [I + S]^{-1}[g]$$

or

$$y = g - S[g] + S^2[g] - \cdots + (-1)^n S^n[g] + \cdots \tag{3.4.18}$$

This is the Neumann series in the present case. It is an easy matter to prove its convergence and that $[I + S]^{-1}$ is a bounded linear operator on $C[0, \omega]$ to itself. (Cf. Theorem 1.4.2.)

For our present purposes it is enough to carry through the argument for $g(x) = 1$ and x. For $0 \le s \le \omega$ we have

$$|\lambda - q(s)| \le |\lambda| + \|q\| \equiv M^2 \tag{3.4.19}$$

where $\|q\|$ is the sup norm of q in $C[0, \omega]$. We have now

$$|S[g](x)| \le M^2 \int_0^x (x - s)|g(s)|\, ds \le \tfrac{1}{2}M^2x^2\|g\|.$$

Proceeding in this manner we see that

$$|S[1](x)| \le \frac{1}{2!} M^2x^2, \qquad |S[x](x)| \le \frac{1}{3!} M^2x^3,$$

$$\cdots\cdots\cdots\cdots\cdots\cdots$$

$$|S^n[1](x)| \le \frac{1}{(2n)!} M^{2n}x^{2n}, \qquad |S^n[x](x)| \le \frac{1}{(2n+1)!} M^{2n}x^{2n+1},$$

$$\cdots\cdots\cdots\cdots\cdots\cdots$$

Adding we see that for $0 \le x \le \omega$

$$|y_1(x, \lambda)| \le \cosh(Mx) < \exp\{[|\lambda| + \|q\|]^{1/2}x\} \tag{3.4.20}$$

and the same estimate holds for $|y_2(x, \lambda)|$ if $|\lambda| > 1$. It follows that

$$\limsup_{|\lambda|\to\infty} \frac{\log\log|y_1(x, \lambda)|}{\log|\lambda|} \le \frac{1}{2} \limsup_{|\lambda|\to\infty} \frac{\log[|\lambda| + \|q\|] + 2\log x}{\log|\lambda|} = \frac{1}{2}.$$

Moreover,

$$\limsup_{|\lambda|\to\infty} \frac{\log|y_1(x, \lambda)|}{|\lambda|^{1/2}} \le \limsup_{|\lambda|\to\infty} \frac{[|\lambda| + \|q\|]^{1/2}x}{|\lambda|^{1/2}} = x \le \omega.$$

The same estimates hold for $|y_2(x, \lambda)|$, and hence for any linear combination of $y_1(x, \lambda)$ and $y_2(x, \lambda)$. ∎

Finally we shall consider a problem where both the differential equation and the initial conditions are of an unconventional type. This problem also illustrates *the method of expanding a solution of a differential equation in a power series in terms of a parameter*. This is an important device often used in applications.

Let $b_1(x), b_2(x), \ldots, b_n(x)$ be n given functions of $C[a, b]$, $b - a < \infty$, such that $\inf b_j(x) = \beta_j > 0$, $j = 1, 2, \ldots, n$. We define the following sequence of differential operators. Let $D = d/dx$ and set

$$\begin{aligned} A_1 &= b_n(x)D, \\ A_2 &= b_{n-1}(x)DA_1, \\ &\cdots\cdots\cdots \\ A &= A_n = b_1(x)DA_{n-1}. \end{aligned} \tag{3.4.21}$$

We shall see later that the domain of A is a non-void subset of $C[a, b]$. After these conventions have been laid down we state and prove

Theorem 3.4.3. *The differential equation*

$$A[y] - \lambda y = 0$$

with the initial conditions

$$y(a) = y_{01}, \quad A_1[y](a) = y_{02}, \ldots, \quad A_{n-1}[y](a) = y_{0n}, \tag{3.4.22}$$

has a unique solution $y(x, \lambda)$ which, for each fixed x in $[a, b]$, is an entire function of λ of order at most $1/n$. It is of normal type of this order.

Proof. We shall attempt to find the solution as a power series in λ

$$y(x, \lambda) = \sum_{n=0}^{\infty} y_n(x)\lambda^n. \tag{3.4.23}$$

We substitute this series in (3.4.20) and note that the result must be an identity in λ. This gives the conditions

$$A[y_0(x)] = 0, \qquad A[y_k(x)] = y_{k-1}(x), \qquad k > 0. \tag{3.4.24}$$

We have also to satisfy the initial conditions. This we can do by choosing $y_0(x)$ so that it satisfies (3.4.22) while the $y_k(x)$ with $k > 0$ shall vanish at $x = a$ together with $A_1[y_k], A_2[y_k], \ldots, A_{n-1}[y_k]$.

Our first condition is

$$A[y_0(x)] = 0 \qquad \text{or} \qquad b_1(x)DA_{n-1}[y_0(x)] = 0.$$

This shows that $A_{n-1}[y_0(x)]$ must be a constant, the value of which is given as y_{0n} by the last initial condition. Hence

$$A_{n-1}[y_0] = y_{0n}$$

or

$$DA_{n-2}[y_0(x)] = \frac{y_{0n}}{b_2(x)}\cdot$$

This gives

$$A_{n-2}[y_0(x)] = y_{0,n-1} + y_{0,n}\int_a^x \frac{ds_1}{b_2(s_1)},$$

where we have used the appropriate initial condition to determine the constant of integration. After n steps we have

$$y_0(x) = y_{01} + y_{02}\int_a^x \frac{ds}{b_n(s)} + y_{03}\int_a^x \frac{ds_1}{b_n(s_1)}\int_a^{s_1} \frac{ds_2}{b_{n-1}(s_2)} + \cdots$$
$$+ y_{0,n}\int_a^x \frac{ds_1}{b_n(s_1)}\int_a^{s_1} \frac{ds_2}{b_{n-1}(s_2)}\cdots\int_a^{s_{n-2}} \frac{ds_{n-1}}{b_2(s_{n-1})}\cdot \tag{3.4.25}$$

This function is annihilated by the operator A and it satisfies the appropriate conditions.

Next we have to solve

$$A[y_1(x)] = y_0(x),$$

where $y_1, A_1[y_1], A_2[y_1], \ldots, A_{n-1}[y_1]$ are supposed to vanish at $x = a$. This gives

$$y_1(x) = \int_a^x \frac{ds_1}{b_n(s_1)}\int_a^{s_1} \frac{ds_2}{b_{n-1}(s_2)}\cdots\int_a^{s_{n-2}} \frac{ds_{n-1}}{b_2(s_{n-1})}\int_a^{s_{n-1}} \frac{y_0(s_n)\,ds_n}{b_1(s_n)}\cdot \tag{3.4.26}$$

This expression defines a linear integral operator T on $C[a, b]$ to itself such that

$$y_1(x) = T[y_0(\cdot)](x). \tag{3.4.27}$$

We have quite generally

$$y_n(x) = T[y_{n-1}(\cdot)](x) = T^n[y_0(\cdot)](x). \tag{3.4.28}$$

We note in passing that every function of the form

$$T[f(\cdot)](x), \qquad f \in C[a, b], \tag{3.4.29}$$

belongs to the domain of A, in fact

$$A\{T[f(\cdot)]\} = f. \tag{3.4.30}$$

All the terms of the power series are well defined. It remains to prove convergence and to estimate the sum. It is clear that $y_0(x) \in C[a, b]$. Let $\|y_0\|$ denote its sup norm. Further we can find a $\beta > 0$ such that

$$b_j(x) \geq \beta, \qquad j = 1, 2, \ldots, n.$$

This shows that

$$|T[y_0](x)| \leq \frac{\beta^{-n}}{(n-1!)} \int_a^x (x-s)^{n-1} |y_0(s)|\, ds$$

$$\leq \frac{1}{n!} [(x-a)/\beta]^n \|y_0\|.$$

Hence

$$|T^2[y_0](x)| \leq \frac{\beta^{-2n}}{n!(n-1)!} \int_a^x (x-s)^{n-1}(s-a)^n\, ds \|y_0\|$$

$$= \frac{1}{(2n)!} [(x-a)/\beta]^{2n} \|y_0\|,$$

and by complete induction we obtain

$$|y_k(x)| \leq \frac{1}{(kn)!} \left(\frac{x-a}{\beta}\right)^{kn} \|y_0\|. \tag{3.4.31}$$

It follows that the series (3.4.23) converges absolutely and uniformly for x in $[a, b]$ and λ in any compact subset of the complex plane. Moreover, we have

$$|y(x, \lambda)| < \exp\left\{\frac{x-a}{\beta} |\lambda|^{1/n}\right\} \|y_0\|. \tag{3.4.32}$$

This estimate, crude as it is, proves the assertion.

We have assumed that $b < \infty$. This is not essential as long as $\inf b_j(x) > 0$ for all j. In the inequality (3.4.32) we have to replace $\|y_0\|$ by $\max_{0 \leq t \leq x} |y_0(t)|$ and this is the only change required. ▮

Expanding the solutions in terms of a parameter is a device of old standing in celestial mechanics. In the 1890's, Henri Poincaré gave a famous set of lectures on this discipline, in which he put this method on a firm basis. In this connection he also laid the foundation for the theory of infinite determinants and for asymptotic divergent series.

EXERCISE 3.4

1. Consider the equation
$$y' = \lambda + \cos y, \qquad y(0) = 0,$$
where the variables are real. Discuss the estimate furnished by Theorem 3.4.1 for $|y(x, \lambda) - y(x, 0)|$.

2. What bounds can be obtained for
$$|\mathrm{sn}\,(x, k) - \sin x|, \qquad |\mathrm{cn}\,(x, k) - \cos x|, \qquad |\mathrm{dn}\,(x, k) - 1|$$
for real values of x, $|x| \leq K$, and $0 < k < 1$, using Theorem 3.4.1? Note that this $K = K(k)$ should not be confused with the Lipschitz constant.

3. The elliptic functions sn (x, k), cn (x, k), dn (x, k) can be expanded in powers of the parameter k^2. Find the first three terms in each of the expansions.

4. Solve the system
$$y_1'(x) = \lambda y_2(x), \qquad y_1(0) = 1,$$
$$y_2'(x) = x y_1(x), \qquad y_2(0) = 0,$$
by expanding y_1 and y_2 in powers of λ. Prove convergence for all finite λ and all finite x.

5. The equation
$$(x^3 y')' - \lambda y = 0$$
has two solutions which are such that
$$y_1(x, \lambda) - 1 \to 0, \quad y_2(x, \lambda) - x \to 0 \qquad \text{as} \qquad x \to +\infty.$$
Express these solutions as power series in λ, compute the coefficient functions, and show that the series converge for all x, $x \neq 0, \infty$, and all finite λ.

6. The "hyper-Bessel" equation
$$[x^{4+\alpha} y'']'' + \lambda y = 0, \qquad 0 < \alpha,$$
has four solutions which for large positive x are of the form
$$x[1 + R_1], \quad 1 + R_2, \quad x^{-1-\alpha}[1 + R_3], \quad x^{-2-\alpha}[1 + R_4]$$
with $R_j = O(x^{-\alpha})$. Expand the solutions in powers of λ, compute the coefficient functions of x and α, and show that the series converge for all x, $x \neq 0, \infty$, and all finite λ. Show that they are entire functions of λ of order $\frac{1}{4}$.

7. Find the analogue of Theorem 3.4.2 for the case
$$y^{(n)} + [\lambda - q(x)]y = 0.$$

The proof of Theorem 3.4.2 suggests that the following functional inequalities are valid. Note that the transformation
$$f(x) \to \frac{1}{k} \int_0^x \sinh k(x - s) f(s)\, ds, \ 0 < k$$
is linear bounded and order-preserving on any space $C[0, \omega]$.

8. If $F(x)$ has continuous first and second order derivatives, if $F(0) = F'(0) = 0$, if $g(x) \in C[0, \omega]$, and if

$$F''(x) - k^2F(x) \leq g(x),$$

then

$$F(x) \leq \frac{1}{k}\int_0^x \sinh k(x - s)g(s)\, ds.$$

9. If $f(x)$ and $g(x)$ belong to $C[0, \omega]$ if $g(x) \geq 0$, and if

$$f(x) \leq g(x) + k^2 \int_0^x (x - s)f(s)\, ds$$

then

$$f(x) \leq g(x) + k \int_0^x \sinh k(x - s)g(s)\, ds.$$

10. Use either of the preceding inequalities to prove Theorem 3.4.2.

COLLATERAL READING

For modern aspects of the problems discussed in this chapter consult

COPPEL, W. A., *Stability and Asymptotic Behavior of Differential Equations*, (Chapter I), Heath, Boston (1965).

HALANAY, A., *Differential Equations. Stability, Oscillations, Time Lags*, (Introduction), Academic Press, New York, (1966).

Reference has been made to

BENDIXSON, I., "Démonstration de l'existence de l'intégral d'une équation aux dérivées partielles linéaires," *Bull. Soc. Math. de France*, **24**, 220–225 (1896).

GRONWALL, T. H., "Note on the derivative with respect to a parameter of the solutions of a system of differential equations," *Annals of Math.*, (2) **20**, 292–296 (1918).

PEANO G., "Generalità sulle equazioni differenziali ordinarie," *Atti della R. Accademia delle Szienze di Torino*, **33**, 9–18 (1897–98).

POINCARÉ, H., *Les méthodes nouvelles de la mécanique céleste*, 3 vols. Gauthier-Villars, Paris (1892, 1893, 1899).

4 ABSTRACT SPACES

In this chapter we collect some results concerning abstract spaces and linear operators which will be used later.

There are six sections: Some Concepts of Functional Analysis, Banach Algebras, The Resolvent, Gelfand's Representation Theorem, Operational Calculus, and The Commutator Operator.

4.1 SOME CONCEPTS OF FUNCTIONAL ANALYSIS

We refer the reader to Section 1.1 for the notion of a linear vector space, and to Section 1.2 for metric spaces. Notions of a norm and of a complete metric space are to be found in the latter section.

Definition 4.1.1. *A normed linear vector space complete in the metric determined by the norm is called a Banach space, or B-space for short.*

Linear transformations (= mappings, operators) were introduced in Section 1.2 and have figured ever since. We formulate a definition for B-spaces.

Definition 4.1.2. *Let $\mathfrak{X}$ and $\mathfrak{Y}$ be B-spaces over the same scalar field $F(= C$ or $R^1)$. Then T is a linear operator on $\mathfrak{X}$ to $\mathfrak{Y}$ of domain $\mathfrak{D}$ in $\mathfrak{X}$ and range $\mathfrak{R}$ in $\mathfrak{Y}$ if $\mathfrak{D}$ is a linear subspace and if*

$$T(x_1 + x_2) = T(x_1) + T(x_2), \qquad \forall x_1, x_2 \in \mathfrak{D}, \tag{4.1.1}$$

$$T(\alpha x) = \alpha T(x), \qquad \forall x \in \mathfrak{D}, \qquad \forall \alpha \in F. \tag{4.1.2}$$

We have clearly

$$T(0) = 0, \tag{4.1.3}$$

where the zero element of $\mathfrak{X}$ figures on the left, and on the right that of $\mathfrak{Y}$. We denote by $\mathfrak{N}[T]$, called the *null space* of T, the set of all elements x which are annihilated by T,

$$T(x) = 0, \qquad \text{iff} \qquad x \in \mathfrak{N}[T]. \tag{4.1.4}$$

If $\mathfrak{N}(T) = \{0\}$, the mapping $x \to T(x)$ is *one-to-one*, it is *onto* if $\mathfrak{R} = \mathfrak{Y}$.

Definition 4.1.3. *The operator T is bounded if there exists a constant M such that*

$$\|T(x)\| \leq M\|x\|, \qquad \forall x \in \mathfrak{D}. \tag{4.1.5}$$

The least such M is called the norm of T and written $\|T\|$. We have

$$\|T\| = \sup_{\|x\|=1} \|Tx\|.$$

Theorem 4.1.1. *A linear bounded operator T on $\mathfrak{X}$ to $\mathfrak{Y}$ such that $\mathfrak{D}$ is dense in $\mathfrak{X}$ can be extended to all of $\mathfrak{X}$. The extension T^0 is also a linear bounded operator with $\mathfrak{D}(T^0) = \mathfrak{X}$ and $\|T^0\| = \|T\|$.*

Proof. Let $x_0 \in \mathfrak{X} \ominus \mathfrak{D}$ and let $\{x_n\} \subset \mathfrak{D}$ with $\lim x_n = x_0$. Then

$$\|T(x_m) - T(x_n)\| = \|T(x_m - x_n)\| \leq \|T\|\,\|x_m - x_n\| \to 0$$

as $m, n \to \infty$. Hence $\{T(x_n)\}$ is a Cauchy sequence in $\mathfrak{Y}$ and since $\mathfrak{Y}$ is complete

$$\lim T(x_n) \equiv T^0(x_0)$$

exists. In this manner T^0 is defined in $\mathfrak{X} \ominus \mathfrak{D}$ and in $\mathfrak{D}$ we set $T^0 = T$. The resulting operator T^0 is clearly linear, $\mathfrak{D}(T^0) = \mathfrak{X}$, and since

$$\|T(x_n)\| \leq \|T\|\,\|x_n\| \to \|T\|\,\|x\|,$$

we conclude that $\|T^0\| \leq \|T\|$. But by the definition of the norm of T, for given $\varepsilon > 0$ there can be found $x \in \mathfrak{D}$ for which $\|x\| = 1$ and

$$\|T\| - \varepsilon \leq \|Tx\| = \|T^0x\| \leq \|T^0\|.$$

Since ε was arbitrary, we have $\|T^0\| = \|T\|$. ∎

We denote the set of all linear bounded operators on $\mathfrak{X}$ to $\mathfrak{Y}$ by $\mathfrak{E}(\mathfrak{X}, \mathfrak{Y})$. This is also a B-space if we define the arithmetic operations and the norm properly. We set

$$(T_1 + T_2)(x) = T_1(x) + T_2(x), \qquad (\alpha T)(x) = \alpha T(x) \tag{4.1.6}$$

and let the norm of T be defined by Definition 4.1.3. We have to show that $\mathfrak{E}(\mathfrak{X}, \mathfrak{Y})$ is complete in this metric. Suppose that $\{T_n\}$ is a Cauchy sequence in $\mathfrak{E}(\mathfrak{X}, \mathfrak{Y})$. Then $\{T_n(x)\}$ is a Cauchy sequence in $\mathfrak{Y}$ for every $x \in \mathfrak{X}$ so that

$$\lim_{n\to\infty} T_n(x) \equiv T(x)$$

exists. Here T is obviously linear and it is bounded; for $\|T_n\|$ is bounded, $\|T_n\| \leq M$, so that

$$\|T(x)\| = \lim_{n\to\infty} \|T_n(x)\| \leq M\|x\|.$$

Finally, we note that if $\varepsilon > 0$ is given, then there exists an N such that $\|T_m - T_n\| < \varepsilon$ for $m, n > N$. This gives

$$\|T_n(x) - T_m(x)\| \leq \varepsilon\|x\|,$$

and, passing to the limit with n,

$$\|T_m(x) - T(x)\| \leq \varepsilon\|x\|, \qquad \text{whence} \qquad \|T_m - T\| \leq \varepsilon,$$

so that $\lim_{m\to\infty} \|T_m - T\| = 0$. Hence $\mathfrak{E}(\mathfrak{X}, \mathfrak{Y})$ is complete.

It was observed above that if $\mathfrak{N}[T] = \{0\}$, then the mapping $x \to T(x)$ is (1, 1). This means that there exists an inverse transformation T^{-1} on $\mathfrak{Y}$ to $\mathfrak{X}$ such that

$$T^{-1}[T(x)] = x, \qquad \forall x \in \mathfrak{D}, \tag{4.1.7}$$

$$T[T^{-1}(y)] = y, \qquad \forall y \in \mathfrak{R}. \tag{4.1.8}$$

It is clear that T^{-1} is linear if T is linear, but boundedness is not so easy to detect. We have the following result, which we state without proof.

Theorem 4.1.2. *Let the bounded linear transformation T map $\mathfrak{X}$ onto $\mathfrak{Y}$ in a* (1, 1) *manner; then the inverse transformation T^{-1} is also bounded.*

We note that T^{-1} is bounded iff there is a positive number m such that

$$\|T(x)\| \geq m\|x\|, \qquad \forall x \in \mathfrak{D}. \tag{4.1.9}$$

We leave the verification to the reader.

Among the various B-spaces $\mathfrak{E}(\mathfrak{X}, \mathfrak{Y})$, two are particularly important, namely the cases (i) $\mathfrak{Y} = \mathfrak{X}$, and (ii) $\mathfrak{Y} = F$. In the first case we write $\mathfrak{E}(\mathfrak{X})$ instead of $\mathfrak{E}(\mathfrak{X}, \mathfrak{X})$. This is the linear vector space of all linear bounded transformations on $\mathfrak{X}$ to $\mathfrak{X}$. Actually $\mathfrak{E}(\mathfrak{X})$ is an algebra if we define products by

$$(T_1T_2)(x) = T_1[T_2(x)], \qquad \forall x. \tag{4.1.10}$$

Since

$$\|T_1T_2\| \leq \|T_1\|\,\|T_2\|, \tag{4.1.11}$$

this is a normed algebra. Being complete, it is a B-algebra in the terminology of the next section.

In the second case, we write $\mathfrak{E}(\mathfrak{X}, F) = \mathfrak{X}^*$, known as the *adjoint space.*

Definition 4.1.2. *A function on $\mathfrak{X}$ having values in the scalar field F is called a functional; thus $\mathfrak{X}^*$ is the space of all linear bounded functionals on $\mathfrak{X}$.*

Functionals are denoted by x^* or similar symbol. The reader should note that x and x^* are used as generic elements of $\mathfrak{X}$ and $\mathfrak{X}^*$; the notation is not meant to imply that x and x^* are related.

The space $\mathfrak{X}^*$ is not void since it always contains the zero functional which annihilates every element of $\mathfrak{X}$. Actually, any B-space carries enough functionals to distinguish between the elements. Without attempting to prove the assertions, let us mention the existence of linear bounded functionals with the following properties:

1. *If* $x_0 \neq 0$, $x_0 \in \mathfrak{X}$, *there exists an* $x_0^* \in \mathfrak{X}^*$ *such that* $x_0^*(x_0) = \|x_0\|$ *and* $\|x_0^*\| = 1$.
2. *If* $\mathfrak{X}_0 \subset \mathfrak{X}$ *is a linear subspace of* $\mathfrak{X}$ *that is not dense in* $\mathfrak{X}$, *then there is an* $x_1^* \in \mathfrak{X}^*$ *such that* $x_1^*(\mathfrak{X}_0) = 0$ *and* $\|x_1^*\| = 1$.
3. *If* x_1 *and* $x_2 \in \mathfrak{X}$, $x_1 \neq x_2$, *there exists an* $x_2^* \in \mathfrak{X}^*$ *such that* $x_2^*(x_1) \neq x_2^*(x_2)$. *In particular, this implies that the only element that annihilates all functionals is the zero element.*

We shall have to consider functions on real or complex numbers having their values in a B-space $\mathfrak{X}$. Since we have a metric in $\mathfrak{X}$, it is possible to define boundedness, continuity, and differentiability of the function in question in an obvious manner. We follow the classical pattern, simply replacing absolute values by norms. Likewise, we can integrate a continuous function over a real interval or over a rectifiable arc in the complex plane. The usual discussion of Riemann sums and of Riemann-Stieltjes sums carries over to the abstract case. The resulting integral has the usual properties of linearity with respect to the integrand, additivity with respect to the domain of integration, and the norm of the integral does not exceed the integral of the norm. We refer to Hille and Phillips, *Functional Analysis and Semi-Groups*, for further details.

The theory of holomorphic functions with values in $\mathfrak{X}$ calls for some observations. Let Δ be a *domain* (= open connected set) in the complex plane, $f(\zeta)$ a function on complex numbers to $\mathfrak{X}$ defined in Δ. Suppose that $f(\zeta)$ is continuous and differentiable in Δ. The latter assumption implies the existence of a function $f'(\zeta)$ defined in Δ with values in $\mathfrak{X}$ such that

$$\lim_{\eta \to 0} \left\| \frac{1}{\eta} [f(\zeta + \eta) - f(\zeta)] - f'(\zeta) \right\| = 0. \tag{4.1.12}$$

If $x^* \in \mathfrak{X}^*$ is any linear bounded functional on $\mathfrak{X}$, then this relation implies that

$$\lim_{\eta \to 0} \left\{ \frac{1}{\eta} (x^*[f(\zeta + \eta)] - x^*[f(\zeta)]) - x^*[f'(\zeta)] \right\} = 0,$$

i.e. the complex-valued function $x^*[f(\zeta)]$ is holomorphic in the sense of Cauchy and

$$x^*[f'(\zeta)] = \frac{d}{d\zeta} x^*[f(\zeta)].$$

Now let Γ be a simple closed rectifiable curve which together with its interior lies in Δ. Then

$$\int_\Gamma f(\tau)\, d\tau$$

is defined as an abstract Riemann-Stieltjes integral. We form

$$x^*\left\{\int_\Gamma f(\tau)\, d\tau\right\} = \int_\Gamma x^*[f(\tau)]\, d\tau = 0.$$

The first step follows from the definition of the integrals as limits of Riemann-Stieltjes sums, the second from the well-known property of Cauchy holomorphic functions. Here x^* is any element of $\mathfrak{X}^*$, and we know that the only element of $\mathfrak{X}$ that annihilates all functionals is the zero element. Hence

$$\int_\Gamma f(\tau)\, d\tau = 0. \tag{4.1.13}$$

In the same manner we prove

$$f(\zeta) = \frac{1}{2\pi i}\int_\Gamma \frac{f(\tau)\, d\tau}{\tau - \zeta} \tag{4.1.14}$$

for ζ interior to Γ. Once we have the Cauchy integral for $\mathfrak{X}$-valued holomorphic functions, then we have the whole Cauchy apparatus: the existence and representation by integrals of derivatives of $f(\zeta)$ of all orders, the existence of Taylor and Laurent expansions convergent in the norm in the largest circle or annulus where $f(\zeta)$ is holomorphic, and so on.

We have also a form of the *principle of the maximum*: *if* $\|f(\zeta)\| \le M$ *on* Γ, *then the same inequality holds in the interior of* Γ. For a circular disk, this is immediate. From

$$f(\zeta) = \frac{1}{2\pi}\int_0^{2\pi} f(\zeta + \rho\, e^{i\theta})\, d\theta, \tag{4.1.15}$$

it follows that

$$\|f(\zeta)\| \le \max_\theta \|f(\zeta + \rho\, e^{i\theta})\|.$$

This shows that $\|f(\zeta)\|$ cannot have a maximum anywhere in the domain where $f(\zeta)$ is holomorphic. This is a form of the principle of the maximum and it implies the assertion made above.

In closing this brief survey of the principles of functional analysis, let us recall some special B-spaces of importance to function theory and the theory of differential equations. The reader is already familiar with $C[a, b]$, the space of all functions continuous in the closed interval $[a, b]$ with the metric defined by the sup norm. He has also encountered $L(a, b)$, the space of all measurable functions integrable in the sense of Lebesgue. Here the elements are actually equivalence classes, all members of which have the same Lebesgue integral. The norm is

$$\|f\|_1 = \int_a^b |f(t)|\, dt. \tag{4.1.16}$$

We have also "higher" Lebesgue spaces $L_p(a, b)$, $1 < p < \infty$. Again the elements are equivalence classes of measurable functions and

$$\|f\|_p = \left\{\int_a^b |f(t)|^p\, dt\right\}^{1/p}. \tag{4.1.17}$$

The class L_q with

$$\frac{1}{p} + \frac{1}{q} = 1 \tag{4.1.18}$$

is said to be *conjugate* to L_p. Finally we mention $BV[a, b]$, the class of functions of bounded variation in $[a, b]$. We cannot take $V_a^b[f]$, the *total variation* of f, as norm of f since this would assign the norm 0 to all constant functions. A suitable norm is, for example,

$$\|f\|_V = |f(a)| + 2V_a^b[f]. \tag{4.1.19}$$

The mysterious factor "2" is inserted to make sure that the norm of a product does not exceed the product of the norms. We recall that

$$V_a^b[f] = \sup \sum_{j=0}^{n} |f(t_{j+1}) - f(t_j)|$$

for any partition of $[a, b]$ by points $\{t_j\}$.

EXERCISE 4.1

1. Let $\mathfrak{X} = C[0, 1]$ and define

$$T[f](x) = \int_0^x f(t)\, dt, \qquad 0 \le x \le 1.$$

Show that this is a linear bounded transformation on $\mathfrak{X}$ to $\mathfrak{X}$. Is the range dense in $\mathfrak{X}$? Show that the mapping is (1, 1) and determine T^{-1}.

2. Let $\mathfrak{X} = C[0, 1]$ and define

$$T[f](x) = f(x) - \int_0^x \sinh(x - s) f(s)\, ds, \qquad 0 \le x \le 1.$$

Show that this is a linear bounded transformation on $\mathfrak{X}$ to $\mathfrak{X}$. In order to prove that the mapping is one-to-one it is necessary (and sufficient) to show that the equation

$$f(x) = \int_0^x \sinh(x - s) f(s)\, ds$$

implies $f(x) \equiv 0$. Show that a solution in $\mathfrak{X}$ must be twice differentiable and reduce the problem to a uniqueness question for a differential equation.

3. If $\mathfrak{X} = C[0, 1]$ and if $g(t) \in BV[0, 1]$ is fixed, show that

$$x^*[f] = \int_0^1 f(t)\, dg(t)$$

is a linear bounded functional on $\mathfrak{X}$ with $\|x^*\| = V_0^1[g]$.

4. A particular functional on $C[0, 1]$ is given by $f(t_0)$, the value of f at $t = t_0$, $0 \leq t_0 \leq 1$. What is the corresponding function g? Show that this functional is not merely linear but also *multiplicative*, that is $x^*[fg] = x^*[f]x^*[g]$.
5. The functional of the preceding problem is annihilated by certain elements of $C[0, 1]$. What is the algebraic structure of $\mathfrak{N}[x^*]$?
6. If $g(t) \in C[a, b]$, show that

$$x^*[f] = \int_a^b g(t)\, df(t)$$

is a linear bounded functional on $BV[a, b]$. This is not the most general functional, however.

7. If $\mathfrak{X} = L_2(0, 2\pi)$ and if g is a fixed element of L_2, then

$$x^*[f] = \int_0^{2\pi} f(t)g(t)\, dt$$

is a linear bounded functional on $\mathfrak{X}$. Prove this, using the Bouniakovski-Schwarz inequality to find $\|x^*\|$. All functionals on $\mathfrak{X}$ are of this form.

8. How should g be chosen in order that x^* annihilate all trigonometric polynomials of degree ≤ 2?
9. How should g be chosen in order that $x^*[f] = \|f\|$ for a given $f \in L_2$?
10. Find a functional on L_2 which takes on different values for $\sin t$ and $\cos t$.
11. If $\mathfrak{X} = L_p(0, 2\pi)$ and g is a fixed element of the conjugate space L_q, show that

$$x^*[f] = \int_0^{2\pi} f(t)g(t)\, dt$$

is a linear bounded functional on $\mathfrak{X}$. Use Hölder's inequality to find the norm of x^*.

12. Carry through the proof of (4.1.14).

4.2 BANACH ALGEBRAS

An abstract set $\mathfrak{A}$ is called an *algebra* if it is a linear vector space in which multiplication of elements is also defined so that $x \in \mathfrak{A}$, $y \in \mathfrak{A}$ implies $xy \in \mathfrak{A}$. This clearly also implies that $yx \in \mathfrak{A}$ and $\mathfrak{A}$ is said to be a *commutative* or *Abelian algebra* if

$$xy = yx, \qquad \forall x, y, \tag{4.2.1}$$

otherwise *non-commutative*. Multiplication is supposed to be associative

$$(xy)z = x(yz). \tag{4.2.2}$$

We also assume the distributive laws

$$x(y + z) = xy + xz, \qquad (x + y)z = xz + yz, \tag{4.2.3}$$

and that scalar multiplication commutes with multiplication so that

$$\alpha x \beta y = \alpha\beta xy. \tag{4.2.4}$$

An algebra may have a *unit element e* such that

$$ex = xe = x, \qquad \forall x. \tag{4.2.5}$$

If $\mathfrak{A}$ has a unit element e, some elements x may have *inverses*. We say that x *is regular if it has an inverse*, i.e. an element y such that

$$xy = yx = e. \tag{4.2.6}$$

We set

$$y = x^{-1}. \tag{4.2.7}$$

An element x which is not regular is said to be *singular*.

Theorem 4.2.1. *The regular elements form a group* $\mathfrak{G}$.

Proof. If x and $y \in \mathfrak{G}$, then

$$xyy^{-1}x^{-1} = e, \qquad y^{-1}x^{-1}xy = e, \tag{4.2.8}$$

so that xy has the inverse $y^{-1}x^{-1}$. Further, if $x \in \mathfrak{G}$ so does x^{-1} since $(x^{-1})^{-1} = x$. ▮

Definition 4.2.1. $\mathfrak{B}$ *is a Banach algebra* (= B-algebra) *if* $\mathfrak{B}$ *is an algebra as well as a B-space and if, in addition,*

$$\|xy\| \le \|x\| \, \|y\|. \tag{4.2.9}$$

If $\mathfrak{B}$ has a unit element, $\|e\| \ge 1$. It is always possible to introduce an equivalent norm such that

$$\|e\| = 1. \tag{4.2.10}$$

We shall always assume that this has been done.

Theorem 4.2.2. *If* $\mathfrak{B}$ *is a B-algebra, then the sphere*

$$\|x - e\| < 1 \tag{4.2.11}$$

belongs to $\mathfrak{G}$.

Proof. The geometric series

$$e + (e - x) + (e - x)^2 + \cdots + (e - x)^n + \cdots \tag{4.2.12}$$

converges in norm to an element of $\mathfrak{B}$ by (4.2.11). If the series is multiplied by

$$x = e - (e - x)$$

on the right or on the left, all terms cancel except e so that (4.2.12) is the inverse of x. ∎

Theorem 4.2.3. *The group $\mathfrak{G}$ is an open set in the normed metric.*

Proof. We have to show that, if $x_0 \in \mathfrak{G}$, then also a small neighborhood of x_0 is in $\mathfrak{G}$. The argument is based on the preceding theorem. We have

$$x = x_0 - (x_0 - x) = x_0[e - x_0^{-1}(x_0 - x)].$$

This is the product of two factors of which the first has an inverse by assumption. By Theorem 4.2.2 the second factor has an inverse if

$$\|x_0^{-1}(x_0 - x)\| = \|e - x_0^{-1}x\| < 1.$$

This is satisfied, e.g. if

$$\|x - x_0\| < (\|x_0^{-1}\|)^{-1}$$

and this is a neighborhood of x_0. ∎

We shall need the following lemma concerning so-called *subadditive sequences.*

Lemma 4.2.1. *If $\{a_n\}$ is a sequence of real numbers and if for all m and n*

$$a_{m+n} \le a_m + a_n, \tag{4.2.13}$$

then

$$\lim_{n\to\infty} \frac{a_n}{n} = \beta \qquad \textit{where} \qquad \beta = \inf \frac{a_n}{n}. \tag{4.2.14}$$

Here $-\infty \le \beta < \infty$.

Proof. If $\varepsilon > 0$ is given and if β is finite, we can find a k such that

$$\frac{a_k}{k} < \beta + \varepsilon.$$

If $n = mk + d$ with $0 \le d \le k - 1$, we have

$$\beta \le \frac{a_n}{n} = \frac{a_{mk+d}}{mk + d} \le \frac{m}{mk + d} a_k + \frac{a_d}{mk + d},$$

$$= \frac{mk}{mk + d} \frac{a_k}{k} + \frac{a_d}{mk + d} < \beta + \varepsilon + \frac{a_d}{mk + d},$$

so that

$$\beta \le \liminf \frac{a_n}{n} \le \limsup \frac{a_n}{n} \le \beta + \varepsilon.$$

Since ε is arbitrary, this proves the assertion when β is finite. We leave the case $\beta = -\infty$ to the reader. ▌

We cannot exclude the possibility that $\beta = -\infty$; this is shown by the sequence $\{-n^p\}$ where $p > 1$.

The lemma gives the following result, which is due to I. M. Gelfand.

Theorem 4.2.4. *If* $x \in \mathfrak{B}$, *then*

$$\lim_{n \to \infty} \|x^n\|^{1/n} \equiv r(x) \tag{4.2.15}$$

exists and $0 \leq r(x) \leq \|x\|$.

Proof. If x is *nilpotent* and $x^p = 0$, then $x^n = 0$ for $n \geq p$. In this case $r(x) = 0$. Leaving this case to one side, we may assume that $x^n \neq 0$ for all n so that

$$a_n = \log \|x^n\|$$

is well defined. Here

$$a_{m+n} = \log \|x^{m+n}\| \leq \log \|x^m\| + \log \|x^n\| = a_m + a_n.$$

By the lemma

$$\lim \frac{1}{n} \log \|x^n\| \equiv \beta$$

exists and $-\infty \leq \beta < \infty$. Since

$$a_n \leq n a_1,$$

we see that $\beta \leq \log \|x\|$. We have $r(x) = e^\beta$ where the exponential is 0 by definition if $\beta = -\infty$. ▌

The quantity $r(x)$ is known as the *spectral radius* of x for reasons that will become evident in the next section.

An element $q \in \mathfrak{B}$ with $r(q) = 0$ is called a *quasi-nilpotent*. It is clear that a nilpotent element is also quasi-nilpotent but the converse is not necessarily true. Any quasi-nilpotent element is singular. This will be proved later.

Among the singular elements figure the so-called *divisors of zero*. We say that an element $a \neq 0$ is a divisor of zero if there exists an element $b \neq 0$ such that either

$$ab = 0 \quad \text{or} \quad ba = 0. \tag{4.2.16}$$

Since the product of regular elements is regular and since 0 is singular, we conclude that both a and b must be singular.

An element x with

$$x^2 = x \tag{4.2.17}$$

is said to be *idempotent*. This equation is of course satisfied by the zero and the unit elements. Since

$$x(x - e) = 0,$$

we see that if $x \neq 0, e$, then x is singular. If the equation (4.2.17) is satisfied by an element $P \in \mathfrak{E}(\mathfrak{X})$, then P is said to be a *projection* (operator).

The presence of divisors of zero in the algebra makes manipulations somewhat hazardous and the question arises, is it possible to find products which are not zero. In certain algebras this is indeed possible.

Definition 4.2.2. [N. Jacobson] *An algebra $\mathfrak{A}$ is called a prime ring if $xzy = 0$ for all $z \in \mathfrak{A}$ implies that either x or y is* 0.

In other words, if $\mathfrak{A}$ is a prime ring and if $x \neq 0$, $y \neq 0$, then there exists a z such that $xzy \neq 0$.

Let us finally give some examples of B-algebras. We have already observed that $C[a, b]$ is a B-algebra under the sup norm. It is commutative and has a unit element but it is not a prime ring. Similarly, $BV[a, b]$ is a commutative B-algebra with unit element. It is not a prime ring, in fact, no commutative algebra where there are divisors of zero can be a prime ring.

The matrix algebra $\mathfrak{M}_n$ is a non-commutative B-algebra under the norm

$$\|\mathcal{A}\| = \max_j \sum_{k=1}^{n} |a_{jk}|.$$

Here the unit matrix $\mathcal{E}$ serves as unit element. $\mathfrak{M}_n$ is a prime ring. For if $\mathcal{X} \neq 0$ there is at least one element $x_{jk} \neq 0$. Suppose that $x_{j\alpha} \neq 0$. Similarly, if $\mathcal{Y} \neq 0$, there is an element $y_{\beta k} \neq 0$. We can then take $\mathfrak{Z}$ as the matrix which has a 1 in the place (α, β) and 0 elsewhere. Then $\mathcal{X}\mathfrak{Z}\mathcal{Y}$ has the element $x_{j\alpha} y_{\beta k}$ in the place (j, k) and is consequently not the zero matrix.

One of the largest and most important classes of B-algebras is formed by the operator algebras $\mathfrak{E}(\mathfrak{X})$ introduced in the preceding section. Such an algebra is non-commutative and has as unit element the identity operator I. R. Loy has called attention to the fact that $\mathfrak{E}(\mathfrak{X})$ is a prime ring. The proof is based on the following lemma, which is due to J. L. B. Gamlen.

Lemma 4.2.2. *If $x_0, y_0 \in \mathfrak{X}$, $\|x_0\| = 1$, then there exists an operator $T \in \mathfrak{E}(\mathfrak{X})$ such that $T[x_0] = y_0$ and $\|T\| = \|y_0\|$.*

Proof. It was observed above that there exists a linear bounded functional $x^* \in X^*$ such that $x^*(x_0) = \|x_0\| = 1$ and $\|x^*\| = 1$. We then set $T[x] = y_0 x^*(x)$ which has the desired properties. ▮

Theorem 4.2.5. *$\mathfrak{E}(\mathfrak{X})$ is a prime ring.*

Proof. Let $A, B \in \mathfrak{E}(\mathfrak{X})$, $A \neq 0$, $B \neq 0$. Then there exist elements u_0, y_0 such that $B[u_0] \neq 0$, $A[y_0] \neq 0$. Write $x_0 = Bu_0$ and suppose that $\|x_0\| = 1$ as we may do. Then by the preceding lemma, there exists an operator $T \in \mathfrak{E}(\mathfrak{X})$ such that $T[x_0] = y_0$, that is $TB[u_0] = y_0$, so that $ATB[u_0] = A[y_0] \neq 0$, and ATB is not the zero operator. ▮

In Sections 9.6 and 10.6, we shall consider a special type of B-algebras known as *star algebras*. Here there is an additional operation defined, denoted by a star and known as *conjugation* or *involution*. In this connection x^* is an element of the algebra and must not be confused with the generic notation for a functional which is an element of the adjoint space. The following definition involves the concept of spectrum, which is defined in the next section. It is more convenient to have all assumptions in one place.

Definition 4.2.3. *A complex B-algebra $\mathfrak{B}$ is said to be a star algebra if it satisfies the assumptions:*

i) *For each $x \in \mathfrak{B}$ there is a unique $x^* \in \mathfrak{B}$ and $(x^*)^* = x$.*
ii) $(x + y)^* = x^* + y^*$.
iii) $(\alpha x)^* = \bar{\alpha} x^*$.
iv) $(xy)^* = y^* x^*$.
v) $\|x^* x\| = \|x\|^2$.

We designate $\frac{1}{2}(x + x^*)$ and $1/2i(x - x^*)$ as the real and imaginary parts of x, respectively. An element such that $x^* = x$ is said to be symmetric. It coincides with its real part. We postulate further:

vi) *Symmetric elements have real spectra.*
vii) *Symmetric elements with non-negative real spectra form a positive cone $\mathfrak{B}^+$, i.e. the set is closed under addition, multiplication by positive numbers, and passage to the limit.*
viii) *Elements of the form $xx^* \in \mathfrak{B}^+$.*

Symmetric elements with positive (negative) spectra are said to be positive (negative) and (vii) *is understood to imply that for positive elements sums and positive multiples are also positive.*

For a symmetric element x, condition (v) gives

$$\|x^2\| = \|x\|^2,$$

more generally

$$\|x^{2n}\| = \|x\|^{2n}$$

whence it follows that

$$r(x) = \|x\| \quad \text{if} \quad x^* = x, \tag{4.2.18}$$

where $r(x)$ is the spectral radius.

Note that for all x condition (v) implies

$$\|x^*\| = \|x\|. \tag{4.2.19}$$

EXERCISE 4.2

1. Verify that the norm (4.1.19) satisfies (4.2.9).
2. Construct a divisor of zero in $C[0, 1]$.
3. If T is defined as in Problem 1 of Exercise 4.1, find $T^n[f]$ and determine $\|T^n\|$. Show that T is a quasinilpotent element of the operator algebra $\mathfrak{E}(C[0, 1])$.
4. Determine the spectral radii of the matrices $\begin{pmatrix} 1 & 0 \\ 1 & 1 \end{pmatrix}$ and $\begin{pmatrix} 1 & 0 \\ 0 & 2 \end{pmatrix}$ and compare with the norms.
5. The matrix $\begin{pmatrix} 0 & 0 \\ 1 & 1 \end{pmatrix}$ determines a linear transformation T on R^2 to R^2 as in (1.3.17). Show that T is a projection and that the matrix is an idempotent.
6. In the algebra $C[0, 1]$ define f^* by $f^*(t) = \overline{f(t)}$ where the bar indicates the complex conjugate. Show that $C[0, 1]$ becomes a star algebra under this definition, the norm being the sup norm. [*Hint*: The spectrum of f is the range of $f(t)$.]
7. Show that $\mathfrak{M}_n$ becomes a star algebra under the definition $\mathcal{A}^* = (\bar{a}_{kj})$ if $\mathcal{A} = (a_{jk})$. Verify that $(\mathcal{A}\mathcal{A}^*\mathbf{x}, \mathbf{x}) = (\mathcal{A}^*\mathbf{x}, \mathcal{A}^*\mathbf{x})$ to prove (viii). Use the operator norm (1.3.25).
8. If $|\mu| < 1$ and P is a projection, sum the series
$$I + P\mu + P^2\mu^2 + \cdots + P^n\mu^n + \cdots.$$
9. Verify that a commutative algebra with zero divisors cannot be a prime ring.
10. Let $\sum_{-\infty}^{\infty} |a_n|^2$ and $\sum_{-\infty}^{\infty} |b_n|^2$ be convergent and define the following transformations on $L_2(0, 2\pi)$:
$$T_1[f](x) = \sum_{-\infty}^{\infty} a_k f_{2k}\, e^{2kix}, \qquad T_2[f](x) = \sum_{-\infty}^{\infty} b_k f_{2k+1}\, e^{(2k+1)ix},$$
where
$$f \sim \sum_{-\infty}^{\infty} f_n\, e^{nix}.$$
Show that they are elements of $\mathfrak{E}[L_2]$ and find $\|T_1\|$ and $\|T_2\|$.
11. Show that $T_1T_2 = T_2T_1$ is the zero operator that annihilates all of L_2. If
$$S[f](x) = e^{ix}f(x),$$
evaluate $T_1ST_2[f]$ and $T_2ST_1[f]$.
12. If $\mathfrak{B} = \mathfrak{M}_n$, show that $[\det(\mathcal{A})]^p$ is a non-linear bounded functional on $\mathfrak{B}$ which is multiplicative, p positive integer.
13. If $f(\zeta)$ is a $\mathfrak{B}$-valued function holomorphic in the domain Δ, prove that the spectral radius of $f(\zeta)$ cannot have a local maximum in Δ.

4.3 THE RESOLVENT

Let $\mathfrak{B}$ be any B-algebra with unit element e. Until further notice, $\mathfrak{B}$ shall be non-commutative.

We have seen that regular elements play a particularly important role in an algebra. With this in mind we shall consider the regularity of

$$\lambda e - x \equiv x_\lambda, \tag{4.3.1}$$

where λ is any complex number and x is a fixed element of $\mathfrak{B}$. The values of λ fall into two mutually exclusive categories, those for which x_λ is regular and those for which x_λ is singular. The first set is the *resolvent set* of x, denoted by $\rho(x)$, the latter the *spectrum*, denoted by $\sigma(x)$.

Theorem 4.3.1. *The resolvent set is an open unbounded set in the complex plane and*

$$\rho(x) \supset (\lambda \mid |\lambda| > r(x)), \tag{4.3.2}$$

where $r(x)$ is the spectral radius of x. The spectrum is a bounded closed set confined to the disk

$$|\lambda| \leq r(x) \tag{4.3.3}$$

and there is at least one point of $\sigma(x)$ on the boundary.

Proof. That $\rho(x)$ is open follows from Theorem 4.2.3. For large values of λ we have

$$(\lambda e - x)^{-1} = \frac{e}{\lambda} + \sum_{n=1}^{\infty} \frac{x^n}{\lambda^{n+1}}. \tag{4.3.4}$$

The series converges in norm for

$$|\lambda| > r(x)$$

and diverges for any λ with $|\lambda| < r(x)$, by the definition of radius of convergence and of spectral radius. In the first case, if the series is multiplied by $\lambda e - x$, either on the right or on the left, the resulting product is e, i.e. the series represents $(\lambda e - x)^{-1}$ in its region of convergence.

The spectrum is the complement of the resolvent set; the latter being open, the former must be closed. It is clear that $\sigma(x)$ must be confined to the disk (4.3.3). If $\sigma(x)$ could be confined to a smaller disk with center at the origin, then the series (4.3.4) would converge in some region $|\lambda| > r$ with $r < r(x)$ and this is impossible. Hence there must be at least one point of $\sigma(x)$ on the circle $|\lambda| = r(x)$. ∎

We note that the open set $\rho(x)$ need not be connected. In fact it can have infinitely many disjoint components. One of these contains the point at infinity and is frequently referred to as the *principal component* of the resolvent set.

Wherever the inverse of x_λ exists we shall write

$$(\lambda e - x)^{-1} \equiv R(\lambda, x). \tag{4.3.5}$$

This is a function of two variables, λ and x. It satisfies a functional equation with respect to each of these variables. These will now be derived.

From the definition of the resolvent it follows that

$$(\lambda e - x)R(\lambda, x) = R(\lambda, x)(\lambda e - x) = e, \qquad \forall \lambda \in \rho(x). \tag{4.3.6}$$

Suppose now that λ and μ belong to $\rho(x)$. Then

$$(\lambda e - x)R(\lambda, x) \qquad = e,$$
$$R(\mu, x)(\mu e - x) = e.$$

Multiply the first equation on the right by $R(\mu, x)$, the second on the left by $R(\lambda, x)$ and subtract the results. After cancellation we get

$$(\lambda - \mu)R(\lambda, x)R(\mu, x) = R(\mu, x) - R(\lambda, x). \tag{4.3.7}$$

This will be called the *first resolvent equation* in the following.

Similarly, if $\lambda \in \rho(x) \cap \rho(y)$

$$(\lambda e - x)R(\lambda, x) = e,$$
$$R(\lambda, y)(\lambda e - y) \qquad = e.$$

Here we multiply the first equation on the left by $R(\lambda, y)$, the second on the right by $R(\lambda, x)$ and subtract the results. After cancellation we obtain

$$R(\lambda, y)(y - x)R(\lambda, x) = R(\lambda, y) - R(\lambda, x). \tag{4.3.8}$$

This is the *second resolvent equation.*

These equations were first noted in the theory of linear integral equations around 1910. We shall derive some consequences.

Leaving out the variable x, we can write the first equation

$$(\lambda - \mu)R(\lambda)R(\mu) = R(\mu) - R(\lambda). \tag{4.3.9}$$

Here $R(\lambda)$ is a function on complex numbers to the B-algebra $\mathfrak{B}$ and it commutes with $R(\mu)$. Suppose that there is such a function $R(\lambda)$ which satisfies (4.3.9) in some domain Δ of the complex plane and which is bounded in Δ, say $\|R(\lambda)\| \leq M$. Then for λ and μ in Δ

$$\|R(\lambda) - R(\mu)\| \leq M^2|\lambda - \mu|,$$

so $R(\lambda)$ is continuous in Δ. But then

$$\lim_{\mu \to \lambda} \frac{R(\lambda) - R(\mu)}{\lambda - \mu} = -[R(\lambda)]^2, \tag{4.3.10}$$

i.e. $R(\lambda)$ is a differentiable function in Δ. This implies the existence of derivatives of all orders and

$$R^{(n)}(\lambda) = (-1)^n n!\,[R(\lambda)]^{n+1}. \tag{4.3.11}$$

We conclude that $R(\lambda)$ is a $\mathfrak{B}$-valued analytic function of λ, holomorphic in any domain where it is defined and bounded. Hence, for $\lambda_0 \in \Delta$,

$$R(\lambda) = \sum_{n=0}^{\infty} (\lambda_0 - \lambda)^n [R(\lambda_0)]^{n+1}. \tag{4.3.12}$$

We started out with a resolvent equation, i.e. an equation satisfied by regular elements of $\mathfrak{B}$. However, it may not be that the function R defined by (4.3.12) is regular, in the sense that all the values $R(\lambda)$ furnished by the series when it converges, are regular elements of $\mathfrak{B}$. It has this property iff $R(\lambda_0)$ is regular. In fact, we can get a local solution of (4.3.9) by choosing an arbitrary element a of $\mathfrak{B}$, regular or singular, and forming the series

$$R(\lambda) = \sum_{0}^{\infty} (\lambda_0 - \lambda)^n a^{n+1}. \tag{4.3.13}$$

This converges iff

$$|\lambda - \lambda_0| r(a) < 1,$$

and for such λ, $R(\lambda)$ is a regular element of $\mathfrak{B}$ iff a is regular.

Applied to the resolvent $R(\lambda, x)$ which is a solution of (4.3.9), the preceding results show that $R(\lambda, x)$ is a holomorphic function of λ in each of the components of $\rho(x)$. It should be observed that in (4.3.7) λ and μ might be in different components of $\rho(x)$.

Equation (4.3.8) can be subjected to a similar analysis. Here we deal with a function $R(x)$ on $\mathfrak{B}$ to $\mathfrak{B}$ which satisfies

$$R(y)(y - x)R(x) = R(y) - R(x) \tag{4.3.14}$$

in some domain (= open connected set) $\mathfrak{D}$ of $\mathfrak{B}$. Here again boundedness of $\|R(x)\|$ in $\mathfrak{D}$ implies continuity since then a Lipschitz condition

$$\|R(y) - R(x)\| \le M^2 \|x - y\|$$

holds in $\mathfrak{D}$. Continuity in its turn implies a type of differentiability. If $x \in \mathfrak{D}$ and z is any element of $\mathfrak{B}$ while α is a complex number, then

$$y = x + \alpha z$$

is in $\mathfrak{D}$ for all sufficiently small values of $|\alpha|$. This gives

$$\lim_{\alpha \to 0} \frac{1}{\alpha} [R(x + \alpha z) - R(x)] = R(x) z R(x). \tag{4.3.15}$$

Higher derivatives, defined in a similar manner, also exist, and we have Taylor expansions of the form

$$R(x + \alpha z) = R(x) + \sum_{n=1}^{\infty} \alpha^n R(x)[zR(x)]^n, \tag{4.3.16}$$

where it must be remembered that normally z and $R(x)$ do not commute, so we cannot separate powers of z from powers of $R(x)$ in the products. This series converges in norm iff

$$|\alpha| r[zR(x)] < 1, \tag{4.3.17}$$

a fortiori it converges for

$$|\alpha| \, \|z\| \, \|R(x)\| < 1. \tag{4.3.18}$$

Here again the applications to the resolvent case are of interest. Suppose that $R(x) = R(\lambda_0, x)$ so that $\lambda_0 \in \rho(x)$. Then we conclude from (4.3.18) that $\lambda_0 \in \rho(x + \alpha z)$ provided

$$|\alpha| \, \|z\| \, \|R(\lambda_0, x)\| < 1.$$

This has several implications. Thus if $\lambda_0 \in \rho(x)$, there is a sphere in $\mathfrak{B}$

$$\|y - x\| < [\|R(\lambda_0, x)\|]^{-1} \tag{4.3.19}$$

such that λ_0 belongs to $\rho(y)$ for every such y. This shows that the set of those x in $\mathfrak{B}$ whose resolvent sets contain a given complex number λ_0 is open.

Secondly, similar considerations obviously apply to the spectrum of x. The set $\sigma(x)$ is compact and so is the set

$$\{\lambda \mid d[\lambda, \sigma(x)] \le \varepsilon\}.$$

We can cover the latter set by a finite number of open ε-disks. Let Ω_ε denote the union of these disks and let Γ_ε be the boundary of Ω_ε. Then Γ_ε consists of at least one and at most a finite number of closed rectifiable curves each made up of a finite number of circular arcs. Let P_ε be the complement of the interior of Ω_ε. Then $R(\lambda, x)$ exists in P_ε and is bounded there. This is clearly the case in each of the finitely many bounded components of P_ε and in the infinite component, $R(\lambda, x) \to 0$ as $\lambda \to \infty$. Hence $R(\lambda, x)$ is also bounded in the infinite component. Suppose that

$$\|R(\lambda, x)\| \le M_\varepsilon, \qquad \forall \lambda \in P_\varepsilon. \tag{4.3.20}$$

Here all points of P_ε belong to $\rho(x)$ and by (4.3.19) they also belong to $\rho(y)$ provided

$$\|y - x\| \le (M_\varepsilon)^{-1}. \tag{4.3.21}$$

This asserts that

$$\sigma(y) \subset \Omega_\varepsilon \tag{4.3.22}$$

when (4.3.21) holds. This is a form of continuity for σ as a function from $\mathfrak{B}$ into the class of compact subsets of the complex plane.

Any bounded closed set in the complex plane can be a $\sigma(x)$. In fact, given any such set Σ we can find a B-algebra $\mathfrak{B}$ and an element x thereof whose spectrum with respect to $\mathfrak{B}$ coincides with Σ. At the present juncture, we are mainly interested in the structure of $R(\lambda, x)$ near an isolated point of $\sigma(x)$. We can get the desired result from the first resolvent equation, using an argument due to M. Nagumo. Since the equation is invariant under a translation

$$(\lambda, \mu) \to (\lambda + \lambda_0, \mu + \lambda_0),$$

we can place the isolated singularity at the origin without loss of generality.

Suppose that $R(\lambda)$ is a solution of (4.3.9) with an isolated singularity at $\lambda = 0$. We have then a Laurent expansion

$$R(\lambda) = \sum_{-\infty}^{\infty} c_n \lambda^n. \tag{4.3.23}$$

Substituting this in (4.3.9), we obtain

$$\sum_{-\infty}^{\infty} c_n \frac{\lambda^n - \mu^n}{\lambda - \mu} = -\sum_{-\infty}^{\infty}\sum_{-\infty}^{\infty} c_k c_m \lambda^k \mu^m,$$

where $c_k c_m = c_m c_k$ for all k and m. On the left-hand side c_n is multiplied by

$$\begin{aligned} \lambda^{n-1} + \lambda^{n-2}\mu + \cdots + \mu^{n-1}, &\qquad \text{if } n \geq 1, \\ 0, &\qquad \text{if } n = 0, \\ -(\lambda^n\mu^{-1} + \lambda^{n-1}\mu^{-2} + \cdots + \lambda^{-1}\mu^n), &\qquad \text{if } n < 0. \end{aligned}$$

This shows that there are no terms in λ^n or μ^n if $n < 0$ and no mixed products $\lambda^k\mu^m$ with k and m having opposite signs. This implies that

$$c_k c_m = 0, \qquad k \geq 0, \qquad m \leq -1.$$

Thus we can write

$$R^+(\lambda) = \sum_{0}^{\infty} c_k \lambda^k, \qquad R^-(\lambda) = \sum_{m=-1}^{-\infty} c_m \lambda^m \tag{4.3.24}$$

with

$$R(\lambda) = R^+(\lambda) + R^-(\lambda)$$

and

$$R^+(\lambda)R^-(\mu) = 0 \tag{4.3.25}$$

for all admissible λ and μ. Substituting this expression for $R(\lambda)$ into (4.3.9) we see that $R^+(\lambda)$ and $R^-(\lambda)$ separately satisfy this equation.

Here $R^+(\lambda)$ is holomorphic at $\lambda = 0$ and the general form of a holomorphic solution of (4.3.9) is given by formula (4.3.13) where we set $\lambda_0 = 0$.

This gives

$$R^+(\lambda) = \sum_0^\infty (-\lambda)^n a^{n+1}.$$

Here a is any element of $\mathfrak{B}$, but we shall see that the orthogonality condition (4.3.25) imposes a restriction.

We know some solutions of (4.3.9) which are holomorphic at infinity, but possibly not the most general ones, so we write down the conditions to be satisfied by the coefficients c_{-n}. These are

$$c_{-n} = c_{-1}c_{-n} = c_{-2}c_{-n+1} = \cdots = c_{-n}c_{-1}.$$

Here we set

$$c_{-1} = j, \qquad c_{-2} = q$$

and find that j is an idempotent

$$j^2 = j, \qquad q = jq = qj.$$

We then get

$$c_{-n} = q^{n-1}, \qquad n = 2, 3, \ldots,$$

and

$$R^-(\lambda) = j\lambda^{-1} + \sum_{n=2}^\infty q^{n-1}\lambda^{-n}.$$

We summarize the results as

Theorem 4.3.2. *If $\lambda = 0$ is an isolated singularity of a solution $R(\lambda)$ of* (4.3.9), *then*

$$R(\lambda) = \sum_{n=0}^\infty a^{n+1}(-\lambda)^n + j\lambda^{-1} + \sum_{n=2}^\infty q^{n-1}\lambda^{-n}. \tag{4.3.26}$$

Here

$$aj = ja = 0, \qquad j^2 = j, \qquad q = qj = jq, \tag{4.3.27}$$

and q is quasi-nilpotent, i.e.

$$\|q^n\|^{1/n} \to 0 \qquad \text{or} \qquad r(q) = 0. \tag{4.3.28}$$

The first relation under (4.3.27) is induced by the orthogonality of R^+ and R^-. Since $R^-(\lambda)$ is supposed to be holomorphic for $|\lambda| > 0$, (4.3.28) must hold. In the particular case where the isolated singularity is a pole of order $p > 1$, we have $q^p = 0$ and q is nilpotent. We note that the residue of $R(\lambda)$ at $\lambda = 0$ is j, an idempotent.

This discussion applies to any solution of (4.3.9), in particular to a resolvent $R(\lambda, x)$. In this case two more relations must hold, namely

$$xa = ax = j - e, \qquad q = jx = xj. \tag{4.3.29}$$

These relations are obtained by substituting the expansion (4.3.26) in the identity

$$(\lambda e - x)R(\lambda, x) = e,$$

equating the constant terms, and setting the coefficient of λ^{-1} equal to 0.

If $\mathfrak{B} = \mathfrak{E}(\mathfrak{X})$ is an operator algebra, it is convenient to classify the spectral values of T into three subsets, the *point spectrum* $P\sigma(T)$, the *residual spectrum* $R\sigma(T)$, and the *continuous spectrum* $C\sigma(T)$. Here a spectral value $\lambda = \alpha$ belongs to

i) *$P\sigma(T)$ if $\alpha I - T$ is not* (1, 1), *i.e. there exists an $x_0 \in \mathfrak{X}$, $x_0 \neq 0$, such that $Tx_0 = \alpha x_0$;*

ii) *$R\sigma(T)$ if $\alpha I - T$ is* (1, 1) *but $(\alpha I - T)(\mathfrak{X})$ is not dense in $\mathfrak{X}$;*

iii) *$C\sigma(T)$ if $\alpha I - T$ is* (1, 1) *and $(\alpha I - T)(\mathfrak{X})$ is dense in $\mathfrak{X}$ but $(\alpha I - T)(\mathfrak{U})$ is not bounded away from* 0 *where $\mathfrak{U}$ is the unit sphere in $\mathfrak{X}$: $\mathfrak{U} = (x \mid \|x\| = 1)$.*

If $\lambda = \alpha$ is an isolated point of $\sigma(T)$, which is a pole of the resolvent, then $\alpha \in P\sigma(T)$.

This follows from the generalization of (4.3.26) to a pole at $\lambda = \alpha$ rather than at $\lambda = 0$. We have then

$$R(\lambda, T) = \sum_{n=0}^{\infty} A^{n+1}(\alpha - \lambda)^n + \frac{J}{\lambda - \alpha} + \sum_{n=2}^{m} \frac{Q^{n-1}}{(\lambda - \alpha)^n}, \qquad (4.3.30)$$

where

$$QJ = JQ = Q, \qquad Q^m = 0, \qquad Q = J(T - \alpha I) = (T - \alpha I)J.$$

Since Q^{m-1} is not the zero operator, there exists an x_0, $x_0 \neq 0$, such that $Q^{m-1}x_0 \neq 0$. Then

$$(\alpha I - T)[Q^{m-1}x_0] = (\alpha I - T)JQ^{m-1}x_0 = -Q^m x_0 = 0.$$

Hence $\lambda = \alpha$ belongs to $P\sigma(T)$.

EXERCISE 4.3

1. If $\mathfrak{B} = \mathfrak{M}_2$ and $x = \begin{pmatrix} 1 & 0 \\ 1 & 1 \end{pmatrix}$, find $\sigma(x)$ and $R(\lambda, x)$.
2. If $a \in \mathfrak{B}$ is an idempotent, $a \neq 0, e$, find $R(\lambda, a)$.
3. If $q \in \mathfrak{B}$ is a quasi-nilpotent, find $R(\lambda, q)$.
4. If formula (4.3.26) represents $R(\lambda, x)$, show that $xa^2 = -a$.
5. Under the same assumptions, express j, q, and a in terms of x, algebraically and also analytically.
6. If T is a linear transformation from C^n to C^n, prove that $\sigma(T)$ coincides with $P\sigma(T)$.

7. Let $\mathfrak{X} = C[0, \infty]$ and define $T[f](t) = f(t + a)$ where a is a fixed positive number. Find $\sigma(T)$ and classify its points.
8. Does Cauchy's residue theorem hold in a B-algebra? If so, formulate and prove it.
9. Suppose that $x \in \mathfrak{B}$ and $\sigma(x)$ consists of a finite number of points $\lambda_1, \lambda_2, \ldots, \lambda_n$. Suppose that j_α is the residue of $R(\lambda, x)$ at $\lambda = \lambda_\alpha$. Prove that

$$e = \sum_1^n j_\alpha \qquad \text{and} \qquad j_\alpha j_\beta = j_\beta j_\alpha = \delta_{\alpha\beta} j_\alpha.$$

This decomposition of e is known as a *resolution of the identity.*
10. If the zero element is the only quasi-nilpotent element in $\mathfrak{B}$, show that an isolated singularity of $R(\lambda)$ is necessarily a simple pole.
11. What is the Neumann series used in the proof of Theorem 3.4.2? Express it as a resolvent of an operator and show that the latter is a quasi-nilpotent.
12. Consider $\mathfrak{E}[C[0, 1]]$ and let

$$T[f](t) = \int_0^t f(s)\, ds.$$

Find $R(\lambda, T)$ and $\sigma(T)$.
13. Answer the same question for

$$T[f](t) = \int_0^t (t - s) f(s)\, ds.$$

14. If $\mathfrak{X} = C[0, a]$, if $K(s) \in L(0, a) \cap C(0, a]$, and if

$$T[g](t) = \int_0^t K(s) g(s)\, ds,$$

find $R(\lambda, T)$. What is $\sigma(T)$? Compare the result with Theorem 1.5.7 and re-interpret the latter.

4.4 GELFAND'S REPRESENTATION THEOREM

For the case of a *commutative* B-algebra $\mathfrak{B}$ over the complex field with unit element e, I. M. Gelfand has found an elegant representation based on the *residue class algebras modulo a maximal ideal.* Any such algebra turns out to be isomorphic to the complex field.

We say that $\mathfrak{i}$ is an ideal in $\mathfrak{B}$ if (i) $x, y \in \mathfrak{i}$ implies $x + y \in \mathfrak{i}$, and (ii) $x\mathfrak{B} \subset \mathfrak{i}$. We note that (i) and (ii) imply, in particular, that $\mathfrak{i}$ is a linear subspace of $\mathfrak{B}$. Every algebra $\mathfrak{B}$ contains the trivial ideals $\{0\}$ and $\mathfrak{B}$, known as the *null ideal* and the *unit ideal*, respectively, and the algebra is said to be *simple* if these are the only ideals. Thus the algebra of complex numbers is simple. If $\mathfrak{B}$ is not simple, then it contains other ideals, said to be *proper*. Such an ideal is said to be *maximal* if it is contained in no other proper ideal. Any ideal $\mathfrak{i}$ is either maximal or is contained in a maximal ideal. We do not prove this; the usual proof is based on Zorn's Lemma. We proceed to discuss the structure of maximal ideals, supposed to exist. We use $\mathfrak{m}$ as generic notation for maximal ideals.

Lemma 4.4.1. *An element x of $\mathfrak{B}$ is regular iff it belongs to no maximal ideal of $\mathfrak{B}$.*

Proof. If x is regular and belongs to an ideal $\mathfrak{i}$, then $xx^{-1} = e \in \mathfrak{i}$ and $\mathfrak{i} = \mathfrak{B}$. Hence, a regular element belongs to no maximal ideal. On the other hand, if x is singular, then $\mathfrak{i} = x\mathfrak{B}$ is a proper ideal containing x, and hence x belongs to some maximal ideal. Thus the condition is necessary as well as sufficient. ∎

Corollary. *If $\mathfrak{B}$ is simple, then all its elements are regular, excepting only the zero element.*

For there are no proper ideals, hence no singular elements except $x = 0$. ∎

Actually a sharper statement holds.

Theorem 4.4.1. *A simple commutative B-algebra over the complex field and with a unit element is isomorphic to the complex field.*

Proof. If $x \in \mathfrak{B}$, then $\sigma(x)$ is not void, i.e. there is at least one value of λ for which $\lambda e - x$ is singular. But the zero element is the only singular element, so there is a complex number α such that $x = \alpha e$. Thus there is a (1, 1) correspondence between $\mathfrak{B}$ and the complex field C and this correspondence is obviously an isomorphism. ∎

We recall that an isomorphism is a correspondence such that sums are mapped onto sums and products onto products.

Suppose now that $\mathfrak{B}$ is not simple and let $\mathfrak{m}$ be a maximal ideal in $\mathfrak{B}$. We note that $\mathfrak{m}$ as a point set in $\mathfrak{B}$ is closed. For the closure of $\mathfrak{m}$ is seen to be an ideal containing $\mathfrak{m}$ and since $\mathfrak{m}$ is maximal either $\bar{\mathfrak{m}} = \mathfrak{B}$ or $\bar{\mathfrak{m}} = \mathfrak{m}$. The first alternative would imply that some regular elements of $\mathfrak{B}$ belong to $\mathfrak{m}$ and this is impossible. Hence, $\bar{\mathfrak{m}} = \mathfrak{m}$ and $\mathfrak{m}$ is closed. The algebra $\mathfrak{B}$ breaks up into equivalence classes with respect to $\mathfrak{m}$. Two elements x_1 and x_2 belong to the same *residue class* (= equivalence class) iff $x_1 - x_2 \in \mathfrak{m}$. We denote residue classes by X, Y, and so on and define

$$X = x + \mathfrak{m} = \{x + z \mid z \in \mathfrak{m}\}. \tag{4.4.1}$$

X is referred to as the residue class generated by x modulo $\mathfrak{m}$. The residue classes form a *quotient algebra* $\mathfrak{B}/\mathfrak{m}$ and this algebra can be made into a B-algebra by a suitable definition of the norm. We have first to define the algebraic operations in $\mathfrak{B}/\mathfrak{m}$. If

$$X = x + \mathfrak{m}, \qquad Y = y + \mathfrak{m}, \qquad \alpha \in C, \tag{4.4.2}$$

we set

$$X + Y = x + y + \mathfrak{m}, \quad \alpha X = \alpha x + \mathfrak{m}, \quad XY = xy + \mathfrak{m}. \quad (4.4.3)$$

We note that if we add any two elements belonging to the classes X and Y, not necessarily distinct, then we obtain an element of the class $X + Y$, and similar considerations hold for the other algebraic operations.

It is clear that the unit element of $\mathfrak{B}/\mathfrak{m}$ is the class

$$\mathfrak{E} = e + \mathfrak{m}. \quad (4.4.4)$$

We define the norm of X to be

$$\|X\| = \inf(\|x\| \mid x \in X). \quad (4.4.5)$$

It is not difficult to verify that this convention defines a norm and that $\mathfrak{B}/\mathfrak{m}$ is complete in the resulting metric.

Theorem 4.4.2. *If $\mathfrak{m}$ is a maximal ideal in $\mathfrak{B}$, then the B-algebra $\mathfrak{B}/\mathfrak{m} = \{X\}$ is simple and hence isomorphic to the complex field.*

Proof. We have to show that if $\mathfrak{I}$ is an ideal in $\mathfrak{B}/\mathfrak{m}$ distinct from the null ideal, then $\mathfrak{I} = \mathfrak{B}/\mathfrak{m}$, i.e. the unit ideal. Suppose, contrariwise, that $\mathfrak{I}$ is proper and let $\mathfrak{i}^*$ be the set of all elements of $\mathfrak{B}$ belonging to the various residue classes which together constitute $\mathfrak{I}$. It is clear that $\mathfrak{m} \subset \mathfrak{i}^*$. Further, if x and y belong to $\mathfrak{i}^*$, then X and Y belong to $\mathfrak{I}$ and hence $x + y \in \mathfrak{i}^*$. Suppose that $x \in \mathfrak{i}^*$ and $X = \{x + \mathfrak{m}\}$. If then y is any element of $\mathfrak{B}$ and if $Y = \{y + \mathfrak{m}\}$, then XY belongs to $\mathfrak{I}$ so that $xy \in \mathfrak{i}^*$. This shows that $\mathfrak{i}^*$ is an ideal containing $\mathfrak{m}$ and this is possible iff $\mathfrak{i}^* = \mathfrak{B}$, the unit ideal of $\mathfrak{B}$. But then $\mathfrak{I}$ must be the unit ideal of $\mathfrak{B}/\mathfrak{m}$ as asserted. ∎

Corollary. *The quotient algebra $\mathfrak{B}/\mathfrak{m}$ is made up of the residue classes $X_\alpha = \alpha e + \mathfrak{m}$ where α ranges over the complex field.*

The theorem asserts that the mapping $\mathfrak{B} \to \mathfrak{B}/\mathfrak{m}$ maps each element x of $\mathfrak{B}$ on a complex number α, namely that α for which x is an element of $\alpha e + \mathfrak{m}$. Thus we have a mapping

$$x \to \alpha, \quad x \equiv \alpha e \,(\text{mod } \mathfrak{m}) \quad (4.4.6)$$

and we denote α by $x(\mathfrak{m})$. The properties of $x(\mathfrak{m})$ are given by *Gelfand's representation theorem*:

Theorem 4.4.3. *If $\mathfrak{B}$ is a commutative complex B-algebra with unit element e and if $\mathfrak{m}$ is any maximal ideal of $\mathfrak{B}$, then the mapping $x \to x(\mathfrak{m})$ has the following properties:*

i) $(x + y)(\mathfrak{m}) = x(\mathfrak{m}) + y(\mathfrak{m})$,

ii) $(\alpha x)(\mathfrak{m}) = \alpha x(\mathfrak{m})$,

iii) $(xy)(\mathfrak{m}) = x(\mathfrak{m})y(\mathfrak{m})$,

iv) $e(\mathfrak{m}) = 1$,

v) $0(\mathfrak{m}) = 0$.

vi) *If x is regular then $x(\mathfrak{m}) \neq 0$ and*

$$x^{-1}(\mathfrak{m}) = [x(\mathfrak{m})]^{-1}.$$

vii) $x(\mathfrak{m}) \in \sigma(x)$,

viii) $|x(\mathfrak{m})| \leq r(x)$, *the spectral radius of x.*

ix) *If $\lambda \in \sigma(x)$, then there exists a maximal ideal $\mathfrak{m}_0$ such that $x(\mathfrak{m}_0) = \lambda$.*

x) *If $x(\mathfrak{m}) = 0$ for all $\mathfrak{m}$, then x is quasi-nilpotent.*

Proof. The first three properties are simply restatements of the definitions (4.4.3), together with the fact that each element of $\mathfrak{B}/\mathfrak{m}$ is of the form $\alpha e + \mathfrak{m}$. Since $e \in e + \mathfrak{m}$ and $0 \in \mathfrak{m}$, (iv) and (v) follow. If x is regular, x cannot belong to $\mathfrak{m}$ and must belong to some residue class $\alpha e + m$ with $\alpha \neq 0$. This gives $x(\mathfrak{m}) = \alpha \neq 0$. Then by (iii)

$$1 = e(\mathfrak{m}) = (xx^{-1})(\mathfrak{m}) = x(\mathfrak{m})x^{-1}(\mathfrak{m})$$

and this implies (vi). If $x \in \alpha e + \mathfrak{m}$, then $\alpha e - x \in \mathfrak{m}$, i.e. $\alpha e - x$ is singular and $\alpha \in \sigma(x)$ as asserted in (vii). This implies (viii) by the definition of the spectral radius. To prove (ix), we note that if $\alpha \in \sigma(x)$, then $\alpha e - x$ is singular and can be embedded in a maximal ideal $\mathfrak{m}_0$ with respect to which $x(\mathfrak{m}_0) = \alpha$. Finally, if $x(\mathfrak{m}) = 0$ for all $\mathfrak{m}$, then $\sigma(x) = \{0\}$, so $r(x) = 0$, that is, $\lim_{n \to \infty} \|x^n\|^{1/n} = 0$ and x is quasi-nilpotent as stated by (x). ∎

There is a slightly different way of describing the situation and this is in terms of *bounded linear multiplicative functionals.* Let $\mathfrak{m}$ be a fixed maximal ideal and write $x(\mathfrak{m})$ as $\mu(x)$. The mapping

$$x \to \mu(x)$$

defines a functional μ, and properties (i)–(iii) express that

i') $$\mu(x + y) = \mu(x) + \mu(y),$$

ii') $$\mu(\alpha x) = \alpha\mu(x),$$

iii') $$\mu(xy) = \mu(x)\mu(y),$$

so that μ is multiplicative as well as linear; while (viii) implies

viii') $$|\mu(x)| \leq \|x\|,$$

so that μ is also bounded.

Conversely, if $\mu(x)$ is a bounded linear multiplicative functional on $\mathfrak{B}$, then the null space $\mathfrak{N}[\mu]$ of μ is a maximal ideal. It is easily shown that $\mathfrak{N}[\mu]$ is an ideal and that $\mu(e) = 1$, so that the ideal is proper. If $\mathfrak{N}[\mu]$ were not a maximal ideal, we could embed $\mathfrak{N}[\mu]$ in a maximal ideal $\mathfrak{m}$. If $x_0 \in \mathfrak{m} \ominus \mathfrak{N}[\mu]$, we have $\mu(x_0) \neq 0$. Then

$$\mu[\mu(x_0)e - x_0] = \mu(x_0)\mu(e) - \mu(x_0) = 0$$

so that $\mu(x_0)e - x_0 \in \mathfrak{N}[\mu] \subset \text{m}$. Since $x_0 \in \mathfrak{m}$, we see that $[\mu(x_0)e - x_0] + x_0 = \mu(x_0)e \in \mathfrak{m}$. But no regular element can belong to a maximal ideal, so we conclude that $\mathfrak{N}[\mu]$ is already maximal. Thus there is a (1, 1) correspondence between the bounded linear multiplicative functionals $\mu(x)$ and the maximal ideals of $\mathfrak{B}$.

To illustrate these concepts, let us consider the B-algebra $C[0, 1]$. The elements of $\mathfrak{B}$ are the functions f continuous on the closed interval $[0, 1]$, and the norm is the sup norm. The spectrum $\sigma(f)$ of f coincides with the range of f since $(\lambda - f)^{-1} \in \mathfrak{B}$ iff λ is not in the range of f. In Problem 4 of Exercise 4.1, we encountered a class of bounded linear multiplicative functionals on $\mathfrak{B}$ where $\mu[f] = f(t_0)$ and t_0 is any fixed point in the interval $[0, 1]$. We note that $\mu[f_0] \in \sigma(f_0)$ and that, if $\lambda \in \sigma(f_0)$, then there exists a functional μ_0 with $\mu_0[f_0] = \lambda$. We have merely to find a point t_0 where $f_0(t_0) = \lambda$ and then $\mu_0[f_0] = f_0(t_0) = \lambda$. We already know from Problem 5 of the same exercise that $\mathfrak{N}[\mu]$ is an ideal. We now know that the null space of μ is actually a maximal ideal. (See further Exercise 4.4.)

Gelfand's theorem is very useful when it comes to analyzing the spectra of elements of a B-algebra. In this instance, to start with the restriction to commutative algebras is a nuisance; however, this may be obviated by a simple device. We embed the element or elements under consideration in a commutative subalgebra of $\mathfrak{B}$ which is large enough so that spectra are unchanged. This means that the subalgebra must be closed under inversion. In other words, if a regular element belongs to the subalgebra so does its inverse. In more detail the procedure is as follows.

Let $a_1, a_2, \ldots, a_n$ be elements of $\mathfrak{B}$ which commute, and form the subalgebra $\mathfrak{A}$ generated by

$$e, a_1, a_2, \ldots, a_n$$

so that $\mathfrak{A}$ consists of all polynomials in these elements. Then $\mathfrak{A}$ is Abelian. Next we form $\mathfrak{A}^c$, the *first commutant* of $\mathfrak{A}$. This is the set of all elements of $\mathfrak{B}$ which commute with $a_1, a_2, \ldots, a_n$ and hence with all elements of $\mathfrak{A}$. We note that if $\mathfrak{A}_1$ and $\mathfrak{A}_2$ are algebras and $\mathfrak{A}_1 \subset \mathfrak{A}_2$ then $\mathfrak{A}_2^c \subset \mathfrak{A}_1^c$. It is easily seen that $\mathfrak{A}^c$ is also an algebra with unit element e. Moreover, $\mathfrak{A}^c$ is closed in the normed metric. The algebra $\mathfrak{A}^c$ need not be Abelian but its commutant $\mathfrak{A}^{cc}$ has this property. This can be seen as follows. Now $\mathfrak{A}^{cc}$ is made up of all elements of $\mathfrak{B}$ which commute with the elements of $\mathfrak{A}^c$. It is clear that $\mathfrak{A} \subset \mathfrak{A}^{cc}$ and since $\mathfrak{A} \subset \mathfrak{A}^c$ we have $\mathfrak{A}^{cc} \subset \mathfrak{A}^c$. Now if x and y belong to $\mathfrak{A}^{cc}$ and if z is any element of $\mathfrak{A}^c$, then $xz = zx$ by the definition of $\mathfrak{A}^{cc}$. But since $\mathfrak{A}^{cc} \subset \mathfrak{A}^c$ we can take $z = y$, that is x and y commute. Thus $\mathfrak{A}^{cc}$ is actually Abelian as asserted above. Furthermore, if x is a regular element of $\mathfrak{B}$ and also belongs to $\mathfrak{A}^{cc}$ and if z is any element of $\mathfrak{A}^c$, then

$$xz = zx \quad \text{implies} \quad zx^{-1} = x^{-1}z,$$

so that $x^{-1} \in \mathfrak{A}^{cc}$. Thus $\mathfrak{A}^{cc}$ is closed under inversion. This implies that the spectral properties of x with respect to $\mathfrak{A}^{cc}$ are the same as its spectral properties with respect to $\mathfrak{B}$. Hence for a study of the spectral properties of the elements of $\mathfrak{A}$ we can use Gelfand's theorem applied to the Abelian Banach subalgebra $\mathfrak{A}^{cc}$.

EXERCISE 4.4

It is desired to prove that all bounded linear multiplicative functionals on $C[0, 1]$ are of the form $\mu[f] = f(t_0)$, $0 \leq t_0 \leq 1$. This is accomplished in four steps. Assume that μ is such a functional and verify that

1. The formula is true for $f(t) = t$.
2. It is true for $f(t) = t^n$, n any positive integer.
3. It is true for any polynomial.
4. Use the approximation theorem of Weierstrass to prove that it holds for any element of $C[0, 1]$.
5. Prove that $\mathfrak{A}^c$ is an algebra as asserted in the text.
6. Given the matrix $\mathcal{A} = \left(\begin{smallmatrix} 0 & 1 \\ 1 & 0 \end{smallmatrix}\right)$, find what subalgebra $\mathfrak{A}$ of $\mathfrak{M}_2$ is generated by $\mathcal{E}$ and $\mathcal{A}$. Find $\mathfrak{A}^c$, show that $\mathfrak{A}^c$ is Abelian and $\mathfrak{A}^{cc} = \mathfrak{A}^c$.
7. Given the matrix $\mathcal{A}$ of the preceding problem, find its spectrum as an element of $\mathfrak{M}_2$. We use $\mathcal{A}$ as left- and right-hand multipliers in $\mathfrak{M}_2$, i.e. we consider the mappings

   $$\mathcal{Y} = \mathcal{A} \cdot \mathcal{X}, \qquad \mathcal{Z} = \mathcal{X} \cdot \mathcal{A}.$$

   Determine the spectra of the operators $A\cdot$ and $\cdot A$ as elements of $\mathfrak{E}(\mathfrak{M}_2)$.
8. The elements of $\mathfrak{A}^{cc}$ in Problem 6 are matrices of the form $\mathcal{B} = \left(\begin{smallmatrix} a & b \\ c & d \end{smallmatrix}\right)$, where c and d are certain functions of a and b. Show that the only bounded linear multiplicative functionals are $\mu_1(\mathcal{B}) = a + b$ and $\mu_2(\mathcal{B}) = a - b$.
9. The space $L_2(0, 2\pi)$ is a commutative B-algebra without unit element under convolution

   $$(f_1 * f_2)(t) = \frac{1}{2\pi} \int_0^{2\pi} f_1(t - s) f_2(s)\, ds.$$

   Show that the Fourier coefficients are bounded linear and multiplicative functionals on this space.

4.5 OPERATIONAL CALCULUS

Every student of advanced mathematics is aware of the fundamental importance of the Cauchy kernel in classical complex function theory. From the abstract point of view the Cauchy kernel $(\zeta - z)^{-1}$ is a resolvent, the simplest of all resolvents; it satisfies the first resolvent equation as a function of ζ and the second as a function of z. Once the study of more general algebras than that of complex numbers was broached, it became natural to replace Cauchy kernels by resolvents of elements of the algebra. Matrices formed the first such algebra to be studied and we find resolvents in the works of G. Frobenius and H. Poincaré in the 1890's. The systematic use of resolvents leads to a branch of functional analysis known as *operational calculus*, the elements of which will be given below.

Let $\mathfrak{B}$ be a complex non-commutative B-algebra with unit element e. Let $\mathfrak{D}$ be a bounded domain (= bounded open connected set) in $\mathfrak{B}$. Given any x in $\mathfrak{D}$, its spectrum $\sigma(x)$ is a bounded closed set in the complex plane. Set

$$\Delta = \bigcup_{x \in \mathfrak{D}} \sigma(x). \tag{4.5.1}$$

This is a bounded set. Let us cover Δ by ε-disks so that every point of Δ is the center of a closed disk of radius ε. The union of all these disks is denoted by Δ_ε. Now Δ_ε need not be connected but it is made up of at most a finite number of maximal connected components. Let Γ_ε be the boundary of Δ_ε. Without restricting the generality we may assume that Γ_ε is rectifiable. It consists of a finite number of simple closed curves, to each of which we give an orientation such that in describing Γ_ε the contiguous part of Δ_ε is on the left side of the path. (See Figure 4.1.)

Now let $\mathfrak{F}$ be the class of functions $f(\lambda)$ locally holomorphic in the interior and continuous on Δ_ε. This means that $f(\lambda)$ is holomorphic on each

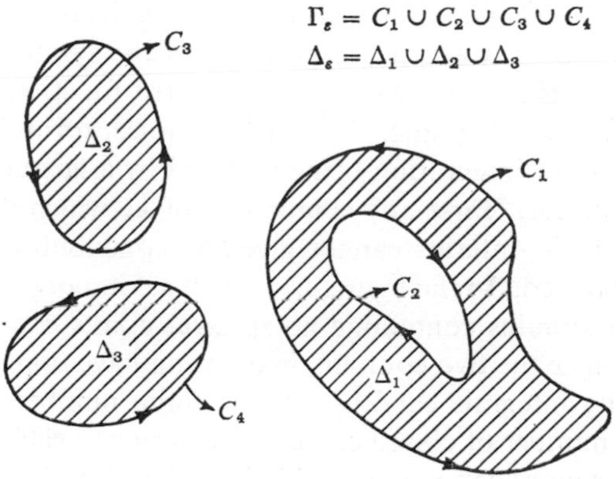

Figure 4.1

component of Δ_ε, but not necessarily holomorphic in a domain containing all components. That is, the restrictions of f to the components of Δ_ε are all holomorphic functions. In the figure we have three components and we may take $f(\lambda) = \lambda$ on the first component, $= 1$ on the second, and $= 0$ on the third. This function is locally holomorphic on the components but evidently not holomorphic in a domain containing parts of more than one component.

The set $\mathfrak{F}$ is clearly an algebra and it becomes a B-algebra under the sup norm $\|f\| = \max_{\lambda\in\Delta_\varepsilon} |f(\lambda)|$. For any $f \in \mathfrak{F}$ and any $x \in \mathfrak{D}$ we now define

$$f(x) = \frac{1}{2\pi i}\int_{\Gamma_\varepsilon} f(\lambda)R(\lambda; x)\,d\lambda. \tag{4.5.2}$$

Since the set Γ_ε belongs to $\rho(x)$ for every $x \in \mathfrak{D}$ and to the domain of continuity for every $f \in \mathfrak{F}$ and since Γ_ε is rectifiable, for each x the integral defines an element of $\mathfrak{B}$. It also defines a mapping f of $\mathfrak{D}$ into $\mathfrak{B}$. We denote the set of all such mappings by $\mathfrak{B}(\mathfrak{D})$. Again, the set $\mathfrak{B}(\mathfrak{D})$ is clearly an algebra and it can be normed by the sup norm

$$\|f\| = \sup_{x\in\mathfrak{D}} \|f(x)\|.$$

It is not claimed that $\mathfrak{B}(\mathfrak{D})$ is complete under this norm but it is easy to see that if $\|f_n - f\| \to 0$ holds in $\mathfrak{F}$ then $\|f_n - f\| \to 0$ holds in $\mathfrak{B}(\mathfrak{D})$. The mapping of $\mathfrak{F}$ on $\mathfrak{B}(\mathfrak{D})$ is an *isomorphism*, i.e. sums go into sums and products into products. The second property is rather striking. The proof that $(fg)(x) = f(x)g(x)$ is based on the use of the first resolvent equation to simplify the double integral that represents the product together with Cauchy's integral. The details are left to the reader. The only isomorphism with the stated continuity properties which can hold between $\mathfrak{F}$ and $\mathfrak{B}(\mathfrak{D})$ is that given by (4.5.2) provided it maps 1 into e and λ into x. We do not need the uniqueness property so we shall not prove it.

On the other hand, it may be worth while to justify the notation $f(x)$. Suppose that in formula (4.5.2) we substitute successively $f(\lambda) = 1$, λ, and λ^n. The results should be e, x and x^n, respectively, if the symbolism is meaningful. This is indeed the case. We have substituted functions $f(\lambda)$ which are holomorphic in the whole plane. For such a choice, formula (4.5.2) can be simplified, the path of integration being replaced by a large circle containing all of Δ_ε in its interior. First any component of Γ_ε which does not contain some part of Δ_ε in its interior cannot give any contribution to the integral and may be suppressed. In the figure, C_2 is such a component. Two contours which bound an annulus containing no spectral points can be deformed so as to coincide. Since the two contours in question have opposite orientation, the corresponding integrals cancel. After a finite number of steps we are left with a finite number of closed curves, all exterior to each other, and each containing one or more components of Δ_ε in its interior. These contours can be deformed into a single contour with this property, and this contour may be taken as a circle with center at $\lambda = 0$. On the circle we now have the convergent series

$$R(\lambda; x) = \frac{e}{\lambda} + \sum_{n=1}^{\infty} \frac{x^n}{\lambda^{n+1}}.$$

Termwise integration gives

$$\frac{1}{2\pi i} \int_{|\lambda|=r} \lambda^n R(\lambda; x)\, d\lambda = x^n (n > 0) \tag{4.5.3}$$

as asserted. For $n = 0$ the right member becomes e instead. By the linearity of the mapping it follows that if $f(\lambda) = P(\lambda)$ is a polynomial in λ, then $f(x) = P(x)$ is the corresponding polynomial in x.

By the continuity property this extends to any function $f(\lambda)$ which is holomorphic in a circular disk $|\lambda| < R$ containing Δ_ε in its interior. Thus if

$$f(\lambda) = \sum_{0}^{\infty} \alpha_n \lambda^n, \quad |\lambda| < R, \qquad \text{then} \qquad f(x) = \sum_{0}^{\infty} \alpha_n x^n, \quad x \in \mathfrak{D}, \tag{4.5.4}$$

where the second series converges in the topology of $\mathfrak{B}$ since the spectral radius of x is necessarily $< R$. These observations serve as a justification for the notation $f(x)$.

The notation involves two letters, f and x. We can fix either one and vary the other. If we let x be a fixed element of $\mathfrak{B}$, then we can apply (4.5.2) to a wider class of functions f. All we now need is that $f(\lambda)$ be locally holomorphic on $\sigma(x)$. We cover $\sigma(x)$ by circular ε-disks, the union of which replaces Δ_ε in the preceding discussion. If $\Gamma_{\varepsilon,x}$, the boundary of $\Delta_{\varepsilon,x}$ is rectifiable and if $f(\lambda)$ is locally holomorphic on $\Delta_{\varepsilon,x}$, we define

$$f(x) = \frac{1}{2\pi i} \int_{\Gamma_{\varepsilon,x}} f(\lambda) R(\lambda, x)\, d\lambda. \tag{4.5.5}$$

Suppose that μ is a complex number not included in the range of $f(\lambda)$ on $\Delta_{\varepsilon,x}$. Then $[\mu - f(\lambda)]^{-1}$ is also locally holomorphic in $\Delta_{\varepsilon,x}$. Since products go into products,

$$[\mu - f(\lambda)][\mu - f(\lambda)]^{-1} = 1$$

implies that

$$[\mu e - f(x)][\mu e - f(x)]^{-1} = e,$$

or $R[\mu, f(x)]$ exists for any such μ. Hence, every number μ which is not in the range of $f(\lambda)$ on $\Delta_{\varepsilon,x}$ belongs to the resolvent set of $f(x)$. Since ε is arbitrary this shows that the spectrum of $f(x)$ is included in the range of f on $\sigma(x)$ for which we write $f[\sigma(x)]$. Actually we have the sharper relation

$$\sigma[f(x)] = f[\sigma(x)], \tag{4.5.6}$$

known as the *spectral mapping theorem of Gelfand.* This can be sharpened still further: when $\mathfrak{B} = \mathfrak{E}(\mathfrak{X})$, the algebra of linear bounded operators on a Banach space $\mathfrak{X}$, the *point spectrum of the operator T is mapped onto the point spectrum of the operator $f(T)$*, and so on. We state this without a proof.

Let us now fix $f \in \mathfrak{F}$ and vary x in $\mathfrak{D}$. The function $f(x)$ defined by (4.5.2) is *Fréchet analytic* in $\mathfrak{D}$. This means the existence of the *Fréchet differential*

$$\lim_{\alpha \to 0} \frac{1}{\alpha} [f(x + \alpha z) - f(x)] \equiv \delta f[x, z] \tag{4.5.7}$$

and the resulting Taylor expansions. Here α is any complex number, z any element of $\mathfrak{B}$, x any element of $\mathfrak{D}$. If $|\alpha|$ is sufficiently small, then $x + \alpha z \in \mathfrak{D}$. Cf. formula (4.3.15) which gives the Fréchet differential of a solution of the second resolvent equation. We can apply this to $R(\lambda, x)$ for any $\lambda \in \Gamma_\varepsilon$ and any $x \in \mathfrak{D}$. In the classical case the analyticity of Cauchy's integral resides in the Cauchy kernel. Here likewise *the Fréchet analyticity of $f(x)$ is induced by the Fréchet analyticity of the resolvent as a function of x.* Take any fixed $x \in \mathfrak{D}$, any $z \in \mathfrak{B}$ with $\|z\| \leq 1$ and any α with $|\alpha| \leq \delta(x)$, where

$$\delta(x) < [\max_{\lambda \in \Gamma_\varepsilon} \|R(\lambda, x)\|]^{-1}. \tag{4.5.8}$$

Formula (4.3.18) and the subsequent discussion shows that with these limitations on x, z and α the element $x + \alpha z \in \mathfrak{D}$ and $\|R(\lambda, x + \alpha z)\|$ is bounded uniformly with respect to λ on Γ_ε, α with $|\alpha| \leq \delta(x)$, and z with $\|z\| \leq 1$.

It follows for α and z restricted as indicated that

$$\frac{1}{\alpha} [f(x + \alpha z) - f(x)] = \frac{1}{2\pi i} \int_{\Gamma_\varepsilon} f(\lambda) \frac{1}{\alpha} [R(\lambda, x + \alpha z) - R(\lambda, x)] \, d\lambda.$$

Here by (4.3.16)

$$\frac{1}{\alpha} [R(\lambda, x + \alpha z) - R(\lambda, x)] = R(\lambda, x) z R(\lambda, x) + O(\alpha),$$

where the estimate $O(\alpha)$ holds uniformly in λ and z. It follows that we can pass to the limit under the sign of integration to obtain

$$\delta f(x, z) = \frac{1}{2\pi i} \int_{\Gamma_\varepsilon} f(\lambda) R(\lambda, x) z R(\lambda, x) \, d\lambda. \tag{4.5.9}$$

This shows the existence of the *first Fréchet differential.*

In the same manner one shows the existence of higher order differentials as well as the *Taylor expansion*

$$f(x + \alpha z) = f(x) + \sum_{n=1}^{\infty} \alpha^n \frac{1}{2\pi i} \int_{\Gamma_\varepsilon} f(\lambda) R(\lambda, x) [z R(\lambda, x)]^n \, d\lambda, \tag{4.5.10}$$

valid for $|\alpha| < \delta(x)$, $\|z\| \leq 1$. This expansion is obtainable from (4.3.16) after multiplication by $f(\lambda)$ and term by term integration along Γ_ε. This is permitted by the uniform convergence of the series (4.3.16) with respect to λ, α, and z.

EXERCISE 4.5

1. If a is a regular element of $\mathfrak{B}$, show that $\sigma(axa^{-1}) = \sigma(x)$ for all x.
2. If $x \in \mathfrak{D}$, $f \in \mathfrak{F}$ and a is regular, show that
$$f(axa^{-1}) = af(x)a^{-1}.$$
3. We can define exp (x) either by the operational calculus, i.e. by formula (4.5.2), or by the exponential series. Show that the two definitions agree.
4. Does the relation $\exp(x + y) = \exp(x)\exp(y)$ hold for arbitrary elements x, y in $\mathfrak{B}$? Give sufficient conditions for the validity of the formula.
5. If j is idempotent commuting with x, show that $2\pi ij$ is a "period" of exp (x), i.e.
$$\exp(x + 2\pi ij) = \exp(x).$$
6. Give sufficient conditions on x for $\sqrt{x}$ to be definable by (4.5.2).
7. Same question for $\log x$.
8. Find the set of all matrices in $\mathfrak{M}_2$ the squares of which are the unit matrix.
9. Let j be an idempotent, $j \neq 0, e$. Use the spectral mapping theorem to show that $\sigma(j) = \{0, 1\}$.
10. If $\sigma(x) = \{\alpha\}$, show that $x = \alpha e + q$ where q is quasi-nilpotent.
11. Prove that $(fg)(x) = f(x)g(x)$ using the hints given in the text.
12. If $f(\lambda)$ is locally holomorphic on an open set Δ containing $\sigma(x)$ and if $\alpha \in \sigma(x)$, then
$$g(\lambda, \alpha) = \frac{f(\lambda) - f(\alpha)}{\lambda - \alpha}$$
is also locally holomorphic in Δ. This implies that
$$g(x, \alpha)(\alpha e - x) = f(\alpha)e - f(x).$$
Use this relation to complete the proof of the spectral mapping theorem.
13. Use the same identity to prove the *fine structure theorem*, i.e. the fact that point, continuous, and residual spectra of x and of $f(x)$ correspond under the mapping.

4.6 THE COMMUTATOR OPERATOR

This section is devoted to a study of the commutator operator which plays an important role in the theory of linear differential equations and of some generalizations.

Let $\mathfrak{B}$ be a complex non-commutative B-algebra with unit element e. Let $a \in \mathfrak{B}$ but not to its *center*, i.e. a shall not commute with all elements of $\mathfrak{B}$. We define three linear bounded operators on $\mathfrak{B}$ to $\mathfrak{B}$, namely $\mathbf{L}_a$, $\mathbf{R}_a$, and $\mathbf{C}_a$, where

$$\mathbf{L}_a x = ax, \qquad \mathbf{R}_a x = xa, \qquad \mathbf{C}_a x = ax - xa \tag{4.6.1}$$

so that

$$\mathbf{C}_a = \mathbf{L}_a - \mathbf{R}_a. \tag{4.6.2}$$

The problem before us is to study these operators and in particular their spectral properties. The first two operators are simple:

Lemma 4.6.1. *We have* $\sigma(\mathbf{L}_a) = \sigma(\mathbf{R}_a) = \sigma(a)$.

Proof. The spectra of $\mathbf{L}_a$ and $\mathbf{R}_a$ are with respect to the operator algebra $\mathfrak{E}(\mathfrak{B})$ while that of a is with respect to $\mathfrak{B}$ itself. We note that if $\alpha \in \sigma(a)$, then $\alpha e - a$ is a singular element of $\mathfrak{B}$. It follows that for any $x \in \mathfrak{B}$

$$(\alpha I - \mathbf{L}_a)x \qquad \text{and} \qquad (\alpha I - \mathbf{R}_a)x$$

are singular elements of $\mathfrak{B}$. Such elements are not dense in $\mathfrak{B}$, in particular all elements in the sphere

$$\|y - e\| < 1$$

are regular. It follows that $\alpha \in \sigma(\mathbf{L}_a) \cap \sigma(\mathbf{R}_a)$. More precisely, α belongs either to the residual spectra or to the point spectra of $\mathbf{L}_a$ and $\mathbf{R}_a$. If $\alpha e - a$ is a divisor of 0 and if

$$(\alpha e - a)b = 0, \qquad \text{then} \qquad \alpha \in P\sigma(\mathbf{L}_a),$$

while if

$$b(\alpha e - a) = 0, \qquad \text{then} \qquad \alpha \in P\sigma(\mathbf{R}_a).$$

In any case $\sigma(a)$ is a subset of $\sigma(\mathbf{L}_a)$ as well as of $\sigma(\mathbf{R}_a)$.

On the other hand, if $\alpha \in \sigma(\mathbf{L}_a)$, say, then $\alpha I - \mathbf{L}_a$ does not have an inverse belonging to $\mathfrak{E}(\mathfrak{B})$. This means that in the equation

$$(\alpha e - a)y = x$$

$\alpha e - a$ cannot be a regular element of $\mathfrak{B}$, for if it were then y would be obtained by multiplying x on the left by $(\alpha e - a)^{-1}$; that is, the inverse of $\alpha I - \mathbf{L}_a$ would exist, have domain $\mathfrak{B}$, and therefore belong to $\mathfrak{E}(\mathfrak{B})$. Thus $\alpha \in \sigma(a)$. In the same way we show that $\sigma(\mathbf{R}_a) \subset \sigma(a)$. Thus we have proved the assertion and in addition we have shown that the continuous spectra are void. ▌

The spectral properties of $\mathbf{C}_a$ are more complicated.

Theorem 4.6.1. *The spectrum of* $\mathbf{C}_a$ *is included in the difference set* $\{\alpha - \beta \mid \alpha \in \sigma(a), \beta \in \sigma(a)\}$.

Proof. We use Gelfand's representation theorem. Let $\mathfrak{A}$ be the commutative algebra generated by the three operators I, $\mathbf{L}_a$, and $\mathbf{R}_a$. Let $\mathfrak{A}^{cc}$ be the second commutant of $\mathfrak{A}$. Let μ be any bounded linear multiplicative functional on $\mathfrak{A}^{cc}$. Then

$$\mu(\mathbf{C}_a) = \mu(\mathbf{L}_a) - \mu(\mathbf{R}_a) \tag{4.6.3}$$

and

$$\mu(\mathbf{C}_a) \in \sigma(\mathbf{C}_a), \qquad \mu(\mathbf{L}_a) \in \sigma(a), \qquad \mu(\mathbf{R}_a) \in \sigma(a).$$

This shows that any spectral value of $\mathbf{C}_a$ belongs to the difference set. Moreover, as μ runs through all the admissible functionals then $\mu(\mathbf{C}_a)$, $\mu(\mathbf{L}_a)$, and $\mu(\mathbf{R}_a)$ run through the spectra of $\mathbf{C}_a$, $\mathbf{L}_a$, and $\mathbf{R}_a$, respectively, but we have no assurance that every element of the difference set is actually represented in $\sigma(\mathbf{C}_a)$. ∎

The value 0 is always present in $\sigma(\mathbf{C}_a)$. Any element $x \in \mathfrak{B}$ which commutes with a is annihilated by $\mathbf{C}_a$ so $0 \in P\sigma(\mathbf{C}_a)$ and any such x is a characteristic vector. Since every power of a commutes with a, we conclude that the dimension of the null space $\mathfrak{N}[\mathbf{C}_a]$ is at least equal to the dimension of the space spanned by

$$e, a, a^2, \ldots, a^n, \ldots$$

Suppose now that $\gamma = \alpha - \beta$ is a member of the difference set and that $\gamma \neq 0$. Under certain circumstances we can assert that $\gamma \in \sigma(\mathbf{C}_a)$.

Theorem 4.6.2. *If $\alpha \in P\sigma(\mathbf{L}_a)$ and $\beta \in P\sigma(\mathbf{R}_a)$ and if $x \neq 0$, $y \neq 0$ are such that $\mathbf{L}_a x = \alpha x$, $\mathbf{R}_a y = \beta y$, then either $xy = 0$ or $\alpha - \beta \in P\sigma(\mathbf{C}_a)$.*

Proof. We have

$$(\alpha - \beta)xy - axy + xya = 0, \tag{4.6.4}$$

whence the conclusion follows. ∎

Theorem 4.6.3. *If $\mathfrak{B}$ is a prime ring in the sense of Definition* 4.2.2 *and if the assumptions of the preceding theorem hold, then $\alpha - \beta \in P\sigma(\mathbf{C}_a)$.*

Proof. By assumption we can find a $z \in \mathfrak{B}$ such that $xzy \neq 0$. The conclusion then follows from

$$(\alpha - \beta)xzy - axzy + xzya = 0. \ ∎ \tag{4.6.5}$$

Corollary. *If $\mathfrak{B} = \mathfrak{M}_n$ is a matrix algebra, then $\mathbf{C}_a$ has a pure point spectrum which coincides with the difference set $\{\alpha - \beta \mid \alpha \in \sigma(a), \beta \in \sigma(a)\}$.*

Proof. In this case the spectra of $\mathbf{L}_a$ and of $\mathbf{R}_a$ are pure point spectra and Theorem 4.6.3 applies since $\mathfrak{M}_n$ is a prime ring. ∎

The characteristic vectors of $\mathbf{C}_a$ are rather special.

Lemma 4.6.2. *If $\mathbf{C}_a x = \gamma x$, $\gamma \neq 0$, then x is nilpotent.*
This is a consequence of the following

Theorem 4.6.4. *If γ_1 and γ_2 are non-zero elements of $P\sigma(\mathbf{C}_a)$ and if $\mathbf{C}_a x = \gamma_1 x$, $\mathbf{C}_a y = \gamma_2 y$, then either $xy = 0$ or $\gamma_1 + \gamma_2 \in P\sigma(\mathbf{C}_a)$ and $\mathbf{C}_a xy = (\gamma_1 + \gamma_2)xy$.*

Proof. The verification is immediate. ▮

From this we conclude that

$$\mathbf{C}_a x^n = n\gamma x^n \tag{4.6.6}$$

so that either $n\gamma \in P\sigma(\mathbf{C}_a)$ or $x^n = 0$. Since $\mathbf{C}_a$ is a bounded operator with

$$\|\mathbf{C}_a\| \leq 2\|a\|,$$

it follows that the second alternative must hold at least for $n|\gamma| > 2\|a\|$. This proves Lemma 4.6.2. ▮

We shall need an expression for the resolvent of $\mathbf{C}_a$ which is due to Yu. L. Daletsky (1953). Let us cover $\sigma(a)$ by ε-disks, one closed disk of radius ε for each point of $\sigma(a)$ and let Σ_ε be the union of these disks. Let

$$\Delta_\varepsilon = \Sigma_\varepsilon - \Sigma_\varepsilon, \tag{4.6.7}$$

i.e. the set of all points $\lambda = \lambda_1 - \lambda_2$ with λ_1 and λ_2 in Σ_ε. The sets Σ_ε and Δ_ε are bounded sets having a finite number of closed maximal components. See Figure 4.2 where Σ_ε has two components and Δ_ε three. Without restricting the generality, we may suppose that Γ_ε, the boundary of Σ_ε, is made up of rectifiable curves, circles in the figure. We suppose that Γ_ε is oriented in the usual manner so that each component of Γ_ε has a component of Σ_ε on the left-hand side in the positive orientation. Finally we denote the complement of Δ_ε by Λ_ε.

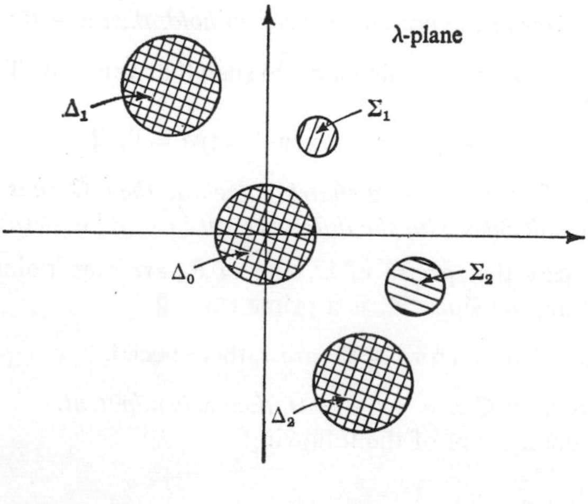

Figure 4.2

Theorem 4.6.5. *For every choice of* $\lambda \in \Lambda_\varepsilon$ *the resolvent* $\mathbf{R}(\lambda, \mathbf{C}_a)$ *exists and is given by*

$$\mathbf{R}(\lambda, \mathbf{C}_a)x = \frac{1}{(2\pi i)^2}\int_{\Gamma_\varepsilon}\int_{\Gamma_\varepsilon} \frac{R(\alpha, a)xR(\beta, a)}{\lambda - \alpha + \beta}\, d\alpha\, d\beta. \tag{4.6.8}$$

Proof. To see that the integral exists we note first that the various contours which form Γ_ε lie in the resolvent set of a. Hence $R(\alpha, a)$ and $R(\beta, a)$ are holomorphic functions of α and β on the contours of integration. The denominator $\lambda - \alpha + \beta$ is holomorphic and bounded away from 0. For if $\alpha \in \Gamma_\varepsilon$, $\beta \in \Gamma_\varepsilon$, then $\alpha - \beta$ lies on the boundary of Δ_ε and λ is by assumption in $C(\Delta_\varepsilon) = \Lambda_\varepsilon$ and thus has a positive distance from Δ_ε. This implies that $\lambda - \alpha + \beta$ is bounded away from 0. Thus the integral exists and defines a function of λ holomorphic in each of the components of Λ_ε. There is only one such component in the figure, but in general there could be a finite number.

Let us denote the right member of (4.6.8) by y and form

$$(\lambda I - \mathbf{C}_a)y = \lambda y - ay + ya.$$

We can rewrite the second member as

$$\int\int (\lambda - \alpha + \beta)Q\, d\alpha\, d\beta + \int\int (\alpha e - a)Q\, d\alpha\, d\beta$$
$$- \int\int Q(\beta e - a)\, d\alpha\, d\beta \equiv I_1 + I_2 - I_3, \tag{4.6.9}$$

where Q stands for the integrand in (4.6.8). The first term in this sum reduces to

$$\frac{1}{2\pi i}\int_{\Gamma_\varepsilon} R(\alpha, a)\, d\alpha\; x\; \frac{1}{2\pi i}\int_{\Gamma_\varepsilon} R(\beta, a)\, d\beta. \tag{4.6.10}$$

Here the two integrals are both equal to e so that

$$I_1 = x.$$

To see the first step we note that an integral around the spectrum can be reduced to an integral taken along a large circle $|\alpha| = r$, where formula (4.3.4) is valid and termwise integration is permitted. This gives the desired result.

Since $(\alpha e - a)R(\alpha, a) = e$, we see that

$$I_2 = x\frac{1}{2\pi i}\int_{\Gamma_\varepsilon} R(\beta, a)\left\{\frac{1}{2\pi i}\int_{\Gamma_\varepsilon}\frac{d\alpha}{\lambda + \beta - \alpha}\right\} d\beta = 0.$$

Here the numerical integral is 0. For the integral can be non-zero only if $\lambda - \alpha + \beta = 0$ for some $\beta \in \Gamma_\varepsilon$, $\alpha \in \Sigma_\varepsilon$. If such β and such α exist, then we have $\lambda = \alpha - \beta \in \Sigma_\varepsilon - \Sigma_\varepsilon = \Delta_\varepsilon$ so $\lambda \notin \Lambda_\varepsilon$ and this is a contradiction. In the same manner it is seen that

$$I_3 = \frac{1}{2\pi i}\int_{\Gamma_\varepsilon} R(\alpha, a)\left\{\frac{1}{2\pi i}\int_{\Gamma_\varepsilon} \frac{d\beta}{\lambda + \beta - \alpha}\right\} d\alpha \cdot x = 0.$$

Thus $(\lambda I - \mathbf{C}_a)y = x$ and in the same manner it is shown that

$$\mathbf{R}(\lambda, \mathbf{C}_a)(\lambda I - \mathbf{C}_a)x = x$$

as asserted. ∎

Using the resolvent we can give a more precise form to Theorem 4.6.2. The following result, with a different proof, is due to S. R. Foguel (1957). His argument applies to a more general situation than the one here studied.

Theorem 4.6.6. *Suppose that γ is an isolated point of the difference set $\{\alpha - \beta \mid \alpha \in \sigma(a), \beta \in \sigma(a)\}$ and that the equation*

$$\gamma = \alpha - \beta \tag{4.6.11}$$

has only a finite number of solutions (α, β) in $\sigma(a)$, say

$$(\alpha_1, \beta_1), (\alpha_2, \beta_2), \ldots, (\alpha_p, \beta_p).$$

Suppose moreover that α_k is a pole of $R(\alpha, a)$ of order m_k and β_k is a pole of order n_k, $k = 1, 2, \ldots, p$.

Then γ is a pole of $\mathbf{R}(\lambda, \mathbf{C}_a)$ of order not exceeding $\max(m_k + n_k - 1)$. *The order is exactly this number if $\mathfrak{B}$ is a prime ring.*

Proof. We have two decompositions of $\sigma(a)$

$$\sigma(a) = \{\alpha_1, \alpha_2, \ldots, \alpha_p\} \cup \sigma_1 = \{\beta_1, \beta_2, \ldots, \beta_p\} \cup \sigma_2. \tag{4.6.12}$$

Here σ_1 and σ_2 are the complementary parts of $\sigma(a)$ in each case. We use the first decomposition with the α-integrals, the second with the β-integrals. We note that (4.6.11) is not satisfied by $\alpha = \alpha_k$, $\beta \in \sigma_2$ or by $\alpha \in \sigma_1$, $\beta = \beta_k$. Corresponding to these decompositions we have two coverings of $\sigma(a)$ by ε-disks. We suppose that ε is so small that each of the disks with centers at $\alpha_1, \ldots, \alpha_p, \beta_1, \ldots, \beta_p$ contains one and only one spectral value. Further, the p disks covering $\alpha_1, \ldots, \alpha_p$ shall have no point in common with each other and with the covering of σ_1 and a similar condition shall hold for the β-covering.

The right-hand side of (4.6.8) can now be broken up into a sum of $(p + 1)^2$ integrals $I_{\mu,\nu}$, say:

$$\mathbf{R}(\lambda, \mathbf{C}_a)x = \sum_1^{p+1}\sum_1^{p+1} I_{\mu,\nu}. \tag{4.6.13}$$

We proceed to describe and discuss the integrals.

A. Consider an $I_{\mu,\nu}$ with $1 \leq \mu \leq p$, $1 \leq \nu \leq p$. This is a double integral over $|\alpha - \alpha_\mu| = \varepsilon$, $|\beta - \beta_\nu| = \varepsilon$. We substitute the representations of $R(\alpha, a)$ and of $R(\beta, a)$ valid at a pole. These are of the form

$$R(\alpha, a) = \frac{j}{\alpha - \sigma} + \sum_{2}^{m} \frac{q^{k-1}}{(\alpha - \sigma)^k} + \sum_{0}^{\infty} b^{k+1}(\sigma - \alpha)^k.$$

Cf. formula (4.3.30). If the series are multiplied out and integrated termwise the result is a set of terms of the form $cx\tilde{c}$ multiplied by a numerical integral

$$J_{k,l} = \frac{1}{(2\pi i)^2} \int\int (s - \sigma)^{-k}(t - \tau)^{-l}(\lambda - s + t)^{-1}\, ds\, dt.$$

Here c and $\tilde{c}$ are certain elements of $\mathfrak{B}$, we have written s, t, σ, τ instead of α, β, α_μ, β_ν, and k and l are arbitrary integers. We can reduce the integral to the form

$$J_{k,l} = \frac{1}{(2\pi i)^2} \int\int u^{-k}v^{-l}(\lambda - \sigma + \tau - u + v)^{-1}\, du\, dv, \qquad (4.6.14)$$

where $|u| = \varepsilon$, $|v| = \varepsilon$. Here

$$J_{k,l} = \begin{cases} 0 & \text{if } k \leq 0 \quad \text{or} \quad l \leq 0, \\ (-1)^{l-1} \dfrac{(k + l - 2)!}{(k - 1)!(l - 1)!} (\lambda - \sigma + \tau)^{-k-l+1}, & k > 0, l > 0. \end{cases} \qquad (4.6.15)$$

It is assumed that $|\lambda - \sigma + \tau| > 2\varepsilon$. To verify these values of $J_{k,l}$ we can use the expansion

$$\sum_{j=0}^{\infty} (\lambda - \sigma + \tau)^{-j-1}(u - v)^j u^{-k}v^{-l}$$

for the integrand and integrate termwise with respect to u and v. The result is 0 unless one of the factors $(u - v)^j$ when expanded by the binomial theorem gives rise to a term in

$$u^{k-1}v^{l-1}.$$

This cannot happen if either $k \leq 0$ or $l \leq 0$, and if they are both >0 we must have $j = k + l - 2$ and the integral has the value stated.

Thus we see that each integral $I_{\mu,\nu}$ with $1 \leq \mu \leq p$, $1 \leq \nu \leq p$, is a rational function of λ with coefficients in $\mathfrak{B}$. More precisely, $I_{\mu,\nu}$ is a polynomial in $(\lambda - \alpha_\mu + \beta_\nu)^{-1}$ of degree not exceeding $m_\mu + n_\nu - 1$. Each of these functions has a single pole which is located at $\lambda = \gamma$ iff $\mu = \nu$. The diagonal terms $I_{\mu,\mu}$ add up to a polynomial in $(\lambda - \gamma)^{-1}$ of degree not exceeding max $(m_\mu + n_\mu - 1)$. We have also to take into account the $\mathfrak{B}$-valued coefficients. The highest term in $I_{\mu,\mu}$ is multiplied by

$$q_\mu^{m_\mu - 1} x \, \tilde{q}_\mu^{n_\mu - 1}, \tag{4.6.16}$$

i.e. x is multiplied on the left by the $(m_\mu - 1)^{\text{th}}$ power of the nilpotent of $R(\alpha, a)$ at $\alpha = \alpha_\mu$ and on the right by the $(n_\mu - 1)^{\text{th}}$ power of the nilpotent of $R(\beta, a)$ at $\beta = \beta_\mu$. These are the coefficients of the highest powers of $(\alpha - \alpha_\mu)^{-1}$ and $(\beta - \beta_\mu)^{-1}$, respectively. The product in (4.6.16) may be 0 for some values of x, but if $\mathfrak{B}$ is a prime ring we can be sure that the product does not vanish for all values of x. In particular, we can choose x so that the term corresponding to the maximal value of $m_\mu + n_\mu - 1$ is not 0. If there are several terms having the maximal degree, we can preserve one and annihilate the others by replacing x by $j_\mu x$ where j_μ is the idempotent at $\alpha = \alpha_\mu$. This follows from the fact that $q_\mu j_\mu = q_\mu$ while $q_\nu j_\mu = 0$.

B. It remains to consider the integrals $I_{\mu,\nu}$ with μ or $\nu = p + 1$. If $\mu = p + 1$, the α-integral is taken along a contour surrounding σ_1, if $\nu = p + 1$, the β-integral surrounds σ_2. A simple argument shows that each of these $2p + 1$ integrals is a holomorphic function of λ in a neighborhood of $\lambda = \gamma$.

Combining the results under A and B we see that $\mathbf{R}(\lambda, \mathbf{C}_a)$ has a pole at $\lambda = \gamma$ and the order of this pole is as stated. ∎

As observed by Daletzky the methods used in the present section apply to a much larger class of operators on $\mathfrak{B}$. Let a and b be two elements of $\mathfrak{B}$ neither of which commutes with all elements of $\mathfrak{B}$. We note that

$$\mathbf{L}_a \mathbf{R}_b = \mathbf{R}_b \mathbf{L}_a. \tag{4.6.17}$$

Let η_{jk}, $0 \le j \le m$, $0 \le k \le n$, be given complex numbers and form the operator $\mathbf{T}_{a,b}$ defined by

$$\mathbf{T}_{a,b} x = \sum_0^m \sum_0^n \eta_{jk} a^j x b^k \tag{4.6.18}$$

and set

$$P(\alpha, \beta) = \sum_0^m \sum_0^n \eta_{jk} \alpha^j \beta^k. \tag{4.6.19}$$

Most of the theorems listed above carry over to this more general situation and we state the results without proof.

Theorem 4.6.7. *The spectrum of* $\mathbf{T}_{a,b}$ *is contained in the set*

$$\{P(\alpha, \beta) \mid \alpha \in \sigma(a), \beta \in \sigma(b)\}.$$

Proof by Gelfand's theorem.

Theorem 4.6.8. *If* $\mathbf{L}_a x = \alpha x$, $\mathbf{R}_b y = \beta y$, $x \neq 0$, $y \neq 0$, *then either* $xy = 0$ *or* $P(\alpha, \beta) \in P\sigma(\mathbf{T}_{a,b})$. *If* $\mathfrak{B}$ *is a prime ring the second conclusion is valid.*

Here $\mathbf{T}_{a,b}(xzy) = P(\alpha, \beta)(xzy)$.

Theorem 4.6.9. *Let* Σ_ε^1 *and* Σ_ε^2 *be the set of points at distances not exceeding* ε *from* $\sigma(a)$ *and* $\sigma(b)$, *respectively, and let* Γ_ε^1 *and* Γ_ε^2 *be their oriented boundaries supposed to be rectifiable curves. Set* $\Delta_\varepsilon = P[\Sigma_\varepsilon^1, \Sigma_\varepsilon^2]$ *and let* Λ_ε *be the complement of* Δ_ε. *Then for* $\lambda \in \Lambda_\varepsilon$

$$\mathbf{R}(\lambda, \mathbf{T}_{ab})x = \frac{1}{(2\pi i)^2}\int_{\Gamma_\varepsilon^1}\int_{\Gamma_\varepsilon^2} \frac{R(\alpha, a)xR(\beta, b)}{\lambda - P(\alpha, \beta)}\, d\alpha\, d\beta. \tag{4.6.20}$$

Operate on the integral by $\lambda I - \mathbf{T}_{a,b}$ and use the properties of $R(\alpha, a)$ and $R(\beta, b)$.

Finally, Foguel's theorem also carries over, though the argument is more laborious. Here the maximal order of the pole is not necessarily reached even if $\mathfrak{B}$ is a prime ring for besides factors $cx\tilde{c}$ we have also numerical coefficients which are partial derivatives of $[\lambda - P(u, v)]^{-1}$ evaluated at $u = \alpha_k$, $v = \beta_k$, and they may vanish.

Theorem 4.6.10. *Let* γ *be an isolated point of the set* $\{P(\alpha, \beta) \mid \alpha \in \sigma(a), \beta \in \sigma(b)\}$ *and let the equation*

$$P(\alpha, \beta) = \gamma \tag{4.6.21}$$

have only a finite number of solutions

$$(\alpha_1, \beta_1), \ldots, (\alpha_p, \beta_p), \alpha_k \in \sigma(a), \beta_k \in \sigma(b).$$

Suppose that $\alpha = \alpha_k$ *is a pole of* $R(\alpha, a)$ *of order* m_k *and* $\beta = \beta_k$ *a pole of* $R(\beta, b)$ *of order* n_k. *Then* γ *is a pole of* $\mathbf{R}(\lambda, \mathbf{T}_{a,b})$ *of order not exceeding* $\max(m_k + n_k - 1)$.

EXERCISE 4.6

1. If a is nilpotent, show that $\mathbf{C}_a$ is also nilpotent and compare the degrees of nilpotency.
2. If a is idempotent, show that $\mathbf{C}_a^3 = \mathbf{C}_a$ and find $\mathbf{R}(\lambda, \mathbf{C}_a)$ in closed form.
3. Compare the result obtained in the preceding problem with that obtainable by evaluating the integral (4.6.8).
4. If a is idempotent and $\mathbf{J}_a x = \frac{1}{2}(ax + xa)$, compute $\mathbf{R}(\lambda, \mathbf{J}_a)x$ using (4.6.20).
5. Compute $\mathbf{R}(\lambda, \mathbf{J}_a)x$ directly.
6. Prove Theorem 4.6.7.
7. Prove Theorem 4.6.9.

8. In proving Theorem 4.6.10 we encounter integrals similar to (4.6.14). Find these integrals and evaluate them.
9. Complete the proof of Theorem 4.6.10.

COLLATERAL READING

For most of Chapter 4 the reader can consult

HILLE, E., and R. S. PHILLIPS, *Functional Analysis and Semi-Groups*, American Mathematical Society Colloquium Series, Vol. 31, Providence, R.I. (1957).

Only the first five chapters are relevant here and §§4.4–4.6, 5.2, 5.3 can be omitted. See also

RICKART, C. E., *General Theory of Banach Algebras*, Van Nostrand, Princeton, N.J. (1960).

For Section 4.6 see

DALETSKY, YU. L., "On the asymptotic solution of a vector differential equation" (Russian), *Doklady Akad. Nauk*, **92**, 881–884 (1953).

FOGUEL, S. R., "Sums and products of commuting spectral operators," *Arkiv för Matematik*, **3**, 449–461 (1957).

For the matrix case see

LAPPO-DANILEVSKY, J. A., *Théorie des systèmes des équations différentielles linéaires*, 3 vols. Chelsea, New York (1953).

See in particular §22 of the first of the thirteen memoirs collected and published after the author's death by the Akademia Nauk. The brilliant author was born in 1896 and died in 1931.

5 LINEAR DIFFERENTIAL EQUATIONS WITH ALMOST CONSTANT COEFFICIENTS

The systematic discussion of linear differential equations will start in the present chapter with a survey of the theory of equations with constant or asymptotically constant coefficients. More general questions involving variable coefficients will be treated in Appendix B and Chapter 6.

There are four sections: Constant Coefficients, The Matrix Case, Infinite Matrices, and Asymptotically Constant Coefficients.

5.1 CONSTANT COEFFICIENTS

In classical analysis a linear differential equation with constant coefficients is of the form

$$y^{(n)} + a_1 y^{(n-1)} + \cdots + a_{n-1} y' + a_n y = 0, \tag{5.1.1}$$

where the a's are real or complex numbers. It is often useful to consider the corresponding linear differential operator $P(D)$ defined by

$$P(D)[y] \equiv D^n y + a_1 D^{n-1} y + \cdots + a_{n-1} Dy + a_n I y \tag{5.1.2}$$

in terms of which the differential equation becomes

$$P(D)[y] = 0. \tag{5.1.3}$$

The starting-point in the discussion is the observation that

$$P(D)[e^{\omega t}] = P(\omega)\, e^{\omega t}, \tag{5.1.4}$$

where ω is an arbitrary complex number. It follows that if ω is a root of the so-called *characteristic equation*

$$P(\omega) \equiv \omega^n + a_1 \omega^{n-1} + \cdots + a_{n-1}\omega + a_n = 0, \tag{5.1.5}$$

then $y = e^{\omega t}$ is a solution of (5.1.1). If the roots of this equation are

$$\omega_1, \omega_2, \ldots, \omega_n, \tag{5.1.6}$$

then each of the functions

$$e^{\omega_j t} \tag{5.1.7}$$

is a solution of (5.1.1).

In the enumeration (5.1.6) of the roots, each root is supposed to be repeated as often as is indicated by its multiplicity. Let us start with the case where the roots are simple. Then the n functions (5.1.7) are distinct. Moreover, they are linearly independent. For if a relation

$$C_1 e^{\omega_1 t} + C_2 e^{\omega_2 t} + \cdots + C_n e^{\omega_n t} \equiv 0 \tag{5.1.8}$$

would hold, then the relations obtained by differentiating any number of times must also hold, i.e.

$$C_1\omega_1^k e^{\omega_1 t} + C_2\omega_2^k e^{\omega_2 t} + \cdots + C_n\omega_n^k e^{\omega_n t} \equiv 0. \tag{5.1.9}$$

Taking $k = 0, 1, 2, \ldots, n-1$ we obtain a system of n equations linear in $C_1, C_2, \ldots, C_n$ which must hold for all values of t, in particular for $t = 0$. Since the system is homogeneous it has non-trivial solutions for the C's iff the determinant is zero. But this is a Vandermonde determinant and

$$\begin{vmatrix} 1 & 1 & \cdots & 1 \\ \omega_1 & \omega_2 & \cdots & \omega_n \\ \omega_1^2 & \omega_2^2 & \cdots & \omega_n^2 \\ \cdot & \cdot & \cdots & \cdot \\ \omega_1^{n-1} & \omega_2^{n-1} & \cdots & \omega_n^{n-1} \end{vmatrix} = \prod_{1 \le j < k \le n} (\omega_k - \omega_j) \tag{5.1.10}$$

is not 0 if the ω's are distinct. This shows that the functions (5.1.7) are linearly independent. The argument also shows that the system of equations

$$\omega_1^k C_1 + \omega_2^k C_2 + \cdots + \omega_2^k C_n = b_k, \quad k = 0, 1, 2, \ldots, n-1, \tag{5.1.11}$$

has a unique solution if the b's are given complex numbers.

Now the differential operator $P(D)$ is linear, i.e.

$$P(D)[C_1 y_1 + C_2 y_2] = C_1 P(D)[y_1] + C_2 P(D)[y_2] \tag{5.1.12}$$

for any constants C_1, C_2 and any functions $y_1(t)$, $y_2(t)$ having derivatives of order $\le n$. This implies that

$$y(t) \equiv C_1 e^{\omega_1 t} + C_2 e^{\omega_2 t} + \cdots + C_n e^{\omega_n t} \tag{5.1.13}$$

is a solution of (5.1.1) for any choice of the constants C_j. Moreover, it is the general solution of (5.1.1) in the following sense. We know that a solution of (5.1.1) is uniquely determined by its initial values, say by the values of

$$y(0), y'(0), y''(0), \ldots, y^{(n-1)}(0).$$

But if these values are $b_0, b_1, b_2, \ldots, b_{n-1}$, respectively, then the equations (5.1.11) determine uniquely a set of constants $C_1, C_2, \ldots, C_n$ such that the exponential polynomial in the right member of (5.1.13) has the same initial values at $t = 0$ as the given solution $y(t)$. Since the exponential polynomial is a solution and initial values determine solutions uniquely, it follows that $y(t)$ coincides with the exponential polynomial, provided the constants $C_1, C_2, \ldots, C_n$ satisfy (5.1.11). This is what we mean by saying that the exponential polynomial gives the general solution of (5.1.1).

This argument presupposes that the roots ω_j are distinct, and it breaks down if this is not the case, since the functions (5.1.7) are no longer linearly independent. Suppose that the characteristic equation (5.1.5) has $\omega = \alpha$ as a k-fold root. This means that in the right member of (5.1.4) $P(\omega)$ has $(\omega - \alpha)^k$ as a factor. This in turn implies that any partial derivative of the right member with respect to ω will vanish for $\omega = \alpha$ provided its order $j \leq k - 1$. An application of the theorem of H. A. Schwarz on mixed partials shows that

$$\frac{\partial^j}{\partial \omega^j} P(D)[e^{\omega t}] = P(D)\left[\frac{\partial^j}{\partial \omega^j} e^{\omega t}\right] = P(D)[t^j e^{\omega t}], \tag{5.1.14}$$

so that

$$e^{\alpha t}, t\, e^{\alpha t}, \ldots, t^{k-1} e^{\alpha t} \tag{5.1.15}$$

are now solutions of (5.1.1). Hence

$$(C_1 + C_2 t + \cdots + C_k t^{k-1})\, e^{\alpha t} \tag{5.1.16}$$

is also a solution.

Taking into account the other roots, some of which may also be multiple roots, we obtain a solution of the form

$$y(t) \equiv \sum_{j=1}^{p} (C_{j1} + \cdots + C_{j,k_j} t^{k_j - 1})\, e^{\omega_j t}, \tag{5.1.17}$$

where

$$\sum_{1}^{p} k_j = n.$$

This expression involves n arbitrary constants and, unless all the C's are 0, the function cannot vanish identically, i.e. the n constituents

$$t^k e^{\omega_j t}$$

are linearly independent. It is decidedly more complicated to prove this than the case handled above.

The argument used above could be modified, but the non-vanishing of the determinant which replaces the Vandermonde determinant is not so easy to prove directly. Instead, we shall use a function theoretical approach which is informative and gives the non-vanishing of the determinant as a by-product. We denote the right member of (5.1.17) by $F(t)$, and note that $F(t)$ is a holomorphic function of t so that, if it vanishes on an interval of the real axis, it must vanish everywhere in the complex plane. We may assume that the distinct ω's are numbered according to increasing real parts so that

$$\Re(\omega_1) \leq \Re(\omega_2) \leq \cdots \leq \Re(\omega_p). \tag{5.1.18}$$

If several ω's have the same real parts, we number this subset according to increasing imaginary parts. We have, by assumption

$$F(t)\,e^{-\omega_p t} = \sum_{j=1}^{p} P_j(t)\,e^{(\omega_j-\omega_p)t} \equiv 0,$$

where $P_j(t)$ is a polynomial in t of degree $k_j - 1$. If $\Re(\omega_{p-1}) < \Re(\omega_p)$, the last relation shows that there is a positive number γ such that

$$F(t)\,e^{-\omega_p t} = P_p(t) + o(e^{-\gamma t}), \qquad t \to +\infty.$$

Such an expression cannot be identically 0 unless $P_p(t) \equiv 0$ and this requires that all coefficients of the P_p are 0. If now all inequalities in (5.1.18) are strict, then we can use the same device to show step by step that

$$P_{p-1}(t) \equiv 0, \ldots, P_2(t) \equiv 0, P_1(t) \equiv 0,$$

and this requires that all coefficients C_{jk} are 0.

If, however, equality holds in one or more places in (5.1.18) the procedure must be modified. We set

$$\omega_j - \omega_p = \alpha_j + i\beta_j.$$

Suppose now, to fix the ideas, that

$$\Re(\omega_p) = \Re(\omega_{p-1}) = \cdots = \Re(\omega_{p-k+1}) > \Re(\omega_{p-k}).$$

We have then

$$\alpha_p = \alpha_{p-1} = \cdots = \alpha_{p-k+1} = 0, \qquad \alpha_j < 0 \quad \text{for} \quad j < p-k+1,$$

$$\beta_p = 0, 0 > \beta_{p-1} > \cdots > \beta_{p-k+1}.$$

We can now find a small positive angle θ so that

$$\alpha_j + \beta_j \sin\theta < 0, j = p-1, p-2, \ldots, 1. \tag{5.1.19}$$

There is no difficulty for $j = p-1, \ldots, p-k+1$ for then $\alpha_j = 0$ and $\beta_j < 0$, but for $j < p-k+1$ we may have to contend with positive numbers β_j. Since $\alpha_j < 0$ we can still satisfy the conditions. We have

$$P_p(t) + P_{p-1}(t)\,e^{i\beta_{p-1}t} + \cdots + P_{p-k+1}(t)\,e^{i\beta_{p-k+1}t}$$
$$+ P_{p-k}(t)\,e^{(\alpha_{p-k}+i\beta_{p-k})t} + \cdots + P_1(t)\,e^{(\alpha_1+i\beta_1)t} = 0.$$

This implies that once θ has been chosen subject to (5.1.19) we can find a positive number γ such that

$$P_p(t) + O(e^{-\gamma|t|}) \equiv 0,$$

when $|t|$ is allowed to become infinite and $\arg t = \theta$. Again, this is impossible unless $P_p(t) \equiv 0$, so all the coefficients of P must vanish. This procedure is general and can be used to prove successively that all the polynomials are identically zero and hence that all coefficients $C_{jk} = 0$.

It follows that the n constituent solutions of formula (5.1.17) are linearly independent. From this we conclude that the conditions

$$y(0) = b_0, y'(0) = b_1, \ldots, y^{(n-1)}(0) = b_{n-1}$$

determine the coefficients $C_{j,k}$ in (5.1.17) uniquely. For if they did not, the functions

$$t^k e^{\omega_j t}$$

must be linearly dependent, and we have seen that this cannot be the case. Thus the general solution of (5.1.1) is now given by (5.1.17).

It is worth while analyzing the idea underlying the linear independence proof. It is the following. Given a function $F(t)$ defined by (5.1.17), then we can find a straight line in the complex plane such that when t goes to ∞ along this line in one of the two possible directions, then $F(t)$ has a dominant term which must vanish identically, if $F(t)$ is to have this property. This means that the corresponding coefficients must be 0. Varying the approach to ∞, we can successively eliminate all terms and find that $F(t) \equiv 0$, iff all the coefficients are 0.

Besides the homogeneous equation (5.1.1) we have also to consider the non-homogeneous case

$$P(D)y = f(t), \tag{5.1.20}$$

where $f(t)$ is a function continuous in the interval under consideration. Let $U(t)$ denote the general solution of (5.1.1) and let $Y(t)$ be a particular solution of (5.1.20). Then the general solution of (5.1.20) is given by

$$y(t) = Y(t) + U(t), \tag{5.1.21}$$

as is shown by substitution.

The problem is then reduced to finding a particular solution of (5.1.20). Here several general methods are available and also a number of special devices applicable to important special cases.

In the first order case, we have

$$y' - \alpha y = f(t) \tag{5.1.22}$$

and

$$D[e^{-\alpha t}y(t)] = e^{-\alpha t}f(t).$$

This gives

$$y(t) = e^{-\alpha a}y(a)\, e^{\alpha t} + \int_a^t e^{\alpha(t-s)}f(s)\, ds. \tag{5.1.23}$$

In particular, we see that the solution of (5.1.22) which vanishes at $t = a$ is

$$Y(t; a, 0) = \int_a^t e^{\alpha(t-s)}f(s)\, ds. \tag{5.1.24}$$

We can reduce the nth order case to the first order one in the following manner. Suppose that

$$P(D) = \prod_{j=1}^{n} (D - \omega_j),$$

where each ω_j is repeated as often as is indicated by its multiplicity as a root of the characteristic equation. We then set

$$\prod_{j=2}^{n} (D - \omega_j)y = y_1, \tag{5.1.25}$$

so that

$$(D - \omega_1)y_1 = f(t).$$

This gives

$$y_1(t) = C_1\, e^{\omega_1 t} + \int_a^t e^{\omega_1(t-s)} f(s)\, ds.$$

Next we set

$$\prod_{j=3}^{n} (D - \omega_j)y = y_2, \tag{5.1.26}$$

so that

$$(D - \omega_2)y_2 = y_1.$$

Hence

$$y_2(t) = C_2\, e^{\omega_2 t} + \int_a^t e^{\omega_2(t-s)} \left\{ C_1\, e^{\omega_1 s} + \int_a^s e^{\omega_1(s-s_1)} f(s_1)\, ds_1 \right\} ds.$$

If $\omega_2 \neq \omega_1$, this reduces to

$$y_2(t) = C_1^*\, e^{\omega_1 t} + C_2^*\, e^{\omega_2 t} + \int_a^t e^{\omega_2(t-s)} \int_a^s e^{\omega_1(s-s_1)} f(s_1)\, ds_1\, ds.$$

If, however, $\omega_2 = \omega_1$, the second term becomes

$$C_2^* t\, e^{\omega_1 t}$$

instead. In any case, we see that the particular solution of

$$(D - \omega_1)(D - \omega_2)y_2 = f, \tag{5.1.27}$$

which vanishes together with its first derivative at $t = a$, is

$$Y(t; a, 0, 0) = \int_a^t e^{\omega_2(t-s)} \int_a^s e^{\omega_1(s-s_1)} f(s_1)\, ds_1\, ds. \tag{5.1.28}$$

By complete induction we find that

$$Y(t) = \int_a^t e^{\omega_n(t-s)} \int_a^s e^{\omega_{n-1}(s-s_1)} \cdots \int_a^{s_{n-2}} e^{\omega_1(s_{n-2}-s_{n-1})} f(s_{n-1})\, ds_{n-1} \cdots ds \tag{5.1.29}$$

is the particular solution of (5.1.20), which vanishes at $t = a$ together with its derivatives of order $\leq n - 1$.

Thus we have found a particular solution of (5.1.20). If it is desired to find the particular solution for which

$$y(a) = b_0, y'(a) = b_1, \ldots, y^{(n-1)}(a) = b_{n-1},$$

we first determine a solution $U(t)$ of the homogeneous equation with these initial values and to it we add $Y(t)$ defined by (5.1.29). The sum $U(t) + Y(t)$ is the desired solution.

This is a general method applicable to all n^{th} order equations with constant coefficients. Two other general methods formulated for second order equations are to be found in Problems 13 and 14 of Exercise 5.1. In the exercise the reader will also find a number of special devices. We discuss one such device here.

Formula (5.1.4) shows that the equation

$$P(D)[y] = a\, e^{\omega t} \tag{5.1.30}$$

is satisfied by

$$y = \frac{a}{P(\omega)}\, e^{\omega t},$$

provided $P(\omega) \neq 0$. If $P(\omega) = 0$ but $P'(\omega) \neq 0$, we use (5.1.14) and obtain the solution

$$y = \frac{a}{P'(\omega)}\, t\, e^{\omega t}.$$

EXERCISE 5.1

1. Find the solution of
$$y'' - k^2 y = f(t), \qquad k > 0,$$
which vanishes for $t = 0$ together with its first derivative.

2. If $f \in L(0, \infty) \cap C[0, \infty)$ find the solution of
$$y'' + k^2 y = f(t), \qquad k > 0,$$
which, together with its first derivative, tends to 0 as $t \to +\infty$.

3. Find the solution of
$$y''' - 3y'' + 3y' - y = e^t, \quad y(0) = y'(0) = 0, \quad y''(0) = 1.$$

4. Find the solution of (5.1.30) if ω is a k-fold root of the characteristic equation.

5. Suppose that $f(t)$ is a polynomial in t of degree k. Show that the equation
$$P(D)y = f(t)$$

has a solution that is a polynomial in t. Determine the degree of the latter under different assumptions on P and indicate how this solution can be found.

6. If $P(i\beta) \neq 0$, show that the equation
$$P(D)y = a \sin \beta t$$
has a solution of the form
$$y = A \sin \beta t + B \cos \beta t.$$

7. Discuss the equation
$$(D^2 + \beta^2)y = \sin \beta t.$$

8. Determine the general form of the solution of
$$y'' + y = \frac{1}{t}$$
and find if any solution is holomorphic at $t = 0$.

9. Prove by induction that
$$P(D)[e^{\omega t}y(t)] = e^{\omega t}P(D + \omega)[y(t)].$$

Formally, the equation
$$(D - \omega)y = f$$
implies that
$$y = \frac{1}{D - \omega} f = -\omega^{-1}\left(1 - \frac{D}{\omega}\right)^{-1} f$$
$$= -\omega^{-1}f - \omega^{-2}Df - \omega^{-3}D^2f - \cdots - \omega^{-n-1}D^nf - \cdots$$

This is a formal replacement of an integral operator [see Eq. (5.1.23)] by a differential operator of infinite order. The series becomes meaningful only if f has derivatives of all orders. Even if this is the case the series need not converge or represent a solution.

10. If f is a polynomial of degree n, the series breaks off after the $(n + 1)^{\text{th}}$ term. Verify that the result is actually a solution.

11. If $f = e^{\alpha t}$ and $|\alpha| < |\omega|$ show that the series converges, find its sum and show that the sum is a solution.

12. Use an adaptation of this method to solve
$$(D - 1)^3(D - 2)y = x^2.$$

13. Let P be a polynomial of degree 2 and leading coefficient 1, let $u_1(t)$ and $u_2(t)$ be two linearly independent solutions of $P(D)U = 0$. Let
$$W(s; u_1, u_2) = \begin{vmatrix} u_1'(s) & u_2'(s) \\ u_1(s) & u_2(s) \end{vmatrix}.$$
Show that $W(s; u_1, u_2) \neq 0$ for all s and verify that
$$y(t) = c_1u_1(t) + c_2u_2(t) + \int_a^t \begin{vmatrix} u_1(t) & u_2(t) \\ u_1(s) & u_2(s) \end{vmatrix} \frac{f(s)\, ds}{W(s; u_1, u_2)}$$

is the general solution of $P(D)y = f$. (The formulas are stated in a form which carries over immediately to the case of a second order equation with variable coefficients.)

14. Under the same assumptions on P, u_1, u_2, the solution of $P(D)y = f$ can be found by the following method, known as *variation of the parameters*. Determine two functions $c_1(t)$ and $c_2(t)$ such that $c_1'(t)u_1(t) + c_2'(t)u_2(t) \equiv 0$ and $c_1(t)u_1(t) + c_2(t)u_2(t)$ satisfies $P(D)y = f$. Show that the result agrees with that of Problem 13.
15. The Euler equation

$$x^n y^{(n)}(x) + a_1 x^{n-1} y^{(n-1)}(x) + \cdots + a_{n-1} x y'(x) + a_n y(x) = 0$$

can be reduced to an equation with constant coefficients by setting $x = e^t$. It is also possible to solve the equation by essaying a solution of the form x^ρ. Work out both methods. What equation must ρ satisfy?

5.2 THE MATRIX CASE

The theory of linear differential equations with constant coefficients gains in simplicity and clarity by passing over to matrices. The basic homogeneous equations are

$$\mathbf{y}'(t) = \mathcal{A}\mathbf{y}(t) \tag{5.2.1}$$

and

$$\mathcal{Y}'(t) = \mathcal{A}\mathcal{Y}(t). \tag{5.2.2}$$

Here $\mathcal{A} \in \mathfrak{M}_n$ is an n by n matrix of constants, $\mathcal{A} = (a_{jk})$. Further, $\mathbf{y}(t)$ is a vector, a function on R^1 to R^n, while $\mathcal{Y}(t)$ is a function on R^1 to $\mathfrak{M}_n$. It is normally necessary to replace R^1 by C^1 and R^n by C^n to gain full generality.

The theory is usually presented for the first equation, and the second is neglected. We shall take the second equation as basic and the first will play a subsidiary role. Actually there is not much difference between the resulting theories. If $\mathcal{Y}(t)$ is a solution of the second equation, then anyone of the column vectors of the matrix $\mathcal{Y}(t)$ is a solution of the first equation. Conversely, any n solutions of (5.2.1) written as column vectors, form a matrix $\mathcal{Y}(t)$ which satisfies the second equation. If the n vectors are linearly independent, then their determinant, $\det \mathcal{Y}(t)$, is $\neq 0$ and we say that $\mathcal{Y}(t)$ is a *fundamental solution* of (5.2.2). Conversely, if $\mathcal{Y}(t)$ is fundamental, then its column vectors give n linearly independent solutions of (5.2.1).

We can find a solution of (5.2.2) by inspection. It is

$$\mathcal{Y}(t; 0, \mathcal{E}) = \exp(\mathcal{A}t), \tag{5.2.3}$$

where, as usual, the exponential function is defined by the series

$$\exp(\mathcal{A}t) = \mathcal{E} + \sum_{k=1}^{\infty} \frac{t^k}{k!} \mathcal{A}^k.$$

We recall that $\mathfrak{M}_n$ is a B-algebra under the norm

$$\|\mathcal{A}\| = \max_j \sum_{k=1}^n |a_{jk}|. \tag{5.2.4}$$

We have then

$$\left\| \sum_m^p \frac{t^k}{k!} \mathcal{A}^k \right\| \le \sum_m^p \frac{|t|^k}{k!} \|\mathcal{A}\|^k.$$

This tends to 0 as $m \to \infty$ for all $p > m$, uniformly with respect to t for $|t| \le R$. Hence the exponential series converges in norm and uniformly with respect to t on compact sets.

The series can be differentiated termwise. Again the resulting series is uniformly convergent in norm and its sum is

$$\mathcal{A} \exp (\mathcal{A}t) = \exp (\mathcal{A}t)\mathcal{A}.$$

It follows that $\mathcal{Y}(t; 0, \mathcal{E})$ is indeed a solution of (5.2.2). As indicated by the notation, it is the unique solution which reduces to $\mathcal{E}$ for $t = 0$. If we want the solution $\mathcal{Y}(t; 0, \mathcal{B})$ which reduces to $\mathcal{B}$ for $t = 0$, we form

$$\mathcal{Y}(t; 0, \mathcal{B}) = \mathcal{Y}(t; 0, \mathcal{E})\mathcal{B}. \tag{5.2.5}$$

It is obvious by substitution that this is a solution and that it has the correct initial value. Since the solution is unique, it is given by (5.2.5).

We recall that $\exp(\mathcal{A}t)$ is a regular element of the algebra $\mathfrak{M}_n$ and that its inverse is $\exp(-\mathcal{A}t)$. We conclude that $\mathcal{Y}(t; 0, \mathcal{B})$ is regular, iff $\mathcal{B}$ is regular. Thus $\mathcal{Y}(t; 0, \mathcal{B})$ is a fundamental solution of (5.2.2) iff $\mathcal{B}$ is a regular matrix. If this is the case, then for any choice of $\mathcal{C}$ in $\mathfrak{M}_n$

$$\mathcal{Y}(t; 0, \mathcal{C}) = \mathcal{Y}(t; 0, \mathcal{B})\mathcal{B}^{-1}\mathcal{C}, \tag{5.2.6}$$

i.e. any solution of (5.2.2) is a constant multiple of an arbitrary fundamental solution.

The discussion can be carried over to an arbitrary non-commutative B-algebra $\mathfrak{B}$ with unit element e. The equation (5.2.2) corresponds to

$$y'(t) = ay(t), \tag{5.2.7}$$

where a and $y(t)$ are elements of $\mathfrak{B}$. The function

$$y(t; 0, e) = \exp (at) \tag{5.2.8}$$

is the basic solution of (5.2.7) which takes the initial value e for $t = 0$. Further,

$$y(t; 0, b) = \exp (at)b \tag{5.2.9}$$

is the unique solution with the initial value b for $t = 0$. It is a fundamental solution iff b is a regular element of the algebra. In this case

$$y(t; 0, c) = y(t; 0, b)b^{-1}c, \tag{5.2.10}$$

so the analogy with the matrix case is perfect at least on this relatively elementary level.

We shall study $\mathcal{Y}(t; 0, \mathcal{E})$ in more detail. Here the alternate definition of the exponential function by the resolvent integral (see Section 4.5) is advantageous. We have

$$\exp(\mathcal{A}t) = \frac{1}{2\pi i}\int_\Gamma e^{\lambda t}\mathcal{R}(\lambda, \mathcal{A})\, d\lambda, \tag{5.2.11}$$

where Γ surrounds the spectrum of $\mathcal{A}$ once in the positive sense and $\mathcal{R}(\lambda, \mathcal{A})$ is the resolvent of $\mathcal{A}$. We recall that in the matrix case $\mathcal{R}(\lambda, \mathcal{A})$ is holomorphic save for a finite number of poles located at the roots of the characteristic equation. More precisely,

$$\mathcal{R}(\lambda, \mathcal{A}) = \sum_{j=1}^{p}\left\{\frac{\mathcal{E}_j}{\lambda - \lambda_j} + \frac{\mathcal{Q}_j}{(\lambda - \lambda_j)^2} + \cdots + \frac{\mathcal{Q}_j^{k_j - 1}}{(\lambda - \lambda_j)^{k_j}}\right\}, \tag{5.2.12}$$

where the summation extends over the p distinct roots λ_j. Further we recall that the $\mathcal{E}_j$'s are idempotents giving a resolution of the identity

$$\sum_{j=1}^{p} \mathcal{E}_j = \mathcal{E},\ \mathcal{E}_j\mathcal{E}_k = \mathcal{E}_k\mathcal{E}_j = \delta_{jk}\mathcal{E}_j,$$

while the $\mathcal{Q}_j$'s are nilpotent elements with

$$\mathcal{E}_j\mathcal{Q}_j = \mathcal{Q}_j\mathcal{E}_j = \mathcal{Q}_j,\ \mathcal{Q}_j\mathcal{Q}_k = \mathcal{O}, \quad j \neq k,\ \mathcal{Q}_j^{k_j} = \mathcal{O}.$$

Substituting this expression for $\mathcal{R}(\lambda, \mathcal{A})$ into (5.2.11) and integrating termwise we obtain

$$\exp(\mathcal{A}t) = \sum_{j=1}^{p}\left\{\mathcal{E}_j + \mathcal{Q}_j t + \cdots + \frac{1}{(k_j - 1)!}\mathcal{Q}_j^{k_j - 1} t^{k_j - 1}\right\} e^{\lambda_j t}, \tag{5.2.13}$$

where

$$\sum_{1}^{p} k_j = n.$$

Formula (5.2.13) expresses $\exp(\mathcal{A}t)$ as a sum of elementary exponential functions multiplied by polynomials whose coefficients are the singular matrices which figure in the partial fraction expansion of the resolvent of $\mathcal{A}$.

It will be important for later applications to estimate the rate of growth of $\|\exp(\mathcal{A}t)\|$ in terms of t for large values of t. It is clear that

$$\|\exp(\mathcal{A}t)\| \leq \exp(\|\mathcal{A}\| t), \quad 0 < t, \tag{5.2.14}$$

but this is usually not good enough for the applications which we have in mind. Suppose that

$$\Re(\lambda_1) \leq \Re(\lambda_2) \leq \cdots \leq \Re(\lambda_p). \tag{5.2.15}$$

We may assume that if $\Re(\lambda_j) = \Re(\lambda_{j+1})$ then $k_j \leq k_{j+1}$. Formula (5.2.13) then shows that we can find a constant M such that for $t \geq 1$

$$\|\exp(\mathcal{A}t)\| \leq Mt^{k_p-1}\exp[\Re(\lambda_p)t]. \tag{5.2.16}$$

In particular, if $\Re(\lambda_p) < 0$, i.e. if all characteristic values have negative real parts, then $\|\exp(\mathcal{A}t)\|$ is bounded for all values of $t \geq 0$ and tends exponentially to zero as $t \to +\infty$. If we have merely $\Re(\lambda_p) = 0$, then $\|\exp(\mathcal{A}t)\|$ is bounded provided $k_p = 1$, but it does not tend to 0 when $t \to \infty$.

In the more general case of $\exp(at)$, $a \in \mathfrak{B}$, we usually have to be satisfied with cruder estimates. This goes back to the more general nature of $R(\lambda, a)$. If the latter has only a finite number of poles and no other singularities, then an expansion of the form (5.2.13) holds and (5.2.16) is true with $\mathcal{A}$ replaced by a. This must be regarded as exceptional, however. We still have the representation

$$\exp(at) = \frac{1}{2\pi i}\int_\Gamma e^{\lambda t}R(\lambda, a)\,d\lambda, \tag{5.2.17}$$

where Γ surrounds the spectrum of a. Suppose that

$$\max[\Re(\lambda) \mid \lambda \in \sigma(a)] = \alpha. \tag{5.2.18}$$

This means that $\sigma(a)$ is located in the half plane $\Re(\lambda) \leq \alpha$. We can then choose Γ in the halfplane $\Re(\lambda) \leq \alpha + \varepsilon$. Then

$$|e^{\lambda t}| \leq \exp[(\alpha + \varepsilon)t], \qquad \lambda \in \Gamma, 0 < t.$$

Suppose that on Γ

$$\|R(\lambda, a\| \leq M(\varepsilon)$$

and that L is the length of Γ. Then we have

$$\|\exp(at)\| \leq \frac{1}{2\pi}LM(\varepsilon)\exp[(\alpha + \varepsilon)t], \qquad 0 < t. \tag{5.2.19}$$

This estimate is not much worse than (5.2.16) and normally cannot be replaced by anything essentially better. Again we see that if the spectrum of a lies in the open left half-plane, then $\|\exp(at)\|$ goes exponentially to zero as t becomes infinite.

Let us now consider the non-homogeneous case. Again we have two possibilities

$$\mathbf{y}'(t) = \mathcal{A}\mathbf{y}(t) + \mathbf{f}(t) \tag{5.2.20}$$

and

$$\mathcal{Y}'(t) = \mathcal{A}\mathcal{Y}(t) + \mathcal{F}(t). \tag{5.2.21}$$

Here $\mathbf{f}(t)$ is a vector on R^1 to R^n or on C^1 to C^n while $\mathcal{F}(t)$ is a matrix on R^1 or C^1 to $\mathfrak{M}_n$. Both are given functions of t. If $\mathcal{F}(t)$ is a singular matrix all column vectors of which are equal to $\mathbf{f}(t)$ and if $\mathcal{Y}(t)$ is a solution of the second equation, then any column vector of $\mathcal{Y}(t)$ satisfies the first equation. If $\mathcal{F}(t)$ does not satisfy this severe restriction, a more general theory arises.

Let us set

$$\mathcal{U}(t) = \mathcal{U}(t; 0, E) = \exp(\mathcal{A}t) \tag{5.2.22}$$

and form

$$\mathcal{Y}(t) = \mathcal{U}(t)\mathcal{B} + \int_0^t \mathcal{U}(t)[\mathcal{U}(s)]^{-1}\mathcal{F}(s)\,ds. \tag{5.2.23}$$

We have then

$$\begin{aligned}\mathcal{Y}'(t) &= \mathcal{A}\mathcal{U}(t)\mathcal{B} + \mathcal{F}(t) + \mathcal{A}\int_0^t \mathcal{U}(t)[\mathcal{U}(s)]^{-1}\mathcal{F}(s)\,ds \\ &= \mathcal{A}\mathcal{Y}(t) + \mathcal{F}(t),\end{aligned}$$

so that $\mathcal{Y}(t)$ is obviously a solution of (5.2.21) with initial value $\mathcal{B}$ for $t = 0$ Moreover, it is the only such solution.

The solution is given here in the form of (5.2.23) in order to have a representation that carries over to the case where $\mathcal{A}$ is no longer a constant matrix. In the constant case it is simpler to write the solution

$$\mathcal{Y}(t) = \exp(\mathcal{A}t)\mathcal{B} + \int_0^t \exp[(t - s)\mathcal{A}]\mathcal{F}(s)\,ds. \tag{5.2.24}$$

This is an immediate generalization of formula (5.1.23) to which it reduces if $n = 1$.

The formalism extends to the $\mathfrak{B}$-algebra case. If the differential equation is

$$y'(t) = ay(t) + f(t) \tag{5.2.25}$$

with a, $y(t)$ and $f(t)$ elements of $\mathfrak{B}$, then

$$y(t) = \exp(at)b + \int_0^t \exp[(t - s)a]f(s)\,ds \tag{5.2.26}$$

is the solution which takes on the value $b \in \mathfrak{B}$ for $t = 0$. More generally,

$$y'(t) = a(t)y(t) + f(t), \qquad y(0) = b, \tag{5.2.27}$$

has the unique solution

$$y(t) = u(t)b + \int_0^t u(t)[u(s)]^{-1}f(s)\,ds, \tag{5.2.28}$$

where

$$u'(t) = a(t)u(t), \qquad u(0) = e. \tag{5.2.29}$$

This is known as the *variation of constants formula*. The existence of $[u(s)]^{-1}$ will be shown in Section 6.1.

For the discussion below, in Section B.3, it is necessary to know when an equation of type (5.2.20) has polynomial solutions. We say that $\mathbf{P}(t)$ is a *vector polynomial* in t if it is a polynomial in t with coefficients which are constant vectors in C^n. We start with an elementary case:

Lemma 5.2.1. *Suppose that* $\mathbf{f}(t)$ *is a vector polynomial of degree* $k \geq 0$ *and that* $\mathcal{A}$ *is a non-singular constant matrix. Then*

$$\mathbf{y}'(t) = \mathcal{A}\mathbf{y}(t) + \mathbf{f}(t)$$

has a unique polynomial solution given by

$$\mathbf{y}(t) = -\mathcal{A}^{-1}\mathbf{f}(t) - \mathcal{A}^{-2}\mathbf{f}'(t) - \mathcal{A}^{-3}\mathbf{f}''(t) - \cdots - \mathcal{A}^{-k-1}\mathbf{f}^{(k)}(t). \quad (5.2.30)$$

Proof. Substitute the last expression in the differential equation and note that $\mathbf{f}^{(k+1)}(t) \equiv 0$. It is a particular solution and the general solution differs from it by

$$\exp(\mathcal{A}t)\mathbf{v}, \qquad \mathbf{v} \in C^n.$$

Since $\lambda = 0$ is not a characteristic root of $\mathcal{A}$, formula (5.2.13) shows that no choice of the constant vector $\mathbf{v} \neq 0$ will reduce $\exp(\mathcal{A}t)\mathbf{v}$ to a polynomial in t. Hence there is a unique solution and its degree is the same as that of $\mathbf{f}$. ▮

Corollary. *If* $\mathcal{A}$ *is non-singular, the homogeneous differential equation has no non-trivial polynomial solution.*

In order to continue the discussion we have to take a closer look at formula (5.2.12). Here k_j *is the multiplicity of* λ_j *as a root of the characteristic equation of* $\mathcal{A}$, but is not necessarily the order of the pole of the resolvent at $\lambda = \lambda_j$. In other words,

$$\mathcal{Q}_j = (\mathcal{A} - \lambda_j\mathcal{E})\mathcal{E}_j \quad (5.2.31)$$

may be a nilpotent of lower order than k_j. The exact order is m_j which is the multiplicity of λ_j as a root of the so-called *minimal equation* of $\mathcal{A}$. Here $1 \leq m_j \leq k_j$. We shall not discuss the minimal equation, however.

The resolution of the identity

$$\mathcal{E} = \mathcal{E}_1 + \mathcal{E}_2 + \cdots + \mathcal{E}_p$$

leads to a corresponding decomposition of C^n into subspaces

$$C^n = X_1 \oplus X_2 \oplus \cdots \oplus X_p, \qquad X_j = \mathcal{E}_j(C^n). \quad (5.2.32)$$

It follows that every vector $\mathbf{x} \in C^n$ has a unique representation

$$\mathbf{x} = \mathbf{x}_1 + \mathbf{x}_2 + \cdots + \mathbf{x}_p, \qquad \mathbf{x}_j = \mathcal{E}_j(\mathbf{x}) \in X_j. \quad (5.2.33)$$

The space X_j is known as the *root space* of $\mathcal{A}$ for $\lambda = \lambda_j$. This term refers to the following situation.

Since $\mathcal{Q}_j^{k_j} = 0$, it naturally annihilates every vector, in particular those of X_j. But for such a vector $\mathcal{E}_j\mathbf{x} = \mathbf{x}$ and, since $\mathcal{E}_j$ commutes with $\mathcal{A}$,

$$\mathbf{0} = \mathcal{Q}_j^{k_j}\mathbf{x} = [(\mathcal{A} - \lambda_j\mathcal{E})\mathcal{E}_j]^{k_j}\mathbf{x} = (\mathcal{A} - \lambda_j\mathcal{E})^{k_j}\mathbf{x}.$$

Hence every $x_j \in X_j$ is a characteristic vector of the matrix

$$(\mathcal{A} - \lambda_j \mathcal{E})^{k_j} \qquad \text{for} \quad \lambda = 0,$$

and no $\mathbf{x}_0 \notin X_j$ can have this property. In particular, for $\lambda = 0$, all the characteristic vectors of $\mathcal{A} - \lambda_j \mathcal{E}$ belong to X_j for they are annihilated already by the first power of $\mathcal{A} - \lambda_j \mathcal{E}$. These vectors form the so-called *characteristic space* (or eigen space) V_j of $A - \lambda_j E$ and in this general situation V_j is normally a proper subspace of X_j.

Lemma 5.2.2. *A singular matrix $\mathcal{B}$ for which $\lambda = 0$ is a characteristic root of multiplicity m has at most m linearly independent characteristic vectors.*

Proof. The rank of such a matrix (= rank of the corresponding determinant) is at least $n - m$. It follows that the equation

$$\mathcal{B}\mathbf{x} = \mathbf{0}$$

has at most m linearly independent solutions. ▌

We now return to the space X_j. It is annihilated by the matrix $(\mathcal{A} - \lambda_j \mathcal{E})^{k_j}$ which is a singular matrix having $\lambda = 0$ as a characteristic root of multiplicity k_j. For $\mathcal{A} - \lambda_j \mathcal{E}$ has $\lambda = 0$ as root of multiplicity k_j and the characteristic roots of $\mathcal{B}^k$ are the kth powers of the characteristic roots of $\mathcal{B}$. Hence $(\mathcal{A} - \lambda_j \mathcal{E})^{k_j}$ has at most k_j linearly independent characteristic vectors. But they span X_j so that

$$\dim (X_j) \leq k_j.$$

On the other hand

$$\sum_{j=1}^{p} \dim (X_j) = n, \qquad \sum_{j=1}^{p} k_j = n.$$

It follows that

$$\dim (X_j) = k_j \tag{5.2.34}$$

and we have proved

Lemma 5.2.3. *The dimension of the root space X_j equals the multiplicity of the characteristic root λ_j.*

We can now return to the differential equation (5.2.20) for the singular case and start with the homogeneous equation.

Lemma 5.2.4. *If $\mathcal{A}$ is singular and $\lambda = 0$ is a k-fold characteristic root with idempotent $\mathcal{P}$ and nilpotent $\mathcal{Q}$, then the equation*

$$\mathbf{y}'(t) = \mathcal{A}\mathbf{y}(t) \tag{5.2.35}$$

has k linearly independent polynomial solutions of the form

$$\mathbf{y}(t) = \left\{\mathcal{P} + \mathcal{Q}t + \frac{1}{2!}\mathcal{Q}^2 t^2 + \cdots + \frac{1}{(k-1)!}\mathcal{Q}^{k-1}t^{k-1}\right\}\mathbf{v}, \tag{5.2.36}$$

where $\mathbf{v}$ *runs through a system of linearly independent basis vectors of the root space of* $\mathcal{A}$ *for* $\lambda = 0$.

Proof. That these vector polynomials are solutions follows from (5.2.13) if we multiply the expression there given for exp $(\mathcal{A}t)$ on the right by a vector $\mathbf{v}$ belonging to the root space of $\mathcal{A}$ for $\lambda = 0$. To apply the formula we identify λ_1 with 0, $\mathcal{E}_1$ with $\mathcal{I}$, $\mathcal{Q}_1$ with $\mathcal{Q}$. If now $\mathbf{v} \in X_1$, then $\mathbf{v}$ is annihilated by $\mathcal{E}_j$ and $\mathcal{Q}_j$ for $j \neq 1$. In this case there are k linearly independent choices for $\mathbf{v}$ and hence k linearly independent solutions since any linear relation between the functions $\mathbf{y}(t)$ involves the corresponding linear relation between the $\mathbf{v}$'s. Each solution is a vector polynomial in t of degree at most $k - 1$. ∎

In order to handle the non-homogeneous singular case we need one more auxiliary result from matrix algebra.

Lemma 5.2.5. *If* $\mathcal{A}$ *is a singular matrix, if* $\lambda = 0$ *is a characteristic root of multiplicity* k, *and if* X_1 *is the corresponding root space, then there exist* k *linearly independent vectors* $\mathbf{v}_1, \mathbf{v}_2, \ldots, \mathbf{v}_k$ *in* X *such that*

$$\begin{aligned} \mathcal{A}\mathbf{v}_1 &= \mathbf{0}, \\ \mathcal{A}\mathbf{v}_2 &= \alpha_{21}\mathbf{v}_1, \\ &\cdots\cdots\cdots\cdots \\ \mathcal{A}\mathbf{v}_k &= \alpha_{k1}\mathbf{v}_1 + \alpha_{k2}\mathbf{v}_2 + \cdots + \alpha_{k,k-1}\mathbf{v}_{k-1}. \end{aligned} \tag{5.2.37}$$

Proof. If $X_1 = V_1$, this is trivial, for any choice of k linearly independent vectors in X_1 forms as basis with the desired property, all coefficients α_{jk} being zero.

If $V_1 \subset X_1$, we can find an integer m, $m \leq k$, such that $\mathcal{A}^m\mathbf{v} = 0$ for all $\mathbf{v} \in X_1$. If m is the least such integer, there exists a vector $\mathbf{v}_0 \in X_1$ such that $\mathcal{A}^{m-1}\mathbf{v}_0 \neq 0$. We then set

$$\mathbf{v}_1 = \mathcal{A}^{m-1}\mathbf{v}_0, \mathbf{v}_2 = \mathcal{A}^{m-2}\mathbf{v}_0, \ldots, \mathbf{v}_m = \mathbf{v}_0$$

and observe that

$$\mathcal{A}\mathbf{v}_1 = \mathbf{0}, \mathcal{A}\mathbf{v}_j = \mathbf{v}_{j-1}, \qquad j = 2, 3, \ldots, m.$$

It is a simple matter to show that these vectors are linearly independent and they all belong to X_1 since any vector which is annihilated by some power of $\mathcal{A}$ belongs to X_1. If $m = k$, we are through. If not, let W_m be the subspace of X spanned by $\mathbf{v}_1, \mathbf{v}_2, \ldots, \mathbf{v}_m$, and consider the quotient space $X^* = X_1/W_m$. Its elements are residue classes $(\mathbf{w} + W_m)$ and X^* is mapped into itself by $\mathcal{A}$. Let $m_1 \leq m$ be the least integer such that $\mathcal{A}^{m_1}$ maps X^* into the zero element $(\mathbf{0} + W_m)$ while there exists at least one residue class, $(\mathbf{w}_0 + W_m)$ say, which is not annihilated by $\mathcal{A}^{m_1-1}$. We then set

$$\mathbf{v}_{m+1} = \mathcal{A}^{m_1-1}\mathbf{w}_0, \mathbf{v}_{m+2} = \mathcal{A}^{m_1-2}\mathbf{w}_0, \ldots, \mathbf{v}_{m+m_1} = \mathbf{w}_0.$$

These new vectors, together with $\mathbf{v}_1, \ldots, \mathbf{v}_m$, are linearly independent and satisfy equations of the form (5.2.37). We can repeat the process until we reach a set of k vectors. Since we get at least one new admissible basis vector each time, the process comes to an end. ∎

We can now state and prove the main result due to H. Kneser (1950).

Theorem 5.2.1. *Let $\mathcal{A}$ be a singular matrix with $\lambda = 0$ a characteristic root of multiplicity k. Let $\mathbf{f}(t)$ be a vector polynomial of degree p. Then the equation*

$$\mathbf{y}'(t) = \mathcal{A}\mathbf{y}(t) + \mathbf{f}(t) \tag{5.2.38}$$

has solutions which are vector polynomials of degree $\leq k + p$ and the manifold of such solutions is of dimension k.

Proof. Let X_1 be the root space of $\mathcal{A}$ for $\lambda = 0$ and let $\mathbf{v}_1, \mathbf{v}_2, \ldots, \mathbf{v}_k$ be a basis of X_1 the A-transforms of which satisfy equations of type (5.2.37). Then every vector $\mathbf{v} \in C^n$ admits a unique representation

$$\mathbf{v} = \beta_1\mathbf{v}_1 + \beta_2\mathbf{v}_2 + \cdots + \beta_k\mathbf{v}_k + \mathbf{w},$$

where $\mathbf{w} \in C^n \ominus X_1 \equiv X_0$. We note that $\mathcal{A}$ restricted to X_0 is non-singular, i.e. there exists a regular matrix $\mathcal{C}$ such that

$$\mathcal{A}\mathbf{x} = \mathcal{C}\mathbf{x} \qquad \text{for} \quad \mathbf{x} \in X_0.$$

This follows from the fact that $\mathcal{A}\mathbf{x} = \mathbf{0}$ for $\mathbf{x} \in X_0$ implies $\mathbf{x} = \mathbf{0}$.

We now represent the vectors $\mathbf{f}$ and $\mathbf{y}$ in the form

$$\mathbf{f}(t) = f_1(t)\mathbf{v}_1 + \cdots + f_k(t)\mathbf{v}_k + \mathbf{f}_0(t), \tag{5.2.39}$$

$$\mathbf{y}(t) = y_1(t)\mathbf{v}_1 + \cdots + y_k(t)\mathbf{v}_k + \mathbf{y}_0(t) \tag{5.2.40}$$

where $\mathbf{f}_0(t)$ and $\mathbf{y}_0(t)$ lie in X_0. Substitution into (5.2.38) gives

$$\sum_{j=1}^{k} y_j'(t)\mathbf{v}_j + \mathbf{y}_0'(t) = \sum_{j=1}^{k} y_j(t) \sum_{m=1}^{j-1} \alpha_{jm}\mathbf{v}_m + \mathcal{C}\mathbf{y}_0(t)$$
$$+ \sum_{j=1}^{k} f_j(t)\mathbf{v}_j + \mathbf{f}_0(t).$$

Since the representation in terms of basis vectors is unique, we can identify coefficients of $\mathbf{v}_j$ on both sides. This leads to the system

$$y_j'(t) = \sum_{m=j+1}^{k} \alpha_{mj}y_m(t) + f_j(t), \qquad j = 1, 2, \ldots, k, \tag{5.2.41}$$

$$\mathbf{y}_0'(t) = \mathcal{C}\mathbf{y}_0(t) + \mathbf{f}_0(t). \tag{5.2.42}$$

We attack the equations in the first set in reversed order. Since

$$y_k'(t) = f_k(t),$$

$y_k(t)$ is determined up to an arbitrary constant of integration and is a polynomial of degree $1 + \deg(f_k) \le p + 1$. Since

$$y_{k-1}'(t) = \alpha_{k,k-1}y_k(t) + f_{k-1}(t),$$

another integration will give $y_{k-1}(t)$. In this way we determine successively $y_k, y_{k-1}, \ldots, y_2, y_1$. Here $y_j(t)$ involves $k - j + 1$ integrations and its degree does not exceed $p + k - j + 1$.

Next, since $\mathfrak{C}$ is regular, (5.2.42) has the unique solution

$$\mathbf{y}_0(t) = -\mathfrak{C}^{-1}\mathbf{f}_0(t) - \mathfrak{C}^{-2}\mathbf{f}_0'(t) - \cdots - \mathfrak{C}^{-p-1}\mathbf{f}_0^{(p)}(t),$$

a polynomial of the same degree as $\mathbf{f}_0$. Combining these expressions we obtain $\mathbf{y}(t)$. ▌

The solution is not unique owing to the k constants of integration. Let $\mathbf{p}^0(t)$ be the particular solution corresponding to taking each constant of integration to be 0. The general solution is then of the form

$$\mathbf{p}^0(t) + \mathbf{P}(t), \tag{5.2.43}$$

where $\mathbf{P}(t)$ is a vector polynomial of degree $\le k - 1$ taking values in X_1. If $C_1, \ldots, C_k$ are the successive constants of integration, then

$$\mathbf{P}(0) = (C_k, C_{k-1}, \ldots, C_2, C_1)$$

and $\mathbf{P}(t)$ is uniquely determined by $\mathbf{P}(0)$. It follows that the dimension of the manifold of solutions (5.2.43) is the same as that of the vectors $\mathbf{P}(0)$ which is k since every vector in X_1 is a possible $\mathbf{P}(0)$.

EXERCISE 5.2

Find the canonical expansion (5.2.13) for $\exp(\mathcal{A}t)$ if $\mathcal{A}$ is

1. $\begin{bmatrix} 1 & 1 \\ 0 & 1 \end{bmatrix}$.

2. $\begin{bmatrix} 1 & 1 & 0 \\ 0 & 1 & 0 \\ 0 & 0 & 1 \end{bmatrix}$. Note that $\lambda = 1$ is a pole of order 2 (not 3) of $\mathfrak{R}(\lambda, \mathcal{A})$.

Find the solution of (5.2.21) if

3. $\mathcal{A}$ is as in No. 1 and

$$\mathcal{F}(t) = \begin{bmatrix} 1 & t \\ 0 & 1 \end{bmatrix}.$$

4. $\mathcal{A}$ is as in No. 2 and

$$\mathcal{F}(t) = \begin{bmatrix} 1 & t & t^2 \\ t & t^2 & 1 \\ t^2 & 1 & t \end{bmatrix}.$$

5. If $\mathcal{J}$ is an idempotent matrix, find $\exp(\mathcal{J}t)$ and estimate its norm for $t > 0$.
6. If $\mathcal{Q}$ is a nilpotent matrix, find $\exp(\mathcal{Q}t)$ and estimate its norm for $t > 0$.
7. If $q \in \mathfrak{B}$ is quais-nilpotent, show that

$$\lim_{t\to\infty} t^{-1} \log \| \exp(qt)\| = 0.$$

8. How should α be chosen in order that

$$\lim_{t\to\infty} e^{-\alpha t} \exp(\mathcal{A}t) = 0?$$

9. Show that there is a half-plane $\Re(\lambda) > \alpha$ in which the integral

$$\int_0^\infty e^{-\lambda s} \exp(\mathcal{A}s)\, ds$$

converges in norm and equals $\mathcal{R}(\lambda, \mathcal{A})$. This formula may be regarded as the inverse of (5.2.11).

10. Determine the spectrum of $\exp(\mathcal{A}t)$. If $\mu(t)$ is a spectral value, show the existence of a matrix $\mathcal{X}$, $\mathcal{X} \neq 0$, such that $\mathcal{X}$ is independent of t and $\exp(\mathcal{A}t)\mathcal{X} = \mu(t)\mathcal{X}$.
11. Suppose that $\Re(\lambda_{p-1}) < \Re(\lambda_p)$ and show that

$$\lim_{n\to\infty} \|\exp(\mathcal{A}nt)\|^{1/n} = \exp[\Re(\lambda_p)t], \qquad 0 < t.$$

12. Verify that the rank of a matrix with 0 as a characteristic root of multiplicity m is at least $n - m$.
13. Verify that the vectors $\mathbf{v}_j$ introduced in the proof of Lemma 5.2.5 are linearly independent.
14. Take $k = 3$ and find $\mathbf{P}(t)$ explicitly in terms of C_1, C_2, C_3 and the coefficients α_{jk}.

5.3 INFINITE MATRICES

Let us consider briefly some aspects of the theory of differential equations involving infinite matrices. There is no question of a systematic discussion; even if such a discussion were possible, it could not be confined to the available space. Instead we shall point out some of the novel features which arise in the infinite case.

First let us observe that the discussion of the equation

$$\mathcal{Y}'(t) = \mathcal{A}\mathcal{Y}(t) \tag{5.3.1}$$

presents no novel features, if the matrix $\mathcal{A}$ belongs to the B-algebra $\mathfrak{M}_\infty$ made up of matrices $\mathcal{B}$ for which

$$\|\mathcal{B}\| = \sup_j \sum_{k=1}^{\infty} |b_{jk}| < \infty. \tag{5.3.2}$$

Here the equation has the unique solution

$$\mathcal{Y}(t; 0, \mathcal{E}) = \exp(\mathcal{A}t) \tag{5.3.3}$$

belonging to $\mathfrak{M}_\infty$ and taking on the value $\mathcal{E}$ at $t = 0$.

We are likely to run into a much more complicated situation when $\mathcal{A}$ no longer belongs to $\mathfrak{M}_\infty$. We have had glimpses of this possibility already in Section 2.2. There we saw that the equation

$$\mathbf{y}'(t) = (j\delta_{jk})\mathbf{y}(t), \; \mathbf{y}(0) = \left\{\frac{1}{n^3}\right\} \tag{5.3.4}$$

has a unique solution in (l) for $t \leq 0$ but no solution for $t > 0$. Thus the equation distinguishes between left and right or, with t as time variable, between past and future. Similarly, the equation

$$\mathbf{y}'(t) = ((-1)^j j\delta_{jk})\mathbf{y}(t), \; \mathbf{y}(0) = \left\{\frac{1}{n^3}\right\}, \tag{5.3.5}$$

has no solution in (l) for any $t \neq 0$. This may be regarded as a defect of the space rather than of the equation. There are abstract spaces to which the solution belongs for all t. Let L be the space of all sequences $\{x_n\}$ such that

$$\|\{x_n\}\| \equiv \sum_1^\infty e^{-n^2}|x_n| < \infty, \tag{5.3.6}$$

then obviously for all t

$$\left\{\frac{1}{n^3}\, e^{(-1)^n nt}\right\} \in L.$$

There are other simple equations exhibiting various peculiar features. A rich source of such equations are the so-called *equations of Kolmogorov* in the theory of stochastic processes. A matrix $\mathcal{A} = (a_{jk})$ is a *Kolmogorov matrix* if the following three conditions are satisfied:

i) $a_{jj} < 0$,
ii) $a_{jk} \geq 0$ if $j \neq k$, and
iii) $\sum_{k=1}^\infty a_{jk} \leq 0$ for $j = 1, 2, 3, \ldots$

If $\mathcal{A}$ is a Kolmogorov matrix, then the equation

$$\mathcal{Y}'(t) = \mathcal{A}\mathcal{Y}(t) \tag{5.3.7}$$

is satisfied by a probability matrix $\mathcal{P}(t) = (p_{jk}(t))$, not necessarily unique where $0 \leq p_{jk}(t) \leq 1$ and $\sum_{k=1}^\infty p_{jk}(t) \leq 1$. Besides these "respectable" solutions, we may expect a profusion of "pathological" solutions of no interest to probability. But they are of interest to the theory of differential equations and we shall be concerned with some special cases.

The choice

$$a_{n,n-1} = n - 1, \quad a_{nn} = -n, \quad a_{n,n+1} = 1, \quad a_{jk} = 0 \quad \text{otherwise,} \tag{5.3.8}$$

gives a Kolmogorov matrix. Taking a column of the $\mathcal{Y}(t)$-matrix we are led to the system of equations

$$\begin{aligned} y_1'(t) &= -y_1(t) + y_2(t), \\ y_2'(t) &= y_1(t) - 2y_2(t) + y_3(t), \\ &\cdots\cdots\cdots\cdots \\ y_n'(t) &= (n-1)y_{n-1}(t) - ny_n(t) + y_{n+1}(t), \\ &\cdots\cdots\cdots\cdots \end{aligned} \tag{5.3.9}$$

We construct solutions of this system by the following device. Let $f(t)$ be a function defined in some interval where it has derivatives of all orders. The function may be analytic but this is not necessary for the argument. We set arbitrarily

$$y_1(t) = f(t). \tag{5.3.10}$$

If this value is substituted in the first equation, we see that $y_2(t)$ is uniquely determined in terms of $f(t)$. Then the second equation will give $y_3(t)$ and so on. We get

$$\begin{aligned} y_2(t) &= f'(t) + f(t), \\ y_3(t) &= f''(t) + 3f'(t) + f(t) \\ &\cdots\cdots\cdots\cdots \\ y_{n+1}(t) &= P_n(D)[f], \qquad D = \frac{d}{dt}, n \geq 1. \end{aligned} \tag{5.3.11}$$

Here $P_n(\lambda)$ is a polynomial of degree n having positive integral coefficients.

These polynomials are closely related to the matrix $\mathcal{A}$; in fact, they are components of a characteristic vector of $\mathcal{A}$ corresponding to the characteristic value λ. Thus if we set

$$(\lambda\mathcal{E} - \mathcal{A})\mathbf{x}(\lambda) = 0, \ \mathbf{x}(\lambda) = \{x_n(\lambda)\}, \tag{5.3.12}$$

then we get the system of equations

$$\begin{aligned} x_2(\lambda) &= (\lambda + 1)x_1(\lambda), \\ x_3(\lambda) &= (\lambda + 2)x_2(\lambda) - x_1(\lambda), \\ &\cdots\cdots\cdots\cdots \\ x_{n+1}(\lambda) &= (\lambda + n)x_n(\lambda) - (n-1)x_{n-1}(\lambda), \\ &\cdots\cdots\cdots\cdots \end{aligned} \tag{5.3.13}$$

If we set $x_1(\lambda) \equiv 1$, then $x_{n+1}(\lambda) = P_n(\lambda)$.

It is desired to show that the polynomials defined by (5.3.13) are the same as those which figure in (5.3.11). We note that if

$$P_n(\lambda) = (\lambda + n)P_{n-1}(\lambda) - (n - 1)P_{n-2}(\lambda),$$

then for any f having derivatives of all orders we have the identity

$$P_n(D)f = (D + n)P_{n-1}(D)f - (n - 1)P_{n-2}(D)f,$$

whence

$$DP_{n-1}(D)f = (n - 1)P_{n-2}(D)f - nP_{n-1}(D)f + P_n(D)f.$$

Thus, if we set

$$P_n(D)[f](t) \equiv y_{n+1}(t),$$

then

$$y_n'(t) = (n - 1)y_{n-1}(t) - ny_n(t) + y_{n+1}(t),$$

i.e. the equations (5.3.11) are satisfied and the identity of the polynomials is proved.

The polynomial $P_n(\lambda)$ is of the form

$$P_n(\lambda) = \lambda^n + a_{1,n}\lambda^{n-1} + a_{2,n}\lambda^{n-2} + \cdots + a_{n-1,n}\lambda + 1, \quad (5.3.14)$$

where obviously all coefficients are integers. Using an induction argument we can show that $a_{j,n} > 0$ for all j and n. We set $\lambda = 1$ and write $P_n(1) = S_n$. Substituting in (5.3.13) and adding the first n equations we get the recursion formula

$$S_n = nS_{n-1} + 1. \quad (5.3.15)$$

Since $S_1 = 1$, it is an easy matter to verify by induction that

$$S_n \leq 3 \cdot n! - 1. \quad (5.3.16)$$

It follows that

$$|P_n(\lambda)| < 3n! \max(1, |\lambda|^n) \quad (5.3.17)$$

and consequently for all λ

$$\{P_n(\lambda)\} \in L. \quad (5.3.18)$$

If suitable restrictions are imposed on the rate of growth of $|f^{(n)}(t)|$ as a function of n, we can also attain that

$$\{P_n(D)[f](t)\} \in L. \quad (5.3.19)$$

For this to be the case it is sufficient that there exist positive numbers c, k, and M such that for all n and all t in $[a, b]$

$$|f^{(n)}(t)| \leq Mc^n(n!)^k. \quad (5.3.20)$$

If f is analytic, then such an estimate holds automatically with $k = 1$ on any compact subset of the domain of definition. But if f is merely supposed to have derivatives of all orders, then (5.3.20) is a restriction.

Combining (5.3.17) and (5.3.20) we see that if $c \leq 1$

$$|P_n(D)[f](t)| \leq 3Mc^n(n!)^{k+1} \tag{5.3.21}$$

and (5.3.19) obviously holds.

An interesting special case is obtained by taking

$$f(t) = \exp(-t^{-2}), \qquad t \neq 0, f(0) = 0.$$

This function has derivatives of all orders and it may be shown that (5.3.20) holds, say for $k = 2$ and some choice of c. The importance of this example lies in the fact that, t being real, $f(t)$ has derivatives of all orders at $t = 0$ and all these derivatives are zero. This in turn implies that the corresponding functions $P_n(D)[f](t)$ vanish at $t = 0$ together with all their derivatives. This means that the equations (5.3.9) have a solution, not identically zero, which is in L such that the initial values for $t = 0$ are given by the zero vector. Such a solution is known as a *null solution.*

The existence of a null solution implies that the initial value problem for (5.3.9) does not have a unique solution since we can always add a null solution to whatever solution has been found. We observe that, in the present case, not merely does the solution vector vanish for $t = 0$ but also the derived vectors of all orders.

The system (5.3.9) offers several interesting features. We have noted solutions depending upon an arbitrary function and the existence of null solutions with resulting lack of uniqueness of initial value problems. We observe also the existence of analytic solutions with singular points the position and nature of which have no apparent relation to the coefficient matrix $\mathcal{A}$.

The following example exhibits somewhat different features. The system is not a Kolmogoroff equation in the sense used above, but the transposed matrix is a Kolmogoroff matrix and both types occur in the theory of probability. We take

$$a_{jk} = 0,\ k < j,\ a_{jj} = -j,\ a_{jk} = 1,\ k > j, \tag{5.3.22}$$

so that the system becomes

$$y_j'(t) + jy_j(t) = \sum_{k=j+1}^{\infty} y_k(t), \qquad j = 1, 2, 3, \ldots \tag{5.3.23}$$

Here the equations are meaningless unless the series on the right are convergent. This suggests that we should look for solutions in (l). Such solutions can be found by different methods. The following is due to G. E. H. Reuter (oral communication).

Suppose that the system has a solution in (l) for $t > 0$ and that $\{y_n(0)\}$ is a given element of (l). We set

$$z_n(t) = \sum_{k=n+1}^{\infty} y_k(t).$$

Then $\{z_n(t)\}$ is the sequence of remainders of a convergent series. We have

$$y_n(t) = z_{n-1}(t) - z_n(t)$$

which we substitute in (5.3.23). We know that $y_n(t)$ is differentiable for $t > 0$; we suppose that $z_n(t)$ has the same property so that

$$y_n'(t) = z_{n-1}'(t) - z_n'(t).$$

This gives

$$z_{n-1}'(t) + nz_{n-1}(t) = z_n'(t) + (n + 1)z_n(t).$$

It follows that the right member is independent of n and is a function of t alone. We set this function equal to $f(t)$.

The original initial value problem has now been transformed into the following form. Solve

$$z_n'(t) + (n + 1)z_n(t) = f(t),\ z_n(0) = \left\{\sum_{n+1}^{\infty} y_k(0)\right\}, \tag{5.3.24}$$

Here $f(t)$ is supposed to be a given function which we assume to be continuous for $t \geq 0$. The solution is immediate

$$z_n(t) = z_n(0)\, e^{-(n+1)t} + \int_0^t e^{(n+1)(s-t)} f(s)\, ds. \tag{5.3.25}$$

Replacing n by $n - 1$ and subtracting we get

$$y_n(t) = z_{n-1}(0)\, e^{-nt} - z_n(0)\, e^{-(n+1)t} + \int_0^t e^{n(s-t)}(1 - e^{s-t}) f(s)\, ds. \tag{5.3.26}$$

As $t \to 0$ we see that

$$y_n(t) \to z_{n-1}(0) - z_n(0) = y_n(0).$$

Further

$$\sum_1^{\infty} |y_n(t)| \leq \sum_1^{\infty} |z_{n-1}(0) - z_n(0)\, e^{-t}|\, e^{-nt} + \int_0^t e^{s-t}\, |f(s)|\, ds. \tag{5.3.27}$$

The sum on the right is dominated by

$$\sum_1^{\infty} |y_n(0)|\, e^{-nt} + \sum_1^{\infty} |z_n(0)|\, (1 - e^{-t})\, e^{-nt}.$$

This shows that the series in (5.3.27) converges for $t \geq 0$, uniformly in t on any finite interval $[0, \omega]$. On the other hand, the series normally diverges for every $t < 0$.

We can differentiate (5.3.26) with respect to t and verify that the equations (5.3.23) are satisfied. Thus we have obtained a solution vector $\{y_n(t)\}$ in (l) valid for any $t > 0$. This solution depends upon the initial values and also upon an arbitrary continuous function $f(t)$. Thus we have infinitely many solutions corresponding to the same initial vector $\{y_n(0)\}$. In particular, choosing $y_n(0) = 0$ for all n we get null solutions for any choice of $f(t)$. The equation distinguishes between past and future. It is not sufficient to define $f(t)$ for all t; unless the initial vector is chosen in a very special manner, the solution cannot be continued for negative values of t.

We have assumed the existence of $z_n'(t)$ for all $t > 0$. The assumption that $f(t)$ is continuous is sufficient to ensure this as is easily verified. This assumption also ensures the existence of $y_n''(t)$ for all t. We have

$$y_n''(t) = n^2 z_{n-1}(0)\, e^{-nt} - (n+1)^2 z_n(0)\, e^{-(n+1)t} + \int_0^t e^{n(s-t)}[n^2 - (n+1)^2\, e^{s-t}] f(s)\, ds + f(t),$$

and this shows that $y_n'''(t)$ exists iff $f'(t)$ exists. This is in great contrast to the situation in the previous problem where derivatives of all orders exist.

These indications should convince the reader that in dealing with infinite matrix equations nothing can be taken for granted.

EXERCISE 5.3

1. Why is $P_n(0) = 1$?
2. Verify (5.3.15).
3. Show that $y_n(t) = P_{n-1}(\lambda)e^{\lambda t}$ is a solution of (5.3.9).
4. Express $a_{j,n}$ in terms of $a_{k,n-1}$ and $a_{k,n-2}$. Show by induction that
$$a_{j-1,n} - a_{j-2,n-1} > a_{j-2,n-1} - a_{j-3,n-2} > 0$$
and use this to show that $a_{j,n} > 0$.
5. For $0 < t \leq \frac{1}{2}$ we can estimate the derivatives of $\exp(-t^{-2})$ by the following argument. We have
$$D^n \exp(-t^{-2}) = \frac{n!}{2\pi i}\int_\Gamma \exp(-s^{-2})(s-t)^{-n-1}\, ds$$
where Γ is made up of two circular arcs $u^2 + v^2 = \pm 2v$, $0 < u < 2t$, and the line $u = 2t$ where $s = u + iv$. The distance from t to Γ is $(1 + t^2)^{1/2} - 1$ and the maximum value of $|\exp(-s^{-2})|$ is reached at the two right vertices of Γ. Use this to estimate the integral and find an upper bound for the estimate as a function of t for fixed n.
6. Prove (5.3.27) and complete the proof of the uniform convergence.
7. Let $f(s) > 0$ for all real s and suppose that $y_n(0) = -n^{-2}$. Prove divergence of the series in the left member of (5.3.27) for $t < 0$.
8. Suppose that $f(t)$ is a bounded measurable function of t not necessarily continuous anywhere. Prove the existence of $y'(t)$ for $t > 0$ by forming the difference quotient and passing to the limit. Show that (5.3.26) still defines a solution of the system (5.3.23) and show that $y_n''(t)$ need not exist for all t but only almost everywhere.

9. An alternate method of solving (5.3.23) is to introduce $F(t) = \sum_{n=1}^{\infty} y_n(t)$ as the known function, assumed to be continuous, and to recover the component functions $y_n(t)$ by recurrence from the equations

$$y_n'(t) + ny_n(t) = F(t) - y_1(t) - \cdots - y_n(t).$$

Solve the first two equations.

10. In using the preceding method one has to prove that $\sum_1^n y_k(t) \to F(t)$ as $n \to \infty$. This leads, among other things, to the problem of finding

$$\lim_{n\to\infty} n \int_0^t e^{n(s-t)} F(s)\, ds.$$

Show that the limit is $F(t)$.

5.4 ASYMPTOTICALLY CONSTANT COEFFICIENTS

We return to finite matrices and now assume that the equation is of the form

$$\mathcal{Y}'(t) = [\mathcal{A}_0 + \mathcal{A}_1(t)]\mathcal{Y}(t). \tag{5.4.1}$$

Here $\mathcal{A}_0$ is a constant n by n matrix, $\mathcal{A}_1(t)$ is defined and continuous for $0 \le t < \infty$ and shall also satisfy some integrability condition to be specified later. In some sense or other, $\mathcal{A}_1(t)$ is considered as a small *perturbation* for large values of t and the problem is to decide to what extent the properties of $\mathcal{Y}(t)$ reflect those of $\mathcal{U}(t)$, the solution of the equation

$$\mathcal{U}'(t) = \mathcal{A}_0\mathcal{U}(t), \tag{5.4.2}$$

where there is no perturbation. In particular we are concerned with boundedness and asymptotic behavior of $\mathcal{Y}(t) - \mathcal{U}(t)$. This is a fascinating problem with an extensive literature. We can give only a few results and for further details and other aspects of the problem we refer to the references at the end of this chapter.

We start by proving a result on boundedness.

Theorem 5.4.1. *If for some real* β,

$$\limsup_{t\to+\infty} \exp(-\beta t)\|\mathcal{U}(t)\| < \infty \tag{5.4.3}$$

for every solution of (5.4.2) *and if*

$$\int_0^\infty \|\mathcal{A}_1(s)\|\, ds < \infty, \tag{5.4.4}$$

then

$$\limsup_{t\to+\infty} \exp(-\beta t)\|\mathcal{Y}(t)\| < \infty \tag{5.4.5}$$

for every solution of (5.4.1). *In particular, if the solutions of* (5.4.2) *are bounded so are those of* (5.4.1).

Proof. Suppose that

$$\mathcal{Y}(0) = \mathcal{B}.$$

We have then

$$\mathcal{Y}(t) = \exp(\mathcal{A}_0 t)\mathcal{B} + \int_0^t \exp[\mathcal{A}_0(t - s)]\mathcal{A}_1(s)\mathcal{Y}(s)\,ds \tag{5.4.6}$$

as shown by differentiation. By assumption we can find an M such that

$$\|\exp(\mathcal{A}_0 t)\| \leq M \exp(\beta t),\ 0 \leq t.$$

We have then

$$\|\mathcal{Y}(t)\| \leq M\|\mathcal{B}\| \exp(\beta t) + M \int_0^t \exp[\beta(t - s)]\|\mathcal{A}_1(s)\|\ \|\mathcal{Y}(s)\|\,ds$$

whence

$$\exp(-\beta t)\|\mathcal{Y}(t)\| \leq M\|\mathcal{B}\| + M \int_0^t \|\mathcal{A}_1(s)\| \exp(-\beta s)\|\mathcal{Y}(s)\|\,ds$$

and, by Theorem 1.5.7,

$$\exp(-\beta t)\|\mathcal{Y}(t)\| \leq M\|\mathcal{B}\| \exp\left[M \int_0^t \|\mathcal{A}_1(s)\|\,ds\right] \tag{5.4.7}$$

proving (5.4.5). ∎

Next let us have a look at the case where $\mathcal{A}_0$ is the zero matrix. This implies that $\mathcal{Y}(t)$ is bounded. We shall show that it tends to a limit. This is actually a special case of a result to be proved in Chapter 6, Theorem 6.4.4.

Theorem 5.4.2. *If $\mathcal{U}(t)$ is a solution of*

$$\mathcal{U}'(t) = \mathcal{A}_1(t)\mathcal{U}(t), \tag{5.4.8}$$

where $\|\mathcal{A}_1(t)\| \in L(0, \infty)$, then there exists a constant matrix $\mathcal{U}_0$ such that

$$\lim_{t\to\infty} \mathcal{U}(t) = \mathcal{U}_0. \tag{5.4.9}$$

Here $\mathcal{U}_0 = 0$ iff $\mathcal{U}(t) \equiv 0$.

Proof. Let us define

$$\mathcal{W}(t) \equiv \mathcal{U}(t) + \int_t^\infty \mathcal{A}_1(s)\mathcal{U}(s)\,ds. \tag{5.4.10}$$

The integral exists since $\|\mathcal{A}_1(s)\| \in L(0, \infty)$ and $\|\mathcal{U}(s)\|$ is bounded by Theorem 5.4.1. Then

$$\mathcal{W}'(t) = \mathcal{U}'(t) - \mathcal{A}_1(t)\mathcal{U}(t) \equiv 0$$

and

$$\mathcal{W}(t) = \mathcal{U}_0,$$

a constant matrix. This gives

$$\mathcal{U}(t) = \mathcal{U}_0 - \int_t^\infty \mathcal{A}_1(s)\mathcal{U}(s)\,ds \tag{5.4.11}$$

and this implies (5.4.9). We can estimate the rate of convergence to the limit in the usual manner. Since

$$\|\mathcal{U}(t)\| \le \|\mathcal{U}_0\| + \int_t^\infty \|\mathcal{A}_1(s)\| \, \|\mathcal{U}(s)\| \, ds,$$

we have

$$\|\mathcal{U}(t)\| \le \|\mathcal{U}_0\| \exp\left[\int_t^\infty \|\mathcal{A}_1(s)\| \, ds\right]$$

and

$$\|\mathcal{U}(t) - \mathcal{U}_0\| \le \|\mathcal{U}_0\| \left\{\exp\left[\int_t^\infty \|\mathcal{A}_1(s)\| \, ds\right] - 1\right\}. \tag{5.4.12}$$

Cf. Problem 7, Exercise 1.5. It is clear that $\mathcal{U}_0 = 0$ iff $\mathcal{U}(t) \equiv 0$. ▮

We prove next a generalization of this result for the case when $\mathcal{A}_0 \neq 0$ under fairly severe restrictions on $\|\mathcal{A}_1(t)\|$.

Theorem 5.4.3. *Suppose that $\mathcal{Y}(t)$ is a solution of* (5.4.1) *and that*

$$\int_0^\infty \|\exp(-\mathcal{A}_0 s)\mathcal{A}_1(s) \exp(\mathcal{A}_0 s)\| \, ds < \infty. \tag{5.4.13}$$

Then there exists a matrix $\mathcal{U}_0$ such that

$$\lim_{t\to\infty} \exp(-\mathcal{A}_0 t)\mathcal{Y}(t) = \mathcal{U}_0. \tag{5.4.14}$$

Here $\mathcal{U}_0 = 0$ iff $\mathcal{Y}(t) \equiv 0$.

Proof. Let us set

$$\mathcal{Y}(t) = \exp(\mathcal{A}_0 t)\mathcal{U}(t). \tag{5.4.15}$$

Then

$$\mathcal{A}_0 \exp(\mathcal{A}_0 t)\mathcal{U}(t) + \exp(\mathcal{A}_0 t)\mathcal{U}'(t) = \mathcal{A}_0 \exp(\mathcal{A}_0 t)\mathcal{U}(t) + \mathcal{A}_1(t) \exp(\mathcal{A}_0 t)\mathcal{U}(t)$$

or

$$\mathcal{U}'(t) = \exp(-\mathcal{A}_0 t)\mathcal{A}_1(t) \exp(\mathcal{A}_0 t)\mathcal{U}(t).$$

By virtue of (5.4.13) the assumptions of the preceding theorem are satisfied and we conclude the existence of a constant matrix $\mathcal{U}_0$ such that

$$\lim_{t\to\infty} \mathcal{U}(t) = \mathcal{U}_0. \tag{5.4.16}$$

Formula (5.4.12) also applies and gives the estimate

$$\|\mathcal{U}(t) - \mathcal{U}_0\| \le \|\mathcal{U}_0\| \left\{\exp\left[\int_t^\infty \|\exp(-\mathcal{A}_0 s)\mathcal{A}_1(s) \exp(\mathcal{A}_0 s)\| \, ds\right] - 1\right\}. \tag{5.4.17}$$

These relations obviously imply (5.4.14). ▮

Condition (5.4.13) is rather severe. Suppose that the spectrum of $\mathcal{A}_0$ is confined to the open strip

$$\alpha < \Re(\lambda) < \beta. \tag{5.4.18}$$

We have then for $0 \le s$

$$\|\exp(\mathcal{A}_0 s)\| \le M \exp(\beta s), \ \|\exp(-\mathcal{A}_0 s)\| \le M \exp(-\alpha s)$$

so that (5.4.13) holds if

$$\int_0^\infty \exp[(\beta - \alpha)s] \|\mathcal{A}_1(s)\| \, ds < \infty. \tag{5.4.19}$$

In certain cases we can circumvent this condition, however.

Theorem 5.4.4. *Suppose that $\mathcal{A}_0 = \gamma \mathcal{I}$ where γ is a complex number with positive real part and $\mathcal{I}$ is an idempotent matrix. Suppose further that*

$$\mathcal{A}_1(s) = \mathcal{I}\mathcal{A}_1(s). \tag{5.4.20}$$

If now $\|\mathcal{A}_1(s)\| \in L(0, \infty)$, we have

$$\mathcal{Y}(t) = \exp(\gamma \mathcal{I} t)[\mathcal{U}_0 + \mathcal{R}(t)], \tag{5.4.21}$$

where $\mathcal{R}(t) = \mathcal{I}\mathcal{R}(t)$ and there is an a, $a > 0$, such that

$$\|\mathcal{R}(t)\| \le \|\mathcal{U}_0\| \left\{ \exp\left[a \int_t^\infty \|\mathcal{A}_1(s)\| \, ds \right] - 1 \right\}. \tag{5.4.22}$$

If $\mathcal{I}\mathcal{Y}(0) = \mathcal{Y}(0)$, then $\mathcal{I}\mathcal{U}_0 = \mathcal{U}_0$ and $\mathcal{I}\mathcal{Y}(t) = \mathcal{Y}(t)$ for all t.

Proof. We have

$$\exp(-\gamma \mathcal{I} s) = \mathcal{I} \exp(-\gamma s) + (\mathcal{E} - \mathcal{I}),$$
$$\exp(\gamma \mathcal{I} s) = \mathcal{I} \exp(\gamma s) + (\mathcal{E} - \mathcal{I}),$$

so that

$$\begin{aligned} \exp(-\gamma \mathcal{I} s)\mathcal{A}_1(s) \exp(\gamma \mathcal{I} s) &= \mathcal{I}\mathcal{A}_1(s)\mathcal{I} + \mathcal{I}\mathcal{A}_1(s)(\mathcal{E} - \mathcal{I}) \exp(-\gamma s) \\ &\quad + (\mathcal{E} - \mathcal{I})\mathcal{A}_1(s)\mathcal{I} \exp(\gamma s) + (\mathcal{E} - \mathcal{I})\mathcal{A}_1(s)(\mathcal{E} - \mathcal{I}) \\ &= \mathcal{A}_1(s)\mathcal{I} + \mathcal{A}_1(s)(\mathcal{E} - \mathcal{I}) \exp(-\gamma s), \end{aligned}$$

since the other terms drop out by virtue of (5.4.20). It is clear that the norm of this expression does not exceed some constant a times $\|\mathcal{A}_1(s)\|$. We can take $a = 1 + 2\|\mathcal{I}\|$, for instance. Hence condition (5.4.13) is satisfied as soon as $\|\mathcal{A}_1(s)\| \in L(0, \infty)$. It follows that the preceding theorem applies and shows the existence of a constant matrix $\mathcal{U}_0$ and a remainder term $\mathcal{R}(t)$, satisfying (5.4.22), such that (5.4.21) holds. Here

$$\begin{aligned} \mathcal{R}(t) &= -\int_t^\infty \exp(-\gamma \mathcal{I} s)\mathcal{A}_1(s) \exp(\gamma \mathcal{I} s)\mathcal{Y}(s) \, ds \\ &= -\int_t^\infty \mathcal{A}_1(s)[\mathcal{I} + (\mathcal{E} - \mathcal{I}) \exp(-\gamma s)]\mathcal{Y}(s) \, ds. \end{aligned}$$

This shows that $\mathcal{T}\mathcal{R}(t) = \mathcal{R}(t)$. Since

$$\mathcal{Y}(0) = \mathcal{U}_0 + \mathcal{R}(0) = \mathcal{U}_0 + \mathcal{T}\mathcal{R}(0),$$

we see that $\mathcal{T}\mathcal{Y}(0) = \mathcal{Y}(0)$ implies $\mathcal{T}\mathcal{U}_0 = \mathcal{U}_0$ and hence $\mathcal{T}\mathcal{Y}(t) = \mathcal{T}\mathcal{U}_0 + \mathcal{T}\mathcal{R}(t) = \mathcal{U}_0 + \mathcal{R}(t) = \mathcal{Y}(t)$ as asserted. ∎

It stands to reason that asymptotic relations should hold between $\mathcal{Y}(t)$ and $\exp(\mathcal{A}_0 t)$ under less restrictive assumptions than those of the last two theorems. This is indeed the case, and general results in this direction were proved by R. Bellman (1946) and by N. Levinson (1947). We shall give here essentially the results of Bellman.

Theorem 5.4.5. *Suppose that the matrix $\mathcal{A}_0$ has real distinct characteristic roots, $\lambda_1 < \lambda_2 < \cdots < \lambda_n$, and that*

$$\|\mathcal{A}_1(t)\| \in L(0, \infty). \tag{5.4.23}$$

Then the equation (5.4.1) *has a solution of the form*

$$\mathcal{Y}(t) = \sum_{k=1}^{n} [\mathcal{T}_k + \mathcal{R}_k(t)]\, e^{\lambda_k t}, \tag{5.4.24}$$

where $\mathcal{T}_k$ is the idempotent of $\mathcal{A}_0$ belonging to λ_k, i.e. $\mathcal{A}_0\mathcal{T}_k = \lambda_k\mathcal{T}_k$, and

$$\lim_{t\to\infty} \|\mathcal{R}_k(t)\| = 0. \tag{5.4.25}$$

Remark. The prototype of this theorem for linear differential equations of order n is due to H. Poincaré (1885). It has been shown by Levinson that the restriction to real distinct roots is not essential. We restrict ourselves to this simple case.

Proof. We start by reducing equation (5.4.1) to a more convenient normal form. Since $\mathcal{A}_0$ has distinct characteristic roots it can be reduced to diagonal form, i.e. there is a regular matrix $\mathcal{C}$ such that

$$\mathcal{C}\mathcal{A}_0\mathcal{C}^{-1} \equiv \mathcal{A} = (\delta_{jk}\lambda_k). \tag{5.4.26}$$

We set

$$\mathcal{C}\mathcal{Y}(t)\mathcal{C}^{-1} = \mathfrak{Z}(t),\ \mathcal{C}\mathcal{A}_1(t)\mathcal{C}^{-1} = \mathcal{B}(t)$$

and obtain

$$\mathfrak{Z}'(t) = [\mathcal{A} + \mathcal{B}(t)]\mathfrak{Z}(t), \tag{5.4.27}$$

where $\|\mathcal{B}(t)\| \in L(0, \infty)$.

Our problem is now to find an integral equation for $\mathfrak{Z}(t)$ which we can solve. Actually it is easier to deal with the individual elements $z_{jk}(t)$ of $\mathfrak{Z}(t)$. They satisfy the following system of equations

$$\begin{aligned} z_{jk}(t) &= \int_a^t e^{\lambda_j(t-s)} \left\{\sum_{m=1}^{n} b_{jm}(s) z_{mk}(s)\right\} ds, \qquad 1 \le j < k, \\ z_{jk}(t) &= \delta_{jk}\, e^{\lambda_k t} - \int_t^\infty e^{\lambda_j(t-s)} \left\{\sum_{m=1}^{n} b_{jm}(s) z_{mk}(s)\right\} ds,\ k \le j \le n, \end{aligned} \tag{5.4.28}$$

where $k = 1, 2, \ldots, n$. Here a is at our disposal, it will be chosen so large that

$$\beta \equiv \int_a^\infty \|\mathcal{B}(s)\| \, ds < \tfrac{1}{3}, \tag{5.4.29}$$

and $t > a$. If these equations can be solved, differentiation shows that the corresponding matrix $(z_{jk}(t))$ satisfies (5.4.27). We can simplify by writing

$$z_{jk}(t) = e^{\lambda_k t} v_{jk}(t). \tag{5.4.30}$$

Substitution shows that the v_{jk} satisfy the system

$$\begin{aligned} v_{jk}(t) &= \int_a^t \exp\,[(\lambda_j - \lambda_k)(t - s)] \left\{ \sum_{m=1}^n b_{jm}(s) v_{mk}(s) \right\} ds, \qquad 1 \le j < k, \\ v_{jk}(t) &= \delta_{jk} - \int_t^\infty \exp\,[(\lambda_j - \lambda_k)(t - s)] \left\{ \sum_{m=1}^n b_{jm}(s) v_{mk}(s) \right\} ds, \qquad k \le j. \end{aligned} \tag{5.4.31}$$

The two systems are equivalent; if one has a solution, so does the other.

We apply the method of successive approximations to the second system using

$$v_{jk}^{(0)}(t) = \delta_{jk}$$

as the initial approximation. This gives

$$v_{jk}^{(1)}(t) = \int_a^t \exp\,[(\lambda_j - \lambda_k)(t - s)] b_{jk}(s) \, ds, \qquad j < k,$$

$$v_{jk}^{(1)}(t) = \delta_{jk} - \int_t^\infty \exp\,[(\lambda_j - \lambda_k)(t - s)] b_{jk}(s) \, ds, \qquad k \le j.$$

Since the exponents are negative or zero in the respective intervals of integrations and $|b_{jk}(s)| \le \|\mathcal{B}(s)\|$ is in $L(0, \infty)$, the integrals exist and we obtain the estimate

$$|v_{jk}^{(1)}(t) - \delta_{jk}| < \beta$$

for all j and k. Suppose we have verified for some integer p the existence of the approximation and also the estimate

$$|v_{jk}^{(p)}(t) - v_{jk}^{(p-1)}(t)| < \beta^p, \qquad j, k = 1, 2, \ldots, n, \; a < t. \tag{5.4.32}$$

We have then for $j < k$

$$\begin{aligned} &|v_{jk}^{(p+1)}(t) - v_{jk}^{(p)}(t)| \\ &\quad \le \int_a^t \exp\,[(\lambda_j - \lambda_n)(t - s)] \left\{ \sum_{m=1}^n |b_{jm}(s)| \, |v_{mk}^{(p)}(s) - v_{mk}^{(p-1)}(s)| \right\} ds \\ &\quad \le \beta^p \int_a^t \sum_{m=1}^n |b_{jm}(s)| \, ds \le \beta^p \int_a^t \|\mathcal{B}(s)\| \, ds \le \beta^{p+1}, \end{aligned}$$

and this holds also for $j > k$. Since the induction hypothesis holds for $p = 1$, the inequality (5.4.32) holds for all p.

It follows that the series

$$v_{jk}(t) = v_{jk}^{(0)}(t) + \sum_{p=1}^{\infty} [v_{jk}^{(p)}(t) - v_{jk}^{(p-1)}(t)] \tag{5.4.33}$$

are absolutely convergent for all j, k and for $t > a$. Thus the solutions $v_{jk}(t)$ of the system (5.4.31) exist as bounded differentiable functions for $t > a$. Moreover

$$|v_{jk}(t) - \delta_{jk}| < \frac{\beta}{1 - \beta}. \tag{5.4.34}$$

We set

$$\mathfrak{V}(t) \equiv (v_{jk}(t)). \tag{5.4.35}$$

We now see that the functions $z_{jk}(t)$ of (5.4.30) exist and form a matrix $\mathfrak{Z}(t)$ satisfying (5.4.27).

Let $\mathfrak{E}_{kk}$ be the matrix with a one in the place (k, k) and zeros elsewhere and set

$$\mathfrak{Z}_k(t) = \mathfrak{Z}(t)\mathfrak{E}_{kk}. \tag{5.4.36}$$

The matrices $\mathfrak{Z}(t)$ and $\mathfrak{Z}_k(t)$ have the same k^{th} column, the other columns of $\mathfrak{Z}_k(t)$ are occupied by zeros. We set

$$\mathfrak{Z}_k(t) = [\mathfrak{E}_{kk} + \mathfrak{R}_k^*(t)]\, e^{\lambda_k t}, \tag{5.4.37}$$

where

$$\mathfrak{R}_k^*(t) = [\mathfrak{V}(t) - \mathfrak{E}]\mathfrak{E}_{kk}, \tag{5.4.38}$$

that is $\mathfrak{R}_k^*(t)$ is a matrix whose k^{th} column agrees with that of $\mathfrak{V}(t) - \mathfrak{E}$ and all other elements are 0. Using (5.4.34) we see that

$$\|\mathfrak{R}_k^*(t)\| < \frac{\beta}{1 - \beta}, \qquad a < t. \tag{5.4.39}$$

Actually we have a much stronger result, namely

$$\lim_{t \to \infty} \|\mathfrak{R}_k^*(t)\| = 0. \tag{5.4.40}$$

To get this we return to the integral equations (5.4.31). We know that they have bounded solutions. For $j < k$ we have the inequality

$$|v_{jk}(t)| \le \int_a^t \exp[(\lambda_j - \lambda_k)(t - s)] \left\{\sum_{m=1}^{n} |b_{jm}(s)|\, |v_{mk}(s)|\right\} ds.$$

In the right member

$$|v_{mk}(s)| < |v_{kk}(s)| < \tfrac{3}{2}, \qquad m \neq k,$$

by (5.4.34) and the choice of a. Further

$$\sum_{m=1}^{n} |b_{jm}(s)| \leq \|\mathcal{B}(s)\|.$$

Hence

$$|v_{jk}(t)| \leq \tfrac{3}{2} \int_a^t \exp\,[(\lambda_j - \lambda_k)(t - s)]\|\mathcal{B}(s)\|\, ds, \qquad 1 \leq j < k. \quad (5.4.41)$$

Similarly we get

$$|v_{jk}(t) - \delta_{jk}| \leq \tfrac{3}{2} \int_t^\infty \exp\,[(\lambda_j - \lambda_k)(t - s)]\|\mathcal{B}(s)\|\, ds, \qquad k \leq j. \quad (5.4.42)$$

The last expression tends to 0 when $t \to \infty$ since $(\lambda_j - \lambda_k)(t - s) \leq 0$ in the interval of integration.

The integral in (5.4.41) we break into two parts: the integral from a to $\frac{1}{2}t$ and the integral from $\frac{1}{2}t$ to t. They are dominated by

$$\tfrac{3}{2}\beta \exp\,[\tfrac{1}{2}(\lambda_j - \lambda_k)t] \quad \text{and} \quad \tfrac{3}{2} \int_{t/2}^t \|\mathcal{B}(s)\|\, ds,$$

respectively. Since $\lambda_j < \lambda_k$, both expressions tend to 0 as $t \to \infty$. Hence we have shown that

$$\lim_{t \to \infty} |v_{jk}(t) - \delta_{jk}| = 0 \quad (5.4.43)$$

for all j and k and this implies (5.4.40).

We can now return to equation (5.4.1). Its solution is

$$\mathcal{Y}(t) = \mathcal{C}^{-1}\mathfrak{Z}(t)\mathcal{C}.$$

Here

$$\mathcal{C}^{-1}\mathcal{E}_{kk}\mathcal{C} \equiv \mathcal{J}_k \quad (5.4.44)$$

is clearly an idempotent of $\mathfrak{M}_n$ and a simple calculation shows that

$$\mathcal{A}_0\mathcal{J}_k = \mathcal{J}_k\mathcal{A}_0 = \lambda_k\mathcal{J}_k. \quad (5.4.45)$$

For

$$\mathfrak{R}_k(t) = \mathcal{C}^{-1}\mathfrak{R}_k^*(t)\mathcal{C}$$

we get

$$\lim_{t = \infty} \|\mathfrak{R}_k(t)\| = 0$$

if (5.4.40) holds. This proves formulas (5.4.24) and (5.4.25). We observe that the matrices $\mathfrak{Z}_k(t)$ are linearly independent for large values of t so that $\mathfrak{Z}(t)$ is a fundamental solution of (5.4.27) for large t and hence for all t. This implies that $\mathcal{Y}(t)$ is a fundamental solution of (5.4.1). ∎

We observe that Theorems 5.4.1 to 5.4.4 extend to the case of a general B-algebra with only verbal changes. On the other hand, Theorem 5.4.5 is more special and extensions are doubtful.

We can apply Theorem 5.4.5 to various equations of the type

$$y^{(n)} + [a_1 + F_1(t)]y^{(n-1)} + \cdots + [a_n + F_n(t)]y = 0 \tag{5.4.46}$$

which can be reduced to the matrix case just treated. The essential assumption is that

$$F_j(t) \in L(0, \infty), \qquad j = 1, 2, \ldots, n. \tag{5.4.47}$$

The corresponding matrix $\mathcal{A}_0$ is

$$\mathcal{A}_0 = \begin{bmatrix} 0 & 1 & 0 & \cdots & 0 \\ 0 & 0 & 1 & \cdots & 0 \\ \cdot & \cdot & \cdot & \cdot & \cdot \\ 0 & 0 & 0 & \cdots & 1 \\ -a_n & -a_{n-1} & -a_{n-2} & \cdots & -a_n \end{bmatrix}, \tag{5.4.48}$$

while $\mathcal{A}_1(t)$ is obtained if in $\mathcal{A}_0$ we replace the ones by zeros and a_k by $F_k(t)$. From Theorem 5.4.5 we then conclude that equation (5.4.46) has n solutions of the form

$$y_k(t) = e^{\lambda_k t}[1 + o(1)], \qquad k = 1, 2, \ldots, n, \tag{5.4.49}$$

provided the roots of the characteristic equation are real and distinct.

It is clear that the other theorems also have applications to n^{th} order linear equations. The following special case is of considerable importance for the applications and will figure repeatedly in later chapters.

Theorem 5.4.6. *Given the second order linear differential equation*

$$y''(t) + [a^2 - F(t)]y(t) = 0, \; 0 < a, \; F(t) \in L(0, \infty). \tag{5.4.50}$$

Then every solution $y(t)$ of (5.4.50) is bounded and there is a uniquely determined function $w(t)$ with the following three properties:

$$y(t) = w(t) - \frac{1}{a}\int_t^\infty \sin a(s - t)F(s)y(s)\, ds, \tag{5.4.51}$$

$$w''(t) + a^2 w(t) = 0, \tag{5.4.52}$$

$$|y(t) - w(t)| \le \max_{0<s} |w(s)| \left\{\exp\left[\frac{1}{a}\int_t^\infty |F(s)|\, ds\right] - 1\right\}. \tag{5.4.53}$$

Proof. It is easier to give a direct proof than to reduce the theorem to previously known results. We start with a non-trivial solution $y(t)$ of (5.4.50) and choose a solution $w_0(t)$ of (5.4.52) with the same initial values at $t = 0$

$$w_0(0) = y(0), \; w_0'(0) = y'(0).$$

We then form the Volterra equation

$$v(t) = w_0(t) + \frac{1}{a}\int_0^t \sin a(t - s)F(s)v(s)\, ds. \tag{5.4.54}$$

We do not have to solve this equation, it only serves as an intermediary step. We observe, however, that $v(t)$ is a solution of (5.4.50), as is seen by repeated differentiation. Moreover, since $v(0) = w_0(0) = y(0)$, $v'(0) = w_0'(0) = y'(0)$, it follows that $v(t)$ and $y(t)$ are identical. From (5.4.54) we obtain the functional inequality

$$|v(t)| \le M_0 + \frac{1}{a}\int_0^t |F(s)|\,|v(s)|\,ds, \quad M_0 = \max |w_0(s)|,$$

and the resulting estimate

$$|v(t)| \le M_0 \exp\left[\frac{1}{a}\int_0^t |F(s)|\,ds\right].$$

This shows that $y(t) = v(t)$ is bounded for all $t \ge 0$.

This being the case we can obviously form the function $w(t)$ of formula (5.4.51), i.e.

$$w(t) = y(t) + \frac{1}{a}\int_t^\infty \sin a(s - t)F(s)y(s)\,ds$$

and twofold differentiation shows that $w(t)$ satisfies (5.4.52). Thus, to every given solution $y(t)$ of (5.4.50) corresponds a uniquely defined solution $w(t)$ of the sine equation (5.4.52) such that

$$\lim\,[y(t) - w(t)] = 0.$$

In terms of this function $w(t)$ the solution $y(t)$ also satisfies the singular Volterra equation (5.4.51). This gives the inequality

$$|y(t)| \le M + \frac{1}{a}\int_t^\infty |F(s)|\,|y(s)|\,ds, \qquad M = \max_{0<s} |w(s)|,$$

and this in its turn implies (5.4.53). In later chapters we shall be concerned with the extension of this theorem to the complex plane. ▮

EXERCISE 5.4

1. Under the assumptions of Theorem 5.4.2 it follows that $\|\mathcal{A}_1(t)\mathcal{U}(t)\| \in L(0, \infty)$. Show that this implies the existence of $\lim_{t\to\infty} \mathcal{U}(t)$.
2. Let η be a real or complex number. Let $\mathcal{Y}(t)$ be any solution of (5.4.1) and set
$$\mathcal{Y}(t) = e^{\eta t}\mathfrak{Z}(t).$$
Show that $\mathfrak{Z}(t)$ satisfies an equation of the same form as $\mathcal{Y}(t)$ but with a different constant matrix, $\mathcal{B}$ say. How are the characteristic roots of $\mathcal{B}$ related to those of $\mathcal{A}_0$?
3. The transformation used in the preceding problem can be used to shift the spectrum of the constant matrix to a more favorable position. How should η be chosen in order that $\mathfrak{Z}(t)$ should become a bounded matrix?

4. Is (5.4.21) valid without the restriction $\Re(\gamma) > 0$?
5. Verify the expression for $\exp(\gamma \mathfrak{J} t)$ given in the proof of Theorem 5.4.4.
6. Show that (5.4.24) is valid under the weaker assumption $\Re(\lambda_1) < \Re(\lambda_2) < \cdots < \Re(\lambda_n)$.
7. Show that $v_{jk}(t) \in L(a, \infty)$ if $j \neq k$ while $v_{jj}(t) - 1$ has this property if $t\|\mathcal{A}_1(t)\|$ does.
8. What are the matrices $\mathcal{A}_0$ and $\mathcal{A}_1(t)$ corresponding to equation (5.4.50) and find $\exp(\mathcal{A}_0 t)$.
9. Discuss Eq. (5.4.50) when $a = 0$. Find the asymptotic form of the solutions.
10. If $J_\alpha(x)$ denotes the Bessel function of order α and the first kind, then $\sqrt{x}\, J_\alpha(x)$ satisfies

$$y''(x) + \left\{1 - \frac{\alpha^2 - \frac{1}{4}}{x^2}\right\} y(x) = 0.$$

Theorem 5.4.6 applies in the interval $(1, \infty)$. What does it assert concerning the asymptotic behavior of $J_\alpha(x)$ for large x?
11. Suppose $\alpha = \pm\frac{1}{2}$. What form does the assertion take now?
12. For small values of x the equation

$$x^2y'' + xy' - [a^2 + f(x)]y = 0, \qquad 0 < a,$$

may have solutions of the form $x^\rho[1 + o(1)]$. Find suitable conditions on f and determine ρ.

COLLATERAL READING

Further problems connected with the subject matter of Sections 5.1 and 5.2 are found in most books on differential equations. See also

HILLE, E., *Analysis*, Vols. I and II, Blaisdell, New York (1964, 1965), cf. Sections 7.6 of Vol. I and 20.6 of Vol. II.

For the theory of Kolmogoroff's equations, see

DOOB, J. L., "Markoff chains—denumerable case," *Trans. Amer. Math. Soc.* **58**, 455–473 (1945).

See also

HILLE, E., and R. S. PHILLIPS, *Functional Analysis and Semi-Groups.* American Mathematical Society Colloquium Lectures, Vol. 31, Providence, R.I. (1957). In particular, Section 23.12.

The examples discussed in Section 5.3 are taken from the author's paper:

HILLE, E., "Pathology of infinite systems of linear first order differential equations with constant coefficients," *Annali di Matematica pura ed applicata* (4). **55**, 133–148 (1961).

The reader who wants to penetrate deeper into the subject matter of Section 5.4 would do well to consult the surveys:

BELLMAN, R., *A Survey of the Theory of Boundedness, Stability, and Asymptotic Behavior of Solutions of Linear and Non-Linear Differential and Difference Equations*, NAVEXOS P-596, Office of Naval Research, Washington, D.C. (1949).

CESARI, L., *Asymptotic Behavior and Stability Problems in Ordinary Differential Equations*, Ergebnisse der Mathematik. N.S., 16, Springer Verlag (1959).

COPPEL, W. A., *Stability and Asymptotic Behavior of Differential Equations*, Heath, Boston (1965).

The following papers were referred to in the text:

BELLMAN, R., "The boundedness of solutions of linear differential equations," *Duke Math. Journal*, **14**, 83–97 (1947).

LEVINSON, N., "The asymptotic nature of the solutions of linear systems of differential equations," *Duke Math. Journal*, **15**, 111–126 (1948).

The discussion of polynomial solution vectors at the end of Section 5.2 is based on

KNESER, H., "Die Reihenentwicklung bei schwach singulären Stellen linearer Differentialgleichungen," *Archiv der Mathematik*, **2**, 413–419 (1949–50).

For additional information on matrices consult

GANTMACHER, F. R., *The Theory of Matrices*, 2 vols., Chelsea, New York (1959).

Appendix B

LINEAR DIFFERENTIAL EQUATIONS IN THE COMPLEX DOMAIN

To facilitate the reading of this treatise the general theory of linear differential equations has been split into two parts. This Appendix is devoted to what might be referred to as the classical part of the theory: the nth order linear equations, systems of first order linear equations, and matrix equations. Chapter 6 is devoted to first order linear differential equations over a Banach algebra. The Appendix serves partly as an introduction to the abstract theory. In order to avoid too much duplication, proofs have been held to a minimum in the Appendix, and some of the more abstract topics, which are easier to handle in the general setting, have been omitted here. Thus the presentation is partly expository, especially in Section B.4.

The reader is referred to Chapter 7 for a discussion of linear second order differential equations in the complex domain, in particular, the classical equations.

The reader who is not interested in the abstract theory can omit Chapter 6 and restrict his reading of Appendix C to the first section.

There are four sections in Appendix B: Existence and independence; Regular singular points; The method of H. Kneser; and Irregular singular points.

B.1 EXISTENCE AND INDEPENDENCE

Our first concern is with linear n^{th} order differential equations

$$P_0(z)w^{(n)} + P_1(z)w^{(n-1)} + \cdots + P_n(z)w = 0, \tag{B.1.1}$$

where the coefficients $P_k(z)$ are holomorphic functions of z in some domain (= open connected set) D of the complex plane and where $P_0(z) \neq 0$ in D. It is often desirable to replace this equation by a system of first order equations:

$$w_j' = \sum_{k=1}^{n} a_{jk}(z)w_k, \qquad j = 1, 2, \ldots, n. \tag{B.1.2}$$

This may also be written as a vector matrix differential equation

$$\mathbf{w}' = \mathcal{A}(z)\mathbf{w} \tag{B.1.3}$$

or simply as a matrix differential equation

$$\mathcal{W}' = \mathcal{A}(z)\mathcal{W}. \tag{B.1.4}$$

Here $\mathcal{A}(z) = (a_{jk}(z))$ is an n by n matrix whose elements are holomorphic in D. The vector $\mathbf{w}$ is a column vector

$$\mathbf{w} = \begin{bmatrix} w_1 \\ \vdots \\ w_n \end{bmatrix} \tag{B.1.5}$$

made up of a solution of (B.1.2), and $\mathcal{W} \in \mathfrak{M}_n$ is a matrix made up n such column vectors.

The passage from (B.1.1) to (B.1.2) can be made via the substitution

$$w_1 = w,\ w_2 = w', \ldots, w_n = w^{(n-1)} \tag{B.1.6}$$

which leads to a system (B.1.2) with

$$\left.\begin{aligned} a_{j,j+1}(z) &= 1, \\ a_{jk}(z) &= 0,\ k \neq j+1, \end{aligned}\right\} j = 1, 2, \ldots, n-1,$$
$$a_{nk}(z) = -\frac{P_{n-k}(z)}{P_0(z)}, \qquad k = 1, 2, \ldots, n. \tag{B.1.7}$$

Other substitutions are possible and may be preferable for special purposes.

Let $z_0 \in D$ and give n complex numbers

$$w_{01}, w_{02}, \ldots, w_{0n}. \tag{B.1.8}$$

Then (B.1.1) has a unique solution

$$w(z; z_0, w_{01}, \ldots, w_{0n}) \tag{B.1.9}$$

which is defined and holomorphic in some neighborhood of $z = z_0$ and satisfies

$$w(z_0) = w_{01},\ w'(z_0) = w_{02}, \ldots, w^{(n-1)}(z_0) = w_{0n}. \tag{B.1.10}$$

This solution may be constructed with the aid of the method of successive approximations. Suppose that D is a *star domain* with respect to $z = z_0$, that is if $z_1 \in D$ so does the straight line segment joining z_0 and z_1. Here

$$\frac{P_1(z)}{P_0(z)}, \frac{P_2(z)}{P_0(z)}, \ldots, \frac{P_n(z)}{P_0(z)}$$

are supposed to be holomorphic in D. It may then be shown that

$$w(z; z_0, w_{01}, \ldots, w_{0n})$$

is also holomorphic in D for any choice of the initial values $w_{01}, \ldots, w_{0n}$.

Similarly, suppose that the n^2 functions $a_{jk}(z)$ are holomorphic in the star domain D. We then say that $\mathcal{A}(z)$ is holomorphic in D. Take the n

numbers in (B.1.8) as the components of a column vector $\mathbf{w}_0$. Then there is a unique vector-valued function

$$\mathbf{w}(z; z_0, \mathbf{w}_0) \tag{B.1.11}$$

holomorphic in D where it satisfies (B.1.3) and its components satisfy (B.1.2). Furthermore

$$\mathbf{w}(z_0; z_0, \mathbf{w}_0) = \mathbf{w}_0. \tag{B.1.12}$$

Let us now have given n vectors

$$\mathbf{w}_{01}, \mathbf{w}_{02}, \ldots, \mathbf{w}_{0n}$$

linearly independent over the complex field, i.e. for complex numbers $C_1, C_2, \ldots, C_n$ the vector equation

$$C_1\mathbf{w}_{01} + C_2\mathbf{w}_{02} + \cdots + C_n\mathbf{w}_{0n} = \mathbf{0}$$

implies

$$C_1 = C_2 = \cdots = C_n = 0.$$

To each such initial vector $\mathbf{w}_{0k}$ corresponds a unique solution vector $\mathbf{w}_k(z)$ of (B.1.3). Using these n vectors as columns of a matrix we get a solution $\mathfrak{W}(z)$ of (B.1.4). We write this solution

$$\mathfrak{W}(z; z_0, \mathfrak{W}_0) \tag{B.1.13}$$

where $\mathfrak{W}_0$ is the matrix the columns of which are the initial vectors $\mathbf{w}_{0k}$. In this context, $\mathfrak{W}_0$ is referred to as the *initial matrix*. It should be noted that if $\mathfrak{W}(z)$ is a solution of (B.1.4) and if $\mathfrak{W}_1$ is an arbitrary constant matrix, then

$$\mathfrak{W}(z)\mathfrak{W}_1$$

is also a solution of (B.1.4), while $\mathfrak{W}_1\mathfrak{W}(z)$ ordinarily is not. This observation shows that

$$\mathfrak{W}(z; z_0, \mathfrak{W}_0) = \mathfrak{W}(z; z_0, \mathfrak{E})\mathfrak{W}_0, \tag{B.1.14}$$

for both sides are solutions and the initial matrices coincide; hence the identity follows.

It is important to note that *if the initial vectors are linearly independent so are the solution vectors* and hence $\mathfrak{W}(z)$ is a regular (= invertible) element of $\mathfrak{M}_n$ for all z in D. This means that $\mathfrak{W}(z)$ *is regular iff* $\mathfrak{W}_0$ *is.*

Now a matrix $\mathfrak{B}(z)$ is regular iff its determinant

$$\beta(z) = \det\,[\mathfrak{B}(z)] \neq 0.$$

We shall derive a differential equation for

$$\omega(z) = \det\,[\mathfrak{W}(z)]. \tag{B.1.15}$$

The simplest case is that of Eq. (B.1.1) where the relevant determinant

$$\omega(z) = |w_k^{(j-1)}(z)|$$

is known as the *Wronskian* after the Polish mathematician Count Hoëné Wronski (1778–1853). In more detail it equals

$$\omega(z) = \begin{vmatrix} w_1(z) & w_2(z) & \cdots & w_n(z) \\ w_1'(z) & w_2'(z) & \cdots & w_n'(z) \\ \cdot & \cdot & \cdot & \cdot \\ w_1^{(n-1)}(z) & w_2^{(n-1)}(z) & \cdots & w_n^{(n-1)}(z) \end{vmatrix}. \tag{B.1.16}$$

Now the derivative of a determinant is the sum of n determinants obtained by differentiating one row at a time. Applying this procedure to $\omega(z)$ we obtain $n - 1$ determinants with equal rows which vanish accordingly. The nth determinant differs from $\omega(z)$ by the elements in the nth row being n^{th} derivatives instead of $(n - 1)^{\text{th}}$. Now

$$w_k^{(n)} = -\frac{P_1}{P_0} w_k^{(n-1)} - \cdots - \frac{P_n}{P_0} w_k$$

and if these expressions are substituted in the nth determinant we obtain a sum of n determinants, only one of which is not identically zero. The remaining term gives the equation

$$\omega'(z) = -\frac{P_1(z)}{P_0(z)} \omega(z) \tag{B.1.17}$$

and

$$\omega(z) = \omega(z_0) \exp\left\{-\int_{z_0}^{z} \frac{P_1(t)}{P_0(t)} dt\right\}. \tag{B.1.18}$$

This formula goes back to N. H. Abel (1802–1829). It is also valid in the real domain if the ratios $P_k(t)/P_0(t)$ are continuous functions of t. From (B.1.18) we conclude that $\omega(z) \neq 0$ in D provided $\omega(z_0) \neq 0$. Thus $\omega(z_0) \neq 0$ is a sufficient condition that the n solution vectors be linearly independent and the corresponding solution matrix $\mathfrak{W}(z)$ be invertible. In particular, this implies that the n solutions $w_1(z), w_2(z), \ldots, w_n(z)$ are linearly independent in D. For a relation

$$C_1 w_1(z) + C_2 w_2(z) + \cdots + C_n w_n(z) \equiv 0$$

holding in some subdomain of D where the C's are fixed constants not all 0, implies the same relation satisfied by the kth order derivatives, $k = 1, 2, \ldots$. Taking the first n of these equations, we see that their determinant must be $\equiv 0$ or $\omega(z) \equiv 0$.

Since the solution of (B.1.17) is unique, *the condition*

$$\omega(z_0) \neq 0 \tag{B.1.19}$$

is necessary as well as sufficient for the linear independence of the solution vectors.

For the matrix case formula (B.1.18) generalizes to

$$\omega(z) = \omega(z_0) \exp\left\{\int_{z_0}^{z} \operatorname{tr}\,[\mathcal{A}(t)]\,dt\right\} \tag{B.1.20}$$

where *the trace of a matrix is* by definition *the sum of the elements in the main diagonal*:

$$\operatorname{tr}\,[\mathcal{A}(t)] = \sum_{j=1}^{n} a_{jj}(t). \tag{B.1.21}$$

The conclusion is the same as in the nth order case, namely

Theorem B.1.1. *The solution matrix $\mathcal{W}(z)$ is either regular everywhere in D or nowhere.*

Proof. The argument that leads to (B.1.20) is more delicate than that which gave (B.1.18). Let z and $z + h$ be two points in D such that the line segment $[z, z + h]$ also lies in D. Suppose further that the solution matrix is invertible at z. There are such points z for, if $\mathcal{W}(z_0)$ is regular, then there exists a full neighborhood of z_0 at all points of which $[\mathcal{W}(z)]^{-1}$ exists. Then

$$\begin{aligned}\mathcal{W}(z + h) &= \mathcal{W}(z) + h\mathcal{W}'(z) + O(h^2)\\ &= \mathcal{W}(z) + h\mathcal{A}(z)\mathcal{W}(z) + O(h^2).\end{aligned}$$

Since $\omega(z) \neq 0$ by assumption,

$$\omega(z + h) = \det\{\mathcal{E} + h\mathcal{A}(z) + O[h^2\mathcal{W}^{-1}(z)]\}\omega(z)$$

and

$$\frac{1}{h}[\omega(z + h) - \omega(z)] = \frac{1}{h}\{\det(\mathcal{E} + h\mathcal{A}(z) + O[h^2\mathcal{W}^{-1}(z)]) - 1\}\omega(z).$$

In the right member, the entry in the place (j, k) in the determinant is

$$\delta_{jk} + h a_{jk}(z) + O(h^2).$$

Hence the determinant equals

$$1 + h\sum_{j=1}^{n} a_{jj}(z) + O(h^2).$$

It follows that the right member tends to the limit

$$\left\{\sum_{j=1}^{n} a_{jj}(z)\right\}\omega(z)$$

as $h \to 0$. Hence the left member has a limit and

$$\omega'(z) = \left\{\sum_{j=1}^{n} a_{jj}(z)\right\}\omega(z) \tag{B.1.22}$$

results. This is under the assumption that $\omega(z) \neq 0$. Now $\omega(z)$ is a holomorphic function in D since $\mathcal{W}(z)$ has this property. It is then either identically zero in D or its zeros, if any, are isolated. The first alternative is excluded if, as we assume, $\omega(z_0) \neq 0$. We have then in some neighborhood of $z = z_0$

$$\omega(z) = \omega(z_0) \exp\left\{\int_{z_0}^{z} \operatorname{tr}\,[\mathcal{A}(t)]\, dt\right\}.$$

Here the right member is holomorphic in D and $\neq 0$. It follows that the holomorphic function $\omega(z)$ is represented by (B.1.20) in D and hence $\neq 0$ there.

So far we have only shown that $\omega(z_0) \neq 0$ implies $\omega(z) \neq 0$ in D. It should also be shown that $\omega(z_0) = 0$ implies $\omega(z) \equiv 0$. Suppose contrariwise that there is a $z_1 \in D$ such that $\omega(z_1) \neq 0$.

By the preceding argument

$$\omega(z) = \omega(z_1) \exp\left\{\int_{z_1}^{z} \operatorname{tr}\,[\mathcal{A}(t)]\, dt\right\}$$

in D, where the path of integration is some rectifiable curve leading from z_1 to z. Since D is simply-connected, all such paths are equivalent. This formula holds also at $z = z_0$ and contradicts the assumption that $\omega(z_0) = 0$. ▮

EXERCISE B.1

1. Apply the method of successive approximations to (B.1.3), show that the approximations converge uniformly in any bounded domain D_0 which is a star domain with respect to $z = z_0$ and the closure of which is contained in D, and show that $\mathbf{w}(z; z_0, \mathbf{w}_0)$ is holomorphic in D.
2. The functions t^2 and $t^2 \operatorname{sgn} t$ are continuous together with their first order derivatives in any finite interval $(-a, a)$. Verify that they are linearly dependent in $(-a, 0)$ and $(0, a)$ but not in $(-a, a)$. Show that the Wronskian is zero in any interval.

Find the Wronskians if

3. $y'' + P(t)y = 0$.
4. $[(1 - t^2)y']' + n(n + 1)y = 0$ (Legendre's equation).
5. Show that (B.1.18) holds for continuous functions of a real variable. How should the proof be modified?
6. Answer the same question for (B.1.20).
7. Find the Wronskian if $[K(z)w'(z)]' + G(z)w(z) = 0$.
8. A set of n solutions of (B.1.1) is called a *fundamental system*, if the solutions are linearly independent. Show that this implies and is implied by their Wronskian being $\neq 0$.

9. A solution matrix $\mathfrak{W}(z)$ of (B.1.4) is said to be *fundamental* if the column vectors are linearly independent. Show that this implies and is implied by $\mathfrak{W}(z)$ being a regular element of $\mathfrak{M}_n$.
10. The following equation has been considered by T. Kato (1955). Let $\mathfrak{P}(t) \in \mathfrak{M}_n$, $-a < t < a$, be a projection (= idempotent) matrix, $\mathfrak{P}(t) = [\mathfrak{P}(t)]^2$, and continuously differentiable. Let $\mathfrak{W}(t)$ satisfy

$$\mathfrak{W}'(t) = [\mathfrak{P}'(t)\mathfrak{P}(t) - \mathfrak{P}(t)\mathfrak{P}'(t)]\mathfrak{W}(t), \qquad \mathfrak{W}(0) = \mathfrak{E}.$$

Show that $\mathfrak{P}(t)\mathfrak{W}(t)$ satisfies the same equation and $\mathfrak{P}(t)\mathfrak{W}(t) = \mathfrak{W}(t)\mathfrak{P}(0)$.

B.2 REGULAR SINGULAR POINTS

The solution matrix $\mathfrak{W}(z)$ of (B.1.4) can be continued analytically along any path which permits analytic continuation of $\mathfrak{A}(z)$. In general a singular point of $\mathfrak{A}(z)$ is also a singular point of $\mathfrak{W}(z)$; moreover, the nature of the singularity of $\mathfrak{W}(z)$ is apt to be more complicated than that of $\mathfrak{A}(z)$. Thus a simple pole of $\mathfrak{A}(z)$ may lead to a transcendental critical point of $\mathfrak{W}(z)$, a multiple pole may introduce an essential singularity, and so on.

We shall restrict ourselves to the case where $\mathfrak{A}(z)$ is holomorphic save for poles and start with the case of a simple pole placed at the origin to simplify the notation. The equation is then of the form

$$z\mathfrak{W}'(z) = \mathfrak{P}(z)\mathfrak{W}(z) \tag{B.2.1}$$

or in equivalent vector form

$$z\mathbf{w}'(z) = \mathfrak{P}(z)\mathbf{w}(z). \tag{B.2.2}$$

Here

$$\mathfrak{P}(z) = \big(P_{jk}(z)\big) \tag{B.2.3}$$

is holomorphic for $|z| < R$ and $\mathfrak{P}(0) \neq 0$. We say that $z = 0$ is a *regular singular point* of the equations.

The systematic study of linear differential equations in the neighborhood of a singular point was initiated by Lazarus Fuchs (1833–1902) in 1866 and followed up by G. Frobenius (1849–1917) in 1873. They discussed the nth order linear equation

$$z^n w^{(n)} + z^{n-1}B_1(z)w^{(n-1)} + \cdots + zB_{n-1}(z)w' + B_n(z)w = 0 \tag{B.2.4}$$

under the assumption that the functions $B_k(z)$ are holomorphic at $z = 0$ while at least one of the functions

$$z^{-k}B_k(z)$$

is not holomorphic there. Fuchs referred to such a singularity as a "*Bestimmtheitstelle*," later German terminology is "*schwach singuläre Stelle*." The term "*stark singuläre Stelle*" refers to an irregular singular point which in the matrix case corresponds to a pole of order >1.

In view of the lasting importance of the nth order linear case, we shall briefly outline the procedure of Fuchs before taking up the generalization to the matrix case. It is advantageous to rewrite (B.2.4) in a different form by introducing the differential operator ϑ defined by

$$\vartheta f = zf'(z). \tag{B.2.5}$$

The powers of ϑ are defined by recurrence

$$\vartheta^k f = \vartheta[\vartheta^{k-1} f], \qquad k = 2, 3, \ldots$$

It is a simple matter to show by induction that

$$z^k f^{(k)}(z) = \vartheta(\vartheta - I)\cdots(\vartheta - (k - 1)I)f(z), \tag{B.2.6}$$

where I is the identity operator. Hence (B.2.4) may be written

$$\sum_{k=1}^{n} B_{n-k}(z)\vartheta(\vartheta - I)\cdots(\vartheta - (k - 1)I)w(z) + B_n(z)w(z) = 0. \tag{B.2.7}$$

Here we expand the polynomials in ϑ and collect the terms containing the same power of ϑ. The result is of the form

$$\sum_{k=0}^{n} P_{n-k}(z)\vartheta^k w = 0, \qquad P_0 \equiv 1. \tag{B.2.8}$$

We note that

$$\vartheta z^s = sz^s$$

for any constant s. More generally,

$$\vartheta \sum_{m=0}^{\infty} c_m z^{s+m} = \sum_{m=0}^{\infty} (s + m)c_m z^{s+m},$$

provided one of the series has a positive radius of convergence. This suggests trying to find solutions of (B.2.8) of the form

$$\sum_{m=0}^{\infty} c_m z^{s+m}, \tag{B.2.9}$$

where s and the c's are complex numbers to be determined. Substituting the series in (B.2.8) we obtain

$$\sum_{k=0}^{n} \sum_{j=0}^{\infty} P_{n-k,j} z^j \sum_{m=0}^{\infty} c_m (m + s)^k z^{m+s} \equiv 0, \tag{B.2.10}$$

where

$$P_m(z) = \sum_{j=0}^{\infty} P_{mj} z^j. \tag{B.2.11}$$

The terms of lowest degree in (B.2.10) correspond to $j = m = 0$ and are

$$\left\{\sum_{k=0}^{n} P_{n-k,0}s^k\right\}c_0 z^s.$$

This vanishes iff

$$f_0(s) \equiv \sum_{k=0}^{n} P_{n-k,0}s^k = 0. \tag{B.2.12}$$

Here $P_{n-k,0} = P_{n-k}(0)$. We conclude that s must be a root of this equation which is known as the *indicial equation* of (B.2.8) at $z = 0$. Define

$$f_j(s) \equiv \sum_{k=0}^{n} P_{n-k,j}s^k, \qquad j = 1, 2, \ldots \tag{B.2.13}$$

Then (B.2.10) will vanish identically if, for $m = 0, 1, 2, \ldots$

$$c_m f_0(s + m) + c_{m-1} f_1(s + m - 1) + \cdots + c_0 f_m(s) = 0. \tag{B.2.14}$$

Choose s as a root of $f_0(s) = 0$, take $c_0 = 1$, and proceed to determine $c_1, c_2, \ldots$ successively. This can be done, provided

$$f_0(s + m) \neq 0 \tag{B.2.15}$$

for all roots s_j and all positive integers m, in other words, provided the roots of the indicial equation do not differ by integers. If, in addition, the roots are distinct, we obtain n linearly independent series solutions

$$w_k(z) = \sum_{m=0}^{\infty} c_{mk} z^{m+s_k}, \tag{B.2.16}$$

where $s_1, s_2, \ldots, s_n$ are the roots of the indicial equation. We omit a convergence proof since this will be covered by the corresponding proof for the matrix case.

For the case in which the roots of the indicial equation are not distinct or differ by integers, G. Frobenius developed a method to obtain a complete set of linearly independent solutions based on a perturbation argument, differentiation with respect to the parameter s, and passage to the limit. We shall develop this method for the B-algebra case in Section 6.6.

Let us note in passing that for the normal form (B.2.4) the indicial equation becomes

$$\sum_{k=1}^{n} s(s - 1)(s - 2)\cdots(s - (k - 1))P_{n-k}(0) + P_n(0) = 0. \tag{B.2.17}$$

It is a simple matter to pass from the normal form (B.2.8) to a matrix equation of type (B.2.1). It suffices to set

$$w_1 = w, \qquad w_2 = \vartheta w, \ldots, w_n = \vartheta w_{n-1}. \tag{B.2.18}$$

The corresponding matrix $\mathfrak{P}(z)$ is

$$\begin{bmatrix} 0 & 1 & 0 & \cdots & 0 & 0 \\ 0 & 0 & 1 & \cdots & 0 & 0 \\ \cdot & \cdot & \cdot & \cdots & \cdot & \cdot \\ 0 & 0 & 0 & \cdots & 0 & 1 \\ -P_n & -P_{n-1} & -P_{n-2} & \cdots & -P_2 & -P_1 \end{bmatrix} = \mathfrak{P}(z). \qquad \text{(B.2.19)}$$

We observe that the indicial equation (B.2.12) is simply the characteristic equation of the matrix $\mathfrak{P}(0)$.

We now turn to the general matrix case (B.2.1). We shall consider the equivalent first order system

$$\vartheta w_j = \sum_{k=1}^{n} P_{jk}(z) w_k, \qquad j = 1, 2, \ldots, n, \qquad \text{(B.2.20)}$$

which we try to satisfy by series of the form

$$w_k(z, s) = \sum_{m=0}^{\infty} c_{km}(s) z^{s+m}, \qquad k = 1, 2, \ldots, n, \qquad \text{(B.2.21)}$$

where the c's and the parameter s is to be determined.

The first general discussion of regular singular points of systems of linear first order differential equations is due to L. Sauvage (1886) who showed how to compute the series, and proved their convergence and the linear independence of the resulting solutions. There are algebraic complications just as in the nth order case: actually the postulated form of the solution holds only if the characteristic roots of the matrix $\mathfrak{P}(0)$ are incongruent modulo 1. If this is the case, n linearly independent solution vectors are obtained by assigning to s successively the values $s_1, s_2, \ldots, s_n$, the characteristic roots in question. But if this assumption does not hold, then the coefficients are in general polynomials of bounded degree in $\log z$.

In the following we shall give two proofs: one valid for the case $s_j - s_k \not\equiv 0 \pmod 1$, $j \neq k$, and a second one in the next section which holds without restrictions on the roots. The first is an arrangement of the proof given by the author in 1925, the second is due to H. Kneser (1950) and is based on Theorem 5.2.1.

Theorem B.2.1. *If the characteristic roots s_k of the matrix $P(0)$ are such that $s_j - s_k \not\equiv 0 \pmod 1$, then the system* (B.2.20) *has a set of n linearly independent solution vectors of the form* (B.2.21) *where $s = s_j$, $j = 1, 2, \ldots, n$, and the series converge for z, $z \neq 0$, in the disk where $\mathfrak{P}(z)$ is holomorphic.*

Proof. Let

$$P_{jk}(z) = \sum_{m=0}^{\infty} p_{jkm} z^m \tag{B.2.22}$$

and substitute the series (B.2.21) into the system (B.2.20). This gives identities

$$\sum_{m=0}^{\infty} (s + m) c_{jm}(s) z^{s+m} \equiv \sum_{m=0}^{\infty} \left\{ \sum_{k=1}^{n} \sum_{\alpha=0}^{m} p_{jk\alpha} c_{k,m-\alpha}(s) \right\} z^{s+m},$$

where $j = 1, 2, \ldots, n$. Equating coefficients of terms involving the same power of z, we obtain

$$\sum_{k=1}^{n} [\delta_{jk}(s + m) - p_{jk0}] c_{km}(s) = \sum_{k=1}^{n} \sum_{\alpha=1}^{m} p_{jk\alpha} c_{k,m-\alpha}(s), \tag{B.2.23}$$

where $j = 1, 2, \ldots, n$, $m = 0, 1, 2, \ldots$.

For $m = 0$ we obtain the homogeneous system

$$\sum_{k=1}^{n} (\delta_{jk} s - p_{jk0}) c_{k0}(s) = 0, \qquad j = 1, 2, \ldots, n, \tag{B.2.24}$$

whose determinant must vanish:

$$f(s) = |\delta_{jk} s - p_{jk0}| = \det [s\mathcal{E} - \mathcal{P}(0)] = 0. \tag{B.2.25}$$

This equation is satisfied by the characteristic roots of $\mathcal{P}(0)$, by assumption not congruent modulo 1. In particular, there are no multiple roots. Thus the parameter s must be one of the characteristic roots s_j of $\mathcal{P}(0)$.

The determinant of the system (B.2.23) is seen to be $f(s + m)$ and by assumption this does not vanish for any $s = s_j$, $m > 0$. Denote the cofactor of $\delta_{jk} s - p_{jk0}$ in the determinant $f(s)$ by $f_{jk}(s)$. We can then solve (B.2.23) to obtain

$$f(s + m) c_{jm}(s) = \sum_{\beta=1}^{n} f_{j\beta}(s + m) \sum_{k=1}^{n} \sum_{\alpha=1}^{m} p_{\beta k\alpha} c_{k,m-\alpha}(s), \qquad m \geq 1. \tag{B.2.26}$$

From these equations we can determine the $c_{jm}(s)$ successively in terms of the $c_{k0}(s)$.

It is advantageous to carry out the convergence proof for the formal solution series without specifying the value of s. Let ρ be so large that

$$|s_j| < \rho, \qquad \forall j.$$

Delete from the disk $|s| < \rho$ the disks

$$|s - s_j - m| < \varepsilon, \qquad j = 1, 2, \ldots, n, \qquad m = 1, 2, \ldots,$$

and denote the remaining part by Δ. If ε is chosen sufficiently small, all points s_j will be in Δ. We can then find two positive numbers δ and μ such that for all $m \geq 1, j, k = 1, 2, \ldots, n$, and s any point in Δ

$$|f(s+m)| > \delta(\rho+m)^n, \qquad |f_{jk}(s+m)| < \mu(\rho+m)^{n-1}. \tag{B.2.27}$$

Suppose that for some fixed M and r

$$|p_{jkm}| \leq Mr^{-m}, \qquad \forall j, k, m. \tag{B.2.28}$$

This implies that $\mathfrak{F}(z)$ is holomorphic at least for $|z| < r$. Conversely, if $\mathfrak{F}(z)$ is holomorphic for $|z| < R$ and $0 < r < R$, then we can find an M such that (B.2.28) holds. These estimates applied to (B.2.26) lead to

$$\delta(\rho+m)^n|c_{jm}(s)| \leq \sum_{\beta=1}^{n} \mu(\rho+m)^{n-1} \sum_{k=1}^{n}\sum_{\alpha=0}^{m-1} Mr^{\alpha-m}|c_{k\alpha}(s)|$$

whence

$$(\rho+m)r^m|c_{jm}(s)| \leq \frac{\mu}{\delta} Mn \sum_{\alpha=0}^{m-1}\sum_{k=1}^{n} r^{\alpha}|c_{k\alpha}(s)|. \tag{B.2.29}$$

Let us introduce a sequence of positive numbers C_j such that

$$(\rho+m)C_m = a\sum_{j=0}^{m-1} C_j, \qquad a = \frac{\mu}{\delta} Mn^2. \tag{B.2.30}$$

Here C_0 is at our disposal. We choose it so large that

$$|c_{j0}(s)| < C_0, \qquad \forall j, \qquad s \in \Delta.$$

It is then seen by induction that

$$r^m|c_{jm}(s)| < C_m, \qquad \forall j, m, \qquad s \in \Delta. \tag{B.2.31}$$

In (B.2.30) we replace m by $m + 1$ and subtract to obtain

$$(\rho+m+1)C_{m+1} = (\rho+m+a)C_m \tag{B.2.32}$$

whence

$$C_m = \frac{(\rho+a)(\rho+a+1)\cdots(\rho+a+m-1)}{(\rho+1)(\rho+2)\cdots(\rho+m)} C_0.$$

The fraction is the general coefficient of a hypergeometric series

$$F(\rho+a, 1, \rho+1; x).$$

It follows that the series for $z^{-s}w_j(z, s)$ is dominated by a hypergeometric series

$$z^{-s}w_j(z,s) \ll C_0F(\rho+a, 1, \rho+1; z/r), \qquad \forall j. \tag{B.2.33}$$

It follows that the formal series $w_j(z, s)$ converge for $0 < |z| < r$, uniformly with respect to s in Δ.

In particular, for $s = s_k$, $k = 1, 2, \ldots, n$, we obtain n solution vectors

$$\{w_j(z, s_k)\}, \qquad j, k = 1, 2, \ldots, n. \tag{B.2.34}$$

For if $s = s_\alpha$, we can find n numbers $c_{k0}(s_\alpha)$, not all 0, which satisfy (B.2.24) and then proceed to compute $c_{km}(s_\alpha)$ from (B.2.26). As we have just seen, the resulting formal series are absolutely convergent for $|z| < r$. It follows that the operations performed in order to obtain the equations (B.2.23) are legitimate. Hence the formal series are actual solutions of the system (B.2.20) as asserted.

It remains to show that the n solutions corresponding to $s = s_1, s_2, \ldots, s_n$ are actually linearly independent. This can be proved in various ways. Since the roots are incongruent modulo 1, the following method gives a simple proof. Suppose that we had a linear relation between the solution vectors. This would imply corresponding linear relations between their components, say

$$C_1 w_j(z, s_1) + C_2 w_j(z, s_2) + \cdots + C_n w_j(z, s_n) \equiv 0 \tag{B.2.35}$$

for $j = 1, 2, \ldots, n$. If here we let z describe a small circle Γ: $|z| = \varepsilon\, e^{i\theta}$, $0 \leq \theta \leq 2\pi$, about the origin, the power z^{s_k} is multiplied by the factor

$$\exp(2\pi i s_k) \equiv \omega_k.$$

Formula (B.2.35) is an identity between analytic functions and remains valid for the new determinations of $w_j(z, s_k)$. Repeating this procedure $n - 1$ times we obtain the relations

$$C_1 w_j(z, s_1)\omega_1^p + C_2 w_j(z, s_2)\omega_2^p + \cdots + C_n w_j(z, s_n)\omega_n^p = 0,$$

where $p = 0, 1, 2, \ldots, n - 1$ and $w_j(z, s_k)$ stands for the original determination made single-valued by a cut along the negative real axis. This set of n linear equations will have a non-trivial solution iff the determinant

$$|\omega_k^{j-1}| = 0.$$

This is a Vandermonde determinant whose value is the product of the differences $\omega_j - \omega_k$, $j \neq k$. It can vanish iff there are two distinct integers j and k such that $\omega_j = \omega_k$ and this implies that $s_j - s_k \equiv 0 \pmod 1$ against our assumption. It follows that we have obtained a fundamental system of solution vectors. ∎

The reader will have noticed that in the preceding proof there was hardly any use made of matrix methods. It is perfectly feasible to find a solution of (B.2.1) as a matrix series

$$\mathfrak{W}(z) = \sum_{m=0}^{\infty} \mathfrak{C}_m z^{\mathfrak{A}_0 + m}, \tag{B.2.36}$$

where $\mathcal{C}_m \in \mathfrak{M}_n$, $\mathcal{C}_0 = \mathcal{E}$, and

$$z^{\mathcal{A}_0} = \sum_1^n \mathcal{T}_j z^{s_j}, \quad \mathcal{T}_j^2 = \mathcal{T}_j. \tag{B.2.37}$$

The coefficients $\mathcal{C}_m$ can be found by substitution in the equation which leads to a set of commutator equations

$$m\mathcal{E} - (\mathcal{C}_m\mathcal{A}_0 - \mathcal{A}_0\mathcal{C}_m) = \mathcal{B}_m. \tag{B.2.38}$$

In this appendix we want to avoid using the theory of such equations already developed in Section 4.6. They will figure prominently in Chapter 6. The argument given above is elementary and would enable us to compute the $\mathcal{C}$'s if so desired. The reader who wants to examine the matrix approach will find an excellent detailed account in the monograph by J. A. Lappo-Danilevsky (1896–1931). Mention should also be made of earlier work by G. D. Birkhoff (1884–1944) and L. Schlesinger (1864–1933).

It was stated earlier that normally the solution $\mathcal{W}(z)$ has a more complicated singularity than does $\mathcal{A}(z)$. This is not always the case, however. Thus the equation

$$z\mathcal{W}'(z) = \begin{pmatrix} 0 & 1 \\ -6 & 5 \end{pmatrix} \mathcal{W}(z) \tag{B.2.39}$$

has a regular singular point at $z = 0$. It is satisfied by

$$\mathcal{W}(z) = \begin{pmatrix} z^2 & z^3 \\ 2z^2 & 3z^3 \end{pmatrix}. \tag{B.2.40}$$

This function is holomorphic in the finite plane including the origin. It is algebraically regular except at the origin. Thus there is no function theoretical singularity at $z = 0$ but there is an algebraic singularity instead.

So far only singularities at $z = 0$ have been discussed. The point $z = a$ is a regular singular point if the equation (B.1.4) may be written

$$(z - a)\mathcal{W}'(z) = \mathcal{Q}(z)\mathcal{W}(z), \tag{B.2.41}$$

where $\mathcal{Q}(z)$ is holomorphic at $z = a$ and $\mathcal{Q}(a) \neq 0$. Similarly the nth order linear equation has a regular singular point at $z = a$, if it may be written

$$(z - a)^n w^{(n)} + (z - a)^{n-1} C_1(z) w^{(n-1)} + \cdots + (z - a) C_{n-1}(z) w' + C_n(z) w = 0, \tag{B.2.42}$$

where the functions $C_k(z)$ are holomorphic at $z = a$ while at least one of the functions

$$(z - a)^{-k} C_k(z)$$

is not.

We still have the point at infinity. To investigate this point we use the substitution

$$z = \frac{1}{s} \tag{B.2.43}$$

and make the convention that $z = \infty$ *is a regular singular point of the original equation if* $s = 0$ *is a regular singular point of the transformed equation.* We now note that

$$\vartheta f = z\frac{df}{dz} = -s\frac{df}{ds} \equiv -\theta f. \tag{B.2.44}$$

It follows that (B.2.1) is transformed into

$$s\mathfrak{W}' = -\mathfrak{F}(1/s)\mathfrak{W}, \tag{B.2.45}$$

where the prime now denotes differentiation with respect to s. By our convention, $z = \infty$ is a regular singular point of (B.2.1) if $\mathfrak{F}(z)$ is holomorphic at infinity and $\mathfrak{F}(\infty) \neq 0$. The corresponding result for the nth order case will be needed sufficiently often to justify our stating it as a theorem.

Theorem B.2.2. *If the functions $P_k(z)$ are holomorphic at $z = \infty$ then*

$$\vartheta^n w + P_1(z)\vartheta^{n-1}w + \cdots + P_{n-1}(z)\vartheta w + P_k(z)\, w = 0 \tag{B.2.46}$$

has a regular singular point at $z = \infty$ which may reduce to a regular point in exceptional cases.

Proof. The transformation (B.2.43) gives

$$(-1)^n\theta^n w + (-1)^{n-1}P_1(1/s)\theta^{n-1}w + \cdots - P_{n-1}(1/s)\theta w + P_n(1/s)w = 0.$$

Since each $P_j(z)$ is holomorphic at $z = \infty$, the functions $P_j(1/s)$ are holomorphic at $s = 0$. The equation is then of type (B.2.8) at $s = 0$, whence it follows that the point $z = \infty$ is normally a regular singular point. Here we have to say "normally" for it may happen that the point $s = 0$ is not singular at all. Thus if the transformed equation is

$$\theta^2 w - \theta w = 0,$$

this is the same as

$$s^2 w'' = 0, \; w(s) = a + bs,$$

and the singularity is only apparent. The corresponding matrix equation still has a regular singular point at $s = 0$, but it is an algebraic rather than a function theoretical singularity. ∎

A linear differential equation which has no other singularities than regular singular points is said to belong to the *Fuchsian class.* The term applies both to n^{th} order linear equations and to first order matrix equations. The coefficients of such an equation have to be rational functions satisfying rather severe restrictions. (See Problem 10 below and Section 6.7.)

EXERCISE B.2

1. Verify (B.2.6).
2. Conversely, show the existence of positive integers C_{mk} such that

$$\vartheta^k f(z) = z^k f^{(k)}(z) + C_{1k} z^{k-1} f^{(k-1)}(z) + \cdots + C_{k-1,k} z f'(z).$$

   Compute the coefficients for $k = 3$.
3. If

$$\mathcal{J}(z) = \begin{pmatrix} 0 & 1 \\ 1 & 0 \end{pmatrix},$$

   show that a solution matrix is given by

$$\tfrac{1}{2}(\mathcal{J} + \mathcal{E})z + \tfrac{1}{2}(\mathcal{J} - \mathcal{E})z^{-1}.$$

4. If

$$\mathcal{J}(z) = \begin{pmatrix} 0 & 1 \\ -1 & 0 \end{pmatrix},$$

   show that a solution matrix is given by

$$\mathcal{E} \cos(\log z) + \mathcal{J} \sin(\log z).$$

5. If $\mathcal{J}(z)$ is defined by (B.2.19), show that the indicial equation (B.2.12) for the Eq. (B.2.8) coincides with the characteristic equation for the matrix $\mathcal{J}(0)$.
6. If n power series $\sum_{m=0}^{\infty} c_{km} z^m$, $k = 1, 2, \ldots, n$, are linearly dependent, what relations must hold between the coefficients?
7. Given n series of the form $\sum_{m=0}^{\infty} c_{km} z^{m+s_k}$ where $s_j \not\equiv s_k \pmod 1$, show that they are necessarily linearly independent using function theoretical considerations. Assume to start with that $\Re(s_j) < \Re(s_k)$ if $j < k$ and then remove this restriction.
8. Show that the equation $\vartheta^3 w - 3\vartheta^2 w + 2\vartheta w = 0$ has only an apparent singularity at $z = 0$. Find the solution.
9. Find the corresponding matrix equation and a solution matrix. Show that the latter is algebraically but not function theoretically singular at $z = 0$.
10. If $\mathcal{W}'(z) = \mathcal{A}(z)\mathcal{W}(z)$ belongs to the Fuchsian class, show that $\mathcal{A}(z)$ is a rational function with simple poles and vanishes at ∞.
11. Under what conditions on P and Q does

$$w'' + P(z)w' + Q(z)w = 0$$

   belong to the Fuchsian class?

Find the singular points of the following second order equations, determine which are regular singular, and find the indicial equations at these points.

12. $zw'' + w' + zw = 0.$

13. $z^2w'' + (z^2 - a^2 + \frac{1}{4})w = 0.$

14. $(1 - z^2)w'' - 2zw' + a(a + 1)w = 0.$

15. $z(1 - z)w'' + [c - (a + b + 1)z]w' - abw = 0.$

16. Prove that the function defined by the power series

$$\sum_{n=1}^{\infty} n^k z^n, \qquad k \text{ positive integer},$$

has a pole of order $k + 1$ at $z = 1$ and that this is its only singularity.

B.3 THE METHOD OF H. KNESER

In order to handle regular singular points where some of the roots of the characteristic or indicial equation are congruent modulo 1 we shall use the elegant method devised by H. Kneser (1950).

Theorem B.3.1. *Let*

$$\mathfrak{F}(z) = \sum_{m=0}^{\infty} \mathcal{A}_m z^m, \qquad \mathcal{A}_m \in \mathfrak{M}_n, \tag{B.3.1}$$

convergent for $|z| < R$. *Then the equation*

$$z\mathbf{w}'(z) = \mathfrak{F}(z)\mathbf{w}(z) \tag{B.3.2}$$

has n linearly independent solution vectors of the form

$$\mathbf{w}_j(z, r) = \sum_{m=0}^{\infty} \mathbf{p}_{jmr}(\log z)z^{r+m}, \qquad j = 1, 2, \ldots, n. \tag{B.3.3}$$

Here r runs through the distinct characteristic roots of the matrix $\mathcal{A}_0$ *and the* $\mathbf{p}_{jmr}(t)$ *are vector polynomials in t of degree* $\leq n - 1$. *The series converge for* $0 < |z| < R$.

Proof. We substitute

$$\mathbf{w}(z) = \sum_{m=0}^{\infty} \mathbf{p}_m(\log z)z^{r+m} \tag{B.3.4}$$

in (B.3.2) obtaining

$$\sum_{m=0}^{\infty} [\mathbf{p}_m'(\log z) + (r + m)\mathbf{p}_m(\log z)]z^{r+m} = \sum_{m=0}^{\infty} \left\{ \sum_{j=0}^{m} \mathcal{A}_{m-j}\mathbf{p}_j(\log z) \right\} z^{r+m}.$$

Here the coefficients of like powers of z must be identical so that

$$\mathbf{p}_m'(t) + (r + m)\mathbf{p}_m(t) = \sum_{j=0}^{m} \mathcal{A}_{m-j}\mathbf{p}_j(t), \qquad t = \log z,$$

or

$$\mathbf{p}'_m(t) + [(r+m)\mathcal{E} - \mathcal{A}_0]\mathbf{p}_m(t) = \sum_{j=0}^{m-1} \mathcal{A}_{m-j}\mathbf{p}_j(t), \tag{B.3.5}$$

where $m = 0, 1, 2, \ldots$. In particular, for $m = 0$,

$$\mathbf{p}'_0(t) + (r\mathcal{E} - \mathcal{A}_0)\mathbf{p}_0(t) = 0. \tag{B.3.6}$$

The corollary to Lemma 5.2.1 asserts that this equation has a non-trivial polynomial solution iff the matrix

$$r\mathcal{E} - \mathcal{A}_0$$

is singular, that is r must be a characteristic value of $\mathcal{A}_0$.

Let us denote by $d(r, \mathcal{A}_0)$ the multiplicity of r as a characteristic value of $\mathcal{A}_0$ with similar notation for other matrices. It is understood that $d(r, \mathcal{A}_0) = 0$ means that r is not a characteristic value. Suppose now that $d(r_\alpha, \mathcal{A}_0) = k_\alpha > 0$. Then, by Lemma 5.2.4, Eq. (B.3.6) has k_α linearly independent polynomial solutions of the form

$$\mathbf{p}_0(t) = \left\{\mathcal{J}_\alpha + \mathcal{Q}_\alpha t + \frac{1}{2!}\mathcal{Q}_\alpha^2 t^2 + \cdots + \frac{1}{(k_\alpha - 1)!}\mathcal{Q}_\alpha^{k_\alpha - 1} t^{k_\alpha - 1}\right\}\mathbf{v}. \tag{B.3.7}$$

Let X_α be the root space of $\mathcal{A}_0$ for $r = r_\alpha$, $\mathcal{J}_\alpha$ the idempotent and $\mathcal{Q}_\alpha$ the corresponding nilpotent element. The vector $\mathbf{v}$ is one of the k_α basis vectors of X_α. We see that $\mathbf{p}_0(t)$ is of degree $\leq k_\alpha - 1$, the exact degree being $m_\alpha - 1$, if m_α is the multiplicity of r_α as a root of the minimal equation of $\mathcal{A}_0$.

We now take $r = r_\alpha$ and fix $\mathbf{v} = \mathbf{v}_\alpha$ as one of the basis vectors of X_α. Once this is done $\mathbf{p}_0(t)$ is a definite vector polynomial and we proceed to determine $\mathbf{p}_1(t), \mathbf{p}_2(t), \ldots$ from the recurrence relations (B.3.5). As long as $d(r_\alpha + m, \mathcal{A}_0) = 0$, i.e. as long as the matrices $(r_\alpha + m)\mathcal{E} - \mathcal{A}_0$ are non-singular, Lemma 5.2.1 gives a unique expression for $\mathbf{p}_m(t)$ in terms of the preceding polynomials $\mathbf{p}_0(t), \mathbf{p}_1(t), \ldots, \mathbf{p}_{m-1}(t)$. Moreover all these polynomials are of degree $\leq k_\alpha - 1$.

Ambiguity and increase in the degree will occur only if we encounter an m such that $d(r_\alpha + m, \mathcal{A}_0) > 0$. Here we have to resort to Theorem 5.2.1 which presents us with a solution manifold of dimension $d(r_\alpha + m, \mathcal{A}_0)$ and polynomial vectors whose degrees exceed those of the preceding polynomials by at most $d(r_\alpha + m, \mathcal{A}_0)$. From this manifold we select the particular solution which corresponds to taking all constants of integration equal to 0, i.e. the solution denoted by $\mathbf{p}^0(t)$ in the proof of Theorem 5.2.1. Note that replacing $\mathbf{p}^0(t)$ by some other admissible solution amounts to adding some determination of $w(z, r_\alpha + m)$ to $w(z, r_\alpha)$. Suppose that the arithmetic progression

$$r_\alpha, r_\alpha + 1, r_\alpha + 2, \ldots, r_\alpha + m, \ldots$$

contains K_α characteristic values of $\mathcal{A}_0$, each value counted with its proper multiplicity. We have then

$$d(r_\alpha + m, \mathcal{A}_0) = 0 \qquad \text{for} \qquad K_\alpha < m$$

and for such values of m equation (B.3.5) has one and only one polynomial solution.

Let d_m denote the degree of $\mathbf{p}_m(t)$. Then

$$d_m \leq K_\alpha - 1 \leq n - 1 \tag{B.3.8}$$

for all m and all α. To prove this, note that

$$\sum_{m=0}^{\infty} d(r_\alpha + m, \mathcal{A}_0) = K_\alpha.$$

Further, by Theorem 5.2.1,

$$d_m \leq D_{m-1} + d(r_\alpha + m, \mathcal{A}_0), \qquad D_k = \max_{0 \leq j < k} d_j.$$

By induction we obtain

$$d_m \leq d_0 + \sum_1^m d(r_\alpha + k, \mathcal{A}_0) \leq D_0 + K_\alpha - k_\alpha \leq K_\alpha - 1 \leq n - 1,$$

since $D_0 = d_0 \leq k_\alpha - 1$ and $\sum k_\alpha = n$.

It follows that for $r = r_\alpha$ there are k_α formal series (B.3.3) where the $\mathbf{p}_{jmr}(\log z)$ are uniquely determined vector polynomials in $\log z$, each of degree $\leq K_\alpha - 1$. These polynomials may reduce to constant vectors. This will be the case if (1) $\mathfrak{Q}_\alpha = 0$ and (2) $K_\alpha = k_\alpha$; in other words, if the root space X_α is spanned by the characteristic vectors corresponding to $r = r_\alpha$ and there is no root space X_β with $r_\beta = r_\alpha + m$ for any positive integer m. The first of these conditions is also necessary for the absence of logarithms.

If we now let r_α run through the distinct characteristic values of $\mathcal{A}_0$, we obtain

$$\sum_\alpha d(r_\alpha, \mathcal{A}_0) = n$$

formal solution vectors. It remains to prove the convergence of the series (B.3.3) so obtained and to prove the linear independence.

To prove convergence we proceed as follows. Let D be a simply-connected domain whose closure lies in the punctured disk $0 < |z| < R$ and let T be its image under the mapping $t = \log z$. Take a ρ such that $0 < \rho < R$ and $z \in D$ implies $|z| < \rho$. Set

$$\alpha_k = \|\mathcal{A}_k\|, \qquad A(\rho) = \sum_0^{\infty} \alpha_k \rho^k, \tag{B.3.9}$$

where

$$\|\mathcal{A}\| = \max_j \sum_{k=1}^{n} |a_{jk}|, \qquad \mathcal{A} = (a_{jk}).$$

Consider once more the equation (B.3.5) for m large. For $m > |r_\alpha| + \alpha_0$ the matrix $(r_\alpha + m)\mathcal{E} - \mathcal{A}_0$ is non-singular and its inverse admits of the expansion

$$\mathcal{R}(r_\alpha + m, \mathcal{A}_0) = \sum_{k=0}^{\infty} \mathcal{A}_0^k (r_\alpha + m)^{-k-1} \tag{B.3.10}$$

and the estimate

$$\|\mathcal{R}(r_\alpha + m, \mathcal{A}_0)\| \le (m - |r_\alpha| - \alpha_0)^{-1}. \tag{B.3.11}$$

Let us set

$$\mathbf{q}_m(t) = \sum_{j=0}^{m-1} \mathcal{A}_{m-j} \mathbf{p}_j(t). \tag{B.3.12}$$

Since $(r_\alpha + m)\mathcal{E} - \mathcal{A}_0$ is non-singular for the values of m under consideration, Lemma 5.2.1 gives

$$\mathbf{p}_m(t) = \mathcal{R}(r_\alpha + m, \mathcal{A}_0)\mathbf{q}_m(t) - \mathcal{R}^2(r_\alpha + m, \mathcal{A}_0)\mathbf{q}_m'(t) + \mathcal{R}^3(r_\alpha + m, \mathcal{A}_0)\mathbf{q}_m''(t) - \cdots \tag{B.3.13}$$

This series breaks off after a finite number of terms since $\mathbf{q}_m(t)$ is a polynomial of degree $\le K_\alpha - 1$, the maximal degree of the $\mathbf{p}$'s.

We have to prove that each of the series

$$\sum_{m=0}^{\infty} \mathbf{p}_m(\log z) z^{r_\alpha + m}$$

converges uniformly in some domain D, say

$$0 < \varepsilon < |z| < \rho, \qquad |\arg z| < \pi. \tag{B.3.14}$$

The formal series will then define an actual solution of (B.3.2) in D. The series may be written in the form

$$z^{r_\alpha} \sum_{k=0}^{K_\alpha - 1} (\log z)^k \mathbf{v}_k(z), \tag{B.3.15}$$

where $\mathbf{v}_k(z)$ is a power series in z with vector coefficients. These power series must converge for $|z| < R$ since every solution of (B.3.2) is holomorphic in

$$0 < |z| < R, \ |\arg z| < \pi. \tag{B.3.16}$$

Hence it is sufficient to prove that for any choice of ρ, $\rho < R$, the sequence

$$\{\sup_{z \in D} \|\mathbf{p}_m(\log z)\| \rho^m\} \tag{B.3.17}$$

is bounded.

To prove this we need some estimates of the polynomials $\mathbf{p}_m(t)$ and $\mathbf{q}_m(t)$ and of their derivatives for $t \in T$, the image under $t = \log z$ of the domain D of (B.3.14) where $\rho < R$. Set

$$b_j = \max_k \sup_{t \in T} \|\mathbf{p}_j^{(k)}(t)\|, \qquad c_j = \max_k \sup_{t \in T} \|\mathbf{q}_j^{(k)}(t)\|. \tag{B.3.18}$$

These numbers are finite since $\mathbf{p}_j$ and $\mathbf{q}_j$ are polynomials of bounded degree.

Now for $m > |r_\alpha| + \alpha_0 + 1 \equiv a + 1$ formulas (B.3.11) and (B.3.13) give, for $t \in T$,

$$\|\mathbf{p}_m(t)\| \le \frac{c_m}{m - a - 1},$$

and repeated differentiation shows that this may be strengthened to

$$b_m \le \frac{c_m}{m - a - 1}. \tag{B.3.19}$$

On the other hand, (B.3.12) leads to

$$\|\mathbf{q}_m(t)\| \le \sum_{j=0}^{m-1} \alpha_{m-j} b_j,$$

and repeated differentiation gives

$$c_m \le \sum_{j=0}^{m-1} \alpha_{m-j} b_j. \tag{B.3.20}$$

Combining we get

$$b_m \le \frac{1}{m - a - 1} \sum_{j=0}^{m-1} \alpha_{m-j} b_j,$$

whence

$$\begin{aligned} b_m \rho^m &\le \frac{1}{m - a - 1} \sum_{j=0}^{m-1} \alpha_{m-j} \rho^{m-j} b_j \rho^j \\ &\le \frac{1}{m - a - 1} \left\{ \sum_{k=1}^{m} \alpha_k \rho^k \right\} \max_{j<m} (b_j \rho^j) \\ &\le \frac{1}{m - a - 1} [A(\rho) - \alpha_0] \max_{j<m} (b_j \rho^j). \end{aligned}$$

Suppose now that m is so large that

$$m > A(\rho) + |r_\alpha| + 1.$$

Then

$$b_m \rho^m < \max_{j<m} (b_j \rho^j) \tag{B.3.21}$$

and

$$\lim_{k\to\infty} b_k\rho^k = 0.$$

It follows that the sequence

$$\{b_m\rho^m\} \tag{B.3.22}$$

is bounded and, *a fortiori*, so is (B.3.17).

Hence all the formal series (B.3.3) are convergent in norm for z satisfying (B.3.14). Thus they represent actual solutions and as such converge in norm in the domain (B.3.16).

We have still to prove linear dependence. Now a linear relation between the solution vectors (B.3.3) implies a corresponding relation between the various functions

$$(\log z)^k z^{r_\alpha+m}\mathbf{v}_{jkm}$$

which enter in the definition of the solutions: comparison can be made only between terms involving the same exponents k and $r_\alpha + m$. If this condition is satisfied, the corresponding vectors $\mathbf{v}_{jkm}$ must be linearly dependent. Suppose that the characteristic roots r_α are numbered so that

$$\Re(r_1) \le \Re(r_2) \le \cdots \le \Re(r_\alpha) \le \cdots,$$

where $\Im(r_\alpha) < \Im(r_{\alpha+1})$ if $\Re(r_\alpha) = \Re(r_{\alpha+1})$. As above k_α denotes the multiplicity of r_α. The sum

$$\sum_{j=1}^{n} C_j\mathbf{w}_j(z)$$

contains the subsum

$$\sum_{j=1}^{k_1} C_j\mathbf{v}_j \cdot z^{r_1}$$

which must be identically zero if the solutions are linearly dependent. This implies

$$\sum_{j=1}^{k_1} C_j\mathbf{v}_j = \mathbf{0},$$

i.e. a relation between the basis vectors of the root space X_1. This gives

$$C_1 = C_2 = \cdots = C_{k_1} = 0.$$

The same argument applies for all the other root spaces as long as the corresponding roots r_β are not congruent modulo 1 to one of the preceding r_α's. Suppose that the first time this occurs is for $r_\beta = r_\alpha + m$. We have then a relation of the form

$$z^{r_\alpha+m}\sum C_j'\mathbf{v}_{j\alpha m} + z^{r_\beta}\sum C_j''\mathbf{v}_{j\beta 0} = \mathbf{0}.$$

The first sum formally involves k_α terms but is actually empty since each C_j' is 0 by virtue of the linear independence of the k_α solutions corresponding to $r = r_\alpha$. The second sum involves k_β terms. Here the vectors $\mathbf{v}_{j\beta 0}$ form a basis of X_β and are consequently linearly independent so each $C_j'' = 0$. In this manner we show successively that all $C_j = 0$ so the solutions are linearly independent. ∎

EXERCISE B.3

1. In formula (B.3.15) set $z^{r_\alpha}\mathbf{v}_k(z) = \mathbf{V}_k(z)$ and show that

$$z\mathbf{V}_k'(z) - \mathcal{A}(z)\mathbf{V}_k(z) = -(k+1)\mathbf{V}_{k+1}(z),$$

$k = 0, 1, 2, \ldots, p$, if the pth power of $\log z$ is the highest power actually present. Show, in particular, that $\mathbf{V}_p(z)$ satisfies the original equation.

2. Kneser's Lemma. Suppose that the series

$$\mathcal{A}(z) = \sum_{k=0}^{\infty} \mathcal{A}_k z^k, \qquad \mathbf{v}(z) = \sum_{k=0}^{\infty} \mathbf{v}_k z^k$$

with $\mathcal{A}_k \in \mathfrak{M}_n$, $\mathbf{v}_k \in C^n$, converge for $|z| \le R$. If the series $\sum \mathbf{w}_m z^{p+m}$ is a formal solution of the equation

$$z\mathbf{w}'(z) = \mathcal{A}(z)\mathbf{w}(z) + z^p\mathbf{v}(z),$$

show that the series converges for $0 < |z| < R$.

3. Using the preceding results, give an alternate convergence proof for the series (B.3.3).

4. Determine characteristic roots, root spaces and the functions $\mathbf{p}_0(t)$ and $\mathbf{p}_1(t)$, if

$$\mathcal{A}(z) = \begin{pmatrix} z & z \\ z & 1 + 2z \end{pmatrix}.$$

B.4 IRREGULAR SINGULAR POINTS

An nth order linear differential equation has an irregular singular point at infinity if in the representation (B.2.46), i.e.

$$\sum_{j=0}^{n} P_j(z)\vartheta^{n-j}w = 0, \qquad P_0(z) \equiv 1,$$

at least one of the functions P_j is not holomorphic at ∞. We restrict ourselves to the case where $z = \infty$ is at most a pole for the coefficients. The formula

$$\vartheta^k w = z^k w^{(k)} + C_{1,k} z^{k-1} w^{(k-1)} + \cdots + C_{k-1,k} z w'$$

shows that in the transformed equation

$$z^n w^{(n)} + \sum_{j=1}^{n} Q_j(z) z^{n-j} w^{(n-j)} = 0$$

at least one of the functions $Q_j(z)$ has a pole at infinity. We divide by z^n and rewrite the equation as

$$w^{(n)} + \sum_{j=1}^{n} p_j(z) w^{(n-j)} = 0. \tag{B.4.1}$$

We now see that $z = \infty$ is an irregular singular point, if at least one of the functions

$$z^j p_j(z) \tag{B.4.2}$$

has a pole at infinity.

Let us define the order of $p_j(z)$ at infinity. If $p_j(z) \equiv 0$ we write $\mu_j = -\infty$, otherwise define the order μ_j so that

$$p_j(z) = z^{\mu_j} \pi_j(z), \tag{B.4.3}$$

where $\pi_j(z)$ is holomorphic at $z = \infty$ and $\pi_j(\infty) \neq 0$.

Definition B.4.1. *Set*

$$g = 1 + \max_{1 \le j \le n} (\mu_j / j) \tag{B.4.4}$$

and call g the grade of the irregular singular point at infinity.

The term "rank" is more commonly used than "grade." We shall use "rank" later in a related sense for matrix equations. The grade can be any positive rational number p/k with $1 \le k \le n$, while rank is usually taken to be an integer.

For a discussion we shall need the solution of an elementary *Minimax Problem.*

Lemma B.4.1. *Let $\mu_1, \mu_2, \ldots, \mu_n$ be n given real numbers and set*

$$\mu = \max_{1 \le j \le n} (\mu_j / j). \tag{B.4.5}$$

Then for any choice of n real numbers $\alpha_1, \alpha_2, \ldots, \alpha_n$ the largest of the $2n - 1$ numbers

$$\alpha_2 - \alpha_1, \alpha_3 - \alpha_2, \ldots, \alpha_n - \alpha_{n-1}, \tag{B.4.6}$$

$$\mu_1, \mu_2 - (\alpha_n - \alpha_{n-1}), \mu_3 - (\alpha_n - \alpha_{n-2}), \ldots, \mu_n - (\alpha_n - \alpha_1)$$

is not less than μ and there exists at least one choice of the α's for which the maximum equals μ.

Proof. Let m be the infimum of the maximum in (B.4.6) for any choice of the α's. It is clear that $m \ge \mu_1$. Further, if $j \ge 2$, the larger of the two numbers

$$\mu_j - (\alpha_n - \alpha_{n-j+1}) \quad \text{and} \quad \alpha_{n-j+2} - \alpha_{n-j+1}$$

is at least equal to

$$\tfrac{1}{2}[\mu_j - (\alpha_n - \alpha_{n-j+2})].$$

If now $j \geq 3$, the larger of this number and $\alpha_{n-j+3} - \alpha_{n-j+2}$ is at least equal to

$$\tfrac{1}{3}[\mu_j - (\alpha_n - \alpha_{n-j+3})],$$

and so on. It follows that $m \geq \mu_j/j$ for $j = 1, 2, \ldots, n$.

Now suppose that

$$\mu = \mu_k/k$$

and if there are several possible values for k, take the least one. We then choose

$$\alpha_j = (j-1)\mu, \quad j = 1, 2, \ldots, n. \tag{B.4.7}$$

This gives

$$\mu_j - (\alpha_n - \alpha_{n-j+1}) = \mu_j - (j-1)\mu \leq \mu,$$

i.e. a choice for which $m = \mu$. ∎

The following theorem was proved by Helge von Koch in 1918 (with $g + \varepsilon$ instead of g), using infinite determinants, and by Oscar Perron in 1919, using the Lyapunov–Birkhoff method.

Theorem B.4.1. *Every solution of* (B.4.1) *satisfies*

$$|w(z)| \leq B \exp(K|z|^g) \tag{B.4.8}$$

for $|z|$ large and suitably chosen B and K.

Proof. To show this we reduce the equation to matrix form and bring Theorem 1.5.7 to bear on the result. The reduction can be made in many different ways; here we use a procedure that will give a coefficient matrix $\mathcal{A}(z)$ of least possible rate of growth.

To this end set

$$w_j = z^{-(j-1)\mu} w^{(j-1)}, \quad j = 1, 2, \ldots, n, \tag{B.4.9}$$

where μ is given by (B.4.5). For the column vector $\mathbf{w}(z)$ formed by the w_j's this leads to the equation

$$\mathbf{w}'(z) = \mathcal{A}(z)\mathbf{w}(z), \tag{B.4.10}$$

where the matrix $\mathcal{A}(z) = (a_{jk}(z))$ has the elements

$$\begin{aligned} a_{j,j}(z) &= -(j-1)\mu/z,\ a_{j,j+1}(z) = z^{\mu},\ j = 1, 2, \ldots, n-1, \\ a_{n,\beta}(z) &= -z^{-(n-\beta)\mu} p_{n-\beta+1}(z),\ \beta = 1, 2, \ldots, n-1, \\ a_{n,n}(z) &= -(n-1)\mu/z - p_1(z), \end{aligned} \tag{B.4.11}$$

all other elements being 0.

We may assume $\mu > -1$. The order at infinity of the elements of $\mathcal{A}(z)$ in the first $n - 1$ rows is at most μ and equals μ for the elements above the main diagonal. The order of $a_{n,\beta}(z)$ is

$$\mu_{n-\beta+1} - (n - \beta)\mu \le \mu$$

by Lemma B.4.1 and this holds also for $\beta = n$. Hence we can find M and R such that $a_{jk}(z)$ is holomorphic for $0 < R \le |z| = r < \infty$ and

$$|a_{jk}(z)| \le Mr^{\mu}. \tag{B.4.12}$$

This gives

$$\|\mathcal{A}(z)\| \le nMr^{\mu}. \tag{B.4.13}$$

Take a z_0 with $R < |z_0|$, let the initial value of $\mathbf{w}(z)$ be given at $z = z_0$ and integrate (B.4.10) radially from z_0 to z. Thus

$$\mathbf{w}(z) = \mathbf{w}(z_0) + \int_{z_0}^{z} \mathcal{A}(s)\mathbf{w}(s)\, ds$$

and

$$\|\mathbf{w}(z)\| \le \|\mathbf{w}(z_0)\| + \int_{z_0}^{z} \|\mathcal{A}(s)\|\, \|\mathbf{w}(s)\|\, |ds|$$

$$\le \|\mathbf{w}(z_0)\| + nM \int_{z_0}^{z} |s|^{\mu} \|\mathbf{w}(s)\|\, |ds|.$$

By the generalization of Theorem 1.5.7 in Problem 6, Exercise 1.5 this implies

$$\|\mathbf{w}(z)\| \le \|\mathbf{w}(z_0)\| \exp\left\{\frac{nM}{\mu + 1}\,[|z|^{\mu+1} - |z_0|^{\mu+1}]\right\}.$$

If $|\arg z| \le \pi$, then $\|\mathbf{w}(z_0)\|$ is bounded on $|z| = r_0$. If its least upper bound is C, then (B.4.8) is seen to hold with

$$K = \frac{nM}{\mu + 1}, \qquad B = C \exp(-Kr_0^{\mu+1}).$$

Note that the inequality for the solution vector implies the same inequality for its first component $w_1(z)$ which is a solution of (B.4.1). ▌

It follows from Lemma B.4.1 that of all substitutions of the form

$$w_j = z^{-\alpha_j} w^{(j-1)}, \tag{B.4.14}$$

the one chosen, namely (B.4.9), gives the lowest bound for the rate of growth of the solutions for radial approach to ∞. Another matter is, of course, in what sense the result is the best possible of its kind. As in all such problems the meaning of the "best possible of its kind" is open to various interpretations. Here we can make the following assertion:

For each positive rational $g = p/k$, *there exists a linear differential equation of order* k *for which* $z = \infty$ *is an irregular singularity of grade* g *which has a solution* $w(z)$ *such that*

$$\lim |z|^{-g} \log |w(z)| > 0 \tag{B.4.15}$$

for radial approach to ∞, *a finite number of directions excepted.*

If ω is a primitive k^{th} root of unity we can take

$$w(z) = \sum_{j=0}^{k-1} \exp(\omega^j z^g). \tag{B.4.16}$$

This is an entire function of z that satisfies (B.4.15) as well as a differential equation of the form

$$w^{(k)} - \sum_{j=1}^{k-1} c_{jk} z^{-j} w^{(k-j)} - g^k z^{k(g-1)} w = 0 \tag{B.4.17}$$

Here the c_{jk} are polynomials in g. It is clear that $z = \infty$ is an irregular singular point of grade g. Here g is given. It would be more satisfactory to give the integers $\mu_1, \mu_2, \ldots, \mu_n$, and then construct the differential equation with the desired properties.

Equation (B.4.1) has solutions of the form

$$w(z) = z^\sigma F(z), \tag{B.4.18}$$

where $F(z)$ is holomorphic in $R < |z| < \infty$. It follows that $F(z)$ can be expanded in a Laurent series in this annulus. The exponent σ can be determined modulo 1 and the coefficients of the series can be found by the use of *infinite determinants*. This was done by Helge von Koch (1870–1924) in 1892.

The known facts about the rate of growth of $w(z)$ suggest the possibility of finding solutions of the form

$$z^\sigma \exp[P(z)]N(z), \tag{B.4.19}$$

where $P(z)$ is a polynomial in z or in some fractional power of z and $N(z)$ is an expansion in descending powers of z or of $z^{1/k}$. In general the series $N(z)$ is formal and does not converge but may be *asymptotic in the sense of Poincaré*. One reason for the divergence is that the function $F(z)$ of (B.4.18) has in general an essential singularity at $z = \infty$. By Picard's theorem, $F(z)$ takes on every value infinitely often in any neighborhood of $z = \infty$ with at most one exception. On the other hand, if $w(z)$ is represented by (B.4.19) with a convergent series $N(z)$, then $w = 0$ must be a Picard value for $w(z)$. This is possible, of course, but must be considered exceptional so that convergent expansions (B.4.19) are less likely to exist.

Such series in integral powers of z were introduced by L. W. Thomé in 1872, who called them *normal series*, while series in fractional powers of z

go back to the 1885 Paris thesis of Eugène Fabry (1856–1944). They are called *subnormal series.*

Actually expansions with divergent $N(z)$ are the more useful. Here a second phenomenon comes into play, that of *Stokes* (after George Gabriel Stokes 1819–1903). The neighborhood of an irregular singular point is not a homogeneous medium with respect to behavior of the solutions. On the contrary, the neighborhood breaks up into complementary regions, usually sectorial in shape, in each of which the solution has a different asymptotic behavior.

Equation (B.4.17) with $g = 2$, $k = 2$ and

$$w(z) = \exp(z^2) + \exp(-z^2)$$

can be taken as a simple illustration. Here there are four sectors

$$S_j\colon \tfrac{1}{4}(2j-3)\pi < \arg z < \tfrac{1}{4}(2j-1)\pi, \qquad j = 1, \ldots, 4.$$

In the interior of S_1 and S_3

$$\lim_{z\to\infty} w(z)\exp(-z^2) = 1$$

while in the interior of S_2 and S_4 we have instead

$$\lim_{z\to\infty} w(z)\exp(z^2) = 1.$$

It is exceptional that a solution has the same asymptotic behavior in a full neighborhood of the singularity. For a study of an irregular singular point we have to determine the basic sectors and for each sector the corresponding asymptotic expansions (B.4.19).

We shall not carry out this delicate and laborious determination. For the second order case we refer to Section 7.4, where the transformation of Liouville, conformal mapping, and asymptotic integration are used to get a fairly complete picture of the behavior of the solutions at an irregular singular point placed at $z = \infty$.

Let us remark in passing that there is a close relation between our problem for Eq. (B.4.1) and the theory of the *algebroid functions* satisfying the equation

$$Y^n + p_1(z)Y^{n-1} + \cdots + p_{n-1}(z)Y + p_n(z) = 0. \tag{B.4.20}$$

For large values of $|z|$ this equation is satisfied by n functions

$$Y_1(z),\ Y_2(z), \ldots,\ Y_n(z). \tag{B.4.21}$$

The corresponding functions

$$\exp\left[\int^z Y_1(s)\,ds\right], \ldots, \exp\left[\int^z Y_n(s)\,ds\right] \tag{B.4.22}$$

are approximate solutions of (B.4.1) roughly in the same sense as the *determining factors* $\exp[P(z)]$ for the various sectors are approximate solutions.

The observation goes back to Anders Wiman (1865–1959) and details have been worked out in an Uppsala dissertation by Mogens Matell (1924).

If $N(z)$ is an asymptotic series in powers of $1/z$, valid in a right half-plane, the divergent series can often be replaced by a convergent *factorial series* of the form

$$a_0 + \sum_{m=1}^{\infty} \frac{m!a_m}{z(z+\gamma)\cdots(z+(m-1)\gamma)}. \tag{B.4.23}$$

This device was first used by J. Horn in 1915 and was studied in great detail by W. J. Trjitzinsky (1935). Formal series in terms of $z^{-1/k}$ can be handled similarly by factorial series in $z^{1/k}$. Trjitzinsky has shown that not all formal series arising in this theory are amenable to such treatment. Here the salient fact is whether or not the function $N(z)$ or, alternately, some function $N(az^k)$ admits of a representation by a Laplace integral

$$\int_0^{\infty} \exp(-zt)f(t)\,dt, \tag{B.4.24}$$

where $f(t)$ is analytic and satisfies certain conditions.

Laplace contour integrals

$$\oint \exp(zt)U(t)\,dt \tag{B.4.25}$$

have been used by H. Poincaré (1886) to represent solutions of linear differential equations of type (B.4.1). They are effective if $g \le 1$. For $g = 2$, E. Cunningham (1906) has examined representations by contour double integrals

$$\oint\oint \exp(zs + \tfrac{1}{2}z^2t)U(s, t)\,ds\,dt \tag{B.4.26}$$

and has indicated generalizations to p-tuple integrals for $g = p$. Cf. Sections 6.8 and 6.9, where similar questions are considered for $\mathfrak{B}$-valued functions.

We turn now to the matrix case

$$\mathcal{W}'(z) = z^{p-1}\mathcal{A}(z)\mathcal{W}(z). \tag{B.4.27}$$

Here p is a positive integer, $\mathcal{A}(z)$ is holomorphic for $R < |z| \le \infty$ and $\mathcal{A}(\infty) \ne 0$. We call p the *rank* of the singular point $z = \infty$. Proceeding as in the nth order linear case we obtain

Theorem B.4.2. *If* $\mathcal{W}(z)$ *is a solution of* (B.4.27), *then there are constants* B *and* K *such that for* $R < R_1 \le |z|$ *and* $|\arg z| \le \pi$

$$\|\mathcal{W}(z)\| \le B\exp(K|z|^p). \tag{B.4.28}$$

The proof is left to the reader.

Choosing $\mathcal{A}(z) = \mathcal{E}$, we see that the estimate is the best possible for the admissible range of matrices $\mathcal{A}(z)$. This does not mean that it is necessarily a good estimate.

The further development of the theory is largely tied to the nature of the characteristic roots of the matrix $\mathcal{A}(\infty)$. If these are distinct the situation is relatively simple. We state without proof:

Theorem B.4.3. *If the characteristic roots of $\mathcal{A}(\infty)$ are all distinct, say $\lambda_1, \lambda_2, \ldots, \lambda_n$, there exist n scalar polynomials $P_k(z)$ and n exponents $\sigma_1, \sigma_2, \ldots, \sigma_n$, such that*

$$\mathcal{W}(z) = \mathcal{N}(z)\mathcal{D}(\cdots, \exp[P_k(z) + \sigma_k \log z], \cdots) \qquad \text{(B.4.29)}$$

is a fundamental solution of (B.4.27). *Here*

$$P_k(z) = \frac{1}{p}\lambda_k z^p + \lambda_{k,1} z^{p-1} + \cdots + \lambda_{k,k-1} z, \qquad \text{(B.4.30)}$$

$\mathcal{D}(\cdots)$ is a diagonal matrix with the stated element in the kth place. The curvilinear sectors are bounded by infinite branches of the curves

$$C_{jk} : \Re[P_j(z)] = \Re[P_k(z)] \qquad \text{(B.4.31)}$$

and for each sector there is a matrix series $\mathcal{N}(z)$ in powers of $1/z$ which is asymptotic to the function.

If there are multiple characteristic roots, several complications arise. There is a polynomial P_j for each of the distinct roots, but this may now be a polynomial in $z^{1/k}$ for some positive integer k. Similarly the $\mathcal{N}(z)$'s may proceed after powers of $z^{-1/k}$. The simple diagonal matrix is replaced by a diagonal block matrix, the kth block being

$$[P_k(z) + \sigma_k \log z]\mathfrak{I}_k + \log z\mathfrak{Z}_k. \qquad \text{(B.4.32)}$$

Here $\mathfrak{I}_k$ and $\mathfrak{Z}_k$ have the same dimension as the root space of the corresponding λ_k; $\mathfrak{I}_k$ is the unit matrix, $\mathfrak{Z}_k$ a square matrix with zeros and/or ones in the first subdiagonal and zeros elsewhere. It follows that $\exp[\log z\mathfrak{Z}_k]$ is a polynomial in $\log z$.

There are several reduction problems associated with (B.4.27). The first of these concerns the form of $\mathcal{A}(z)$. Instead of the infinite series

$$\mathcal{A}(z) = \sum_{k=0}^{\infty} \mathcal{A}_k z^{-k}$$

it would be advantageous to have a polynomial in $1/z$ of as low a degree as possible. The idea is to choose a multiplier $\mathcal{M}(z)$ such that setting

$$\mathcal{W} = \mathcal{M}(z)\mathcal{Y}$$

the function $\mathcal{Y}(z)$ satisfies an equation

$$\mathcal{Y}'(z) = z^{p-1}\left\{\sum_{j=0}^{s} \mathcal{B}_j z^{-j}\right\}\mathcal{Y}(z), \qquad \text{(B.4.33)}$$

where s is as small as possible.

G. D. Birkhoff, who did pioneering work in the theory now before us, pointed out the possibility of making such a reduction. In 1909 and in 1913, he gave two methods with a view to showing that one can make $s \leq p$. His argument has been questioned; in 1953, F. R. Gantmacher, and in 1959, P. Masani gave counter examples for $p = 0$ (the regular singular case!) indicating that Birkhoff's claims could not be maintained. In 1963 H. L. Turrettin attempted to make clear to what extent Birkhoff was right and to what extent he was wrong. He found that a cut-off is always possible: there exists some finite s for which (B.4.33) holds though possibly $s > p$. For the contested case $p = 0$, he found that $s = 1$ comes out of a correct application of Birkhoff's first method and $s = 0$ out of his second. For $p > 0$ Birkhoff's second method can still be made to give $s = p$, provided the characteristic roots of $\mathcal{A}_0$ are all distinct while the case with multiple roots remains obscure.

The second reduction problem is a Poincaré-Birkhoff problem. As observed above, Poincaré had used a Laplace transformation (B.4.25) to study the case $p = 1$. Here the function $U(t)$ satisfies a linear differential equation having only regular singular points. This can be interpreted as reducing a problem involving rank unity to one involving rank zero. In 1909 Birkhoff applied generalized Laplace integrals to the corresponding matrix problem for an arbitrary rank p. Again there was a reduction of rank from p to 0, but he ran into some difficulties in doing this and had to postulate certain facts that he could not prove. Again this gap in his discussion has been filled by Turrettin, who in 1963 showed that it is possible to make a direct reduction of the rank from p to 1 at the expense of increasing the order of the underlying matrix algebra.

The third reduction problem should really have been the first: how is Eq. (B.4.27) reduced to a normal form from which one can discern (i) if fractional powers are present and, if so, what powers, and (ii) the detailed structure of the matrices $\mathfrak{J}_k$? For this question we have again to refer to the investigations of Turrettin (1955, 1963). Reference should also be made to papers by Masuo Hukuhara (1937) and J. Horn (1938).

EXERCISE B.4

1. Determine the coefficients c_{jk} in (B.4.17) for $k = 2$ and 3.
2. Show that the equation

$$zw'' + (1 - z)w' - w = 0$$

is satisfied by $w_1 = \exp(z)$, $w_2 = \int_0^\infty \exp(-t)(t + z)^{-1}\,dt$ (z not real negative). Show that

$$\sum_{k=0}^{\infty} (-1)^k k!\, z^{-k-1}$$

is a formal solution which represents $w_2(z)$ asymptotically in the cut plane, i.e. for all n

$$\lim z^n\left[w_2(z) - \sum_{k=0}^{n-1} (-1)^k k!z^{-k-1}\right] = 0,$$

if the distance of z from the negative real axis becomes infinite.

3. Given the equation

$$w'' - (z^3 + z^2)w' + (z^5 - 2z)w = 0.$$

Here $g = 4$. Verify that

$$w_1 = \exp\left(\tfrac{1}{3}z^3\right) \qquad \text{and} \qquad w_2 = \exp\left(\tfrac{1}{3}z^3\right)\int_0^z \exp\left(\tfrac{1}{4}t^4 - \tfrac{1}{3}t^3\right) dt$$

are linearly independent solutions. Determine the asymptotic behavior of w_2 in the sectors of the plane determined by $\arg z = \pm\frac{1}{8}\pi + k\frac{1}{2}\pi$. [*Hint*: In some of these sectors a suitable integration by parts will give the desirable information.]

4. Find the corresponding functions $Y_1(z)$ and $Y_2(z)$ and compare

$$\exp\left[\int^z Y_1(s)\, ds\right] \qquad \text{and} \qquad \exp\left[\int^z Y_2(s)\, ds\right]$$

with the known solutions.

5. If $f(t)$ is holomorphic in the right half-plane and admits of a convergent expansion

$$f(t) = \sum_{n=0}^{\infty} c_n(1 - e^{-t})^n$$

with $c_n = O(n^k)$ for some fixed $k \geq 0$, show that

$$\int_0^{\infty} e^{-zt} f(t)\, dt = \sum_{n=0}^{\infty} \frac{c_n n!}{z(z+1)\cdots(z+n)},$$

where the series is absolutely convergent for $\Re(z) > k + 1$.

6. Show that $w_2(z)$ defined in No. 2 satisfies the conditions for expansion in such a factorial series.

7. The equation

$$\mathcal{W}'(z) = \begin{pmatrix} 0 & 1 \\ (2z)^{-1} & -(4z)^{-1} \end{pmatrix} \mathcal{W}(z)$$

is of rank 1 at ∞. Here the matrix $\mathcal{A}(\infty)$ has double characteristic roots 0, 0, and fractional powers occur. Show that a solution matrix is given by

$$\begin{pmatrix} \exp(\sqrt{z}) & \exp(-\sqrt{z}) \\ \dfrac{1}{2\sqrt{z}}\exp(\sqrt{z}) & -\dfrac{1}{2\sqrt{z}}\exp(-\sqrt{z}) \end{pmatrix}$$

$$= \begin{pmatrix} 1 & 1 \\ \dfrac{1}{2\sqrt{z}} & -\dfrac{1}{2\sqrt{z}} \end{pmatrix} \mathfrak{D}[\exp(\sqrt{z}), \exp(-\sqrt{z})].$$

COLLATERAL READING

SCHLESINGER, L., *Handbuch der Theorie der linearen Differentialgleichungen*, Vols. 1, 2:1, 2:2, B. G. Teubner, Leipzig (1895, 1897, 1898),

contains a magistral presentation of the subject. Group-theoretical and invariantive aspects occupy the first 226 pages of Vol. 2:1.

HORN, J., *Gewöhnliche Differentialgleichungen beliebiger Ordnung*, Sammlung Schubert, L. G. J. Göschen, Leipzig (1905),

is less elaborate and more readable. For a modern presentation, see

CODDINGTON, E. A., and NORMAN LEVINSON, *Theory of Ordinary Differential Equations*, McGraw-Hill, New York (1955).

Here chapters 4 and 5 give an excellent account of regular and irregular singular points with emphasis on the matrix case.

For the Fuchs–Frobenius theory, see

FROBENIUS, G., "Ueber die Integration der linearen Differentialgleichungen durch Reihen," *J. für Math.* **76**, 214–235 (1873).

FUCHS, L., "Zur Theorie der linearen Differentialgleichungen mit veränderlichen Coeffizienten," *J. für Math.* **66**, 121–160 (1866); **68**, 345–385 (1868).

HILLE, E., "Miscellaneous questions in the theory of differential equations. I. On the method of Frobenius," *Annals of Math.* (2) **27**, 195–198 (1926).

KNESER, H., "Die Reihenentwicklung bei schwach singulären Stellen linearer Differentialgleichungen," *Archiv der Mathematik*, **2** 413–419 (1949–50).

LAPPO-DANILEVSKY, I. A., *Mémoires sur la théorie du systèmes des équations différentielles linéaires*, Trav. Inst. Phys.-Math. Stekloff, 3 volumes (1934, 1935, 1936). Reprinted Chelsea, New York (1953).

SAUVAGE, L., "Sur les solutions régulières d'un système d'équations différentielles," *Ann. Ecole Norm. Sup.* (3) **3** 391–404 (1886); **5**, 7–22 (1888) and **6**, 157–182 (1889).

SAUVAGE, L., "Théorie générale des systèmes d'équations différentielles linéaires et homogènes," *Ann. de Toulouse*, **8**, 1–24 (1895); *ibid.* **9**, 25–100.

References for Section B.4:

BIRKHOFF, G. D., "Singular points of ordinary differential equations," *Trans. Amer. Math. Soc.* **10**, 436–470 (1909).

BIRKHOFF, G. D., "Equivalent singular points of ordinary linear differential equations," *Math. Annalen*, **74**, 134–139 (1913).

CUNNINGHAM, E., "On linear differential equations of rank unity," *Proc. London Math. Soc.* (2) **4**, 374–383 (1907).

FABRY, E., "Sur les intégrales des équations différentielles linéaires à coefficients rationnels," *Thèse*, Paris (1885).

GANTMACHER, F. R., *The Theory of Matrices*, Vol. 2, Chelsea, New York (1959). Russian original, Moscow (1953).

HILB, E., "Lineare Differentialgleichungen im komplexen Gebiet," *Encyklopädie der Math. Wissenschaften*, Vol. II.2. B. G. Teubner, Leipzig (1915), pp. 471–562.

HORN, J., "Über eine Classe linearer Differentialgleichungen," *Math. Annalen*, **50**, 525–565 (1897).

HORN, J., "Integration linearer Differentialgleichungen durch Laplacesche Integrale und Fakultätenreihen," *Jahresbericht Deutschen Math. Ver.* **24**, 309–329 (1915).

HORN, J., "Laplacesche Integrale, Binomialkoeffizientenreihen und Gammaquotientenreihen," *Math. Zeitschrift*, **21**, 85–95 (1924).

HORN, J., "Unbestimmtheitsstellen linearer Differentialgleichungen mit mehrfachen Wurzeln der characteristischen Gleichung," *Math. Zeitschrift*, **44**, 481–506 (1930).

HUKUHARA, M., "Sur les points singuliers des équations différentielles linéaires, II," *Journ. Fac. Sci. Hokkaido Imp. Univ.* **5**, 123–166 (1937).

VON KOCH, H., "Sur les déterminants infinis et les équations différentielles linéaires," *Acta Math.* **16**, 217–295 (1892).

VON KOCH, H., "Un théorème sur les intégrales irrégulières des équations différentielles linéaires et son application au problème de l'intégration," *Arkiv. Mat., Astr. Fys.* **13**, No. 15, 18 pp. (1918).

LYAPUNOV, A., "Sur la stabilité du mouvement dans un cas particulier," *Ann. de Toulouse* (2) **9**, 203–469 (1908); Russian original, *Comm. Soc. math. Charkov*, (2) **2**, 1–94 (1891).

MASANI, P., "On a result of G. D. Birkhoff on linear differential systems," *Proc. Amer. Math. Soc.* **10**, 696–698 (1959).

MATELL, M., "Asymptotische Eigenschaften gewisser linearer Differentialgleichungen," Uppsala (1924), 67 pp.

PERRON, O., "Über einen Satz des Herrn Helge von Koch über die Integrale linearer Differentialgleichungen," *Math. Zeitschrift*, **3**, 161–174 (1919).

POINCARÉ, H., "Sur les intégrales irregulières des équations linéaires," *Acta Math.* **8**, 295–344 (1886).

STERNBERG, W., "Über die asymptotische Integration von Differentialgleichungen," *Math. Annalen*, **81**, 119–186 (1920).

THOMÉ, L. W., "Zur Theorie der linearen Differentialgleichungen," *J. für Math.* **74** (1872), **75**, **76** (1873), and many later volumes; summaries of work in Vols. **96** (1884) and **122** (1900).

TRJITZINSKY, W. J., "Laplace integrals and factorial series in the theory of linear differential and linear difference equations," *Trans. Amer. Math. Soc.* **37**, 80–146 (1935).

TURRETTIN, H. L., "Convergent solutions of ordinary linear homogeneous differential equations in the neighborhood of an irregular singular point," *Acta Math.* **93**, 27–66 (1955)

TURRETTIN, H. L., "Reduction of ordinary differential equations to the Birkhoff canonical form," *Trans. Amer. Math. Soc.* **107**, 485–507 (1963).

TURRETTIN, H. L., "Reducing the rank of ordinary differential equations," *Duke Math. J.* **30**, 271–274 (1963).

TURRETTIN, H. L., "Solvable related equations pertaining to turning point problems. In Symposium on: Asymptotic Solutions of Differential Equations and their Applications," Publication No. 13 of the Mathematics Research Center U.S. Army, The University of Wisconsin, pp. 37–52, Wiley, New York (1964).

6 LINEAR DIFFERENTIAL EQUATIONS IN BANACH ALGEBRAS

In this chapter we develop the general theory of linear differential equations for functions of a complex variable having values in a Banach algebra. The latter is normally assumed to be non-commutative and to have a unit element, though in some problems we consider a commutative algebra without unit element. In many respects the treatment is complementary to the discussion in the preceding Appendix B where emphasis was on functions of a complex variable, either complex valued or having values in a matrix algebra.

Various aspects of the second order case are developed in the five chapters of Part II. There the emphasis is on real or complex valued solutions, and B-algebras are scarcely mentioned. However, star algebras play a basic role in Section 9.6 and figure also in Section 10.7, while matrix algebras figure also in Sections C.2 and C.3.

The present chapter has nine sections: Fundamental Solutions; Analytic Continuation. The Monodromy Group; Approach to a Singular Point; The Integrable Case; Regular Singular Points; The Method of Frobenius; The Fuchsian Class; Irregular Singular Points, $p = 1$; Irregular Singular Points, $p > 1$.

6.1 FUNDAMENTAL SOLUTIONS

Let $\mathfrak{B}$ be a non-commutative B-algebra with unit element e. Reference will often be made to the special case $\mathfrak{B} = \mathfrak{M}_n$, the algebra of n by n matrices.

We plan to discuss first order linear differential equations with $\mathfrak{B}$-valued solutions. We are mostly concerned with the normal form

$$y'(t) = F(t)y(t) \tag{6.1.1}$$

but the form

$$v'(t) = v(t)G(t) \tag{6.1.2}$$

will also receive some attention. Before going any further, let us note that other forms are possible such as

$$u'(t) = F(t)u(t)G(t), \tag{6.1.3}$$

$$H(t)w'(t) = w(t). \tag{6.1.4}$$

The reader can undoubtedly conceive of still further possibilities. Here the theory of (6.1.2) does not differ essentially from that of (6.1.1) while (6.1.3) presents new and difficult problems. So does (6.1.4), unless $H(t)$ is a regular element of the algebra so that we can multiply on the left by the inverse of $H(t)$ and obtain an equation of type (6.1.1). We shall not consider such equations excepting occasional special problems.

In (6.1.1) $F(t)$ is supposed to be a $\mathfrak{B}$-valued function of a real variable, defined and continuous in some interval (a, b). The extension to complex variables will come shortly.

Theorem 6.1.1. *Let $a < c < b$ and let y_0 be a given element of $\mathfrak{B}$. Then the initial value problem*

$$y'(t) = F(t)y(t), \qquad y(c) = y_0$$

has a unique solution in (a, b).

Proof. We can use the method of successive approximations with $y_0(t) = y_0$. This leads to a sequence of functions $\{y_m(t)\}$ continuous and differentiable in (a, b). If

$$\|F(t)\| \le M \qquad \text{for} \quad a + \varepsilon \le t \le b - \varepsilon,$$

then the usual estimates give

$$\|y_m(t) - y_{m-1}(t)\| \le \|y_0\| \frac{M^m}{m!} |t - c|^m, \tag{6.1.5}$$

and hence uniform convergence in norm of the approximations in

$$[a + \varepsilon, b - \varepsilon]$$

and convergence in (a, b). The limit $y(t)$ is clearly the unique solution of the initial value problem. We have tacitly assumed (a, b) to be finite, the necessary modifications in the infinite case are obvious. ▮

In the same manner we prove

Theorem 6.1.2. *The initial value problem*

$$v'(t) = v(t)G(t), \qquad v(c) = v_0,$$

has a unique solution in (a, b).

The extension to complex variables is of basic importance and offers some novel features. We now suppose that $F(z)$ is a function on complex numbers to the algebra $\mathfrak{B}$ which is holomorphic in some part of the complex plane. We make this more precise by introducing the so-called *Mittag-Leffler star* $\mathbf{A}(z_0; F)$ of $F(z)$ with respect to the initial point z_0. The star $\mathbf{A}(z_0; F)$ is the set of all points z_1 such that $F(z)$ is holomorphic at all points of the straight line segment joining z_0 and z_1, the end-points included. Thus if z_2 is a boundary point of $\mathbf{A}(z_0; F)$, then either $z = z_2$ is a singular point of $F(z)$ for radial approach to z_2 from z_0 or else analytic continuation along the ray leads to a singularity before z_2 is reached. We emphasize that $\mathbf{A}(z; F)$ is a star domain with respect to $z = z_0$, that is if $z_1 \in \mathbf{A}(z_0; F)$ so do all points on the line segment $[z_0, z_1]$. We have now

Theorem 6.1.3. *If $F(z)$ is holomorphic at $z = z_0$, then the initial value problem*

$$w'(z) = F(z)w(z), \qquad w(z_0) = w_0 \in \mathfrak{B}, \tag{6.1.6}$$

has a unique solution $w(z; z_0, w_0)$ holomorphic in $\mathbf{A}(z_0; F)$. Similarly the initial value problem

$$v'(z) = v(z)G(z), \qquad v(z_0) = v_0 \in \mathfrak{B}, \tag{6.1.7}$$

has a unique solution holomorphic in $\mathbf{A}(z_0; G)$.

Proof. This also follows from the method of successive approximations. It is enough to sketch the proof for (6.1.6). Let $\mathbf{A}_0$ be a bounded star domain with respect to $z = z_0$ and contained in $\mathbf{A}(z_0; F)$. Since the closure of $\mathbf{A}_0$ is compact, there are positive numbers M and ρ such that

$$\|F(z)\| \le M, \quad |z - z_0| \le \rho, \quad z \in \mathbf{A}_0.$$

We have then $w_0(z) = w_0$ and

$$w_m(z) = w_0 + \int_{z_0}^{z} F(t)w_{m-1}(t)\,dt,$$

where each $w_m(z)$ is holomorphic in $\mathbf{A}_0$. Further

$$\|w_m(z) - w_{m-1}(z)\| \le \int_{z_0}^{z} \|F(t)\|\,\|w_{m-1}(t) - w_{m-2}(t)\|\,|dt|.$$

If now for some m

$$\|w_{m-1}(t) - w_{m-2}(t)\| \le \|w_0\| \frac{M^{m-1}}{(m-1)!} |t - z_0|^{m-1}, \tag{6.1.8}$$

then

$$\|w_m(z) - w_{m-1}(z)\| \le \|w_0\| \frac{M^m}{(m-1)!} \int_{z_0}^{z} |t - z_0|^{m-1}|dt|$$

$$= \|w_0\| \frac{M^m}{m!} |z - z_0|^m \le \|w_0\| \frac{1}{m!} (\rho M)^m.$$

Since (6.1.8) is clearly valid for $m = 2$, it holds for all m. Hence the series

$$w_0(z) + \sum_{m=1}^{\infty} [w_m(z) - w_{m-1}(z)] \equiv w(z) \tag{6.1.9}$$

converges uniformly in norm in $\mathbf{A}_0$ and the sum of the series is a holomorphic function of z in $\mathbf{A}_0$. Here $\mathbf{A}_0$ is an arbitrary star domain in $\mathbf{A}(z_0; F)$. Thus $w(z)$ exists everywhere in $\mathbf{A}(z_0; F)$ as a $\mathfrak{B}$-valued holomorphic function of z. We have clearly

$$w(z) = w_0 + \int_{z_0}^{z} F(t)w(t)\,dt, \tag{6.1.10}$$

so that $w(z) \equiv w(z; z_0, w_0)$ is the desired solution of (6.1.6). Uniqueness follows by the usual argument. ▮

Thus we see that the solutions have no singularities other than those of $F(z)$ plus possibly the point at infinity. This has been proved for rectilinear continuation from $z = z_0$, but we shall show below that the same result holds for analytic continuation along arbitrary paths.

Theorem 6.1.4. *We have*

$$\begin{aligned} w(z; z_0, w_0) &= w(z; z_0, e)w_0, \\ v(z; z_0, v_0) &= v_0 v(z; z_0, e). \end{aligned} \tag{6.1.11}$$

The same type of results holds for real variables.

Proof. Consider the first relation. Here both sides are solutions of (6.1.6) and have the same initial value w_0 at $z = z_0$. Hence they are identical. The same argument holds for the second relation. ▮

Theorem 6.1.5. *The solution $w(z; z_0, e)$ is a regular element of $\mathfrak{B}$ for z in $\mathbf{A}(z_0; F)$. More generally, $w(z; z_0, w_0)$ is regular in $\mathfrak{B}$ iff w_0 has this property. The same result holds for real variables in any interval of continuity.*

Proof. The following simple argument was suggested by W. A. Coppel. Let $W(z)$ and $V(z)$ denote the solutions of

$$w'(z) = F(z)w(z), \qquad w(z_0) = e,$$

$$v'(z) = -v(z)F(z), \qquad v(z_0) = e,$$

respectively. Then $W(z)$ and $V(z)$ are holomorphic in $\mathbf{A}(z_0; F)$. Further

$$V(z)W'(z) + V'(z)W(z) \equiv 0. \tag{6.1.12}$$

This together with $W(z_0) = V(z_0) = e$ gives

$$V(z)W(z) = e,$$

so that $V(z)$ is the left inverse of $W(z)$ in $\mathbf{A}(z_0; F)$. On the other hand, from $W(z_0) = e$ it follows that $W(z)$ has a two-sided inverse in some neighborhood of $z = z_0$. In this neighborhood

$$[W(z)]^{-1} = V(z), \qquad V(z)W(z) = W(z)V(z) = e. \tag{6.1.13}$$

But the last relation is a functional equation satisfied by the functions $V(z)$ and $W(z)$ and, by the Law of Permanency of Functional Equations, it holds as long as both $V(z)$ and $W(z)$ are holomorphic and hence for $z \in \mathbf{A}(z_0; F)$. Hence $W(z) = w(z; z_0, e)$ is regular in $\mathbf{A}(z_0; F)$.

In the relation

$$w(z; z_0, w_0) = w(z; z_0, e)w_0$$

the first factor on the right is regular in $\mathbf{A}(z_0; F)$. Hence the left member will be regular iff w_0 is regular and then for all z in $\mathbf{A}(z_0; F)$.

Suppose now that $F(t)$ is merely continuous on a real interval (a, b) and $W(c) = V(c) = e$ for some c, $a < c < b$. We still have that $V(t)$ and $W(t)$ exist in (a, b) and satisfy

$$V(t)W(t) = e.$$

Again we have that $W(t)$ is regular in some interval $(c - h, c + h)$ and there

$$[W(t)]^{-1} = V(t), \qquad V(t)W(t) = W(t)V(t) = e.$$

To extend these relations to all of (a, b) we may resort to a step-by-step argument. Let $\delta > 0$ be fixed and let c_0 be any point in $[a + \delta, b - \delta]$. We can then find an η independent of c_0 such that

$$\|w(t; c_0, e) - e\| \le \tfrac{1}{2} \quad \text{for} \quad |t - c_0| \le \eta.$$

For such values of t the function $w(t; c_0, e)$ is then a regular element of $\mathfrak{B}$. If now, for example, $c + h - \frac{1}{2}\eta < c_0 < c + h$, we have

$$w(t; c, e) = w(t; c_0, e)w(c_0; c, e)$$

and hence regular in an interval which extends beyond $c + h$ by a fixed amount $> \frac{1}{2}\eta$. This can be repeated and in a finite number of steps all points in $[a + \delta, b - \delta]$ have been reached. It follows that $w(t; c, e)$. is actually regular everywhere in (a, b). ∎

Corollary. *For an arbitrary choice of points z_1 and z in $\mathbf{A}(z_0; F) \cap \mathbf{A}(z_1; F)$*

$$w(z; z_0, e) = w(z; z_1, e)w(z_1; z_0, e). \tag{6.1.14}$$

Definition 6.1.1. *A solution $w(z; z_0, w_0)$ is said to be fundamental iff every solution holomorphic in some neighborhood of $z = z_0$ can be written $w(z; z_0, w_0)w_1$, $w_1 \in \mathfrak{B}$.*

Theorem 6.1.5 then leads to

Theorem 6.1.6. *A solution $w(z; z_0, w_0)$ is fundamental iff w_0 is regular.*

The proof is left to the reader.

We see that a non-fundamental solution of (6.1.6) is a singular element of $\mathfrak{B}$ for all z.

Certain functionals of fundamental solutions are of some interest. Let μ be a *complex valued multiplicative functional* defined and continuous on $\mathfrak{B}$. We postulate the existence of such a functional, not much seems to be known about them. Moreover, we shall require that μ be *Fréchet analytic* on some neighborhood of e in $\mathfrak{B}$. This implies that μ satisfies local Lipschitz conditions and

$$\delta\mu(e; g) \equiv \lim_{\eta \to 0} \frac{1}{\eta} [\mu(e + \eta g) - \mu(e)] \tag{6.1.15}$$

exists for all $g \in \mathfrak{B}$. Since

$$\mu(e) = \mu(e^2) = [\mu(e)]^2,$$

it follows that $\mu(e) = 0$ or 1. The former choice gives $\mu(a) = 0$ for all $a \in \mathfrak{B}$ and is of no interest to us. Hence we take $\mu(e) = 1$ and find that $\mu(a) \neq 0$ for all regular elements of $\mathfrak{B}$ since

$$\mu(a)\mu(a^{-1}) = \mu(e) = 1.$$

Under these assumptions we obtain

Theorem 6.1.7. *If μ is a non-trivial multiplicative functional, Fréchet analytic at $a = e$, and if w_0 is regular, then for $z \in \mathbf{A}(z_0; F)$*

$$\mu[w(z; z_0, w_0)] = \exp\left\{\int_{z_0}^{z} \delta\mu[e; F(t)]\, dt\right\}\mu(w_0). \tag{6.1.16}$$

Proof. To abbreviate we write $w(z)$ for $w(z; z_0, w_0)$. Then

$$\begin{aligned} w(z + \eta) &= w(z) + \eta w'(z) + O(\eta^2) \\ &= [e + \eta F(z)]w(z) + O(\eta^2) \\ &= \{e + \eta F(z) + O(\eta^2)[w(z)]^{-1}\}w(z). \end{aligned}$$

Hence

$$\mu[w(z + \eta)] = \mu[e + \eta F(z)] + O(\eta^2)\mu[w(z)]$$

and, by the local Lipschitz condition,

$$\frac{1}{\eta}\{\mu[w(z + \eta)] - \mu[w(z)]\} = \frac{1}{\eta}\{\mu[e + \eta F(z)] + O(\eta^2) - 1\}\mu[w(z)].$$

Letting $\eta \to 0$, we get by (6.1.15)

$$\frac{d}{dz}\mu[w(z)] = \delta\mu[e; F(z)]\mu[w(z)]. \tag{6.1.17}$$

Integration gives the desired result.

The proof presupposes that w_0 is regular so that $w(z)$ has the same property and $[w(z)]^{-1}$ exists. The formula may be trivially true in other cases, however.

Corollary. *Formula* (6.1.16) *holds for singular* w_0 *for any multiplicative functional which vanishes on the singular elements.*
For then both sides of (6.1.16) are zero.

As an illustration let $\mathfrak{B} = \mathfrak{M}_n$ with elements $\mathcal{A}, \mathcal{B}, \ldots$ and the unit element $\mathcal{E}$. It is well known that

$$\mu(\mathcal{A}) = \det(\mathcal{A}) \tag{6.1.18}$$

is a multiplicative bounded functional on $\mathfrak{M}_n$. Here

$$\det(\mathcal{E} + \eta\mathcal{F}) = 1 + \eta \operatorname{tr}[\mathcal{F}] + O(\eta^2)$$

so that

$$\delta\mu(\mathcal{E}, \mathcal{F}(z)) = \operatorname{tr}[\mathcal{F}(z)],$$

and we obtain formula (B.1.20) for this choice of $\mathfrak{B}$ and μ.

Finally, if μ is linear as well as multiplicative we are led to the formula

$$\mu[w(z)] = \mu(w_0) \exp\left\{\int_{z_0}^{z} \mu[F(t)]\, dt\right\}. \tag{6.1.19}$$

EXERCISE 6.1

1. What is the analogue of Theorem 6.1.5 for Eq. (6.1.7)? Of Definition 6.1.1 and Theorem 6.1.6?
2. What is the analogue of Theorem 6.1.7?
3. As an example of a singular equation of type (6.1.4) take

$$qw'(z) = w(z)$$

where q is a nilpotent element of $\mathfrak{B}$. Show that $w(z) \equiv 0$ is the only solution.

4. Suppose instead that q is quasi-nilpotent and that $n\|q^n\|^{1/n} \to 0$. Assume $w(z)$ to be holomorphic is some part of the z-plane and show that the only such solution is $w(z) \equiv 0$. [*Hint*: Use Cauchy's inequalities for the derivatives of a holomorphic function.]
5. Verify that $\det(\mathcal{A})$ is a continuous multiplicative functional on $\mathfrak{M}_n$.
6. If $p > 0$ is a fixed number, verify that $|\det(\mathcal{A})|^p$ is a multiplicative functional on $\mathfrak{M}_n$. Is it Fréchet analytic at $\mathcal{E}$?
7. Verify (6.1.19).
8. Fill in the missing details at the end of the proof of Theorem 6.1.5.
9. Show that Theorem 6.1.3 remains valid if $\mathfrak{B}$ does not have a unit element. If there is no unit element, Definition 6.1.1 still makes sense and may perhaps be taken as the definition of a fundamental solution. Theorem 6.1.6 obviously becomes meaningless in this new situation.

The space $L_2(0, 2\pi)$ can be made into a commutative B-algebra without unit element under the usual norm and with products defined by convolution, i.e.

$$[f_1 * f_2](t) = \frac{1}{2\pi} \int_0^{2\pi} f_1(t - s) f_2(s)\, ds.$$

The Fourier coefficients are linear and multiplicative functionals on this algebra by Problem 9 of Exercise 4.4.

10. Solve the differential equation

$$w'(z) = F(z) * w(z)$$

on this space, i.e. solve the equation

$$\frac{\partial}{\partial z} w(z, t) = \frac{1}{2\pi} \int_0^{2\pi} F(z, t - s) w(z, s)\, ds,$$

where

$$F(z, t) \sim \sum_{-\infty}^{\infty} F_n(z) e^{nit}, \quad \sum_{-\infty}^{\infty} |F_n(z)|^2 < \infty, \quad |z| < r,$$

and the functions $F_n(z)$ are holomorphic in $|z| < r$. Assume a Fourier series for the solution

$$w(z, t) \sim \sum_{-\infty}^{\infty} w_n(z) e^{nit}, \quad w_n(0) = w_{n0}, \quad \sum_{-\infty}^{\infty} |w_{n0}|^2 < \infty,$$

Determine the coefficients, show that they are holomorphic in $|z| < r$, and that the solution belongs to $L_2(0, 2\pi)$.

11. Does Theorem 6.1.7 have an analogue in this case?
12. For what initial values is the solution fundamental?

6.2 ANALYTIC CONTINUATION. THE MONODROMY GROUP

We return to Eq. (6.1.6) and the solution $w(z; z_0, e)$ defined in $\mathbf{A}(z_0; F)$. Let $z_1 \in \mathbf{A}(z_0; F)$, $z_1 \neq z_0$, and set $w(z_1; z_0, e) = w_1$. There is a unique solution $w(z; z_1, e)$ defined in $\mathbf{A}(z_1; F)$ and

$$w(z; z_0, e) = w(z; z_1, e) w_1, \qquad z \in \mathbf{A}(z_0; F) \cap \mathbf{A}(z_1; F). \tag{6.2.1}$$

The right member of this equation gives the analytic continuation of $w(z; z_0, e)$ in $\mathbf{A}(z_1; F)$. Given a finite set of points z_k with

$$z_k \in \mathbf{A}(z_{k-1}; F),$$

we obtain a sequence of analytic continuations of the form

$$w(z; z_k, e) w_k w_{k-1} \cdots w_1$$

which represent $w(z; z_0, e)$ in $\mathbf{A}(z_k; F)$, $k = 1, 2, \ldots, m$, provided the analytic continuation is made along the polygonal line with vertices at $z_0, z_1, \ldots, z_m$.

Suppose that $z_0 \in \mathbf{A}(z_m; F)$. After describing the closed polygon $z_0, z_1, \ldots, z_m, z_0$ we arrive at $z = z_0$ with the value

$$w_{m+1}w_m \cdots w_2w_1$$

which is normally different from the initial value e. We note that each w_k is a regular element of $\mathfrak{B}$; hence their product is also regular.

Consider the set of all rectifiable curves C beginning and ending at $z = z_0$ along which $F(z)$ can be continued analytically. To simplify matters we assume that $F(z)$ is single-valued in its domain of existence and has only a finite number of isolated singular points and/or singular lines in any finite sub-domain. The most important case is that in which $F(z)$ is a rational function of z and then the assumptions are trivially satisfied. Since a rectifiable curve can be approximated arbitrarily closely by polygonal lines, there is no loss of generality in assuming C to be a closed polygon which, however, may intersect itself.

We shall assign an *orientation* to such polygons. If C is a simple closed polygon, then by the Jordan curve theorem C separates the plane into two sets, the interior of C and the exterior. C has positive orientation if the so-called *winding number* of C with respect to an interior point is $+1$. The same polygonal line described in the negative sense (winding number -1 for interior points) will be denoted by $-C$.

For a curve C that intersects itself we use a parametric representation

$$z = z(t), \quad 0 < t < 1, \quad z(0) = z(1) = z_0,$$

where $z(t)$ is continuous and piecewise linear. This induces an orientation of C where $z_1 = z(t_1)$ precedes $z_2 = z(t_2)$ if $t_1 < t_2$. There is a uniquely determined minimal simple closed sub-polygon Π of C which contains z_0 as a vertex. This orientation is positive if the induced orientation of Π is positive in the previously defined sense, otherwise negative. Again we use C for positively oriented curves and $-C$ for negatively oriented ones.

For each admissible, positively oriented polygon C there is a regular element $m(C)$ of $\mathfrak{B}$ such that continuation along C carries

$$w(z; z_0, e) \quad \text{into} \quad w(z; z_0, e)m(C) \tag{6.2.2}$$

while continuation along $-C$ carries

$$w(z; z_0, e) \quad \text{into} \quad w(z; z_0, e)[m(C)]^{-1}. \tag{6.2.3}$$

If we first describe C_1 and follow this by a circuit along C_2, the net result is to carry

$$w(z; z_0, e) \quad \text{into} \quad w(z; z_0, e)m(C_2)m(C_1). \tag{6.2.4}$$

We call $m(C)$ the *substitution* associated with C. The set of all substitutions $m(C)$ forms the *group of monodromy* of Eq. (6.1.6) with respect to the point

$z = z_0$. As defined, the group $\mathfrak{G}$ depends upon the choice of z_0 but it will be shown that this dependence is only apparent since all these groups turn out to be isomorphic. It will then be permissible to speak of *the group* $\mathfrak{G}$ *of the equation.*

Lemma 6.2.1. *If the simple closed polygon C does not contain any singularities of F(z) in its interior, then*

$$m(C) = e. \tag{6.2.5}$$

Proof. This is obvious if C lies entirely in $\mathbf{A}(z_0; F)$. In the general case we argue as follows. We recall that a polygon C may be triangulated, i.e. we can join some of the vertices of C by diagonals in the interior of C in such a manner that the polygon plus the diagonals used form a set of triangles. (See Figure 6.1.)

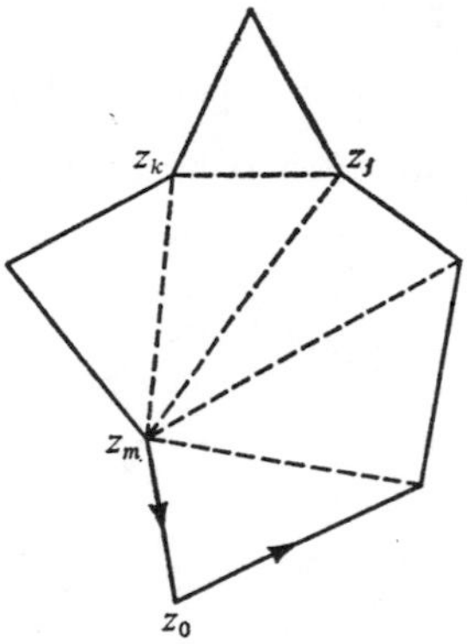

Figure 6.1

Consider a diagonal leading from $z = z_j$ to z_k where $0 < j < k < m$. Continuing $w(z; z_0, e)$ along C we reach z_j with the value w_j and z_k with the value w_k and get back to $z = z_0$ with a value w_{m+1}. If $w_{m+1} \neq e$, we say that C is a *path of non-uniqueness.* Suppose now that we proceed from z_j to z_k along the diagonal instead and reach z_k with a value w^*. There are two possibilities.

(i) $w^* = w_k$. In this case, replace the polygonal line $z_j, z_{j+1}, \ldots, z_k$ by the diagonal z_j, z_k to obtain a new admissible polygon C^*

$$C^*: z_0, z_1, \ldots, z_j, z_k, \ldots, z_m, z_0.$$

Here $m(C^*) = m(C)$ and C^* has fewer vertices than C.

(ii) $w^* \neq w_k$. In this case, the polygon

$$C': z_j, z_{j+1}, \ldots, z_k, z_j$$

is also a path of non-uniqueness in the interior of which $F(z)$ has no singularities. Again C' has fewer vertices than C.

In either case we see that the assumption that C is a path of non-uniqueness for analytic continuation of $w(z; z_0, e)$, there being no singularities of F inside C, leads to the conclusion that there are other paths of non-uniqueness with a smaller number of vertices. We can continue the reduction until we reach a triangle which is also a path of non-uniqueness and which does not contain any singularities of F in its interior or on the perimeter. If $z = z_j$ is one of the three vertices of the triangle, then the latter is completely contained in $\mathbf{A}(z_j; F)$ where the solution is single-valued. Thus the assumption that C is a path of non-uniqueness leads to a contradiction and (6.2.5) must hold. ∎

Lemma 6.6.2. *If C_1 and C_2 are admissible paths from z_0 to z_0, if C_1 and C_2 have no points in common except for $z = z_0$, and if the path $C_1 - C_2$ has no singular points of F in its interior, then*

$$m(C_1) = m(C_2). \tag{6.2.6}$$

Proof. See Figure 6.2. Here

$$m(C_1 - C_2) = [m(C_2)]^{-1}m(C_1) \tag{6.2.7}$$

and $C_1 - C_2$ is a path of uniqueness so that $m(C_1 - C_2) = e$ and (6.2.6) follows. ∎

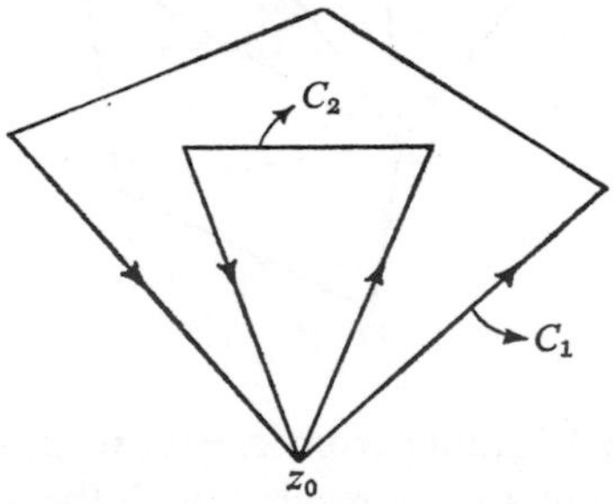

Figure 6.2

Lemma 6.2.3. *If the singular points and singular lines of F are finite in number, then the group $\mathfrak{G}(z_0)$ is finitely generated, i.e. there is a finite set of elements $g_1, g_2, \ldots, g_p$ of $\mathfrak{B}$ such that for any admissible path C*

$$m(C) = (g_{j_\beta})^{\alpha_\beta} (g_{j_{\beta-1}})^{\alpha_{\beta-1}} \cdots (g_{j_1})^{\alpha_1}, \tag{6.2.8}$$

where $\alpha_1, \alpha_2, \ldots, \alpha_\beta$ are positive or negative integers and $j_1, j_2, \ldots, j_\beta$ are integers selected from the set $1, 2, \ldots, p$.

Proof. Let the singular points be $\zeta_1, \zeta_2, \ldots, \zeta_k$, the finite singular lines $l_1, l_2, \ldots, l_m$, and set $k + m = p$. We disregard singular lines extending to infinity. If $z = \infty$ is an isolated singularity of the equation, then it is to be included in the set $\{\zeta_j\}$. We surround each of the singularities by a polygonal loop beginning and ending at $z = z_0$. The loop is supposed to surround the singularity once and only once in the positive sense and to leave all other singularities on the outside. A loop around the point at infinity, if required, can be taken as a large circle outside all the finite singularities joined to z_0 by a suitably chosen double line. Here the orientation of the circle is negative with respect to the origin to make it positive with respect to ∞.

To each loop C_j corresponds a substitution $m(C_j)$. We set

$$m(C_j) = g_j. \tag{6.2.9}$$

These elements of $\mathfrak{B}$ are ordinarily distinct from each other and from e. Given an admissible path C we can find an equivalent union of loops C_j, say

$$\alpha_1 C_{j_1} + \alpha_2 C_{j_2} + \cdots + \alpha_\beta C_{j_\beta}. \tag{6.2.10}$$

Here order is essential. We start by describing α_1 times the loop C_{j_1}, followed by C_{j_2} described α_2 times and so on. Here each α is an integer, positive if the loop is described in the positive sense, negative otherwise. It may happen that two consecutive C_j's are the same. In this case we can contract the formula replacing

$$\alpha_1 C_j + \alpha_2 C_j \qquad \text{by} \qquad (\alpha_1 + \alpha_2) C_j.$$

It should be noted that two equal loops separated by one or more distinct loops cannot be contracted. In replacing C by (6.2.10) repeated use is made of Lemmas 6.2.1. and 6.2.2.

The details are left to the reader. It is suggested that he draw a number of simple figures to convince himself that he can carry out the reduction in any given case. Induction on the number of singularities suffices for the general case.

The reduction (6.2.10) leads directly to (6.2.8). The representation of C by (6.2.10) is not necessarily unique since there may be linear relations between the loops. Such a relation always holds if there is a loop for infinity. This ambiguity is immaterial for our present purposes: all we want to show is that the group $\mathfrak{G}(z_0)$ has a finite set of generators, namely $g_1, g_2, \ldots, g_p$. We do not claim that this is the minimum number of generators nor that the representation of $m(C)$ by these generators is unique. ∎

Lemma 6.2.4. *The group $\mathfrak{G}$ is independent of the initial point z_0 in the sense that if $z_1 \neq z_0$ is a point where $F(z)$ is holomorphic, then there exists a regular element g of $\mathfrak{B}$ such that*

$$\mathfrak{G}(z_1) = g^{-1}\mathfrak{G}(z_0)g. \tag{6.2.11}$$

Proof. Join z_0 and z_1 by a rectifiable arc, a line segment if possible. Describing this arc from z_1 to z_0 carries

$$w(z; z_1, e) \qquad \text{into} \qquad w(z; z_0, e)g$$

for some choice of g which may depend upon the arc. Here g is a regular element of $\mathfrak{B}$. Now let z describe the loop C_j from z_0 to z_0 used in the proof of Lemma 6.2.3. We return to z_0 with the new determination

$$w(z; z_0, e)g_jg$$

and proceeding along the arc from z_0 to z_1 this is changed into

$$w(z; z_1, e)g^{-1}g_jg.$$

Now C_j plus the arc from z_1 to z_0 and back is a loop C_j' with respect to z_1. This shows that the substitutions

$$g^{-1}g_jg, \qquad j = 1, 2, \ldots, p, \tag{6.2.12}$$

form a set of generators of the group $\mathfrak{G}(z_1)$ and this proves (6.2.11). ▌

Thus the group $\mathfrak{G}(z_1)$ is the transform of $\mathfrak{G}(z_0)$ under the transformation g. The two groups are isomorphic since for all j, k

$$g^{-1}g_jg_kg = g^{-1}g_jgg^{-1}g_kg. \tag{6.2.13}$$

Hence *there is a unique abstract monodromy group* $\mathfrak{G}$.

The substitutions g_j and $g^{-1}g_jg$ have the same spectra since, if either side exists,

$$(\lambda e - g^{-1}g_jg)^{-1} = g(\lambda e - g_j)^{-1}g^{-1}. \tag{6.2.14}$$

EXERCISE 6.2

1. Consider the equation in $\mathfrak{M}_2$

$$\mathcal{W}'(z) = \mathcal{A}(z-1)^{-1}\mathcal{W}(z), \qquad \mathcal{A} = \begin{pmatrix} 0 & \alpha \\ \alpha & 0 \end{pmatrix}.$$

Show that

$$\frac{1}{2}\left(\mathcal{E} + \frac{1}{\alpha}\mathcal{A}\right)(z-1)^{\alpha} + \frac{1}{2}\left(\mathcal{E} - \frac{1}{\alpha}\mathcal{A}\right)(z-1)^{-\alpha}$$

is a fundamental solution.

2. Show that the group of the preceding equation has a single generator $g = \exp(2\pi i\mathcal{A})$. If α is an integer, the solution is single-valued and the group reduces to the identity. If α is not an integer the group is *cyclic* and is finite iff α is rational.

3. In No. 1, replace $\mathcal{A}$ by the matrix

$$\mathcal{B} = \begin{pmatrix} 0 & 1 \\ 0 & 0 \end{pmatrix}.$$

Find a solution matrix and determine the group.

4. Suppose that (6.1.6) has singularities at $z = 0, 1, \infty$ and nowhere else. Take $z_0 = \frac{1}{2}$ and lay loops C_0 and C_1 around 0 and 1. Set $m(C_j) = g_j$. Find a path such that $m(C) = g_1g_0^{-1}g_1^{-1}g_0$. Draw a figure. Such double loops play an important role in the theory of complex integration, in particular in finding solutions of the equation in the form of definite integrals.

6.3 APPROACH TO A SINGULAR POINT

We shall now be concerned with the behavior of the solution for approach to a singularity and start with the real case.

The differential equation

$$y'(t) = F(t)y(t) \tag{6.3.1}$$

is given, where $F(t)$ is a $\mathfrak{B}$-valued function of t continuous for $0 < t \leq \tau$. If F ceases to be continuous at $t = 0$, what can be said concerning the solution $y(t)$ as t decreases to 0? It will be seen that the behavior is largely determined by the integrability properties of $\|F(t)\|$ in the interval $(0, \tau]$.

Theorem 6.3.1. *If $y(t)$ satisfies (6.3.1), $y(\tau)$ being given, and if $F(t)$ is continuous on $(0, \tau]$, then $y(t)$ satisfies, $0 < t \leq \tau$,*

$$\|y(\tau)\| \exp\left[-\int_t^\tau \|F(s)\|\,ds\right] \leq \|y(t)\| \leq \|y(\tau)\| \exp\left[\int_t^\tau \|F(s)\|\,ds\right]. \tag{6.3.2}$$

Proof. Let $0 < \alpha < \beta < \tau$ and note that

$$y(\beta) - y(\alpha) = \int_\alpha^\beta F(s)y(s)\,ds. \tag{6.3.3}$$

Hence

$$\|y(\beta)\| \leq \|y(\alpha)\| + \int_\alpha^\beta \|F(s)\|\,\|y(s)\|\,ds$$

and by Theorem 1.5.7 this implies that

$$\|y(\beta)\| \leq \|y(\alpha)\| \exp\left[\int_\alpha^\beta \|F(s)\|\,ds\right].$$

In particular, for $\alpha = t$, $\beta = \tau$, the result may be written

$$\|y(\tau)\| \exp\left[-\int_t^\tau \|F(s)\|\,ds\right] \leq \|y(t)\|.$$

This is the lower bound in (6.3.2).

To get the upper bound, set

$$t = \tau - x, \quad y(t) = w(x), \quad F(t) = G(x)$$

to obtain

$$w'(x) = -G(x)w(x) \tag{6.3.4}$$

and

$$w(x) = w(0) - \int_0^x G(s)w(s)\,ds, \qquad 0 \leq x < \tau. \tag{6.3.5}$$

Hence

$$\|w(x)\| \le \|w(0)\| + \int_0^x \|G(s)\| \, \|w(s)\| \, ds$$

and

$$\|w(x)\| \le \|w(0)\| \exp\left[\int_0^x \|G(s)\| \, ds\right].$$

Returning to the old variables we obtain the upper bound in (6.3.2). ∎

Corollary. *If as* $t \downarrow 0$

$$\|y(t)\| \exp\left[\int_t^\tau \|F(s)\| \, ds\right] \to 0, \tag{6.3.6}$$

then $y(t) \equiv 0$.

It is also of interest to discuss the behavior of the solution for large values of t assuming $F(t)$ to be defined. We obtain

Theorem 6.3.2. *If* $y(t)$ *is a solution of* (6.3.1), $y(\tau)$ *being given, and if* $F(t)$ *is continuous for* $\tau \le t < \infty$, *then for* $t > \tau$

$$\|y(\tau)\| \exp\left[-\int_\tau^t \|F(s)\| \, ds\right]$$

$$\le \|y(t)\| \le \|y(\tau)\| \exp\left[\int_\tau^t \|F(s)\| \, ds\right]. \tag{6.3.7}$$

Corollary. *If as* $t \uparrow \infty$

$$\|y(t)\| \exp\left[\int_\tau^t \|F(s)\| \, ds\right] \to 0, \tag{6.3.8}$$

then $y(t) \equiv 0$.

These results can be extended to the complex plane. Take

$$w'(z) = F(z)w(z), \tag{6.3.9}$$

where $F(z)$ is an analytic function with a singularity at $z = 0$. This may be an isolated singular point or an accessible point on a singular line. To allow for both possibilities we assume $F(z)$ to be holomorphic in a sector

$$\alpha < \arg z < \beta, \qquad 0 < |z| \le R.$$

We can apply Theorem 6.3.1 to each of the rays $\arg z = \theta$ and obtain

Theorem 6.3.3. *For all* r, $0 < r < R$, $\alpha < \theta < \beta$,

$$\|w(R\exp(i\theta))\| \exp\left[-\int_r^R \|F(s\exp(i\theta))\| \, ds\right]$$

$$\le \|w(r\exp(i\theta))\|$$

$$\le \|w(R\exp(i\theta))\| \exp\left[\int_r^R \|F(s\exp(i\theta))\| \, ds\right]. \tag{6.3.10}$$

Similar relations hold for approach to infinity in a sector. It should be noted that the factor $\|w(R \exp(i\theta))\|$ is bounded away from 0 and ∞, if θ is restricted to a compact subset of (α, β). On such a set one can usually also find majorants and minorants for $\|F(r \exp(i\theta))\|$, independent of θ, and thus obtain simpler estimates for $\|w(r \exp(i\theta))\|$. The most important case for the applications is that where $z = 0$ and $z = \infty$ are isolated singular points. This case will be considered in some detail below.

EXERCISE 6.3

Determine the bounds (6.3.2) if $F(t)$ is

1. $t^{-\alpha}$, $0 < \alpha < 1$.
2. t^{-1}.
3. $t^{-\alpha}$, $1 < \alpha$.
4. Determine the bounds (6.3.7) in these three cases.
5. Find the explicit solution of (6.3.1) if $\mathcal{F}(t) = \mathcal{A}t^{-\alpha}$ where $\mathcal{A}$ is a constant diagonal matrix with distinct characteristic roots. If $\tau = 1$, $\|\mathcal{Y}(\tau)\| = 1$, compare the *a priori* estimates with those obtainable from the explicit solution.

   Take $\mathfrak{B} = \mathfrak{M}_2$ and

$$z\mathcal{W}'(z) = \mathcal{A}\mathcal{W}(z), \qquad \mathcal{W}(1) = \mathcal{E},$$

and let $z \to 0$ along the logarithmic spiral $r = \exp(-\theta)$. Express the solution as a function of θ if $\mathcal{A}$ equals

6. $\begin{pmatrix} 0 & 1 \\ -1 & 0 \end{pmatrix}$.
7. $\begin{pmatrix} 0 & 1 \\ 1 & 0 \end{pmatrix}$.
8. Let

$$\mathcal{A}(t) = \begin{pmatrix} 0 & 1 \\ 0 & 0 \end{pmatrix}.$$

Estimate the rate of growth of $\|\mathcal{Y}(t)\|$ as $t \to +\infty$ using (i) Theorem 6.3.2 and (ii) the explicit solution.

The methods of this section may be used to estimate solutions of linear n^{th} order equations. In the second order case

$$w'' + P(t)w = 0,$$

set $w = w_1$, $tw' = w_2$ and reduce to the matrix case. Apply this device to estimate $w(t)$ for

9. $P = t^{-1}$, $t \to 0$.
10. $P = 1 - at^{-2}$, $t \to 0$.
11. $P = t^n$, $t \to \infty$.
12. $P = e^t$, $t \to -\infty$.

6.4 THE INTEGRABLE CASE

We shall now make a closer examination of the results obtained in the preceding section and start with the case where $\|F(t)\|$ is integrable down to 0. In this case (6.3.2) shows that the solution is bounded away from 0 and ∞ as $t \downarrow 0$. A much stronger result holds, however.

Theorem 6.4.1. *If* $\|F(t)\| \in L(0, \tau)$, *then every solution of* (6.3.1) *tends to a finite limit as* $t \downarrow 0$ *and this limit is* 0 *iff* $y(t) \equiv 0$.

We base the proof on the following

Theorem 6.4.2. *If* $\|F(t)\| \in L(0, \tau)$, *then the equation*

$$y'(t) = F(t)y(t), \qquad 0 < t \le \tau, \tag{6.4.1}$$

with the boundary condition $y(t) \to e$ *as* $t \downarrow 0$ *has a unique solution* $y(t; 0, e)$.

Proof. We rewrite (6.4.1) as an integral equation

$$y(t) = e + \int_0^t F(s)y(s)\, ds. \tag{6.4.2}$$

If this equation has a unique solution, then $y(t)$ must also satisfy (6.4.1) and the boundary condition. We can solve (6.4.2) by successive approximations with

$$y_0(t) = e, \qquad y_m(t) = e + \int_0^t F(s)y_{m-1}(s)\, ds. \tag{6.4.3}$$

Here $y_1(t)$ exists since $\|F(s)\| \in L(0, \tau)$. It is found that all approximations exist and are differentiable functions for $0 < t$. The usual estimates apply and show the convergence of $y_m(t)$ to a limit $y(t) \equiv y(t; 0, e)$ that satisfies (6.4.2) and hence also (6.4.1) and the boundary condition. Moreover, by Theorem 1.5.7

$$\|y(t; 0, e) - e\| \le \exp\left[\int_0^t \|F(s)\|\, ds\right] - 1. \tag{6.4.4}$$

This is obviously a fundamental solution of (6.4.1) and uniqueness may be proved using Theorem 2.3.2 with $K(s) = \|F(s)\|$. ∎

Proof of Theorem 6.4.1. We now return to the solution $y(t; \tau, e)$ of (6.4.1) with $y(\tau) = e$. Since both $y(t; 0, e)$ and $y(t; \tau, e)$ are fundamental solutions, we can express one in terms of the other. Thus

$$y(t; \tau, e) = y(t; 0, e)[y(\tau; 0, e)]^{-1},$$

since this is true for $t = \tau$. Hence

$$\lim_{t \downarrow 0} y(t; \tau, e) = [y(\tau; 0, e)]^{-1}$$

and more generally

$$\lim_{t \downarrow 0} y(t; \tau, w_0) = [y(\tau; e, 0)]^{-1} w_0. \blacksquare \tag{6.4.5}$$

The extension to the complex plane involves a delicate point. We assume $F(z)$ to be holomorphic in the sector

$$\alpha < \arg z < \beta, \qquad 0 < |z| \le R. \tag{6.4.6}$$

Further, $\|F(r \exp (i\theta))\|$ shall belong to $L(0, R)$ for each fixed θ in (α, β). Here some type of uniformity is desirable. The assumption made below is convenient although more restrictive than necessary.

Theorem 6.4.3. *Suppose that $F(z)$ is holomorphic in the sector* (6.4.6) *and suppose there is a function $K(r)$ in $C(0, R] \cap L(0, R)$ such that*

$$\|F(r \exp (i\theta))\| \le K(r), \qquad \alpha < \theta < \beta. \tag{6.4.7}$$

Then the equation

$$w'(z) = F(z)w(z) \tag{6.4.8}$$

has a unique solution $w(z; 0, e)$ such that

$$\lim_{r \downarrow 0} w(r \exp (i\theta); 0, e) = e, \tag{6.4.9}$$

uniformly in θ. Further, every solution of (6.4.8) *tends to a finite limit as $r \downarrow 0$. Here the limit is independent of θ and exists uniformly with respect to θ.*

Proof. The existence of $w(z; 0, e)$ is shown as in the real case and (6.4.4) is now replaced by

$$\|w(z; 0, e) - e\| \le \exp \left[\int_0^{|z|} K(r)\, dr\right] - 1. \tag{6.4.10}$$

This shows the uniform convergence of $w(z; 0, e)$ in the sector. If z_0 is any point in the sector and if $w(z; z_0, e)$ is the corresponding solution of (6.4.8), then

$$w(z; z_0, e) = w(z; 0, e)[w(z_0; 0, e)]^{-1} \tag{6.4.11}$$

and

$$\lim w(z; z_0, e) = [w(z_0; 0, e)]^{-1} \tag{6.4.12}$$

uniformly in the sector. $\blacksquare$

Finally we can extend the discussion to an infinite interval. The result is essentially Theorem 5.4.2 formulated for B-algebras.

Theorem 6.4.4. *Let $\|F(t)\| \in L(\tau, \infty)$. Then every solution of*

$$y'(t) = F(t)y(t) \tag{6.4.13}$$

tends to a finite limit as $t \uparrow \infty$ and this limit is 0 iff $y(t) \equiv 0$.

Proof. As in the proof of Theorem 6.4.1, consider the integral equation

$$y(t) = e - \int_t^\infty F(s)y(s)\,ds. \tag{6.4.14}$$

It has a unique solution $y(t; \infty, e)$ which tends to e as $t \uparrow \infty$. This is proved by successive approximations. The solution is fundamental and every solution of (6.4.13) is of the form

$$y(t) = y(t; \infty, e)a, \qquad a \in \mathfrak{B}.$$

Hence $\lim_{t\uparrow\infty} y(t) = a \neq 0$ unless $y(t) \equiv 0$. ▮

EXERCISE 6.4

1. Consider the equation

$$\mathcal{W}'(z) = \mathcal{A}z^{-1/2}\mathcal{W}(z), \qquad \mathcal{A} = \begin{pmatrix} 0 & 1 \\ 1 & 0 \end{pmatrix}.$$

Verify that the assumptions of Theorem 6.4.3 are satisfied with $\alpha = -\pi$, $\beta = \pi$, $K(r) = r^{-1/2}$. Show that

$$\mathcal{W}(z; 0, \mathcal{E}) = \mathcal{E}\cosh(2z^{1/2}) + \mathcal{A}\sinh(2z^{1/2}).$$

2. In the preceding problem replace $\mathcal{A}$ by

$$\mathcal{B} = \begin{pmatrix} 0 & 1 \\ 0 & 0 \end{pmatrix}$$

and find $\mathcal{W}(z; 0, \mathcal{E})$.

3. In Problem 1 replace $z^{-1/2}$ by $\log z$ (principal value!) and find $\mathcal{W}(z; 0, \mathcal{E})$.

4. Fill in the missing details in the proof of Theorem 6.4.2.

5. Let $p(t)$ and $q(t)$ be continuous in [0, 1] and let $0 \le \alpha < 1$. Show that the differential equation

$$t^{2\alpha}y''(t) + t^{2\alpha-1}[\alpha + tp(t)]y'(t) + q(t)y(t) = 0$$

has a fundamental system $y_1(t)$, $y_2(t)$ such that

$$y_1(t) \to 1, \qquad y_2(t) \to 0,$$
$$t^\alpha y_1'(t) \to 0, \qquad t^\alpha y_2'(t) \to 1$$

as $t \downarrow 0$. This is no longer true for $\alpha = 1$ as is seen, e.g. by taking $p(t) \equiv 0$, $q(t) \equiv 1$.

6. Do the theorems of Sections 6.3 and 6.4 remain valid for solutions of Eq. (6.1.7)?

6.5 REGULAR SINGULAR POINTS

We now turn to the case where $\|F(t)\|$ is not integrable down to 0. A particularly simple instance is that where there are two positive numbers m and M such that

$$m \le t\|F(t)\| \le M, \qquad 0 < t \le \tau. \tag{6.5.1}$$

Here (6.3.2) gives

$$\|y(\tau)\|\left(\frac{t}{\tau}\right)^M \le \|y(t)\| \le \|y(\tau)\|\left(\frac{\tau}{t}\right)^M, \qquad 0 < t \le \tau. \tag{6.5.2}$$

The extension to the complex plane is immediate. We note in particular the following special case.

Theorem 6.5.1. *Let $P(z) = zF(z)$ be holomorphic in some disk $|z| \le R$ and let $P(0) = a \ne 0$ so that $F(z)$ has a simple pole of residue a at $z = 0$. If $|\arg z| \le \alpha$, then there are positive constants $b(\alpha)$, $B(\alpha)$ and M such that*

$$b(\alpha)|z|^M \le \|w(z)\| \le B(\alpha)|z|^{-M} \tag{6.5.3}$$

for any solution $w(z)$ of

$$zw'(z) = P(z)w(z). \tag{6.5.4}$$

Here $b(\alpha)$ and $B(\alpha)$ depend upon the solution as well as upon α, while

$$M = \max_{|z| \le R} \|P(z)\|. \tag{6.5.5}$$

Proof. Apply (6.3.10). By the principle of the maximum

$$M \ge \|a\|. \blacksquare \tag{6.5.6}$$

For the matrix case, $\mathfrak{B} = \mathfrak{M}_n$, such an estimate of the rate of growth of the solutions for approach to a regular singular point was given by G. D. Birkhoff in 1913. This *a priori* estimate shows that a solution cannot approach either 0 or ∞ faster than a power of $|z|$. Of course, the solution may stay away both from 0 and ∞. What it actually does depends upon the spectrum of a.

In analogy with the matrix case we say that (6.5.4) has a *regular singular point* at the origin. More generally, the equation

$$w'(z) = F(z)w(z)$$

is said to have a regular singular point at a finite point $z = \alpha$ if $F(z)$ has a simple pole at $z = \alpha$. We have also to examine the point at infinity.

If $z = \infty$ is a singular point of $F(z)$, then it is *ipso facto* a singularity of $w(z)$ and actually an *irregular singular point* which is of finite *rank* iff $z = \infty$ is a pole of $F(z)$. On the other hand, if $F(z)$ is holomorphic at $z = \infty$, we cannot conclude that $w(z)$ is holomorphic there. Here the integrability test shows what to expect. If $F(z)$ has a zero at $z = \infty$ of at least the second order, then $\|F(z)\|$ is integrable, the point at infinity is a regular point of the equation where we can solve the initial value problem, and the solution is actually holomorphic. If $F(z)$ has a zero merely of the first order, then $z = \infty$ is a regular singular point. Finally, if $F(z)$ is holomorphic at $z = \infty$ and tends to a limit $\neq 0$, then $z = \infty$ is an irregular singular point of rank one. At this juncture we are concerned only with the regular singular case. Applying the usual technique we get

Theorem 6.5.2. *If $P(z) = zF(z)$ is holomorphic at $z = \infty$ and if $P(\infty) = a \neq 0$, then $z = \infty$ is a regular singular point of Eq.* (6.5.4). *The solution satisfies estimates of the form*

$$b(\alpha)|z|^{-M} \leq \|w(z)\| \leq B(\alpha)|z|^{M}, \tag{6.5.7}$$

where $M \geq \|a\|$, $|\arg z| \leq \alpha$.

We return to Eq. (6.5.4) supposed to have a regular singular point at the origin. Just as in the matrix case, we shall find series solutions valid in a punctured disk in which $P(z)$ is holomorphic. Suppose now that

$$P(z) = \sum_{n=0}^{\infty} a_n z^n, \qquad |z| < R, \tag{6.5.8}$$

and assume the existence of a solution of the form

$$w(z) = \sum_{m=0}^{\infty} c_m z^{m+a_0}. \tag{6.5.9}$$

This type of series is suggested by formula (B.2.26). Just as in the matrix case, we shall find that this type of series is suitable iff a_0 has no spectral values congruent modulo 1. We concentrate on this case here and take up the general case in the next section.

First we must explain what is meant by z^a, if z is a complex number and a an element of $\mathfrak{B}$. There are two expressions available:

$$z^a = \exp(a \log z) \qquad \text{or} \qquad z^a = \frac{1}{2\pi i}\int_C z^{\lambda} R(\lambda, a)\, d\lambda. \tag{6.5.10}$$

They agree fortunately. We restrict z so that $0 < |z| < \infty$, $-\pi < \arg z \leq \pi$. Then

$$\log z = \log |z| + i \arg z, \qquad z^{\lambda} = \exp(\lambda \log z)$$

are uniquely defined. The contour C surrounds $\sigma(a)$, the spectrum of a, once and only once in the positive sense. Finally $R(\lambda, a)$ is as usual the resolvent of a or $(\lambda e - a)^{-1}$. We can think of z^{m+a_0} either as

$$z^m z^{a_0} = z^{a_0} z^m \qquad \text{or as} \qquad z^{(me + a_0)}.$$

The two interpretations agree.

Theorem 6.5.3. *Suppose that a_0 satisfies one of the following conditions:* (i) *a_0 belongs to the center of $\mathfrak{B}$,* (ii) *no two spectral values of a_0 differ by an integer. We can then take $c_0 = e$ in* (6.5.9) *and determine $c_1, c_2, \ldots, c_m, \ldots$ uniquely in terms of the a_k's. The resulting series for $w(z)$ converges in norm for $0 < |z| < R$ and satisfies* (6.5.4) *. It is a fundamental solution.*

Proof. Substitution of (6.5.8) and (6.5.9) in (6.5.4) gives

$$\sum_{m=0}^{\infty} c_m(me + a_0)z^{m+a_0} = \sum_{k=0}^{\infty} a_k z^k \sum_{m=0}^{\infty} c_m z^{m+a_0}$$
$$= \sum_{m=0}^{\infty} \left(\sum_{k=0}^{m} a_{m-k}c_k \right) z^{m+a_0},$$

assuming convergence in norm of the series involved. For this to be an identity we must have

$$c_0 a_0 = a_0 c_0,$$
$$c_m(me + a_0) = \sum_{k=0}^{m} a_{m-k}c_k, \qquad m = 1, 2, 3, \ldots$$

Since we want a fundamental solution, the leading term of the series (6.5.9) must be a regular element of $\mathfrak{B}$ for $z \neq 0$ and this is the case iff c_0 is regular. The simplest choice is

$$c_0 = e.$$

The equations for the determination of the coefficients then become

$$mc_m - (a_0 c_m - c_m a_0) = \sum_{k=0}^{m-1} a_{m-k}c_k, \qquad m = 1, 2, 3, \ldots \tag{6.5.11}$$

We now consider the two cases separately.

i) *The element a_0 belongs to the center of $\mathfrak{B}$.*

This implies that a_0 commutes with all elements of $\mathfrak{B}$ so the equations reduce to

$$mc_m = \sum_{k=0}^{m-1} a_{m-k}c_k, \qquad m = 1, 2, 3, \ldots \tag{6.5.12}$$

Here $c_0 = e$ is given, so the coefficients c_m can be determined successively in terms of the a_k's. The convergence of the resulting series can be proved in various ways. Here is a simple majorant argument in the spirit of Theorem 2.5.1. Set

$$A(z) \equiv \sum_{k=0}^{\infty} \alpha_k z^k \qquad \text{where} \qquad \alpha_k = \|a_k\| \tag{6.5.13}$$

and consider the auxiliary equation

$$zU'(z) = A(z)U(z), \tag{6.5.14}$$

where $U(z)$ is a complex number. The solution is immediate:

$$U(z) = z^{\alpha_0}\exp\left[\int_0^z [A(s) - \alpha_0]s^{-1}ds\right]\cdot \tag{6.5.15}$$

The exponential is holomorphic in the disk $|z| < R$ and in no larger disk, if R is the exact radius of convergence of (6.5.8). Set

$$U(z) = \sum_{m=0}^{\infty} \gamma_m z^{m+\alpha_0}. \tag{6.5.16}$$

Then $\gamma_0 = 1$ and

$$m\gamma_m = \sum_{k=0}^{m-1} \alpha_{m-k}\gamma_k, \qquad m = 1, 2, 3, \ldots$$

On the other hand, we have $\|c_0\| = 1$ and (6.5.12) gives

$$m\|c_m\| \le \sum_{k=0}^{m-1} \alpha_{m-k}\|c_k\|, \qquad m > 0.$$

It follows that

$$\|c_m\| \le \gamma_m \tag{6.5.17}$$

for all m and the series (6.5.9) converges in norm for $0 < |z| < R$. Hence the formal solution is an actual solution of (6.5.4). It is a fundamental solution for the first term z^{a_0} is a regular element of $\mathfrak{B}$ for $0 < |z| < \infty$ and the sum of the series lies in a small neighborhood of the first term if $|z|$ is small. Hence the sum is regular in a punctured neighborhood of $z = 0$ and by Theorem 6.1.5 and the discussion in Section 6.2 this implies that $w(z)$ is a fundamental solution at points z which are not singular points of the equation.

ii) *No two spectral values of a_0 differ by an integer.*

We may of course assume that condition (i) does not hold so that a_0 does not commute with all elements of $\mathfrak{B}$. The corresponding commutator operator $\mathbf{C}_{a_0}$ defined by

$$\mathbf{C}_{a_0}x = a_0x - xa_0 \tag{6.5.18}$$

is then non-trivial. We refer to Section 4.6 for the properties of the commutator used in the following. Equations (6.5.11) now become

$$(me - \mathbf{C}_{a_0})c_m = \sum_{k=0}^{m-1} a_{m-k}c_k. \tag{6.5.19}$$

We recall that

$$\sigma[\mathbf{C}_a] \subset \sigma(a_0) - \sigma(a_0). \tag{6.5.20}$$

Our basic assumption is that no integer belongs to the difference set. It follows that the Eqs. (6.5.19) can be solved successively for $m = 1, 2, 3, \ldots$ Thus

$$c_m = \mathbf{R}(m, \mathbf{C}_{a_0})\left\{\sum_{k=0}^{m-1} a_{m-k}c_k\right\} \tag{6.5.21}$$

in terms of the resolvent of the commutator. Thus the formal solution is well defined, if not explicitly known.

For the convergence proof a different type of majorant argument is preferable. To prove that the radius of convergence of the formal series is $\geq R$, it is sufficient to show that the terms of the series are bounded in norm for $z = \rho$ for any ρ with $0 < \rho < R$. Since

$$\|\mathbf{C}_{a_0}\| \leq 2\|a_0\| = 2\alpha_0, \tag{6.5.22}$$

we get from (6.5.19) the inequality

$$(m - 2\alpha_0)\|c_m\| \leq \sum_{k=0}^{m-1} \alpha_{m-k}\|c_k\|$$

which is non-trivial for $m > 2\alpha_0$. Let ρ be chosen as stated. Then

$$(m - 2\alpha_0)\|c_m\|\rho^m \leq \sum_{k=0}^{m-1} \alpha_{m-k}\rho^{m-k}\|c_k\|\rho^k$$

$$\leq [A(\rho) - \alpha_0] \max_{k<m} \{\|c_k\|\rho^k\},$$

where $A(\rho)$ is defined by (6.5.13). Choose

$$N > A(\rho) + \alpha_0.$$

Then for $m > N$

$$\|c_m\|\rho^m \leq \max_{k \leq N} \{\|c_k\|\rho^k\} \equiv M(\rho). \tag{6.5.23}$$

This shows that

$$\|c_k\|\rho^k \leq M(\rho) \tag{6.5.24}$$

for all k, i.e. the terms of the series (6.5.9) are bounded in norm for $z = \rho$. Since this holds for every $\rho < R$, it follows that the series converges in norm for $0 < |z| < R$. Thus the formal solution is an actual solution and it is obviously fundamental by the argument given above in case (i). ∎

EXERCISE 6.5

1. Solve $zw'(z) = (\alpha e + az)w(z)$ where α is a complex number and $a \in \mathfrak{B}$.
2. Show that formula (6.5.12) is valid in case (ii) if a_0 commutes with a_n for all n.

3. Let f_1 and f_2 be elements of $L_2(0, 2\pi)$ and set $P(z, t) = f_1(t) + zf_2(t)$. Solve the equation

$$z \frac{\partial}{\partial z} w(z, t) = P(z, t) * w(z, t)$$

where the asterisk denotes convolution with respect to t. Cf. No. 10, Exercise 6.1.

The remaining problems are concerned with the algebra of bounded linear operators on $C[-1, 1]$ to itself. The operator A takes $f(t)$ into $tf(t)$, the operator N takes $f(t)$ into $f(-t)$.

4. What is the action of $R(\lambda, A)$ and for what values of λ is it defined? What is the action of z^A?
5. Same questions for $R(\lambda, N)$ and z^N.
6. Show that $R(\lambda, \mathbf{C}_A)N[f](t) = (\lambda - 2t)^{-1}f(-t)$. Formula (4.6.8) may be used for the proof. Thus the spectrum of $\mathbf{C}_A$ is the interval $[-2, -2]$.

Solve the following differential operator equations:

7. $zT'(z) = (A + zI)T(z)$.
8. $zU'(z) = [A + zR(2, A)]U(z)$.
9. $zV'(z) = (\frac{1}{3}A + zN)V(z)$.

6.6 THE METHOD OF FROBENIUS

We come now to the case where some spectral values of a_0 are congruent modulo 1. In the matrix case, this contingency is handled either by the method of Frobenius (1873) or by that of H. Kneser (1950). Neither of these methods can cope with the general situation in a B-algebra, but by imposing some restrictions on the spectrum of a_0 which are automatically satisfied in a matrix algebra, we can adapt the argument of Frobenius to the problem on hand.

Theorem 6.6.1. *Suppose that $a_0 \in \mathfrak{B}$ satisfies the assumptions:*

i) *positive integers in the difference set are isolated points of the set and for any positive integer n the equation*

$$\alpha - \beta = n \tag{6.6.1}$$

has at most a finite number of solutions with α and β in $\sigma(a_0)$,

ii) *each such α and β is a pole of $R(\lambda, a_0)$.*

Then there is a positive integer p and $p + 1$ power series such that

$$\sum_{j=0}^{p} (\log z)^j \sum_{m=0}^{\infty} c_{mj} z^{m+a_0} \tag{6.6.2}$$

is a solution of (6.5.4). *The series converge in norm for* $0 < |z| < R$ *and the solution is fundamental in the punctured disk.*

Proof. The assumptions on $\sigma(a_0)$ imply that $\mathbf{R}(n, \mathbf{C}_{a_0})$ exists for all positive integers n with at most a finite number of exceptions and the exceptional values are poles of $\mathbf{R}(\lambda, \mathbf{C}_{a_0})$ by Foguel's Theorem 4.6.6. Let the exceptional values be $n_1, n_2, \ldots, n_k$ where

$$1 \leq n_1 < n_2 < \cdots < n_k \leq 2\alpha_0$$

and let their orders as poles of $\mathbf{R}(\lambda, \mathbf{C}_{a_0})$ be $m_1, m_2, \ldots, m_k$, respectively. Set

$$m_1 + m_2 + \cdots + m_k = p. \tag{6.6.3}$$

We can now find a $\delta > 0$ such that each disk $|\lambda - n| < \delta$ contains at most one spectral singularity of $\mathbf{C}_{a_0}$. For $n = n_1, n_2, \ldots, n_k$ there is such a singularity in the disk and it is a pole of $\mathbf{R}(\lambda, \mathbf{C}_{a_0})$ located at the center of the disk. For all other values of $n > 0$ the disk contains no spectral points.

Let σ be a complex number, $0 < |\sigma| < \delta$, and consider the series

$$w(z, \sigma) \equiv \sum_{m=0}^{\infty} c_m(\sigma) z^{a_0 + m + \sigma}. \tag{6.6.4}$$

Since $\sigma \neq 0$ this cannot be a solution of the differential equation (6.5.4), but we can choose the coefficients $c_m(\sigma)$ so that $w(z, \sigma)$ satisfies a non-homogeneous linear equation where the perturbation term is small in norm when $|\sigma|$ is small. To this end, let us form

$$[\vartheta - P(z)]w(z, \sigma).$$

Here we substitute the series for $P(z)$ and $w(z, \sigma)$, multiply out, and rearrange the result according to ascending powers of z. We obtain

$$\sum_{m=0}^{\infty} [c_m(\sigma)(a_0 + m + \sigma) - \sum_{j=0}^{m} a_{m-j} c_j(\sigma)] z^{a_0 + m + \sigma}.$$

For $m = 0$ the coefficient of $z^{a_0 + \sigma}$ is

$$\sigma c_0(\sigma) + c_0(\sigma) a_0 - a_0 c_0(\sigma).$$

We choose

$$c_0(\sigma) = \sigma^p e, \tag{6.6.5}$$

where p is defined by (6.6.3). For $m > 0$ we choose $c_m(\sigma)$ so that the coefficient of $z^{a_0 + m + \sigma}$ is 0. This gives

$$(m + \sigma) c_m(\sigma) - a_0 c_m(\sigma) + c_m(\sigma) a_0 = \sum_{j=0}^{m-1} a_{m-j} c_j(\sigma). \tag{6.6.6}$$

Since $\mathbf{R}(m + \sigma, \mathbf{C}_{a_0})$ is well defined for $0 < |\sigma| < \delta$, we get

$$c_m(\sigma) = \mathbf{R}(m + \sigma, \mathbf{C}_{a_0}) \left\{ \sum_{j=0}^{m-1} a_{m-j} c_j(\sigma) \right\} \tag{6.6.7}$$

for $m = 1, 2, 3, \ldots$ The successive determination of the coefficients $c_m(\sigma)$ can be carried out and, if the resulting series converges, we see that $w(z, \sigma)$ satisfies the equation

$$z \frac{\partial}{\partial z} w(z, \sigma) = P(z)w(z, \sigma) + \sigma^{p+1} z^{a_0 + \sigma}. \tag{6.6.8}$$

Let us now examine the analytical nature of the coefficients $c_m(\sigma)$ as functions of σ. If $1 < n_1$, then $\mathbf{R}(1 + \sigma, \mathbf{C}_{a_0})$ is holomorphic in the disk $|\sigma| < \delta$ and

$$c_1(\sigma) = \mathbf{R}(1 + \sigma, \mathbf{C}_{a_0})[a_1 c_0(\sigma)] = \sigma^p \mathbf{R}(1 + \sigma, \mathbf{C}_{a_0})[a_1]$$

is holomorphic in the disk and has a zero of order p at $\sigma = 0$. The same applies for $m = 2, 3, \ldots, n_1 - 1$. For $m = n_1$ the situation is different. The formula is

$$c_{n_1}(\sigma) = \mathbf{R}(n_1 + \sigma, \mathbf{C}_{a_0}) \left[\sum_{j=0}^{n_1 - 1} a_{n_1 - j} c_j(\sigma) \right] \cdot$$

Here the resolvent operates on a holomorphic function of σ which has a zero of order not less than p at $\sigma = 0$, but the resolvent has a pole at $\sigma = 0$ of order exactly m_1. The result is that $c_{n_1}(\sigma)$ exists and is holomorphic in the disk and it has a zero at $\sigma = 0$ of order at least $p - m_1$. For $m = n_1 + 1, \ldots, n_2 - 1$ the resolvent is holomorphic and operates on a holomorphic function with a zero of order at least $p - m_1$ at $\sigma = 0$. Hence these coefficients are holomorphic in the disk and each of them has a zero of multiplicity $\geq p - m_1$ at $\sigma = 0$. For $m = n_2$ there is again a change: $\mathbf{R}(n_2 + \sigma, \mathbf{C}_{a_0})$ has a pole of order m_2 and it operates on a holomorphic function with a zero of order $\geq p - m_1$ at $\sigma = 0$. Hence $c_{n_2}(\sigma)$ is holomorphic in the disk and has a zero at $\sigma = 0$ of multiplicity $\geq p - m_1 - m_2$. In this way we continue. Each function $c_m(\sigma)$ is holomorphic in the disk; if $n_j \leq m < n_{j+1}$, there is a zero of multiplicity at least

$$p - m_1 - m_2 - \cdots - m_j$$

at $\sigma = 0$. For $m \geq n_k$ the $c_m(\sigma)$ normally do not vanish at $\sigma = 0$.

It is desired to show that the series

$$\sum_{m=0}^{\infty} c_m(\sigma) z^m$$

converges for $|z| < R$, $|\sigma| < \delta$, uniformly on compact subsets. To this end it suffices to show that the sequence

$$\{\| c_m(\sigma) \| \rho^m\} \tag{6.6.9}$$

is bounded for any fixed ρ, $0 < \rho < R$, uniformly with respect to σ for $|\sigma| \leq \varepsilon < \delta$. We can proceed as in the proof of the second part of Theorem 6.5.3. The basic inequality for $|\sigma| \leq \varepsilon$ is now

$$(m - \varepsilon - 2\alpha_0)\|c_m(\sigma)\|\rho^m \leq [A(\rho) - \alpha_0] \max_{k<m} \|c_k(\sigma)\|\rho^k$$

and for $m > N > A(\rho) + \alpha_0 + \varepsilon$ this implies

$$\|c_m(\sigma)\|\rho^m \leq \max_{|\sigma|\leq\varepsilon} \max_{k\leq N} \|c_k(\sigma)\|\rho^k \equiv M(\rho, \varepsilon).$$

This shows that the sequence (6.6.9) is uniformly bounded for $|\sigma| \leq \varepsilon$.

It follows that the series (6.6.4) converges for all z and σ with $0 < |z| < R$, $|\sigma| < \delta$. This implies that $w(z, \sigma)$ satisfies Eq. (6.6.8) since the operations performed to compute the coefficients are legitimate. Further, the series being uniformly convergent, its sum is an analytic function of σ as well as of z. This implies the existence of mixed partials of all orders and relations like

$$\frac{\partial}{\partial z}\frac{\partial^p}{\partial \sigma^p} w(z, \sigma) = \frac{\partial^p}{\partial \sigma^p}\frac{\partial}{\partial z} w(z, \sigma). \tag{6.6.10}$$

Moreover, the partials can be found by termwise differentiation of the series (6.6.4).

Now Eq. (6.6.8) together with the analyticity of $w(z, \sigma)$ in z and σ show that

$$\lim_{\sigma\to 0} w(z, \sigma)$$

exists and satisfies (6.5.4). This is of doubtful value, however, since the limit would normally be a singular element of $\mathfrak{B}$ and, possibly, identically zero.

In such circumstances it is best to resort to differentiation with respect to σ before passing to the limit. The perturbation term

$$\sigma^{p+1} z^{\alpha_0 + \sigma}$$

vanishes for $\sigma = 0$ together with its partials with respect to σ of order $\leq p$. Differentiating (6.6.8) p times with respect to σ and using (6.6.10) we get

$$z\frac{\partial}{\partial z}\frac{\partial^p}{\partial \sigma^p} w(z, \sigma) = P(z)\frac{\partial^p}{\partial \sigma^p} w(z, \sigma) + \frac{\partial^p}{\partial \sigma^p}[\sigma^{p+1} z^{\alpha_0+\sigma}].$$

If we now let $\sigma \to 0$, the perturbation term vanishes and

$$\left\{\frac{\partial^p}{\partial \sigma^p} w(z, \sigma)\right\}_{\sigma=0} \equiv W(z) \tag{6.6.11}$$

is a solution of (6.5.4). Moreover, it is a fundamental solution.

This fact will come out in our study of the structure of $W(z)$. We note that $W(z)$ has an expansion of the type (6.6.2), for each time we differentiate a power

$$z^{a_0+m+\sigma}$$

with respect to σ, a factor $\log z$ is introduced. Since

$$\lim_{\sigma\to 0}\frac{\partial^p}{\partial\sigma^p}[\sigma^p z^{a_0+\sigma}] = p!z^{a_0},$$

it is seen that

$$c_{00} = p!e \neq 0 \tag{6.6.12}$$

and a regular element of $\mathfrak{B}$. We note further that

$$c_{0j} = 0 \quad \text{for} \quad j > 0.$$

These are not the only vanishing coefficients. In fact

$$c_{mj} = 0 \quad \text{for} \quad 0 \leq m < n_1, \quad 0 < j.$$

Logarithmic terms begin to appear for $m = n_1$, but we still have

$$c_{n_1,j} = 0 \quad \text{for} \quad m_1 < j.$$

More logarithmic terms involving higher powers of $\log z$ appear for $m = n_2$ and so on. Finally, $(\log z)^p$ will appear in general for $m = n_k$ and no higher powers of $\log z$ can arise.

As observed above, the p times derived series converges uniformly in σ, so we can pass to the limit and the limit $W(z)$ is a solution of (6.5.4). It is a fundamental solution since the leading term

$$p!z^{a_0}$$

is a regular element of $\mathfrak{B}$ for $0 < |z| < \infty$. ∎

The matrix case is completely covered by Theorems 6.5.3 and 6.6.1 for in this case $a_0 = \mathcal{A}_0$ has no spectral singularities but poles. By Foguel's theorem, the spectrum of $\mathbf{C}_{\mathcal{A}_0}$ reduces to a finite pure point spectrum to which our considerations apply.

On the other hand, equations of quite simple appearance may present an integration problem to which the method of Frobenius does not apply. As an example we may take the operator equation

$$zW'(z) = (A + zJ)W(z), \tag{6.6.13}$$

where $\mathfrak{B}$ is the algebra of linear bounded operators on $C[-1, 1]$ to itself and A and J take $f(t)$ into $tf(t)$ and $\int_0^t f(s)\,ds$, respectively. Here $\mathbf{C}_A$ has a continuous spectrum covering the interval $[-2, 2]$ and A does not commute with J. It is not clear if the solution admits of an expansion of type (6.6.2). At any rate we cannot find it.

EXERCISE 6.6

1. Find the resolvent of $\mathcal{A}$ and compute $z^{\mathcal{A}}$ if

$$\mathcal{A} = \begin{pmatrix} 0 & 1 \\ 1 & 0 \end{pmatrix}.$$

2. For the same choice of $\mathcal{A}$, consider the commutator defined by $\mathcal{A}$. Show that $(\mathbf{C}_{\mathcal{A}})^3 = 4\mathbf{C}_{\mathcal{A}}$ and use this to prove that

$$\mathbf{R}(\lambda, \mathbf{C}_{\mathcal{A}}) = \frac{\mathbf{I}}{\lambda} + \frac{1}{(\lambda^2 - 4)}\mathbf{C}_{\mathcal{A}} + \frac{1}{\lambda(\lambda^2 - 4)}(\mathbf{C}_{\mathcal{A}})^2.$$

3. Consider the differential equation

$$z\mathfrak{W}'(z) = (\mathcal{A} + z\mathfrak{Q})\mathfrak{W}(z), \qquad \mathfrak{Q} = \begin{pmatrix} 0 & 1 \\ 0 & 0 \end{pmatrix},$$

and $\mathcal{A}$ as above. Show that in the notation of Theorem 6.6.1, $n_1 = 2$, $m_1 = 1$, $p = 1$. Compute $\mathfrak{C}_1(\sigma)$ and $\mathfrak{C}_2(\sigma)$, verify that they are holomorphic at $\sigma = 0$ and find $\mathfrak{C}_1(0)$ and $\mathfrak{C}_2(0)$.

4. Let $\mathfrak{B}$ be the algebra of linear bounded operators on $C[-1, 1]$ to itself and let N be the operator which takes $f(t)$ into $f(-t)$. Consider the equation

$$zU'(z) = \left(N + \sum_{m=1}^{\infty} A_m z^m\right)U(z).$$

Show that the conditions of Theorem 6.6.1 are satisfied and that $n_1 = 2$, $m_1 = p = 1$.

5. In the notation of Theorem 6.6.1 suppose that $p = 2$ and write the solution in the form

$$w(z) = w_0(z) + 2w_1(z)\log z + w_2(z)[\log z]^2.$$

Show that $w_2(z)$ and $w_1(z) + w_2(z)\log z$ are also solutions.

6. Prove that the latter solutions are necessarily singular elements of $\mathfrak{B}$.

7. Prove the assertion in No. 5 by letting z describe circuits about the origin and noting that the solutions form a linear vector space.

8. If a parameter α is introduced in Eq. (6.6.13) as a factor of A and if $|\alpha| < \frac{1}{2}$, then a solution of the modified equation will exist by Theorem 6.5.3. Examine the analytic character of this solution as a function of α. Is it possible to reach $\alpha = 1$ by analytic continuation?

6.7 THE FUCHSIAN CLASS

In analogy with the matrix case *the differential equation*

$$w'(z) = F(z)w(z)$$

in a B-algebra is said to belong to the Fuchsian class if all its singularities are regular singular points. This condition implies that there are only a finite number of singularities, since a cluster point of poles would be a singularity of higher order. Suppose the finite singularities are located at

$$z = \alpha_1, \alpha_2, \ldots, \alpha_m.$$

Then each point $z = \alpha_k$ must be a simple pole of $F(z)$ and the point at infinity is either a regular point or a regular singular point of the equation, so that $F(z)$ must vanish at infinity at least to the first order. These properties require that $F(z)$ is a rational function of z with simple poles and vanishes at infinity, i.e.

$$F(z) = \sum_{k=1}^{m} \frac{a_k}{z - \alpha_k}, \qquad a_k \in \mathfrak{B}. \tag{6.7.1}$$

Thus the equation is

$$w'(z) = \left\{\sum_{k=1}^{m} \frac{a_k}{z - \alpha_k}\right\} w(z). \tag{6.7.2}$$

The point at infinity is regular or regular singular according as

$$\sum_{k=1}^{m} a_k = 0 \qquad \text{or not.}$$

The simplest case $m = 1$ with

$$w'(z) = a(z - \alpha)^{-1} w(z)$$

is trivial and has the solution

$$w(z) = (z - \alpha)^a b,$$

where b is an arbitrary element of $\mathfrak{B}$.

The case $m = 2$ can be brought to the normal form

$$w'(z) = \left\{\frac{a}{z} + \frac{b}{1 - z}\right\} w(z) \tag{6.7.3}$$

by a suitable linear transformation of the independent variable. We refer to this case as the *abstract hypergeometric equation* since it reduces to the classical hypergeometric equation if $\mathfrak{B} = \mathfrak{M}_2$ and the matrices a and b are suitably chosen. See below.

The Eq. (6.7.3) is trivial iff $a = b$, in which case

$$\left(\frac{z}{1 - z}\right)^a$$

is a solution. We exclude this case in the following.

We begin the discussion of (6.7.3) by deriving a fundamental solution at the singular point $z = 0$. We then show that the equation admits a group of transformations acting on z and on the vector

$$\begin{pmatrix} a \\ b \end{pmatrix}$$

which enables us to write down fundamental solutions at the other singular points $z = 1$ and $z = \infty$.

We start with the solution at $z = 0$. Suppose that the difference set

$$\{\gamma \mid \gamma = \alpha - \beta, \alpha \in \sigma(a), \beta \in \sigma(a)\} \tag{6.7.4}$$

does not contain any integers >0. Then (6.7.3) has a canonical solution at the origin of the form

$$H(z; a, b) = \sum_{k=0}^{\infty} c_k z^{a+k}, \qquad c_0 = e. \tag{6.7.5}$$

Let us write

$$\mathbf{R}(k, \mathbf{C}_a) = \mathbf{R}_k. \tag{6.7.6}$$

Then the c_k's satisfy the recurrence relations

$$c_k = \mathbf{R}_k[b(c_0 + c_1 + \cdots + c_{k-1})]$$

from which the coefficients may be computed. We obtain

$$c_1 = \mathbf{R}_1 b, \quad c_2 = \mathbf{R}_2(I + b\mathbf{R}_1)b, \quad c_3 = \mathbf{R}_3(I + b\mathbf{R}_2)(I + b\mathbf{R}_1)b,$$

and, generally,

$$c_k = \mathbf{R}_k(I + b\mathbf{R}_{k-1})(I + b\mathbf{R}_{k-2})\cdots(I + b\mathbf{R}_1)b. \tag{6.7.7}$$

Here it is to be observed that $\mathbf{R}_p$ is a linear bounded operator on $\mathfrak{B}$ to $\mathfrak{B}$ and must not be treated as an element of $\mathfrak{B}$. The order of the factors in (6.7.7) is essential and each $\mathbf{R}_p$ operates on everything that follows it in the product. I is the identity operator. This gives

$$H(z; a, b) = \left\{e + \sum_{n=1}^{\infty}\left[\mathbf{R}_n \prod_{k=1}^{n-1}(I + b\mathbf{R}_{n-k})b\right]z^n\right\}z^a. \tag{6.7.8}$$

This formula can perhaps claim some measure of elegance; to use it for an effective computation of $H(z; a, b)$ is another matter. To show that it is not purely ornamental, we shall carry through the computation in a special case where the properties of a and b lead to much simplification.

We take a and b so that

$$a^2 = e, \quad a \neq e, \quad ab - ba = -2b, \quad b \neq 0. \tag{6.7.9}$$

Such a choice is possible if, e.g., $\mathfrak{B} = \mathfrak{M}_2$. Here $\sigma(a) = \{-1, 1\}$ so that $\sigma(\mathbf{C}_a) = \{-2, 0, 2\}$. We obtain

$$z^a = \tfrac{1}{2}(e + a)z + \tfrac{1}{2}(e - a)z^{-1}. \tag{6.7.10}$$

Further

$$(\mathbf{C}_a)^3 = 4\mathbf{C}_a \tag{6.7.11}$$

so that

$$\mathbf{R}(\lambda, \mathbf{C}_a) = \frac{1}{\lambda} I + \frac{1}{\lambda^2 - 4}\mathbf{C}_a + \frac{1}{\lambda(\lambda^2 - 4)}(\mathbf{C}_a)^2. \tag{6.7.12}$$

This form of the resolvent would indicate potential trouble in the computation of the coefficients since $\lambda = 2$ is in the spectrum. Actually this does not materialize thanks to the choice of b. Here b is a characteristic vector of $\mathbf{C}_a$ for $\lambda = -2$. This gives

$$\mathbf{R}(\lambda, \mathbf{C}_a)b = \frac{1}{\lambda + 2} b \tag{6.7.13}$$

since

$$\frac{1}{\lambda} - \frac{2}{\lambda^2 - 4} + \frac{4}{\lambda(\lambda^2 - 2)} = \frac{1}{\lambda + 2}.$$

Further, the higher powers of b do not enter in the picture since $b^k = 0$, $k > 1$. This follows from Theorem 4.6.4 according to which either $b^k = 0$ or $\lambda = -2k$ is a characteristic value of $\mathbf{C}_a$. The latter cannot be the case for $k > 1$ so we must have $b^k = 0$, $k > 1$. This implies that formula (6.7.7) reduces to

$$c_k = \mathbf{R}_k b = \frac{1}{k + 2} b.$$

Hence we are left with

$$H(z; a, b) = \left\{e + b \sum_{k=1}^{\infty} \frac{z^k}{k + 2}\right\}[\tfrac{1}{2}(e + a)z + \tfrac{1}{2}(e - a)z^{-1}]. \tag{6.7.14}$$

The infinite series reduces to

$$z^{-2}[\log(1 - z)^{-1} - z - \tfrac{1}{2}z^2].$$

The canonical solution at $z = 1$ is of the form

$$H(1 - z; -b, -a) = \sum_{n=0}^{\infty} d_n(1 - z)^{n-b}, \tag{6.7.15}$$

where the H-notation will be justified below. Here

$$(1 - z)^{-b} = e - b \log(1 - z)$$

and the basic resolvents are defined by

$$\mathbf{R}(\lambda, -b)x = \frac{x}{\lambda} - \frac{bx}{\lambda^2},$$

$$\mathbf{R}(\lambda, \mathbf{C}_{-b})x = \frac{x}{\lambda} + \frac{xb - bx}{\lambda^2} - \frac{2}{\lambda^3} bxb.$$

The coefficients d_n are linear forms in e, a, b, and ab which may be computed from (6.7.7). The result is too complicated for reproduction.

Equation (6.7.3) admits of a set of transformations which leave it formally invariant. These go back to E. Kummer (1810–1893), who, in 1836, published a study of the hypergeometric equation where they play a basic role. These transformations form a group of six elements, the so-called *anharmonic group*, here denoted by $\mathfrak{A}$. In the classical case, to attain formal invariance it is necessary to supplement the fractional linear transformations on z, induced by $\mathfrak{A}$, by transformations on w. (See Section 7.1.) In our situation there is no need to change the dependent variable. Moreover, the same group $\mathfrak{A}$ enters in the transformation of the coefficient vector $[a, b]$. Our point of departure is a set of six two by two matrices which form a group under matrix multiplication. They are

$$\mathcal{E} = \begin{pmatrix} 1 & 0 \\ 0 & 1 \end{pmatrix}, \quad \mathcal{S} = \begin{pmatrix} 0 & -1 \\ -1 & 0 \end{pmatrix}, \quad \mathcal{T} = \begin{pmatrix} -1 & 1 \\ 0 & 1 \end{pmatrix},$$
$$\mathcal{S}\mathcal{T} = \begin{pmatrix} 0 & -1 \\ 1 & -1 \end{pmatrix}, \quad \mathcal{T}\mathcal{S} = \begin{pmatrix} -1 & 1 \\ -1 & 0 \end{pmatrix}, \quad \mathcal{T}\mathcal{S}\mathcal{T} = \begin{pmatrix} 1 & 0 \\ 1 & -1 \end{pmatrix}. \tag{6.7.16}$$

The basic identities are

$$\mathcal{S}^2 = \mathcal{T}^2 = (\mathcal{T}\mathcal{S}\mathcal{T})^2 = \mathcal{E}, \quad (\mathcal{S}\mathcal{T})^3 = (\mathcal{T}\mathcal{S})^3 = \mathcal{E}, \quad \mathcal{T}\mathcal{S}\mathcal{T} = \mathcal{S}\mathcal{T}\mathcal{S}. \tag{6.7.17}$$

We also note that $\mathcal{T}\mathcal{S}$ is the inverse of $\mathcal{S}\mathcal{T}$.

We shall also need a notion of *conjugacy*. If $\mathcal{U} \in \mathfrak{A}$, we set

$$\mathcal{U}^* = \mathcal{T}\mathcal{S}\mathcal{T}\mathcal{U}\mathcal{T}\mathcal{S}\mathcal{T} \tag{6.7.18}$$

and refer to $\mathcal{U}^*$ as the *conjugate* of $\mathcal{U}$. This gives the following pairs of conjugate matrices and transformations:

$$(\mathcal{E}, \mathcal{E}), (\mathcal{S}, \mathcal{T}), (\mathcal{S}\mathcal{T}, \mathcal{T}\mathcal{S}), (\mathcal{T}\mathcal{S}\mathcal{T}, \mathcal{T}\mathcal{S}\mathcal{T}). \tag{6.7.19}$$

It is clear that

$$(\mathcal{U}^*)^* = \mathcal{U}.$$

Further, $\mathcal{E}$ and $\mathcal{T}\mathcal{S}\mathcal{T}$ are self-conjugate.

If $\mathcal{U} \in \mathfrak{A}$ and

$$\mathcal{U} = \begin{pmatrix} \alpha & \beta \\ \gamma & \delta \end{pmatrix},$$

we define

$$\mathfrak{U}(z) = \frac{\alpha z + \beta}{\gamma z + \delta}, \tag{6.7.20}$$

$$\mathfrak{U}\begin{pmatrix} a \\ b \end{pmatrix} = \begin{pmatrix} \alpha a + \beta b \\ \gamma a + \delta b \end{pmatrix}. \tag{6.7.21}$$

Thus the six transforms of z under the anharmonic group are

$$z, \frac{1}{z}, 1 - z, \frac{1}{1-z}, \frac{z-1}{z}, \frac{z}{z-1}, \tag{6.7.22}$$

respectively, those of the coefficient vector

$$\begin{pmatrix} a \\ b \end{pmatrix}, \begin{pmatrix} -b \\ -a \end{pmatrix}, \begin{pmatrix} b-a \\ b \end{pmatrix}, \begin{pmatrix} -b \\ a-b \end{pmatrix}, \begin{pmatrix} b-a \\ -a \end{pmatrix}, \begin{pmatrix} a \\ a-b \end{pmatrix}, \tag{6.7.23}$$

respectively.

We have now the basic transformation theorem:

Theorem 6.7.1. *The transformations*

$$s = \mathfrak{U}(z), \begin{pmatrix} a^* \\ b^* \end{pmatrix} = \mathfrak{U}^*\begin{pmatrix} a \\ b \end{pmatrix} \tag{6.7.24}$$

carry equation (6.7.3) *into*

$$\frac{dw}{ds} = \left(\frac{a^*}{s} + \frac{b^*}{1-s}\right) w. \tag{6.7.25}$$

Verification is left to the reader.

This means that, knowing one solution of (6.7.3), we know six which we can write in the form

$$H\left(\mathfrak{U}(z); \mathfrak{U}^*\begin{pmatrix} a \\ b \end{pmatrix}\right), \qquad \mathfrak{U} \in \mathfrak{A}, \tag{6.7.26}$$

or in more detail

$$H(z; a, b), H\left(\frac{1}{z}; b-a, b\right), H(1-z; -b, -a)$$

$$H\left(\frac{1}{1-z}; b-a, -a\right), H\left(\frac{z-1}{z}; -b, a-b\right), H\left(\frac{z}{z-1}; a, a-b\right). \tag{6.7.27}$$

We denote these solutions by H_1 to H_6.

They are defined by convergent series in ascending powers of the first argument $\mathfrak{U}[z]$, multiplied on the right by $[\mathfrak{U}[z]]^{a^*}$. Here we are tacitly assuming that all spectral difference sets for the a^* are free of integers. Note that there are only three sets to consider, namely those corresponding to a, b, $a - b$. The series representations are valid in the domains

$$|z| < 1, |z| > 1, |z-1| < 1, |z-1| > 1, \Re(z) > \tfrac{1}{2}, \Re(z) < \tfrac{1}{2}, \tag{6.7.28}$$

respectively. See Figure 7.1.

We recall that there are constant elements c_{jk} such that

$$H_j = H_k c_{jk}, \qquad j, k = 1, 2, \ldots, 6. \tag{6.7.29}$$

Some of these transition constants can be found explicitly. The determination is easy when H_j and H_k have representations valid in a neighborhood of the same singular point. There are three such pairs (H_1, H_6), (H_2, H_4), (H_3, H_5), with representations valid in neighborhoods of $z = 0, \infty, 1$, respectively.

Let us consider the first pair which gives

$$c_{16} = (H_6)^{-1}H_1 = (z-1)^a z^{-a}\left\{\sum_{k=0}^{\infty} b_k[z/(z-1)]^k\right\}\left\{\sum_{m=0}^{\infty} c_m z^m\right\} z^a$$

with obvious notation. This being independent of z we can find its value by letting z tend to 0 along the positive real axis. Since $b_0 = c_0 = e$, the multiplier of $(z-1)^a$ is of the form

$$e + z^{-a}G(z)z^a \quad \text{with} \quad \|G(z)\| \leq C|z|.$$

For $\|a\| < \frac{1}{2}$ this tends to e as $z \to 0$. The same conclusion is valid if $\|a - \alpha e\| < \frac{1}{2}$ for some complex α. To evaluate the limit of $(z-1)^a$ and similar expressions, we restrict z by introducing cuts in the z-plane, say along the real axis from $-\infty$ to 0 and from 1 to $+\infty$. At $z = \frac{1}{2}$ take

$$\arg z = \arg(1 - z) = 0, \ \arg(z-1) = -\pi.$$

This gives

$$c_{61} = \exp(\pi i a), \ c_{16} = \exp(-\pi i a), \tag{6.7.30}$$

By the identity theorem for Fréchet analytic functions (see Hille-Phillips, Functional Analysis and Semi-Groups, p. 111, Theorem 3.16.4) the restriction imposed on a may be removed. For $\exp(\pi i a)$ is Fréchet analytic for all a, while $(H_6)^{-1}H_1$, evaluated say at $z = \frac{1}{4}$, is Fréchet analytic at least for $\|a\| < \frac{1}{2}$ since for such values of a all resolvents entering in the coefficients of H_1 and H_6 are Fréchet analytic. This implies that (6.7.30) holds for all a for which H_1 and H_6 are defined. Similarly

$$\begin{aligned} c_{53} &= \exp(\pi i b), & c_{35} &= \exp(-\pi i b), \\ c_{42} &= \exp[\pi i(b-a)], & c_{24} &= \exp[\pi i(a-b)], \end{aligned} \tag{6.7.31}$$

when the solutions are defined. Determination of the other constants would be of some interest.

Let us now derive the classical hypergeometric equation from the abstract case. We take $\mathfrak{B} = \mathfrak{M}_2$ and set $a = \mathcal{A}$, $b = \mathcal{B}$, $\mathfrak{C} = \mathcal{A} - \mathcal{B}$. The problem is to determine $\mathcal{A}$ and $\mathfrak{C}$ so that

$$z(1-z)\mathfrak{W}'(z) = (\mathcal{A} - \mathfrak{C}z)\mathfrak{W}(z)$$

is equivalent to the ordinary second order linear equation. Here we replace $\mathfrak{W}(z)$ by one of its column vectors

$$\begin{pmatrix} w(z) \\ zw'(z) \end{pmatrix},$$

where $w(z)$ shall be a solution of the classical hypergeometric equation. This gives the vector-matrix equation

$$z(1-z)\begin{pmatrix} w'(z) \\ zw''(z) + w'(z) \end{pmatrix} = (\mathcal{A} - \mathcal{C}z)\begin{pmatrix} w(z) \\ zw'(z) \end{pmatrix}$$

and hence the system of equations

$$z(1-z)w'(z) = (a_{11} - c_{11}z)w(z) + (a_{12} - c_{12}z)zw'(z),$$

$$z(1-z)[zw''(z) + w'(z)] = (a_{21} - c_{21}z)w(z) + (a_{22} - c_{22}z)zw'(z),$$

if $\mathcal{A} = (a_{jk})$, $\mathcal{C} = (c_{jk})$. The first equation becomes an identity if

$$a_{11} = c_{11} = 0, \; a_{12} = c_{12} = 1.$$

If we choose

$$a_{21} = 0,$$

the second equation becomes divisible by z and reduces to

$$z(1-z)w''(z) + [1 - a_{22} - (1 - c_{22})z]w'(z) + c_{21}w = 0.$$

Here we set

$$a_{22} = 1 - \gamma, \; c_{21} = -\alpha\beta, \; c_{22} = -\alpha - \beta$$

and obtain the well-known equation

$$z(1-z)w''(z) + [\gamma - (1 + \alpha + \beta)z]w'(z) - \alpha\beta w(z) = 0. \tag{6.7.32}$$

For a discussion of this equation along classical lines, see Section 7.1. Before leaving this topic we note that the corresponding matrices are

$$\mathcal{A} = \begin{pmatrix} 0 & 1 \\ 0 & 1-\gamma \end{pmatrix}, \qquad \mathcal{B} = \begin{pmatrix} 0 & 0 \\ -\alpha\beta & 1 + \alpha + \beta - \gamma \end{pmatrix}. \tag{6.7.33}$$

In Section B.2 there was a brief mention of the Fuchsian class of nth order linear differential equations, but a closer characterization of the coefficients still remains to be done. We require that all singularities are regular singular points. This implies that the coefficients of the equation are rational functions of z. Hence, clearing fractions, we can write the equation

$$\sum_{j=0}^{n} P_j(z)w^{(n-j)}(z) = 0 \tag{6.7.34}$$

where the P_j's are polynomials. The singularities are given by the zeros of $P_0(z)$ plus possibly the point at infinity. Suppose that the distinct zeros of $P_0(z)$ are

$$\alpha_1, \alpha_2, \ldots, \alpha_m,$$

and set

$$P(z) = (z - \alpha_1)(z - \alpha_2)\cdots(z - \alpha_m). \tag{6.7.35}$$

If $z = \alpha_k$ is to be a regular singular point,

$$\frac{P_j(z)}{P_0(z)}(z - \alpha_k)^j, \qquad j = 1, 2, \ldots, n$$

must be holomorphic at $z = \alpha_k$, or

$$\frac{P_j(z)}{P_0(z)}[P(z)]^j, \qquad j = 1, 2, \ldots, n$$

must be holomorphic in the finite plane. We may assume that

$$P_0(z) = [P(z)]^n. \tag{6.7.36}$$

Then the conditions imply that

$$P_j(z) = [P(z)]^{n-j}Q_j(z), \qquad j = 1, 2, \ldots, n, \tag{6.7.37}$$

where Q_j is a polynomial.

The degrees of these polynomials are severely restricted, if the point at infinity is also to be at most regular singular. In fact this implies

$$\deg [Q_j] \le j(m - 1), \qquad j = 1, 2, \ldots, n. \tag{6.7.38}$$

An equivalent condition is that

$$z^j \frac{Q_j(z)}{[P(z)]^j} \tag{6.7.39}$$

be holomorphic at infinity.

The proof is somewhat lengthy so we shall carry through the argument for $n = 3$. This exhibits the method. We are then dealing with an equation

$$w''' + p_1(z)w'' + p_2(z)w' + p_3(z)w = 0 \tag{6.7.40}$$

where the p_j's are holomorphic for $R < |z| < \infty$. For the following argument it is not necessary that the p_j's are rational. Putting

$$z = \frac{1}{s}$$

we get a result which may be written

$$s^3w''' + s^2[6 - zp_1(z)]w'' \\ + s[6 - 2zp_1(z) + z^2p_2(z)]w' - z^3p_3(z)w = 0, \tag{6.7.41}$$

where now the primes indicate differentiation with respect to s. If this equation is to admit the point $s = 0$ as a regular singular point, it is necessary that each of the functions

$$6 - zp_1(z),\ 6 - 2zp_1(z) + z^2p_2(z),\ z^3p_3(z) \tag{6.7.42}$$

be holomorphic at $z = \infty$, that is at $s = 0$. This will be the case iff

$$zp_1(z), \qquad z^2p_2(z), \qquad z^3p_3(z)$$

have this property. The condition is sufficient for $z = \infty$ to be either regular or regular singular. This is condition (6.7.39) for the case $n = 3$. The general case is handled by the same method.

Thus it is seen that conditions (6.7.36) to (6.7.38) are necessary and sufficient in order that Eq. (6.7.34) belong to the Fuchsian class. It is perhaps permitted to observe that the abstract case is simpler!

Let us return to the general equation (6.7.2) to obtain a representation of the solution for all non-singular values of z. For the matrix case, such a representation was found by J. A. Lappo-Danilevsky (posthumous publication, 1933), who followed up indications in papers by Fuchs and Poincaré.

Mark the points $\alpha_1, \alpha_2, \ldots, \alpha_m$ in the complex plane and denote by S the universal covering surface of the extended plane punctured at $z = \alpha_1, \alpha_2, \ldots, \alpha_m$ and ∞. This is the least Riemann surface on which each of the functions $\log(z - \alpha_j)$ is holomorphic. Let β be a point of the surface and introduce a family of functions.

$$L_\beta(\alpha_{j_1}, \alpha_{j_2}, \ldots, \alpha_{j_n}; z), \tag{6.7.43}$$

known as *hyperlogarithms* and defined by

$$\begin{aligned} L_\beta(\alpha_j; z) &= \int_\beta^z \frac{ds}{s - \alpha_j} = \log\frac{z - \alpha_j}{\beta - \alpha_j}, \\ L_\beta(\alpha_{j_1}, \ldots, \alpha_{j_n}, \alpha_{j_{n+1}}; z) &= \int_\beta^z L_\beta(\alpha_{j_1}, \ldots, \alpha_{j_n}; s)\frac{ds}{s - \alpha_{j_{n+1}}} \end{aligned} \tag{6.7.44}$$

Here $j_1, \ldots, j_n$ take on the values $1, 2, \ldots, m$. These functions are 0 at $z = \beta$ and are single-valued and holomorphic on S. If Γ is any rectifiable path on S from β to z of length L and if its distance from the branch points of S is δ, then

$$|L_\beta(\alpha_{j_1}, \ldots, \alpha_{j_n}; z)| \le \frac{1}{n!}\left(\frac{L}{\delta}\right)^n. \tag{6.7.45}$$

This is clearly true for $n = 1$ and is proved by complete induction on n. We have now *Lappo-Danilevsky's representation theorem.*

Theorem 6.7.2. For any z on S

$$w(z; \beta, e) = e + \sum_{n=1}^{\infty} \left\{ \sum a_{j_1} a_{j_2} \cdots a_{j_n} L_\beta(\alpha_{j_n}, \alpha_{j_{n-1}}, \ldots, \alpha_{j_1}; z) \right\} \tag{6.7.46}$$

where the second summation extends over all ordered products of n factors formed from the elements $a_1, a_2, \ldots, a_m$.

Proof. To prove convergence, note that

$$\begin{aligned}\|\sum a_{j_1} a_{j_2} \cdots a_{j_n} L_\beta(\alpha_{j_n}, \alpha_{j_{n-1}}, \ldots, \alpha_{j_1}; z)\| \\ &\le \frac{1}{n!}\left(\frac{L}{\delta}\right)^n \sum \|a_{j_1} a_{j_2} \cdots a_{j_n}\| \\ &\le \frac{1}{n!}\left(\frac{L}{\delta}\right)^n \left(\sum_{j=1}^{m} \|a_j\|\right)^n.\end{aligned}$$

It follows that the series converges and

$$\|w(z; \beta, e) - e\| \le \exp\left\{\frac{L}{\delta} \sum_{j=1}^{m} \|a_j\|\right\} - 1. \tag{6.7.47}$$

It remains to show that the differential equation is satisfied. By (5.7.44)

$$\frac{d}{dz} L_\beta(\alpha_{j_n}, \ldots, \alpha_{j_2}, \alpha_{j_1}; z) = \frac{1}{z - \alpha_{j_1}} L_\beta(\alpha_{j_n}, \ldots, \alpha_{j_2}; z).$$

It is clearly permitted to differentiate the series termwise and this gives

$$w'(z; \beta, e) = \sum_{n=1}^{\infty} \left\{ \sum \frac{1}{z - \alpha_{j_1}} a_{j_1} a_{j_2} \cdots a_{j_n} L_\beta(a_{j_n}, \ldots, \alpha_{j_2}; z) \right\}.$$

If in this multiple series we collect the terms for which j_1 has the fixed value k, we see that $(z - \alpha_k)^{-1}$ is multiplied by $a_k w(z; \beta, e)$, the series satisfies Eq. (6.7.2) and its initial value at $z = \beta$ is e. Hence the sum of the series equals the solution $w(z; \beta, e)$ defined in Section 6.1, where $\beta = z_0$. This justifies the notation. Incidentally, if we should apply the method of successive approximations to Eq. (6.7.2) we would get precisely the series (6.7.46).

EXERCISE 6.7

1. Suppose $m = 2$ in Eq. (6.7.2). Show how to obtain the normal form (6.7.3).
2. Show that $H(z; a, b) = z^\alpha(1 - z)^\beta H(z; a - \alpha e, b + \beta e)$.
3. What form does the series $H(z; a, b)$ take if a and b commute?
4. Show that conditions (6.7.9) can be satisfied in $\mathfrak{M}_2$ by non-trivial matrices.

5. Carry through the integration of (6.7.3) at $z = 0$ if $a = j$, $b = bj$, $jb = 0$, where j is an idempotent of $\mathfrak{B}$, $j \neq 0, e$.
6. Same question if $a = j$, $bj = 0$, $jb = b$.
7. Let $F_0, F_1, F_2 \in L_2(0, 2\pi)$ and find the solution of the hypergeometric convolution equation

$$z(1 - z)w_z(z, t) = [F_1(t) + zF_2(t)]*w(z, t)$$

such that $w(\frac{1}{2}, t) = F_0(t)$ and $w(z, t)$ is holomorphic in the z-plane cut along the real axis from $-\infty$ to 0 and from 1 to $+\infty$.
8. Verify (6.7.17) and (6.7.19).
9. If $\mathcal{S}$ is defined by (6.7.16), find $\mathbf{R}(\lambda, \mathbf{C}_{\mathcal{S}})$.
10. Verify Theorem 6.7.1. It is enough to take $\mathfrak{U} = \mathcal{S}$ and $\mathfrak{U} = \mathcal{C}$. Why?
11. Why are (6.7.38) and (6.7.39) equivalent?
12. Show that the point at infinity is a regular point (not singular) for Eq. (6.7.40) if

$$6z - z^2p_1(z), \quad 6z^2 - 2z^3p_1(z) + z^4p_2(z) \quad \text{and} \quad z^6p_3(z)$$

are holomorphic at infinity.
13. Find a similar condition for regularity at infinity in the second order case $w'' + p_1(z)w' + p_2(z)w = 0$.
14. Verify that the hypergeometric equation (6.7.32) belongs to the Fuchsian class and that the point at infinity is regular singular unless $\alpha = 0, \beta = 1$ or $\alpha = 1, \beta = 0$.

The next two relations are due to Lappo-Danilevsky in the matrix case.

15. Prove that

$$L_\beta(\alpha_1, \alpha_2; z) + L_\beta(\alpha_2, \alpha_1; z) = L_\beta(\alpha_1; z)L_\beta(\alpha_2; z).$$

16. If a and b commute with $[b, a] = ba - ab$, show that the series (6.7.46) reduces to

$$\exp\{-L_\beta(1, 0; z)[b, a]\}\left(\frac{z}{\beta}\right)^a\left(\frac{z - 1}{\beta - 1}\right)^{-b}$$

6.8 IRREGULAR SINGULAR POINTS, $p = 1$

We place the singularity at infinity, which point is supposed to be accessible in a sector. Consider the equation

$$w'(z) = F(z)w(z), \tag{6.8.1}$$

where $F(z)$ is a $\mathfrak{B}$-valued function holomorphic in a sector S: $R < |z| < \infty$, $|\arg z| < \alpha$, and

$$\|F[r \exp(i\theta)]\| \le Mr^{p-1}, \tag{6.8.2}$$

p being a positive integer. Referring to Theorem 6.3.3 and subsequent comments, we conclude that any non-trivial solution of (6.8.1) satisfies the double inequality (cf. (B.4.28) for the matrix case)

$$A_1 \exp\left[-\frac{1}{p} Mr^p\right] \leq \|w(z)\| \leq A_2 \exp\left[\frac{1}{p} Mr^p\right], \tag{6.8.3}$$

where A_1 and A_2 are positive numbers that depend upon the initial value of $w(z)$ and the opening of the sector. Simple examples show that the estimate is the best of its kind.

We turn now to the case where F is given by an expansion

$$F(z) = z^{p-1} \sum_{n=0}^{\infty} a_m z^{-m},\ a_m \in \mathfrak{B},\ R < |z|. \tag{6.8.4}$$

We say that $z = \infty$ is an *irregular singular point of rank p*. Actually we shall restrict ourselves to the case where $zF(z)$ is a polynomial of degree p. The resulting equation

$$zw'(z) = \left\{\sum_{k=0}^{p} a_k z^{p-k}\right\} w(z), \qquad a_0 \neq 0, \tag{6.8.5}$$

will be said to be of *Birkhoff's canonical form* in analogy with the matrix case. (See the comments concerning formula (B.4.33).) In view of the baffling situation in the matrix case, it does not seem likely that reduction to canonical form will be readily proved in general B-algebras. Equation (6.8.5) may well imply severe restriction of the generality; there will be other severe restrictions that have to be made for the sake of the method.

Equation (6.8.5) involves $p + 1$ $\mathfrak{B}$-valued parameters, the coefficients $a_0, a_1, \ldots, a_p$. It is natural to ask for transformations which preserve the form of the equation but shift the parameters. The substitution

$$w(z) = y(z) \exp\left\{\frac{\beta_0}{p} z^p + \frac{\beta_1}{p-1} z^{p-1} + \cdots + \beta_{p-1} z\right\} z^{\beta_p} \tag{6.8.6}$$

has this property and the new values of the parameters are

$$a_0 - \beta_0 e,\ a_1 - \beta_1 e, \ldots, a_p - \beta_p e,$$

respectively. This device will be used below to shift spectral singularities when needed.

The problem before us is to find representations of the solution of (6.8.5) valid in some partial neighborhood of infinity such as a sector. Of the various possible methods, that of Poincaré and Birkhoff, based on the use of the Laplace transform, seems most attractive, even, as it turns out, it cannot cope with the general situation.

We start with the case $p = 1$ and will consider $p > 1$ in the next section. Thus the equation is

$$zw'(z) = (a_0 z + a_1)w(z). \tag{6.8.7}$$

In analogy with the matrix case we set

$$w(z) = \int_C u(t) \exp(zt)\, dt, \tag{6.8.8}$$

where the function $u(t)$ and the path of integration C are to be determined. Substitution and integration by parts yields

$$(te - a_0)u(t) \exp(zt)|_C = \int_C [(te - a_0)u'(t) + (a_1 + e)u(t)] \exp(zt)\, dt.$$

This is satisfied if we can find a solution $u(t)$ of

$$(te - a_0)u'(t) + (a_1 + e)u(t) = 0$$

or, equivalently,

$$u'(t) = -R(t; a_0)(a_1 + e)u(t), \tag{6.8.9}$$

where as usual $R(t; a_0)$ denotes the resolvent of a_0, and if, for this $u(t)$, we can find a path C such that the integrated part vanishes in the limits:

$$(te - a_0)u(t) \exp(zt)|_C = 0. \tag{6.8.10}$$

Such a path would normally surround a part of the spectrum of a_0 and extend to infinity in such a direction that

$$\lim \exp(zt) = 0. \tag{6.8.11}$$

Owing to the factor $a_1 + e$ in the right member of (6.8.9), not all spectral singularities of a_0 are necessarily singularities of $u(t)$. Here we may exclude the case $a_1 = -e$ where the solution is elementary and may be read off by inspection. The point at infinity is not affected and is a regular singular point of $u(t)$ as long as $a_1 + e \neq 0$. For $|t| > r(a_0)$, the spectral radius of a_0,

$$tu'(t) = -\left[a_1 + e + \sum_{m=1}^{\infty} a_0^m (a_1 + e)t^{-m}\right] u(t). \tag{6.8.12}$$

If the difference set

$$[\gamma \mid \gamma = \alpha - \beta,\ \alpha \in \sigma(a_1),\ \beta \in \sigma(a_1)]$$

does not contain any integers > 0, Eq. (6.8.12) has a solution

$$u(t) = \left[e + \sum_{k=1}^{\infty} c_k t^{-k}\right] t^{-a_1 - e} \tag{6.8.13}$$

where the series converges for $|t| > r(a_0)$.

We can use this solution to form the integral (6.8.8). To fix the ideas, suppose that $\Re(z) > 0$. We can then take for C a loop surrounding $\sigma(a_0)$ and the negative real axis. More precisely, let C consist of the semi-circle $|t| = r(a_0) + 1$, $\Re(t) > 0$, and the two lines $\Im(t) = \pm[r(a_0) + 1]$, $\Re(t) \leq 0$, described in the positive sense so that $\arg t$ goes from $-\pi$ to $+\pi$. Since on C

$$\|u(t)\| \leq M|t|^{\|a_1\|-1}, \tag{6.8.14}$$

the integral exists and

$$\|te - a_0\| \; \|u(t)\| \exp[\Re(zt)] \to 0$$

as $\Re(t) \to -\infty$ along C. Hence this choice of $u(t)$ and of C gives a solution of (6.8.7), an entire function of z times a power of z.

To derive the series for this and other solutions, we shall need a definition of the gamma function on $\mathfrak{B}$. More precisely, we shall consider the *reciprocal gamma function* which always exists while the gamma function itself may not. Write

$$\frac{1}{\Gamma(\lambda)} = \frac{1}{\Gamma}(\lambda).$$

This is an entire function of the scalar variable λ which is representable by a power series, an infinite product, and Hankel's integral. In any one of these representations we can replace λ by an element a of $\mathfrak{B}$ and thus obtain equivalent definitions of $(1/\Gamma)(a)$. The infinite product shows that $(1/\Gamma)(a)$ is a singular element of $\mathfrak{B}$ iff one of the elements $a, a + e, \ldots, a + ne, \ldots$ is singular. It also gives relations like

$$\frac{1}{\Gamma}(a)\frac{1}{\Gamma}(e - a) = \frac{1}{\pi}\sin(\pi a) \tag{6.8.15}$$

and the functional equation

$$a\frac{1}{\Gamma}(a + e) = \frac{1}{\Gamma}(a). \tag{6.8.16}$$

Hankel's integral is what is especially needed here, and it gives

$$\frac{1}{\Gamma}(a) = \frac{1}{2\pi i}\int_C t^{-a}\exp(t)\,dt, \tag{6.8.17}$$

where C is a loop surrounding the negative real axis of the type described above and $a \in \mathfrak{B}$.

Substituting the series (6.8.13) in the integral (6.8.8) and integrating termwise as is permitted by the uniform convergence, we obtain a result which simplifies to

$$w(z) = 2\pi i \sum_{k=0}^{\infty} c_k \frac{1}{\Gamma}[a_1 + (k + 1)e]\, z^{a_1 + k}. \tag{6.8.18}$$

This is an entire function of z of order 1 multiplied by z^{a_1} as asserted above. It is a fundamental solution unless $a_1 + e$ is singular. The order follows from the *a priori* estimate (6.8.3) with $p = 1$ and may be confirmed by estimating the coefficients using (6.8.17). This is a solution in good standing of (6.8.7) but it tell us nothing about the asymptotic behavior of $w(z)$.

To get such information we must tackle the singularities of (6.8.9) that stem from the spectral set of a_0. This set may be any closed set in the disk $(t|\ |t| \leq r(a_0))$. In order to get anywhere we must impose assumptions on $\sigma(a_0)$. The following will serve our needs.

Hypothesis I. 1) *There exists an isolated point $\alpha_1 \in \sigma(a_0)$ and $\sigma(a_0) \ominus \{\alpha_1\}$ does not separate α_1 from the point at infinity.*

2) *α_1 is a simple pole of $R(t; a_0)$.*

3) *If j is the residue idempotent of $R(t; a_0)$ at $t = \alpha$, then the difference set of $\sigma[j(a_1 + e)]$ contains no integers $\neq 0$.*

Here (1) and (2) are necessary for the desired type of results; (3) will sometimes be achieved by a preliminary transformation of the type (6.8.6) to replace a_1 by $a_1 + \eta e$, η a complex number. This happens, e.g. in the matrix case, for which see below. If

$$ja_1 j = \beta j, \tag{6.8.19}$$

β complex number, we can again satisfy I(3). For here $\sigma[j(a_1 + e)] = \{0, \beta + 1\}$ and (6.8.6) may be used to ensure that β is not an integer.

We now have

$$R(t; a_0)(a_1 + e) = \frac{j(a_1 + e)}{t - \alpha_1} + \sum_{n=0}^{\infty} b^{n+1}(a_1 + e)(\alpha_1 - t)^n, \tag{6.8.20}$$

where $jb = bj = 0$ and the series converges for $|t - \alpha_1| < [r(b)]^{-1}$ and $r(b)$ is the spectral radius of b. Hence (6.8.9) is satisfied by

$$u(t) = \sum_{k=0}^{\infty} b_k(t - \alpha_1)^{-j(a_1+e)+k},\ b_0 = e, \tag{6.8.21}$$

by Theorem 6.5.3. The series converges in the same disk as the resolvent series. By Hypothesis I(1), $u(t)$ may be continued outside the disk, if the singularities of $R(t; a_0)(a_1 + e)$ are avoided and, in particular, there exists a path l from $t = \alpha_1$ to $t = \infty$ along which $u(t)$ may be continued analytically. Here the part of l outside a large circle is at our disposal and may be taken as a horizontal straight line going to the left or the right according as $\Re(z) > 0$ or < 0.

We can take C as a loop in the resolvent set of a_0 closely surrounding the path l. Since (6.8.14) holds on the distant part of l, (6.8.10) is satisfied and the corresponding integral (6.8.8) is a solution of (6.8.7). The asymptotic behavior of this solution can be found by a method which at first sight seems to be doomed to failure: one substitutes the series (6.8.21) in the integral and integrates termwise. This is completely unjustified but leads to the desired result!

We may assume that α_1 is real positive. If not, a preliminary use of (6.8.6) affecting only a_0 will achieve this. Consider one of the integrals obtained by the substitution:

$$\int_C (t - \alpha_1)^{-j(a_1+e)+k} \exp(zt)\, dt.$$

To fix the ideas, suppose that $\Re(z) > 0$. We can then straighten out C so that it becomes a loop surrounding the line segment $(-\infty, \alpha_1)$ of the real axis. Set $t = \alpha_1 + s/z$ to obtain

$$z^{j(a_1+e)-k-1} \exp(\alpha_1 z) \int_C s^{-j(a_1+e)+k} \exp(s)\, ds$$

$$= 2\pi i \frac{1}{\Gamma} [j(a_1 + e) - ke]\, z^{j(a_1+e)-k-1} \exp(\alpha_1 z),$$

using (6.8.17) and a suitable rotation of the path of integration. Multiplying by b_k and summing for k, one obtains the formal result

$$w(z) \sim 2\pi i \left\{ \sum_{k=0}^{\infty} b_k \frac{1}{\Gamma} [j(a_1 + e) - ke]\, z^{j(a_1+e)-k-1} \right\} \exp(\alpha_1 z). \quad (6.8.22)$$

Unless $b_k = 0$ for almost all k, the series diverges since the reciprocal gamma function grows as a factorial. Nevertheless the expansion is an asymptotic series in the sense of Poincaré and represents the solution in the right half-plane. In the first approximation the solution behaves as

$$z^{j(a_1+e)-1} \exp(\alpha_1 z). \quad (6.8.23)$$

For the question of asymptotic representation, see the next section.

The procedure also applies in the left half-plane. The same series is obtained, but normally it represents a different solution. Such solutions may be expected to be singular elements of $\mathfrak{B}$ since $j(a_1 + e)$ is singular and hence also $(1/\Gamma)[j(a_1 + e)]$. If there are several spectral values of a_0 which satisfy Hypothesis I, then to each of them will correspond an asymptotic representation of a particular integral obtained by making appropriate changes in formula (6.8.22) of coefficients b_k, idempotent j, and spectral value α. In particular, if there are only a finite number of spectral values of a_0, all of which satisfy Hypothesis I, then we have a set of linearly independent solutions which may be combined to form a fundamental solution. In particular, $w(z)$ of (6.8.18) will then be the sum of solutions of known asymptotic behavior.

This situation arises in the matrix case, $\mathfrak{B} = \mathfrak{M}_n$,

$$z\mathcal{U}'(z) = (\mathcal{B}_0 z + \mathcal{B}_1)\mathcal{U}(z),$$

provided the characteristic values of $\mathcal{B}_0$ are all distinct. If this is the case and if $\mathcal{B}$ is so chosen that $\mathcal{B}\mathcal{B}_0\mathcal{B}^{-1} \equiv \mathcal{A}_0 = (\delta_{jk}\alpha_k)$, then $\mathcal{W}(z) = \mathcal{B}\mathcal{U}(z)\mathcal{B}^{-1}$ satisfies

$$z\mathcal{W}'(z) = (\mathcal{A}_0 z + \mathcal{A}_1)\mathcal{W}(z), \qquad \mathcal{A}_1 = \mathcal{B}\mathcal{B}_1\mathcal{B}^{-1}. \tag{6.8.24}$$

Consider the kth characteristic value α_k of $\mathcal{A}_0$ and let $\mathcal{E}_k$ be the corresponding residue idempotent of $\mathcal{R}(t; \mathcal{A}_0)$. Then $\mathcal{E}_k$ has a 1 in the place (k, k) and 0 elsewhere. We have

$$-j(a_1 + e) = -\mathcal{E}_k(\mathcal{A}_1 + \mathcal{E}).$$

If $\mathcal{A}_1 = (a^1_{km})$, then the right member is the matrix whose k^{th} row is

$$-\delta_{km} - a^1_{km},$$

while all other elements are 0. The characteristic values of this matrix are 0, repeated $n - 1$ times, and $-1 - a^1_{kk}$. We may assume that the latter number is not a positive integer; if this is not so, this can be achieved by a preliminary transformation of type (6.8.6) affecting only $\mathcal{A}_1$. The preceding discussion applies and gives a set of n linearly independent solution vectors for the right half-plane, and n for the left. The elements of the kth column vector behave asymptotically as constant multiples of

$$z^{\beta_k} \exp(\alpha_k z), \qquad \beta_k = a^1_{kk},$$

as $z \to \infty$ in the half-plane in question.

Several important second order linear differential equations have equivalent matrix equations of type (6.8.24). Here $\mathfrak{B} = \mathfrak{M}_2$. Thus, if we set

$$\mathcal{A}_0 = \begin{pmatrix} 0 & 0 \\ 0 & a \end{pmatrix}, \qquad \mathcal{A}_1 = \begin{pmatrix} 0 & 1 \\ a & -b \end{pmatrix}, \tag{6.8.25}$$

and take

$$\mathcal{W}(z) = \begin{pmatrix} w_1(z) & w_2(z) \\ w_1'(z) & w_2'(z) \end{pmatrix},$$

then $w_j(z)$ satisfies

$$zw''(z) + (b - a)w'(z) - aw(z) = 0, \tag{6.8.26}$$

a form of the confluent hypergeometric equation. As a second example take

$$\mathcal{A}_0 = \begin{pmatrix} 0 & 1 \\ -1 & 0 \end{pmatrix}, \qquad \mathcal{A}_1 = \begin{pmatrix} 0 & 0 \\ 0 & -2a - 1 \end{pmatrix}. \tag{6.8.27}$$

Here $w_i(z)$ satisfies

$$zw''(z) + (2a + 1)w'(z) + zw(z) = 0. \tag{6.8.28}$$

The substitution $u = z^a w$ takes this into Bessel's equation

$$z^2u''(z) + zu'(z) + (z^2 - a^2)u(z) = 0. \tag{6.8.29}$$

Bessel's equation is discussed in Section 7.3, and the confluent equation in Section 7.5, where the asymptotic behavior of the solutions is treated at some length.

EXERCISE 6.8

1. Take $\mathfrak{B} = \mathfrak{M}_2$,

$$\mathcal{A}_0 = \begin{pmatrix} 0 & 1 \\ \beta^2 & 0 \end{pmatrix}, \qquad \mathcal{A}_1 = \begin{pmatrix} 0 & 0 \\ 0 & 1 \end{pmatrix},$$

   where β is real positive. Determine the characteristic values of $\mathcal{A}_0$, find the residue idempotents $\mathfrak{J}$, find the characteristic values of $\mathfrak{J}(\mathcal{A}_1 + \mathcal{E})$, and find the leading terms in the asymptotic expansions.
2. Answer the same questions if $\mathcal{A}_0$ and $\mathcal{A}_1$ are given by (6.8.25).
3. Answer the same questions if $\mathcal{A}_0$ and $\mathcal{A}_1$ are given by (6.8.27).
4. Given the equation

$$z^2w''(z) - (\alpha z^2 + \beta z)w'(z) - \gamma w(z) = 0.$$

   Reduce to a matrix equation of type (6.8.24), using w, zw' for the column vectors.
5. The preceding second order equation has a formal solution which is a power series in $1/z$. Find the coefficients and prove that the series diverges.
6. Suppose that $j \in \mathfrak{B}$ is an idempotent and that $b \in \mathfrak{B}$ satisfies $jb = b$, $bj = 0$. Solve Eq. (6.8.7) with $a_0 = j$, $a_1 = b$.
7. How is (6.8.13) obtained?
8. What is the form of the infinite product of $(1/\Gamma)(a)$?
9. Verify (6.8.15)–(6.8.17).
10. If N is the operator that takes $f(s)$ into $f(-s)$ in the space $C[-1, 1]$, find the action of $(1/\Gamma)(N + kI)$, k integer or zero.
11. Determine the spectrum of $j(a_1 + e)$ if (6.8.19) holds.

6.9 IRREGULAR SINGULAR POINTS, $p > 1$

We now turn to the case where the rank p is greater than 1. Here we follow the discussion given by J. B. Miller (1963). The equation is given as

$$zw'(z) = \left\{\sum_{k=0}^{p} a_{p-k}z^k\right\} w(z), \qquad a_j \in \mathfrak{B}, \tag{6.9.1}$$

but we shall find it advantageous to consider the class of equations

$$zW'(z) = \left\{ \sum_{k=0}^{p} b_{p-k} z^k \right\} W(z), \tag{6.9.2}$$

where

$$b_j = a_j - \beta_j e, \qquad j = 0, 1, 2, \ldots, p, \tag{6.9.3}$$

and the β's are arbitrary complex numbers. We recall that (6.9.2) arises when the transformation (6.8.6) is applied to (6.9.1).

Equation (6.9.2) will be solved using Poincaré's method as extended by Birkhoff. We assume the existence of a solution of the form

$$W(z) = \int_C \exp(tz^p) \left\{ \sum_{k=1}^{p} z^{p-k} u_k(t) \right\} dt, \tag{6.9.4}$$

where the functions $u_1, u_2, \ldots, u_p$ and the path C are to be determined.

Substitution of (6.9.4) in (6.9.2) and rearrangement of terms yields

$$\int_C \exp(tz^p) \left\{ \sum_{k=0}^{2p} z^{2p-k} U_k(t) \right\} dt = 0, \tag{6.9.5}$$

where

$$U_k(t) = \begin{cases} (pte - b_0)u_k(t) - \displaystyle\sum_{j=1}^{k-1} b_j u_{k-j}(t), & 1 \le k \le p, \\ (2p - k)u_{k-p}(t) - \displaystyle\sum_{j=k-p}^{p} b_j u_{k-j}(t), & p + 1 \le k \le 2p. \end{cases} \tag{6.9.6}$$

Setting

$$\begin{aligned} \sum_{k=1}^{2p} z^{2p-k} U_k(t) &= \sum_{k=p+1}^{2p} z^{2p-k} U_k + z^p \sum_{k=1}^{p} z^{p-k} U_k \\ &\equiv S_1(z, t) + z^p S_2(z, t) \end{aligned} \tag{6.9.7}$$

and integrating by parts in (6.9.5), we get

$$\int_C \exp(tz^p) \left[S_1(z, t) - \frac{\partial}{\partial t} S_2(z, t) \right] dt + [S_2(z, t) \exp(tz^p)]_C = 0. \tag{6.9.8}$$

It follows that (6.9.4) will satisfy (6.9.2), if the $u_k(t)$ can be chosen so that

$$S_1(z, t) = \frac{\partial}{\partial t} S_2(z, t)$$

identically in z and if also a path C can be found such that

$$[S_2(z, t) \exp(tz^p)]_C = 0.$$

The first condition requires that

$$U_{k+p}(t) = U_k'(t), \qquad k = 1, 2, \ldots, p. \tag{6.9.9}$$

These equations together with (6.9.6) give a system of p linear first order differential equations for $u_1, u_2, \ldots, u_p$. We shall write these equations in matrix form. To this end we introduce vector fields and matrices over the algebra $\mathfrak{B}$.

Let $\mathfrak{B}_p = \mathfrak{B}_p(\mathfrak{B})$ be the Banach space of vectors composed of p components belonging to $\mathfrak{B}$, with the complex numbers as scalar field, and norm

$$|\boldsymbol{v}| = \|x_1\| + \|x_2\| + \cdots + \|x_p\|, \tag{6.9.10}$$

if $\boldsymbol{v} = (x_1, x_2, \ldots, x_p)$. Similarly, let $\mathfrak{M}_p = \mathfrak{M}_p(\mathfrak{B})$ be the B-algebra of p by p matrices $\mathsf{X} = (x_{jk})$ where $x_{jk} \in \mathfrak{B}$ and the norm is

$$|\mathsf{X}| = \max_j \sum_{k=1}^{p} \|x_{jk}\|. \tag{6.9.11}$$

We define $a\mathsf{X} = (ax_{jk})$, $\mathsf{X}a = (x_{jk}a)$.

Define A and B as the triangular matrices

$$\mathsf{A} = \begin{bmatrix} b_0 & & & & \\ b_1 & b_0 & & & \\ \cdot & \cdot & \cdot & & \\ \cdot & \cdot & \cdot & \cdot & \\ b_{p-1} & b_{p-2} & b_1 & \cdot & b_0 \end{bmatrix}, \tag{6.9.12}$$

$$\mathsf{B} = \begin{bmatrix} e + b_p & b_{p-1} & b_{p-2} & \cdot & b_1 \\ & 2e + b_p & b_{p-1} & \cdot & b_2 \\ & & \cdot & \cdot & \cdot \\ & & & \cdot & b_{p-1} \\ & & & & pe + b_p \end{bmatrix}$$

and let $\mathsf{U}(t)$ be a solution of the matrix equation

$$(\mathsf{A} - pt\mathsf{E})\mathsf{U}'(t) = \mathsf{B}\mathsf{U}(t)$$

or equivalently

$$\mathsf{U}'(t) = -\mathsf{R}(pt; \mathsf{A})\mathsf{B}\mathsf{U}(t). \tag{6.9.13}$$

Then any column vector $\boldsymbol{u}(t) = [u_1(t), \ldots, u_p(t)]$ of $\mathsf{U}(t)$ gives a solution of the vector matrix equation

$$\boldsymbol{u}'(t) = -\mathsf{R}(pt; \mathsf{A})\mathsf{B}\boldsymbol{u}(t). \tag{6.9.14}$$

If the components of $\boldsymbol{u}(t)$ are substituted in the integral (6.9.4) we obtain a solution of (6.9.2) for a suitable choice of the path C. If $\mathsf{U}(t)$ is a fundamental solution of (6.9.13), then the column vectors are linearly independent and such a matrix gives p linearly independent solutions of (6.9.2). Any non-zero solution $\mathsf{U}(t)$ gives at least one acceptable choice of $u_1, \ldots, u_p$ and a non-zero solution of (6.9.2).

We need an explicit expression for $\mathsf{R}(\lambda; \mathsf{A})$, the resolvent of A. Since A is a lower triangular matrix, we may expect its resolvent to have the same form. If X is the required matrix, we can compute its elements successively by equating corresponding elements in the identity

$$\mathsf{X}(\lambda \mathsf{E} - \mathsf{A}) = \mathsf{E}.$$

In this way one obtains

$$\mathsf{R}(\lambda; \mathsf{A}) = \begin{bmatrix} R & & & & \\ S_1 & R & & & \\ S_2 & S_1 & R & & \\ \cdot & \cdot & \cdot & \cdot & \\ S_{p-1} & S_{p-2} & S_{p-3} & \cdot & R \end{bmatrix}, \tag{6.9.15}$$

where $R = R(\lambda; b_0)$, the resolvent of b_0, and

$$\begin{aligned} S_1 &= Rb_1R, \\ S_2 &= Rb_2R + Rb_1Rb_1R, \\ &\cdot\ \cdot\ \cdot\ \cdot\ \cdot\ \cdot\ \cdot\ \cdot\ \cdot\ \cdot \\ S_k &= \sum_{(k)} Rb_{j_1}Rb_{j_2}R \cdots Rb_{j_h}R. \end{aligned} \tag{6.9.16}$$

Here the symbol under the summation sign indicates that the sum is taken over all ordered partitions $(j_1, j_2, \ldots, j_h)$ of k,

$$j_1 + j_2 + \cdots + j_h = k, \qquad j_1 \geq 1, j_2 \geq 1, \ldots, j_h \geq 1.$$

It is seen that the singularities of $\mathsf{R}(pt; \mathsf{A})$ occur precisely at the singularities of $R(pt; b_0)$. In general, a simple pole of the latter will produce a p-fold pole in the former. Our object will be to impose suitable restrictions on the spectrum of $a_0 = b_0 + \beta_0 e$ and choices of the parameters $\beta_0, \beta_1, \ldots, \beta_p$ so that $\mathsf{R}(pt; \mathsf{A})$ exhibits at least one simple pole. To this end we postulate, with Miller:

Hypothesis II. 1) *The spectrum of* a_0 *contains an isolated point* $\lambda = \lambda_0$ *which is a simple pole of* $R(\lambda; a_0)$. *Let the corresponding residue idempotent be* j.
2) $\sigma(a_0) \ominus \{\lambda_0\}$ *is non-empty, but there is a sector* $\vartheta_1 < \arg(\lambda - \lambda_0) < \vartheta_2$ *free from spectral values.*
3) *To any* $a \in \mathfrak{B}$ *there is a complex number* α *such that*

$$jaj = \alpha j. \tag{6.9.17}$$

Here II(1) is necessary for the auxiliary equation to have a regular singular point. If this were not the case, then the method breaks down completely since there is no point in considering an auxiliary equation which is more complicated than the given equation. As we shall see, condition II(1) is partly redundant: that the isolated singularity reduces to a simple pole follows from II(3) for $a = a_0$. Hypothesis II(2) will be used only in the choice of the path C and in discussing the asymptotic behavior of $W(z)$. Finally, II(3) is a very severe and artificial-looking assumption. Be that as it may, it is almost essential for the success of the method. Actually it would be sufficient if II(3) held in a subalgebra generated by $e, a_0, a_1, \ldots, a_p, j, c$, where

$$c = \lim_{\lambda \to \lambda_0} (e - j)R(\lambda; a_0). \tag{6.9.18}$$

We have $\sigma(a_0) = \sigma(b_0) + \beta_0$. This means that $R(\lambda, b_0)$ has a simple pole at $\lambda = \lambda_0 - \beta_0$ with residue idempotent j. We can shift this pole to $\lambda = 0$ by choosing the parameter β_0 which is at our disposal:

$$\beta_0 = \lambda_0. \tag{6.9.19}$$

With this choice of β_0 and hence of b_0

$$j = \frac{1}{2\pi i} \int_\gamma R(\lambda, b_0)\, d\lambda, \tag{6.9.20}$$

where γ is a small circle about the origin. Now $\mathsf{R}(\lambda; \mathsf{A})$ will also have a pole at the origin and the corresponding residue idempotent J is the residue at the origin of the matrix (6.9.15). Since the residue of a matrix is the matrix of the residues we have

$$\mathsf{J} = \begin{bmatrix} j & & & & \\ r_1 & j & & & \\ r_2 & r_1 & j & & \\ \cdot & \cdot & \cdot & \cdot & \\ r_{p-1} & r_{p-2} & \cdot & r_1 & j \end{bmatrix}, \tag{6.9.21}$$

where

$$r_\nu = \frac{1}{2\pi i} \int_\gamma S_\nu\, d\lambda. \tag{6.9.22}$$

We have to show that it is possible to choose the remaining parameters $\beta_1, \beta_2, \ldots, \beta_p$ so that $\mathsf{R}(\lambda; \mathsf{A})$ has only a simple pole at $\lambda = 0$. For this purpose it is necessary and sufficient to show that each function S_k can be made to have at most a simple pole at $\lambda = 0$. We note that the diagonal elements R of the matrix (6.9.15) already have this property. We start with

$$\begin{aligned} S_1 &= R(\lambda, b_0) b_1 R(\lambda, b_0) \\ &= \left[\frac{1}{\lambda} j + \sum_{n=0}^{\infty} c^{n+1}(-\lambda)^n\right] b_1 \left[\frac{1}{\lambda} j + \sum_{n=0}^{\infty} c^{n+1}(-\lambda)^n\right] \\ &= \frac{1}{\lambda^2} j b_1 j + \frac{1}{\lambda}(j b_1 c + c b_1 j) + O(1), \end{aligned}$$

where c is defined by (6.9.18). It follows that S_1 will have a simple pole at $\lambda = 0$ iff $jb_1j = 0$. Since

$$jb_1j = j(a_1 - \beta_1 e)j = (\alpha_1 - \beta_1)j$$

by assumption, it follows that we must choose

$$\beta_1 = \alpha_1,\ b_1 = a_1 - \alpha_1 e. \tag{6.9.23}$$

If this is done, then S_1 has at most a simple pole at $\lambda = 0$.

We then use an induction argument. Assume that, for some $k < p - 1$, the poles at $\lambda = 0$ of $R, S_1, \ldots, S_k$ have, by choice of $\beta_1, \beta_2, \ldots, \beta_k$, been reduced to orders ≤ 1. Now

$$\begin{aligned} S_{k+1} &= \sum_{(k+1)} Rb_{i_1}R\cdots Rb_{i_h}R \\ &= Rb_1S_k + Rb_2S_{k-1} + \cdots + Rb_kS_1 + Rb_{k+1}R \\ &= \left(\frac{1}{\lambda}j + \cdots\right)b_1\left(\frac{1}{\lambda}r_k + \cdots\right) + \cdots + \left(\frac{1}{\lambda}j + \cdots\right)b_k\left(\frac{1}{\lambda}r_1 + \cdots\right) \\ &\quad + \left(\frac{1}{\lambda}j + \cdots\right)b_{k+1}\left(\frac{1}{\lambda}j + \cdots\right) \equiv \frac{1}{\lambda^2}g_{k+1} + \frac{1}{\lambda}r_{k+1} + \cdots. \end{aligned}$$

Here

$$g_{k+1} = jb_1r_k + jb_2r_{k-1} + \cdots + jb_kr + jb_{k+1}j \tag{6.9.24}$$

must be annihilated by a suitable choice of the parameter β_{k+1}. To show that this is possible we use the identities

$$r_\nu j + r_{\nu-1}r_1 + \cdots + r_1r_{\nu-1} + jr_\nu = r_\nu, \qquad \nu = 0, 1, \ldots, p-1, \tag{6.9.25}$$

obtained by comparing corresponding elements in the matrix identity $\mathsf{J}^2 = \mathsf{J}$. This gives

$$g_{k+1} = \sum_{\nu=0}^{k} j\left(\sum_{\mu=\nu}^{k} b_{k-\mu+1}r_{\mu-\nu}\right)r_\nu. \tag{6.9.26}$$

Now let the numbers $\theta_{\nu+1}$, $\nu = 1, 2, \ldots, p-1$, be defined by

$$j(b_1r_\nu + b_2r_{\nu-1} + \cdots + b_{\nu-1}r_2 + b_\nu r_1)j = \theta_{\nu+1}j \tag{6.9.27}$$

under assumption (6.9.17). Then (6.9.24) becomes

$$\begin{aligned} g_{k+1} = \theta_{k+1}j + g_kr_1 + g_{k-1}r_2 + \cdots \\ + g_2r_{k-1} + g_1r_k + j(a_{k+1} - \beta_{k+1}e)j. \end{aligned}$$

The induction hypothesis implies that $g_1 = g_2 = \cdots = g_k = 0$, so

$$g_{k+1} = (\theta_{k+1} + \alpha_{k+1} - \beta_{k+1})j,$$

where

$$ja_\nu j = \alpha_\nu j, \qquad \nu = 1, 2, \ldots, p-1, \tag{6.9.28}$$

and choice of β_{k+1} so that $g_{k+1} = 0$ is possible. Thus S_{k+1} has at most a pole of order 1 at $\lambda = 0$ and the desired result follows by complete induction. The β's are determined by

$$\beta_\nu = \theta_\nu + \alpha_\nu, \qquad \nu = 1, 2, \ldots, p-1. \tag{6.9.29}$$

Here we define $\theta_1 = 0$ and determine $\beta_1, \theta_2, \beta_2, \theta_3, \ldots, \beta_{p-1}$ successively by using (6.9.29) and (6.9.27) alternately, so that $g_1 = g_2 = \cdots = g_{p-1} = 0$.

It should be noted that each of the residues $r_1, \ldots, r_{p-1}$ is a multinomial in $b_1, b_2, \ldots, b_{p-1}, c, j$ so that at this stage we use the basic hypothesis (6.9.17) only on elements of the subalgebra $\mathfrak{B}_0$ of $\mathfrak{B}$ generated by $e, a_0, a_1, \ldots, a_{p-}, c, j$.

Actually, under the sole assumption

$$ja_0j = \alpha_0 j \tag{6.9.30}$$

we can prove that an isolated spectral singularity of a_0 at $\lambda = \lambda_0$ must be a simple pole. Since j commutes with a_0

$$j(a_0 - \lambda_0 e) = j^2(a_0 - \lambda_0 e) = j(a_0 - \lambda_0 e)j = (\alpha_0 - \lambda_0)j.$$

Here are two possibilities.

i) $\alpha_0 = \lambda_0$. We note that $jR(\lambda; b_0)$ has $\lambda = 0$ as its only singularity while $(e - j)R(\lambda; b_0)$ is holomorphic at $\lambda = 0$. Now for $\lambda \neq 0$

$$jR(\lambda; b_0) = \frac{1}{\lambda}j + \sum_{n=1}^{\infty} \frac{1}{\lambda^{n+1}}(jb_0)^n = \frac{1}{\lambda}j.$$

Hence

$$R(\lambda; b_0) = jR(\lambda; b_0) + (e - j)R(\lambda; b_0) = \frac{1}{\lambda}j + H(\lambda),$$

where $H(\lambda)$ is a $\mathfrak{B}$-valued function holomorphic at $\lambda = 0$. Hence the isolated spectral singularity of $R(\lambda, b_0)$ at $\lambda = 0$ is necessarily a simple pole.

ii) $\alpha_0 \neq \lambda_0$. Here

$$jR(\lambda, b_0) = \lambda^{-1}j + \sum_{n=1}^{\infty} \lambda^{-n-1}(\alpha_0 - \lambda_0)^n j = (\lambda - \alpha_0 + \lambda_0)^{-1}j$$

which is holomorphic at $\lambda = 0$. Now $(e - j)R(\lambda, b_0)$ is holomorphic at $\lambda = 0$ so $R(\lambda, b_0)$ must have the same property. This contradicts the assumption that $\lambda = 0$ is a spectral singularity. Thus we see that the second alternative must be rejected: α_0 must equal λ_0.

We assume henceforth that $\lambda = 0$ is a simple pole of $R(\lambda, b_0)$ with residue j, and that the parameters $\beta_1, \beta_2, \ldots, \beta_{p-1}$ have been chosen so that $\mathsf{R}(\lambda; \mathsf{A})$ also has a simple pole at $\lambda = 0$ with residue J. The corresponding auxiliary equation (6.9.13) now has a regular singular point at $t = 0$ and may be written

$$t\mathsf{U}'(t) = -t\mathsf{R}(pt; \mathsf{A})\mathsf{B}\mathsf{U}(t) = \left(\sum_{n=0}^{\infty} \mathsf{C}_n t^n\right)\mathsf{U}(t) \tag{6.9.31}$$

where the critical first coefficient is

$$\mathsf{C} = \mathsf{C}_0 = -\frac{1}{p}\,\mathsf{JB}. \tag{6.9.32}$$

The series converges in some disk $|t| < \rho$ with $\rho > 0$.

This equation will certainly belong to the class discussed in Section 6.6, if the resolvent of C is a rational function of λ. For then $\mathsf{R}(\lambda; \mathsf{K})$, the resolvent of K, the commutator of C, will also be a rational function of λ by Foguel's Theorem 4.6.6. This turns out to be the case here. Miller has proved

Theorem 6.9.1. *The spectrum of* C *is the set*

$$\left\{0, -\frac{1}{p}, -\frac{2}{p}, \ldots, -1\right\} \tag{6.9.33}$$

and each of these points is a pole of $\mathsf{R}(\lambda; \mathsf{C})$ *of order exactly* 1.

Since the algebra of linear bounded operators on $\mathfrak{M}_p$ is a prime ring by Theorem 4.2.5, Foguel's Theorem 4.6.6 gives the

Corollary. *All spectral singularities of* K *are simple poles. There is a pole at* $\lambda = 1$ *and at no other positive integer.*

The proof of the theorem is long and complicated, so reluctantly we omit it here and refer to the original article (pp. 218–226, *Acta Mathematica*, **110** (1963)).

It follows that Theorem 6.6.1 applies and only one differentiation is necessary to obtain the fundamental solution. (See formula (6.6.11) with $p = 1$.) Note that this p has nothing to do with the rank of our equation. Thus we have

$$\mathsf{U}_1(t) = \lim_{\sigma \to 0} \frac{\partial}{\partial \sigma}\, \mathsf{U}(t, \sigma), \tag{6.9.34}$$

where $\mathsf{U}(t, \sigma)$ is found by the construction given in the proof of Theorem 6.6.1. In the proof it was also observed that a solution is given by

$$\mathsf{U}_0(t) = \lim_{\sigma \to 0} \mathsf{U}(t, \sigma). \tag{6.9.35}$$

For the case here considered Miller has computed the leading coefficients of these solutions in terms of various operators, *loc. cit.*, p. 226. The formulas show that $\mathsf{U}_0(t)$ is always singular and may possibly vanish identically while $\mathsf{U}_1(t)$ is a fundamental solution.

It remains now to obtain the solution of (6.9.1) using the generalized Laplace integral (6.9.4) where $u_1, u_2, \ldots, u_p$ form a column vector of a solution matrix $\mathsf{U}(t)$ of the auxiliary equation (6.9.13) and the path C is suitably chosen. The latter can now be chosen. By Hypothesis II(2) the resolvent $R(\lambda; b_0)$ is holomorphic in the open sector $\vartheta_1 < \arg \lambda < \vartheta_0$.

Denote by Σ_0 any closed interior sector, i.e. a region $\vartheta_1 < \vartheta_1^* \leq \arg \lambda \leq \vartheta_2^* < \vartheta_2$, $0 \leq |\lambda|$. Then

$$\sup \| t\mathsf{R}(pt; \mathsf{A})\mathsf{B} \| = M < \infty. \tag{6.9.36}$$

Using Theorems 6.5.1 and 6.5.3 one sees that

$$\| \mathsf{U}(t) \| < K_1 |t|^M, \ |t| > \tfrac{1}{2}\rho, \tag{6.9.37}$$

$$\| \mathsf{U}(t) \| < K_2 |t|^{-M}, \ |t| \leq \tfrac{1}{2}\rho, \tag{6.9.38}$$

for $t \in \Sigma_0$ where the constants K_1 and K_2 depend upon the solution, upon ρ and upon Σ_0.

Let L be any ray in Σ_0. We take the contour C as a loop coming from infinity along L, encircling the origin once in a positive sense, and returning to infinity along L. If z is such that

$$\Re(tz^p) < 0 \quad \text{for} \quad t \text{ on } L, \tag{6.9.39}$$

then the estimate (6.9.37) shows that the integral (6.9.4) converges and the endpoint condition

$$\lim S_2(z, t) \exp(tz^p) = 0$$

is satisfied if $t \to \infty$ along L. Thus any non-zero solution $\mathsf{U}(t)$ of (6.9.13) determines a solution of (6.9.2) for z lying in an appropriate sector and from $W(z)$ we pass to the solution $w(z)$ of (6.9.1) with the aid of the transformation (6.8.6).

We want to get the asymptotic expansion of $W(z)$ in a sector. For this purpose it would be more convenient to consider solutions of the auxiliary equation which do not involve logarithms, but we can handle the general case with little additional trouble. We have

$$\mathsf{U}_1(t) = [\mathsf{S}_1(t) + \mathsf{S}_2(t) \log t]t^{\mathsf{C}}, \tag{6.9.40}$$

where

$$\mathsf{S}_1(t) = \sum_{n=0}^{\infty} \mathsf{A}_n t^n, \ \mathsf{S}_2(t) = \sum_{n=1}^{\infty} \mathsf{B}_n t^n. \tag{6.9.41}$$

Here the coefficients are supposed to be known and the series converge in norm for $|z| < \rho$, a positive number. Denote the Nth partial sums of these series by $\mathsf{S}_{1,N}(t)$ and $\mathsf{S}_{2,N}(t)$, respectively. We have then

$$\begin{aligned} \mathsf{W}(z) &\equiv \int_C \exp(tz^p)\mathsf{U}_1(t)\, dt \\ &= \int_C \exp(tz^p)\{\mathsf{U}_1(t) - [\mathsf{S}_{1,N}(t) + \mathsf{S}_{2,N}(t) \log t]t^{\mathsf{C}}\}\, dt \\ &\quad + \int_C \exp(tz^p)\mathsf{S}_{1,N}(t)t^{\mathsf{C}}\, dt + \int_C \exp(tz^p)\mathsf{S}_{2,N}(t)t^{\mathsf{C}} \log t\, dt \\ &\equiv \mathsf{I}_{1,N}(z) + \mathsf{I}_{2,N}(z) + \mathsf{I}_{3,N}(z). \end{aligned}$$

We may choose the ray L in Σ_0 so that tz^p is real negative for t on L. This puts a limitation on z. If Σ_0 is the sector $\vartheta_1^* \leq \arg t \leq \vartheta_2^*$, then the discussion applies for z in the sector

$$\Psi_1 : \frac{1}{p}(\pi - \vartheta_2^*) \leq \arg z \leq \frac{1}{p}(\pi - \vartheta_1^*) \tag{6.9.42}$$

as well as for z in the sectors $\Psi_2, \Psi_3, \ldots, \Psi_p$ obtained by rotating Ψ_1 through angles $(2\pi)/p, (4\pi)/p, \ldots, [2(p-1)\pi]/p$, respectively.

The integrals entering in I_2 and I_3 can be evaluated explicitly and will give the asymptotic expansion of $\mathsf{W}(z)$, provided that it can be shown that, in some sense to be specified, the norm of I_1 is small as $z \to \infty$. The integrals in I_2 are of the form

$$\int_C \exp(tz^p) t^a \, dt = z^{-p(a+e)} \int_{C_0} s^a \exp(s) \, ds.$$

Here a is supposed to belong to a B-algebra with unit element e, and C_0 is a loop around the negative real axis in the s-plane. By (6.8.17) the result is

$$2\pi i \frac{1}{\Gamma}(-a) \, z^{-p(a+e)}.$$

Here we substitute $a = \mathsf{C} + n\mathsf{E}$, $e = \mathsf{E}$, multiply on the left by A_n, and sum for n to obtain

$$\mathsf{I}_{2,N}(z) = 2\pi i \sum_{n=0}^{N} \mathsf{A}_n \frac{1}{\Gamma}(-\mathsf{C} - n\mathsf{E}) \, z^{-p(\mathsf{C}+(n+1)\mathsf{E})}. \tag{6.9.43}$$

The integrals in I_3 on the other hand are of the form

$$\int_C \exp(tz^p) \, t^a \log t \, dt.$$

Here we set $tz^p = s$, which is real negative, and obtain

$$z^{-p(a+e)} \int_{C_0} \exp(s) s^a (\log s - p \log z) \, ds$$

$$= z^{-p(a+e)} \left[\int_{C_0} s^a \exp(s) \log s \, ds - p 2\pi i \log z \frac{1}{\Gamma}(-a) \right].$$

The remaining integral

$$\int_{C_0} s^a \exp(s) \log s \, ds \tag{6.9.44}$$

differs from the typical integral under I_2 by the factor $\log s$. Now if a were a scalar variable, we would obtain (6.9.44) simply by differentiating

$$\int_{C_0} s^a \exp(s) \, ds = 2\pi i \frac{1}{\Gamma}(-a)$$

with respect to a, obtaining

$$-2\pi i\left(\frac{1}{\Gamma}\right)'(-a)$$

which in this case would be well defined. It is still well defined, if a is any element of a B-algebra, since $(1/\Gamma)'$ is an entire function. But differentiation with respect to an element of an algebra, in particular under a sign of integration, is not well defined. The result is correct but we have to produce a better argument. To prove that

$$\int_{C_0} s^a \exp(s) \log s \, ds = -2\pi i\left(\frac{1}{\Gamma}\right)'(-a) \tag{6.9.45}$$

we use operational calculus. (See Section 4.5.)

We have then by definition

$$\left(\frac{1}{\Gamma}\right)'(a) = \frac{1}{2\pi i}\int_c \left(\frac{1}{\Gamma}\right)'(\lambda)R(\lambda; a)\, d\lambda,$$

where c is a simple closed rectifiable curve surrounding the spectrum of a in the positive sense. Here we substitute

$$\left(\frac{1}{\Gamma}\right)'(\lambda) = -\frac{1}{2\pi i}\int_{C_0} s^{-\lambda}\exp(s)\log s\, ds$$

which is obtained from Hankel's integral for $1/\Gamma(\lambda)$. This gives

$$\begin{aligned}\left(\frac{1}{\Gamma}\right)'(a) &= -\frac{1}{2\pi i}\int_c \left\{\frac{1}{2\pi i}\int_{C_0} s^{-\lambda}\exp(s)\log s\, ds\right\}R(\lambda; a)\, d\lambda \\ &= -\frac{1}{2\pi i}\int_{C_0}\exp(s)\log s\left\{\frac{1}{2\pi i}\int_C s^{-\lambda}R(\lambda; a)\, d\lambda\right\} ds \\ &= -\frac{1}{2\pi i}\int_{C_0} s^{-a}\exp(s)\log s\, ds\end{aligned}$$

as asserted. Since the double integral involved in this argument is absolutely convergent in norm, the order of integration may be changed, and the last step follows again from the operational calculus applied to the definition of s^{-a}.

Going back to I_3 we see that

$$\begin{aligned}\mathsf{I}_{3,N}(z) = -2\pi i\sum_{n=1}^{N}\mathsf{B}_n&\left\{\left(\frac{1}{\Gamma}\right)'(-\mathsf{C}-n\mathsf{E})\right. \\ &\left.+\, p\log z\,\frac{1}{\Gamma}(-\mathsf{C}-n\mathsf{E})\right\}z^{-p[\mathsf{C}+(n+1)\mathsf{E}]}.\end{aligned} \tag{6.9.46}$$

It remains to show that $\|\mathsf{I}_1\|$ is small. Let the contour C be thought of as the union of

C_1: those parts of the two arms along L for which $|t| > \frac{1}{2}\rho$,

C_2: the parts of the arms along L for which $\delta < |t| < \frac{1}{2}\rho$,

C_3: a positive circuit of the origin along $|t| = \delta$.

We may assume without loss of generality that $\frac{1}{2}\rho < 1$. On C_2 and C_3 we can write

$$\mathsf{S}_1(t) - \sum_0^N \mathsf{A}_n t^n = \frac{t^{N+1}}{2\pi i}\int_{C_0} \frac{\mathsf{S}_1(\zeta)\,d\zeta}{\zeta^{N+1}(\zeta - t)}$$

where $C_4 = \{\zeta \mid |\zeta| = \frac{3}{4}\rho\}$ and there is a similar relation for

$$\mathsf{S}_2(t) - \sum_1^N \mathsf{B}_n t^n.$$

On C_2 and C_3 we can find a finite number M_1 such that $\|\mathsf{S}_1(t)\| \leq M_1$, $\|\mathsf{S}_2(t)\| \leq M_1$. Hence

$$\left\|\int_{C_2 \cup C_3} \exp(tz^p)\{[\mathsf{S}_1(t) - \mathsf{S}_{1,N}(t)] + \log t[\mathsf{S}_2(t) - \mathsf{S}_{2,N}(t)]t^{\mathsf{C}}\}\,dt\right\|$$

$$\leq 3M_1(\tfrac{3}{4}\rho)^{-N-1}\int_{C_2\cup C_3} |\exp(tz^p)|\,|t|^{N+1}(1 + |\log t|)\|t^{\mathsf{C}}\|\,dt. \quad (6.9.47)$$

Write $|t| = \tau$. Then on $C_2 \cup C_3$

$$\|t^{\mathsf{C}}\| \leq \exp[\gamma(|\log \tau| + 2\pi)] = \exp(2\pi\gamma)\tau^{-\gamma}, \qquad \gamma = \|\mathsf{C}\|,$$

since $\tau \leq 1$. On C_2, $\exp(tz^p) = \exp(-\tau|z|^p)$, while on C_3, $|\exp(tz^p)| \leq \exp(\delta|z|^p)$.

The factor $1 + |\log t|$ which occurs in the integral is more of a nuisance than a complication. It cannot exceed $1 + 2\pi + |\log \tau|$ and, for $0 < \tau < 1$, this expression is dominated by $(1 + 2\pi)\tau^{-1/2}$. Making this replacement in the integral, we see that

$$\left\|\int_{C_2}\right\| < 2(1 + 2\pi)\exp(2\pi\gamma)\Gamma(N + \tfrac{3}{2} - \gamma)|z|^{-p(N+3/2-\gamma)},$$

$$\left\|\int_{C_3}\right\| < 2\pi(1 + 2\pi)\,\delta^{N+3/2-\gamma}\exp(\delta|z|^p + 2\pi\gamma). \quad (6.9.48)$$

The first bound is independent of δ so we may let $\delta \to 0$ when $N > \gamma - \frac{3}{2}$.

The contribution of C_1 to I_1 is dominated by

$$\int_{C_1} \exp(-\tau|z|^p)\,|\mathsf{U}_1(t)|\,|dt| + \sum_{n=0}^{N} |\mathsf{A}_n| \int_{C_1} \exp(-\tau|z|^p)\,|t^{\mathsf{C}}|\,|t|^n\,|dt| + \sum_{n=1}^{N} |\mathsf{B}_n| \int_{C_1} \exp(-\tau|z|^p)\,|t^{\mathsf{C}}|\,|t|^n\,|\log t|\,|dt| \equiv Q_1 + Q_2 + Q_3.$$

In estimating these integrals we make use of the following inequality, the verification of which is left to the reader. For ξ and η positive, and α real

$$\int_{\eta}^{\infty} \exp(-\xi\tau)\tau^{\alpha}\,d\tau < 2\frac{1}{\xi}\,\eta^{\alpha}\exp(-\xi\eta), \tag{6.9.49}$$

if $\xi > 2|\alpha| \max(1, \eta^{-1})$.

Formula (6.9.37) shows that

$$Q_1 < 2K_1 \int_{\rho/2}^{\infty} \exp(-\tau|z|^p)\tau^M\,d\tau.$$

Here we take $\xi = |z|^p$, $\eta = \frac{1}{2}\rho \leq 1$, $\alpha = M$, and get

$$Q_1 < 4K_1(\tfrac{1}{2}\rho)^M|z|^{-p}\exp(-\tfrac{1}{2}\rho|z|^p), \tag{6.9.50}$$

valid for $|z|^p > (4/\rho)M$.

The integrals in Q_2 contain

$$|t^{\mathsf{C}}| \leq \exp(2\pi\gamma)\max(\tau^{\gamma}, \tau^{-\gamma}) < \exp(2\pi\gamma)[\tau^{\gamma} + \tau^{-\gamma}].$$

Using (6.9.49) again we get

$$Q_2 < M_2|z|^{-p}\exp(-\tfrac{1}{2}\rho|z|^p), \tag{6.9.51}$$

where

$$M_2 = 4\exp(2\pi\gamma)[(\tfrac{1}{2}\rho)^{\gamma} + (\tfrac{1}{2}\rho)^{-\gamma}]\left(\sum_{n=0}^{\infty} |\mathsf{A}_n|(\tfrac{1}{2}\rho)^n\right),$$

and this estimate is valid for $|z|^p > 4/\rho(N + \gamma)$.

In Q_3 both $|t^{\mathsf{C}}|$ and $|\log t|$ cause complications but a simple argument shows that

$$|t^{\mathsf{C}}|\,|\log t| < 2\pi\exp(2\pi\gamma)[(\tfrac{1}{2}\rho)^{\gamma+1/2} + (\tfrac{1}{2}\rho)^{-\gamma-1/2}].$$

This gives

$$Q_3 < M_3|z|^{-p}\exp(-\tfrac{1}{2}\rho|z|^p) \tag{6.9.52}$$

with

$$M_3 = 4\pi \exp(2\pi\gamma)[(\tfrac{1}{2}\rho)^{\gamma+1/2} + (\tfrac{1}{2}\rho)^{-\gamma-1/2}]\left[\sum_{n=1}^{\infty} |\mathsf{B}_n| (\tfrac{1}{2}\rho)^n\right],$$

valid for

$$|z|^p > \frac{4}{\rho}(N + \gamma + \tfrac{1}{2}). \tag{6.9.53}$$

Combining (6.9.50) to (6.9.52), we see that there is a constant M_4, independent of N, such that

$$Q_1 + Q_2 + Q_3 < M_4|z|^{-p} \exp(-\tfrac{1}{2}\rho|z|^p) \tag{6.9.54}$$

for large N and z satisfying (6.9.53).

Combining (6.9.47), (6.9.48), and (6.9.54) we see that

$$\|\mathsf{I}_{1,N}(z)\| < M_4|z|^{-p} \exp(-\tfrac{1}{2}\rho|z|^p) + M_5\left(\frac{4}{3\rho}\right) \Gamma(N + \tfrac{3}{2} - \gamma)|z|^{-p(N+3/2-\gamma)} \tag{6.9.55}$$

where M_4 and M_5 are independent of N. This shows that for any $\varepsilon > 0$

$$\lim_{z\to\infty} |z|^{p(N+3/2-\gamma-\varepsilon)}\|\mathsf{I}_{1,N}(z)\| = 0 \tag{6.9.56}$$

when $z \to \infty$ in one of the sectors $\Psi_1, \ldots, \Psi_p$.

What we have shown so far is that if

$$\mathsf{W}(z) = \int_C \exp(tz^p)\mathsf{U}_1(t)\, dt, \tag{6.9.57}$$

and if z lies in one of the sectors $\Psi_1, \Psi_2, \ldots, \Psi_p$, then

$$\lim_{z\to\infty} |z|^{p(N+3/2-\gamma-\varepsilon)}\|\mathsf{W}(z) - \mathsf{I}_{2,N}(z) - \mathsf{I}_{3,N}(z)\| = 0. \tag{6.9.58}$$

Closer estimates are obtainable from (6.9.55).

To pass from $\mathsf{W}(z)$ to the solution $W(z)$ of (6.9.2), we take a non-zero column vector of W and form the inner product with the vector

$$\mathfrak{z}_p = (z^{p-1}, z^{p-2}, \ldots, z, 1). \tag{6.9.59}$$

If the kth column is admissible and if $\boldsymbol{e}_k$ is the vector with e in the kth place and 0 elsewhere, then the inner product can be written symbolically

$$W(z) = \mathfrak{z}_p\mathsf{W}(z)\boldsymbol{e}_k. \tag{6.9.60}$$

This is an element of $\mathfrak{B}$. Its norm does not exceed the product of the norms of the factors in the appropriate space. Now $\|\mathfrak{z}_p\| < p|z|^{p-1}$ if $1 < |z|$, and $\|\boldsymbol{e}_k\| = 1$. This gives Miller's asymptotic representation theorem:

Theorem 6.9.2. *Assuming Hypothesis* II *with* II(3) *only for the subalgebra* $\mathfrak{B}_0$ *generated by* $a_0, a_1, \ldots, a_p$, c, e, *and* j *and with* $\beta_0, \beta_1, \ldots, \beta_p$ *defined by* (6.9.19), (6.9.27), *and* (6.9.29), *then the corresponding equation* (6.9.2) *has a solution* $W(z)$ *such that for* z *in any of the sector* $\Psi_1, \ldots, \Psi_p$ *and any* $N > 2 - \gamma$

$$\lim_{z\to\infty} |z|^{p(N+1/2-\gamma-\varepsilon)+1} \| W(z) - z_p[\mathsf{I}_{2,N}(z) + \mathsf{I}_{3,N}(z)]e_k \| = 0. \tag{6.9.61}$$

Here $\mathsf{I}_{2,N}(z)$ *and* $\mathsf{I}_{3,N}$ *are given by* (6.9.43) *and* (6.9.46), *respectively.*

A final remark: this mode of proving asymptotic expansions at an irregular singular point goes back to J. Horn (1897) for the nth order linear case.

EXERCISE 6.9

1. According to Miller

$$\mathsf{R}(\lambda; \mathsf{C}) = \sum_{k=0}^{p} \mathsf{I}_k \left(\lambda + \frac{k}{p}\right)^{-1}$$

where the I's are mutually orthogonal idempotents. Compute the coefficients $(1/\Gamma)(-\mathsf{C} - n\mathsf{E})$ which figure in the asymptotic expansion. Show that they become infinite as $\Gamma(n + 1 - 1/p)$.

2. Show that the discussion in Section 6.9 is valid if the coefficients a_k are orthogonal idempotents.

3. Let $\mathfrak{B} = \mathfrak{M}_2$ and let $\mathfrak{B}_0$ be the subalgebra of matrices of the form

$$\mathcal{A} = \begin{pmatrix} a & b \\ -b & a \end{pmatrix}$$

where a, b are real or complex numbers. Show that $\mathfrak{B}_0$ contains only two non-trivial idempotents $\mathfrak{J}_1$ and $\mathfrak{J}_2$ and that $\mathfrak{J}_1\mathcal{A} = (a + bi)\mathfrak{J}_1$ and $\mathfrak{J}_2\mathcal{A} = (a - bi)\mathfrak{J}_2$.

4. Show that the Birkhoff–Miller theory applies if $a_0, \ldots, a_p$ belong to the algebra $\mathfrak{B}_0$ of the preceding problem.

5. Show that the theory applies to the system

$$zw_1' = P(z)w_1 + Q(z)w_2,$$
$$zw_2' = -Q(z)w_1 + P(z)w_2,$$

where P and Q are polynomials.

6. If $P(z) = 1$, $Q(z) = z^2$, find the corresponding matrices $\mathcal{A}_0$, $\mathcal{A}_1$, $\mathcal{A}_2$, the spectrum of $\mathcal{A}_0$, the residue idempotent at one of the poles of the resolvent of $\mathcal{A}_0$, and carry through the reduction to the canonical form (6.9.2). Does the same form correspond to both characteristic values of $\mathcal{A}_0$?

7. If P and Q are as in the preceding problem, show that w_1 and w_2 satisfy the equation

$$z^2w'' - 3zw' + (z^4 + 3)w = 0.$$

COLLATERAL READING

This chapter is essentially an elaboration of the author's paper

"Linear differential equations in Banach algebras," *Proc. International Symposium on Linear Spaces*, Jerusalem, pp. 263–273 (1960).

See also

"Some aspects of differential equations in B-algebras," *Proc. Conference on Functional Analysis*, U.C.I. (1966), pp. 185–194; Thompson Book Co., Washington, D.C. (1967).

G. D. Birkhoff's equivalence problem for analytic matrices (See end of Section B.4) has been generalized to analytic operator functions operating in a Hilbert space by

HELSON, Henry, "Vectorial function theory," *Proc. London Math. Soc.* (3) **17**, 499–504 (1967).

Helson's elegant analysis unfortunately throws no light on the problem of reduction to Birkhoff's normal form (6.8.5).

Section 6.9 is based on

MILLER, J. B., "Solution in Banach algebras of differential equations with irregular singular points," *Acta Math.* **110**, 209–231 (1963).

These papers seem to be the only ones in existence which have a bearing on the problem of extending the classical theory of linear differential equations in the complex domain to Banach algebras. There is, however, a considerable literature on differential equations in Banach spaces. For various aspects of this theory, see

AGMON, S., and L. NIRENBERG, "Properties of solutions of ordinary differential equations in Banach space," *Comm. Pure Appl. Math.* **16**, 121–239 (1963).

MASSERA, J. L., and J. J. SCHÄFFER, *Linear Differential Equations and Function Spaces*, Academic Press, New York (1966).

Appendix C
RICCATI'S EQUATION

Of all non-linear equations, that of Riccati

$$y'(z) = f_0(z) + f_1(z)y(z) + f_2(z)[y(z)]^2$$

can claim to be the most important. One reason is its close connection with the second order linear case; another is the fact that the equation has movable singularities which are simple poles. We could also mention the structure of the solutions, in particular that the general solution is a fractional linear function of the constant of integration.

In the present appendix we study this equation, essentially formal theory and the properties in the complex plane. For the role of Riccati's equation in the general theory of non-linear equations in the complex domain, see Chapter 12. Riccati equations on the real line will figure in Chapter 9.

We also study some Riccati matrix equations mainly in the complex domain, a study which seems to have been neglected by earlier writers in this field. This study presupposes a discussion of second order linear matrix equations in the complex domain. Here it is not the function theoretical properties of the solutions which stand in the foreground, but their algebraic properties as elements of a matrix algebra. Some Riccati equations in a Banach star algebra figure in Section 9.6.

There are three sections: The classical Riccati equation; Second order linear matrix equations; and Matrix Riccati equations.

C.1 THE CLASSICAL RICCATI EQUATION

Some special equations of the type

$$y' = f_0(z) + f_1(z)y + f_2(z)y^2 \tag{C.1.1}$$

were studied by Jacopo Francesco, Count Riccati (1676–1754) in the 1720's. Hence this class of equations is referred to as Riccati's equation.

It is closely connected with the linear second order equation

$$w'' + P(z)w' + Q(z)w = 0. \tag{C.1.2}$$

In fact, setting

$$y(z) = -\frac{1}{f_2(z)}\frac{w'(z)}{w(z)}, \tag{C.1.3}$$

we see that $w(z)$ satisfies the equation

$$w''(z) - \left\{\frac{f_2'(z)}{f_2(z)} + f_1(z)\right\}w'(z) + f_0(z)f_2(z)w(z) = 0 \tag{C.1.4}$$

which is of type (C.1.2) with

$$P(z) = -\frac{f_2'(z)}{f_2(z)} - f_1(z), \qquad Q(z) = f_0(z)f_2(z). \tag{C.1.5}$$

Since the general solution of (C.1.4) is of the form

$$w(z) = C_1w_1(z) + C_2w_2(z), \tag{C.1.6}$$

where C_1 and C_2 are arbitrary constants and $w_1(z)$, $w_2(z)$ are two linearly independent solutions, it follows that the general solution of (C.1.1) is

$$y(z) = -\frac{1}{f_2(z)}\frac{C_1w_1'(z) + C_2w_2'(z)}{C_1w_1(z) + C_2w_2(z)}.$$

Actually the solution does not depend upon two arbitrary constants. Setting

$$C = \frac{C_2}{C_1}$$

we obtain

$$y(z) = -\frac{1}{f_2(z)}\frac{w_1'(z) + Cw_2'(z)}{w_1(z) + Cw_2(z)}, \tag{C.1.7}$$

involving only one arbitrary constant. We note that *the solution is a fractional linear function of C*. Cf. Exercise 3.2, Problem 7 for a special case of this observation. (See also Theorem 12.1.3.)

This fact has important consequences, for a fractional linear transformation is uniquely determined by three of its transforms. Let

$$v = \frac{a + bu}{c + du}, \quad ad - bc \neq 0, \tag{C.1.8}$$

be the transformation. In the present case $u = C$ and a, b, c, d are fixed functions of z. Give u four complex values

$$u_1, u_2, u_3, u_4$$

and let

$$v_1, v_2, v_3, v_4$$

be the corresponding values of v. We introduce the cross-ratio

$$R(z_1, z_2, z_3, z_4) = \frac{z_1 - z_3}{z_1 - z_4} : \frac{z_2 - z_3}{z_2 - z_4} \tag{C.1.9}$$

and find that

$$R(v_1, v_2, v_3, v_4) = R(u_1, u_2, u_3, u_4). \tag{C.1.10}$$

This is obtained by an elementary but lengthy computation.

In the present case this means that the cross-ratio of four solutions of Riccati's equation is a constant since

$$R(y_1, y_2, y_3, y_4) = R(C_1, C_2, C_3, C_4), \tag{C.1.11}$$

if y_j is the solution obtained by setting $C = C_j$ in (C.1.7).

Thus, knowing three solutions y_1, y_2, y_3 we know all solutions. The general solution is expressible as

$$y(z) = \frac{[y_1(z) - y_3(z)]y_2(z) - \lambda[y_2(z) - y_3(z)]y_1(z)}{[y_1(z) - y_3(z)] - \lambda[y_2(z) - y_3(z)]}, \tag{C.1.12}$$

where λ is an arbitrary parameter. Here also the solution is a fractional linear function of the parameter.

If f_0, f_1, f_2 are taken as analytic functions of z, formula (C.1.4) shows that $w(z)$ has possible singularities at the singular points of f_0, f_1, f_2, at the zeros of f_2, and, possibly also at the point of infinity. Let S denote the union of these points. The points of S are the *fixed singularities* of $y(z)$. If we know the analytical character of $w_1(z)$ and $w_2(z)$ in a neighborhood of a point of S, then we also know the behavior of $y(z)$ at this point. In addition $y(z)$ has *movable singularities* the position of which depend upon the value of C (or of λ). These are the zeros of the denominator in (C.1.7), i.e. the points determined by

$$C_1 w_1(z) + C_2 w_2(z) = 0.$$

Since the zeros of a solution of (C.1.4) are simple, these movable singular points are simple poles of $y(z)$. If such a pole is located at $z = a$, the residue is

$$-\frac{1}{f_2(a)}.$$

In (C.1.7) we can let $C \to \infty$. The limit

$$-\frac{1}{f_2(z)} \frac{w_2'(z)}{w_2(z)}$$

is also a solution of (C.1.1).

We note that a Riccati equation is formally invariant under fractional linear transformations. Thus, if we substitute in (C.1.1)

$$y = \frac{\alpha + \beta v}{\gamma + \delta v}, \tag{C.1.13}$$

where α, β, γ, δ are arbitrary constants with $\alpha\delta - \beta\gamma \neq 0$, then v satisfies the Riccati equation

$$\begin{aligned}(\beta\gamma - \alpha\delta)v' = {} & [\gamma^2 f_0 + \alpha\gamma f_1 + \alpha^2 f_2] \\ & + [2\gamma\delta f_0 + (\alpha\delta + \beta\gamma)f_1 + 2\alpha\beta f_2]v \qquad \text{(C.1.14)} \\ & + [\delta^2 f_0 + \beta\delta f_1 + \beta^2 f_2]v^2.\end{aligned}$$

In particular, $1/y$ satisfies the equation

$$-v' = f_2(z) + f_1(z)v + f_0(z)v^2. \qquad \text{(C.1.15)}$$

Since the zeros of y are the poles of v, we conclude that the movable zeros of $y(z)$ are simple.

Suppose that $z = a$ does not belong to the set S. We can then determine uniquely a solution of (C.1.15) with the initial value

$$v(a) = 0.$$

This solution is holomorphic in some neighborhood of $z = a$ where it has a power series expansion

$$v(z) = c_1(z - a) + c_2(z - a)^2 + \cdots$$

with

$$c_1 = -f_2(a) \neq 0$$

since $z = a$ is not a zero of $f_2(z)$. It follows that

$$y(z) = \frac{1}{v(z)} = -\frac{1}{f_2(a)}\frac{1}{z - a} + \sum_{n=0}^{\infty} b_n(z - a)^n. \qquad \text{(C.1.16)}$$

This implies that any point $a \notin S$ can be the site of a simple pole of a suitably chosen solution of (C.1.1).

We note that *while Riccati's equation has movable poles, all branch points of the solutions* if any *are fixed.* In fact, *Riccati's equation is the only first order equation, rational in y, with fixed branch points.* (See Section 12.1.)

So far we have based the study of Riccati's equation on the associated second order linear equation. We can also proceed in the opposite direction: valuable information concerning the solutions of second order equations is obtainable from the associated Riccati equation. Suppose that (C.1.2) is given where we assume P and Q to be holomorphic in some domain D of the complex plane. We now set

$$\frac{w'}{w} = -y \qquad \text{(C.1.17)}$$

and obtain

$$y'(z) = Q(z) - P(z)y(z) + [y(z)]^2 \qquad \text{(C.1.18)}$$

as the associated Riccati equation. This device is used repeatedly in Chapter 9 for real valued functions.

EXERCISE C.1

1. The equation $y' = 1 - y^2$ has a solution which becomes infinite as $z = x$ real decreases to 0. Show that $xy(x) \to 1$. Show that this solution is positive and decreasing for all $x > 0$ and tends to the limit $+1$ as $x \to +\infty$. Does the equation have any constant solutions?
2. The very similar equation $y' = 1 - y^3$ has solutions with movable branch points. Show that for the solution which becomes infinite at $z = 0$ we have $x^{1/2}y(x) \to \frac{1}{2}\sqrt{2}$ instead and that the other properties remain the same as in the preceding problem.
3. Verify (C.1.10).
4. If y_1, y_2, y_3, y_4 are four distinct solutions of

$$y' - f_0 - f_1 y - f_2 y^2 = 0,$$

then substituting these solutions we get a system of four linear equations known to have the non-trivial solution $1, -f_0, -f_1, -f_2$. This requires that the corresponding determinant with j^{th} row

$$y_j' \quad 1 \quad y_j \quad y_j^2, \qquad j = 1, 2, 3, 4,$$

must be identically zero. Show that the determinant is the numerator of the derivative of $\mathcal{R}(y_1, y_2, y_3, y_4)$ and hence that the cross-ratio is a constant.
5. The asymptotic behavior of solutions of Riccati's equation for large values of $|z|$ can sometimes be studied by reducing the equation to one which is asymptotic to the tangent equation $Y_0' = 1 + Y_0^2$ [P. Boutroux, 1913]. Find numbers α, β such that

$$y' = z^m + z^n y^2, \qquad m \neq -n,$$

is reduced to

$$\frac{dY}{dZ} = 1 + Y^2 + \frac{n - m}{n + m + 2}\frac{Y}{Z}$$

by the transformation

$$Z = \frac{1}{\alpha} z^\alpha, \qquad y = z^\beta Y.$$

6. Assuming that $Y(Z)$ has a pole at $Z = Z_0$ where $\Im(Z_0)$ is large and that $Y(Z) = \tan(Z - Z_0) + O(Z^{-1})$ for large values of $|Z|$, what is the general pattern of the distributions of the poles of $y(z)$ for large values of $|z|$?
7. Reduce the equation

$$y'(z) = 1 + f_2(z)y^2$$

to an approximate tangent equation by the transformation

$$Z = \int^z [f_2(s)]^{1/2}\, ds, \qquad Y = [f_2(z)]^{1/2} y.$$

C.2 SECOND ORDER LINEAR MATRIX EQUATIONS

With a view to studying the Riccati matrix equation, we have first to devote some time to linear second order matrix equations of the form

$$\mathfrak{W}''(z) + \mathfrak{P}(z)\mathfrak{W}'(z) + \mathfrak{Q}(z)\mathfrak{W}(z) = 0, \tag{C.2.1}$$

where $\mathfrak{P}$, $\mathfrak{Q}$, $\mathfrak{W}$ are n by n matrices

$$\mathfrak{P}(z) = \{p_{jk}(z)\},\ \mathfrak{Q}(z) = \{q_{jk}(z)\},\ \mathfrak{W}(z) = \{w_{jk}(z)\}, \quad j, k = 1, 2, \ldots, n.$$

We assume $\mathfrak{P}$ and $\mathfrak{Q}$ are holomorphic at some point $z = z_0$ and denote by $\mathbf{A}(z_0; \mathfrak{P}, \mathfrak{Q})$ the Mittag-Leffler star of $\mathfrak{P}$ and $\mathfrak{Q}$ with respect to z_0. If $z_1 \in \mathbf{A}$, the $2n^2$ functions $p_{jk}(z)$ and $q_{jk}(z)$ are holomorphic at all points on the ray joining z_0 and z_1, while if z_2 is a boundary point of $\mathbf{A}$, then at least one of these functions becomes singular somewhere on the ray joining z_0 and z_2.

The existence theorem here takes the form

Theorem C.2.1. *If $\mathfrak{W}_0$ amd $\mathfrak{W}_1$ are given n by n constant matrices, then there exists a unique matrix function*

$$\mathfrak{W}(z; z_0, \mathfrak{W}_0, \mathfrak{W}_1)$$

which is holomorphic in $\mathbf{A}(z_0; \mathfrak{P}, \mathfrak{Q})$ where it satisfies (C.2.1) *and has the given initial values*

$$\mathfrak{W}(z_0; z_0, \mathfrak{W}_0, \mathfrak{W}_1) = \mathfrak{W}_0,\ \mathfrak{W}'(z_0; z_0, \mathfrak{W}_0, \mathfrak{W}_1) = \mathfrak{W}_1.$$

Proof. The argument is the same as in the first order case, in fact it would be possible to reduce the theorem to the first order case for $(2n)$ by $(2n)$ matrices. For our purposes, however, the matrices $\mathfrak{W}(z)$ and $\mathfrak{W}'(z)$ are the important objects and it is more convenient to work directly with (C.2.1). This equation we transform into an integral equation

$$\mathfrak{W}(z) = \mathfrak{W}_0 + [\mathfrak{W}_1 + \mathfrak{P}(z_0)\mathfrak{W}_0](z - z_0) - \int_{z_0}^{z} \{\mathfrak{P}(t) + (z - t)[\mathfrak{P}'(t) + \mathfrak{Q}(t)]\}\mathfrak{W}(t)\, dt \tag{C.2.2}$$

which obviously calls for an integration by parts. The latter equation we can solve by successive approximations. If D is any bounded subdomain of $\mathbf{A}$, star-shaped with respect to z_0, then trivial estimates show that the approximations converge uniformly in D to a matrix function $\mathfrak{W}(z)$ holomorphic in D which satisfies the differential as well as the integral equations and assumes the correct initial values at $z = z_0$. Since D is arbitrary, the limit exists everywhere in $\mathbf{A}$ and has the stated properties. Uniqueness of the solution is obvious. ▮

Let $\mathfrak{E}$ denote the unit matrix, $\mathfrak{O}$ the zero matrix, and consider the two solutions

$$\mathfrak{W}(z; z_0, \mathfrak{O}, \mathfrak{E}) \quad \text{and} \quad \mathfrak{W}(z; z_0, \mathfrak{E}, \mathfrak{O}).$$

We have then

$$\mathfrak{W}(z; z_0, \mathfrak{W}_0, \mathfrak{W}_1) = \mathfrak{W}(z; z_0, \mathcal{O}, \mathcal{E})\mathfrak{W}_1 + \mathfrak{W}(z; z_0, \mathcal{E}, \mathcal{O})\mathfrak{W}_0 \quad \text{(C.2.3)}$$

for both sides of the equation are solutions of (C.2.1) and they have the same initial values at $z = z_0$. By the uniqueness of the solution, (C.2.3) must be an identity.

Just as in the first order case, we can obtain the analytic continuation of our solution in $\mathbf{A}(z_1; \mathcal{T}, \mathcal{Q})$ if $z_1 \in \mathbf{A}(z_0; \mathcal{T}, \mathcal{Q})$. The continuation of the solution is again the solution of the continuation of the equation along a broken line. In particular, suppose that $\mathcal{T}$ and $\mathcal{Q}$ are single-valued and we have a closed polygonal line Π beginning and ending at $z = z_0$ along which the coefficients may be continued. We then arrive at $z = z_0$ with a solution of (C.2.1) which is necessarily of the form

$$\mathfrak{W}(z; z_0, \mathcal{O}, \mathcal{E})\mathfrak{W}_3 + \mathfrak{W}(z; z_0, \mathcal{E}, \mathcal{O})\mathfrak{W}_2, \quad \text{(C.2.4)}$$

where $\mathfrak{W}_2$ and $\mathfrak{W}_3$ are constant matrices. We have a transformation

$$(\mathfrak{W}_0, \mathfrak{W}_1) \to (\mathfrak{W}_2, \mathfrak{W}_3)$$

associated with the path Π. The set of all such transformations forms a group, just as in the first order case.

The function theoretical singularities of $\mathfrak{W}(z)$ are fixed and coincide with those of $\mathcal{T}(z)$ and $\mathcal{Q}(z)$. On the other hand, the algebraic singularities are movable. In this context, $z = a$ *is an algebraic singularity of* $\mathfrak{W}(z)$ *if* $\mathfrak{W}(a)$ *is a singular element of the matrix algebra* $\mathfrak{M}_n$. This is equivalent to saying that

$$\Delta(z) = \det\,[\mathfrak{W}(z)] \quad \text{(C.2.5)}$$

has a zero at $z = a$. Now in the first order case

$$\mathfrak{W}'(z) = \mathcal{F}(z)\mathfrak{W}(z),$$

the algebraic singularities are trivial in the sense that once singular, always singular, i.e. the solution $\mathfrak{W}(z; a, \mathfrak{W}_0)$ is singular and then for all z iff $\mathfrak{W}_0$ is singular. The second order case is totally different.

We may have

$$\mathfrak{W}(z) \not\equiv 0, \Delta(z) \equiv 0,$$

but this is exceptional. Here $\Delta(z)$ is an analytic function of z and its zeros are naturally subjected to the limitations which the analytic character of $\Delta(z)$ imposes on its zeros. Thus they cannot cluster at a point $z = a$, where $\mathcal{T}$ and $\mathcal{Q}$ are holomorphic. There does not seem to be any obvious restrictions imposed by the fact that $\Delta(z)$ is the determinant of a solution of a second order linear differential equation.

We note that $\mathfrak{W}(z)$ may be algebraically regular for all z while $\mathfrak{W}'(z)$ is identically singular. Thus if $\mathcal{A}^2 = 0$, the equation

$$\mathfrak{W}'' - \mathcal{A}\mathfrak{W} = 0 \quad \text{(C.2.6)}$$

is satisfied by

$$\mathfrak{W}(z) = \mathcal{E} + \tfrac{1}{2}\mathcal{A}z^2 \quad \text{with} \quad [\mathfrak{W}(z)]^{-1} = \mathcal{E} - \tfrac{1}{2}\mathcal{A}z^2$$

and $\mathfrak{W}'z = \mathcal{A}z$ which is identically singular.

Both $\mathfrak{W}_0$ and $\mathfrak{W}_1$ may be singular and still $\mathfrak{W}(z; z_0, \mathfrak{W}_0, \mathfrak{W}_1)$ may have only isolated algebraic singularities. Take $n = 2$, $z_0 = 0$,

$$\mathfrak{W}_0 = \begin{pmatrix} 0 & 0 \\ 0 & 1 \end{pmatrix}, \qquad \mathfrak{W}_1 = \begin{pmatrix} 0 & 0 \\ 1 & 0 \end{pmatrix} \tag{C.2.7}$$

and the equation

$$\mathfrak{W}'' + \begin{pmatrix} -S & C - 2 \\ -1 - S & C - 1 \end{pmatrix}\mathfrak{W}' + \begin{pmatrix} 1 & 0 \\ 1 & 0 \end{pmatrix}\mathfrak{W} = 0,$$

where

$$C = \cosh z, \qquad S = \sinh z.$$

The equation is chosen so that

$$\mathfrak{W}(z) = \begin{pmatrix} C - 1 & 0 \\ S & 1 \end{pmatrix}$$

is the solution satisfying the given initial conditions. Here

$$\Delta(z) = C - 1 = \cosh z - 1$$

which has a double zero at each of the points $z = n\pi i$, $n = 0, \pm 1, \pm 2, \ldots$, and $\mathfrak{W}(z)$ is algebraically singular only at these points. Here again all matrices $\mathfrak{W}^{(n)}(z)$ are identically singular.

This example raises an important question. Suppose $z = a$ is an isolated algebraic singularity of a solution $\mathfrak{W}(z)$ of (C.2.1) and define *the order of the singularity as the order of the zero of* $\Delta(z) = \det \mathfrak{W}(z)$ *at* $z = a$.

Is there any limitation on the order?

This question does not seem to have been properly investigated, but the prevailing opinion among those who have given the matter a thought, including for a long time the present author, appears to be that the order is $\leq n$, the order of the matrix algebra. This is not the case, however, as shown by simple counter examples.

The situation is quite complicated, but the following general pattern is discernible. For each n there are singular matrices $\mathfrak{W}_0$ and $\mathfrak{W}_1$, independent of $\mathfrak{P}$ and $\mathfrak{Q}$, such that, if $z = a$ is not a singular point of $\mathfrak{P}$ or $\mathfrak{Q}$, then $\mathfrak{W}(z; a, \mathfrak{W}_0, \mathfrak{W}_1)$ has an algebraic singularity of order m at $z = a$ where $n \leq m \leq \infty$. Here $m = \infty$ means that $\Delta(z) \equiv 0$. Normally $m = n$, but may take on any preassigned value $> n$, if $\mathfrak{P}$ and $\mathfrak{Q}$ are suitably specified.

To verify this in detail would be very laborious, but we shall give some results for $n = 2$ and $n = 3$ which have a bearing on the problem. For $n = 2$ we may take $\mathfrak{W}_0$ and $\mathfrak{W}_1$ as in (C.2.7) while for $n = 3$

$$\mathfrak{W}_0 = \begin{bmatrix} 0 & 0 & 0 \\ 0 & 0 & 0 \\ 1 & 0 & 0 \end{bmatrix}, \qquad \mathfrak{W}_1 = \begin{bmatrix} 0 & 0 & 0 \\ 0 & 1 & 0 \\ 0 & 0 & 1 \end{bmatrix} \tag{C.2.8}$$

will do. In neither case is the choice unique. In general one takes the $2n$ unit vectors in E^{2n} as column vectors of a matrix. One selects n of them; the upper half of these vectors gives a possible $\mathfrak{W}_0$-matrix, the lower half the corresponding $\mathfrak{W}_1$.

If $n = 2$, it is a simple matter to verify that $\Delta(z)$ and $\Delta'(z)$ vanish at $z = a$ if $\mathfrak{W}_0$ and $\mathfrak{W}_1$ are chosen as in (C.2.7). For $\Delta''(z)$ one obtains under the same assumption

$$\Delta''(a) = -p_{12}(a).$$

If this quantity is 0, then

$$\Delta'''(z) = 2q_{12}(a) - p'_{12}(a).$$

Thus the condition for an algebraic singularity of order at least 4 at $z = a$ is

$$p_{12}(a) = 0,\ p'_{12}(a) = 2q_{12}(a)$$

under the stated initial conditions. The labor involved in repeated differentiation grows exponentially with the order of the derivative, but the principle is clear. Note that the conditions obtained depend upon the choice of the initial conditions.

For $n = 3$ and $\mathfrak{W}_0$, $\mathfrak{W}_1$ given by (C.2.8) moderate labor gives

$$\Delta(a) = \Delta'(a) = \Delta''(a) = 0$$

while the vanishing of $\Delta'''(a)$ imposes a restriction on the coefficients.

In the general case it is an easy matter to exhibit a solution matrix which has an algebraic singularity of order n at $z = a$. In fact

$$\mathfrak{W}(z; a, \mathfrak{O}, \mathfrak{E})$$

will do. For its elements are of the form

$$w_{jk}(z) = (z - a)[\delta_{jk} + O(z - a)]$$

and

$$\Delta(z) = (z - a)^n[1 + O(z - a)].$$

Let us return to the case $n = 2$ and consider equations of the special form

$$\mathfrak{W}''(z) = \mathfrak{F}(z)\mathfrak{W}(z), \qquad \mathfrak{F} = \{f_{jk}\}. \tag{C.2.9}$$

A simple calculation gives

$$\Delta''(z) = [f_{11}(z) + f_{22}(z)]\,\Delta(z) + 2\Delta_1(z), \tag{C.2.10}$$

where $\Delta(z) = \det \mathfrak{W}(z)$, $\Delta_1(z) = \det \mathfrak{W}'(z)$. This relation shows that, if, at $z = a$, the matrix $\mathfrak{W}(z)$ is singular while $\mathfrak{W}'(z)$ is not, then $z = a$ can be an algebraic singularity of at most the order 2. In the opposite direction it shows that $\mathfrak{W}(z)$ is identically singular iff $\mathfrak{W}'(z)$ has this property. Further, if $\mathfrak{W}(z)$ is singular of the order m and $\mathfrak{W}'(z)$ of the order m_1 then

$$m = m_1 + 2. \tag{C.2.11}$$

The important point here is that $m > m_1$. It would be interesting to know if these properties generalize to the case $n > 2$.

We shall need the following elementary

Lemma C.2.1. *Let the matrix function $\mathfrak{W}(z)$ be holomorphic in the disk $|z - a| < \eta$. Let $\Delta(z) = \det [\mathfrak{W}(z)]$ have a zero of the exact order m at $z = a$. Then there exists a ρ, $\rho \leq \eta$, such that $[\mathfrak{W}(z)]^{-1}$ is holomorphic in $0 < |z - a| < \rho$ and has a pole of order $\leq m$ at $z = a$. The order is exactly m unless all first order minors of $\Delta(z)$ vanish at $z = a$.*

Proof. This follows from the representation

$$\Delta(z)[\mathfrak{W}(z)]^{-1} = (A_{kj}(z)) \tag{C.2.12}$$

where $A_{kj}(z)$ is the algebraic complement of $w_{kj}(z)$ in the expansion of $\Delta(z)$. The right-hand side is a holomorphic function of z in $|z - a| < \rho$ and the leading term in its Taylor expansion at $z = a$ is $(A_{kj}(a))$ which reduces to the zero matrix iff each $A_{kj}(a) = 0$. ▮

EXERCISE C.2

1. Deduce (C.2.2) and give a convergence proof.
2. Construct a solution of (C.2.6) which is identically singular.
3. If $\mathfrak{W}_0$ and $\mathfrak{W}_1$ are given by (C.2.7), compute $\Delta''(a)$ and $\Delta'''(a)$.
4. Verify (C.2.10) and (C.2.11). The latter relation should be modified if the trace of $\mathcal{F}(z)$ vanishes at $z = a$. How?
5. Determine the matrix $\mathfrak{T}(z)$ such that
$$\mathfrak{W} = \begin{pmatrix} z & z^2 \\ 1 & 1 + 2z \end{pmatrix}$$
satisfies the equation
$$\mathfrak{W}'' + \mathfrak{T}(z)\mathfrak{W}' + \mathfrak{W} = 0.$$
6. Consider the Eq. (C.2.9) in $\mathfrak{M}_3$. Take $\mathfrak{W}_0$ and $\mathfrak{W}_1$ as in (C.2.8) and find the condition for $\mathfrak{W}(z)$ to have an algebraic singularity of order 4 at $z = a$.
7. Let
$$\mathfrak{W}(z) = \begin{pmatrix} \frac{1}{6}z^3 & \frac{1}{2}z^2 \\ z & 1 + \frac{1}{2}z^2 \end{pmatrix}$$
and show that $[\mathfrak{W}(z)]^{-1}$ has a triple pole at the origin. Compute the coefficient of z^{-3}.

8. If $\mathcal{W}(z)$ is defined as in the preceding problem, discuss the behavior of $[\mathcal{W}'(z)]^{-1}$ at $z = 0$.

C.3 MATRIX RICCATI EQUATIONS

There are several possible generalizations of Riccati's equation to matrices. Here we shall restrict ourselves to equations in the algebra $\mathfrak{M}_n$ of n by n matrices of the form

$$\mathcal{Y}'(z) = \mathcal{A}(z) + \mathcal{B}(z)\mathcal{Y}(z) + \mathcal{Y}(z)\mathcal{C}(z)\mathcal{Y}(z) \tag{C.3.1}$$

and

$$\mathcal{V}'(z) = \mathcal{C}(z) - \mathcal{V}(z)\mathcal{B}(z) + \mathcal{V}(z)\mathcal{A}(z)\mathcal{V}(z). \tag{C.3.2}$$

These equations are *associates* of each other in the sense that if $\mathcal{Y}(z)$ has an inverse then

$$-[\mathcal{Y}(z)]^{-1} = \mathcal{V}(z) \tag{C.3.3}$$

is a solution of (C.3.2) and vice versa. In order to give anything like a complete discussion of one of these equations it is necessary to consider also its associate.

We assume that the coefficients $\mathcal{A}(z)$, $\mathcal{B}(z)$, $\mathcal{C}(z)$ are holomorphic in the finite plane save for poles. Moreover, $\mathcal{A}(z)$ and $\mathcal{C}(z)$ shall be regular elements of $\mathfrak{M}_n$, except for isolated points. Let S denote the set of all exceptional points.

Suppose now that $z = a$ does not belong to the set S and let $\mathcal{Y}_0$ and $\mathcal{V}_0$ be given constant, non-singular matrices. Let D be a simply-connected domain not containing any points of S and let $a \in D$. Then the existence theorems show that there is a neighborhood $N(a)$ of $z = a$ in which the equation (C.3.1) has a unique solution $\mathcal{Y}(z)$ with

$$\mathcal{Y}(a) = \mathcal{Y}_0$$

and (C.3.2) has a unique solution $\mathcal{V}(z)$ with

$$\mathcal{V}(z) = \mathcal{V}_0$$

and these solutions are holomorphic in $N(a)$. At this stage the assumption that $\mathcal{Y}_0$ and $\mathcal{V}_0$ are non-singular is superfluous, but if it holds and if

$$\mathcal{V}_0 = -\mathcal{Y}_0^{-1}$$

then (C.3.3) holds in $N(a)$.

To study equation (C.3.1) we introduce a function $\mathcal{W}(z)$ defined implicitly by

$$\mathcal{Y}(z) = -[\mathcal{C}(z)]^{-1}\mathcal{W}'(z)[\mathcal{W}(z)]^{-1}. \tag{C.3.4}$$

We note that $[\mathcal{C}(z)]^{-1}$ exists and is holomorphic in D. Substituting this expression for $\mathcal{Y}(z)$ in (C.3.1) we find that $\mathcal{W}(z)$ must be a solution of the second order matrix equation

$$\mathcal{W}''(z) + \mathcal{P}(z)\mathcal{W}'(z) + \mathcal{Q}(z)\mathcal{W}(z) = 0 \qquad \text{(C.3.5)}$$

with

$$\mathcal{P}(z) = -\mathcal{C}(z)\mathcal{B}(z)[\mathcal{C}(z)]^{-1} - \mathcal{C}'(z)[\mathcal{C}(z)]^{-1},$$

$$\mathcal{Q}(z) = \mathcal{C}(z)\mathcal{A}(z), \qquad \text{(C.3.6)}$$

functions holomorphic in D.

The solution of (C.3.5) is uniquely defined by its initial values $\mathcal{W}_0$ and $\mathcal{W}_1$ and we have

$$\mathcal{W}(z; a, \mathcal{W}_0, \mathcal{W}_1) = \mathcal{W}(z; a, \mathcal{O}, \mathcal{E})\mathcal{W}_1 + \mathcal{W}(z; a, \mathcal{E}, \mathcal{O})\mathcal{W}_0.$$

We have now to choose a particular solution that will satisfy (C.3.4) in $N(a)$. This may be achieved by choosing

$$\mathcal{W}_0 = \mathcal{E},\ \mathcal{W}_1 = -\mathcal{C}(a)\mathcal{Y}_0 \qquad \text{(C.3.7)}$$

so that

$$\mathcal{W}(z) = \mathcal{W}(z; a, \mathcal{E}, -\mathcal{C}(a)\mathcal{Y}_0) \qquad \text{(C.3.8)}$$

is the required solution.

Now by Theorem C.2.1 this solution exists in $\mathbf{A}(a; \mathcal{P}, \mathcal{Q})$ as a holomorphic function of z. Moreover, the solution can be continued everywhere in D which is supposed to be simply-connected. Thus $\mathcal{W}(z)$ and $\mathcal{W}'(z)$ exist everywhere in D and (C.3.4) holds as long as the right-hand side is meaningful, i.e. for all z, save for the algebraic singularities of $\mathcal{W}(z)$. We note that $\mathcal{W}(z)$ cannot be identically singular in D since $\mathcal{W}(a) = \mathcal{E}$. Hence the algebraic singularities of $\mathcal{W}(z)$ are isolated. They are movable and clearly depend upon the choice of $\mathcal{Y}_0$. We have the following

Theorem C.3.1. *The movable singularities of $\mathcal{Y}(z)$ in D are poles located at algebraic singularities of $\mathcal{W}(z)$. Likewise, the movable singularities of $\mathcal{V}(z)$ are poles located at algebraic singularities of $\mathcal{W}'(z)$. Associated functions $\mathcal{Y}(z)$ and $\mathcal{V}(z)$ may have a pole in common. There is no limitation on the order of the poles.*

Proof. The first two assertions follow from Lemma C.2.1. Let $z = b$, $b \in D$, be an algebraic singularity of $\mathcal{W}(z)$ and/or $\mathcal{W}'(z)$. To take into account the various possibilities we set

$$c(z) = \det[\mathcal{C}(z)],\ y(z) = \det[\mathcal{Y}(z)],\ v(z) = \det[\mathcal{V}(z)],$$
$$w_0(z) = \det[\mathcal{W}(z)],\ w_1(z) = \det[\mathcal{W}'(z)]. \qquad \text{(C.3.9)}$$

We recall that

$$\mathcal{V}(z) = -[\mathcal{Y}(z)]^{-1} = \mathcal{W}(z)[\mathcal{W}'(z)]^{-1}\mathcal{C}(z).$$

We have then

$$y(z) = (-1)^n \frac{w_1(z)}{c(z)w_0(z)} = (-1)^n \frac{1}{v(z)} \tag{C.3.10}$$

as identities between Cauchy analytic functions. Here $c(z) \neq 0$ in D while $w_0(z)$ and $w_1(z)$ may have a finite number of zeros. By assumption $z = b$ is one of these. To fix the ideas, we suppose that $z = b$ is a zero of $w_0(z)$ of order m and a zero of $w_1(z)$ of order m_1 where m and m_1 are non-negative integers and at least one is positive. Then in some neighborhood of $z = b$

$$y(z) = (z - b)^{m_1 - m} f(z), \tag{C.3.11}$$

where $f(z)$ is holomorphic and $f(b) \neq 0$. Since we do not know if $f(z)$ is the determinant of a matrix function holomorphic at $z = b$, this relation is of doubtful value. The integers m and m_1 are decisive for the behavior of $\mathcal{Y}(z)$ and $\mathcal{V}(z)$ at $z = b$ rather than their difference $m - m_1$.

Since $\mathcal{W}(z)$ is holomorphic at $z = b$ and its determinant $w_0(z)$ has a zero of order m there, Lemma C.2.1 shows that $[\mathcal{W}(z)]^{-1}$ is holomorphic save for a possible pole at $z = b$. Moreover, the order of the pole is at most m. If $m = 0$, this means that $\mathcal{Y}(z)$ is holomorphic at $z = b$ where it has an algebraic singularity of order m_1. In the general case we see that $\mathcal{Y}(z)$ has a pole at $z = b$ of order at most m. If $m > m_1$, (C.3.11) shows that $y(z)$ becomes infinite as $z \to b$ and $\mathcal{Y}(z)$ must have a pole there. If $m \leq m_1$, $\mathcal{Y}(z)$ may be holomorphic at $z = b$.

Let us now consider $\mathcal{V}(z)$. Here we note that $\mathcal{W}'(z)$ is holomorphic at $z = b$ and its determinant $w_1(z)$ has a zero of order m_1 there. It follows again by Lemma C.2.1 that $[\mathcal{W}'(z)]^{-1}$ has a pole of order at most m_1 there and the same holds for $\mathcal{V}(z)$. We see that $\mathcal{V}(z)$ cannot be holomorphic at $z = b$ if $m < m_1$.

In order to prove the remaining statements, we exhibit an example of a Riccati matrix equation and corresponding solutions $\mathcal{Y}(z)$ and $\mathcal{V}(z)$ which exhibit poles of high order at $z = 0$. We take

$$\mathcal{Y}'(z) = \mathcal{A}(z) + [\mathcal{Y}(z)]^2, \qquad \mathcal{A}(z) = -\begin{pmatrix} 1 & z^k \\ 0 & 1 \end{pmatrix}, \tag{C.3.12}$$

where $k \geq 0$ is an integer. Here $\mathcal{A}(z)$ is holomorphic and algebraically regular in the finite plane. We solve the equation in the usual manner by setting

$$\mathcal{Y}(z) = -\mathcal{W}'(z)[\mathcal{W}(z)]^{-1}$$

and find that $\mathcal{W}(z)$ satisfies the equation

$$\mathcal{W}''(z) + \mathcal{A}(z)\mathcal{W}(z) = 0.$$

We take $z = 0$ and the initial conditions given by (C.2.7). The four components of $\mathcal{W}(z)$ are

$$w_{11}(z) = \int_0^z \sinh(z - t)t^k \sinh t\, dt = \frac{z^{k+3}}{(k+2)(k+3)}\{1 + O(z^2)\},$$

$$w_{12}(z) = \int_0^z \sinh(z - t)t^k \cosh t\, dt = \frac{z^{k+2}}{(k+1)(k+2)}\{1 + O(z^2)\},$$

$$w_{21}(z) = \sinh z,$$

$$w_{22}(z) = \cosh z.$$

Here

$$w_0(z) = -\frac{2z^{k+3}}{(k+1)(k+2)(k+3)}\{1 + O(z^2)\}$$

and

$$\lim_{z\to 0} w_0(z)\mathcal{W}'(z)[\mathcal{W}(z)]^{-1} = \begin{pmatrix} 0 & 0 \\ 1 & 0 \end{pmatrix}\begin{pmatrix} 1 & 0 \\ 0 & 0 \end{pmatrix} = \begin{pmatrix} 0 & 0 \\ 1 & 0 \end{pmatrix},$$

so that

$$\lim_{z\to 0} z^{k+3}\mathcal{Y}(z) = \tfrac{1}{2}(k+1)(k+2)(k+3)\begin{pmatrix} 0 & 0 \\ 1 & 0 \end{pmatrix}. \tag{C.3.13}$$

Thus $\mathcal{Y}(z)$ has a pole of order $k + 3$ at $z = 0$.

We now consider $\mathcal{V}(z)$. Here

$$w_1(z) = -\frac{z^{k+1}}{k+1}\{1 + O(z^2)\}.$$

Thus the order of the pole of $\mathcal{V}(z)$ at $z = 0$ is at most $k + 1$. As a matter of fact the true order is k. To see this we need only the first two terms in the Maclaurin series, namely

$$\mathcal{W}(z) = \begin{pmatrix} 0 & 0 \\ 0 & 1 \end{pmatrix} + \begin{pmatrix} 0 & 0 \\ 1 & 0 \end{pmatrix} z + \cdots,$$

$$w_1(z)[\mathcal{W}'(z)]^{-1} = -\begin{pmatrix} 0 & 1 \\ 0 & 0 \end{pmatrix} + \begin{pmatrix} 1 & 0 \\ 0 & 0 \end{pmatrix} z + \cdots,$$

Hence

$$\mathcal{W}(z)w_1(z)[\mathcal{W}'(z)]^{-1} = -\begin{pmatrix} 0 & 0 \\ 0 & 1 \end{pmatrix} z + \cdots \tag{C.3.14}$$

and

$$\lim_{z\to 0} z^k\mathcal{V}(z) = (k+1)\begin{pmatrix} 0 & 0 \\ 0 & 1 \end{pmatrix}. \tag{C.3.15}$$

Thus $\mathcal{V}(z)$ has a pole of order k at $z = 0$ as asserted. There is obviously an abnormal concentration of poles at the origin in this case. Both $\mathcal{Y}(z)$ and $\mathcal{V}(z)$ have infinitely many poles but, except for $z = 0$, they are at most double poles. ∎

The equation

$$\mathcal{Y}'(z) = -[\mathcal{Y}(z)]^2 \tag{C.3.16}$$

is worthy of special attention. It arises in resolvent theory. Cf. (4.3.11) with $n = 1$. We take first the matrix case, $\mathcal{Y} \in \mathfrak{M}_n$. Here if $\mathcal{M}$ is any constant matrix $\in \mathfrak{M}_n$, then

$$\mathfrak{R}(z, \mathcal{M}) = (z\mathcal{E} - \mathcal{M})^{-1} \tag{C.3.17}$$

is a solution of (C.3.16). The solution which takes on the value $\mathcal{Y}_0$ at $z = a$ is given by

$$\mathcal{Y}_0[\mathcal{E} + (z - a)\mathcal{Y}_0]^{-1}. \tag{C.3.18}$$

The resolvent of a matrix has only polar singularities. We refer to formula (5.2.12) which we rewrite as

$$\mathfrak{R}(z, \mathcal{M}) = \sum_{j=1}^{p} \left\{\frac{\mathcal{E}_j}{z - z_j} + \frac{\mathcal{Q}_j}{(z - z_j)^2} + \cdots + \frac{\mathcal{Q}^{k_j - 1}}{(z - z_j)^{k_j}}\right\}, \tag{C.3.19}$$

where the summation extends over the distinct characteristic roots z_j of $\mathcal{M}$. Here $p \leq n$, $\sum k_j = n$, $\mathcal{E}_j$ is an idempotent, $\mathcal{Q}_j$ a nilpotent matrix.

The situation changes radically, if we consider equation (C.3.16) in an arbitrary Banach algebra $\mathfrak{B}$. The spectrum of an element $M \in \mathfrak{B}$ may now be an arbitrary bounded closed point set. Here $R(z, M)$ exists in the resolvent set $\rho(M)$ which is open but may break up into countably many disjoint components. In each of the latter $R(z, M)$ satisfies (C.3.16). Thus there may be singular lines and by Theorem 4.3.2 isolated singularities may be essential singularities.

EXERCISE C.3

1. If the solution $\mathcal{Y}(z)$ of (C.3.12) is defined as above, show that its poles are located at the zeros of the entire function

$$F(z) \equiv \int_0^z \sinh^2 (z - t)\; t^k\, dt.$$

Show that

$$F''(z) = 4F(z) + \frac{2}{k + 1}\, z^{k+1}$$

and deduce from this that the poles can be at most double except for $z = 0$.

2. Construct a solution of (C.3.12) which has merely a double pole at $z = 0$. Is this possible?

3. Given the equation

$$\mathcal{Y}' = \mathcal{E} + \mathcal{Y}\begin{pmatrix} 1 & 0 \\ 0 & 0 \end{pmatrix}\mathcal{Y} \quad \text{with} \quad \mathcal{Y}(0) = \begin{pmatrix} 0 & -1 \\ -1 & 0 \end{pmatrix}.$$

Find the solution and determine the location and multiplicity of its poles. [*Hint*: Since $\mathfrak{C}(z)$ is singular, the substitution (C.3.4) is meaningless. A possible method is to replace the matrix equation by a system of equations for the four components.]

4. Knowing that the solution $\mathfrak{Y}(z)$ of (C.3.16) is a resolvent and that $\mathfrak{Y}(z)$ is holomorphic at $z = z_0$, find $\mathcal{M}$ in the representation $\mathfrak{Y}(z) = \mathfrak{R}(z, \mathcal{M})$.
5. What is the associated equation of (C.3.16)? Find $\mathfrak{V}(z)$.
6. Determine a (two-valued) matrix function whose square equals $\mathfrak{R}(z, \mathcal{M})$ for $|z| > r(\mathcal{M})$, the spectral radius of $\mathcal{M}$.
7. Let $\mathfrak{P} = \mathfrak{P}^2$, $\mathfrak{P}\mathfrak{Q} = \mathfrak{Q}\mathfrak{P} = \mathfrak{Q}$, $\mathfrak{Q}^m = 0$, and

$$\mathfrak{R}(z) = (z - a)^{-1}\left[\mathfrak{P} + \sum_{j=1}^{m-1} \mathfrak{Q}^j(z - a)^{-j}\right].$$

Show that

$$[\mathfrak{R}(z)]^{1/2} = (z - a)^{-1/2}\left\{\mathfrak{P} + \sum_{j=1}^{m-1} (-1)^j\binom{-\frac{1}{2}}{j}\mathfrak{Q}^j(z - a)^{-j}\right\}.$$

Use this to represent the square root in the whole plane in the preceding problem and extend to k^{th} roots.

8. Formally the equation $\mathfrak{Z}'(z) = -\frac{1}{2}[\mathfrak{Z}(z)]^3$ can be reduced to a Riccati equation by setting $[\mathfrak{Z}(z)]^2 = \mathfrak{Y}(z)$. What information can be obtained about its solutions with the aid of this method? Generalize to higher powers!

COLLATERAL READING

A brief discussion of the classical Riccati equation in the complex domain is found in

INCE, E. L., *Ordinary differential equations*, Dover reprint, New York (1944), pp. 293–295.

Relevant matrix theory is almost exclusively concerned with functions of a real variable. For this side of the theory see

BARRETT, J. H., "Matrix systems of second order differential equations," *Portugaliae Mathematica*, **14**, 79–89 (1955).

LEVIN, J. J., "On the matrix Riccati equation," *Proc. Amer. Math. Soc.* **10**, 519–524 (1959).

LEVIN, J. J., and S. S. SHATZ, "Riccati algebras," *Duke Math. J.* **30**, 579–594 (1963).

REID, W. T., "A matrix differential equation of the Riccati type," *Amer. J. Math.* **68**, 237–246 (1946).

WHYBURN, W. M., "Existence and oscillation theorems for non-linear differential equations of the second order," *Trans. Amer. Math. Soc.* **30**, 848–854 (1928).

Further references are to be found in these papers and at the end of Chapter 9. We note in conclusion that Levin has extended formula (C.1.11) for cross-ratios to the matrix case.

PART II

Linear Second Order Differential Equations

7 SPECIAL LINEAR SECOND ORDER DIFFERENTIAL EQUATIONS

In this chapter we shall discuss some of the linear second order differential equations which arise most frequently in the applications. It is impossible to give adequate coverage of this important part of the subject and stay within reasonable bounds. For most of the equations there exist large monographs where the reader who so desires can find further details. Mixed in with the special theory, the reader will find various general considerations such as closure of orthogonal systems, the Liouville transformation, a method of asymptotic integration, and Floquet's theorem.

There are six sections: The Hypergeometric Equation; Legendre's Equation; Bessel's Equation; Asymptotic Integration; On the Confluent Hypergeometric Equation; and Mathieu's Equation.

7.1 THE HYPERGEOMETRIC EQUATION

This time-honored equation reads

$$z(1 - z)w'' + [\gamma - (\alpha + \beta + 1)z]w' - \alpha\beta w = 0, \tag{7.1.1}$$

where the three parameters α, β, γ are arbitrary complex numbers. Among the many mathematicians who have worked on this equation should be mentioned in particular Euler, Gauss, Kummer, and Riemann. Other names will occur below. The equation belongs to the Fuchsian class. There are three singular points, 0, 1, and ∞. The corresponding indicial equations have the roots

$$0, 1 - \gamma; 0, \alpha + \beta - \gamma; \alpha, \beta, \tag{7.1.2}$$

respectively. Note that at infinity the roots are the exponents of $1/z$ and not of z itself. We see that exceptional cases will arise

at $z = 0$, if γ is an integer,
at $z = 1$, if $\alpha + \beta - \gamma$ is an integer, and
at $z = \infty$, if $\alpha - \beta$ is an integer.

Assuming γ not zero or a negative integer, the hypergeometric series gives a solution. We set

$$F(a, b, c; z) = 1 + \sum_{n=1}^{\infty} \frac{(a)_n(b)_n}{(1)_n(c)_n} z^n, \tag{7.1.3}$$

where

$$(a)_n = a(a+1)(a+2)\cdots(a+n-1). \tag{7.1.4}$$

We find then that

$$w_{01}(z) = F(\alpha, \beta, \gamma; z) \tag{7.1.5}$$

is a solution holomorphic at $z = 0$. The series converges for $|z| < 1$. The solution, however, exists also outside of the unit circle as we shall see. We notice at this point that for arbitrary values of γ, the problem of finding a solution of (7.1.1) which is holomorphic at $z = 0$ and takes on the value 1 there, has a unique solution, namely $w_{01}(z)$. This observation is known as *Kummer's principle* after Eduard Kummer.

The hypergeometric equation admits of a number of transformations on the variables which take it into a similar equation in the new variables with a new set of parameters. One such transformation is

$$w = z^{1-\gamma}u. \tag{7.1.6}$$

The equation for u is

$$z(1-z)u'' + [2 - \gamma - (\alpha + \beta - 2\gamma + 3)z]u' - (\alpha - \gamma + 1)(\beta - \gamma + 1)u = 0. \tag{7.1.7}$$

If we set

$$a = \alpha - \gamma + 1,\ b = \beta - \gamma + 1,\ c = 2 - \gamma,$$

then (7.1.7) is a hypergeometric equation with the parameters a, b, c. Since $F(a, b, c; z)$ satisfies (7.1.7) we see that

$$w_{02}(z) = z^{1-\gamma}F(\alpha - \gamma + 1, \beta - \gamma + 1, 2 - \gamma; z) \tag{7.1.8}$$

satisfies (7.1.1) provided γ is not a positive integer. If $\gamma = 1$ the two solutions become identical. Thus we see that if γ is not an integer, then $w_{01}(z)$ and $w_{02}(z)$ are linearly independent solutions of (7.1.7) and form a fundamental system. We defer the discussion of the exceptional cases until later.

Since the hypergeometric equation has only regular singular points, it is of the Fuchsian class. The corresponding matrix equation of the Fuchsian class with singular points at $z = 0, 1$, and ∞ is of the form

$$\frac{d\mathfrak{W}}{dz} = \left(\frac{\mathcal{A}}{z} + \frac{\mathcal{B}}{1-z}\right)\mathfrak{W}. \tag{7.1.9}$$

We saw in Section 6.7 that this equation is formally invariant under the transformations of the anharmonic group

$$z \Rightarrow z,\ 1 - z,\ \frac{1}{z},\ \frac{1}{1-z},\ \frac{z}{z-1},\ \frac{z-1}{z}. \tag{7.1.10}$$

Each of these transformations leads to an equation of type (7.1.9), only the matrix "parameters" $\mathcal{A}$ and $\mathcal{B}$ are changed.

One would expect that the hypergeometric equation would be formally invariant under this group. This is not the case, however; only the identity and the reflection

$$z \to 1 - z$$

lead right away to hypergeometric equations. Thus the reflection leads to an equation with parameters

$$\alpha, \beta, \alpha + \beta + 1 - \gamma.$$

It follows that (7.1.1) is satisfied by

$$w_{11}(z) = F(\alpha, \beta, \alpha + \beta + 1 - \gamma; 1 - z), \qquad (7.1.11)$$

$$w_{12}(z) = (1 - z)^{\gamma-\alpha-\beta}F(\gamma - \alpha, \gamma - \beta, \gamma + 1 - \alpha - \beta; 1 - z). \qquad (7.1.12)$$

These solutions exist for $|z - 1| < 1$ provided $\alpha + \beta - \gamma$ is not an integer. They are then linearly independent and form a fundamental system at $z = 1$.

The other anharmonic transformations are not by themselves of invariantive character. We can, however, combine such a transformation of the independent variable with a change of the dependent variable of the form

$$w = z^{\delta}(1 - z)^{\varepsilon}u. \qquad (7.1.13)$$

It is possible to choose δ and ε so that a hypergeometric equation is obtained for u. We list the results obtained in this manner and leave the verification to the reader.

i) $z \to 1/z$, $\delta = -\alpha$, $\varepsilon = 0$. The new parameters are

$$\alpha, \alpha - \gamma + 1, \alpha - \beta + 1.$$

Hence

$$w_{\infty,1}(z) = z^{-\alpha}F(\alpha, \alpha - \gamma + 1, \alpha - \beta + 1; 1/z) \qquad (7.1.14)$$

is a solution. The series converges for $|z| > 1$. Since (7.1.1) is left invariant if α and β are interchanged, it follows that

$$w_{\infty,2}(z) = z^{-\beta}F(\beta, \beta - \gamma + 1, \beta - \alpha + 1; 1/z) \qquad (7.1.15)$$

is also a solution. These functions exist unless $\alpha - \beta$ is an integer. They form a fundamental system at the point at infinity.

ii) $z \to 1/(1 - z)$, $\delta = 0$, $\varepsilon = -\alpha$. The parameters are

$$\alpha, \gamma - \beta, \alpha - \beta + 1$$

and

$$w_{\infty,3}(z) = (z - 1)^{-\alpha}F(\alpha, \gamma - \beta, \alpha - \beta + 1; 1/(1 - z)) \qquad (7.1.16)$$

is a solution. Interchanging α and β we get

$$w_{\infty,4}(z) = (z - 1)^{-\beta}F(\beta, \gamma - \alpha, \beta - \alpha + 1; 1/(1 - z)) \qquad (7.1.17)$$

as a second solution. The hypergeometric series converge for $|z - 1| > 1$ and if $\alpha - \beta$ is not an integer, both solutions exist and form a fundamental system at infinity. The relation between the two fundamental systems will be given below. We take $(z - 1)^{-\alpha}$ rather than $(1 - z)^{-\alpha}$ to simplify the comparison of the two fundamental systems.

iii) $z \to z/(z - 1)$, $\delta = 0$, $\varepsilon = -\alpha$. The parameters are

$$\alpha, \gamma - \beta, \gamma$$

and the corresponding solution is

$$w_{03}(z) = (1 - z)^{-\alpha} F\left(\alpha, \gamma - \beta, \gamma; \frac{z}{z - 1}\right). \tag{7.1.18}$$

Similarly, interchanging α and β we get

$$w_{05}(z) = (1 - z)^{-\beta} F\left(\beta, \gamma - \alpha, \gamma; \frac{z}{z - 1}\right) \tag{7.1.19}$$

as a solution. The reason for the mysterious numbering will become clear later. Actually, the interchange of α and β does not lead to anything new, and it is more interesting to consider the second solution of the transformed equation. We recall that the equation

$$s(1 - s)u'' + [c - (a + b + 1)s]u' - abu = 0$$

is satisfied by

$$s^{1-c} F(a - c + 1, b - c + 1, 2 - c; s).$$

Here we replace a, b, c by either

$$\alpha, \gamma - \beta, \gamma \quad \text{or} \quad \beta, \gamma - \alpha, \gamma$$

and write $z/(z - 1)$ for s. This observation gives two solutions

$$w_{04}(z) = z^{1-\gamma}(1 - z)^{\gamma-\alpha-1} F\left(\alpha + 1 - \gamma, 1 - \beta, 2 - \gamma; \frac{z}{z - 1}\right), \tag{7.1.20}$$

$$w_{06}(z) = z^{1-\gamma}(1 - z)^{\gamma-\beta-1} F\left(\beta + 1 - \gamma, 1 - \alpha, 2 - \gamma; \frac{z}{z - 1}\right). \tag{7.1.21}$$

These four solutions exist for $\Re(z) < \frac{1}{2}$ provided γ is not an integer. Linear independence will be examined later.

iv) $z \to \dfrac{z - 1}{z}$, $\delta = -\alpha$, $\varepsilon = 0$. The parameters are

$$\alpha, \alpha - \gamma + 1, \alpha + \beta + 1 - \gamma.$$

Hence

$$w_{1,3}(z) = z^{-\alpha} F\left(\alpha, \alpha - \gamma + 1, \alpha + \beta + 1 - \gamma; \frac{z - 1}{z}\right), \tag{7.1.22}$$

$$w_{1,5}(z) = z^{-\beta} F\left(\beta, \beta - \gamma + 1, \alpha + \beta + 1 - \gamma; \frac{z - 1}{z}\right) \tag{7.1.23}$$

are solutions. Again we get more solutions by considering the second solution of the transformed equation at the origin. This gives

$$w_{1,4}(z) = z^{\beta-\gamma}(1-z)^{\gamma-\alpha-\beta}F\left(\gamma-\beta, 1-\beta, 1+\gamma-\alpha-\beta; \frac{z-1}{z}\right), \quad (7.1.24)$$

$$w_{1,6}(z) = z^{\alpha-\gamma}(1-z)^{\gamma-\alpha-\beta}F\left(\gamma-\alpha, 1-\alpha, 1+\gamma-\alpha-\beta; \frac{z-1}{z}\right), \quad (7.1.25)$$

another pair of solutions. The last four hypergeometric series converge in the half-plane $\Re(z) > \frac{1}{2}$.

In this manner we obtain a total of sixteen solutions. The power of the method of transformation is not exhausted, however, and we shall find additional solutions below. The solutions are given by infinite series which converge for

$\lvert z\rvert < 1$	in the case of	w_{01} and w_{02},
$\lvert z-1\rvert < 1$	in the case of	w_{11} and w_{12},
$\lvert z\rvert > 1$	in the case of	$w_{\infty,1}$ and $w_{\infty,2}$,
$\lvert z-1\rvert > 1$	in the case of	$w_{\infty,3}$ and $w_{\infty,4}$,
$\Re(z) < \frac{1}{2}$	in the case of	w_{03}, w_{04}, w_{05}, and w_{06},
$\Re(z) > \frac{1}{2}$	in the case of	w_{13}, w_{14}, w_{15}, and w_{16}.

The various domains of convergence are shown in Figure 7.1.

Any three solutions of a linear differential equation of the second order are linearly dependent. Thus any one of the sixteen solutions can be expressed in terms of the solutions of a fundamental system. A number of these relations can be found by inspection. We note the following identities.

$$\begin{aligned} w_{01} &= w_{03} = w_{05}, & w_{02} &= w_{04} = w_{06}, \\ w_{11} &= w_{13} = w_{15}, & w_{12} &= w_{14} = w_{16}, \\ w_{\infty,1} &= w_{\infty,3}, & w_{\infty,2} &= w_{\infty,4}. \end{aligned} \quad (7.1.26)$$

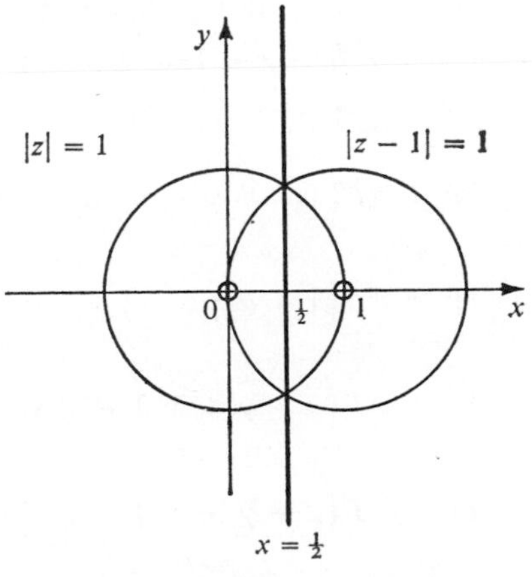

Figure 7.1

These identities are obtained as follows. The three functions $w_{01}(z)$, $w_{03}(z)$, and $w_{05}(z)$ are holomorphic in some neighborhood of the origin where they have the common value 1. It was observed above that (7.1.1) has only one solution with this property, namely $w_{01}(z)$. This gives the first identity. The three solutions involved in the second identity are all of the form $z^{1-\gamma}$ times a function which is holomorphic at $z = 0$ and takes the value 1 there. Since the equation has only one solution with these properties, namely $w_{02}(z)$, the identity follows. A similar argument applies in the remaining cases. In the third and the fourth identities, the solutions exist in some neighborhood of $z = 1$, in the fifth and sixth cases in some neighborhood of infinity.

The integration problem for the hypergeometric equation has many different phases. The first one is to obtain the three fundamental systems

$$w_{01}(z), w_{02}(z); w_{11}(z), w_{12}(z); w_{\infty,1}(z), w_{\infty,2}(z),$$

one for each singular point. In each case the functions are given at the outset by local power series expansions. From the function theoretical point of view an important problem is to obtain analytic continuations of the solutions from the local region of definition to the whole plane. If successful, this will ultimately lead to expressions for one fundamental system in terms of any other fundamental system, i.e. to the group of the equation.

The identities (7.1.26) form partial solutions of the analytic continuation problem. Thus $w_{01}(z)$, originally given in the disk $|z| < 1$, is seen to be represented in the half-plane $\Re(z) < \frac{1}{2}$ by either $w_{03}(z)$ or $w_{05}(z)$. The other identities are capable of similar interpretation.

In 1836 Kummer gave a set of twenty-four solutions of the hypergeometric equation. Of these, sixteen have figured already above. The remaining eight are

$$\begin{aligned}
w_{07}(z) &= (1 - z)^{\gamma-\alpha-\beta}F(\gamma - \alpha, \gamma - \beta, \gamma; z),\\
w_{08}(z) &= z^{1-\gamma}(1 - z)^{\gamma-\alpha-\beta}F(1 - \alpha, 1 - \beta, 2 - \gamma; z),\\
w_{17}(z) &= z^{1-\gamma}F(\alpha - \gamma + 1, \beta - \gamma + 1, \alpha + \beta - \gamma + 1; 1 - z),\\
w_{18}(z) &= z^{1-\gamma}(1 - z)^{\gamma-\alpha-\beta}F(1 - \alpha, 1 - \beta, \gamma - \alpha - \beta + 1; 1 - z),
\end{aligned}$$

$$w_{\infty,5}(z) = z^{\beta-\gamma}(z - 1)^{\gamma-\alpha-\beta}F\left(1 - \beta, \gamma - \beta, \alpha - \beta + 1; \frac{1}{z}\right),$$

$$w_{\infty,6}(z) = z^{\alpha-\gamma}(z - 1)^{\gamma-\alpha-\beta}F\left(1 - \alpha, \gamma - \alpha, \beta - \alpha + 1; \frac{1}{z}\right),$$

$$w_{\infty,7}(z) = z^{1-\gamma}(z - 1)^{\gamma-\alpha-1}F\left(\alpha - \gamma + 1, 1 - \beta, \alpha - \beta + 1; \frac{1}{1 - z}\right),$$

$$w_{\infty,8}(z) = z^{1-\gamma}(z - 1)^{\gamma-\beta-1}F\left(\beta - \gamma + 1, 1 - \alpha, \beta - \alpha + 1; \frac{1}{1 - z}\right).$$

The reader should have no difficulty in determining the regions of convergence of the hypergeometric series. He can also use Kummer's principle to verify the additional identities:

$$\begin{gathered} w_{07} = w_{01}, \qquad w_{08} = w_{02}, \qquad w_{17} = w_{11}, \qquad w_{18} = w_{12}, \\ w_{\infty,5} = w_{\infty,7} = w_{\infty,1}, \qquad w_{\infty,6} = w_{\infty,8} = w_{\infty,2}. \end{gathered} \tag{7.1.27}$$

So far we have excluded the exceptional cases. It is enough to discuss the situation at $z = 0$ where the case $\gamma = p$, an integer, is exceptional. If $p > 0$, $w_{01}(z)$ is still a solution, but the formula for $w_{02}(z)$ breaks down. To get a meaningful second solution at $z = 0$, we can use a continuity argument. For fixed values of z, α and β the series

$$w_{02}(z) = z^{1-\gamma} + \sum_{n=1}^{\infty} \frac{(\alpha - \gamma + 1)_n(\beta - \gamma + 1)_n}{(1)_n(2 - \gamma)_n} z^{n+1-\gamma} \equiv G(\gamma)$$

defines a meromorphic function of γ which has a simple pole at $\gamma = p$. A simple calculation shows that the residue of $G(\gamma)$ at $\gamma = p$ equals

$$(-1)^{p-1} \frac{(\alpha - p + 1)_{p-1}(\beta - p + 1)_{p-1}}{(p - 2)!(p - 1)!} F(\alpha, \beta, p; z) \equiv f_{-1}(z),$$

that is, a solution of (7.1.1) for $\gamma = p$. Here we have assumed tacitly that $p > 1$ and that neither α nor β is one of the numbers

$$1, 2, \ldots, p - 1.$$

The case $p = 1$ requires special handling since then the expressions for $w_{01}(z)$ and $w_{02}(z)$ coincide. For the stated exceptional values of α and β the point $\gamma = p$ is not a pole of $G(\gamma)$ and

$$\lim_{\gamma \to p} G(\gamma)$$

exists as a finite limit and is the desired second solution. Leaving these cases to one side we proceed as follows.

We set

$$C_p(\alpha, \beta) = (-1)^{p-1} \frac{(\alpha - p + 1)_{p-1}(\beta - p + 1)_{p-1}}{(p - 2)!(p - 1)!} \tag{7.1.28}$$

and observe that

$$\Delta \equiv G(\gamma) - C_p(\alpha, \beta) \frac{1}{\gamma - p} F(\alpha, \beta, \gamma; z)$$

is a solution of (7.1.1) for $0 < |\gamma - p| < 1$. Hence, if this expression has a limit as $\gamma \to p$, then the limit will be a solution of (7.1.1) for $\gamma = p$. Now we know that $G(\gamma)$ has an expansion of the form

$$G(\gamma) = \frac{1}{\gamma - p} f_{-1}(z) + f_0(z) + \sum_{n=1}^{\infty} f_n(z)(\gamma - p)^n,$$

convergent for $0 < |\gamma - p| < 1$. Here

$$f_0(z) = \frac{\partial}{\partial \gamma}[(\gamma - p)G(\gamma)]_{\gamma = p}$$

by Taylor's theorem. It follows that

$$\Delta = -C_p(\alpha, \beta)\frac{1}{\gamma - p}[F(\alpha, \beta, \gamma; z) - F(\alpha, \beta, p; z)]$$

$$+ f_0(z) + \sum_{n=1}^{\infty} f_n(z)(\gamma - p)^n,$$

the limit of which is

$$-C_p(\alpha, \beta)\frac{\partial}{\partial \gamma}F(\alpha, \beta, p; z) + f_0(z)$$

$$= -C_p(\alpha, \beta)\frac{\partial}{\partial \gamma}F(\alpha, \beta, p; z) + \frac{\partial}{\partial \gamma}[(\gamma - p)G(\gamma)]_{\gamma = p}.$$

Thus the limit exists and we have merely to carry out the indicated operations.

We omit the details of the calculation which are long and tedious. The result is of the form

$$-C_p(\alpha, \beta)F(\alpha, \beta, p; z)\log z + F_1(\alpha, \beta, p; z), \tag{7.1.29}$$

where

$$F_1(\alpha, \beta, p; z) = z^{1-p} + \sum_{n=1}^{p-2}\frac{(\alpha - p + 1)_n(\beta - p + 1)_n}{(1)_n(2 - \gamma)_n}z^{n+1-p}$$

$$-C_p(\alpha, \beta)\sum_{m=1}^{\infty}\frac{(\alpha)_m(\beta)_m}{(1)_m(p)_m}\sum_{j=0}^{m-1}\left(\frac{1}{\alpha + j} + \frac{1}{\beta + j} - \frac{1}{1 + j} - \frac{1}{p + j}\right)z^m. \tag{7.1.30}$$

We have suppressed a constant multiple of $F(\alpha, \beta, p; z)$, which is also part of the limit, since we are interested only in obtaining a second solution, linearly independent of $w_{01}(z)$. Thus (7.1.29) is a solution of (7.1.1) for $\gamma = p$ and it is clearly linearly independent of $w_{01}(z)$. This solution contains a term in $\log z$ and the reader should note that the multiplier of $\log z$ is a constant multiple of $w_{01}(z)$. This is nothing special for the hypergeometric equation. It holds for any linear second order differential equation having a regular singular point at $z = 0$ such that the roots of the indicial equation differ by an integer. If logarithms do occur which is normally the case, then the equation has a fundamental system of the form

$$w_{01}(z) = z^\rho f_1(z), \qquad w_{02}(z) = w_{01}(z)\log z + z^\sigma f_2(z). \tag{7.1.31}$$

Here ρ and σ are the roots of the indicial equation, $\Re(\rho) \geq \Re(\sigma)$, f_1 and f_2 are power series in z with non-vanishing constant terms.

We have supposed $\gamma = p > 1$. A similar formula holds for $p = 1$, namely

$$-F(\alpha, \beta, 1; z)\log z + \sum_{m=1}^{\infty} \frac{(\alpha)_m(\beta)_m}{(1)_m(1)_m} \sum_{j=0}^{m-1} \left(\frac{1}{\alpha + j} + \frac{1}{\beta + j} - \frac{2}{1 + j}\right) z^m. \quad (7.1.32)$$

This is obtainable as

$$\lim_{\gamma \to 1} \frac{1}{\gamma - 1} [F(\alpha, \beta, \gamma; z) - z^{1-\gamma} F(\alpha - \gamma + 1, \beta - \gamma + 1, 2 - \gamma; z)]$$

and is consequently a solution of (7.1.1) for $\gamma = 1$ which is clearly not a constant multiple of $F(\alpha, \beta, 1; z)$.

The case where γ is a positive integer or 0 leads to similar considerations. Here it is $w_{02}(z)$ that remains valid while $w_{01}(z)$ becomes infinite and cannot be used as a second solution. The method used above can be carried over to this case or we can reduce the discussion to the case $p > 0$ by a suitable change of variable. Similar results hold also at the other singular points when an exceptional set of parameters is present. We do not pursue this matter any further.

Instead we turn to the problem of determining the transit substitutions which express one fundamental system in terms of another. We start with the question of expressing $w_{01}(z)$ and $w_{02}(z)$ in terms of $w_{11}(z)$ and $w_{12}(z)$:

$$\begin{aligned} w_{01}(z) &= Aw_{11}(z) + Bw_{12}(z), \\ w_{02}(z) &= Cw_{11}(z) + Dw_{12}(z). \end{aligned} \quad (7.1.33)$$

We note that the four solutions under consideration have a common domain of definition, namely the set

$$[z \mid |z| < 1, |z - 1| < 1].$$

In particular, the line segment (0, 1) belongs to this domain. The formula involves the powers $z^{1-\gamma}$ and $(1 - z)^{\gamma-\alpha-\beta}$. These are to be given their principal determinations on (0, 1), i.e. for such values of z and for α, β, γ real the powers are real positive numbers. It is assumed that α, β, γ have non-exceptional values so that all solutions are expressible in terms of hypergeometric series.

By the general theory A, B, C, D are independent of z but they are functions of α, β, γ, actually meromorphic functions of these variables. To see this we can differentiate the formulas with respect to z so as to get two more linear equations for A, B, C, D. From these we obtain

$$A = \frac{w_{01}(z)w'_{12}(z) - w'_{01}(z)w_{12}(z)}{w_{11}(z)w'_{12}(z) - w'_{11}(z)w_{12}(z)},$$

identically in z, and similar formulas for B, C, D. Here numerator and denominator are meromorphic functions of α, β, γ and hence the quotient has the same property. Such a function exists for all values of the variables, certain lower dimensional varieties in $C \times C \times C$ excepted. This means that if we can determine A, B, C, D as functions of α, β, γ under suitable restrictions on these parameters, then the expressions so obtained will be valid so long as they define holomorphic functions of α, β, γ regardless of the initial restrictions. This application of the principle of permanency of functional equations will be used repeatedly below.

It will be seen that the desired quantities A, B, C, D are expressible in terms of gamma functions of linear combinations of α, β, γ. Hence we shall need some properties of the gamma function and of the hypergemetric series, which will be the next item on the agenda. We recall that

$$\Gamma(x+1) = x\Gamma(x), \qquad \Gamma(x)\Gamma(1-x) = \frac{\pi}{\sin \pi x}.$$

Further we note that for any fixed a and $|x| \to \infty$ in a sector $|\arg x| < \pi - \varepsilon$, we have

$$\frac{x^a \Gamma(x)}{\Gamma(x+a)} = 1 + O\left(\frac{1}{x}\right). \tag{7.1.34}$$

From this we obtain that the binomial coefficients satisfy

$$(-1)^n \binom{a}{n} = \frac{1}{\Gamma(-a)} n^{-1-a} + O[n^{-2-\Re(a)}] \tag{7.1.35}$$

since

$$(-1)^n \binom{a}{n} = \frac{\Gamma(n-a)}{\Gamma(-a)\Gamma(n+1)}.$$

This enables us to get the asymptotic form of the coefficients of the hypergemetric series. Since

$$\frac{(a)_n(b)_n}{(1)_n(c)_n} = \frac{\Gamma(c)}{\Gamma(a)\Gamma(b)} \frac{\Gamma(n+a)\Gamma(n+b)}{\Gamma(n+1)\Gamma(n+c)},$$

we have

$$\frac{(a)_n(b)_n}{(1)_n(c)_n} = \frac{\Gamma(c)}{\Gamma(a)\Gamma(b)} n^{a+b-c-1} + O(n^{-\delta-2}), \tag{7.1.36}$$

where $\delta = \Re(c - a - b)$. Here a, b, c are assumed to be distinct from 0 and negative integers. This gives

Theorem 7.1.1. *The hypergeometric series is absolutely convergent on* $|z| = 1$ *if* $\delta > 0$. *It converges for* $|z| = 1, z \neq 1$, *if* $-1 < \delta \leq 0$, *and diverges everywhere on* $|z| = 1$ if $\delta \leq -1$.

Proof. The first and the last statements follow directly from (7.1.36). To prove the middle one, we note that $F(a, b, c; e^{i\theta})$ differs from

$$\frac{\Gamma(c)}{\Gamma(a)\Gamma(b)}\left(1 + \sum_{n=1}^{\infty} n^{-d-1} e^{ni\theta}\right), \; d = c - a - b \tag{7.1.37}$$

by an absolutely convergent series. To (7.1.37) we apply summation by parts for $0 < |\theta| \leq \pi$ noting that

$$\left|1 + \sum_{k=1}^{n} e^{ki\theta}\right| \leq \frac{2}{|\theta|}$$

and that

$$|n^{-d-1} - (n+1)^{-d-1}| = \left|(d+1)\int_n^{n+1} u^{-d-2}\,du\right| \leq |d+1|n^{-\delta-2}.$$

Since $-1 < \delta \leq 0$, the transformed series is absolutely convergent, uniformly in θ for $|\theta| \geq \varepsilon > 0$. ▮

If $\delta \leq 0$, the function $F(a, b, c; r)$ becomes infinite as $r \to +1$. If $\delta < 0$, formula (7.1.33) applies and shows that

$$F(a, b, c; r) = O(1) + B(1 - r)^d. \tag{7.1.38}$$

For the moment we restrict ourselves to the case $-1 < \delta < 0$. Using (7.1.35) and the analogue of (7.1.37), we see that (7.1.38) implies

$$\frac{\Gamma(c)}{\Gamma(a)\Gamma(b)}\sum_1^{\infty} n^{-d-1} r^n = O(1) + \frac{B}{\Gamma(-d)}\sum_1^{\infty} n^{-d-1} r^n.$$

Since the series becomes infinite as r increases to 1, this requires that

$$B = \frac{\Gamma(c)\Gamma(a+b-c)}{\Gamma(a)\Gamma(b)}. \tag{7.2.39}$$

We obtained this result by letting $z = r \to 1$ in the first formula (7.1.33). We shall now let $r \to 0$ instead. Here we shall assume the two hypergeometric series on the right to diverge for $z = 0$. The condition for this is the same in both cases, namely

$$\Re(c) > 1.$$

Assuming $2 > \Re(c) > 1$ we then get

$$A\frac{\Gamma(a+b-c+1)}{\Gamma(a)\Gamma(b)}\sum_1^{\infty} n^{c-2}(1-r)^n$$
$$+ B\frac{\Gamma(c-a-b+1)}{\Gamma(c-a)\Gamma(c-b)}\sum_1^{\infty} n^{c-2}(1-r)^n = O(1).$$

Since the series become infinite when $r \to 0$, we conclude that

$$A\frac{\Gamma(a+b-c+1)}{\Gamma(a)\Gamma(b)} + B\frac{\Gamma(c-a-b+1)}{\Gamma(c-a)\Gamma(c-b)} = 0$$

whence

$$A = \frac{\Gamma(c-a-b)\Gamma(c)}{\Gamma(c-a)\Gamma(c-b)}. \tag{7.1.40}$$

Hence we have proved the formula

$$\begin{aligned} F(\alpha, \beta, \gamma; z) &= \frac{\Gamma(\gamma-\alpha-\beta)\Gamma(\gamma)}{\Gamma(\gamma-\alpha)\Gamma(\gamma-\beta)} F(\alpha, \beta, \alpha+\beta-\gamma+1; 1-z) \\ &+ \frac{\Gamma(\alpha+\beta-\gamma)\Gamma(\gamma)}{\Gamma(\alpha)\Gamma(\beta)}(1-z)^{\gamma-\alpha-\beta} \\ &\times F(\gamma-\alpha, \gamma-\beta, \gamma-\alpha-\beta+1; 1-z). \end{aligned} \tag{7.1.41}$$

Similarly we prove

$$\begin{aligned} z^{1-\gamma}F(\alpha-\gamma+1, \beta-\gamma+1, 2-\gamma; z) &= \frac{\Gamma(\gamma-\alpha-\beta)\Gamma(2-\gamma)}{\Gamma(1-\alpha)\Gamma(1-\beta)} F(\alpha, \beta, \alpha+\beta-\gamma+1; 1-z) \\ &+ \frac{\Gamma(\alpha+\beta-\gamma)\Gamma(2-\gamma)}{\Gamma(\alpha-\gamma+1)\Gamma(\beta-\gamma+1)}(1-z)^{\gamma-\alpha-\beta} \\ &\times F(\gamma-\alpha, \gamma-\beta, \gamma-\alpha-\beta+1; 1-z). \end{aligned} \tag{7.1.42}$$

From (7.1.41) we obtain an important result:

$$F(\alpha, \beta, \gamma; 1) = \frac{\Gamma(\gamma-\alpha-\beta)\Gamma(\gamma)}{\Gamma(\gamma-\alpha)\Gamma(\gamma-\beta)} \quad \text{if } \Re(\gamma-\alpha-\beta) > 0. \tag{7.1.43}$$

Our next problem should be to find the transit substitution which expresses the fundamental system at $z = 0$ in terms of that at $z = \infty$. Here we are hampered to start with by the fact that the two domains of definition, $|z| < 1$ and $|z| > 1$, do not overlap. But we have encountered above the solutions w_{03}, w_{05}, w_{07} which all represent w_{01} in the half-plane $\Re(z) < \frac{1}{2}$. If we replace w_{01} and w_{02} by w_{03} and w_{04}, respectively, we obtain a situation to which our method applies. We obtain

$$\begin{aligned} F(\alpha, \beta, \gamma; z) &= (1-z)^{-\alpha}F\left(\alpha, \gamma-\beta, \gamma; \frac{z}{z-1}\right) \\ &= \frac{\Gamma(\beta-\alpha)\Gamma(\gamma)}{\Gamma(\gamma-\alpha)\Gamma(\beta)}(-z)^{-\alpha}F\left(\alpha, \alpha-\gamma+1, \alpha-\beta+1; \frac{1}{z}\right) \\ &+ \frac{\Gamma(\alpha-\beta)\Gamma(\gamma)}{\Gamma(\gamma-\beta)\Gamma(\alpha)}(-z)^{-\beta}F\left(\beta, \beta-\gamma+1, \beta-\alpha+1; \frac{1}{z}\right) \end{aligned} \tag{7.1.44}$$

and

$$(-z)^{1-\gamma}F(\alpha-\gamma+1,\beta-\gamma+1,2-\gamma;z)$$
$$=(-z)^{1-\gamma}(1-z)^{\gamma-\alpha-1}F\left(\alpha-\gamma+1,1-\beta,2-\gamma;\frac{z}{z-1}\right)$$
$$=\frac{\Gamma(\beta-\alpha)\Gamma(2-\gamma)}{\Gamma(1-\alpha)\Gamma(\beta-\gamma+1)}(-z)^{-\alpha}$$
$$\times F\left(\alpha,\alpha-\gamma+1,\alpha-\beta+1;\frac{1}{z}\right)$$
$$+\frac{\Gamma(\alpha-\beta)\Gamma(2-\gamma)}{\Gamma(1-\beta)\Gamma(\alpha-\gamma+1)}(-z)^{-\beta}$$
$$\times F\left(\beta,\beta-\gamma+1,\beta-\alpha+1;\frac{1}{z}\right). \quad (7.1.45)$$

We have replaced powers of z by powers of $-z$ to facilitate the comparison on the negative real axis.

We leave transit substitutions for the time being. Instead we shall take up the representation of hypergeometric functions by definite integrals. We shall be concerned here with a special case of the so-called Euler transformation. Our point of departure is the *Eulerian integral of the first kind*

$$\int_0^1 t^{x-1}(1-t)^{y-1}\,dt=\frac{\Gamma(x)\Gamma(y)}{\Gamma(x+y)},$$

valid for $\Re(x)>0$, $\Re(y)>0$, and the *binomial series*, written

$$(1-zt)^{-a}=\sum_{n=0}^{\infty}\frac{(a)_n}{(1)_n}(zt)^n,$$

valid for $|zt|<1$. Combining these two formulas we get

$$\int_0^1 t^{x-1}(1-t)^{y-1}(1-tz)^{-a}\,dt=\sum_{n=0}^{\infty}\frac{(a)_n\Gamma(x+n)\Gamma(y)}{(1)_n\Gamma(x+y+n)}z^n.$$

Here we have integrated the series termwise. This is permitted for a fixed z with $|z|<1$ since then the series converges uniformly with respect to t in $[0, 1]$. If here we choose

$$x=b,\ y=c-b,$$

we obtain

$$F(a,b,c;z)=\frac{\Gamma(c)}{\Gamma(b)\Gamma(c-b)}\int_0^1 t^{b-1}(1-t)^{c-b-1}(1-zt)^{-a}\,dt, \quad (7.1.46)$$

valid for $\Re(b)>0$, $\Re(c-b)>0$. On the other hand, we can relax the restrictions on z. If the integral is taken along the real axis, all we need is that z is not real and greater than 1. If we cut the z-plane along the positive real axis from $z = 1$ to $z = \infty$, then the integral converges and represents $w_{01}(z)$ in the cut plane. If in addition $\Re(c - b - a) > 0$, we obtain again Eq. (7.1.43) upon letting z approach 1. We can get much more out of integrals of this type.

Setting $t = 1/s$ we get an integral of the form

$$I(\xi, \eta) = \int_\xi^\eta s^{a-c}(s - 1)^{c-b-1}(s - z)^{-a}\, ds. \tag{7.1.47}$$

The kernel $(s - z)^{-a}$ is characteristic of the Euler transform. This transformation is applied to the function $s^{a-c}(s - 1)^{c-b-1}$. The integral is also closely related to the Liouville-Riemann theory of fractional integration, but we shall not explore this angle here. In the case under consideration $\xi = 1$, $\eta = \infty$. These are two of the four branch points of the integrand, the others being 0 and z. It is natural to ask if some other combination of branch points will give a solution of the hypergeometric equation. This is indeed the case; in fact all six possible combinations give solutions. See Figure 7.2 for the paths of integration.

We obtain the following results which are stated without proof.

$$I(1, \infty) = \frac{\Gamma(b)\Gamma(c - b)}{\Gamma(c)} w_{01}(z), \qquad \Re(c - b) > 0,\ \Re(b) > 0,$$

$$I(0, z) = e^{-\pi i(c-b+1)} \frac{\Gamma(a - c + 1)\Gamma(1 - a)}{\Gamma(2 - c)} w_{02}(z),$$
$$\Re(a - c) > -1,\ \Re(a) < 1,$$

$$I(-\infty, 0) = e^{\pi i(a-b+1)} \frac{\Gamma(a - c + 1)\Gamma(b)}{\Gamma(a + b - c + 1)} w_{11}(z),$$
$$\Re(a - c) > -1,\ \Re(b) > 0,$$

$$I(z, 1) = e^{\pi i(c-a-b)} \frac{\Gamma(1 - a)\Gamma(c - b)}{\Gamma(c - a - b + 1)} w_{12}(z), \tag{7.1.48}$$
$$\Re(c - b) > 0,\ \Re(a) < 1,$$

$$I(0, 1) = e^{\pi i(c-b+1)} \frac{\Gamma(a - c + 1)\Gamma(1 - b)}{\Gamma(a - b + 1)} w_{\infty,1}(z),$$
$$\Re(a - c) > -1,\ \Re(c - b) > 0,$$

$$I(z, \infty) = e^{-\pi i a} \frac{\Gamma(1 - a)\Gamma(b)}{\Gamma(b - a + 1)} w_{\infty,2}(z), \qquad \Re(a) < 1,\ \Re(b) > 0.$$

Integration in the complex plane along closed contours gives relations like

$$I(0, 1) + I(1, z) + I(z, 0) = 0, \tag{7.1.49}$$

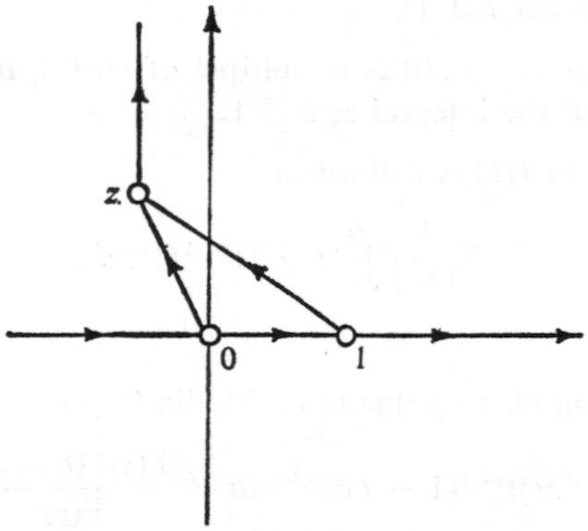

Figure 7.2

which is a linear relation between the three solutions

$$w_{02}(z), \quad w_{1,2}(z), \quad \text{and} \quad w_{\infty,1}(z).$$

There are four such relations corresponding to the four "triangles" formed by the six lines of integration. (See Figure 7.2.) These relations could also be used to compute the transit substitutions.

EXERCISE 7.1

Verify the following relations:

1. $\dfrac{d}{dz} F(a, b, c; z) = \dfrac{ab}{c} F(a + 1, b + 1, c + 1; z)$.
2. $(1 - z)^{-a} = F(a, b, b; z)$.
3. $\arctan z = zF(1, \tfrac{1}{2}, \tfrac{3}{2}; -z^2)$.
4. $\arcsin z = zF(\tfrac{1}{2}, \tfrac{1}{2}, \tfrac{3}{2}; z^2)$.
5. $\lim\limits_{a \to \infty} F\left(a, 1, 1; \dfrac{z}{a}\right) = e^z$.
6. $F(a, b, 1; z^2) = \dfrac{1}{2\pi}\displaystyle\int_0^{2\pi} (1 - ze^{-i\omega})^{-a}(1 - ze^{i\omega})^{-b}\, d\omega$.
7. The elliptic integral $K = \tfrac{1}{2}\pi F(\tfrac{1}{2}, \tfrac{1}{2}, 1; k^2)$.
8. The elliptic integral $K' = \tfrac{1}{2}\pi F(\tfrac{1}{2}, \tfrac{1}{2}, 1; 1 - k^2)$.
9. If $\sum_0^\infty a_n(z - 1)^n$ is a solution of (7.1.1) for $|z - 1| < 1$, find the coefficients by substitution and recurrence.
10. Carry out the transformations that lead to (7.1.14).
11. Same question for (7.1.18).
12. Develop a method to prove that $w_{\infty,8}(z)$ is a solution.
13. Verify (7.1.44).
14. Express $w_{11}(z)$ in terms of $w_{\infty,1}(z)$ and $w_{\infty,2}(z)$.

15. Verify the formula for $I(0, 1)$.

16. If it is known that $I(-\infty, 0)$ is a multiple of $w_{11}(z)$, find the multiplier by finding the limit of the integral as $z \to 1$.

17. If the αth integral of $f(t)$ is defined as

$$\frac{1}{\Gamma(\alpha)} \int_0^z (z - t)^{\alpha - 1} f(t)\, dt,$$

interpret $I(0, z)$.

18. Prove the following identity due to H. Mellin (1896)

$$\int_0^1 F(a, b, s; zt) t^{s-1} (1 - t)^{c-s-1}\, dt = \frac{\Gamma(s)\Gamma(c - s)}{\Gamma(c)} F(a, b, c; z).$$

What happens for $s = a$ or b?

19. Gauss said that two hypergeometric series $F(a, b, c; z)$ and $F(\alpha, \beta, \gamma; z)$ define *contiguous functions* if two of the differences $a - \alpha$, $b - \beta$, $c - \gamma$ are zero while the third is ± 1. He proved relations between such functions. Verify that
$(c - a - 1)F(a, b, c; z) + aF(a + 1, b, c; z) + (1 - c)F(a, b, c - 1; z) = 0.$

20. If $a = \frac{1}{4}$, $b = 1$, $c = \frac{1}{2}$, show that

$$w_{02}(z) = w_{12}(z) = w_{\infty,1}(z)$$

is an algebraic function. Find this function. Are there other algebraic solutions?

21. With the parameters as in the preceding problem form the quotient

$$Q(z) = \frac{w_{02}(z)}{w_{01}(z)}.$$

This function maps the upper half of the z-plane on to the interior of a curvilinear triangle (possibly degenerate) bounded by straight lines and arcs of circles. Describe this triangle, find the sides, the vertices, and the angles.

22. The equation $w^2 + 2w - z = 0$ has a root that goes to zero with z. Express this root as a hypergeometric function.

23. Show that the equation

$$w^3 + 3w - z = 0$$

is satisfied by

$$w = \tfrac{1}{3} z F(\tfrac{1}{3}, \tfrac{2}{3}, \tfrac{3}{2}; -\tfrac{1}{4} z^2), \qquad |z| < 2.$$

24. Where are the singularities of the function $w(z)$ of the preceding problem and what is their nature? Use the hypergeometric transit substitutions to express $w(z)$ in a neighborhood of $z = 2i$.

25. Verify that the hypergeometric equation may be written

$$z(\vartheta + a)(\vartheta + b)w = \vartheta(\vartheta - 1 + c)w, \qquad \vartheta = z \frac{d}{dz}.$$

26. Consider the integral

$$w(z) = \frac{1}{2i}\int \frac{\Gamma(t+a)\Gamma(t+b)\,(-z)^t}{\Gamma(t+1)\Gamma(t+c)\sin \pi t}\,dt$$

taken along the line $\Re(t) = -\frac{1}{2}$, assuming $-a$, $-b$, $-c$ to be to the left of the line. Here $(-z)^t = \exp[t\log(-z)]$ and $|\arg(-z)| < \pi$. Verify that the integral converges and satisfies the hypergeometric equation. Show that the integral equals the sum of the residues of the integrand at the poles to the right of the line of integration and hence is a constant multiple of $w_{01}(z)$.

27. Derive the transit substitution (7.1.44) from the integral in the preceding problem by expressing it as the sum of the residues of the integrand at the poles to the left of the line of integration. [E. W. Barnes, 1908.]

28. Show that $(\sin\theta)^{1-a}$ is a solution of the equation

$$U'' + a\cot\theta \quad U' - (a-1)U = 0$$

and transform the equation into hypergeometric form. Cf. Problem 3, Exercise 7.4.

7.2. LEGENDRE'S EQUATION

This name is given to the equation

$$\frac{d}{dz}\left[(1-z^2)\frac{dw}{dz}\right] + a(a+1)w = 0, \tag{7.2.1}$$

the case where $a = n$, an integer having been considered by A. M. Legendre in 1785. It really is a special case of the hypergeometric equation. In fact, the substitution

$$u = \tfrac{1}{2}(1-z)$$

gives a hypergeometric equation with parameters

$$a+1,\ -a,\ 1.$$

There are three regular singular points $z = 1, -1$, and ∞. The roots of the corresponding indicial equations are

$$0,\ 0;\ 0,\ 0;\ a+1,\ -a,$$

respectively. The holomorphic solution at $z = 1$ is

$$P_a(z) = F(a+1, -a, 1; \tfrac{1}{2}(1-z)). \tag{7.2.2}$$

Using the method which led to formula (7.1.32) we obtain as second solution

$$P_{a,1}(z) = P_a(z)\log\tfrac{1}{2}(1-z) + \sum_{n=1}^{\infty}\frac{(a+1)_n(-a)_n}{(1)_n(1)_n}$$
$$\times \sum_{j=0}^{n-1}\left[\frac{1}{a+1+j} + \frac{1}{-a+j} - \frac{2}{1+j}\right][\tfrac{1}{2}(1-z)]^n. \tag{7.2.3}$$

Since the Eq. (7.2.1) is invariant under the substitution $z = -s$, we see that

$$P_a(-z) \quad \text{and} \quad P_{a,1}(-z) \tag{7.2.4}$$

form a fundamental system at $z = -1$.

At $z = \infty$ a fundamental system is given by

$$Q_a(z) \quad \text{and} \quad Q_{-1-a}(z), \tag{7.2.5}$$

where

$$Q_\alpha(z) = \frac{\Gamma(\frac{1}{2})\Gamma(\alpha+1)}{\Gamma(\alpha+\frac{3}{2})}(2z)^{-1-\alpha}F(\tfrac{1}{2}\alpha+\tfrac{1}{2}, \tfrac{1}{2}\alpha+1, \alpha+\tfrac{3}{2}; z^{-2}). \tag{7.2.6}$$

It is enough to verify that $Q_a(z)$ is a solution since the equation is clearly invariant under the transformation, a goes into $-1 - a$. Note that $P_{-1-a}(z) = P_a(z)$. We leave the verification to the reader.

We exclude the case where $2a$ is an integer.

The problem of finding the transit substitutions presents novel features and the formulas developed in Section 7.1 do not apply to the present case. We can use the method, however, and start with the formula

$$P_a(z) = AP_a(-z) + BP_{a,1}(-z). \tag{7.2.7}$$

For this and subsequent discussion we shall need a couple of further properties of the gamma function. The logarithmic derivative of the gamma function is given by the series

$$\Psi(x) = \frac{\Gamma'(x)}{\Gamma(x)} = -C - \frac{1}{x} - \sum_{n=1}^{\infty}\left[\frac{1}{x+n} - \frac{1}{n}\right]. \tag{7.2.8}$$

This enables us to find the limit of the finite sums occurring in (7.2.3) as $n \to \infty$, namely

$$\lim_{n\to\infty}\sum_{j=0}^{n-1}\left[\frac{1}{a+1+j} + \frac{1}{-a+j} - \frac{2}{j+1}\right]$$
$$= -[\Psi(a+1) + \Psi(-a) + 2C] \equiv -\Delta(a), \tag{7.2.9}$$

where C is Euler's constant. We shall also need the duplication formula for the gamma function

$$\Gamma(2x) = \frac{1}{\sqrt{\pi}}2^{2x-1}\Gamma(x)\Gamma(x+\tfrac{1}{2}). \tag{7.2.10}$$

The functions occurring in (7.2.7) are defined on the line segment $(-1, 1)$ and we shall get the values for A and B by letting z tend to the end-points of this interval. If $z = 1 - r$, $r > 0$, we have

$$P_a(1 - r) = 1 + O(r),$$

$$P_a(-1 + r) = -\frac{1}{\pi}\sin \pi a \sum_{n=0}^{\infty} \frac{\Gamma(a + 1 + n)\Gamma(-a + n)}{[\Gamma(n + 1)]^2}(1 - \tfrac{1}{2}r)^n$$

$$= -\frac{1}{\pi}\sin \pi a \sum_{n=1}^{\infty} \frac{1}{n}(1 - \tfrac{1}{2}r)^n + O(1)$$

$$= \frac{1}{\pi}\sin \pi a \log r + O(1),$$

$$P_{a,1}(-1 + r) = O(r \log r) - \frac{1}{\pi}\sin \pi a\, \Delta(a) \log r + O(1).$$

Comparing coefficients of $\log r$ we see that

$$A - B\,\Delta(a) = 0.$$

On the other hand, if $z = -1 + r$, then

$$P_a(z) = \frac{1}{\pi}\sin \pi a \log r + O(1),$$

$$P_a(-z) = 1 + O(r),$$

$$P_{a,1}(-z) = \log r + O(1) + O(r).$$

Hence we have

$$B = \frac{1}{\pi}\sin \pi a,$$

$$A = \frac{1}{\pi}\sin \pi a\, \Delta(a).$$

Thus we have proved that

$$P_a(z) = \frac{1}{\pi}\sin \pi a\{[\Psi(a + 1) + \Psi(-a) + 2C]P_a(-z) + P_{a,1}(-z)\}. \quad (7.2.11)$$

We have assumed that $2a$ is not an integer. It is clear that the derivation is valid also when a is half of an odd integer. If a is an integer, the formula evidently breaks down, but if we let $a \to n$, a positive integer, then

$$\lim_{a\to n} A(a) = (-1)^n, \qquad \lim_{a \to n} B(a) = 0,$$

and we obtain correctly,

$$P_n(z) = (-1)^n P_n(-z). \quad (7.2.12)$$

In this case $P_a(z)$ reduces to the nth Legendre polynomial, the parity of which is the same as that of n.

Similarly one proves

$$P_{a,1}(z) = \left[\pi \operatorname{cosec} \pi a - \frac{1}{\pi} \sin \pi a \, \Delta^2(a)\right] P_a(-z)$$
$$- \frac{1}{\pi} \sin \pi a \, \Delta(a) P_{a,1}(-z). \tag{7.2.13}$$

We get more elegant formulas for the transit from $z = 1$ to $z = \infty$. Here we note first that for $\Re(z) > 0$

$$P_a(z) = [\tfrac{1}{2}(1 + z)]^{-1-a} F\left(a + 1, a + 1, 1; \frac{z - 1}{z + 1}\right), \tag{7.2.14}$$

this being the analogue of $w_{03}(z)$ of formula (7.1.18). We set

$$P_a(z) = C Q_a(z) + D Q_{-1-a}(z). \tag{7.2.15}$$

In the present case it is enough to make the comparison at infinity. We may assume $\Re(a) > -\frac{1}{2}$. This makes $Q_{-1-a}(z)$ the dominating term in the right member of (7.2.15) and we have

$$Q_{-1-a}(r) = \frac{\Gamma(\frac{1}{2})\Gamma(-a)}{\Gamma(-\frac{1}{2} + a)} (2r)^a [1 + o(1)], \qquad r \to +\infty.$$

On the other hand, (7.2.14) shows that

$$P_a(r) = \left(\frac{2}{r + 1}\right)^{1+a} [\Gamma(a + 1)]^{-2} \sum_{n=1}^{\infty} [n^{2a} + O(n^{2a-1})]\left(1 - \frac{2}{r + 1}\right)^n$$
$$= \left(\frac{2}{r + 1}\right)^{1+a} \frac{\Gamma(2a + 1)}{[\Gamma(a + 1)]^2} \left(\frac{2}{r + 1}\right)^{-1-2a} [1 + o(1)]$$
$$= \frac{\Gamma(a + \frac{1}{2})}{\Gamma(\frac{1}{2})\Gamma(a + 1)} (2r)^a [1 + o(1)].$$

Thus for the leading terms to balance it is necessary that

$$\frac{\Gamma(a + \frac{1}{2})}{\Gamma(\frac{1}{2})\Gamma(a + 1)} = D \frac{\Gamma(\frac{1}{2})\Gamma(-a)}{\Gamma(-a + \frac{1}{2})},$$

so that

$$D = -\frac{1}{\pi} \tan \pi a.$$

Here we have used the formula for $\Gamma(x)\Gamma(1 - x)$ twice. In order to get the expression for C we note that the left member of (7.2.15) is unchanged if we replace a by $-1 - a$. Hence the right member must have the same property and this gives $C = -D$. Thus we have proved

$$P_a(z) = \frac{1}{\pi} \tan \pi a \, [Q_a(z) - Q_{-1-a}(z)]. \tag{7.2.16}$$

Here the assumption that $2a$ is not an integer becomes significant. If $a \to n$, a positive integer, the formula gives the trivial identity

$$P_n(z) = P_n(z).$$

This is trivial, but it is also the correct form of the transit substitution since $P_n(z)$ and $Q_n(z)$ form a fundamental system at $z = \infty$.

The most important case for the applications is that where $a = n$, a positive integer. Here

$$P_n(z) = F(n + 1, -n, 1, \tfrac{1}{2}(1 - z))$$

is clearly a polynomial in z of degree n. These Legendre polynomials have a large number of interesting properties some of which will be listed below or in Exercise 7.2.

We start with

$$P_n(z) = \frac{1}{2^n n!} \frac{d^n}{dz^n} (z^2 - 1)^n. \tag{7.2.17}$$

The formula is easily verified if we note that

$$(z^2 - 1)^n = (z - 1)^n[(z - 1) + 2]^n.$$

Expanding this in powers of $(z - 1)$ and differentiating n times, with respect to z, we obtain the desired result.

We note that $(z^2 - 1)^n$ has n-fold zeros at $z = 1$ and at $z = -1$. Hence, by Rolle's theorem, $P_n(z)$ has n zeros in the interval $(-1, 1)$, i.e. all its zeros are real and lie in $(-1, 1)$.

The polynomials $\{P_n(t)\}$ form an *orthogonal system* for the interval $(-1, 1)$. More precisely we have

$$\int_1^1 P_m(t)P_n(t)\, dt = \delta_{mn} \frac{2}{2m + 1}\cdot \tag{7.2.18}$$

To prove this we use (7.2.17). Suppose $m \leq n$. The integral equals

$$[2^{m+n} m! n!]^{-1} \int_{-1}^{1} \frac{d^m}{dt^m} (t^2 - 1)^m \frac{d^n}{dt^n} (t^2 - 1)^n \, dt.$$

Here we integrate m times by parts, integrating the second factor and differentiating the first. The successive integrated parts vanish in the limits and we are left with

$$(-1)^m [2^{m+n} m! n!]^{-1} \int_{-1}^{1} \frac{d^{2m}}{dt^{2m}} (t^2 - 1)^m \frac{d^{n-m}}{dt^{n-m}} (t^2 - 1)^n \, dt$$

$$= (-1)^m \frac{(2m)!}{2^{m+n} m! n!} \int_{-1}^{1} \frac{d^{n-m}}{dt^{n-m}} (t^2 - 1)^n \, dt.$$

This is 0 if $m < n$. If $m = n$, we get

$$\frac{(2m)!}{[m!]^2} 2^{-2m} \int_{-1}^{1} (1 - t^2)^m \, dt = \frac{2}{2m + 1}$$

as asserted.

Using the same technique we obtain

$$\int_{-1}^{1} P_n(t) t^{n+2k} \, dt = \frac{\Gamma(\frac{1}{2}n + \frac{1}{2} + k)\Gamma(\frac{1}{2}n + 1 + k)}{\Gamma(k + 1)\Gamma(n + \frac{3}{2} + k)}. \tag{7.2.19}$$

This will be used later.

We know that

$$P_n(t) = \sum_{2j \le n} p_{n,j} t^{n-2j}.$$

Conversely we have

$$t^n = \sum_{2j \le n} q_{n,j} P_{n-2j}(t). \tag{7.2.20}$$

The actual values of the coefficients $q_{n,j}$ could be found with the aid of (7.2.18) and (7.2.19). We need the existence of such a formula rather than the precise formula.

Going back to formula (7.2.18), we see that it states that the root mean square average of $P_n(t)$ is $(2n + 1)^{-1/2}$. Actually this is the order of magnitude of $|P_n(t)|$ in most of the interval $(-1, 1)$ and we have

$$|P_n(t)| < 1 \quad \text{for} \quad -1 < t < 1. \tag{7.2.21}$$

To prove this inequality we shall anticipate methods which will be developed more fully in the next chapter. Let $y(t)$ be a solution of

$$(1 - t^2)y''(t) - 2ty'(t) + a(a + 1)y(t) = 0,$$

where $a > 0$, and form the function

$$F(t) = (1 - t^2)[y'(t)]^2 + a(a + 1)[y(t)]^2. \tag{7.2.22}$$

In view of the differential equation,

$$F'(t) = 2t[y'(t)]^2,$$

which is positive or 0 for $0 \le t < 1$. Suppose that

$$y(t) = P_a(t).$$

Then

$$F(t) < F(1) = a(a + 1), \qquad 0 \le t < 1$$

and *a fortiori*

$$|P_a(t)| < 1 \quad \text{for} \quad 0 \le t < 1. \tag{7.2.23}$$

If $a = n$, the parity of $P_n(t)$ as function of t implies the desired relation (7.2.21).

An orthogonal system gives rise to series expansions of the Fourier type. If $f(t) \in L(-1, 1)$, the integrals

$$f_n = (n + \tfrac{1}{2}) \int_{-1}^{1} f(t) P_n(t) \, dt \tag{7.2.24}$$

exist since $P_n(t)$ is continuous and uniformly bounded. They are known as the (Fourier-) Legendre coefficients of $f(t)$ and the formal series

$$\sum_{n=0}^{\infty} f_n P_n(t) \tag{7.2.25}$$

is the (Fourier-) Legendre series of $f(t)$. If f is restricted to belong to $L_2(-1, 1)$, we have Bessel's inequality

$$\sum_{n=0}^{\infty} \frac{|f_n|^2}{n + \frac{1}{2}} \le \int_{-1}^{1} |f(t)|^2 \, dt. \tag{7.2.26}$$

For the derivation, see Problem 19, Exercise 7.2.

Actually we have equality in this relation for all $f \in L_2$. This expresses that $\{P_n(t)\}$ is a *complete orthogonal system* in $L_2(-1, 1)$. In fact, we have the following result which we state for general orthonormal systems for future reference.

Theorem 7.2.1. *Given an orthonormal system $\{\omega_n(t)\}$ for the interval (a, b). The following conditions are equivalent:*

i) *If $f_n = \int_a^b f(s)\overline{\omega_n(s)} \, ds = 0$ for all n and if $f \in L_2(a, b)$, then $f(t) = 0$ for almost all t.*

ii) *Every $f \in L_2(a, b)$ can be approximated arbitrarily closely in the sense of the L_2-norm by finite linear combinations of the ω_k's.*

$$\text{iii)} \int_a^b |f(t)|^2 \, dt = \sum_{n=0}^{\infty} |f_n|^2, \qquad f_n = \int_a^b f(s)\overline{\omega_n(s)} \, ds,$$

for every $f \in L_2(a, b)$.

Proof. (iii) $\Rightarrow$ (ii). Since

$$\int_a^b \left| f(t) - \sum_{k=0}^{n} f_k \omega_k(t) \right|^2 dt = \int_a^b |f(t)|^2 \, dt - \sum_{k=0}^{n} |f_k|^2 \tag{7.2.27}$$

the partial sums of the Fourier series of f converge to f in the metric of L_2 provided (iii) holds. Since the partial sums are finite linear combinations of the ω_j's we see that (ii) holds.

(ii) $\Rightarrow$ (i). Suppose that (ii) holds for a given $f \in L_2$ with $f_n = 0$ for all n. Suppose that

$$\left\| f - \sum_0^n \alpha_j \omega_j \right\| < \varepsilon.$$

Then

$$\|f\|^2 - \sum_{j=0}^n \bar{\alpha}_j \int_a^b f(s)\overline{\omega_j(s)}\, ds - \sum_{j=0}^n \alpha_j \int_a^b \overline{f(s)}\omega_j(s)\, ds + \sum_0^n |\alpha_j|^2 < \varepsilon^2$$

and

$$\|f\|^2 + \sum_0^n |\alpha_j|^2 < \varepsilon^2.$$

Since ε is arbitrary, we must have $\|f\| = 0$ and $f \sim 0$, i.e. (i) holds.

(i) $\Rightarrow$ (iii). Suppose (i) holds, and let f be any element of L_2 and

$$\sum_0^\infty f_n \omega_n,$$

its Fourier series. The partial sums of this series converge in the sense of the metric and, L_2 being a complete metric space, the limit is an element g of the space. Now $h = f - g$ has all its Fourier coefficients equal to 0. Hence $\|h\| = 0$, i.e. the left member of (7.2.27) converges to 0 and this implies that (iii) holds. ∎

The functions $\{P_n(t)\}$ form an orthogonal system but are not orthonormal. We can set

$$\omega_n(t) = (n + \tfrac{1}{2})^{1/2} P_n(t) \tag{7.2.28}$$

and obtain an orthonormal system. We can now prove

Theorem 7.2.2. *The system $\{P_n(t)\}$ is complete in $L_2(a, b)$.*

Proof. In order to avoid misunderstanding, let us denote the Fourier coefficients of f with respect to the system (7.2.28) by f_n^*. To prove completeness it is enough to verify that (i) holds.

Suppose that $f \in L_2(-1, 1)$ and that $f_n^* = 0$ for all n. This shows that

$$\int_{-1}^1 f(t) P_n(t)\, dt = 0$$

for all n and by (7.2.20) this implies

$$\int_{-1}^1 f(t) t^k\, dt = 0$$

for all k or, equivalently,

$$\int_{-1}^1 f(t)(t-1)^k\, dt = 0$$

for all k. But if

$$F(t) = \int_{-1}^{t} f(s)\, ds,$$

then for $k > 0$

$$\int_{-1}^{1} f(t)(t-1)^k\, dt = [F(t)(t-1)^k]_{-1}^{1} - k\int_{-1}^{1} F(t)(t-1)^{k-1}\, dt$$

$$= -k\int_{-1}^{1} F(t)(t-1)^{k-1}\, dt = 0.$$

But $F(t) \in C[-1, 1]$ and by the *approximation theorem of Weierstrass* a continuous function cannot be orthogonal to all polynomials without being identically zero. Hence $F(t) \equiv 0$ and so is its derivative, i.e. $f \sim 0$ and (i) holds. Thus the system $\{P_n(t)\}$ is complete in $L_2(-1, 1)$ and this implies

$$\int_{-1}^{1} |f(t)|^2\, dt = \sum_{n=0}^{\infty} |f_n^*|^2 = 2\sum_{n=0}^{\infty} \frac{|f_n|^2}{2n+1} \tag{7.2.29}$$

as asserted above. This is known as *Parseval's formula* or the *closure relation.* ▮

In the applications Legendre's equation arises, in particular, in connection with the Newtonian potential of a sphere. We speak of $P_a(z)$ and $Q_a(z)$ as *Legendre functions of the first and second kind*, respectively, but also as *spherical harmonics*, sometimes *zonal harmonics* (German: *Kugelfunktionen*). The functions with parameter $a = -\frac{1}{2} + i\mu$ are known as *conical harmonics* (German: *Kegelfunktionen*) since they are connected with the potential theory of a cone.

The potential theory of the sphere leads to the expansion

$$G(z, w) \equiv (1 - 2zw + w^2)^{-1/2} = \sum_{n=0}^{\infty} P_n(z) w^n. \tag{7.2.30}$$

In the physical problems, $z = t$ and $w = r$ are real, $-1 \leq t \leq 1, 0 < r < 1$, but (7.2.30) is an identity between analytic functions and is valid as long as the series is convergent. Here the square root is given the value $+1$ for $z = w = 0$. For fixed z the function $G(z, w)$ has two branch points

$$w_1 = z + (z^2 - 1)^{1/2}, \qquad w_2 = z - (z^2 - 1)^{1/2}$$

and the series converges for

$$|w| < \min(|w|_1, |w_2|).$$

To prove (7.2.30) we note that for $w \neq 1$

$$G(z, w) = (1 - w)^{-1}\left[1 + 2\frac{(1-z)w}{(1-w)^2}\right]^{-1/2}.$$

Repeated use of the binomial series leads to the expansion

$$G(z, w) = \sum_{j=0}^{\infty} \sum_{k=0}^{\infty} (-1)^k \binom{-\frac{1}{2}}{j} \binom{-2j-1}{k} 2^j (1-z)^j w^{j+k}$$

$$= \sum_{n=0}^{\infty} w^n \left[\sum_{j+k=n} (-1)^k 2^j \binom{-\frac{1}{2}}{j} \binom{-2j-1}{k} (1-z)^j \right].$$

Here the coefficient of w^n is clearly a polynomial in $(1 - z)$ of degree n, and, evaluating the binomial coefficients, we find that the polynomial is

$$F(n + 1, -n, 1; \tfrac{1}{2}(1 - z)) = P_n(z)$$

in agreement with (7.2.30). The expansions and rearrangements used in proving these results are clearly legitimate for sufficiently small values of $1 - z$ and w. By analytic continuation the identity then holds when both sides make sense.

$G(z, w)$ is known as the *generating function* of the Legendre polynomials. Some analytical applications of this function will be given in Exercise 7.2.

The last topic of this section centers around the formula of F. Neumann (1848)

$$Q_n(z) = \frac{1}{2} \int_{-1}^{1} \frac{P_n(t)}{z - t}\, dt, \tag{7.2.31}$$

valid for all z not on the line segment $[-1, 1]$. To prove this we note that for $|t| < |z|$

$$\frac{1}{z - t} = \sum_{n=0}^{\infty} \frac{t^n}{z^{n+1}}.$$

After multiplication by $P_n(t)$ the resulting series converges absolutely and uniformly in t for $-1 \le t \le 1$, $|z| > 1$, and may be integrated with respect to t over $[-1, 1]$ termwise. For $m < n$ the integrals are 0 and so is the case if m is of opposite parity to n. The remaining integrals are obtainable from (7.2.19) and a comparison with (7.2.6) shows that the result equals $Q_n(z)$.

This shows that $(2n + 1)Q_n(z)$ is the nth Fourier-Legendre coefficient of $(z - t)^{-1}$. This kernel *qua* function of t belongs to $L_2(-1, 1)$ for z fixed not in $[-1, 1]$. Hence we have the expansion

$$\frac{1}{z - t} = \sum_{n=0}^{\infty} (2n + 1) P_n(t) Q_n(z) \tag{7.2.32}$$

at least in the sense of mean square convergence, i.e. convergence in $L_2(-1, 1)$. Actually the series converges so rapidly that it represents $(z - t)^{-1}$ not merely for $-1 \le t \le 1$ but also for some complex values of t. More precisely, let E be any ellipse in the complex plane with foci at ± 1. Then (7.2.32) is valid, the series being absolutely convergent for any t inside E and any z outside of E. We shall not prove this here.

EXERCISE 7.2

1. Determine the coefficients $q_{n,j}$ in (7.2.20).
2. Show that

$$P_{2n}(0) = (-1)^n \frac{(2n-1)!!}{(2n)!!}$$

where $m!!$ is the product of the positive integers $\leq m$ of the same parity as m. What is $P'_{2n}(0)$?

3. Prove that

$$\lim_{n\to\infty} (\pi n)^{1/2}|P_{2n}(0)| = 1.$$

4. Prove that $P_n(z)$ as a function of n satisfies the linear second order difference equation

$$(n+1)P_{n+1}(z) - (2n+1)zP_n(z) + nP_{n-1}(z) = 0,$$

e.g. by comparing coefficients of powers of w in the identity

$$(1 - 2zw + w^2)G'_w(z, w) = (z - w)G(z, w).$$

The equation, but not the proof, holds for arbitrary real or complex values of n.

5. Show that

$$\int_{-1}^{1} (1 - t^2)[P'_n(t)]^2\, dt = 2\,\frac{n(n+1)}{2n+1}.$$

6. Let the z-plane be cut along the real axis from $z = -1$ to $z = +1$ and set

$$\xi = z + (z^2 - 1)^{1/2}$$

where the square root is real positive when z is real and >1. Show that the curve $|\xi| = r > 1$ is the ellipse passing through the point z and having its foci at ± 1. Show that

$$\limsup_{n\to\infty} |P_n(z)|^{1/n} = |\xi|.$$

7. Show that for $|w| > |\xi|$, we have $G(z, w) = \sum_{n=0}^{\infty} P_n(z)w^{-n-1}$.
8. Show that

$$P_n(z) = \frac{1}{2\pi i}\int_C G(z, w)w^n\, dw$$

where C: $|w| = r > |\xi|$.

9. If $z \to t = \cos\theta$, $0 < \theta < \pi$, from the upper half-plane, $\xi \to e^{i\theta}$. The function $G(t, w)$ is now single-valued in the w-plane cut along the arc of the unit circle from $e^{-i\theta}$ via 1 to $e^{i\theta}$. Show that the path of integration in the preceding problem can be deformed into a closed contour surrounding the cut and use this to obtain the integral

$$P_n(\cos\theta) = \frac{1}{\pi}\sqrt{2}\int_0^{\theta} (\cos\beta - \cos\theta)^{-1/2} \cos(n + \tfrac{1}{2})\beta\, d\beta.$$

This is known as the *Dirichlet–Mehler integral*.

10. What differential equation is satisfied by $P_n(\cos\theta)$ as a function of θ?

11. Show that

$$Q_0(z) = \tfrac{1}{2}\log\frac{z+1}{z-1}, \qquad Q_1(z) = \tfrac{1}{2}z\log\frac{z+1}{z-1} - 1.$$

12. If $-1 < t < 1$, show that

$$\lim_{n\ 0}\,[Q_n(t+i\eta) - Q_n(t-i\eta)] = -\pi i P_n(t).$$

13. Verify that the derivatives of $Q_n(z)$ are obtainable by formal differentiation under the sign of integration in (7.2.31).

14. Show that $n(n+1)(2n+1)Q_n(z)$ are the Fourier-Legendre coefficients of a function in $L_2(-1, 1)$. Use the fact that $Q_n(z)$ satisfies the differential equation plus the information obtainable from the preceding problem. Use this together with the Schwarz inequality to prove that the series in (7.2.32) converges absolutely and uniformly to $(z-t)^{-1}$, $-1 \le t \le 1$.

15. If $f(t) \in L(-1, 1)$ and its Legendre coefficients are $\{f_n\}$ and if z is not on the line segment $[-1, 1]$, prove that

$$\frac{1}{2}\int_{-1}^{1}\frac{f(t)}{z-t}\,dt = \sum_{n=0}^{\infty} f_n Q_n(z),$$

the series being absolutely convergent.

16. Suppose that $F(w)$ is holomorphic in the interior of an ellipse E with foci at ± 1. Assume the validity of the "ellipse theorem" for the convergence of (7.2.32) and show that

$$F(w) = \sum_{n=0}^{\infty} a_n P_n(w), \qquad a_n = \frac{2n+1}{2\pi i}\int_{E_0} F(\omega)Q_n(\omega)\,d\omega$$

and E_0 is any ellipse interior to and confocal with E. Show that this series must coincide with the Fourier-Legendre series of F, which function is clearly in $L_2(-1, 1)$.

17. If $a = -\frac{1}{2} + \mu i$, $\mu > 0$, show that $P_a(t)$ is real for $t > -1$ and positive on $[-1, 1]$.

18. Suppose that a is real, $a > -\frac{1}{2}$ and not an integer, and let the z-plane be cut along the real axis from $-\infty$ to -1. If $z = z + iy$, $x < -1$, $y > 0$, and y decreases to 0, show that the imaginary part of the limit of $P_a(z)$ is $\neq 0$ and find its sign which is a function of a.

19. Find the minimum value of

$$\int_{-1}^{1}\left| f(t) - \sum_{k=0}^{n} c_k P_k(t)\right|^2 dt,$$

if $f(t)$ is a fixed element of $L_2(-1, 1)$ and $c_0, c_1, \ldots, c_n$ range independently of each other over all complex numbers. Use the result to prove (7.2.26).

20. In the notation of (7.2.9), prove that

$$\int_{-1}^{1} P_a(t)P_b(t)\,dt = \frac{2}{\pi^2}\sin \pi a \sin \pi b\,\frac{\Delta(a) - \Delta(b)}{(a - b)(a + b + 1)},$$

where $b \neq a$, $b \neq -a - 1$ and neither a nor b is an integer.

21. Show the existence of a system of Legendre functions $\{P_{a_n}(t)\}$ orthogonal to each other and to $P_{-1/2}(t)$ over the interval $(-1, 1)$.

7.3. BESSEL'S EQUATION

In 1824 the German astronomer, F. W. Bessel, made a study of the perturbations of the planets in which he developed at some length the theory of the solutions of the differential equation

$$z^2w'' + zw' + (z^2 - a^2)w = 0, \tag{7.3.1}$$

assuming the parameter a to be an integer or 0. O. Schlömilch (1857) and R. Lipschitz (1859) proposed to name these functions after Bessel. Special instances of Bessel functions were known much earlier, however. Among the earlier writers on this theme could be mentioned Jakob Bernoulli (1703), his nephew Daniel B. (1732), L. Euler (1764), J. L. Lagrange (1769), and J. Fourier (1822). These authors were led to Bessel functions in investigations devoted to such varied topics as oscillations of heavy chains, oscillations of circular membranes, elliptic motion, and heat conduction in cylinders.

The literature on Bessel's equation has grown enormously. While the earliest monograph, that of Carl Neumann of 1867, quoted only nine papers, the monumental tome of G. N. Watson of 1962 has thirty-six pages of bibliography!

The equation (7.3.1) has a regular singular point at $z = 0$, the roots of the indicial equation being a and $-a$. The point at infinity is an irregular singular point of rank 1.

If a is not an integer or 0, the functions $J_a(z)$ and $J_{-a}(z)$ form a fundamental system. They are known as *Bessel functions of the first kind of order a and $-a$*, respectively. Here

$$J_a(z) = \sum_{k=0}^{\infty} \frac{(-1)^k}{k!\,\Gamma(a + k + 1)}\left(\frac{z}{2}\right)^{2k+a}, \tag{7.3.2}$$

and the series converges for $0 < |z| < \infty$. The choice of the coefficient of z^a is traditional and simplifies the many relations satisfied by these functions.

The roots of the indicial equation differ by an integer if $2a$ is an integer. The general theory tells us that in this case the two canonical solutions may be expected to become linearly dependent and a second solution has to be found which will involve a logarithmic term. This does not happen, however, if $a = n + \frac{1}{2}$, half an odd integer. A simple calculation shows that

$$J_{1/2}(z) = \left(\frac{2}{\pi z}\right)^{1/2} \sin z, \qquad J_{-1/2}(z) = \left(\frac{2}{\pi z}\right)^{1/2} \cos z. \tag{7.3.3}$$

It may be shown that

$$J_{n+1/2}(z) = (-1)^n \left(\frac{2}{\pi}\right)^{1/2} z^{n+1/2} \theta^n \left\{\frac{\sin z}{z}\right\}, \tag{7.3.4}$$

where θ is the differential operator

$$\theta = \frac{1}{z}\frac{d}{dz}. \tag{7.3.5}$$

It follows that

$$J_{n+1/2}(z) = A_n(z) \cos z + B_n(z) \sin z, \tag{7.3.6}$$

where A_n and B_n are polynomials in $z^{-1/2}$. Here formula (7.3.4) is a consequence of (7.3.3) and formula (7.3.13).

Thus the case $a = n + \frac{1}{2}$ leads to no complications. If $a = n$, a positive integer or 0, we have a different situation. Here $J_n(z)$ is a solution but

$$J_{-n}(z) = (-1)^n J_n(z),$$

so a linearly independent second solution must be found. Several different *Bessel functions of the second kind* are to be found in the literature. They differ only by constant multiples of $J_n(z)$ but different physical problems lead to different preferred normalizations.

For a not an integer or 0 we define

$$Y_a(z) = \pi \operatorname{cosec} \pi a \, [J_a(z) \cos \pi a - J_{-a}(z)] \tag{7.3.7}$$

which is obviously a solution of (7.3.1). Here we let $a \to n$. A limit exists which is denoted by $Y_n(z)$ and is the required second solution. This gives

$$Y_n(z) = -\sum_{k=0}^{n-1} \frac{(n-k-1)!}{k!} (\tfrac{1}{2}z)^{-n+2k} + \sum_{k=0}^{\infty} \frac{(-1)^k}{k!(n+k)!} (\tfrac{1}{2}z)^{n+2k} \left\{2 \log (\tfrac{1}{2}z) + 2C - \sum_{1}^{n+k} \frac{1}{m} - \sum_{1}^{k} \frac{1}{m}\right\}, \tag{7.3.8}$$

where C is Euler's constant. We take this as the *canonical form of Bessel's function of the second kind of order n*. We shall also encounter Bessel functions of the third kind later.

The function $J_a(z)$ satisfies a number of functional equations with respect to z or a or both. We note the difference equation

$$zJ_{a+1}(z) - 2aJ_a(z) + zJ_{a-1}(z) = 0 \tag{7.3.9}$$

and the partial difference–differential equation

$$zJ_a'(z) = aJ_a(z) - zJ_{a-1}(z) \tag{7.3.10}$$

which imply

$$J_a'(z) = \tfrac{1}{2}[J_{a-1}(z) - J_{a+1}(z)], \tag{7.3.11}$$

$$J_a'(z) = J_{a-1}(z) - \frac{a}{z} J_a(z). \tag{7.3.12}$$

We can rewrite (7.3.10) as

$$z^{-a-1}J_{a+1}(z) = -\theta[z^{-a}J_a(z)],$$

where θ is the differential operator (7.3.5). By iteration we obtain

$$z^{-a-p}J_{a+p}(z) = (-1)^p\theta^p[z^{-a}J_a(z)] \tag{7.3.13}$$

of which (7.3.4) is a special case.

The basic relations (4.3.9) and (4.3.10) can be obtained from the definition of $J_a(z)$ by comparing coefficients of powers of z on each side of the equation under consideration.

If in (7.3.1) we set $z = iy$, we obtain

$$y^2 \frac{d^2w}{dy^2} + y\frac{dw}{dy} - (y^2 + a^2)w = 0. \tag{7.3.14}$$

If a is real, the coefficients of this equation are real and it has real solutions. Two such solutions are $I_a(y)$ and $I_{-a}(y)$, where

$$I_a(y) = \sum_{k=0}^{\infty} \frac{1}{k!\Gamma(a+k+1)} (\tfrac{1}{2}y)^{a+2k}. \tag{7.3.15}$$

This function differs from $J_a(iy)$ by a factor $\exp(\frac{1}{2}\pi ai)$. It is real positive if $y > 0$ and $a > 0$ and grows exponentially with y. The functions $I_a(y)$ and $I_{-a}(y)$ form a fundamental system of solutions of (7.3.14) unless a is an integer or 0. In the latter case $I_n(y) = I_{-n}(y)$ and a second solution can be found by a suitable modification of $Y_n(iz)$.

Fractional values of a arise in some applications, besides $a = n + \frac{1}{2}$ the case $a = \pm\frac{1}{3}$ is important, but integral values of a are most frequently encountered. The system $\{J_n(z)\}$ has a simple generating function

$$\exp\{\tfrac{1}{2}z(t - t^{-1})\} = \sum_{n=-\infty}^{\infty} J_n(z)t^n. \tag{7.3.16}$$

This relation is proved as follows. We have

$$\begin{aligned}\exp\{\tfrac{1}{2}z(t - t^{-1})\} &= \exp(\tfrac{1}{2}zt)\exp(-\tfrac{1}{2}zt^{-1}) \\ &= \sum_{j=0}^{\infty} \frac{1}{j!}(\tfrac{1}{2}z)^j t^j \cdot \sum_{k=0}^{\infty} \frac{(-1)^k}{k!}(\tfrac{1}{2}z)^k t^{-k} \\ &= \sum_{j=0}^{\infty}\sum_{k=0}^{\infty} \frac{(-1)^k}{j!k!}(\tfrac{1}{2}z)^{j+k}t^{j-k}.\end{aligned}$$

Here the double series is absolutely convergent and may be summed by diagonals, i.e. by first summing over the integers j and k for which $j - k = n$, a fixed integer, and then summing for n. If $n \geq 0$ the coefficient of t^n is

$$\sum_{k=0}^{\infty} \frac{(-1)^k}{k!(n+k)!} (\tfrac{1}{2}z)^{n+2k} = J_n(z)$$

and if $n = -m < 0$

$$(-1)^m \sum_{j=0}^{\infty} \frac{(-1)^j}{j!(m+j)!} (\tfrac{1}{2}z)^{m+2j} = (-1)^m J_m(z) = J_n(z).$$

The desired result follows.

From this expansion, due to Schlömilch, follows a number of interesting relations and inequalities. We set

$$z = iy, \qquad t = -i$$

and obtain the identity

$$e^y = I_0(y) + 2 \sum_{n=1}^{\infty} I_n(y). \tag{7.3.17}$$

The series is convergent for all y. For $y > 0$ all terms are positive, whence it follows that

$$I_0(y) \leq e^y, \quad I_n(y) < \tfrac{1}{2}e^y, \qquad 0 < n. \tag{7.3.18}$$

For $y \leq 0$ we replace y by $|y|$ in these inequalities.

Another interesting relation is found by setting

$$t = e^{i\theta}.$$

This gives

$$e^{iz \sin \theta} = \sum_{-\infty}^{\infty} J_n(z) e^{ni\theta}, \tag{7.3.19}$$

convergent for all z and θ. By the definition of the Fourier coefficients we have

$$J_n(z) = \frac{1}{2\pi} \int_{-\pi}^{\pi} \exp\,[i(z \sin \theta - n\theta)]\, d\theta, \tag{7.3.20}$$

or, in formally real form,

$$J_n(z) = \frac{1}{\pi} \int_0^{\pi} \cos\,(z \sin \theta - n\theta)\, d\theta. \tag{7.3.21}$$

Incidentally, the latter formula was Bessel's original definition of $J_n(z)$. If $z = x > 0$, we see that

$$|J_n(x)| \leq 1, \qquad \forall n, \ \forall x. \tag{7.3.22}$$

The function in the left member of (7.3.19) belongs to $L_2(-\pi, \pi)$ as function of θ and with $z = x + iy$

$$\int_{-\pi}^{\pi} |e^{iz \sin \theta}|^2 \, d\theta = \int_{-\pi}^{\pi} e^{-2y \sin \theta} \, d\theta = 2\pi J_0(2iy) = 2\pi I_0(2y).$$

Applying the closure relation for the orthogonal system $\{e^{ni\theta}\}$ to the function under consideration, we get

$$I_0(2y) = \sum_{-\infty}^{\infty} |J_n(x + iy)|^2. \tag{7.3.23}$$

Since

$$I_0(2y) < e^{2|y|},$$

we see that

$$|J_0(x + iy)| \leq e^{|y|}, \quad |J_n(x + iy)| \leq \frac{1}{\sqrt{2}} e^{|y|}, \qquad 0 < n, \tag{7.3.24}$$

for all x.

These simple inequalities give a fairly good idea of the behavior of $J_n(z)$. They will be supplemented by asymptotic relations later. We note that (7.3.23) implies the curious identity

$$[J_0(z)]^2 + 2 \sum_{n=1}^{\infty} [J_n(z)]^2 \equiv 1. \tag{7.3.25}$$

For this is true when z is real as we see by setting $y = 0$ in (7.3.23). Now the series in the left member is an absolutely convergent series of holomorphic functions which converges uniformly with respect to z in any bounded domain. Hence the sum is holomorphic in the finite plane. A holomorphic function that is 1 on the real axis is identically 1 as asserted.

We attach one more remark to formula (7.3.16). For fixed z the series converges for all finite values of t, $t \neq 0$. This implies

$$\lim_{n \to \infty} |J_n(z)|^{1/n} = 0, \qquad \forall z. \tag{7.3.26}$$

We could use Stirling's formula to get more precise information.

We have encountered two integral representations for $J_n(z)$. Of the large number of such representations for $J_a(z)$, the following is perhaps the most important:

$$J_a(z) = \frac{1}{\Gamma(\frac{1}{2})\Gamma(a + \frac{1}{2})} \left(\frac{z}{2}\right)^a \int_{-1}^{1} (1 - t^2)^{a - 1/2} \cos(zt) \, dt \tag{7.3.27}$$

which is valid for $\Re(a) > -\frac{1}{2}$. To prove this we expand $\cos(zt)$ in powers of zt, multiply by $(1 - t^2)^{a-1/2}$ and integrate termwise over $(-1, 1)$. This is permitted since the series is uniformly convergent. We have

$$\int_{-1}^{1} (1 - t^2)^{a - 1/2} t^{2k} \, dt = \int_{0}^{1} (1 - s)^{a - 1/2} s^{k - 1/2} \, ds = \frac{\Gamma(a + \frac{1}{2})\Gamma(k + \frac{1}{2})}{\Gamma(a + k + 1)}$$

and

$$(2k)! = \frac{2^{2k}}{\Gamma(\frac{1}{2})} k!\Gamma(k + \tfrac{1}{2}),$$

whence the expansion follows.

The integral can also be written

$$J_a(z) = \frac{1}{\Gamma(\frac{1}{2})\Gamma(a + \frac{1}{2})} \left(\frac{z}{2}\right)^a \int_{-1}^{1} (1 - t^2)^{a-1/2} e^{izt}\, dt, \tag{7.3.28}$$

since

$$e^{izt} = \cos(zt) + i \sin(zt)$$

and the integral arising from $\sin(zt)$ is 0.

The last formula is a type of Laplace transform and other integrals of similar form satisfy Bessel's equation. Cf. Section 6.8, where such integrals occur in a more general setting. Suppose that $z = x + iy$ lies in the right half-plane and that a is real and $> \frac{1}{2}$. Consider the integral

$$\frac{1}{\Gamma(\frac{1}{2})\Gamma(a + \frac{1}{2})} (\tfrac{1}{2}z)^a \int_C (1 - t^2)^{a-1/2} e^{izt}\, dt$$

taken in positive sense around the rectangle with vertices at $t = -1, +1, 1 + i\omega, -1 + i\omega$ in the complex t-plane. Here ω is a large positive number. The value of the integral is 0. Now the integral along the upper edge of the rectangle does not exceed a fixed quantity times

$$(\omega^2 + 4)^{a-1/2} \exp(y - x\omega)$$

which goes to 0 when $\omega \to \infty$ since $x > 0$. It follows that $J_a(z)$ is expressible in terms of the two integrals along the lines $t = \pm 1 + is$, $0 < s < \infty$. These two integrals are also *Bessel functions* but *of the third kind.* They were introduced by H. Hankel in 1869.

The integral along $(1, 1 + i\infty)$ can be written

$$\frac{i}{2\Gamma(a + \frac{1}{2})} \left(\frac{2}{\pi z}\right)^{1/2} e^{iz} \int_0^\infty [\tfrac{1}{2}z(-is)(2 + is)]^{a-1/2} e^{-zs}\, d(zs).$$

If z is real positive, we can set $sz = u$ and obtain after some simplification

$$\frac{1}{2\Gamma(a + \frac{1}{2})} \left(\frac{2}{\pi z}\right)^{1/2} \exp[i(z - \tfrac{1}{2}\pi a - \tfrac{1}{4}\pi)] \int_0^\infty e^{-u} u^{a-1/2} \left\{1 + \frac{iu}{2z}\right\}^{a-1/2} du,$$

where again the integral is taken along the positive real axis. We now set

$$H_a^{(1)}(z) = \frac{1}{\Gamma(a + \frac{1}{2})} \left(\frac{2}{\pi z}\right)^{1/2} \exp[i(z - \tfrac{1}{2}\pi a - \tfrac{1}{4}\pi)] \times \int_0^\infty e^{-u} u^{a-1/2} \left\{1 + \frac{iu}{2z}\right\}^{a-1/2} du. \tag{7.3.29}$$

Thus the integral along $(1, 1 + i\infty)$ is

$$-\tfrac{1}{2}H_a^{(1)}(z).$$

Further we define $H_a^{(2)}(z)$ as the function obtained by replacing i by $-i$ in (7.3.29). Then

$$J_a(z) = \tfrac{1}{2}[H_a^{(1)}(z) + H_a^{(2)}(z)]. \tag{7.3.30}$$

In the proof we have assumed z to be real positive. This is obviously not necessary. The integral in (7.3.29) exists as long as the factor $1 + iu/2z$ does not vanish anywhere on the positive real axis in the u-plane. This means that z is confined to the z-plane cut along the negative imaginary axis, i.e.

$$-\tfrac{1}{2}\pi < \arg z < \tfrac{3}{2}\pi.$$

This holds if the integral is supposed to be taken along the positive real axis in the u-plane. Again this is not necessary. We can take any ray

$$\arg u = \alpha, \qquad -\tfrac{1}{2}\pi < \alpha < \tfrac{1}{2}\pi$$

as path of integration. This allows more freedom for z. We can allow

$$-\pi < \arg z < 2\pi, \tag{7.3.31}$$

where the sector is spread out on the Riemann surface of $\log z$.

Similarly $H_a^{(2)}(z)$ is definable in the sector

$$-2\pi < \arg z < \pi. \tag{7.3.32}$$

In the sector (7.3.31) we have

$$H_a^{(1)}(z) = \left(\frac{2}{\pi z}\right)^{1/2} \exp\,[i(z - \tfrac{1}{2}\pi a - \tfrac{1}{4}\pi)]M_1(z), \tag{7.3.33}$$

where $M_1(z)$ is holomorphic and bounded outside a neighborhood of the origin. If $z \to \infty$ in the sector we have

$$\lim M_1(z) = 1.$$

We can get more precise information about the asymptotic behavior of $M_1(z)$ in the sector by expanding

$$\left(1 + \frac{iu}{2z}\right)^{a-1/2}$$

in a Taylor's series with remainder and integrating termwise. The result is of the form

$$M_1(z) = S_m(z) + R_m(z). \tag{7.3.34}$$

Here $S_m(z)$ is the mth partial sum of the divergent hypergeometric series of type ${}_2F_0$:

$$\sum_0^\infty \frac{(\frac{1}{2} + a)_k(\frac{1}{2} - a)_k}{k!}\left(-\frac{i}{2z}\right)^k \equiv {}_2F_0\left(\tfrac{1}{2} + a, \tfrac{1}{2} - a; -\frac{i}{2z}\right) \tag{7.3.35}$$

in the notation of L. Pochhammer modified by E. W. Barnes. More generally,

$$ {}_pF_q(\alpha_1, \ldots, \alpha_p; \beta_1, \ldots, \beta_q; z) = \sum_{k=0}^{\infty} \frac{(\alpha_1)_k \cdots (\alpha_p)_k}{k!(\beta_1)_k \cdots (\beta_q)_k} z^k. $$

Hence an ordinary hypergeometric series is denoted by a symbol ${}_2F_1$, and a Bessel function can be written

$$ J_a(z) = \frac{1}{\Gamma(a + 1)} (\tfrac{1}{2}z)^a {}_0F_1(a + 1; -\tfrac{1}{4}z^2). $$

Fairly simple estimates can be obtained for $R_m(z)$. Here we note merely that

$$ \lim_{z \to \infty} z^{m+1} R_m(z) = \frac{(\frac{1}{2} + a)_{m+1} (\frac{1}{2} - a)_{m+1}}{(m + 1)!} (-\tfrac{1}{2}i)^{m+1}, \tag{7.3.36} $$

if z tends to infinity in the interior of the sector (7.3.31). This implies among other things that

$$ {}_2F_0\left(\tfrac{1}{2} + a, \tfrac{1}{2} - a; -\frac{i}{2z}\right) $$

is an asymptotic power series for $M_1(z)$ in the sector. H. Poincaré in 1885 said that *a formal power series*

$$ \sum_{k=0}^{\infty} a_k z^{-k} $$

represents the function $f(z)$ asymptotically in a sector at infinity if for all m

$$ \lim_{z \to \infty} z^m \left[f(z) - \sum_{k=0}^{m} a_k z^{-k} \right] = 0 $$

for approach to infinity in the sector. Cf. Sections 6.8–6.9.

We have consequently

$$ H_a^{(1)}(z) \sim \left(\frac{2}{\pi z}\right)^{1/2} \exp i(z - \tfrac{1}{2}\pi a - \tfrac{1}{4}\pi)\, {}_2F_0\left(\tfrac{1}{2} + a, \tfrac{1}{2} - a; -\frac{i}{2z}\right) \tag{7.3.37} $$

in the sector (7.3.31). Similarly we obtain the asymptotic representation for $H_a^{(2)}(z)$ by replacing i by $-i$ in the last formula, the representation being asymptotic in the sector (7.3.32).

Combining these formulas we get an asymptotic representation for $J_a(z)$

$$ J_a(z) \sim \left(\frac{2}{\pi z}\right)^{1/2} \{\cos(z - \tfrac{1}{2}a\pi - \tfrac{1}{4}\pi)P(z) + \sin(z - \tfrac{1}{2}a\pi - \tfrac{1}{4}\pi)Q(z)\}, \tag{7.3.38} $$

valid in the sector

$$ -\pi < \arg z < \pi. \tag{7.3.39} $$

Here

$$P(z) = \frac{1}{2}\left[{}_2F_0\left(\tfrac{1}{2} + a, \tfrac{1}{2} - a; -\frac{i}{2z}\right) + {}_2F_0\left(\tfrac{1}{2} + a, \tfrac{1}{2} - a, \frac{i}{2z}\right)\right],$$

$$Q(z) = \tfrac{1}{2}i\left[{}_2F_0\left(\tfrac{1}{2} + a, \tfrac{1}{2} - a; -\frac{i}{2z}\right) - {}_2F_0\left(\tfrac{1}{2} + a, \tfrac{1}{2} - a; \frac{i}{2z}\right)\right]. \tag{7.3.40}$$

Thus $P(z)$ contains only even powers of z^{-1} and $Q(z)$ only odd powers. These series are not merely asymptotic. They are quite good for computation and only a few terms are needed in order to give the functions fairly accurately for values of z of moderate size.

Assuming $z = x > 0$ we see that

$$J_a(x) \sim \left(\frac{2}{\pi x}\right)^{1/2} \cos\left[x - \tfrac{1}{2}\pi(a + \tfrac{1}{2})\right] \tag{7.3.41}$$

with an error which is $O(x^{-3/2})$. This implies, in particular that $J_a(x)$ has infinitely many real positive zeros:

$$x_{a,k} \sim (k + \tfrac{1}{2}a + \tfrac{3}{4})\pi \tag{7.3.42}$$

for large k with an error of $O(k^{-1})$.

We see that the solutions of Bessel's equation behave asymptotically as $z^{-1/2}$ times a solution of the sine equation

$$Y''(z) + Y(z) = 0. \tag{7.3.43}$$

This is no accident. If we set

$$w(z) = z^{-1/2}W(z) \tag{7.3.44}$$

then

$$W''(z) + [1 - (a^2 - \tfrac{1}{4})z^{-2}]W(z) = 0. \tag{7.3.45}$$

This is a sine equation except for the perturbation term

$$(a^2 - \tfrac{1}{4})z^{-2}$$

which is integrable out to infinity. (Cf. Problems 9 and 10 under Exercise 5.4.) Thus the equation comes under the heading of Theorem 5.4.6. There the emphasis was on real variables, but the analysis can be extended to the complex plane and the results applied to Bessel's equation. This will be done for a more general setting in the next section.

EXERCISE 7.3

1. Prove that

$$e^{zu} = J_0(z) + \sum_{n=1}^{\infty} J_n(z)[(u + (u^2 + 1)^{1/2})^n + (u - (u^2 + 1)^{1/2})^n]$$

where the series is absolutely convergent for all z and u. Prove that the coefficient of $J_n(z)$ is actually a polynomial in u of degree n.

2. For $\Re(t) > 0$ verify that

$$O_n(t) \equiv \frac{1}{2}\int_0^\infty e^{-tu}[(u + (u^2 + 1)^{1/2})^n + (u - (u^2 + 1)^{1/2})^n]\,du$$

exists and is a polynomial in $1/t$ of degree $n + 1$. Find the coefficients and show that for fixed $t \neq 0$

$$O_n(t) = 2^{n-1}n!t^{-n-1}\left[1 + O\left(\frac{1}{n}\right)\right].$$

3. Show that the series

$$O_0(t)J_0(z) + 2\sum_{n=1}^{\infty} O_n(t)J_n(z)$$

converges absolutely for $|z| < |t|$ and uniformly if $|z| \leq a < b \leq |t|$.

4. Multiply both sides of the identity in Problem 1 by e^{-tu} and integrate termwise with respect to u from 0 to ∞. Using the result of Problem 2, we see that the right member equals the series in Problem 3, so we get the identity

$$\frac{1}{t - z} = O_0(t)J_0(z) + 2\sum_{n=1}^{\infty} O_n(t)J_n(z).$$

Verify that the procedure is legitimate, say for $0 < z < t$, and extend to $|z| < |t|$ by analytic continuation.

5. Suppose that $f(z)$ is holomorphic in the disk $|z| < r$. Show that $f(z)$ can be expanded in the series

$$f(z) = \sum_{n=0}^{\infty} a_n J_n(z), \qquad a_n = \frac{1}{2\pi i}\int_C f(t)O_n(t)\,dt,$$

where C: $|t| = \rho < r$. This series is due to C. Neumann (1867).

6. Prove that

$$e^{ixt} = \sum_{n=0}^{\infty} i^n(2n + 1)P_n(x)t^{-1/2}J_{n+1/2}(t),$$

where $P_n(x)$ is the nth Legendre polynomial and the series is absolutely convergent for all x and t.

7. The following is a special case of a series studied by O. Schlömilch in 1857. Let $|a_n|$ be bounded and $\sum_1^\infty n^{-1/2}|a_n - a_{n+1}|$ convergent. Show that the series

$$\sum_{n=0}^{\infty} a_n J_0(nx)$$

converges for $0 < x \leq \pi$. Under what assumptions will it converge for $x = 0$?

8. Show that if $J_a(z)$ and $J_{a+1}(z)$ both vanish for $z = z_0$, then $z_0 = 0$.

9. If x_1 and x_2 are consecutive (real) zeros of $J_a(x)$, show that $J_{a+1}(x)$ has a zero in (x_1, x_2).

10. If x and a are positive, show that the functions $P(x)$ and $Q(x)$ of (7.3.40) are real.

11. Suppose known that for x and a positive

$$J_a(x) = \left(\frac{2}{\pi x}\right)^{1/2}\left\{\cos\left[x - \tfrac{1}{2}(a + \tfrac{1}{2})\pi\right] + \frac{1}{x}\,C(x)\right\}.$$

where $|C(x)| \le C$ with C depending on a but not on x. Set

$$\xi_{a,k} = (k + \tfrac{1}{2}a + \tfrac{3}{4})\pi.$$

Let $\delta < \frac{1}{2}$ and consider the interval $(\xi_{a,k} - \delta,\ \xi_{a,k} + \delta)$. Show that such an interval contains a zero of $J_a(x)$ if, for instance

$$\delta(k + \tfrac{1}{2}a + \tfrac{3}{4} - \delta) > \frac{1}{2\pi}\,C.$$

The inequality $\sin t > (2/\pi)t$ for $0 < t < \pi/2$ may be useful.

12. Let $C_a(x)$ be a solution of (7.3.1) for $z = x > 0$ and $a > 0$ and suppose that it is real for such values of x. Show that $C_a(x)$ has infinitely many positive zeros and hence also infinitely many positive extrema (= points where $C_a'(x) = 0$).

13. Let the extrema occur at the points $\{x_k\}$ where

$$a < x_1 < x_2 < \cdots < x_k < \cdots$$

Show that $\{|C_a(x_k)|\}$ is a decreasing sequence by discussing the function

$$[C_a(x)]^2 + \frac{x^2}{x^2 - a^2}\,[C_a'(x)]^2.$$

Cf. the discussion of formula (7.2.22).

14. Assuming the right of applying the differential operator

$$z^2D^2 + zD + z^2I, \qquad D = \frac{d}{dz},$$

termwise to the series

$$\sum_{n=0}^{\infty} a_n J_n(z),$$

what would be the effect? Could the procedure be justified, if, say, the coefficients are bounded?

15. Obtain a formula for $J_{-n-1/2}(z)$ analogous to (7.3.4).

16. Show that the differential equation

$$w'' + zw = 0$$

is satisfied by

$$z^{1/2}J_{1/3}(\tfrac{2}{3}z^{3/2}) \qquad \text{and} \qquad z^{1/2}J_{-1/3}(\tfrac{2}{3}z^{3/2}).$$

17. Generalize this to show that the equation

$$w'' + z^n w = 0, \qquad n > -2,$$

has solutions expressible in terms of Bessel functions of order $\pm 1/(n + 2)$.

18. Find a transformation of the variables which reduces the equation of the preceding problem to a Bessel equation.
19. Show that the Riccati equation
$$y' = z^n + y^2$$
is reducible to a Bessel equation.

7.4 ASYMPTOTIC INTEGRATION.

We shall apply the method used in the proof of Theorem 5.4.6 for a study of the differential equation
$$w'' + [1 - F(z)]w = 0 \tag{7.4.1}$$
in the complex plane. To this end, we have to impose suitable restrictions on $F(z)$ pertaining to holomorphy, boundedness, and integrability. We want to integrate out to infinity and to have enough freedom to be able to deform the path of integration when needed. The following set of assumptions is adequate for our purposes.

Hypothesis F. *$F(z)$ shall be an analytic function such that:*

i) *$F(z)$ is holomorphic in a domain D extending to infinity and located on the Riemann surface of* $\log z$. *D shall contain a sector S: $\alpha \leq \arg z \leq \beta$, $R \leq |z|$ where*
$$-2\pi \leq \alpha < 0 < \beta \leq 2\pi.$$
For $\alpha \leq \theta \leq \beta$ we denote by D_θ that part of S such that if $z \in S$ then the ray $z + re^{i\theta}$ is in S.

ii) $\lim_{n\to\infty} r|F(re^{i\theta})| = 0$ *uniformly in S.*

iii) *For each $z \in D_\theta$, $\alpha \leq \theta \leq \beta$, the integral*
$$\int_0^\infty |F(z + re^{i\theta})|\, dr \tag{7.4.2}$$
exists and the set of all such integrals is bounded, the least upper bound being M.

We note that these assumptions can be satisfied if, e.g. $F(z)$ is a rational function having its poles inside the circle $|z| = R$ and having a zero at infinity of at least the second order. In particular, they are satisfied by $(a^2 - \frac{1}{4})z^{-2}$, the function occurring in the transformed Bessel equation (7.3.45).

The results will be stated in a number of theorems. We start with

Theorem 7.4.1. *Suppose that Hypothesis F holds. Let $w(z)$ be a solution of* (7.4.1) *defined in D_0. Then there exists a solution $w_0(z)$ of the sine equation*
$$w''(z) + w(z) = 0 \tag{7.4.3}$$

such that for all $z = x + iy$ *in* D_0

$$|w(x + iy) - w_0(x + iy)| \leq M(y)\left\{\exp\left[\int_x^\infty |F(s + iy)|\, ds\right] - 1\right\}, \tag{7.4.4}$$

where $M(y) = \max_s |w_0(s + iy)|$.

Proof. We can imitate the method used in the proof of Theorem 5.4.6. We choose a point $x_0 > R$ on the real axis in D_0. If z is any point in D_0 we can find a θ, where

$$\max(\alpha, -\tfrac{1}{2}\pi) < \theta < \min(\beta, \tfrac{1}{2}\pi)$$

such that the points x_0 and z also belong to D_θ. We can then join x_0 and z in D_0 by a path Π made up of at most two straight line segments, one parallel to the real axis, the other parallel to the ray $\arg z = \theta$. No matter how Π is chosen subject to these conditions, we have

$$\int_\Pi |F(t)|\,|dt| \leq 2M$$

by condition F (iii), and this holds uniformly with respect to z in D_0.

Next we determine the solution $w_1(z)$ of (7.4.3) with the initial conditions

$$w_1(x_0) = w(x_0), \qquad w_1'(x_0) = w'(x_0). \tag{7.4.5}$$

We have then, if Π is oriented from x_0 to z,

$$w(z) = w_1(z) + \int_\Pi \sin(z - t)F(t)w(t)\, dt, \tag{7.4.6}$$

as is shown by twofold differentiation and taking into account the initial conditions.

Let $\gamma > 0$ and let $D_0(\gamma)$ be that part of D_0 the points of which have a distance from the real axis not exceeding γ. Suppose that

$$|w_1(z)| \leq K_\gamma, \qquad |\sin(z - t)| \leq K_\gamma$$

for z and t in $D_0(\gamma)$. We have then

$$|w(z)| \leq |w_1(z)| + \int_\Pi |\sin(z - t)|\,|F(t)|\,|w(t)|\,|dt|$$

or

$$|w(z)| \leq K_\gamma + K_\gamma \int_\Pi |F(t)|\,|w(t)|\,|dt|.$$

If here we express t as a function of the arc length on Π, we see that this inequality is of the nature covered by Theorem 1.5.7 and consequently implies

$$|w(z)| \leq K_\gamma \exp\left[K_\gamma \int_\Pi |F(t)|\,|dt|\right] \leq K_\gamma e^{2MK_\gamma}, \tag{7.4.7}$$

so that $|w(z)|$ is uniformly bounded in $D_0(\gamma)$.

We can now form

$$w(z) - \int_z^\infty \sin(t - z)F(t)w(t)\,dt \equiv w_0(z), \tag{7.4.8}$$

where the integral is taken along the line $t = z + r, 0 \le r < \infty$. The integral exists by virtue of condition F (iii) combined with (7.4.7) which is valid if z is confined to $D_0(\gamma)$. Thus $w_0(z)$ is a well defined function holomorphic in D_0 and bounded in any fixed $D_0(\gamma)$. Twofold differentiation gives

$$w_0''(z) + w_0(z) = 0,$$

that is $w_0(z)$ is a particular solution of (7.4.3) uniquely defined in D_0 by the given solution of (7.4.1).

We have then

$$w(z) = w_0(z) + \int_z^\infty \sin(t - z)F(t)w(t)\,dt. \tag{7.4.9}$$

This is a singular Volterra equation for $w(z)$ which has a unique solution, namely the solution of (7.4.1) from which we started. Since

$$|w(x + iy) - w_0(x + iy)| \le \int_x^\infty |F(s + iy)|\,|w(s + iy)|\,ds,$$

Theorem 1.5.7 applies and gives the inequality (7.4.4).

We can solve (7.4.9) by successive approximations setting

$$w_n(z) = w_0(z) + \int_z^\infty \sin(t - z)F(t)w_{n-1}(t)\,dt$$

for $n = 1, 2, 3, \ldots$ Here

$$|w_n(z) - w_{n-1}(z)| \le M(y)\frac{1}{n!}\left[\int_z^\infty |F(t)|\,dt\right]^n,$$

so the approximations converge rapidly to $w(z)$. ∎

The correspondence between the solutions $w(z)$ of (7.4.1) on the one hand, and the solutions $w_0(z)$ of (7.4.3) on the other is one-to-one and the asymptotic properties of $w(z)$ in D_0 are completely determined by those of $w_0(z)$. Now the solutions of the sine equation form three mutually exclusive classes:

1. Solutions that go exponentially to 0 in the upper half-plane, namely the constant multiples of e^{iz}.

2. Solutions that go exponentially to 0 in the lower half-plane, namely constant multiples of e^{-iz}.

3. Oscillatory solutions of the form constant times $\sin(z - z_0)$, where z_0 is an arbitrary complex number.

Once $w_0(z)$ has been chosen, we may expect that its asymptotic properties will carry over to the corresponding function $w(z)$. Formula (7.4.4) indicates that this is indeed the case. The formula suffers from an obvious defect, however. The information is confined to D_0. At best this region is that part of the plane where the points have a distance from the negative real axis of at least R. Even in this most favorable case, the estimates may be quite poor in the left half-plane.

The known results in the Bessel case suggest that for a satisfactory theory it is essential that $\alpha = -2\pi$ and $\beta = 2\pi$. Equation (7.3.45) has solutions of the three types: $z^{1/2}H_a^{(1)}(z)$ goes exponentially to 0 in the upper half-plane, $z^{1/2}H_a^{(2)}(z)$ goes exponentially to 0 in the lower half-plane, and $z^{1/2}J_a(z)$ is oscillatory both in the right and in the left half-planes. But this is not the whole story. The first of these solutions has the same asymptotic representation in the sector

$$-\pi < \arg z < 2\pi,$$

the second solution has the same representation in the sector

$$-2\pi < \arg z < \pi,$$

while $z^{1/2}J_a(z)$ has one asymptotic representation in the right half-plane and another in the left unless a is an integer.

Let us therefore assume

$$\alpha = -2\pi, \qquad \beta = 2\pi,$$

and proceed to a more detailed analysis of the three cases. We start with

Theorem 7.4.2. *Equation* (7.4.1) *has a unique solution* $E^+(z)$ *asymptotic to* e^{iz} *in the sector*

$$-\pi < \arg z < 2\pi.$$

More precisely,

$$|E^+(z)e^{-iz} - 1| \le \exp\left[\int_z^\infty |F(t)|\,|dt|\right] - 1 \tag{7.4.10}$$

where the path of integration is $\arg(t - z)$ *equal to*

$$0 \ \textit{for}\ \ z \in D_0, \quad \tfrac{1}{2}\pi \ \textit{for}\ \ z \in D_{\pi/2}, \quad \textit{and}\ \ \pi \ \textit{for}\ \ z \in D_\pi.$$

Proof. We set

$$E^+(z)e^{-iz} = U(z). \tag{7.4.11}$$

Equation (7.4.9) shows that $U(z)$ satisfies the integral equation

$$U(z) = 1 + \frac{1}{2i}\int_z^\infty [e^{2i(t-z)} - 1]F(t)U(t)\,dt,$$

where the path of integration is $\arg(t - z) = 0$. Here

$$\left|\frac{1}{2i}[e^{2i(t-z)} - 1]\right| \le 1$$

and the usual estimates show that

$$|U(z) - 1| \leq \exp\left[\int_0^\infty |F(z + r)|\,dr\right] - 1 \tag{7.4.12}$$

for all $z \in D_0$. This is the first inequality listed above. In particular this estimate shows that $|U(z)|$ is bounded in D_0 since the integral cannot exceed M by F (iii).

Next we take a $z \in D_0 \cap D_{\pi/2}$ and invoke F(ii). This condition shows that we can rotate the path of integration through an angle of 90° so that it becomes $\arg(t - z) = \frac{1}{2}\pi$ instead. For the integrand is bounded in the sector

$$0 \leq \arg(t - z) \leq \tfrac{1}{2}\pi, \qquad |t - z| \leq r,$$

uniformly with respect to r and is $o(r^{-1})$ as $r \to \infty$. The integral taken along the boundary of the sector is 0 and the integral along the circular part goes to 0 when $r \to \infty$. It follows that

$$\int_z^{z+\infty} = \int_z^{z+i\infty}.$$

The resulting integral equation for $U(z)$ is valid for all $z \in D_{\pi/2}$. Along the new path of integration

$$\left|\frac{1}{2i}\,[e^{2i(t-z)} - 1]\right| < \frac{1}{2}\cdot$$

so for $z \in D_{\pi/2}$ we have the preliminary inequality

$$|U(z) - 1| \leq \tfrac{1}{2}\int_z^{z+i\infty} |F(t)|\,|U(t)|\,|dt|,$$

whence it follows that

$$|U(z) - 1| \leq \exp\left[\tfrac{1}{2}\int_z^{z+i\infty} |F(t)|\,|dt|\right] - 1. \tag{7.4.13}$$

This is a sharper estimate than that stated in the theorem for this case. In particular, $|U(z)|$ is bounded in all of $D_{\pi/2}$.

For $z \in D_{\pi/2} \cap D_\pi$ we can turn the path of integration once more through an angle of 90° and

$$\int_z^{z+i\infty} = \int_z^{z-\infty}.$$

The resulting integral equation for $U(z)$ is valid for all $z \in D_\pi$ and for such values of z we obtain the estimate

$$|U(z) - 1| \leq \exp\left[\int_z^{z-\infty} |F(t)|\,|dt|\right] - 1 \tag{7.4.14}$$

which is the last assertion.

We cannot turn the path of integration any further because the kernel

$$\frac{1}{2i}\,[e^{2i(t-z)} - 1]$$

is not bounded on rays $\arg(t - z) = \theta$ with $\pi < \theta < 2\pi$. ∎

We know that

$$|U(z) - 1| \le e^M - 1$$

in the region $D_0 \cup D_{\pi/2} \cup D_\pi$. If M is large this is not particularly valuable information. It is clear, however, that we can get a much better estimate by imposing stronger restrictions on z. If we trim off strips along the boundary of $\bar{D} = D_0 \cup D_{\pi/2} \cup D_\pi$, we can attain that for any z in what is left of $\bar{D}$ there is at least one admissible integral

$$I(z, \theta) = \int_0^\infty |F(z + r\,e^{i\theta})|\,dr, \qquad 0 \le \theta \le \pi,$$

whose value does not exceed a preassigned positive number M_0. In particular, we denote by D^+ that part of $\bar{D}$ in which

$$\min_\theta I(z, \theta) < \log 2.$$

Then for $z \in D^+$ we have

$$|U(z) - 1| < 1 \qquad \text{and} \qquad U(z) \ne 0. \tag{7.4.15}$$

The Bessel case (7.3.45) is instructive. Here

$$F(z) = (a^2 - \tfrac{1}{4})z^{-2}$$

and

$$\int_{-\infty}^{\infty} |F(x + iy)|\,dy = |a^2 - \tfrac{1}{4}|\,\frac{\pi}{|x|}, \qquad x \ne 0.$$

If the integral is taken along any other line at a distance r from the origin, $|x|$ should be replaced by r in this formula. This shows that D^+ is that part of the sector

$$-\pi \le \arg z \le 2\pi$$

whose distance from the boundary exceeds

$$\delta \equiv |a^2 - \tfrac{1}{4}|\,\frac{\pi}{\log 2}\cdot \tag{7.4.16}$$

This means that we omit the disk $|z| < \delta$ and two strips of width δ along the rectilinear boundary of the sector, one below $\arg z = -\pi$, the other below $\arg z = 2\pi$. This is D^+ and for $z \in D^+$ we have

$$H_a^{(1)}(z) \ne 0.$$

Using the same method we can prove

Theorem 7.4.3. *The equation* (7.4.1) *has a unique solution* $E^-(z)$ *which goes exponentially to* 0 *in the lower half-plane. More precisely,*

$$|E^-(z)\,e^{iz} - 1| \le \exp\left[\int_z^\infty |F(t)|\,|dt|\right] - 1 \tag{7.4.17}$$

in $D = D_0 \cup D_{-\pi/2} \cup D_{-\pi}$ *and the path of integration is* arg $(t - z)$ *equal to*

$$0 \text{ in } D_0, \quad -\tfrac{1}{2}\pi \text{ in } D_{-\pi/2}, \quad \text{and } -\pi \text{ in } D_{-\pi}.$$

We leave the proof to the reader. As above we see that we can find a subset D^- of D where

$$|E^-(z)\,e^{iz} - 1| < 1 \qquad \text{and} \qquad E^-(z) \neq 0.$$

In particular, in the Bessel case it is enough to omit from D the points whose distance from the boundary does not exceed the quantity δ of (7.4.16). The oscillatory case is more complicated. We start by proving

Theorem 7.4.4. *If* $z_0 = x_0 + iy_0$ *is given, the equation* (7.4.1) *has a unique solution* $w_1(z)$ *which is asymptotic to* $\sin(z - z_0)$ *in* D_0 *in the sense that*

$$[\cosh(y - y_0)]^{-1}|w_1(z) - \sin(z - z_0)| \le \exp\left[\int_0^\infty |F(z + s)|\,ds\right] - 1. \tag{7.4.18}$$

There is also a solution $w_2(z)$ *which is asymptotic to* $\sin(z - z_0)$ *in* D_π *in the sense that*

$$[\cosh(y - y_0)]^{-1}|w_2(z) - \sin(z - z_0)| \le \exp\left[\int_0^\infty |F(z - s)|\,ds\right] - 1. \tag{7.4.19}$$

Here normally $w_2(z) \neq w_1(z)$. *Both solutions are oscillatory,* w_1 *in the right half-plane,* w_2 *in the left.*

Further, $w_1(z)$ *can be continued analytically into* D_π *as well as into* $D_{-\pi}$ *and, normally, the continuation is oscillatory in both regions. In particular,* $w_1(z)$ *is oscillatory in* D_π, *if* y_0 *is sufficiently large positive, in* $D_{-\pi}$ *if* y_0 *is sufficiently large negative.*

Remark. We say that the solution is *oscillatory* in a region if it has infinitely many zeros in that region. This theorem gives only qualitative statements which are amplified by quantitative estimates in the next theorem.

Proof. Formula (7.4.18) is read off directly from (7.4.4) since in the present case $M(y) = \cosh(y - y_0)$. The existence and properties of $w_2(z)$ follow from the analogue of Theorem 7.4.1 for the region D_π. The proof carries over step by step or, simpler, by changing z into $-z$ which preserves the form of the equation. The Bessel case shows that normally $w_2(z)$ is distinct from $w_1(z)$ since $J_a(-z) \neq J_a(z)$ unless a is an even integer.

We postpone the discussion of the oscillatory properties until the next theorem. The analytic continuation of $w_1(z)$ into the adjacent regions D_π and $D_{-\pi}$ on the Riemann surface clearly exist. Let us consider the continuation into D_π. By the analogue of Theorem 7.4.1 there exists a solution $w_0(z)$ of (7.4.3) to which the continuation is asymptotic in D_π. Normally $w_0(z)$ would be oscillatory. The alternative is that $w_1(z)$ is a constant multiple of either $E^+(z)$ or $E^-(z)$. The first alternative is clearly excluded since $E^+(z)$ goes to 0 in the upper half-plane and $w_1(z)$ does not. We can exclude the second alternative if $w_1(z)$ is oscillatory in the intersection of D_0, D_π, and D^+ which is the case if y_0 is sufficiently large positive. Similar considerations apply to the continuation of $w_1(z)$ into $D_{-\pi}$ and the continuation of $w_2(z)$ from D_π into the adjacent regions D_0 and $D_{2\pi}$. ▌

For the detailed discussion of the oscillatory case, we shall need the theorem of Rouché which we state as

Lemma 7.4.1. *Let D be a simply-connected domain in the complex plane bounded by a rectifiable curve C. Let f, g, h be functions holomorphic in $D \cup C$ such that*

i) $h = f + g$,

ii) $|f(z)| > g(z)|$ *everywhere on C.*

Then $f(z)$ and $h(z)$ have the same number of zeros in D.

Proof. The assumptions imply that $f(z)$ and $h(z)$ are $\neq 0$ on C. If z describes C once in the positive sense, the argument of $f(z)$ either returns to its original value or increases by a multiple of 2π, say $2N\pi$. Here N is the number of zeros of $f(z)$ in D. Now, with obvious notation,

$$\Delta \arg h(z) = \Delta \arg f(z) + \Delta \arg \left\{1 + \frac{g(z)}{f(z)}\right\}$$

and here the second term on the right is 0 by virtue of condition (ii). It follows that h and f change their arguments by the same amount when C is described and hence have the same number of zeros in D. ▌

We shall use this lemma to discuss the zeros of

$$w_1(z) = \sin(z - z_0) + R(z)$$

in a right half-plane. Here

$$|R(z)| \leq \cosh(y - y_0)\left\{\exp\left[\int_0^\infty |F(z + s)|\, ds\right] - 1\right\}$$

for z in D_0.

Let δ be given, $0 < \delta < \frac{1}{2}\pi$, and let H_δ be a half-plane

$$\Re(z) > \sigma_0$$

such that $z \in D_0$ and

$$\exp\left[\int_0^\infty |F(z+s)|\,ds\right] < 1 + \frac{\sin\delta}{\cosh\delta} \tag{7.4.20}$$

is satisfied. We have then

Theorem 7.4.5. *Let z_0 and H_δ be such that $z_0 - \delta \in H_\delta$ while $z_0 - \pi + \delta$ does not. For $n = 0, 1, 2, \ldots$, let $Q_{n,\delta}$ be the square*

$$|x - z_0 - n\pi| < \delta, \quad |y - y_0| < \delta, \quad z_0 = x_0 + iy_0.$$

Then $w_1(z)$ has one and only one zero in each square $Q_{n,\delta}$ and no other zeros in H_δ.

Remark. Since $\sin(z - z_0)$ is periodic with period 2π, it is no restriction to assume that $\Re(z_0) = x_0$ is large. The condition imposed on z_0 serves to ensure that $Q_{0,\delta}$ lies in H_δ and $Q_{-1,\delta}$ is entirely outside. It does not exclude any z_0 from consideration.

Proof. On the boundary of $Q_{n,\delta}$

$$|\sin(z - z_0)| \geq \sin\delta,$$

where the lower bound is reached for $z = z_0 + n\pi \pm \delta$. On the other hand, the estimate for $|R(z)|$ on the boundary reaches its maximum at the four vertices of the square so that by (7.4.20)

$$|R(z)| < \sin\delta.$$

This shows that condition (ii) of Lemma 7.4.1 is satisfied by

$$f(z) = \sin(z - z_0), \qquad g(z) = R(z)$$

on the perimeter of the square $Q_{n,\delta}$. Since $\sin(z - z_0)$ has a single zero in the square, namely at its center, it follows that $w_1(z)$ has one and only one zero in each square $Q_{n,\delta}$ with $n \geq 0$.

Suppose next that z is anywhere in H_δ outside all the squares $Q_{n,\delta}$. We have

$$|\sin(z - z_0)|^2 = \sin^2(x - x_0) + \sinh^2(y - y_0).$$

Suppose first that $|y - y_0| > \delta$. Then

$$|\sin(z - z_0)| \geq \sinh|y - y_0|,$$

while

$$|R(z)| < \cosh(y - y_0)\frac{\sin\delta}{\cosh\delta} < \cosh(y - y_0)\tanh\delta.$$

Since

$$\sinh|y - y_0| > \cosh(y - y_0)\tanh\delta,$$

if $|y - y_0| > \delta$, it follows that

$$|\sin(z - z_0)| > |R(z)|$$

and $w_1(z)$ cannot vanish for such a value of z.

It remains to consider the rectangles between the squares, i.e.

$$\delta < x - x_0 - n\pi < \pi - \delta, \qquad |y - y_0| \leq \delta.$$

We have now

$$|\sin(z - z_0)| > \sin\delta, \qquad |R(z)| < \sin\delta.$$

and the same conclusion holds.

We have restricted the discussion to a right half-plane. It is clear, however, that if $|y_0|$ is large the method applies to that part of D_0 where (7.4.20) holds.

We observe that a large part of the theory developed here extends to the case of a differential equation

$$w''(z) + [e - F(z)]w(z) = 0 \tag{7.4.21}$$

in a Banach algebra $\mathfrak{B}$ with unit element e. Here the associated wave equation has the solutions

$$a\exp(iz) + b\exp(-iz), \tag{7.4.22}$$

where $a, b \in \mathfrak{B}$. In Hypothesis F, we replace absolute values by norms. The proof of Theorem 7.4.1 carries over, *mutatis mutandis,* and the analogues of Theorem 7.4.2 and 7.4.3 are also valid, i.e. solutions $E^+(z)$ and $E^-(z)$ exist and have the expected asymptotic properties in sectors of opening 3π. What does not carry over so readily are the oscillatory properties described in Theorems 7.4.4 and 7.4.5. There is no difficulty if b is a scalar multiple of a for then the function $w_0(z)$ has infinitely many zeros which form a set $\{z_0 + n\pi\}$ in the complex plane and the corresponding solution of (7.4.21) also has infinitely many zeros $\{z_n\}$ such that

$$\lim_{n\to\infty}(z_n - z_0 - n\pi) = 0.$$

This is an exceptional case, however, and in general the oscillatory properties hold only in an extended sense. Thus, if λ is a bounded linear and multiplicative functional on $\mathfrak{B}$, then $\lambda[w(z)]$ satisfies a scalar differential equation of type (7.4.1) and Theorems 7.4.4 and 7.4.5 apply to this situation. For the matrix case and on the real line there is a well developed theory for the oscillations of the scalar function det $[w(z)]$ and the basic inequalities obtained above form a basis for extending this theory to the complex plane. We do not pursue these extensions any further here.

We return to the scalar case and note that the power of this method of asymptotic integration can be extended by combining it with a transformation introduced by J. Liouville in 1837. This transformation applies to so-called *formally self-adjoint equations* of the form

$$\frac{d}{dz}[K(z)w'(z)] + G(z)w(z) = 0, \tag{7.4.23}$$

where G and K are supposed to have continuous second order derivatives. Introducing

$$Z = \int^z \left[\frac{G(t)}{K(t)}\right]^{1/2} dt, \qquad W = [G(z)K(z)]^{1/4}w \tag{7.4.24}$$

as new variables, we obtain an equation of the form

$$W''(Z) + [1 - F(Z)]W = 0. \tag{7.4.25}$$

Here $F(Z)$ depends upon $G(z)$ and $K(z)$. The most elegant expression is

$$F(Z) = \frac{H''(Z)}{H(Z)}, \qquad H(Z) = [G(z)K(z)]^{1/4}. \tag{7.4.26}$$

A more explicit expression in terms of the old variable z is

$$\begin{aligned} F(Z) = &-\frac{5}{16}\frac{K(z)}{[G(z)]^3}[G'(z)]^2 + \frac{1}{8}\frac{1}{[G(z)]^2}G'(z)K'(z) \\ &-\frac{1}{16}\frac{[K'(z)]^2}{G(z)K(z)} + \frac{1}{4}\frac{1}{G(z)}K''(z) + \frac{1}{4}\frac{K(z)}{[G(z)]^2}G''(z). \end{aligned} \tag{7.4.27}$$

This transformation has a strongly smoothing effect. We shall illustrate this fact on the important case where $G(z)$ and $K(z)$ are polynomials in z:

$$\begin{aligned} G(z) &= a_0z^n + a_1z^{n-1} + \cdots + a_n, \\ K(z) &= z^m + b_1z^{m-1} + \cdots + b_m, \end{aligned} \tag{7.4.28}$$

and

$$m < n + 2 \tag{7.4.29}$$

to ensure that the point at infinity is an irregular singular point. Here Z equals

$$\frac{\sqrt{2a_0}}{n - m + 2} z^{(n-m+2)/2} \tag{7.4.30}$$

times a power series in $1/z$ with constant term 1 convergent for z outside the smallest circle with center at the origin which contains the zeros of $G(z)K(z)$. We assume that the integration of

$$\left[\frac{G(z)}{K(z)}\right]^{1/2}$$

does not lead to a logarithmic term. Such terms can arise only if m and n have the same parity.

If there are no logarithmic terms present, we can expand z in fractional powers of Z. Setting

$$\zeta = [\tfrac{1}{2}Na_0^{-1/2}Z]^{2/N}, \qquad N = n - m + 2, \tag{7.4.31}$$

we have

$$z = \zeta\left[1 + P_1\left(\frac{1}{\zeta}\right)\right] \tag{7.4.32}$$

and this leads to

$$H(Z) = [G(z)K(z)]^{1/4} = a_0^{1/4}\zeta^{(m+n)/4}\left[1 + P_2\left(\frac{1}{\zeta}\right)\right]$$

$$= A_0 Z^{\frac{1}{2}\frac{m+n}{N}}[1 + P_3(Z^{-2/N})]. \tag{7.4.33}$$

Here A_0 is a constant of no importance and the letter P signifies a power series without constant term in the variable indicated. This gives finally

$$F(Z) = \frac{H''(Z)}{H(Z)} = \tfrac{1}{4}(m + n)(3m - n - 4)N^{-2}Z^{-2}[1 + P_4(Z^{-2/N})]. \tag{7.4.34}$$

This expression is valid as long as

$$3m - n - 4 \neq 0.$$

If this is not the case, the expression has to be modified and will start with terms of still lower order.

We see that the transformed equation is one to which the asymptotic integration theory applies and the problem now becomes one of translating the results obtainable for the transformed equation into results for the original equation. This is essentially a question of conformal mapping. The function

$$Z = Z(z)$$

maps partial neighborhoods of $z = \infty$ onto partial neighborhoods of $Z = \infty$. To apply the theorems we must know what domains in the z-plane go into domains containing half-planes: $\Re(Z) > \alpha$, $\Re(Z) < -\alpha$, $\Im(Z) > \beta$, $\Im(Z) < -\beta$. Here it is enough to observe that at $z = \infty$ angles are multiplied by the factor

$$\tfrac{1}{2}N \qquad \text{where} \qquad N = n - m + 2.$$

It follows that we can find N curvilinear sectors $S_1, S_2, \ldots, S_N$ which are mapped alternately upon upper and lower Z-half-planes. Assuming a_0 to be real positive, we find that the boundaries of these sectors have the rays

$$\arg z = \theta_k = k\frac{2\pi}{N}, \qquad k = 0, 1, 2, \ldots, N - 1, \tag{7.4.35}$$

as asymptotes, the sector S_k being "between" the rays $\arg z = \theta_{k-1}$ and θ_k.

For each k there is a *subdominant solution* $e_k^+(z)$ which is asymptotic to

$$z^{-(m+n)/4}\exp\left\{\frac{2}{N}\sqrt{a_0}\, iz^{N/2}[1 + o(1)]\right\} \tag{7.4.36}$$

in the three sectors S_{k-1}, S_k, and S_{k+1} with the convention $S_{-1} = S_N$. If we change i into $-i$ in the last formula we obtain the corresponding *dominant solution* $e_k^-(z)$ which has the same asymptotic expression in S_k, S_{k-1}, and S_{k-2}. Here $e_k^+(z)$ is subdominant in S_k while $e_k^-(z)$ is subdominant in S_{k-1} and we have

$$e_{k-1}^+(z) = e_k^-(z). \tag{7.4.37}$$

A subdominant solution is non-oscillatory on the boundary of the sector where it is subdominant.

Normally a solution $w(z)$ of (7.4.23) with G and K given by (7.4.28) is oscillatory in the transition zones between the sectors. This is to be understood as follows. Outside a sufficiently large circle all zeros of $w(z)$ are to be found in ε-sectors centered on the rays (7.4.35) and if $N > 2$ the distance from the zero to the ray approaches 0. In each of these ε-sectors the number of zeros of absolute value $\leq r$ is

$$\frac{2\sqrt{a_0}}{\pi N} r^{N/2}[1 + o(1)]. \tag{7.4.38}$$

The solutions $e_k^+(z)$ and $e_k^-(z)$ are exceptional in having no zeros in the ε-sectors which are adjacent to their sectors of subdominance. Thus their frequency of zeros is only

$$1 - \frac{2}{N}$$

of the normal amount. In exceptional cases this number can be lowered still further, if a subdominant solution has several non-adjacent sectors of subdominance. As an example we may take the equation

$$w''(z) - [k^2z^{2k-2} + k(k - 1)z^{k-2}]w(z) = 0. \tag{7.4.39}$$

Here $N = 2k$ but the solution

$$e^{z^k}$$

is subdominant in k sectors and has no zeros at all.

The reader will have noticed that the assumption that G and K are polynomials is not essential for the argument or the resulting formulas. We could just as well have assumed that G and K are functions holomorphic in an annulus $R < |z| < \infty$ having poles at infinity of orders n and m, respectively. Moreover, the method applies to some equations where the point at infinity is an irregular singular point of infinite rank. Such examples are found in the Exercise 7.4 and in Section 7.6.

EXERCISE 7.4

1. If $z = x + iy$, show that

$$\int_0^\infty |z + s|^{-2}\, ds = \begin{cases} \dfrac{\arg z}{y}, & 0 < |\arg z| < \pi, \\ \dfrac{1}{x}, & \arg z = 0. \end{cases}$$

2. Find

$$\min_\theta \int_0^\infty |z + re^{i\theta}|^{-2}\, dr.$$

3. Prove that for $a > 1$.

$$\int_0^\infty |z + s|^{-a}\, ds = (a - 1)^{-1} r^{1-a} F(a - 1, 1, \tfrac{1}{2}(a + 1); \sin^2(\tfrac{1}{2}\theta))$$

and prove the transit formula

$$F(a - 1, 1, \tfrac{1}{2}(a + 1); \sin^2(\tfrac{1}{2}\theta)) = -F(a - 1, 1, \tfrac{1}{2}(a + 1); \cos^2(\tfrac{1}{2}\theta)) + 2\sqrt{\pi}\frac{\Gamma(\frac{1}{2}(a + 1))}{\Gamma(\frac{1}{2}a)} |\sin \theta|^{1-a}.$$

4. Consider the matrix equation in $\mathfrak{M}_2$

$$\mathcal{W}''(z) + [\mathcal{E} - \tfrac{1}{4}\mathcal{A} z^{-2}]\mathcal{W}(z) = 0,$$

where $\|\mathcal{A}\| = 1$ and $\mathcal{E}$ is the unit matrix. Let

$$\mathcal{W}_0(z) = \begin{bmatrix} e^{iz} & e^{-iz} \\ e^{-iz} & e^{iz} \end{bmatrix}$$

be a solution of the wave equation and let $\mathcal{W}(z)$ be the corresponding solution of the given equation. Find the zeros of det $[\mathcal{W}_0(z)]$ and show that the zeros of det $[\mathcal{W}(z)]$ are approximated by those of det $[\mathcal{W}_0(z)]$ in the distant part of the right half-plane. Try to obtain quantitative estimates as in the scalar case.

5. Apply the Liouville transformation to the case

$$G(z) = \sum_{n=0}^\infty c_n z^{n-2}, \qquad c_0 \neq 0, \qquad K(z) \equiv 1,$$

where there is a regular singular point at $z = 0$. Note that $F(Z)$ has a constant limit. Estimate the difference between $F(Z)$ and its limit. How is the integration theory to be modified to cover this case?

6. How is the Eq. (7.4.23) transformed if a new independent variable is introduced by $\xi = \int^z [K(t)]^{-1}\, dt$?

7. Same question if instead $T = [K(z)]^{1/2} w$ is taken as the new dependent variable.

8. Verify the equivalence of (7.4.26) and (7.4.27).

9. If $K(z) = z^m$, $G(z) = z^n$, express the solutions in terms of Bessel functions.

10. If $G(z) = -z$, $K(z) \equiv 1$, carry through the Liouville transformation and discuss the resulting equation. Find the three sectors and the asymptotic behavior of the subdominant solutions. Find domains in the z-plane where such a solution can have no zeros.

11. For the same equation determine how the squares $Q_{n,\delta}$ are mapped into the z-plane.

12. Show that the equation $w'' - zw = 0$ is invariant under a 120° rotation of the plane and use this to prove that the sub-dominants are pairwise linearly independent.

13. Carry through thc Liouville transformation for the equation $w'' + e^z w = 0$ and study the conformal mapping involved. Determine the strips in the z-plane which correspond to Z-half-planes. Express the solutions in terms of Bessel functions. Give a qualitative description of the distribution of the zeros in the right half-plane.

14. If $G(z) = \tanh^2 z$, $K(z) \equiv 1$, we have $Z = \log \cosh z$. Set $Z = X + iY$. Show that the curve $X = 1$ divides the z-plane into two infinite regions H^+ and H^- plus infinitely many congruent bounded regions O_n centered on the points $z = (n + \frac{1}{2})\pi i$.

15. Show that the points $z = (n + \frac{1}{2})\pi i$ are regular singular points of the differential equation and determine the roots of the indicial equations. Show that if $w(z)$ is a solution, so is $w(z + \pi i)$.

16. Carry out the Liouville transformation and show the existence of sub-dominant solutions in H^+. Note that z must tend to infinity in such a manner that its distance from both axes becomes infinite. If $e(z)$ is subdominant for $x \to +\infty, y \to +\infty$, show that $e(z + \pi i)$ is also subdominant and hence that $e(z + \pi i) = Ce(z)$ and show that $C = e^{-\pi}$.

17. If $J_\alpha(z)$ is asymptotic to $Cz^{-1/2} \sin (z - x_0)$ as $z \to +\infty$, show that

$$-C \sin x_0 = (\tfrac{1}{2}\pi)^{1/2}(\alpha^2 - \tfrac{1}{4}) \int_0^\infty J_{1/2}(t)J_\alpha(t)\frac{dt}{t}, \alpha > -\tfrac{1}{2}.$$

7.5 ON THE CONFLUENT HYPERGEOMETRIC EQUATION

The hypergeometric equation has three regular singular points at 0, 1, ∞. The function

$$F\left(a, b, c; \frac{z}{b}\right) \tag{7.5.1}$$

satisfies the equation

$$z(b - z)w''(z) + [bc - (a + b + 1)z]w'(z) - abw(z) = 0 \tag{7.5.2}$$

with three regular singular points at $0, b, \infty$. If in this equation we divide by b and let $b \to \infty$, the result is

$$zw''(z) + (c - z)w'(z) - aw(z) = 0. \tag{7.5.3}$$

This equation has only two singularities: $z = 0$ which is a regular point and $z = \infty$ which is an irregular singular point. Since the singular point b of (7.5.2) has been brought into coincidence with the singular point at infinity, we refer to (7.5.3) as a *confluent hypergeometric equation*.

If we apply the same limiting process in (7.5.1) we obtain

$$\lim_{b \to \infty} F\left(a, b, c; \frac{z}{b}\right) = {}_1F_1(a, c; z) \tag{7.5.4}$$

in the notation of (7.3.36). It is a simple matter to show that this is a solution of (7.5.3), corresponding to the root 0 of the indicial equation. The other root is $1 - c$, just as in the hypergeometric case. We note that

$$z^{1-c}F\left(a - c + 1, b - c + 1, 2 - c: \frac{z}{b}\right)$$

is a solution of (7.5.2) for all b. Passing to the limit with b we obtain

$$z^{1-c}{}_1F_1(a - c + 1, 2 - c; z) \tag{7.5.5}$$

which is easily shown to be a second solution of (7.5.3). Here it is assumed that c is not an integer. If c is a negative integer or 0, the first solution becomes meaningless; if $c = 1$, the two solutions coincide, and if c is a positive integer >1, the second solution drops out. In any case, a second solution has to be found by some device or other. We shall not pay any further attention to these exceptional cases.

In Section 7.1 we found four different expressions for the hypergeometric series. The identity

$$F(a, b, c; z) = (1 - z)^{c-a-b}F(c - a, c - b, c; z)$$

carries over to the confluent case. If here we replace z by z/b and let $b \to \infty$, we get

$${}_1F_1(a, c; z) = e^{z}{}_1F_1(c - a, c; -z), \tag{7.5.6}$$

which is due to Kummer.

The same identity can be derived as follows. Substituting

$$w = e^{z}W$$

in Eq. (7.5.3), we see that W satisfies

$$zW'' + (c + z)W' + (c - a)W = 0. \tag{7.5.7}$$

The function

$${}_1F_1(c - a, c; -z)$$

is a solution of (7.5.7) as is seen by inspection. It follows that

$$e^{z}{}_1F_1(c - a, c; -z)$$

is a solution of (7.5.3). Since this function is holomorphic at the origin where it takes the value 1, Kummer's principle shows that it must coincide with ${}_1F_1(a, c; z)$, i.e. (7.5.6) holds.

From the second proof we can also draw the following conclusion:

Lemma 7.5.1. *If $T(a, c; z)$ is an analytic function of its three arguments which satisfies Eq.* (7.5.3), *then the equation is also satisfied by*

$$e^{z}T(c - a, c; -z).$$

The point at infinity is an irregular singularity of (7.5.3) and we have to find the asymptotic behavior of the solutions as $z \to \infty$. The equation is not self-adjoint, but may be made self-adjoint by multiplication by

$$z^{c-1}\, e^{-z}.$$

If, however, we apply the Liouville transformation with

$$G(z) = -az^{c-1}\, e^{-z}, \qquad K(z) = z^{c}\, e^{-z},$$

we obtain a transformed equation where

$$F(Z) = O(Z^2)$$

instead of the expected $O(Z^{-2})$ so the theorems of the preceding section do not apply. The following simple device enables us to get around this difficulty. We set

$$w = e^{z/2}U \tag{7.5.8}$$

and obtain the equation

$$zU'' + cU' - (\tfrac{1}{4}z - \tfrac{1}{2}c + a)U = 0. \tag{7.5.9}$$

To make this equation self-adjoint we need only multiply by

$$z^{c-1}.$$

The result is

$$\frac{d}{dz}\left(z^{c}\frac{du}{dz}\right) - [\tfrac{1}{4}z^{c} - (\tfrac{1}{2}c - a)z^{c-1}]U = 0. \tag{7.5.10}$$

Here the Liouville transformation leads to

$$Z = i\int^{z}\left\{\tfrac{1}{4} - (\tfrac{1}{2}c - a)\frac{1}{t}\right\}^{1/2} dt$$

$$= \tfrac{1}{2}iz - i(\tfrac{1}{2}c - a)\log z + O(1).$$

Using formula (7.4.27) we find that

$$F(Z) = O(z^{-2}) = O(Z^{-2}),$$

so the theory applies.

We have

$$e^{iZ} = e^{-z/2}z^{c/2-a}[1 + o(1)],$$
$$[G(z)K(z)]^{-1/4} = Az^{-c/2}[1 + o(1)].$$

Going back to the original equation we find for the subdominant in the right half-plane

$$e^{+}(z) = z^{-a}[1 + o(1)], \qquad -\tfrac{3}{2}\pi < \arg z < \tfrac{3}{2}\pi, \tag{7.5.11}$$

and for the subdominant in the left half-plane

$$e^{-}(z) = e^{z}z^{a-c}[1 + o(1)], \qquad -\tfrac{1}{2}\pi < \arg z < \tfrac{5}{2}\pi. \tag{7.5.12}$$

It is of some interest to supplement this information by actual asymptotic series. For this purpose we set

$$w = z^{-a}V$$

in (7.5.3) and find that V satisfies

$$V'' - [1 - (2a - c)z^{-1}]V' + a(a + 1 - c)z^{-2}V = 0. \tag{7.5.13}$$

We try to satisfy this equation by a power series in $1/z$, say

$$V(z) = \sum_{n=0}^{\infty} c_n z^{-n}.$$

We take $c_0 = 1$ and obtain the recursion relations

$$[n(n + 1) + (2a - c)n + a(a + 1 - c)]c_n + (n + 1)c_{n+1} = 0.$$

Hence

$$c_n = (-1)^n \frac{(a)_n(a + 1 - c)_n}{(1)_n}.$$

This gives the formal expansion

$$e^{+}(z) = z^{-a}{}_2F_0\left(a, a + 1 - c; -\frac{1}{z}\right) \tag{7.5.14}$$

and similarly

$$e^{-}(z) = e^{z}z^{a-c}{}_2F_0\left(c - a, 1 - a; \frac{1}{z}\right). \tag{7.5.15}$$

These are obviously divergent series but we shall show that they are asymptotic in the sense of Poincaré. It is enough to give the proof for $e^{+}(z)$. We set

$$V(z) = \sum_{k=0}^{n} c_k z^{-k} + R_n(z) \tag{7.5.16}$$

and find that $R_n(z)$ satisfies the non-homogeneous differential equation

$$R_n''(z) - (1 - \alpha z^{-1})R_n'(z) + \beta z^{-2}R_n(z) = \gamma_n z^{-n-2}, \tag{7.5.17}$$

where to abbreviate we set

$$\alpha = 2a - c, \quad \beta = a(a + 1 - c), \quad \gamma_n = -(n + a)(n + a + 1 - c)c_n.$$

We now have the following result:

Theorem 7.5.1 *For every n and ε, $n = 0, 1, 2, \ldots, 0 < \varepsilon$, there is an $M_n(\varepsilon)$ such that*

$$|z^{n+1}R_n(z)| \le M_n(\varepsilon), \qquad |\arg z| \le \tfrac{3}{2}\pi - \varepsilon, \qquad 1 \le |z|. \tag{7.5.18}$$

We base the proof on the following

Lemma 7.5.2 *Let $G(z)$ be holomorphic in the sector S: $|\arg z| < \frac{3}{2}\pi$, $1 < |z|$, on the Riemann surface of* $\log z$. *Let*

$$\int |G(t)|\,|dt| \le M \tag{7.5.19}$$

for all rectilinear paths in the sector. Then the equation

$$U''(z) - U'(z) = G(z) \tag{7.5.20}$$

has the solution

$$U(z) = \int_z^\infty [1 - e^{z-t}]G(t)\,dt, \tag{7.5.21}$$

where $z \in S$ and the path of integration is one of the rays $\arg(t - z) = \frac{1}{2}k\pi$, $k = -1, 0, 1$ *which lies in S. Moreover, this is the only solution of* (7.5.20) *which tends to* 0 *as $z \to \infty$, uniformly in the sector*

$$S_\varepsilon\colon |\arg z| \le \tfrac{3}{2}\pi - \varepsilon, \qquad 1 \le |z|.$$

Proof. Along one of the permissible paths of integration the kernel $1 - e^{z-t}$ does not exceed 2 in absolute value. Hence the integral (7.5.21) exists and obviously tends to 0 in the sector S_ε uniformly with respect to arg z. Twofold differentiation shows that $U(z)$ satisfies the equation (7.5.20). The general solution of this equation is

$$U(z) + A + B\,e^z$$

and this tends to zero in the right half-plane iff $A = B = 0$. ∎

Proof of Theorem 7.5.1. By definition $R_0(z)$ exists and is holomorphic in S. Formula (7.5.11) shows that $R_0(z) \to 0$ as $z \to \infty$ in any sector S_ε: $|\arg z| \le \frac{1}{2}\pi - \varepsilon$. Actually the discussion in Section 7.4 shows that

$$R_0(z) = O(Z^{-1}) = O(z^{-1}).$$

Since

$$R_n(z) = R_0(z) - \sum_1^n c_k z^{-k},$$

it follows that

$$R_n(z) = O(z^{-1})$$

for all large z and all n. Cauchy's integral gives

$$R_n'(z) = \frac{1}{2\pi i}\int_C \frac{R_n(t)}{(t-z)^2}\,dt.$$

Here we can integrate along the circle $|t - z| = r$ and for $z \in S_{2\varepsilon}$ we can choose r so that $\frac{1}{2}|z| > r > |z| \sin \varepsilon$. Then the circle C lies in S_ε at a distance from the origin which exceeds $\frac{1}{2}|z|$. It follows that

$$R_n'(z) = O(z^{-2}),$$

uniformly for z in S_ε. Here n is fixed.

We can now rewrite (7.5.17) as follows:

$$R_n''(z) - R_n'(z) = \alpha z^{-1}R_n'(z) - \beta z^{-2}R_n(z) + \gamma_n z^{-n-2}.$$

Here every term on the right is absolutely integrable along rectilinear paths in S. Since $R_n(z) \to 0$ in S_ε it follows that

$$R_n(z) = \int_z^\infty [1 - e^{z-t}][\alpha t^{-1}R_n'(t) - \beta t^{-2}R_n(t) + \gamma_n t^{-n-2}]\,dt. \tag{7.5.22}$$

We write this equation as

$$Y(z) = f(z) + \int_z^\infty [1 - e^{z-t}]\left\{\frac{\alpha}{t}\,Y'(t) - \frac{\beta}{t^2}\,Y(t)\right\}dt, \tag{7.5.23}$$

where

$$f(z) = \gamma_n \int_z^\infty [1 - e^{z-t}]t^{-n-2}\,dt. \tag{7.5.24}$$

As path of integration we can take any ray $\arg(t - z) = \theta$ with $|\theta| \le \frac{1}{2}\pi$ which lies in S. Along such a path

$$|e^{z-t}| \le 1, \qquad |1 - e^{z-t}| \le 2.$$

We can solve (7.5.23) by the method of successive approximations taking

$$Y_0(z) = f(z),$$

$$Y_k(z) = f(z) + \int_z^\infty [1 - e^{z-t}]\left\{\frac{\alpha}{t}\,Y_{k-1}'(t) - \frac{\beta}{t^2}\,Y_{k-1}(t)\right\}dt$$

for $k > 0$. To prove convergence we have to impose a restriction on n. We assume

$$n + 1 > B \equiv 2(|\alpha| + |\beta|). \tag{7.5.25}$$

We start by assuming $|\arg z| \leq \frac{1}{2}\pi$. We can then take $\arg t = \arg z$ as line of integration. Then

$$|f(z)| \leq 2|\gamma_n| \int_{|z|}^{\infty} s^{-n-2}\, ds = A|z|^{-n-1}, \qquad A = \frac{2|\gamma_n|}{n+1}, \tag{7.5.26}$$

and the same estimate holds for $f'(z)$. Suppose that for some integer k

$$\left.\begin{matrix} |Y_k(z) - Y_{k-1}(z)| \\ |Y_k'(z) - Y_{k-1}'(z)| \end{matrix}\right\} \leq A\left(\frac{B}{n+1}\right)^k |z|^{-n-1}. \tag{7.5.27}$$

We have then for $|z| > 1$

$$\begin{aligned} |Y_{k+1}(z) - Y_k(z)| &\leq 2|\alpha| \int_z^{\infty} \frac{1}{|t|} |Y_k'(t) - Y_{k-1}'(t)|\, |dt| \\ &\quad + 2|\beta| \int_z^{\infty} \frac{1}{|t|^2} |Y_k(t) - Y_{k-1}(t)|\, |dt| \\ &\leq AB\left(\frac{B}{n+1}\right)^k \int_{|z|}^{\infty} s^{-n-2}\, ds \\ &= A\left(\frac{B}{n+1}\right)^{k+1} |z|^{-n-1}. \end{aligned}$$

Since

$$Y_k'(z) = f'(z) - \int_z^{\infty} e^{z-t}\left\{\frac{\alpha}{t} Y_{k-1}'(t) - \frac{\beta}{t^2} Y_{k-1}(t)\right\} dt,$$

we obtain also

$$|Y_{k+1}'(z) - Y_k'(z)| \leq A\left(\frac{B}{n+1}\right)^{k+1} |z|^{-n-1}.$$

Now (7.5.27) is valid for $k = 1$, hence it holds for all k.

It follows that

$$\lim_{k\to\infty} Y_k(z) \equiv Y(z), \qquad \lim_{k\to\infty} Y_k'(z) \equiv Y'(z)$$

exist and

$$|Y(z)| \leq \frac{(n+1)A}{n+1-B} |z|^{-n-1}.$$

Hence we have

$$|R_n(z)| \leq \frac{2|\gamma_n|}{n+1-B} |z|^{-n-1}, \qquad |\arg z| \leq \tfrac{1}{2}\pi, \tag{7.5.28}$$

for

$$n + 1 > 2(|\alpha| + |\beta|).$$

Here

$$\gamma_n = (n+a)(n+a+1-c)c_n,$$

while

$$\alpha = \tfrac{1}{2}c - a, \qquad \beta = a(a+1-c)$$

are independent of n.

We note for $|\arg z| \le \frac{1}{2}\pi$ the bound for $|R_n(z)|$ is that solution of

$$u(r) = 2|\gamma_n| \int_r^\infty s^{-n-2}\,ds + B \int_r^\infty u(s)\,\frac{ds}{s}, \qquad r = |z|, \tag{7.5.29}$$

which satisfies

$$\lim_{r\to\infty} r^B u(r) = 0. \tag{7.5.30}$$

We have assumed $n > B - 1$. For smaller values of n we note that

$$R_k(z) = R_n(z) + c_n z^{-n} + \cdots + c_{k+1} z^{-k-1}.$$

This shows that

$$R_k(z) = O(z^{-k-1}), \qquad \forall k. \tag{7.5.31}$$

Hence we have proved (7.5.18) when z is confined to the right half-plane.

Suppose now that

$$-\tfrac{1}{2}\pi < \arg z < \tfrac{3}{2}\pi.$$

We use $\arg(t - z) = \frac{1}{2}\pi$ as line of integration and obtain as bound for $|R_n(z)|$ the function $V(x, y)$ determined by the analogue of (7.5.29)

$$V(x, y) = 2|\gamma_n| \int_y^\infty (s^2 + x^2)^{-(n+2)/2}\,ds$$

$$+ B \int_y^\infty (s^2 + x^2)^{-1/2} V(x, s)\,ds, \tag{7.5.32}$$

since on the line of integration $|t| = (s^2 + x^2)^{1/2}$, $0 \le s$. This equation gives

$$V_y'(x, y) + B(x^2 + y^2)^{-1/2}\,V(x, y) = -2|\gamma_n|(x^2 + y^2)^{-(n+2)/2}$$

and for $B < n + 1$ we have the integral

$$V(x, y) = 2|\gamma_n|[y + (x^2 + y^2)^{1/2}]^{-B} \int_y^\infty \frac{[s + (x^2 + s^2)^{1/2}]^B}{(x^2 + s^2)^{(n+2)/2}}\,ds. \tag{7.5.33}$$

This is the only integral which satisfies

$$\lim_{y\to+\infty} y^B V(x, y) = 0,$$

the analogue of (7.5.30).

Since

$$0 < \frac{s + (x^2 + s^2)^{1/2}}{(x^2 + s^2)^{1/2}} < 2,$$

we have

$$V(x, y) < 2^{B+1}|\gamma_n|[y + (x^2 + y^2)^{1/2}]^{-B} \int_y^\infty (x^2 + s^2)^{(B-n-2)/2}\,ds. \tag{7.5.34}$$

Here we set

$$x = r\cos\theta, \qquad y = r\sin\theta, \qquad r = |z|,$$

and obtain finally

$$V(x, y) < 2^{B+1}|\gamma_n| I_n^+(\theta) r^{-n-1}, \tag{7.5.35}$$

where

$$I_n^+(\theta) = (1 + \sin\theta)^{-B} \int_{\sin\theta}^{\infty} (\cos^2\theta + s^2)^{(B-n-2)/2}\, ds. \tag{7.5.36}$$

We note that

$$I_n^+(\theta) \le I_n^+(\tfrac{3}{2}\pi - \varepsilon) \quad \text{if} \quad -\tfrac{1}{2}\pi + \varepsilon \le \theta \le \tfrac{3}{2}\pi - \varepsilon. \tag{7.5.37}$$

We have

$$|R_n(z)| \le 2^{B+1} I_n^+(\theta) |z|^{-n-1}, \qquad -\tfrac{1}{2}\pi < \arg z < \tfrac{3}{2}\pi \tag{7.5.38}$$

for $n > B - 1$. The extension to smaller values of n is trivial.

Finally if

$$-\tfrac{3}{2}\pi < \arg z < \tfrac{1}{2}\pi$$

we use $\arg(t - z) = -\frac{1}{2}\pi$ as line of integration and obtain an estimate of the type (7.5.38) but with $I_n^+(\theta)$ replaced by

$$I_n^-(\theta) = (1 - \sin\theta)^{-B} \int_{-\infty}^{\sin\theta} [\cos^2\theta + s^2]^{(B-n-2)/2}\, ds. \tag{7.5.39}$$

The estimates obtained for the three subcases suffice to prove (7.5.18). ▮

There are various special cases of Eq. (7.3.3) which play an important role in the applications. We note first that if $a = -n$ is a negative integer, then ${}_1F_1(a, c; z)$ is a polynomial of degree n in z. We write

$${}_1F_1(-n, 1 + \alpha; z) = \binom{n+\alpha}{n} L_n^{(\alpha)}(z), \qquad \alpha > -1, \tag{7.5.40}$$

and refer to $L_n^{(\alpha)}(z)$ as the nth *Laguerre polynomial of order* α. In the special case $\alpha = 0$ the superscript is often dropped and $L_n(z)$ is the nth *Laguerre polynomial.*

These polynomials have many interesting properties. Let us consider the function

$$G(z, t) = (1 - t)^{-1} \exp\left(-\frac{zt}{1 - t}\right). \tag{7.5.41}$$

For fixed arbitrary z this function is holomorphic for t in the unit circle and can be expanded in a power series

$$G(z, t) = \sum_{n=0}^{\infty} A_n(z) t^n.$$

Here $A_n(z)$ is clearly a polynomial in z and

$$A_n(0) = 1.$$

Partial differentiation shows that

$$z\frac{\partial^2 G}{\partial z^2} + (1 - z)\frac{\partial G}{\partial z} + t\frac{\partial G}{\partial t} = 0.$$

Here we substitute the power series for $G(z, t)$, operate term-by-term and equate the coefficients to 0 obtaining

$$zA_n''(z) + (1 - z)A_n'(z) + nA_n(z) = 0.$$

This is Eq. (7.5.3) for $a = -n$, $c = 1$. It follows that

$$A_n(z) = L_n(z)$$

and

$$(1 - t)^{-1}\exp\left(-\frac{zt}{1 - t}\right) = \sum_{n=0}^{\infty} L_n(z)t^n, \qquad |t| < 1. \tag{7.5.42}$$

We can use this identity to prove that the functions

$$\{e^{-x/2}L_n(x)\}$$

form an orthonormal system for the interval $(0, \infty)$. To this end we consider

$$\int_0^\infty e^{-x}[G(x, t)]^2\,dx = (1 - t)^{-2}\int_0^\infty \exp\left(-x\frac{1 + t}{1 - t}\right)dx$$
$$= (1 - t^2)^{-1}.$$

On the other hand, proceeding formally we get

$$\sum_{m=0}^{\infty}\sum_{n=0}^{\infty} t^{m+n}\int_0^\infty e^{-x}L_m(x)L_n(x)\,dx = \sum_{m=0}^{\infty} t^{2m}, \qquad |t| < 1,$$

identically in t. This shows that

$$\int_0^\infty e^{-x}L_m(x)L_n(x)\,dx = \delta_{mn} \tag{7.5.43}$$

as asserted.

Here the term-by-term integration is justified if the double series

$$\sum_{m=0}^{\infty}\sum_{n=0}^{\infty} |t|^{m+n}\int_0^\infty e^{-x}|L_m(x)|\,|L_n(x)|\,dx$$

is convergent. To prove convergence we can use fairly crude estimates. We have

$$e^{-x/2}L_n(x) = \frac{1}{2\pi i}\int_C (1 - w)^{-1}\exp\left(-\tfrac{1}{2}x\frac{1 + w}{1 - w}\right)w^{-n-1}\,dw.$$

For $n > 0$ we take for C the circle

$$|w| = 1 - \frac{1}{n}$$

and note that

$$\Re\left(\frac{1+w}{1-w}\right) = \frac{1-|w|^2}{|1-w|^2} \geq \frac{1}{2n-1}$$

on C. Further

$$|w^{-n}| \leq 4, \qquad |1-w|^{-1} \leq n.$$

Hence

$$e^{-x/2}|L_n(x)| < 4n \exp\left(-\frac{x}{4n-2}\right) \tag{7.5.44}$$

and

$$\int_0^\infty e^{-x}|L_m(x)|\,|L_n(x)|\,dx \leq 64\,\frac{m^2n^2}{m+n}\,.$$

This estimate suffices to prove the convergence of the double series and, hence, the validity of the integral formulas. The Laguerre polynomials of order α, $\alpha \neq 0$, also form weighted orthogonal systems:

$$\{e^{-x/2}x^{\alpha/2}L_\alpha^{(n)}(x)\}. \tag{7.5.45}$$

Finally we note the formula

$$L_n(z) = \frac{1}{n!}\,e^z\,\frac{d^n}{dz^n}\,z^n\,e^{-z}. \tag{7.5.46}$$

This also generalizes to functions of order α. As a consequence of these formulas we observe that the zeros of a Laguerre polynomial are real positive.

There are several differential equations of importance which are reducible to confluent hypergeometric equations. One of these is Bessel's equation satisfied by *circular cylinder functions.* If in Bessel's equation

$$z^2w'' + zw' + (z^2 - \nu^2)w = 0$$

we set

$$t = 2iz, \qquad w = z^\nu\,e^{iz}u$$

we obtain

$$t\,\frac{d^2u}{dt^2} + (2\nu + 1 - t)\,\frac{du}{dt} - (\nu + \tfrac{1}{2})u = 0 \tag{7.5.47}$$

which is, except for notation, Eq. (7.5.3) with

$$a = \nu + \tfrac{1}{2}, \qquad c = 2a = 2\nu + 1.$$

Another important case is

$$w'' + (\gamma - z^2)w = 0, \tag{7.5.48}$$

known as the *Hermite-Weber equation,* since it was considered by Charles Hermite (1822–1901) in 1865 and by Heinrich Weber (1842–1913) in 1869.

The solutions are known as *parabolic cylinder functions* because they arise in potential problems involving parabolic cylinders. If in (7.5.48) we set

$$t = z^2, \qquad u = e^{z^2/2}w,$$

we obtain the confluent hypergeometric equation

$$t\frac{d^2u}{dt^2} + (\tfrac{1}{2} - t)\frac{du}{dt} + \tfrac{1}{4}(\gamma - 1)u = 0$$

with

$$a = -\tfrac{1}{4}(\gamma - 1), \qquad c = \tfrac{1}{2}.$$

Here the case where

$$\gamma = 2m + 1, \qquad m = 0, 1, 2, \ldots$$

is particularly important. We note that for $\gamma = 4n + 1$

$${}_1F_1(-n, \tfrac{1}{2}; t)$$

is a polynomial in t of degree n while for $\gamma = 4n + 3$

$$t^{1/2}{}_1F_1(-n, \tfrac{3}{2}; t)$$

is $t^{1/2}$ times a polynomial in t of degree n. This means that for $\gamma = 2m + 1$ Eq. (7.5.48) has the solution

$$E_m(z) = e^{-z^2/2}H_m(z), \tag{7.5.49}$$

where $H_m(z)$ is a polynomial, the mth *Hermite polynomial.* These polynomials are normalized differently by different authors. We use here the constant multiplier which is consistent with the definition by the generating function

$$\exp(2zt - t^2) = \sum_0^\infty H_n(z)\frac{t^n}{n!}, \tag{7.5.50}$$

or, equivalently,

$$H_n(z) = (-1)^n e^{z^2}\frac{d^n}{dz^n}(e^{-z^2}). \tag{7.5.51}$$

The functions $E_n(z)$ form an orthogonal system for the interval $(-\infty, \infty)$. To verify this we can use the differential equation. We have

$$E_m''(x) + (2m + 1 - x^2)E_m(x) = 0,$$
$$E_n''(x) + (2n + 1 - x^2)E_n(x) = 0.$$

We multiply the first equation by $E_n(x)$, the second by $E_m(x)$, and subtract. The result can be written

$$\frac{d}{dx}[E_m(x)E_n'(x) - E_n(x)E_m'(x)] = 2(m - n)E_m(x)E_n(x).$$

This identity we integrate between the limits $-\omega$ and ω. The integrated parts tend to 0 as $\omega \to \infty$ giving

$$\int_{-\infty}^{\infty} E_m(x)E_n(x)\,dx = \int_{-\infty}^{\infty} e^{-x^2}H_m(x)H_n(x)\,dx = 0 \tag{7.5.52}$$

if $m \neq n$. This proves orthogonality but does not give the value of the integral for $m = n$. Here we can proceed as in the Laguerre case and use the generating function. Thus

$$\int_{-\infty}^{\infty} e^{-x^2}\, e^{4xt-2t^2}\,dx = \sqrt{\pi}\, e^{2t^2} = \sqrt{\pi}\sum_{0}^{\infty}\frac{2^n}{n!}t^{2n}$$

and

$$\int_{-\infty}^{\infty} e^{-x^2}\left\{\sum_{0}^{\infty} H_n(x)\frac{t^n}{n!}\right\}^2 dx = \sum_{0}^{\infty}\frac{t^{2n}}{(n!)^2}\int_{-\infty}^{\infty} e^{-x^2}[H_n(x)]^2\,dx,$$

so that

$$\int_{-\infty}^{\infty} e^{-x^2}[H_n(x)]^2\,dx = \sqrt{\pi}\,2^n n!. \tag{7.5.53}$$

Termwise integration can be justified as in the Laguerre case.

The function $E_n(z)$ is the subdominant solution of the equation (7.5.48) for $\gamma = 2n + 1$ in the two sectors

$$-\tfrac{1}{4}\pi < \arg z < \tfrac{1}{4}\pi \quad \text{and} \quad \tfrac{3}{4}\pi < \arg z < \tfrac{5}{4}\pi.$$

This is exceptional and such coincidence happens only when γ has the characteristic values $2n + 1$, $n = 0, 1, 2, \ldots$ In general we have

$$Z = \int_{0}^{z} (\gamma - t^2)^{1/2}\,dt = \tfrac{1}{2}iz^2 - \tfrac{1}{2}i\gamma\log z + O(1)$$

and the subdominant in the sector $|\arg z| < \tfrac{1}{4}\pi$ is

$$\exp(-\tfrac{1}{2}z^2)z^{(\gamma-1)/2}\left\{1 + O\left(\frac{1}{z}\right)\right\} \tag{7.5.54}$$

The subdominant in the sector $\tfrac{3}{4}\pi < \arg z < \tfrac{5}{4}\pi$ has the same expression. We obtain the asymptotic expressions for the subdominants in the sectors $\tfrac{1}{4}\pi < \arg z < \tfrac{3}{4}\pi$ and $\tfrac{5}{4}\pi < \arg z < \tfrac{7}{4}\pi$ by changing the minus sign to a plus in (7.5.54).

EXERCISE 7.5

1. Verify that ${}_1F_1(a, a; z) = e^z$.

2. Verify that ${}_1F_1(\tfrac{1}{2}, \tfrac{3}{2}; -z^2) = z^{-1}\int_0^z e^{-t^2}\,dt$.

3. Verify that ${}_1F_1(\alpha, 1 + \alpha; - z) = \alpha z^{-\alpha}e^{z} \int_0^z e^{-t}t^{\alpha-1}\,dt$.

4. Show that the oscillatory solutions of (7.5.3) have their distant zeros in ε-sectors about the imaginary axis.

5. Verify (7.5.46) and generalize for $\alpha \neq 0$.

6. Verify that the functions (7.5.45) are orthogonal using the differential equation in self-adjoint form.

7. Prove that $L_n(z)$ has only real positive zeros.

8. Express $J_\nu(z)$ in terms of functions ${}_1F_1$.

9. Verify that $H_n(z)$ satisfies the differential equation

$$w''(z) - 2zw'(z) + 2nw(z) = 0.$$

10. Find $H_{2n}(0)$.

11. Find $H'_{2n+1}(0)$.

12. Prove that $H_n(z)$ has only real zeros.

13. Get some estimates of $E_n(z)$ sufficiently good to justify the termwise integration used in obtaining (7.5.53).

14. If $\gamma = 0$, express the solutions of (7.5.48) in terms of Bessel functions.

15. If $\gamma = -1$, show that

$$\exp(\tfrac{1}{2}z^2) \int_z^\infty \exp(-t^2)\,dt$$

is a subdominant solution of (7.5.48) for the sector $|\arg z| < \tfrac{1}{4}\pi$ and find subdominant solutions for the other three sectors using similar constructions.

16. The solutions of (7.5.48) are entire functions of z. Show that the number of zeros of such a solution within a disk of radius r is $(2/\pi)r^2 + O(r)$ unless the solution is subdominant and $\gamma \neq 2n + 1$ in which case the number is reduced to one half of the stated expression. What happens when $\gamma = 2n + 1$?

The equation

$$(1 + z^2)^2 w''(z) + \lambda w(z) = 0$$

is known as *Halm's equation.*

17. Show that $z = \pm i$ are regular singular points and find the roots of the corresponding indicial equations in terms of λ. What is the nature of the point at infinity?

18. Find the general solution by the substitution

$$t = \arc\tan z, \qquad u = (1 + z^2)^{-1/2}w.$$

19. Let $z = x$ be real. Find the solution which tends to the limit 1 as (i) $x \to +\infty$, (ii) $x \to -\infty$. What condition must λ satisfy in order that these solutions be identical?

7.6. MATHIEU'S EQUATION

Émile Léonard Mathieu (1835–1890) has had his name attached to a finite group and to the differential equation

$$w''(z) + [a + b \cos 2z]w(z) = 0, \tag{7.6.1}$$

which he discussed in 1868. It is one of the simplest equations with periodic coefficients. The solutions are sometimes called *functions of the elliptic cylinder* since they arise in potential problems for elliptic cylinders. They are entire functions of z of infinite order.

Since the equation is invariant under the transformation $z \to z + \pi$, it follows that if $w(z)$ is a solution so is $w(z + k\pi)$ for any integer k. It is natural to ask if

$$w(z + k\pi) = w(z) \tag{7.6.2}$$

for some particular choice of $w(z)$ and some particular integer k. Actually the physical problems call for solutions of period π or 2π. The existence of periodic solutions will depend upon a suitable relation holding between the parameters a and b. If b is given, there are infinitely many values of a for which a solution of (7.6.1) with the period $k\pi$ will exist.

We start the discussion by examining the solutions on the real axis, assuming a and b to be real. There are real solutions and their behavior on the real axis will depend upon the properties of

$$F(x) = a + b \cos 2x. \tag{7.6.3}$$

This function may keep a constant sign, plus or minus, or it may change its sign infinitely often. We disregard the last possibility for the time being.

Suppose that

$$a < 0, \qquad |b| < |a| \tag{7.6.4}$$

so that $F(x) < 0$ for all x. In this case the real solutions are non-oscillatory on the real axis in the strict sense that the equation

$$w(z)w'(z) = 0 \tag{7.6.5}$$

has at most one real root. This follows from the identity

$$[w(x)w'(x)]_{x_1}^{x_2} - \int_{x_1}^{x_2} [w'(s)]^2 \, ds + \int_{x_1}^{x_2} F(s)[w(s)]^2 \, ds = 0 \tag{7.6.6}$$

To get this relation, we set $z = x$ in (7.6.1), multiply by $w(x)$ and integrate from x_1 to x_2. The first two terms arise when we integrate $w(x)w''(x)$ by parts.

Assuming $F(x) < 0$ for all x and that $w(x)$ is a non-trivial real solution of (7.6.1), we see that the equation (7.6.5) can have at most one real root.

This simple observation leads to a qualitative classification of the real solutions of (7.6.1) according as the solution has a zero or an extremum or neither one nor the other. Solutions of the first type can clearly be either strictly increasing or strictly decreasing, while solutions of the second type keep a constant sign and have a single minimum or a single maximum according as the sign is plus or minus. The existence of such solutions is obvious.

The existence of solutions of type three will be proved in a more general context in Chapter 9. We state what we need here as lemmas without proof.

Lemma 7.6.1. *Let* $G(x) > 0$ *be continuous in* $(-\infty, \infty)$. *Then the equation*

$$y''(x) - G(x)y(x) = 0 \tag{7.6.7}$$

has one and only one solution $y_+(x)$ *passing through* $(0, 1)$ *which is positive and strictly decreasing for all* x *and one and only one solution* $y_-(x)$ *through* $(0, 1)$ *which is positive and strictly increasing for all* x. *Further*

$$[G(x)]^{1/2}y_+(x) \in L_2(0, \infty), \qquad y'_+(x) \in L_2(0, \infty). \tag{7.6.8}$$

Lemma 7.6.2. *If*

$$0 < \alpha^2 \le G(x) \le \beta^2 < \infty, \tag{7.6.9}$$

then the solution $y_+(x)$ *of* (7.6.7) *satisfies*

$$e^{-\beta x} \le y_+(x) \le e^{-\alpha x}, \qquad 0 < x. \tag{7.6.10}$$

These lemmas obviously apply to Mathieu's equation and we can take

$$\alpha = (|a| - |b|)^{1/2}, \qquad \beta = (|a| + |b|)^{1/2}. \tag{7.6.11}$$

Hence if (7.6.4) holds the equation has two uniquely determined solutions $w_+(z)$ and $w_-(z)$ with the following properties:

$$w_+(0) = w_-(0) = 1, \tag{7.6.12}$$

$$\lim_{x\to+\infty} w_+(x) = 0, \qquad \lim_{x\to-\infty} w_-(x) = 0. \tag{7.6.13}$$

We refer to these solutions as the *normalized subdominant solutions* for approach to $+\infty$ and $-\infty$, respectively.

These solutions have been defined for real values of z but the analytic extension can be made to the finite complex plane since all solutions of (7.6.1) are entire functions of z. Further properties of these subdominants are obtainable from the differential equation. We note first that

$$w_-(z) = w_+(-z) \tag{7.6.14}$$

for the right member is a solution, subdominant for approach to $-\infty$ and normalized at $z = 0$. Since the normalized subdominant is unique, (7.6.14) must hold.

Secondly, we note that $w_+(z + \pi)$ is also subdominant for approach to $+\infty$. It follows that $w_+(z + \pi)$ is a constant multiple of $w_+(z)$ and since $w_+(x)$ is decreasing we have

$$w_+(z + \pi) = Cw_+(z), \qquad 0 < C < 1. \tag{7.6.15}$$

We now set

$$C = e^{-\pi\gamma} \tag{7.6.16}$$

and define $P(z)$ by

$$w_+(z) = e^{-\gamma z}P(z). \tag{7.6.17}$$

It follows that

$$P(z + \pi) = P(z), \tag{7.6.18}$$

i.e. $P(z)$ is periodic of period π. By Lemma 7.6.2 we have

$$\alpha \leq \gamma \leq \beta. \tag{7.6.19}$$

We note in particular that γ cannot be 0, i.e. $w_+(z)$ cannot be periodic.

It follows that $w_+(z)$ is subdominant for $z = x + iy$ tending to infinity in such a manner that $x \to +\infty$ while $|y|$ stays bounded. The convergence of $w_+(z)$ to 0 is not uniform with respect to y.

Before leaving the case (7.6.4), that is $F(x) < 0$, let us observe that the equation can have no periodic solution with a real period in this case. For such a solution may be assumed to be real on the real axis. It can then have neither zeros nor extrema since there can be at most one of either kind. It must then be strictly monotone and of constant sign and we have seen that $w_+(z)$ is not periodic.

In case (7.6.4), Mathieu's equation was seen to have two linearly independent solutions of the form

$$w(z) = \exp(-\gamma z)P(z), \qquad P(z + \pi) = P(z). \tag{7.6.20}$$

A similar observation holds for arbitrary values of a and b. In fact, this is a very special case of results obtained by G. Floquet in 1883 concerning systems of differential equations with simply-periodic coefficients. A modern version of Floquet's theorem is given by

Theorem 7.6.1. *Let $\mathfrak{F}(z)$ be a matrix in $\mathfrak{M}_n$ which is holomorphic in a strip $-b < y < b \leq \infty$, $z = x + iy$, and satisfies*

$$\mathfrak{F}(z + \omega) = \mathfrak{F}(z) \tag{7.6.21}$$

for some real ω. Then the differential equation

$$\mathfrak{W}'(z) = \mathfrak{F}(z)\mathfrak{W}(z) \tag{7.6.22}$$

has a fundamental solution of the form

$$\mathfrak{W}(z) = \mathfrak{T}(z)\exp(z\mathfrak{K}). \tag{7.6.23}$$

Here $\mathfrak{T}(z)$ is a regular matrix, holomorphic in the strip $-b < y < b$ and periodic with period ω, and $\mathfrak{K}$ is a constant matrix.

Proof. Suppose that $\mathcal{W}(z)$ is a fundamental solution. Then $\mathcal{W}(z)$ is holomorphic in the strip. The matrix $\mathcal{W}(z + \omega)$ is also a fundamental solution, so there exists a constant regular matrix $\mathcal{A}$ with

$$\mathcal{W}(z + \omega) = \mathcal{W}(z)\mathcal{A}.$$

Since $\mathcal{A}$ is regular, we can define $\log \mathcal{A}$ by

$$\log \mathcal{A} = \frac{1}{2\pi i} \int_C \log \lambda \quad \mathfrak{R}(\lambda, \mathcal{A})\, d\lambda \tag{7.6.24}$$

where C is a simple closed contour surrounding the spectrum of $\mathcal{A}$ once in the positive sense and leaving $\lambda = 0$ on the outside. Here $\log \lambda$ is real on the positive real axis. Set

$$\mathcal{K} = \frac{1}{\omega} \log \mathcal{A} \qquad \text{so that} \qquad \mathcal{A} = \exp [\omega\mathcal{K}]$$

and let

$$\mathcal{W}(z) = \mathcal{T}(z) \exp (z\mathcal{K}).$$

Then

$$\begin{aligned} \mathcal{W}(z + \omega) &= \mathcal{T}(z + \omega) \exp (z\mathcal{K}) \exp (\omega\mathcal{K}) \\ &= \mathcal{T}(z) \exp (z\mathcal{K})\mathcal{A} \end{aligned}$$

so that

$$\mathcal{T}(z + \omega) = \mathcal{T}(z). \tag{7.6.25}$$

It is clear that $\mathcal{T}(z)$ is holomorphic and non-singular in the strip. ∎

The theorem does not extend automatically to arbitrary Banach algebras since regular elements need not have logarithms.

We return to the Mathieu equation where (7.6.20) holds for two solutions, the values of γ being negatives of each other. It is natural to ask if, for some choice of a and b, one γ is 0 or, more generally, a rational multiple of i, so that the corresponding solution is actually periodic. This question has several aspects and one of these leads to *boundary value problems* for (7.6.1).

Suppose that $w(z)$ is a solution of (7.6.1) which is periodic of period ω, a multiple of π. There are three possibilities: $w(z)$ may be even or odd or neither one nor the other. In the third case $w(-z)$ is also a periodic solution of the same period and so are

$$\tfrac{1}{2}[w(z) + w(-z)] \qquad \text{and} \qquad \tfrac{1}{2}[w(z) - w(-z)].$$

The first of these is even, the second is odd. Hence there is no loss of generality to assume that a periodic solution is either even or odd. Thus it satisfies either

$$w'(0) = 0 \qquad \text{or} \qquad w(0) = 0.$$

Consider the second case and impose the additional condition that $w(\pi) = 0$.

Find solutions of Mathieu's equation such that

$$w(0) = 0, \qquad w(\pi) = 0. \tag{7.6.26}$$

These conditions imply

$$w(-z) = -w(z), \qquad w(\pi - z) = -w(\pi + z)$$

respectively, and combining we get

$$w(z + 2\pi) = w(z),$$

i.e. the solution is periodic of period 2π.

In the same manner we see that a solution of

$$w'(0) = 0, \qquad w'(\pi) = 0 \tag{7.6.27}$$

has the period 2π while

$$w(0) = 0, \quad w(\tfrac{1}{2}\pi) = 0 \qquad \text{or} \qquad w'(0) = 0, \quad w'(\tfrac{1}{2}\pi) = 0$$

give period π and

$$w(0) = 0, \qquad w'(\pi) = 0$$

period 4π. Generalizations are obvious.

The boundary condition (7.6.26) cannot be satisfied by a non-trivial solution for arbitrary values of a and b, but, if b is given, there are infinitely many values of a for which Mathieu's equation has solutions satisfying (7.6.26). These values are known as the *characteristic values* of the corresponding boundary value problem. Similar results hold for the other boundary conditions listed above.

In Chapter 8 we shall prove the existence of characteristic values for various classes of boundary value problems under fairly general assumptions. For this reason we restrict ourselves here to some observations which make the existence of characteristic values and functions plausible and show some of their properties if they do exist.

First a remark concerning the function theoretical aspects of the problem. The initial conditions

$$w(0) = 0, \qquad w'(0) = 1$$

determine $w_1(z; a, b)$ as the unique solution of the integral equation

$$w(z) = z - \int_0^z (z - s)(a + b \cos 2s)w(s)\, ds.$$

This is clearly an entire function of a and of b. For $z = x$ real positive, we see that $|w(x)| \equiv u(x)$ satisfies the inequality

$$u(x) \leq x + (|a| + |b|) \int_0^x (x - s)u(s)\, ds.$$

According to Problem 8, Exercise 3.4 this implies that

$$|w_1(x; a, b)| \leq (|a| + |b|)^{-1/2} \sinh [(|a| + |b|)^{1/2}x].$$

It follows that for b fixed the function

$$w_1(\pi; a, b)$$

is an entire function of a whose order is at most $\frac{1}{2}$. Now a transcendental entire function of order $\leq \frac{1}{2}$ has infinitely many zeros $\{a_n(b)\}$ and, moreover, the series

$$\sum_n |a_n(b)|^{-\sigma}$$

converges for any $\sigma > \frac{1}{2}$.

Thus unless $w_1(\pi; a, b)$ should happen to reduce to a polynomial in a for some particular choice of b, we see that the boundary value problem (7.6.26) has infinitely many characteristic values $\{a_n(b)\}$. Actually these values could be computed at least approximately from the equation

$$w_1(\pi; a, b) = 0. \tag{7.6.28}$$

We are interested in periodic solutions of (7.6.1), in particular, solutions of period π or 2π. Now periodicity suggests trigonometric Fourier series rather than power series. Corresponding to the four boundary value problems

$$\begin{aligned} &\text{i) } w'(0) = 0,\ w'(\tfrac{1}{2}\pi) = 0; &&\text{ii) } w(0) = 0,\ w(\tfrac{1}{2}\pi) = 0;\\ &\text{iii) } w'(0) = 0,\ w'(\pi) = 0; &&\text{iv) } w(0) = 0,\ w(\pi) = 0; \end{aligned} \tag{7.6.29}$$

we have the series expansions

$$\begin{aligned} &\text{i) } \sum_{k=0}^{\infty} a_{k,n} \cos 2kz; &&\text{ii) } \sum_{k=1}^{\infty} b_{k,n} \sin 2kz;\\ &\text{iii) } \sum_{k=0}^{\infty} c_{k,n} \cos (2k + 1)z; &&\text{iv) } \sum_{k=0}^{\infty} d_{k,n} \sin (2k + 1)z; \end{aligned} \tag{7.6.30}$$

for the corresponding characteristic functions. These functions are denoted by the symbols

$$\text{i) } \mathrm{ce}_{2n}(z), \quad \text{ii) } \mathrm{se}_{2n}(z), \quad \text{iii) } \mathrm{ce}_{2n+1}(z), \quad \text{iv) } \mathrm{se}_{2n+1}(z),$$

and the notation is such that

$$\lim_{b\to 0} \mathrm{ce}_m(z) = \cos mz, \qquad \lim_{b\to 0} \mathrm{se}_m(z) = \sin mz.$$

The coefficients of the Fourier series are analytic functions of b. If we substitute such a series, say type (iii) under (7.6.30), in Eq. (7.6.1) and simplify the cosine products, we obtain an infinite system of linear equations in infinitely many unknowns, first

$$(1 - a + \tfrac{1}{2}b)c_0 + \tfrac{1}{2}bc_1 = 0,$$

and, for $k = 1, 2, 3, \ldots$,

$$\tfrac{1}{2}b(c_{k-1} + c_{k+1}) + [a - (2k+1)^2]c_k = 0. \tag{7.6.31}$$

Actually we can solve the equations consecutively in terms of c_0, but, unless there is an appropriate relation between a and b, the resulting formal Fourier series will not converge. This is a homogeneous system and we would expect the corresponding determinant to be zero for consistency. This, however, is an *infinite determinant* and serious questions of convergence arise.

Infinite determinants had first been encountered by the American astronomer G. W. Hill (1838–1914) in lunar theory where, what is nowadays known as Hill's equation,

$$w''(z) + \left\{\sum_0^\infty h_k \cos 2kz\right\} w(z) = 0 \tag{7.6.32}$$

plays an important role. The reader will recognize that this equation is reducible to type (7.6.22) to which the Floquet theory applies. Hill's investigation was put on a rigorous basis by Henri Poincaré in connection with the latter's revision of celestial mechanics. G. Mittag-Leffler, with his flair for recognizing important work, republished Hill's paper in *Acta Mathematica*, **8** (1886), and directed the attention of his pupil Helge von Koch to these questions. The latter developed the theory of infinite determinants into a powerful tool and applied it to important problems in the theory of linear differential equations.

The determinants considered by von Koch in his earlier papers are of the form

$$D = \det(\delta_{jk} + a_{jk}), \tag{7.6.33}$$

where

$$\sum_{j=0}^\infty \sum_{k=0}^\infty |a_{jk}| \tag{7.6.34}$$

is convergent. Such determinants are absolutely convergent in a sense that need not be specified here. Further

$$|D| \le P \equiv \prod_{j=0}^\infty \left\{1 + \sum_{k=0}^\infty |a_{jk}|\right\}, \tag{7.6.35}$$

and the same bound holds for all its minors. The system

$$\sum_{k=0}^\infty (\delta_{jk} + a_{jk})x_k = y_j, \qquad j = 0, 1, 2, \ldots \tag{7.6.36}$$

has a unique solution in (m) if $D \neq 0$ and the homogeneous system has solutions in (m) iff $D = 0$.

The system (7.6.31) can be brought to this form by dividing the kth equation by $-(2k+1)^2$. The resulting determinant $D(a, b)$ is absolutely convergent. Computation of the corresponding bound P gives

$$|D(a, b)| \leq \cosh [\tfrac{1}{2}\pi(|a| + |b|)^{1/2}]. \tag{7.6.37}$$

Thus $D(a, b)$ is an entire function of a for b fixed which is of order $\leq \frac{1}{2}$. The characteristic values of the boundary value problem (7.6.29) (iii) are the roots of the equation

$$D(a, b) = 0. \tag{7.6.38}$$

Again the problem of finding the characteristic values leads to the problem of finding the zeros of an entire function of order $\leq \frac{1}{2}$ and we conclude that, if this function is transcendental, there are indeed infinitely many characteristic values.

We leave these considerations and proceed to prove

Theorem 7.6.2. *If b is real, then all characteristic values of the four boundary value problems are real. The corresponding characteristic functions form an orthogonal system in $L_2(-\pi, \pi)$.*

Proof. We need the identity

$$[\overline{w(x)}w'(x)]_\alpha^\beta - \int_\alpha^\beta |w'(s)|^2\, ds + \int_\alpha^\beta (a + b\cos 2s)|w(s)|^2\, ds = 0. \tag{7.6.39}$$

This is the analogue of (7.6.6) for complex valued solutions and is obtained by multiplying (7.6.1) by $\overline{w(x)}$ and integrating from α to β. Here as usual the bar indicates the complex conjugate. If $w(x)$ is one of the characteristic functions of any one of the boundary value problems and if $\alpha = -\pi$, $\beta = \pi$, then the integrated part is zero and we obtain

$$\int_{-\pi}^{\pi} (a + b\cos 2s)|w(s)|^2\, ds = \int_{-\pi}^{\pi} |w'(s)|^2\, ds.$$

Hence, b real implies a real.

The orthogonality of $\text{ce}_m(x)$ and $\text{se}_n(x)$ over the interval $(-\pi, \pi)$ is obvious from the structure of the defining series since we can multiply out and integrate termwise. In order to prove that, e.g. $\text{ce}_m(x)$ and $\text{ce}_n(x)$ are orthogonal, we use the differential equations. If the corresponding parameters are a_m and a_n, we see that

$$\text{ce}_m(x) = u(x), \qquad \text{ce}_n(x) = v(x)$$

satisfy

$$u''(x) + [a_m + b\cos 2x]u(x) = 0,$$
$$v''(x) + [a_n + b\cos 2x]v(x) = 0.$$

This gives

$$\int_{-\pi}^{\pi} [v(x)u''(x) - u(x)v''(x)]\, dx + (a_m - a_n) \int_{-\pi}^{\pi} u(x)v(x)\, dx = 0.$$

Integration by parts shows that the first integral is 0 by virtue of the boundary conditions and the periodicity. Thus $u(x)$ and $v(x)$ are orthogonal in $(-\pi, \pi)$. Pairs $\mathrm{se}_m(x)$ and $\mathrm{se}_n(x)$ are handled in the same manner. ▮

The periodic solutions of (7.6.1), in particular, the functions $\mathrm{ce}_m(z)$ and $\mathrm{se}_m(z)$ are known as *Mathieu functions of the first kind.*

Let us look briefly at the case where $F(x) > 0$ for all x. Here all real solutions of (7.6.1) are oscillatory on the real axis in the sense that every such solution has infinitely many real zeros and hence also infinitely many real extrema. This follows from oscillation theorems to be proved in Chapter 8. There we shall also prove inequalities for the number $N(x_1, x_2; w)$ of zeros of the solution $w(x)$ in the interval (x_1, x_2). In the present case the frequency of the zeros is somewhat uneven; there are more zeros near a maximum of $F(x)$ than near a minimum. If $x_2 - x_1$ is large, $N(x_1, x_2; w)$ is practically independent of w and of the position of x_1 and depends mainly on $x_2 - x_1$. We shall not elaborate on this point at this juncture.

We pass to the complex plane where new interesting features await us. We suppose a and b to be real. The function

$$F(z) = a + b \cos 2z$$

is real on the real axis and on each of the lines

$$x = \tfrac{1}{2}k\pi,$$

where k is 0 or any integer. In particular, on the imaginary axis Mathieu's equation takes the form

$$U''(y) - (a + b \cosh 2y)U(y) = 0, \qquad U(y) = w(iy). \tag{7.6.40}$$

The same form holds on any of the lines $x = k\pi$. Solutions of this equation are known as *associated Mathieu functions.*

To simplify matters here, we assume $a > 0$, $b > 0$. Then the coefficient of $U(y)$ is negative for all values of y, and Lemma 7.6.1 applies. Thus there exist subdominant solutions $U_+(y)$ and $U_-(y)$ such that

$$\lim_{y \to +\infty} U_+(y) = 0, \qquad \lim_{y \to -\infty} U_-(y) = 0$$

and

$$U_+(0) = U_-(0) = 1.$$

Moreover, for reasons of symmetry

$$U_-(y) = U_+(-y).$$

Lemma 7.6.2 does not apply in the present case. We shall find later that

$$U_+(y) = \exp\,[-(\tfrac{1}{2}b)^{1/2}e^y - \tfrac{1}{2}y]\{1 + o(1)\} \qquad (7.6.41)$$

as $y \to +\infty$. We denote the analytic continuation of $U_+(y)$ to the rest of the complex plane by $E(z)$ so that

$$E(iy) = U_+(y).$$

On the line $x = \frac{1}{2}\pi$ Mathieu's equation takes the form

$$V''(y) + [-a + b\cosh 2y]V(y) = 0, \qquad V(y) = w(\tfrac{1}{2}\pi + iy). \quad (7.6.42)$$

Still assuming $a > 0$, $b > 0$ we see that the coefficient of $V(y)$ is positive, for all y if $a < b$, for

$$|y| > \tfrac{1}{2}\log\left\{\frac{1}{b}\,[a + (a^2 - b^2)^{1/2}]\right\} \qquad \text{if} \quad a > b.$$

It follows that any solution of (7.6.1) which is real on one of the lines $x = (k + \frac{1}{2})\pi$ has infinitely many zeros on the line. Moreover the frequency of the oscillation becomes infinite with $|y|$ in the sense that the distance between consecutive zeros is approximately

$$\pi(2/b)^{1/2}\,e^{-|y|} \qquad \text{as} \quad |y| \to \infty.$$

A simple calculation shows that the functions $\mathrm{ce}_m(z)$ and $\mathrm{se}_m(z)$ are either real or purely imaginary on all lines

$$x = \tfrac{1}{2}k\pi.$$

More precisely, $\mathrm{ce}_{2n}(z)$ is real on all these lines while, e.g. $\mathrm{se}_{2n+1}(z)$ is real if k is odd but purely imaginary if k is even. It follows that each Mathieu function of the first kind has infinitely many zeros on each of the lines

$$x = m\pi.$$

In addition there are infinitely many real zeros. It will be shown in Chapter 11 that this accounts for all the zeros of these functions.

The lines

$$x = (k + \tfrac{1}{2})\pi, \qquad k = 0, \pm 1, \pm 2, \ldots$$

together with the real axis divide the complex plane into infinitely many half-strips

$$\begin{aligned} D_k^+ &: [z \mid z = x + iy, (k - \tfrac{1}{2})\pi < x < (k + \tfrac{1}{2})\pi, 0 < y], \\ D_k^- &: [z \mid z = x + iy, (k - \tfrac{1}{2})\pi < x < (k + \tfrac{1}{2})\pi, y < 0]. \end{aligned} \qquad (7.6.43)$$

In each of these half-strips we have a unique normalized subdominant solution, namely

$$E(z - k\pi) \text{ in } D_k^+, \qquad E(k\pi - z) \text{ in } D_k^-, \qquad (7.6.44)$$

where k is any integer or zero.

To study the equation in a half-strip we resort to the Liouville transformation. It is enough to give the discussion for D_0^+. We set

$$Z(z) = \int_0^z [a + b \cos 2s]^{1/2}\, ds, \tag{7.6.45}$$

where the square root is taken to be positive at $s = 0$. Here as above we assume $a > 0$, $b > 0$. The branch points of the square root are then located either on the real axis or on the vertical boundary lines of the half-strips.

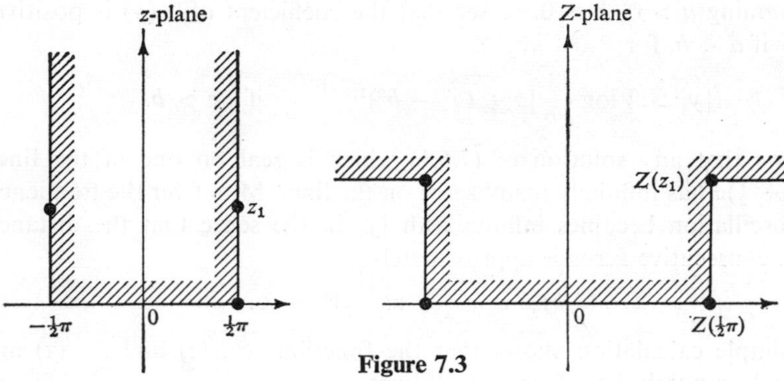

Figure 7.3

It follows that $Z(z)$ is single valued in D_0^+. A simple argument shows that $Z(z)$ maps D_0^+ conformally upon a domain U^+ which contains an upper half-plane and is bounded by five line segments, two vertical and three horizontal. See Figure 7.3 which corresponds to the case where the branch points are of the form

$$(k + \tfrac{1}{2})\pi \pm i\tfrac{1}{2} \log \left\{\frac{1}{b} [a + (a^2 - b^2)^{1/2}]\right\}.$$

There are four vertices, two correspond to the points $\pm\frac{1}{2}\pi$, the others with 270° interior angles to the branch points.

Using the symmetry principle of H. A. Schwarz, we can continue $Z(z)$ analytically across the boundary of D_0^+. Suppose that we enter D_1^+ by crossing the right vertical boundary of D_0^+, above the branch point if $a > b$. The image of D_1^+ under this determination of $Z(z)$ is a domain U_1^-, the mirror image of U^+ with respect to the horizontal line segment farthest to the right. Similarly we get an image U_{-1}^- of D_{-1}^+ by reflecting U^+ in the horizontal line segment farthest to the left.

Now in D_0^+, D_1^+, D_{-1}^+ we have

$$Z(z) = i(\tfrac{1}{2}b)^{1/2}\, e^{-iz} + O(1). \tag{7.6.46}$$

Formula (7.4.27) shows that

$$
\begin{aligned}
F(Z) &= -b\,\frac{b + a\cos 2z + \frac{1}{4}b\sin^2 2z}{(a + b\cos 2z)^3} \\
&= \frac{2}{b}\,e^{2iz} + O(e^{4iz}) = -\frac{1}{4}\frac{1}{Z^2} + o\left(\frac{1}{Z^4}\right),
\end{aligned} \tag{7.6.47}
$$

so the asymptotic integration theory applies. It follows that the subdominant solution in D_0^+ satisfies

$$E(z) = \exp\,[-(\tfrac{1}{2}b)^{1/2}\,e^{-iz} + \tfrac{1}{2}iz]\{C_0 + O(e^{iz})\}, \tag{7.6.48}$$

where $C_0 \neq 0$ is a constant. This confirms (7.6.41). The estimate of the remainder holds uniformly for

$$-\tfrac{3}{2}\pi + \varepsilon \leq x \leq \tfrac{3}{2}\pi - \varepsilon, \qquad 0 < y.$$

In particular, on the lines $x = \pm\pi$ we have

$$E(\pm\pi + iy) = \exp\,[(\tfrac{1}{2}b)^{1/2}\,e^{y} - \tfrac{1}{2}y]\{\pm iC_0 + O(e^{-y})\} \tag{7.6.49}$$

as $y \to \infty$.

The solution $E(z)$ is defined in the whole plane, in particular also in D_0^- where it is dominant and has the asymptotic representation

$$E(z) = \exp\,[(\tfrac{1}{2}b)^{1/2}\,e^{iz} - \tfrac{1}{2}iz]\{C_1 + O(e^{-iz})\} \tag{7.6.50}$$

as $y \to -\infty$.

We shall return to Mathieu's equation in later chapters.

EXERCISE 7.6

1. If a non-trivial solution $y(x)$ of (7.6.7) satisfies the integrability conditions (7.6.8), show that $y(x)$ is strictly monotone and $y(x)y'(x) \neq 0$ for all x.
2. Why does the condition $w(\frac{1}{2}\pi) = 0$ lead to a solution which is an odd function of $z - \frac{1}{2}\pi$ and why does this condition together with $w(0) = 0$ lead to solutions of period π?
3. Change of variable $\cos 2z = s$ transforms (7.6.1) into

$$(1 - s^2)\frac{d^2w}{ds^2} - s\frac{dw}{ds} + \tfrac{1}{4}(a + bs)w = 0.$$

Verify this and show that the points $s = \pm 1$ are regular singular with indicial roots 0, $\frac{1}{2}$. Show that the point at infinity is irregular singular.

4. According to the preceding problem, the transformed equation has solutions of the form

$$A\sum_0^\infty \alpha_n(1 - s)^n + B\sum_0^\infty \beta_n(1 - s)^{n+1/2}.$$

If here we substitute back $s = \cos 2z$ we obtain expansions

$$A \sum_{0}^{\infty} 2^n \alpha_n \sin^{2n} z + B \sum_{0}^{\infty} 2^{n+1/2} \beta_n \sin^{2n+1} z$$

representing solutions of the original equation. This would seem to indicate that (7.6.1) has a periodic general solution for all values of a and b. This is not true. Explain the paradox!

5. Show that $E(z + \pi) = CE(z)$ cannot hold for any value of C.
6. Show that $E(z)$ cannot be periodic of period π or 2π and use this to show that (7.6.1) cannot have two linearly independent solutions with such a period.
7. Show that $E(z)$ and $E(-z)$ are linearly independent.
8. Same question for $E(z)$ and $E(z - \pi)$.
9. Show that a solution of (7.6.1) which is real on the imaginary axis takes on conjugate values at z and $-\bar{z}$.
10. Let $C(z)$ and $S(z)$ be solutions of (7.6.1) determined by the initial conditions
$$C(0) = 1, \quad C'(0) = 0, \quad S(0) = 0, \quad S'(0) = 1.$$
If $E(z) = AC(z) + BS(z)$, show that A is purely imaginary and $B = 1$.
11. Why do the solutions of the boundary value problem (7.6.29) (i) have Fourier series of type (7.6.30) (i)?
12. Find $\lim_{b \to 0} a_n(b)$ for the four boundary value problems.
13. Verify the estimate of $|w_1(\pi; a, b)|$.
14. Find the elements of the determinant $D(a, b)$ and verify that the corresponding bound P is given by the right member of (7.6.37).
15. Verify (7.6.47).
16. Suppose that $a < -b < 0$. Then the zeros of $F(z)$ lie on the lines $x = k\pi$. Let $i\eta$ be the zero in D_0^+ and cut D_0^+ along the imaginary axis from 0 to $i\eta$. Redefine $Z(z)$ by
$$Z(z) = \int_{i\eta}^{z} [a + b \cos 2s]^{1/2}\, ds.$$
Determine the shape of the conformal map of the cut domain under the new choice of $Z(z)$.
17. Does this new choice of $Z(z)$ call for any changes in formulas (7.6.46) to (7.6.50)?
18. Formulate Floquet's theorem for the case of a linear n^{th} order differential equation.

COLLATERAL READING

As a general reference consult the excellent treatise

WHITTAKER, E. T., and G. N. WATSON, *A Course in Modern Analysis*, 4th edition, Cambridge University Press, London (1952). See Chapters 14–17 and 19.

There is much useful information to be found in

INCE, E. L., *Ordinary Differential Equations*, Dover, New York (1944). See Chapters 7, 8, 15, 18, and 20.

KAMKE, E., *Differentialgleichungen: Lösungen und Lösungsmethoden*, Vol. I, 3rd edition, Chelsea (1948).

Kamke gives highly concentrated accounts of the various equations and their solutions with copious references. See in particular his equations:

2.260 (hypergeometric); 2.240 (Legendre); 2.162 (Bessel); 2.87, 2.113, 2.273 (confluent case); 2.365 (Halm); 2.22 (Mathieu), 2.30 (Hill).

Since the solutions of these equations are among the most important special analytic functions, there is an abundance of formulas, relations, and results to be found in the *Bateman papers*. See

ERDÉLYI, A., W. MAGNUS, F. OBERHETTINGER, and F. TRICOMI, *Higher transcendental functions*, 3 volumes, McGraw-Hill, New York (1953, 1955).

For the theory of Hermite, Laguerre, and Legendre polynomials consult

SZEGÖ, G., *Orthogonal polynomials*, American Mathematical Society Colloquium Publications, Vol. 23, 2nd edition, Providence (1948).

The standard treatise on Bessel functions is

WATSON, G. N., *Theory of Bessel functions*, 2nd edition, Cambridge University Press, London (1962).

The method of asymptotic integration used in Section 7.4 and later goes back to the author's papers

"Oscillation theorems in the complex domain," *Trans. Amer. Math. Soc.* **23**, 350–385 (1922).

"An existence theorem," *Ibid.* **26**, 241–248 (1924).

The use of Gronwall's lemma to estimate the remainders is a late addition. Liouville's transformation occurs in his paper

"Second Mémoire sur le développement des fonctions ou parties de fonctions en séries dont les divers termes sont assujétis à satisfaire à une même équation différentielle du second ordre, contenant un paramètre variable," *Journal de Math. pures et appliquées* (1) **2**, 16–35 (1837).

There is a large literature on the confluent hypergeometric case, including several books by F. G. Tricomi. See, in particular his

Fonctions hypergéométriques confluentes, Gauthier-Villars, Paris (1960).

For Mathieu's equation, see the monograph

MCLACHLAN, N. W., *Theory and application of Mathieu functions*, Oxford University Press, Oxford (1947).

The discussion in Section 7.6 is partly based on the author's paper

"On the zeros of Mathieu functions," *Proc. London Math. Soc.* (2) **23**, 185–237 (1924).

For the Floquet theory, see his paper

"Sur les équations différentielles linéaires à coefficients périodiques," *Ann. Sci. Ecole Norm. Sup.* (2) **12**, 47–89 (1883).

For the theory of infinite determinants, see

HILL, G. W., "On the part of the motion of the lunar perigee which is a function of the mean motions of the sun and the moon," *Acta Math.* **8**, 1–36 (1886). (Reprint of earlier paper published in 1877.)

VON KOCH, H., "Sur les déterminants infinis et les équations différentielles linéaires," *Acta Math.* **16**, 217–295 (1892).

For the properties of zeros of entire functions, see the author's *Analytic Function Theory*, Vol. II, Ginn, Boston (1962). Chapter 14, especially p. 231.

8 STURM–LIOUVILLE THEORY

Chapters 8–10 are devoted to the behavior of solutions of a linear second order differential equation on the real line. The coefficients are supposed to be real, so there are real solutions. Such a solution may be *oscillatory* or *non-oscillatory* on the interval (a, b) under consideration. Here we say that the solution is non-oscillatory if it has at most one zero in (a, b), otherwise oscillatory. Introducing a suitable parameter in the equation we can force the solutions to become oscillatory and to satisfy boundary conditions at the endpoints of the interval.

Chapter 8 is devoted to various aspects of oscillation, Chapter 9 to non-oscillation. In Chapter 8 we include a discussion of regular boundary value problems where the interval (a, b) is finite and the points a and b non-singular. Chapter 10 is devoted to singular boundary value problems where at least one of the conditions of regularity does not hold. The foundations for the discussion in Chapter 8 were laid by J. Liouville and C. Sturm (1803–1855) in the 1830's. Though special cases had been considered earlier, the general theory of singular boundary value problems was formulated by Hermann Weyl (1885–1955) in his dissertation of 1909.

There are five sections in Chapter 8: Oscillation Theory, Regular Boundary Value Problems, Prüfer's Method, Another Variant of Prüfer's Method, and Expansion Problems.

8.1 OSCILLATION THEORY

The simple wave equation

$$y''(x) + k^2 y(x) = 0, \tag{8.1.1}$$

where k is a positive constant, has solutions

$$C \sin k(x - x_0),$$

which are clearly oscillatory in $(-\infty, \infty)$. Two features should be noted. The first is the fact that the zeros of linearly independent solutions are *interlaced.* If $y_1(x)$ and $y_2(x)$ are linearly independent and if x_1 and x_2 are consecutive zeros of $y_1(x)$, then $y_2(x)$ has one and only one zero in (x_1, x_2). The second noteworthy feature is that the distance between consecutive zeros is π/k and becomes smaller the larger k is. We would like to generalize these observations to the case of solutions of a differential equation

$$y''(x) + F(x)y(x) = 0 \tag{8.1.2}$$

where $F(x)$ is positive and continuous in some interval (a, b).

Before embarking on this project, some remarks are in order. The first concerns the meaning of the terms "zero" and "consecutive zeros" as applied to the solutions of (8.1.2). We note that such a function $y(x) \not\equiv 0$ is continuous together with its first and second derivatives in (a, b). A point $x = x_1$ is a zero of $y(x)$ if $y(x_1) = 0$. Then $y'(x_1) \equiv \alpha \neq 0$, $y''(x_1) = 0$. We note that $y(x)$ changes its sign as x increasing passes through x_1. To fix the ideas, suppose $\alpha > 0$. Then $y(x)$ is negative in some interval $(x_1 - h_1, x_1)$ and positive in some interval $(x_1, x_1 + h_2)$ where $h_1 > 0$, $h_2 > 0$. We say that x_1 and x_2 are consecutive zeros of $y(x)$, if $x = x_1$ and $x = x_2$ are zeros of $y(x)$ and if $y(x) \neq 0$ for $x_1 < x < x_2$.

Next let us recall a kinematic interpretation of Eqs. (8.1.1) and (8.1.2). The first equation written in the form

$$\ddot{x}(t) + k^2x(t) = 0 \tag{8.1.3}$$

is that of the *harmonic oscillator*. Here $x(t)$ is the position coordinate on the real line at the time t of a particle P moving along the line under the influence of a central force proportional to the distance from P to O and directed toward O. The zeros of $x(t)$ are simply the times of the passage of P through O. The frequency of the oscillations is constant and for given initial data the amplitude is constant.

The equation

$$\ddot{x}(t) + F(t)x(t) = 0 \tag{8.1.4}$$

describes a more general type of rectilinear motion under a central force. The latter is still proportional to the distance of P from O but the factor of proportionality, $F(t)$, depends upon the time t. Here a number of new phenomena present themselves: oscillations vary in frequency and amplitude, there is damping, the force may even be too weak to pull the particle through the center or to prevent it from escaping to infinity. Generally speaking we expect a stronger force to give more frequent oscillations than a weaker one. These heuristic considerations are helpful in suggesting results to be proved by more rigorous methods.

The interlacing of zeros observed above for the harmonic oscillator extends right away to the more general case.

Theorem 8.1.1. *Let $y_1(x)$ and $y_2(x)$ be two linearly independent solutions of* (8.1.2) *and suppose that $y_1(x)$ has at least two zeros in (a, b). If x_1 and x_2 are two consecutive zeros of $y_1(x)$, then $y_2(x)$ has one and only one zero in (x_1, x_2).*

Proof. We may assume that $y_1(x) > 0$ for $x_1 < x < x_2$. We have then $y_1'(x_1) > 0$, $y_1'(x_2) < 0$ since $y_1(x)$ is increasing at $x = x_1$ and decreasing at $x = x_2$. The Wronskian of $y_1(x)$ and $y_2(x)$ is a constant $\neq 0$,

$$y_1(x)y_2'(x) - y_2(x)y_1'(x) = -y_2(x_1)y_1'(x_1). \tag{8.1.5}$$

Evaluating the Wronskian also at $x = x_2$, we get the relation

$$y_2(x_1)y_1'(x_1) = y_2(x_2)y_1'(x_2),$$

whence it follows that

$$\operatorname{sgn} y_2(x_1) = -\operatorname{sgn} y_2(x_2).$$

Hence $y_2(x)$ has at least one zero in (x_1, x_2). On the other hand, there cannot be more than one such zero for if there were two, ξ_1 and ξ_2 say, then we can interchange the roles of the two solutions in the argument and conclude that $y_1(x)$ has at least one zero in (ξ_1, ξ_2). This contradicts our assumption that x_1 and x_2 are consecutive zeros of $y_1(x)$. Hence $y_2(x)$ has exactly one zero in (x_1, x_2). ∎

Thus we see that if there is a solution of (8.1.2) which has two zeros in (a, b), then every solution has at least one zero in (a, b). This is all that can be asserted. Thus for the Eq. (8.1.1) if

$$a = 0, \qquad b = \frac{\pi}{k} + \varepsilon,$$

where ε is small positive, then there are solutions with two zeros in (a, b) but there are also solutions with only one zero. We conclude that there must be some relation between $\min F(x)$ and $b - a$ to ensure oscillatory behavior of the solutions in (a, b).

Even with an infinite interval we cannot be sure. Thus if

$$F(x) = ax^{-2},$$

we have an Euler equation with the solutions

$$Ax^{\rho_1} + Bx^{\rho_2} \qquad \text{with} \qquad \rho_1, \rho_2 = \tfrac{1}{2} \pm (\tfrac{1}{4} - a)^{1/2}.$$

If real, this solution is oscillatory in $(0, \infty)$ iff $a > \frac{1}{4}$. If $a \le \frac{1}{4}$, then every solution has at most one zero.

To proceed with the discussion we need a *comparison theorem* which goes back to Sturm and is an exact formulation of the heuristic principle that a stronger force should give more frequent oscillations than a weaker one.

Theorem 8.1.2. *Consider the two equations*

$$u''(x) + F(x)u(x) = 0, \tag{8.1.6}$$

$$v''(x) + G(x)v(x) = 0, \tag{8.1.7}$$

where $F(x)$ and $G(x)$ are positive, continuous and $G(x) \geq F(x)$ in (a, b). Suppose that the first equation has a solution $u(x)$ having two consecutive zeros at $x = x_1$ and $x = x_2$, $a < x_1 < x_2 < b$. Let $v(x)$ be a solution of the second equation with a zero at $x = x_1$. Then $v(x)$ has at least one zero x_3 with $x_1 < x_3 < x_2$.

Proof. We multiply the first equation by $v(x)$, the second by $u(x)$, subtract the first equation from the second, and integrate from x_1 to x_2. From

$$[u(x)v'(x) - v(x)u'(x)]_{x_1}^{x_2} + \int_{x_1}^{x_2} [G(x) - F(x)]u(x)v(x)\,dx = 0 \qquad (8.1.8)$$

we get

$$-v(x_2)u'(x_2) + \int_{x_1}^{x_2} [G(x) - F(x)]u(x)v(x)\,dx = 0. \qquad (8.1.9)$$

Here we may exclude the trivial case that $G(x) \equiv F(x)$ in (x_1, x_2) which would force $v(x)$ to be a constant multiple of $u(x)$ in (x_1, x_2). Further, without restricting the generality we may assume that $u(x) > 0$ for $x_1 < x < x_2$. This gives $u'(x_2) < 0$. If $v'(x_1) > 0$ and if $v(x)$ were positive in all of (x_1, x_2), then the integral would be positive and

$$-v(x_2)u'(x_2) \geq 0$$

which clearly contradicts (8.1.9). Hence $v(x)$ cannot keep a constant sign throughout the interval (x_1, x_2). ∎

In the same manner we prove the following theorem which develops the same idea.

Theorem 8.1.3. *With the same assumptions on $F(x)$ and $G(x)$, let $u(x)$ and $v(x)$ be solutions of (8.1.6) and (8.1.7) such that*

$$u(x_1) = v(x_1) = 0, \qquad u'(x_1) = v'(x_1) > 0.$$

Suppose that $u(x)$ is increasing in $[x_1, x_2)$ and reaches a maximum at $x = x_2$. Then $v(x)$ reaches a maximum at some point x_3 with $x_1 < x_3 < x_2$.

We leave the proof to the reader.

Next we prove a simple consequence of the comparison theorem.

Theorem 8.1.4. *Suppose that $F(x)$ is continuous in (a, b) and that*

$$0 < m \leq F(x) \leq M. \qquad (8.1.10)$$

If a solution $y(x)$ of (8.1.2) has two consecutive zeros x_1, x_2 then

$$\pi M^{-1/2} \leq x_2 - x_1 \leq \pi m^{-1/2}. \qquad (8.1.11)$$

Proof. We use Theorem 8.1.2 twice. First we take $G(x) \equiv M$. Then

$$v(x) = \sin \sqrt{M}\,(x - x_1)$$

is a solution of

$$v''(x) + Mv(x) = 0.$$

with a zero at $x = x_1$. Since its zeros nearest to x_1 are at the distance $\pi M^{-1/2}$ from x_1, the first part of the inequality (8.1.11) follows from Theorem 8.1.2. The second part is proved in the same manner. ▌

If the solution $y(x)$ has an extremum at $x = \xi$, $x_1 < \xi < x_2$, then the same type of argument shows that

$$\tfrac{1}{2}\pi M^{-1/2} \le \xi - x_1 \le \tfrac{1}{2}\pi m^{-1/2}. \tag{8.1.12}$$

These results have many applications. We shall consider the oscillatory case of Mathieu's equation. Here we have

$$F(x) = a + b\cos 2x$$

with $a > 0$, $b > 0$, $a - b > 0$. Further

$$m = a - b, \qquad M = a + b$$

and Theorem 8.1.4 shows that any real solution has infinitely many real zeros and the distance between consecutive zeros lies between the bounds

$$\pi(a + b)^{-1/2} \quad \text{and} \quad \pi(a - b)^{-1/2}.$$

This has a bearing on the boundary value problems which lead to the Mathieu functions. A function $\text{se}_{2n}(x)$ [for which see formula (7.6.30) (ii)] has zeros at $x = 0$ and $x = \frac{1}{2}\pi$. If these are consecutive zeros, as would be the case for $n = 1$, then we must have

$$a + b \ge 4.$$

A higher bound for $a + b$ is needed if these zeros are not consecutive. If we assume that the subscript $2n$ gives the number of zeros in $(-\frac{1}{2}\pi, \frac{1}{2}\pi)$, then for reasons of symmetry there would be $n - 1$ zeros in $(0, \frac{1}{2}\pi)$ and the least distance between consecutive zeros of $\text{se}_{2n}(x)$ is $\le \pi/(2n)$. This requires that

$$\pi(a + b)^{-1/2} \le \pi(2n)^{-1}$$

or

$$a + b \ge (2n)^2.$$

No better estimate is possible without further information on b since, when b decreases to 0,

$$\lim_{b\to 0} \text{se}_{2n}(x) = \sin(2nx) \qquad \text{and} \qquad \lim_{b\to 0} a_n(b) = (2n)^2.$$

Similar considerations apply to $\text{se}_{2n+1}(x)$.

The inequalities proved here for the parameters in Mathieu's equation are inequalities for the maximum of $F(x)$ in the interval $(-\frac{1}{2}\pi, \frac{1}{2}\pi)$ and can be generalized as follows.

Theorem 8.1.5. *A necessary condition that Eq.* (8.1.2) *have a solution with at least* $n + 1$ *zeros in the interval* (a, b) *is that*

$$\sup_{a<x<b} F(x) > \left(\frac{n\pi}{b - a}\right)^2. \tag{8.1.13}$$

A sufficient condition that every solution have at least n zeros in (a, b) *is that*

$$\inf_{a<x<b} F(x) > \left(\frac{n\pi}{b - a}\right)^2. \tag{8.1.14}$$

Proof. If there exists a solution with $n + 1$ zeros, then the minimum distance between consecutive zeros is $<(b - a)/n$ and (8.1.13) follows from (8.1.11). On the other hand, if (8.1.14) holds, then the maximum distance between consecutive zeros of any fixed solution of (8.1.2) cannot reach $(b - a)/n$ so there must be at least n zeros of the solution under consideration in (a, b). ∎

Equations of type (8.1.2) are not quite general enough for the applications of oscillation theory and we have to consider *self-adjoint equations*

$$\frac{d}{dx}\left[K(x)\frac{dy}{dx}\right] + G(x)y = 0. \tag{8.1.15}$$

We shall prove the extension of Theorem 8.1.2 to this case. The proof will be based upon an identity due to Mauro Picone (1909).

Theorem 8.1.6. *Let* G_1, G_2, K_1, K_2 *be positive and continuous for* $a < x < b$ *where* $G_2(x) > G_1(x)$, $K_1(x) > K_2(x)$. *Let u and v satisfy*

$$[K_1(x)u'(x)]' + G_1(x)u(x) = 0, \tag{8.1.16}$$

$$[K_2(x)v'(x)]' + G_2(x)v(x) = 0, \tag{8.1.17}$$

respectively. Let x_1 *and* x_2 *be a pair of consecutive zeros of* $u(x)$ *in* (a, b). *Then* $v(x)$ *has at least one zero in the open interval* (x_1, x_2).

Proof. Let us consider

$$\frac{d}{dx}\left\{\frac{u}{v}[K_1u'v - K_2v'u]\right\} = u\frac{d}{dx}[K_1u'] - \frac{u^2}{v}\frac{d}{dx}[K_2v'] + \frac{u}{v}(K_1 - K_2)u'v'$$
$$+ \frac{vu' - uv'}{v^2}[K_1u'v - K_2v'u]$$
$$= (G_2 - G_1)u^2 + (K_1 - K_2)(u')^2 + K_2\left[\frac{vu' - uv'}{v}\right]^2.$$

Integration from α to β, $a < \alpha < \beta < b$, gives Picone's formula:

$$\left\{\frac{u}{v}[K_1u'v - K_2v'u]\right\}_\alpha^\beta = \int_\alpha^\beta (G_2 - G_1)u^2\,ds + \int_\alpha^\beta (K_1 - K_2)(u')^2\,ds$$
$$+ \int_\alpha^\beta K_2\left[\frac{vu' - uv'}{v}\right]^2 ds. \tag{8.1.18}$$

Suppose now that $u(x) > 0$ for $x_1 < x < x_2$. If the theorem is false, we may assume $v(x) > 0$ in the same interval, but we allow for the possibility that $v(x)$ may be zero for $x = x_1$ and/or x_2. Take $\alpha = x_1 + \varepsilon$, $\beta = x_2 - \varepsilon$ in (8.1.18) and let $\varepsilon \downarrow 0$. The first two integrals obviously tend to finite positive limits. The integrand of the third integral assumes an indeterminate form at $s = x_1$ if $v(x_1) = 0$ but

$$\lim_{s \to x_1} \frac{v(s)u'(s) - u(s)v'(s)}{v(s)} = 0 \quad \text{or} \quad u'(x_1)$$

according as $v(x_1) = 0$ or not. Similarly at the upper limit. Hence the third integral also exists and the right member of (8.1.18) has a finite positive limit. In the left member

$$\lim_{s \to x_1} \frac{u(s)}{v(s)} [K_1(s)u'(s)v(s) - K_2(s)u(s)v'(s)] = 0$$

regardless of the value of $v(x_1)$. The same is true for $s \to x_2$. This is a contradiction and shows that $v(x)$ must change its sign in (x_1, x_2), i.e. this interval contains at least one zero of $v(x)$. ∎

It is clear that the hypotheses are unnecessarily restrictive. The proof holds if $G_2 \geq G_1$, $K_1 \geq K_2$, provided every interval (α, β) contains a subinterval where either $G_2 > G_1$ or $K_2 > K_1$.

The distance between consecutive zeros of a solution $y(x)$ of (8.1.15) is a constant iff G and K are constants. Sturm observed that consecutive distances form a monotone sequence, if G and K are monotone, one increasing, the other decreasing.

Theorem 8.1.7. *Suppose that $G(x)$ is increasing and $K(x)$ decreasing in (a, b). Let $y(x)$, a solution of* (8.1.15), *have zeros $\{x_k\}$ in (a, b) where $a < x_1 < x_2 < \cdots < x_n < b$. Then*

$$x_2 - x_1 < x_3 - x_2 < \cdots < x_n - x_{n-1}. \tag{8.1.19}$$

If the words "increasing" and "decreasing" are interchanged, then "$<$" is replaced by "$>$." The conclusion is also valid if either G or K is a constant provided the other function has the stated property of monotony.

Proof. We suppose G to be increasing and K to be decreasing. The other possibilities are handled in the same manner. Define

$$\begin{aligned} G_1(s) &= G(s + x_k), & K_1(s) &= K(s + x_k), \\ G_2(s) &= G(s + x_{k+1}), & K_2(s) &= K(s + x_{k+1}), \end{aligned} \qquad 1 \leq k \leq n - 2.$$

Then the equations

$$[K_1(s)u'(s)]' + G_1(s)u(s) = 0,$$

$$[K_2(s)v'(s)]' + G_2(s)v(s) = 0,$$

are satisfied by $y(s + x_k)$ and $y(s + x_{k+1})$, respectively. Hence $u(0) = u(x_{k+1} - x_k) = 0$, $v(0) = v(x_{k+2} - x_{k+1}) = 0$. Since $G_1(s) < G_2(s)$, $K_2(s) < K_1(s)$ by assumption, Theorem 8.1.6 applies and gives $x_{k+1} - x_k < x_{k+2} - x_{k+1}$ as asserted. ▮

As an illustration we take Bessel's equation in the form

$$y''(x) + [1 - (a^2 - \tfrac{1}{4})x^{-2}]y(x) = 0$$

which is satisfied by $x^{1/2}J_a(x)$. Here

$$G(x) = 1 - (a^2 - \tfrac{1}{4})x^{-2}, \qquad K(x) = 1.$$

If $0 < a < \frac{1}{2}$, we see that $G(x) > 0$ for $x > 0$ and decreases to 1 as $x \to +\infty$. If $y(x)$ is any solution whose positive zeros in increasing order form the sequence $\{x_n\}$, then

$$x_{n+1} - x_n < x_{n+2} - x_{n+1}.$$

Thus $\{x_{n+1} - x_n\}$ is an increasing sequence with the limit π. If $a = \frac{1}{2}$, $G(x) \equiv 1$ and the resulting sine equation gives $x_{n+1} - x_n = \pi$ for all n and all real solutions. Finally, if $\frac{1}{2} < a$, $G(x) > 0$ for $x > (a^2 - \frac{1}{4})^{1/2}$ and the zeros $\{x_n\}$ on this interval are such that $\{x_{n+1} - x_n\}$ is a decreasing sequence with the limit π.

In 1963 Lee Lorch and Peter Szego showed that monotony of higher order in the coefficients G and K is reflected in monotony of higher order in the sequence of zeros of the solutions.

Two more comparison theorems are listed in Exercise 8.1. See Problems 9 and 10.

The theorems listed so far have a bearing on the frequency of the oscillations but say nothing about the amplitudes. The following result throws some light on the amplitude problem.

Theorem 8.1.8. *Let G and K be positive, continuously differentiable and strictly monotone in (a, b). Consider the quadratic forms*

$$Q_1[y] \equiv K(x)[y'(x)]^2 + G(x)[y(x)]^2, \tag{8.1.20}$$

$$Q_2[y] \equiv \frac{[y'(x)]^2}{G(x)} + \frac{[y(x)]^2}{K(x)}, \tag{8.1.21}$$

where $y(x)$ is any non-trivial solution of (8.1.15). *Then*

$Q_1[y]$ *is increasing (decreasing), if G is increasing (decreasing) and K decreasing (increasing);*

$Q_2[y]$ *is increasing (decreasing), if G and K are both decreasing (increasing);*

Proof. This is elementary. We differentiate and simplify the result with the aid of the differential equation to obtain

$$Q_1'[y] = G'(x)[y(x)]^2 - K'(x)[y'(x)]^2,$$

$$Q_2'[y] = -\frac{K'(x)}{[K(x)]^2}[y(x)]^2 - \left\{2\frac{K'(x)}{G(x)K(x)} + \frac{G'(x)}{[G(x)]^2}\right\}[y'(x)]^2,$$

whence the assertions follow. ∎

Let $\{\xi_n\}$ be the set of points where $y'(x) = 0$

$$a < \xi_1 < \xi_2 < \cdots < \xi_n < b.$$

Then $|y(\xi_k)|$ can be regarded as the amplitude of the kth wave. Theorem 8.1.9 says that the sequence

$$\{G(\xi_k)[y(\xi_k)]^2\}$$

is increasing (decreasing) if G is increasing (decreasing) and K is decreasing (increasing). On the other hand, the sequence

$$\left\{\frac{[y(\xi_k)]^2}{K(\xi_k)}\right\}$$

is increasing (decreasing) if G and K are decreasing (increasing). If either G or K is a constant, the conditions simplify and we obtain direct information concerning $|y(\xi_k)|$, the amplitudes. Similarly we can obtain information concerning the variation of the slope at the successive zeros. Applications of this device to Legendre polynomials and Bessel functions are to be found in Chapter 7 and further applications are given in the exercise below.

In special cases, the method developed in Section 7.4 gives important and rather precise information concerning oscillatory solutions. We consider

$$[K(x)y'(x)]' + G(x)y(x) = 0, \tag{8.1.22}$$

where G and K are positive and continuous and have continuous first and second order derivatives for $a \le x$. We set

$$X(x) = \int_a^x \left[\frac{G(s)}{K(s)}\right]^{1/2} ds \tag{8.1.23}$$

and carry through the Liouville transformation setting

$$Y(X) = [G(x)K(x)]^{1/4}y(x). \tag{8.1.24}$$

The result is an equation of the form

$$Y''(X) + [1 - F(X)]Y(X) = 0. \tag{8.1.25}$$

We suppose that $X(x)$ maps $a \le x < \infty$ onto $0 < X < \infty$ and that

$$\int_0^\infty |F(X)|\, dX < \infty, \qquad \lim_{x\to\infty} F(X) = 0. \tag{8.1.26}$$

The discussion in Section 7.4 shows that both conditions certainly hold if, e.g. G and K are polynomials in x of degree n and m, respectively, where

$$n \geq m - 1.$$

We have also seen that Mathieu's equation is amenable to this treatment on the vertical lines $x = \frac{1}{2}k\pi$ in the complex plane.

Under these assumptions the transformed equation (8.1.25) has solutions of the form

$$Y(X) = \sin(X - X_0) + R(X), \tag{8.1.27}$$

where $0 \leq X_0 < 2\pi$ and

$$|R(X)| \leq \exp\left[\int_X^\infty |F(S)|\, dS\right] - 1. \tag{8.1.28}$$

This means that the original equation (8.1.22) has real oscillatory solutions of the form

$$y(x) = [G(x)K(x)]^{-1/4}\left(\sin\left\{\int_a^x \left[\frac{G(s)}{K(s)}\right]^{1/2} ds - X_0\right\} + R(X)\right). \tag{8.1.29}$$

Let x_n^* be the root of the equation

$$\int_a^{x_n^*} \left[\frac{G(s)}{K(s)}\right]^{1/2} ds = X_0 + n\pi. \tag{8.1.30}$$

Then for n sufficiently large, $y(x)$ has a zero x_n such that

$$\lim_{n\to\infty} (x_n - x_n^*) = 0 \tag{8.1.31}$$

and the number of zeros of $y(x)$ in the interval (a, ω) is

$$\frac{1}{\pi}\int_a^\omega \left[\frac{G(s)}{K(s)}\right]^{1/2} ds + O(1). \tag{8.1.32}$$

Here the remainder is uniformly bounded with respect to X_0 and ω.

All we need to show is that $Y(X)$ has a single zero in a δ-neighborhood of $X_n = X_0 + n\pi$, if n is sufficiently large. To this end we choose an m so that

$$|R(X_m - \delta)| < \sin\delta, \qquad \delta < \tfrac{1}{2}\pi.$$

Then for $n \geq m$ the sign of $Y(X)$ is the same as that of $\sin(X - X_0)$ at $X = X_n \pm \delta$. Since one of these numbers is positive and the other is negative, $Y(X)$ has at least one zero in the interval $(X_n - \delta, X_n + \delta)$. Further, $\lim_{x\to\infty} F(X) = 0$ so the distance between consecutive zeros of $Y(X)$ tends to the limit π. Thus ultimately there can be at most one zero of $Y(X)$ in an interval of length 2δ. This proves the assertion concerning the zeros of $Y(X)$. Once this has been done, the other assertions follow from the properties of the mapping $x \to X(x)$.

We shall give another asymptotic representation of oscillatory solutions under less restrictive assumptions. This will come as an application of Prüfer's method.

EXERCISE 8.1

1. Let G be positive and continuous in $[0, \infty)$. Show that it is possible to choose G so that every solution $y(x)$ of $y'' + G(x)y = 0$ has at most n zeros in $[0, \infty)$ where n is a preassigned positive integer. [*Hint*: A solution for $n = 1$ is given in the text.]

2. Given $y'' + G(x)y = 0$ with G positive and continuous in $[0, \infty)$ and such that the solutions have infinitely many zeros. Define $y(x, \alpha)$ by the initial condition $y(0) = 1$, $y'(0) = \alpha$. Let $\{x_n(\alpha)\}$ be the sequence of zeros of $y(x, \alpha)$. If $\alpha < \beta$, show that
$$0 < x_1(\alpha) < x_1(\beta) < x_2(\alpha) < \cdots < x_n(\alpha) < x_n(\beta) < x_{n+1}(\alpha) < \cdots$$

3. Show that the conclusion of Theorem 8.1.8 remains valid if either G or K is a constant while the other function is monotone.

4. Consider the modified Bessel equation
$$y'' + [1 - (a^2 - \tfrac{1}{4})x^{-2}]y = 0$$
with $a > \frac{1}{2}$ and a solution $y(x)$ with zeros $\{x_n\}$ and extrema $\{\xi_n\}$ where $\xi_1 < x_1 < \xi_2 < x_2 < \cdots$. What information can you obtain concerning the sequences $\{|y'(x_n)|\}$ and $\{|y(\xi_n)|\}$? Show that $[y(x)]^2 + [y'(x)]^2$ tends to a limit as $x \to \infty$.

5. Given $(1 + x^2)^2y'' + \lambda y = 0$ with $\lambda > 0$. Show that the solutions have only a finite number of real zeros the maximum number depending upon the value of λ. Do the positive zeros form a sequence with monotonic differences?

6. If $a = -\frac{1}{2} + i\mu$, the solutions of Legendre's equation (7.2.1) are oscillatory on $(1, \infty)$. If $\{x_n\}$ is the sequence of zeros in increasing order of a solution $y(x)$, show that the sequence $\{x_{n+1} - x_n\}$ is increasing and diverges to $+\infty$. If $\{\xi_n\}$ is the corresponding sequence of zeros of $y'(x)$, show that $|y(\xi_n)|$ decreases to 0. Estimate the number of zeros x_n in $(1, \omega)$.

7. Mathieu's equation has solutions $w(z)$ which are real on the line $x = \frac{1}{2}\pi$. Let $w(\frac{1}{2}\pi + iy) \equiv U(y)$ be such a solution. Show that if $b > 0$, then $U(y)$ is oscillatory with increasing frequency as $y \to +\infty$. Show that the number of zeros y_n of $U(y)$ with $0 < y_n < \omega$ is
$$\pi^{-1}(\tfrac{1}{2}b)^{1/2}\, e^{\omega} + O(1).$$
Let η_n, $y_n < \eta_n < y_{n+1}$, be the point where $U'(y) = 0$. Show that the sequence $\{|U(\eta_n)|\}$ is decreasing while $\{|U'(x_n)|\}$ is increasing.

8. With the notation of the preceding problem, show that $U(y) \in L_p(0, \infty)$ for each $p > 0$ while $U'(y)$ has this property for no value of p.

Prove the following comparison theorems which are due to Sturm.

9. With the assumptions on G_1, G_2, K_1, K_2 as in Theorem 8.1.6, consider non-trivial solutions $u(x)$ and $v(x)$ in an interval $[A, B]$, $a < A < B < b$, such that

$$u(A) = a_1, \quad u'(A) = b_1, \quad v(A) = a_2, \quad v'(A) = b_2.$$

If $a_1 \neq 0$, suppose that

$$K_1(A)\frac{b_1}{a_1} > K_2(A)\frac{b_2}{a_2}.$$

If $u(x)$ has n zeros in (A, B), then $v(x)$ has at least n zeros there and the kth zero of $v(x)$ is less than the kth zero of $u(x)$ for each k.

10. Under the same assumptions on G_1, G_2, K_1, K_2, suppose that $u(x)$ and $v(x)$ have the same number of zeros in (A, B) and that $u(B) \neq 0$, $v(B) \neq 0$. Then

$$K_1(B)\frac{u'(B)}{u(B)} > K_2(B)\frac{v'(B)}{v(B)}.$$

8.2 REGULAR BOUNDARY VALUE PROBLEMS

We consider a second order quasi-linear differential equation

$$\mathsf{L}[y] \equiv [K(x)y'(x)]' + G(x)y(x) = 0, \tag{8.2.1}$$

where G and K are positive continuous functions in a finite closed interval $[a, b]$. We do not assume $K(x)$ to be differentiable so the meaning of the equation and the existence of solutions are open to question. We encountered a similar situation in Theorem 3.4.2 and the method used there can be applied here to construct solutions of (8.2.1). We can also replace the equation by the equivalent system

$$\begin{aligned} y_1' &= [K(x)]^{-1}y_2, \\ y_2' &= -G(x)y_1, \end{aligned} \tag{8.2.2}$$

to which the existence theorems obviously apply.

Solutions of the equation are usually specified by initial conditions of the form

$$y(a) = \alpha, \qquad y'(a) = \beta,$$

but it is natural to ask if conditions of a different nature will do. This question was originally posed by the demands of mathematical physics. An equation of type (8.2.1) arises in an effort to separate variables in a *wave equation*

$$\frac{\partial}{\partial x}\left\{P(x)\frac{\partial U}{\partial x}\right\} + Q(x)U = \frac{\partial^2 U}{\partial t^2} \tag{8.2.3}$$

or a *diffusion equation*

$$\frac{\partial}{\partial x}\left\{P(x)\frac{\partial T}{\partial x}\right\} + Q(x)T = \frac{\partial T}{\partial t}. \tag{8.2.4}$$

If in the first equation we assume a solution of the form

$$U(x, t) = e^{i\lambda t}y(x), \tag{8.2.5}$$

we find that $y(x)$ satisfies

$$[P(x)y'(x)]' + [Q(x) + \lambda^2]y(x) = 0. \tag{8.2.6}$$

Similarly, substituting

$$T(x, t) = e^{-\lambda^2 t}y(x) \tag{8.2.7}$$

we find that the variables separate and $y(x)$ again satisfies (8.2.6) which is obviously an equation of the type here considered.

The physical problems impose conditions on $U(x, t)$ and $T(x, t)$ which induce boundary conditions on $y(x)$. Thus, if (8.2.3) describes transversal oscillations of a string, it is natural to assume that

$$U(a, t) = 0, \qquad U(b, t) = 0$$

for all t, and this implies the conditions

$$y(a) = 0, \qquad y(b) = 0 \tag{8.2.8}$$

on the solution $y(x)$ of (8.2.6). This is a simple but typical boundary condition. Other physical problems may call for conditions of the form

$$\alpha y'(a) - \beta y(a) = 0, \qquad \gamma y'(b) - \delta y(b) = 0. \tag{8.2.9}$$

The parameter λ occurring in (8.2.5) defines the (time) frequency of the oscillation and we are now facing the problem of deciding whether or not the string, affixed at the ends, admits of oscillations of period $2\pi/\lambda$. In other words, does Eq. (8.2.6) admit of solutions satisfying the boundary conditions (8.2.8)? This is normally not the case for all values of λ. Instead we find that there exists a discrete set of values λ_n such that for $\lambda = \lambda_n$ Eq. (8.2.6) has a solution $y(x, \lambda_n)$, unique up to a constant multiplier, which satisfies the boundary conditions. The set $\{\lambda_n\}$ is known as the *spectrum* of the boundary value problem (or of the equation or of the corresponding differential operator); the numbers λ_n are known as *characteristic values* or *eigenvalues* of the problem and the corresponding functions $y(x, \lambda_n)$ are the *characteristic functions* or *eigenfunctions* (German: *Eigenwert, Eigenfunktion*).

The original demands of physics did not go beyond conditions of type (8.2.9). It should be emphasized that at present we are considering so-called *regular boundary value problems* where the interval is finite, G and K are continuous and positive in $[a, b]$. The typical problems of quantum mechanics are not regular but singular boundary value problems.

From the point of view of functional analysis rather than mathematical physics the problems which we have posed admit of considerable generalization. The solutions $y(x)$ of (8.2.1) belong to the space $C^1[a, b]$, i.e. the space of functions continuous together with their derivatives of the first order on $[a, b]$. The norm on this space can be taken to be

$$\|f\| = \sup |f(t)| + \sup |f'(t)|.$$

The space admits of linear bounded functionals. To every such functional $L[f]$, correspond two functions $g, h \in BV[a, b]$ such that

$$L[f] = \int_a^b f(s)\, dg(s) + \int_a^b f'(s)\, dh(s). \tag{8.2.10}$$

Conversely, every such pair of functions g, h defines a linear bounded functional on $C^1[a, b]$.

Now the left members of (8.2.9) are very special linear functionals corresponding to step functions g and h, having a single jump at $s = a$ or at $s = b$. This suggests replacing the special conditions (8.2.9) by more general conditions. Let L_1 and L_2 be two non-trivial linear bounded functionals on $C^1[a, b]$ and impose the conditions

$$L_1[y] = 0, \qquad L_2[y] = 0 \tag{8.2.11}$$

on the solutions of (8.2.1). We refer to (8.2.11) as *lateral conditions* rather than boundary conditions since, in general, the whole range of $y(x)$ as well as of $y'(x)$ will be relevant and not merely the values at the endpoints.

So far we have had in mind a homogeneous differential equation and homogeneous lateral conditions. The theory demands, however, that we admit a non-homogeneous differential equation

$$\mathsf{L}[y] = R \tag{8.2.12}$$

and non-homogeneous lateral conditions

$$L_1[y] = \sigma, \qquad L_2[y] = \tau. \tag{8.2.13}$$

We now have the following alternatives.

Theorem 8.2.1. *Let y_1 and y_2 be a fundamental system of* (8.2.1). *The boundary value problem*

$$\mathsf{L}[y] = 0, \qquad L_1[y] = 0, \qquad L_2[y] = 0 \tag{8.2.14}$$

has a non-trivial solution iff

$$D[y_1, y_2] = \begin{vmatrix} L_1[y_1] & L_1[y_2] \\ L_2[y_1] & L_2[y_2] \end{vmatrix} = 0. \tag{8.2.15}$$

On the other hand, if $D[y_1, y_2] \neq 0$, then for any choice of $R(x) \in C[a, b]$ and of constants σ and τ the problem

$$\mathsf{L}[y] = R, \qquad L_1[y] = \sigma, \qquad L_2[y] = \tau \tag{8.2.16}$$

has a unique solution.

Proof. If the problem (8.2.14) has a non-trivial solution $y(x)$, then we can find constants C_1 and C_2 not both zero, so that

$$y(x) = C_1 y_1(x) + C_2 y_2(x).$$

It follows that

$$\begin{aligned} C_1 L_1[y_1] + C_2 L_1[y_2] &= 0, \\ C_1 L_2[y_1] + C_2 L_2[y_2] &= 0. \end{aligned} \tag{8.2.17}$$

These equations have a non-trivial solution C_1, C_2, iff (8.2.15) holds. If the rank of the matrix is one, then the ratio $C_1 : C_2$ is uniquely determined, but if the rank is zero, then every solution of $\mathsf{L}[y] = 0$ satisfies the lateral conditions.

Suppose now that $D[y_1, y_2] \neq 0$ and let $Y(x)$ be a particular solution of

$$\mathsf{L}[y] = R.$$

Then the general solution of this equation is

$$Y + C_1 y_1 + C_2 y_2.$$

The lateral conditions now give the relations

$$\begin{aligned} C_1 L_1[y_1] + C_2 L_1[y_2] &= \sigma - L_1[Y], \\ C_1 L_2[y_1] + C_2 L_2[y_2] &= \tau - L_2[Y] \end{aligned} \tag{8.2.18}$$

which determine C_1 and C_2 uniquely. ▮

Let us apply this result to an equation (8.2.6) where we set

$$\lambda^2 = \mu.$$

Thus we are concerned with the equation

$$\mathsf{L}_\mu[y] = [P(x)y'(x)]' + [Q(x) + \mu]y(x) = 0 \tag{8.2.19}$$

and the boundary problem reads

$$\mathsf{L}_\mu[y] = 0, \qquad L_1[y] = 0, \qquad L_2[y] = 0. \tag{8.2.20}$$

We first have to study the fundamental system y_1 and y_2 which we determine from the conditions

$$\begin{aligned} y_1(a, \mu) &= 1, & y_2(a, \mu) &= 0, \\ y_1'(a, \mu) &= 0, & y_2'(a, \mu) &= 1. \end{aligned} \tag{8.2.21}$$

The corresponding solutions are entire functions of μ and so are the values of the functionals L_1 and L_2 for the solutions. The results in Section 3.4 suggest strongly that these entire functions have an order not exceeding $\frac{1}{2}$. Our first task will be to verify this. We shall carry through the argument for $y_1(x, \mu)$.

We set

$$y_1(x, \mu) = \sum_{n=0}^{\infty} u_n(x)\mu^n \tag{8.2.22}$$

and determine the u_n's from the equations

$$\begin{aligned} \mathsf{L}_0[u_0] &= 0, \qquad u_0(a) = 1, \qquad u_0'(a) = 0, \\ \mathsf{L}_0[u_n] &= -u_{n-1}, \qquad u_n(a) = u_n'(a) = 0, \qquad n = 1, 2, 3, \ldots \end{aligned} \tag{8.2.23}$$

Let u_0 and v_0 be the fundamental system of the equation

$$\mathsf{L}_0[y] = 0$$

corresponding to the initial conditions

$$\begin{aligned} u_0(a) &= 1, \qquad v_0(a) = 0, \\ u_0'(a) &= 0, \qquad v_0'(a) = 1, \end{aligned}$$

and denote their Wronskian by $W(x)$. Thus

$$W(x) = \begin{vmatrix} u_0(x) & v_0(x) \\ u_0'(x) & v_0'(x) \end{vmatrix}.$$

We assume $P(x)$ and $Q(x)$ to be positive and continuous in $[a, b]$.

We note first that the function

$$u_0(s)v_0(x) - u_0(x)v_0(s)$$

is a continuously differentiable function of s which vanishes identically for $s = x$. Hence we can find a constant A such that for $a \le s, x \le b$

$$|u_0(s)v_0(x) - u_0(x)v_0(s)| \le A|s - x|.$$

Further we can find constants B, C, and M such that in $[a, b]$

$$|u_0(x)| \le B, \qquad |v_0(x)| \le B(x - a), \qquad P(x) > C, \qquad W(x) > M.$$

For the following compare Problem 13 of Exercise 5.1. We have

$$u_n(x) = -\int_a^x \frac{u_0(s)v_0(x) - u_0(x)v_0(s)}{P(s)W(s)} u_{n-1}(s)\, ds \tag{8.2.24}$$

as is seen by carrying out the operation L_0 on both sides. The boundary condition is obviously satisfied. Using the estimates we see that

$$|u_n(x)| \le \frac{A}{CM} \int_a^x (x - s)|u_{n-1}(s)|\, ds.$$

This says that $|u_n(x)|$ is dominated by a constant multiple of the second integral of $|u_{n-1}(x)|$. Iteration shows that $|u_n(x)|$ is dominated by the nth power of this constant times the $(2n)^{\text{th}}$ integral of $|u_0(x)|$. This gives

$$|u_n(x)| \le B\left(\frac{A}{CM}\right)^n \frac{(x - a)^{2n}}{(2n)!}$$

and the sup norm of this function does not exceed

$$B\left(\frac{A}{CM}\right)^n \frac{(b - a)^{2n}}{(2n)!}.$$

Differentiating (8.2.24) we see that $|u_n'(x)|$ is dominated by a constant multiple of the first integral of $|u_{n-1}(x)|$. This shows that the sup norm of $u_n'(x)$ does not exceed a fixed multiple of

$$B\left(\frac{A}{CM}\right)^{n-1} \frac{(b - a)^{2n-1}}{(2n - 1)!}$$

Adding these two expressions we get an upper bound for the norm of $u_n(x)$ as an element of $C^1[a, b]$.

Multiplying these estimates by $|\mu|^n$ and summing, we get estimates for $\|y_1(\cdot, \mu)\|$ and of $\|y_1'(\cdot, \mu)\|$. Multiplying by the norm of the functional under consideration, we get bounds for

$$|L_1[y_1(\cdot, \mu)]| \quad \text{and} \quad |L_2[y_1(\cdot, \mu)]|.$$

These bounds turn out to be linear combinations of

$$\cosh [D(b - a)|\mu|^{1/2}] \quad \text{and} \quad |\mu|^{1/2} \sinh [D(b - a)|\mu|^{1/2}],$$

where the multiplicative constants are independent of μ but do depend upon the functional. Further

$$D = \left(\frac{A}{CM}\right)^{1/2}.$$

Similar estimates hold for $y_2(x, \mu)$, its norm and functionals.

These estimates suffice to show that

$$L_j[y_k(\cdot, \mu)], \quad j, k = 1, 2,$$

are entire functions of μ of order not exceeding $\frac{1}{2}$. It follows that

$$D[y_1, y_2] = \det (L_j[y_k(\cdot, \mu)]) \equiv D(\mu) \tag{8.2.25}$$

is also an entire function of μ of order not exceeding $\frac{1}{2}$. We have now the alternatives, already familiar to us from the discussion of a special case in Section 7.6: either $D(\mu)$ is a polynomial or else $D(\mu)$ is a transcendental entire function with infinitely many zeros, $\{\mu_n\}$, the characteristic values of the boundary value problem.

In the next section we shall give a rigorous proof of the existence of infinitely many characteristic values for simple classical boundary value problems without any "either or" alternatives. In the meantime we assume the existence of characteristic values and study some of their properties, again in the classical case.

Theorem 8.2.2. *If the boundary conditions are given by* (8.2.9) *where the coefficients* α, β, γ, δ *are real, then the characteristic values* μ_n *are real and the corresponding characteristic functions form an orthogonal system in* $L_2(a, b)$.

Proof. The argument is essentially the same as that used in the proof of Theorem 7.6.1. We assume that μ is a complex characteristic value and that $y(x)$ is the corresponding complex-valued characteristic function. We multiply the equation

$$[P(x)y'(x)]' + [Q(x) + \mu]y(x) = 0$$

by $\overline{y(x)}$, the conjugate of $y(x)$, and integrate the result from a to b. After simplification we have

$$[P(x)\overline{y(x)}y'(x)]_a^b - \int_a^b P(x)|y'(x)|^2\,dx + \int_a^b [G(x) + \mu]|y(x)|^2\,dx = 0.$$

Let us consider the upper limit. Here we have

$$\gamma y'(b) - \delta y(b) = 0.$$

If $\gamma = 0$, this gives $y(b) = 0$ and hence also $\overline{y(b)} = 0$ so the integrated part vanishes in the upper limit. If $\gamma \neq 0$, then

$$P(b)\overline{y(b)}y'(b) = \frac{\delta}{\gamma}P(b)|y(b)|^2,$$

a real number. Similarly we obtain a real number in the lower limit. Thus the integrated part is real. The integrals are obviously real. Hence μ must be real and $y(x)$ is real.

If now μ_1 and μ_2 are two distinct real characteristic values with corresponding characteristic functions $y_1(x)$ and $y_2(x)$, then

$$\{P(x)[y_2(x)y_1'(x) - y_1(x)y_2'(x)]\}_a^b = (\mu_2 - \mu_1)\int_a^b y_1(x)y_2(x)\,dx.$$

Again if $\gamma = 0$, $y_1(b) = y_2(b) = 0$ and the integrated part vanishes in the upper limit. If, however, $\gamma \neq 0$, then

$$y_2(b)y_1'(b) = y_1(b)y_2'(b)$$

and the same result holds. The same holds in the lower limit. Since $\mu_1 \neq \mu_2$,

$$\int_a^b y_1(x)y_2(x)\,dx = 0$$

as asserted. ▮

For general lateral conditions $L_1[y] = 0$, $L_2[y] = 0$ the situation is not clear though Theorem 8.2.2 appears to hold for much more general lateral conditions than those of (8.2.9). An important case where it is valid is that of *periodic boundary conditions*. Here $P(a) = P(b)$ and

$$y(a) = y(b), \qquad y'(a) = y'(b). \tag{8.2.26}$$

A glance at the proof of Theorem 8.2.2 shows such a problem also leads to real characteristic values and the characteristic functions form an orthogonal system for $L_2(a, b)$.

As the last item of this section we give an identity due to Lagrange which we formulate for an nth order linear differential equation. To justify the procedure it is necessary to assume that the coefficients are differentiable. In fact, we assume that $p_j(x)$ is continuous in $[a, b]$ together with its derivatives of order $\leq n - j$, $j = 0, 1, 2, \ldots, n$. We write

$$\mathsf{L}[u] \equiv p_0u^{(n)} + p_1u^{(n-1)} + \cdots + p_{n-1}u' + p_nu. \tag{8.2.27}$$

It is desired to determine a function $v(x)$ such that $v\mathsf{L}[u]$ is an exact derivative. Here we use the identity

$$VU^{(m)} - (-1)^mUV^{(m)} = \frac{d}{dx}\{U^{(m-1)}V - U^{(m-2)}V' + \cdots + (-1)^{m-1}UV^{(m-1)}\} \tag{8.2.28}$$

which is left to the reader to verify. We take

$$m = n - j, \qquad V = p_jv, \qquad U = u$$

and obtain

$$p_jvu^{(n-j)} = \frac{d}{dx}\{u^{(n-j-1)}p_jv - u^{(n-j-2)}(p_jv)' + \cdots + (-1)^{n-j-1}u(p_jv)^{(n-j-1)}\} + (-1)^{n-j}u(p_jv)^{(n-j)}.$$

Here we sum for j from 0 to n and obtain Lagrange's identity:

$$v\mathsf{L}[u] - u\mathsf{L}^*[v] = \frac{d}{dx}P(u, v), \tag{8.2.29}$$

where

$$\mathsf{L}^*[v] = (-1)^n(p_0v)^{(n)} + (-1)^{n-1}(p_1v)^{(n-1)} + \cdots - (p_{n-1}v)' + p_nv \tag{8.2.30}$$

is known as the *adjoint differential expression* to $\mathsf{L}[u]$ and $P(u, v)$ is bilinear and homogeneous in

$$u, u', \ldots, u^{(n-1)},$$
$$v, v', \ldots, v^{(n-1)}.$$

It has been given the name of a *bilinear concomitant*. The equation

$$\mathsf{L}^*[v] = 0 \tag{8.2.31}$$

is known as the *adjoint equation.* The operator L is said to be (*formally*) *self-adjoint* if

$$\mathsf{L}^* = \mathsf{L}. \tag{8.2.32}$$

It should be observed that the differentiability conditions imposed on the p_j's can be relaxed. We need the identity of Lagrange for functions u and v which belong to the domains of the operators L and L*, respectively. Now the adjoint equation has solutions for any choice of continuous functions $p_0, p_1, \ldots, p_n$ with $p_0 \neq 0$ in the interval $[a, b]$ under consideration. It follows that the domains in question are not void and it suffices for the validity of the identity that the p_j's are continuous. In this case $P(u, v)$ is a bilinear and homogeneous form in

$$u, u', \ldots, u^{(n-1)},$$

$$p_n v, (p_{n-1}v)', \ldots, (p_0 v)^{(n-1)}.$$

EXERCISE 8.2

1. Discuss the homogeneous boundary value problem

$$y'' + \lambda^2 y = 0, \qquad y(0) = 0, \qquad y'(\pi) = y(\pi).$$

2. Discuss the non-homogeneous boundary value problem

$$y'' + \lambda^2 y = 0, \qquad y(0) = 1, \qquad y'(\pi) = 0.$$

3. Discuss the boundary value problem for $(0, \pi)$

$$y'' + \lambda^2 y = 0, \qquad y(\tfrac{1}{3}\pi) = 0, \qquad \int_0^\pi y(s)\, ds = 0.$$

Find the characteristic values and functions and show that the functions form an orthogonal system complete in $L_2(0, \pi)$.

4. Discuss the boundary value problem for $(0, \pi)$

$$y'' + \lambda^2 y = 0, \qquad y(0) = 0, \qquad \int_0^\pi s y(s)\, ds = 0.$$

Show that the solutions are of the form $\sin(\lambda_n x)$ where λ_n is a positive root of the transcendental equation

$$\tan \pi\lambda = \pi\lambda.$$

Show that these functions are orthogonal on $(0, \pi)$.

5. Construct the linear functionals involved in the periodic boundary conditions (8.2.26).

6. Discuss the third order problem

$$y''' + \lambda^3 y = 0, \qquad y(0) = y'(0) = 0, \qquad y''(1) = 0.$$

7. State and prove the analogue of Theorem 8.2.1 for an nth order equation and n lateral conditions defined by linear bounded functionals.
8. If $p_n(x) = q(x) + \mu$, discuss the existence of characteristic values. Show that $L_j[y_k(\cdot, \mu)]$, $j, k = 1, 2, \ldots, n$, are entire functions of μ of order $\leq 1/n$ and so is their determinant. Conclusion?
9. Verify (8.2.28).
10. What is the condition that the equation
$$p_0 y'' + p_2 y' + p_2 y = 0$$
be self-adjoint?
11. If the equation of the preceding problem is not self-adjoint, it can be made so by multiplying by a suitable function. Find such a multiplier and give the self-adjoint form of the equation.
12. Is the equation $[P(x)y''(x)]'' + [\mu + Q(x)]y(x) = 0$ self-adjoint?
13. Let $\{\mu_n\}$ be the characteristic values, $\{\omega_n(x)\}$ the corresponding characteristic functions of the boundary value problem (8.2.20). Let $c_1, c_2, \ldots, c_n$ be n arbitrary constants. Show that
$$T(x, t) = \sum_{k=1}^{n} c_k\, e^{-\mu_k t}\, \omega_k(x), \qquad a \leq x \leq b,$$
satisfies the diffusion equation (8.2.4) as well as the lateral conditions for all t.
14. Suppose that the μ_n are real positive and $\mu_n = O(n^2)$. Suppose that the $\{\omega_n(x)\}$ form a complete orthonormal system in $L_2(a, b)$ and that $|\omega_n(x)| \leq M$ for $a \leq x \leq b$ and all n. Let $f \in L_2(a, b)$ and set
$$f_n = \int_a^b f(s)\omega_n(s)\, ds.$$
Show that the series
$$T(x, t) \equiv \sum_{n=1}^{\infty} f_n\, e^{-\mu_n t}\, \omega_n(x)$$
converges for all $t > 0$, uniformly in t and x, $0 < \varepsilon \leq t$, $a \leq x \leq b$. Show that $T(x, t)$ satisfies (8.2.4) and the lateral conditions for $t > 0$ and that
$$\lim_{t \downarrow 0} \int_a^b |T(x, t) - f(x)|^2\, dx = 0.$$
15. Show that there are infinitely many characteristic values if there exists a single value α for which the equation $D(\mu) = \alpha$ has infinitely many roots and that this condition is necessary as well as sufficient.

In (8.2.19) let P, Q, y be elements of a star algebra $\mathfrak{B}$ with unit element e (see Section 4.2). Let P, Q be symmetric and positive definite for $a \leq x \leq b$. Let u_0, v_0 be chosen so that $u_0(a) = e$, $u_0'(a) = 0$, $v_0(a) = 0$, $v_0'(a) = e$. Suppose that
$$W(s) \equiv v_0'(s)u_0(s) - u_0'(s)v_0(s)$$
is algebraically regular in $[a, b]$ and that $u_0(x)$ and $v_0(x)$ commute.

16. Show that the solution of $\mathsf{L}_0[u] = v$, $u(a) = u'(a) = 0$, is

$$u(x) = \int_a^x [v_0(x)u_0(s) - u_0(x)v_0(s)][W(s)]^{-1}[P(s)]^{-1}v(s)\, ds.$$

17. Use this to find $y_1(x, \mu)$, the solution of $\mathsf{L}_\mu[y] = 0$, $y(a) = e$, $y'(a) = 0$. Even though $u_0(x)$ and $v_0(x)$ do commute, the convergence proof may have to be modified and the order of the majorant may turn out to be 1 instead of $\frac{1}{2}$ as in the classical case.
18. Can the classical boundary conditions be generalized to this situation? If so, how should an analogue of Theorem 8.2.1 be formulated and proved?
19. Examine the question of more general lateral conditions. Linear functionals on the space of $\mathfrak{B}$-valued continuously differentiable functions offer a possibility but involves the difficulty that $L[fC]$ need not be a constant multiple of $L[f]$. An alternative would be to consider linear mappings of $C^1([a, b]; \mathfrak{B})$ into $\mathfrak{B}$, assuming $T[fC] = T[f]C$.

8.3 PRÜFER'S METHOD

In 1926, Heinz Prüfer (1896–1934) observed that problems involving zeros and extrema of solutions of linear second order equations and, in particular, boundary value problems could be handled with greater ease by introducing a peculiar type of polar coordinates. With Prüfer we introduce $\rho(x)$ and $\vartheta(x)$ defined by

$$y(x) = \rho(x) \sin \vartheta(x), \qquad P(x)y'(x) = \rho(x) \cos \vartheta(x). \tag{8.3.1}$$

Here $y(x)$ is a non-trivial solution of

$$[P(x)y'(x)]' + Q(x)y(x) = 0 \tag{8.3.2}$$

where $P(x)$ and $Q(x)$ are continuous for $a \le x \le b$ and $P(x) > 0$. Later $Q(x)$ will be made to depend upon a parameter λ and will be a continuous function of (x, λ).

Differentiation of (8.3.1) and using (8.3.2) leads to the two equations

$$\rho'(x) \cos \vartheta(x) - \rho(x) \sin \vartheta(x)\, \vartheta'(x) = -Q(x)\rho(x) \sin \vartheta(x),$$

$$\rho'(x) \sin \vartheta(x) + \rho(x) \cos \vartheta(x)\, \vartheta'(x) = \frac{1}{P(x)}\rho(x) \cos \vartheta(x).$$

Solving for the derivatives we obtain

$$\rho'(x) = \frac{1}{2}\left\{\frac{1}{P(x)} - Q(x)\right\} \sin 2\vartheta(x)\, \rho(x), \tag{8.3.3}$$

$$\vartheta'(x) = \frac{1}{P(x)} \cos^2 \vartheta(x) + Q(x) \sin^2 \vartheta(x). \tag{8.3.4}$$

The second equation involves ϑ alone. If

$$\vartheta(a) = \vartheta_a$$

is given, the equation has a unique solution in $[a, b]$. For the right member is bounded if

$$a \le x \le b, \qquad -\infty < \vartheta < +\infty,$$

and also satisfies a Lipschitz condition with a fixed constant K. The method of successive approximations applies and gives the desired result.

We need a comparison theorem.

Theorem 8.3.1. *Let $\vartheta(x)$ satisfy* (8.3.4) *with the initial condition $\vartheta(a) = \vartheta_a$ and let $\vartheta^*(x)$ satisfy*

$$\vartheta^{*\prime}(x) = \frac{1}{P(x)} \cos^2 \vartheta^*(x) + Q^*(x) \sin^2 \vartheta^*(x) \tag{8.3.5}$$

with $\vartheta^*(a) = \vartheta^*_a$. Here $\vartheta_a \le \vartheta^*_a$ and $Q(x) < Q^*(x)$ for $a \le x \le b$. Then

$$\vartheta(x) < \vartheta^*(x), \qquad a < x \le b. \tag{8.3.6}$$

Proof. At $x = a$ there are three possibilities:

i) $\vartheta_a < \vartheta^*_a$,

ii) $\vartheta_a = \vartheta^*_a \not\equiv 0 \pmod{\pi}$,

iii) $\vartheta_a = \vartheta^*_a \equiv 0 \pmod{\pi}$.

We postpone consideration of case (iii). In the other two cases we see that there is an interval $(a, a + \delta)$ in which (8.3.6) holds. This is obvious in case (i). In case (ii) we have $\vartheta'(a) < \vartheta^{*\prime}(a)$ and the conclusion follows.

If now $a + \delta < b$ we argue as follows. We have supposedly

$$\vartheta(a + \delta) = \vartheta^*(a + \delta).$$

If this quantity is not congruent to 0 modulo π we would have

$$\vartheta'(a + \delta) < \vartheta^{*\prime}(a + \delta)$$

and this implies the existence of an interval $(a + \delta - \eta, a + \delta)$ where

$$\vartheta^*(x) < \vartheta(x)$$

which is absurd.

It remains to consider values of x for which

$$\vartheta(x) = \vartheta^*(x) \equiv 0 \pmod{\pi}.$$

Let c be such a value. We must consider small values of $x - c$. Since

$$\vartheta'(c) = \vartheta^{*\prime}(c) = \frac{1}{P(c)},$$

$\vartheta(x)$ and $\vartheta^*(x)$ are approximately equal and the common value is

$$\frac{1}{P(c)} (x - c) + k\pi$$

up to terms of lower order. We now go back to the differential equations and find that

$$\vartheta^{*\prime}(x) - \vartheta'(x) = \frac{1}{[P(c)]^2}\,[Q^*(c) - Q(c)](x - c)^2$$

up to terms of lower order. This means the existence of an ε-neighborhood of $x = c$ in which $\vartheta^{*\prime}(x) - \vartheta'(x)$ is positive.

Hence, if $c = a$ we see that

$$\vartheta(x) < \vartheta^*(x) \qquad \text{for} \qquad a < x < a + \varepsilon.$$

This disposes of case (iii) which was postponed so far. Next, if $c = a + \delta$, then clearly

$$\vartheta^*(x) < \vartheta(x) \qquad \text{for} \qquad a + \delta - \varepsilon < x < a + \delta$$

which again is a contradiction. It follows that (8.3.6) must hold. Cf. the proof of Theorem 3.3.2 which almost applies to the present situation. ▮

We now introduce a parameter λ in $Q(x)$.

Theorem 8.3.2. *Let $P(x)$ be positive and continuous in $[a, b]$. Let $Q(x, \lambda)$ be defined for $-\infty < \lambda < +\infty$ as a continuous function of (x, λ). Suppose further that, uniformly in x,*

$$\lim_{\lambda \to -\infty} Q(x, \lambda) = -\infty, \qquad \lim_{\lambda \to +\infty} Q(x, \lambda) = +\infty. \tag{8.3.7}$$

Let $0 \le \vartheta_a < \pi$ and let $\vartheta(x, \lambda)$ be the solution of

$$\vartheta'(x) = \frac{1}{P(x)}\cos^2 \vartheta(x) + Q(x, \lambda)\sin^2 \vartheta(x) \tag{8.3.8}$$

with the initial condition $\vartheta(a, \lambda) = \vartheta_a$, then

$$\vartheta(x, \lambda) \ge 0 \qquad \textit{for} \qquad a \le x \le b \quad \textit{and all } \lambda, \tag{8.3.9}$$

$$\lim_{\lambda \to -\infty} \vartheta(b, \lambda) = 0, \qquad \lim_{\lambda \to \infty} \vartheta(b, \lambda) = +\infty. \tag{8.3.10}$$

Proof. Inequality (8.3.9) holds in some interval $(a, a + \delta)$. This is obvious if $\vartheta_a > 0$. On the other hand, if $\vartheta_a = 0$, then $\vartheta'(a, \lambda) = 1/(P(a)) > 0$, so the existence of such an interval is again assured. If the inequality were not true in all of $[a, b]$, there exists a c, $a < c < b$, with $\vartheta(c, \lambda) = 0$. Since $\vartheta'(c, \lambda) = [P(c)]^{-1} > 0$, we see that $\vartheta(x, \lambda) > 0$ in some interval $(c, c + \eta)$ whence it follows that (8.3.9) must hold in all of $[a, b]$.

Next let us prove the first equality under (8.3.10). Choose an A such that $\vartheta_a < A < \pi$ and a B with $0 < B < \pi$. In the (x, ϑ)-plane we join the points (a, A) and (b, B) by a straight line the slope of which is

$$\frac{B - A}{b - a}.$$

On the line segment $\sin \vartheta$ has a positive lower limit. Since $\lim_{\lambda \to -\infty} Q(x, \lambda) = -\infty$, uniformly in x, we can find a λ_0 such that for $\lambda < \lambda_0$ and (x, ϑ) on the line segment

$$\frac{1}{P(x)} \cos^2 \vartheta + Q(x, \lambda) \sin^2 \vartheta < \frac{B - A}{b - a}. \tag{8.3.11}$$

For such values of λ the curve

$$\vartheta = \vartheta(x, \lambda)$$

must stay below the line segment for all x. For if this were not true the curve must intersect the line segment and at such a point its slope must be at least equal to that of the line and this contradicts (8.3.11). This shows that for $\lambda < \lambda_0$

$$0 \leq \vartheta(b, \lambda) \leq B.$$

But B is at our disposal and may be taken arbitrarily small. Hence

$$\lim_{\lambda \to -\infty} \vartheta(b, \lambda) = 0$$

as asserted.

To prove the second inequality we argue as follows. Since

$$\lim_{\lambda \to +\infty} Q(x, \lambda) = +\infty,$$

uniformly in x, we can choose a λ_1 such that

$$\frac{1}{P(x)} \cos^2 \vartheta + Q(x, \lambda) \sin^2 \vartheta > 0$$

for $a \leq x \leq b$, all ϑ, and $\lambda_1 < \lambda$. This says that $\vartheta'(x, \lambda) > 0$ for such values of x and λ. Thus $\vartheta(x, \lambda)$ is an increasing function of x for $\lambda > \lambda_1$.

If λ is large positive, $\vartheta'(x, \lambda)$ is also large positive except in the neighborhood of points x where $\vartheta(x, \lambda)$ is a multiple of π. Let us make this more precise. Choose a large positive M, then there is a $\lambda(M)$ such that

$$Q(x, \lambda) > M \qquad \text{for} \qquad \lambda > \lambda(M).$$

Then

$$\vartheta'(x, \lambda) > M^{1/3}$$

in all subintervals of $[a, b]$ where

$$|\sin \vartheta(x, \lambda)| > M^{-1/3}. \tag{8.3.12}$$

In such an interval $\vartheta(x, \lambda)$ increases by an amount $< \pi$ but close to π if M is large. The mean value theorem of the differential calculus shows that the length of the interval does not exceed $\pi M^{-1/3}$.

Let us estimate the length of an interval where (8.3.12) is not valid. There is a positive lower bound for $\vartheta'(x, \lambda)$. If

$$P(x) \leq P, \qquad a \leq x \leq b,$$

then

$$\vartheta'(x, \lambda) > P^{-1}[1 - M^{-2/3}]$$

in the interval. Hence its length is less than

$$2P(1 - M^{-2/3})^{-1} \arc\sin(M^{-1/3}) < 2\pi P M^{-1/3} \quad \text{if} \quad 2^{3/2} < M.$$

The intervals where (8.3.12) holds alternate with those where it does not hold. There is certainly room for n intervals of each kind in $[a, b]$, if

$$(2P + 1)n\pi M^{-1/3} < b - a. \tag{8.3.13}$$

If this is the case, then

$$\vartheta(b, \lambda) > n\pi - \arc\sin M^{-1/3} + \vartheta_a.$$

Here M is at our disposal and larger values of M permit larger values of n. It follows that

$$\lim \vartheta(b, \lambda) = +\infty$$

as asserted. ∎

We come now to the application of Prüfer's method to boundary value problems with side conditions of the classical type (8.2.9). Here the boundary conditions will appear in a form geared to the use of polar coordinates. The result goes back to Sturm (1836) who considered a special case.

Theorem 8.3.3. *Let $P(x)$ be positive and continuous in $[a, b]$. Let $Q(x, \lambda)$ be real and continuous in (x, λ) for $a \le x \le b$, $-\infty < \lambda < +\infty$, let*

$$Q(x, \lambda_1) < Q(x, \lambda_2) \quad \text{if} \quad \lambda_1 < \lambda_2, \tag{8.3.14}$$

and, uniformly in x,

$$\lim_{\lambda \to -\infty} Q(x, \lambda) = -\infty, \qquad \lim_{\lambda \to +\infty} Q(x, \lambda) = +\infty. \tag{8.3.15}$$

Let

$$\mathsf{L}[y] = [P(x)y'(x)]' + Q(x, \lambda)y(x). \tag{8.3.16}$$

Let ϑ_a and ϑ_b be given, $0 \le \vartheta_a < \pi$, $0 < \vartheta_b \le \pi$, and set

$$L_1[y] = y(a)\cos\vartheta_a - P(a)y'(a)\sin\vartheta_a, \tag{8.3.17}$$

$$L_2[y] = y(b)\cos\vartheta_b - P(b)y'(b)\sin\vartheta_b. \tag{8.3.18}$$

Then the boundary value problem

$$\mathsf{L}[y] = 0, \qquad L_1[y] = 0, \qquad L_2[y] = 0, \tag{8.3.19}$$

has infinitely many real characteristic values $\{\lambda_n\}$:

$$\lambda_0 < \lambda_1 < \lambda_2 < \cdots < \lambda_n < \cdots, \qquad \lim \lambda_n = +\infty.$$

Let $\omega_n(x)$ be the normalized characteristic function corresponding to λ_n. Then $\omega_n(x)$ has exactly n simple zeros in (a, b).

Proof. If we set

$$y(x, \lambda) = \rho(x, \lambda) \sin \vartheta(x, \lambda),$$

$$P(x)y'(x, \lambda) = \rho(x, \lambda) \cos \vartheta(x, \lambda),$$

then $\rho(x, \lambda)$ and $\vartheta(x\ \lambda)$ satisfy (8.3.3) and (8.3.4) with $Q(x, \lambda)$ instead of $Q(x)$. The initial condition

$$\vartheta(a, \lambda) = \vartheta_a \tag{8.3.20}$$

determines $\vartheta(x, \lambda)$ uniquely. By virtue of the preceding theorems and conditions (8.3.14) and (8.4.15), $\vartheta(x, \lambda)$ is an increasing function of λ which is non-negative and

$$\lim_{\lambda \to -\infty} \vartheta(b, \lambda) = 0, \qquad \lim_{\lambda \to +\infty} \vartheta(b, \lambda) = +\infty.$$

Once $\vartheta(x, \lambda)$ is known, we determine $\rho(x, \lambda)$ from

$$\log \rho(x, \lambda) = \frac{1}{2} \int_a^x \left\{ \frac{1}{P(s)} - Q(s, \lambda) \right\} \sin [2\vartheta(s, \lambda)]\, ds \tag{8.3.21}$$

so that $\rho(a, \lambda) = 1$. We note that $\rho(x, \lambda)$ is bounded away from 0 and ∞, though possibly not uniformly in λ. Next observe that

$$\begin{aligned} y(a) \cos \vartheta_a &- P(a)y'(a) \sin \vartheta_a \\ &= \rho(a, \lambda) \sin \vartheta(a, \lambda) \cos \vartheta_a - \rho(a, \lambda) \cos \vartheta(a, \lambda) \sin \vartheta_a \\ &= 0. \end{aligned}$$

It follows that the first boundary condition

$$L_1[y(\cdot, \lambda)] = 0$$

is satisfied by taking

$$y(x, \lambda) = \rho(x, \lambda) \sin \vartheta(x, \lambda) \qquad \text{with} \qquad \rho(a, \lambda) = 1, \quad \vartheta(a, \lambda) = \vartheta_a.$$

The second boundary condition will be satisfied if λ_n can be found so that

$$\vartheta(b, \lambda_n) = \vartheta_b + n\pi, \tag{8.3.22}$$

where n is a positive integer or 0. Note that n cannot be negative since $\vartheta(x, \lambda) \geq 0$ for all (x, λ) and $0 < \vartheta_b \leq \pi$. Since $\vartheta(b, \lambda)$ is an increasing function of λ which takes on every positive value once and only once, it follows that λ_n is uniquely determined and

$$\lambda_0 < \lambda_1 < \lambda_2 < \cdots < \lambda_n < \cdots \qquad \lim_{n \to \infty} \lambda_n = +\infty.$$

To $\lambda = \lambda_n$ corresponds a characteristic function $y(x, \lambda_n)$ which is uniquely defined by the initial conditions. It is advantageous to introduce the normalized characteristic function

$$\omega_n(x) = \left\{ \int_a^b [y(s, \lambda_n)]^2\, ds \right\}^{-1/2} y(x, \lambda_n). \tag{8.3.23}$$

By Theorem 8.2.2 the functions $\omega_n(x)$ form an orthonormal system in $L_2(a, b)$.

It remains to prove that $\omega_n(x)$ has n simple zeros in the open interval (a, b). Since

$$y(x, \lambda_n) = \rho(x, \lambda_n) \sin \vartheta(x, \lambda_n)$$

where the first factor is bounded away from 0 and ∞, it follows that the zeros of $\omega_n(x)$ are located at the points where

$$\vartheta(x, \lambda_n) \equiv 0 \pmod{\pi}.$$

At such a point

$$P(x)y'(x, \lambda_n) = \pm\rho(x, \lambda_n) \neq 0,$$

so each zero is simple. Moreover, if $\vartheta = k\pi$ belongs to the range of $\vartheta(x, \lambda_n)$, then at a point where this value is assumed

$$P(x)\vartheta'(x, \lambda_n) = 1 > 0.$$

Thus, a value $k\pi$ can be assumed at most once by $\vartheta(x, \lambda_n)$ in (a, b). Now

$$\vartheta(a, \lambda_n) = \vartheta_a < \pi, \quad \vartheta(b, \lambda_n) = \vartheta_b + n\pi, \quad 0 < \vartheta_b \leq \pi.$$

Hence the open interval bounded by these two values must belong to the range of $\vartheta(x, \lambda_n)$. If $n > 0$, this interval contains n multiples of π, if $n = 0$ none. Thus $\omega_n(x)$ has at least n zeros in (a, b). There could not be more, however, for if $\vartheta(x_0, \lambda_n) = k\pi$ with $k > n$, then $\vartheta(b, \lambda_n)$ must exceed $(n + 1)\pi$ which is a contradiction. Thus $\omega_n(x)$ has exactly n simple zeros in (a, b). Note that additional zeros may occur at the endpoints, at $x = a$ if $\vartheta_a = 0$, at $x = b$ if $\vartheta_b = \pi$. ∎

In the important case where

$$Q(x, \lambda) = Q(x) + \lambda,$$

we know that all characteristic values are real but, in general, this will not be the case. As a trivial counter example we can take

$$Q(x, \lambda) = Q(x) + \lambda^3$$

where for every real characteristic value λ_n there are two complex ones, $\omega\lambda_n$ and $\omega^2\lambda_n$, with $\omega = \exp(\frac{2}{3}\pi i)$.

For the case where

$$Q(x, \lambda) = Q(x) + \lambda$$

we can use the differential equation for $\vartheta(x, \lambda)$ to obtain fairly good estimates for λ_n.

Theorem 8.3.4. *Suppose that*

$$0 < p \leq P(x) \leq P, \quad q \leq Q(x) \leq Q. \tag{8.3.24}$$

If $y(x, \lambda)$ is a solution of

$$[P(x)y'(x)]' + [Q(x) + \lambda]y(x) = 0$$

with exactly n, $n > 0$, zeros in the open interval (a, b), then if $\lambda > -q$ it must also satisfy the inequality

$$\left(\frac{\pi}{b-a}\right)^2 p(n-1)^2 - Q < \lambda < \left(\frac{\pi}{b-a}\right)^2 P(n+1)^2 - q. \quad (8.3.25)$$

Proof. We have

$$\frac{1}{P}\cos^2\vartheta(x,\lambda) + (q+\lambda)\sin^2\vartheta(x,\lambda)$$
$$< \vartheta'(x,\lambda) < \frac{1}{p}\cos^2\vartheta(x,\lambda) + (Q+\lambda)\sin^2\vartheta(x,\lambda)$$

by formula (8.3.8) together with the assumptions on $P(x)$, $Q(x)$, and λ. To fix the ideas, let $y(x, \lambda)$ satisfy the boundary condition (8.3.17) with $0 \leq \vartheta_a < \pi$ and suppose that $y(x, \lambda)$ has exactly n zeros x_j in (a, b),

$$a < x_1 < x_2 < \cdots < x_n < b.$$

Then $\vartheta(a, \lambda) = \vartheta_a$, $\vartheta(x, \lambda)$ is an increasing function of x and maps the interval $x_j \leq x \leq x_{j+1}$ onto the interval $j\pi \leq \vartheta \leq (j+1)\pi$ in a one-to-one manner. Here $j = 1, 2, \ldots, n-1$. It follows that

$$\int_{j\pi}^{(j+1)\pi}\left\{\frac{1}{p}\cos^2\vartheta + (Q+\lambda)\sin^2\vartheta\right\}^{-1} d\vartheta < x_{j+1} - x_j,$$

while

$$\int_{j\pi}^{(j+1)\pi}\left\{\frac{1}{P}\cos^2\vartheta + (q+\lambda)\sin^2\vartheta\right\}^{-1} d\vartheta > x_{j+1} - x_j.$$

Summing for j we obtain

$$\int_{\pi}^{n\pi}\left\{\frac{1}{p}\cos^2\vartheta + (Q+\lambda)\sin^2\vartheta\right\}^{-1} d\vartheta < x_n - x_1 < b - a,$$

$$\int_{0}^{(n+1)\pi}\left\{\frac{1}{P}\cos^2\vartheta + (q+\lambda)\sin^2\vartheta\right\}^{-1} d\vartheta > b - a.$$

The integrals are elementary. We have

$$\int_0^{\pi/2}(r\cos^2\vartheta + s\sin^2\vartheta)^{-1}\,d\vartheta = \tfrac{1}{2}\pi(rs)^{-1/2}. \quad (8.3.26)$$

Hence

$$(n-1)\pi\left\{\frac{p}{Q+\lambda}\right\}^{1/2} < b - a < (n+1)\pi\left\{\frac{P}{q+\lambda}\right\}^{1/2}.$$

Solving for λ gives (8.3.25).

Corollary. *The inequality* (8.3.25) *is satisfied by the* n^{th} *characteristic value* λ_n.

For $\omega_n(x)$ has exactly n zeros in (a, b).

EXERCISE 8.3

1. With the notation of Theorem 8.3.4 and $\vartheta_a = \frac{1}{2}\pi$, show that the boundary value problem (8.3.19) with $Q(x, \lambda) = Q(x) + \lambda$ has at most one characteristic value less than $-Q$ and no such value if $\vartheta_b \geq \frac{1}{2}\pi$.
2. More generally, show that there is at most one characteristic value less than $-1/p \cot^2 \vartheta_a - Q$ and no such value if $\vartheta_b \geq \vartheta_a$. Here $0 < \vartheta_a < \pi$.
3. Analogous results hold if $Q(x, \lambda) = \lambda Q(x)$ where $q > 0$. If $\vartheta_a = \frac{1}{2}\pi$, show that there is at most one negative characteristic value and none at all if $\vartheta_b \geq \frac{1}{2}\pi$.
4. Similarly, if $\vartheta_a > 0$ show that there is at most one characteristic value less than $-(pq)^{-1} \cot^2 \vartheta_a$ and no such value if $\vartheta_b \geq \vartheta_a$.
5. Verify (8.3.26).

8.4 ANOTHER VARIANT OF PRÜFER'S METHOD

In this section we shall find an asymptotic formula for λ_n and prove that the sup norm of $\omega_n(x)$ is bounded at least when $P(x)$ and $Q(x)$ are continuously differentiable. To this end we use another variant of Prüfer's method. We set

$$\begin{aligned} \left\{\frac{Q(x) + \lambda}{P(x)}\right\}^{1/4} y(x) &= r(x) \sin \theta(x), \\ \left\{\frac{Q(x) + \lambda}{P(x)}\right\}^{-1/4} y'(x) &= r(x) \cos \theta(x), \end{aligned} \tag{8.4.1}$$

where $y(x)$ is supposed to satisfy the equation

$$[P(x)y'(x)]' + [Q(x) + \lambda]y(x) = 0 \tag{8.4.2}$$

and λ is so large that $\min Q(x) + \lambda \equiv q + \lambda > 0$. The differential equations for $r(x)$ and $\theta(x)$ read

$$\frac{r'(x)}{r(x)} = -\frac{1}{4}\frac{Q'(x)}{Q(x) + \lambda} \cos [2\theta(x)] + \frac{1}{4}\frac{P'(x)}{P(x)}\{1 + 2\cos^2 \theta(x)\}, \tag{8.4.3}$$

$$\theta'(x) = \left\{\frac{Q(x) + \lambda}{P(x)}\right\}^{1/2} + \frac{1}{4}\left\{\frac{Q'(x)}{Q(x) + \lambda} + \frac{P'(x)}{P(x)}\right\} \sin [2\theta(x)]. \tag{8.4.4}$$

Before we discuss these equations, there are some comments pertaining to the defining equations (8.4.1). For the solution $y(x, \lambda)$ we have two representations by polar coordinates, one in terms of $\rho(x, \lambda)$ and $\vartheta(x, \lambda)$, the other in terms of $r(x, \lambda)$ and $\theta(x, \lambda)$. The presence in (8.4.1) of the multipliers on the left make for some difference in the behavior of these two sets of functions.

Let us first note what $\vartheta(x, \lambda)$ and $\theta(x, \lambda)$ have in common. Since both functions determine the zeros and extrema of $y(x, \lambda)$, we may assume that they take the same values at such a point. Thus if x_j is the jth zero of $y(x, \lambda)$ in (a, b) we want

$$\vartheta(x_j, \lambda) = \theta(x_j, \lambda) = j\pi.$$

Likewise at the kth extremum

$$\vartheta(\xi_k, \lambda) = \theta(\xi_k, \lambda) = (k - \tfrac{1}{2})\pi.$$

It is to be noted that $\theta(x, \lambda)$ is increasing at each such point as is shown by (8.4.4).

In passing, let us observe that the comparison theorems of Section 8.1 show that

$$\left\{\frac{p}{Q + \lambda}\right\}^{1/2} \pi < x_{j+1} - x_j < \left\{\frac{P}{q + \lambda}\right\}^{1/2} \pi.$$

In particular, if $\lambda = \lambda_n$ and $y(x, \lambda_n)$ is the corresponding non-normalized characteristic function, then by Theorem 8.3.4 λ_n lies between constant multiples of n^2. This shows the existence of fixed positive constants A_1 and A_2 such that

$$A_1 \le n(x_{j+1,n} - x_{j,n}) \le A_2. \tag{8.4.5}$$

We return to $\vartheta(x, \lambda_n)$ and $\theta(x, \lambda_n)$ and ask what relations hold between initial and terminal values of the two functions. We obtain from (8.4.1) the formula

$$\tan \theta(x, \lambda) = \left\{\frac{Q(x) + \lambda}{P(x)}\right\}^{1/2} \frac{y(x, \lambda)}{y'(x, \lambda)}$$

$$= \{P(x)[Q(x) + \lambda]\}^{1/2} \tan \vartheta(x, \lambda). \tag{8.4.6}$$

In particular,

$$\tan \theta(a, \lambda) = \{P(a)[Q(a) + \lambda]\}^{1/2} \tan \vartheta_a.$$

This shows that

$$\theta(a, \lambda) = 0 \quad \text{if} \quad \vartheta_a = 0, \qquad \theta(a, \lambda) = \tfrac{1}{2}\pi \quad \text{if} \quad \vartheta_a = \tfrac{1}{2}\pi.$$

Suppose now that $\vartheta_a \neq 0, \tfrac{1}{2}\pi$. Then

$$\tan \theta(a, \lambda) = [P(a)]^{1/2} \tan \vartheta_a \cdot \lambda^{1/2} + O(\lambda^{-1/2})$$

whence

$$\theta(a, \lambda) = \tfrac{1}{2}\pi - [P(a)]^{-1/2} \cot \vartheta_a \lambda^{-1/2} + O(\lambda^{-1}).$$

Similar results hold for $\theta(b, \lambda)$. We combine the results in the following table.

	ϑ_a	$\theta(a, \lambda_n)$	ϑ_b	$\theta(b, \lambda_n)$
1	0	0	π	$(n + 1)\pi$
2	$\frac{1}{2}\pi$	$\frac{1}{2}\pi$	$\frac{1}{2}\pi$	$(n + \frac{1}{2})\pi$
3	$\neq 0, \frac{1}{2}\pi$	$\frac{1}{2}\pi + O(\lambda_n^{-1/2})$	$\neq \frac{1}{2}\pi, \pi$	$(n + \frac{1}{2})\pi + O(\lambda_n^{-1/2})$

We say that the boundary conditions are of type (j, k) if ϑ_a is taken from line j and ϑ_b from line k of the table.

We now see that

$$\theta(b, \lambda_n) - \theta(a, \lambda_n) = (n + \eta)\pi + O(\lambda_n^{-1/2}) \tag{8.4.7}$$

where η is $0, \frac{1}{2}, 1$ according as (j, k) is

$$\begin{gathered}(2, 2), (2, 3), (3, 2), (3, 3),\\ (1, 2), (1, 3), (2, 1), (3, 1),\\ (1, 1),\end{gathered}$$

respectively. A remainder term is present iff the symbol (j, k) contains a "3."

We shall now use the differential equation (8.4.4) and the preceding discussion to prove

Theorem 8.4.1. *If $P(x)$ and $Q(x)$ are continuously differentiable in $[a, b]$, if $P(x) > 0$ and $P'(x)[P(x)]^{-1/2} \in BV[a\ b]$, and if $Q(x, \lambda) = Q(x) + \lambda$, then the nth characteristic value of Problem (8.3.19) satisfies*

$$\lambda_n^{1/2} = \left\{\int_a^b [P(s)]^{-1/2}\, ds\right\}^{-1} \pi(n + \eta) + O\left(\frac{1}{n}\right) \tag{8.4.8}$$

where η is defined above.

Proof. In (8.4.4) we set $\lambda = \lambda_n$ and integrate from $x = a$ to $x = b$ obtaining

$$\theta(b, \lambda_n) - \theta(a, \lambda_n) = \int_a^b \left\{\frac{Q(x) + \lambda_n}{P(x)}\right\}^{1/2} dx$$
$$+ \int_a^b \left\{\frac{Q'(x)}{Q(x) + \lambda_n} + \frac{P'(x)}{P(x)}\right\} \sin\, [2\theta(x, \lambda_n)]\, dx. \tag{8.4.9}$$

The left member is given by (8.4.7). In the right member the first term dominates. It equals

$$\lambda_n^{1/2} \int_a^b [P(x)]^{-1/2}\, dx + O(\lambda_n^{-1/2}).$$

The remainder is clearly bounded, its first term is actually $O(\lambda_n^{-1})$. The second term is less obvious. Since $\theta'(x, \lambda_n) > 0$ for large λ_n and all x, the arc $\theta(x, \lambda_n)$ is an increasing function of x. We denote its unique inverse by $x_n(\theta)$ and write

$$\int_a^b \frac{P'(x)}{P(x)} \sin [2\theta(x, \lambda_n)]\, dx = \int_{\theta(a,\lambda_n)}^{\theta(b,\lambda_n)} \frac{P'(x_n(\theta))}{P(x_n(\theta))} \frac{1}{\theta'(x)} \sin (2\theta)\, d\theta.$$

Here

$$\theta'(x) = \lambda_n^{1/2}[P(x)]^{-1/2} + O(\lambda_n^{-1/2}),$$

so that the integral under consideration reduces to

$$\lambda_n^{-1/2} \int_{\theta(a,\lambda_n)}^{\theta(b,\lambda_n)} p_n(\theta) \sin 2\theta\, d\theta + O(\lambda_n^{-1})$$

where

$$p_n(\theta) = P'(x)[P(x)]^{-1/2} \qquad \text{with} \qquad x = x_n(\theta).$$

Since $p_n(\theta)$ is of bounded variation in $[\theta(a, \lambda_n), \theta(b, \lambda_n)]$, the total variation being independent of n, it follows that the integral is uniformly bounded. Hence, finally,

$$\pi(n + \eta) = \lambda_n^{1/2} \int_a^b [P(x)]^{-1/2}\, dx + O(\lambda_n^{-1/2})$$

which is equivalent to (8.4.8). ∎

We come now to the behavior of $r(x, \lambda)$. Equation (8.4.3) gives

$$\log \frac{r(x, \lambda)}{r(a, \lambda)} = -\frac{1}{4} \int_a^x \frac{Q'(s)}{Q(s) + \lambda} \cos [2\theta(s, \lambda)]\, ds$$

$$+ \frac{1}{4} \int_a^x \frac{P'(s)}{P(s)} \{1 + 2\cos^2 \theta(s, \lambda)\}\, ds \qquad (8.4.10)$$

which is bounded uniformly with respect to λ, $\lambda > -q + 1$. Hence there exist fixed positive numbers M_1 and M_2 such that

$$M_1 r(a, \lambda) < r(x, \lambda) < M_2 r(a, \lambda). \qquad (8.4.11)$$

This reduces the problem to a discussion of $r(a, \lambda)$. Here the different possibilities of choosing the boundary condition at $x = a$ affect the infinitary behavior of $r(a, \lambda)$ for large values of λ. We recall that $\rho(a, \lambda) \equiv 1$ and we suppose that $y(x, \lambda)$ satisfies the first boundary condition which is characterized by the arc ϑ_a. We have to distinguish between two cases, $\vartheta_a = 0$ and $\vartheta_a \neq 0$. In any case we have

$$\sin \vartheta_a = y(a, \lambda) = \left\{\frac{P(a)}{Q(a) + \lambda}\right\}^{1/4} r(a, \lambda) \sin [\theta(a, \lambda)],$$

$$\cos \vartheta_a = P(a) y'(a, \lambda) = [Q(a) + \lambda]^{1/4} [P(a)]^{3/4} r(a, \lambda) \cos [\theta(a, \lambda)].$$

First we take $\vartheta_a = \theta(a, \lambda) = 0$. Then the second equation gives

$$r(a, \lambda) = \lambda^{-1/4}[P(a)]^{-3/4}\left\{1 + O\left(\frac{1}{\lambda}\right)\right\}. \tag{8.4.12}$$

Next, take $\vartheta_a = \theta(a, \lambda) = \frac{1}{2}\pi$. The first equation gives

$$r(a, \lambda) = \lambda^{1/4}[P(a)]^{-1/4}\left\{1 + O\left(\frac{1}{\lambda}\right)\right\} \tag{8.4.13}$$

and the same estimate holds if $\vartheta_a \neq 0, \frac{1}{2}\pi$. Similar considerations give

$$r(b, \lambda) = O(\lambda^{-1/4}) \quad \text{or} \quad O(\lambda^{1/4}) \tag{8.4.14}$$

according as $\vartheta_b = \pi$ or not. Here it is assumed that $y(x, \lambda)$ satisfies the second boundary condition.

Suppose now that

$$y(x, \lambda) = \left\{\frac{P(x)}{Q(x) + \lambda}\right\}^{1/4} r(x, \lambda) \sin [\theta(x, \lambda)]$$

satisfies the first boundary condition. We see then that

$$y(x, \lambda) = \begin{cases} \lambda^{-1/2}B_0(x, \lambda) \sin [\theta(x, \lambda)] & \text{if } \vartheta_a = 0, \\ B_1(x, \lambda) \sin [\theta(x, \lambda)] & \text{if } 0 < \vartheta_a < \pi, \end{cases} \tag{8.4.15}$$

and there exist positive constants B_1 and B_2 such that

$$B_1 < B_0(x, \lambda) < B_2, \qquad B_1 < B_1(x, \lambda) < B_2, \tag{8.4.16}$$

for $a \leq x \leq b$, $-q + 1 \leq \lambda$. These estimates hold in particular for $\lambda = \lambda_n$.

We now proceed to estimate the L_2-norm of $y(x, \lambda_n)$. We have to distinguish between the two cases $\vartheta_a = 0$ and $\vartheta_a \neq 0$. In the first case

$$\int_a^b |y(x, \lambda_n)|^2\, dx = \lambda_n^{-1} \int_a^b [B_0(x, \lambda_n)]^2 \sin^2 [\theta(x, \lambda_n)]\, dx.$$

Here the integral in the right member lies between B_1^2 and B_2^2 times

$$\int_a^b \sin^2 [\theta(x, \lambda_n)]\, dx = \int_a^b \sin^2 [\theta(x, \lambda_n)] \frac{d\theta(x, \lambda_n)}{\theta'(x, \lambda_n)}.$$

Now $\theta'(x, \lambda_n)$ is positive and $O(\lambda_n^{1/2})$ for large n. More precisely, there exist two positive constants C_1 and C_2 such that

$$C_1\lambda_n^{1/2} \leq \theta'(x, \lambda_n) \leq C_2\lambda_n^{1/2}, \quad a \leq x \leq b, \quad n_0 < n. \tag{8.4.17}$$

Hence the last integral lies between C_2^{-1} and C_1^{-1} times

$$\lambda_n^{-1/2} \int_a^b \sin^2 [\theta(x, \lambda_n)]\, d\theta(x, \lambda_n) = \lambda_n^{-1/2} \int_0^{\theta(b,\lambda_n)} \sin^2 \theta\, d\theta$$

$$= \tfrac{1}{2}\lambda_n^{-1/2}[\theta(b, \lambda_n) + O(1)] = O(1)$$

since $\theta(b, \lambda_n) = (n + \eta)\pi + o(1)$ and $\lambda_n = O(n^2)$. Combining the various inequalities we see that positive constants N_1 and N_2 can be found such that

$$N_1\lambda_n^{-1/2} \le \|y(\cdot, \lambda_n)\|_2 \le N_2\lambda_n^{-1/2}, \qquad \vartheta_a = 0. \tag{8.4.18}$$

Combining this estimate with (8.4.15) and (8.4.16) we see that

$$\omega_n(x) = \frac{y(x, \lambda_n)}{\|y(\cdot, \lambda_n)\|_2}$$

is bounded uniformly in n and x, i.e. there are positive constants A_1 and A_2 such that

$$A_1 \le \|\omega_n(\cdot)\|_C \le A_2 \tag{8.4.19}$$

where $\| \, \|_C$ denotes the sup norm in $C[a, b]$.

This formula is also valid if $\vartheta_a \neq 0$. Since now the factor $\lambda_n^{-1/2}$ is missing in (8.4.15), it is also missing in (8.4.18) and (8.4.19) remains valid.

EXERCISE 8.4

1. Get an approximate value of λ_n if

$$P(x) = (1 + x)^2, \quad Q(x) \equiv 0, \quad y(0) = 0, \quad y(b) = 0$$

and examine what happens to $\lambda_n = \lambda_n(b)$ as $b \to +\infty$.

2. Prove that $\|\omega_n'\|_C = O(\lambda_n^{1/2})$.
3. Prove that $\|\omega_n'\|_2 = O(\lambda_n^{1/2})$ and not $o(\lambda_n^{1/2})$.
4. If $\sum_0^\infty u_n$ converges to the sum U, prove that

$$\lim_{\lambda \to \infty} \sum_{n=0}^{\infty} \frac{\lambda}{\lambda + \lambda_n} u_n = U.$$

This defines a method of *resolvent summability*.

5. A divergent series $\sum_0^\infty u_n$ may be resolvent summable. Thus if $\lambda_n = n^2$, $n = 1, 2, \ldots$, and $u_{2m} = -u_{2m-1} = -1$, the series is divergent but $(C, 1)$-summable to $\frac{1}{2}$. Show that it is also resolvent summable to $\frac{1}{2}$.
6. This raises the general question: If a series is $(C, 1)$-summable to the limit U, is it also resolvent summable and if so to the same limit? Prove or disprove!

8.5 EXPANSION PROBLEMS

For the class of boundary value problems considered in the preceding sections it was shown that there are infinitely many characteristic values, all real, and the corresponding normalized characteristic functions form an orthonormal system in $L_2(a, b)$. Such a system leads to a formal orthogonal series expansion.

If $f(t) \in L_2(a, b)$, we write

$$f(t) \sim \sum_{n=0}^{\infty} f_n \omega_n(t), \qquad f_n = \int_a^b f(s)\omega_n(s)\, ds. \tag{8.5.1}$$

This is the formal expansion of f in the orthonormal system $\{\omega_n\}$. For the following see (7.6.26) and Theorem 7.2.1. Bessel's inequality

$$\sum_{n=0}^{\infty} |f_n|^2 \le \int_a^b |f(s)|^2\, ds \tag{8.5.2}$$

shows the convergence of the series on the left. Here we have equality iff the system $\{\omega_n\}$ is complete in $L_2(a, b)$. If this is the case, we recall that the partial sums of the formal series (8.5.1) converge to f in the sense of the metric of L_2. The main object of the present section is to show that the system $\{\omega_n\}$ is indeed complete in the case of the simple boundary value problems here considered. The proof will require a number of steps.

We consider the differential operator

$$\mathsf{L}_0[y] = [P(t)y'(t)]' + Q(t)y(t) \tag{8.5.3}$$

where $P(t)$ and $Q(t)$ are continuously differentiable functions and $P(t) > 0$ in (a, b). Let X be the domain of L_0. It is that subset of

$$L_2(a, b) \cap C^1[a, b]$$

where $\mathsf{L}_0[y]$ exists and is an element of $L_2(a, b)$. Let X_1 be the subset of X where

$$L_1[y] \equiv y(a) \cos \vartheta_a - P(a)y'(a) \sin \vartheta_a = 0, \tag{8.5.4}$$

X_2 the subset where

$$L_2[y] \equiv y(b) \cos \vartheta_b - P(b)y'(b) \sin \vartheta_b = 0 \tag{8.5.5}$$

and let $X_{1,2} = X_1 \cap X_2$.

In order to conform with the conventions of linear operator theory, we say that μ_n is a characteristic value and ω_n the corresponding normalized characteristic function of the operator L_0 in the space $X_{1,2}$ if

$$\mathsf{L}_0[\omega_n] = \mu_n \omega_n, \qquad \omega_n \in X_{1,2}, \qquad \|\omega_n\|_2 = 1. \tag{8.5.6}$$

Note that in the preceding sections we have considered boundary value problems of the type

$$\mathsf{L}_0[y] + \lambda y = 0, \qquad L_1[y] = 0, \qquad L_2[y] = 0.$$

Our previous results apply the present situation, if we write $\mu = -\lambda$ and $\lambda_n = -\mu_n$. There is no change in ω_n.

What we propose to do is to define and study the resolvent of the operator L_0, i.e. the operator

$$(\mu I - \mathsf{L}_0)^{-1} \equiv \mathsf{R}(\mu, \mathsf{L}_0), \tag{8.5.7}$$

which, as we shall see, maps all of $L_2(a, b)$ into $X_{1,2}$. The set $\{\omega_n\}$ spans a linear subspace of $X_{1,2}$ whose L_2-closure is all of $L_2(a, b)$. This will lead to the main result:

Theorem 8.5.1. *The system $\{\omega_n\}$ is complete in $L_2(a, b)$.*

We start the argument by introducing *Green's function*, so named after the British mathematical physicist George Green (1793–1851), whose brilliant work on potential theory, electricity and magnetism was largely overlooked during his lifetime. This function serves as the kernel in the integral representation of the resolvent. We use a fundamental system of solutions, $y_1(t, \mu)$ and $y_2(t, \mu)$ of the homogeneous equation

$$\mathsf{L}_0[y] = \mu y \tag{8.5.8}$$

such that

$$L_1[y_1] = 0, \qquad L_2[y_2] = 0. \tag{8.5.9}$$

We take the initial values of $y_1(t, \mu)$ at $t = a$ and of $y_2(t, \mu)$ at $t = b$ to be independent of μ. For fixed t the solutions are then entire functions of μ of order $\leq \frac{1}{2}$. For $\mu = \mu_n$ they become linearly dependent. This suggests introducing their Wronskian. The identity of Lagrange gives

$$y_2\mathsf{L}_0[y_1] - y_1\mathsf{L}_0[y_2] = \frac{d}{dt}\{P(t)[y_2(t)y_1'(t) - y_1(t)y_2'(t)]\} = 0 \tag{8.5.10}$$

so that

$$P(t)[y_2(t, \mu)y_1'(t, \mu) - y_1(t, \mu)y_2'(t, \mu)]$$

is independent of t. It is of course a function of μ. Set

$$D(\mu) \equiv P(a)[y_2(a, \mu)y_1'(a, \mu) - y_1(a, \mu)y_2'(a, \mu)]. \tag{8.5.11}$$

This is also an entire function of μ of order $\leq \frac{1}{2}$ and $D(\mu) \neq 0$ for $\mu \in \mathrm{M}$, the μ-plane with the points μ_n deleted. Each μ_n is a simple zero of $D(\mu)$.

We can now define Green's function. For $\mu \in \mathrm{M}$ set

$$G(s, t; \mu) = \begin{cases} [D(\mu)]^{-1}y_1(s, \mu)y_2(t, \mu), & s < t, \\ [D(\mu)]^{-1}y_1(t, \mu)y_2(s, \mu), & t < s. \end{cases} \tag{8.5.12}$$

With the aid of this kernel define

$$\begin{aligned} Y(t, \mu; f) &\equiv \int_a^b G(s, t; \mu)f(s)\, ds \\ &= [D(\mu)]^{-1}\Big\{y_2(t, \mu)\int_a^t y_1(s, \mu)f(s)\, ds \\ &\qquad + y_1(t, \mu)\int_t^b y_2(s, \mu)f(s)\, ds\Big\}. \end{aligned} \tag{8.5.13}$$

Lemma 8.5.1. *$Y(t, \mu; f)$ is the unique solution of the boundary value problem*

$$\mu Y - \mathsf{L}_0[Y] = f, \qquad L_1[Y] = 0, \qquad L_2[Y] = 0 \tag{8.5.14}$$

for any f in $L_2(a, b)$.

Proof. It is clear that the integrals in (8.5.13) exist and define a continuous function of t for every $f \in L_2(a, b)$. Moreover, $Y(t, \mu; f)$ is differentiable and its derivative is given by

$$Y'(t, \mu; f) = [D(\mu)]^{-1}\left\{y_2'(t, \mu) \int_a^t y_1(s, \mu) f(s)\, ds \right.$$
$$\left. + \, y_1'(t, \mu) \int_t^b y_2(s, \mu) f(s)\, ds\right\}. \tag{8.5.15}$$

If f is continuous, this is obtainable by formal differentiation. Two terms involving $f(t)$ appear but cancel. The same result holds for $f \in L_2(a, b)$ as is seen by actually carrying out the limiting process. On the other hand, if we want to show that $Y(t, \mu; f)$ satisfies the differential equation (8.5.14) for all t, we must restrict f to be continuous. Without this assumption the differential equation will hold only for almost all t. Hence we assume $f \in C[a, b]$. This restriction is not severe for the elements of $C[a, b]$ are dense in $L_2(a, b)$ and if the resolvent turns out to be bounded on this dense subspace then it can be extended to all of $L_2(a, b)$ as a bounded operator with the same bound.

The main step in verifying the differential equation is to evaluate

$$D(\mu)[P(t)Y'(t)]' = [P(t)y_2'(t, \mu)]' \int_a^t y_1(s, \mu) f(s)\, ds$$
$$+ \, [P(t)y_1'(t, \mu)]' \int_t^b y_2(s, \mu) f(s)\, ds$$
$$+ \, f(t)P(t)[y_2'(t, \mu)y_1(t, \mu) - y_1'(t, \mu)y_2(t, \mu)].$$

Here the multiplier of $f(t)$ is $-D(\mu)$ by (8.5.11) and

$$[P(t)y_1'(t)]' = [\mu - Q(t)]y_1(t),$$
$$[P(t)y_2'(t)]' = [\mu - Q(t)]y_2(t).$$

Substituting and collecting terms, we obtain

$$\mu Y - \mathsf{L}_0[Y] = f$$

as asserted. ▌

It remains to show that the boundary conditions are satisfied. Set

$$\int_a^b y_1(s, \mu) f(s)\, ds = h_1(\mu), \qquad \int_a^b y_2(s, \mu) f(s)\, ds = h_2(\mu).$$

We have now

$$Y(a, \mu; f) = \frac{h_1(\mu)}{D(\mu)} y_1(a, \mu), \qquad Y(b, \mu; f) = \frac{h_2(\mu)}{D(\mu)} y_2(b, \mu). \quad (8.5.16)$$

If now $\vartheta_a = 0$, $\vartheta_b = \pi$, then $y_1(a, \mu) = y_2(b, \mu) = 0$, so that $Y(t)$ satisfies the same boundary conditions. If, however, either $\vartheta_a \neq 0$ or $\vartheta_b \neq \pi$, we need $Y'(t)$. Here formula (8.5.15) gives

$$Y'(a, \mu; f) = \frac{h_1(\mu)}{D(\mu)} y_1'(a, \mu), \qquad Y'(b, \mu; f) = \frac{h_2(\mu)}{D(\mu)} y_2'(b, \mu). \quad (8.5.17)$$

It follows that

$$\begin{aligned} L_1[Y(\cdot, \mu; f)] &= \frac{h_1(\mu)}{D(\mu)} L_1[y_1(\cdot, \mu)] = 0, \\ L_2[Y(\cdot, \mu; f)] &= \frac{h_2(\mu)}{D(\mu)} L_2[y_2(\cdot, \mu)] = 0, \end{aligned} \quad (8.5.18)$$

so that the boundary conditions also hold.

Lemma 8.5.2. *$G(s, t; \mu)$ is a meromorphic function of μ for fixed s, t and has simple poles at each of the points $\mu = \mu_n$ where the residue is $\omega_n(s)\omega_n(t)$. These are the only poles.*

Proof. All that needs to be done here is to find the residues. Formula (8.5.12) shows that

$$\begin{aligned} \lim_{\mu \to \mu_n} (\mu - \mu_n) G(s, t; \mu) &= c_n y_1(s, \mu_n) y_2(t, \mu_n) \\ &= C_n \omega_n(s) \omega_n(t) \end{aligned}$$

but fails to give us the value of C_n. It is seen by inspection, however, that

$$U = \frac{\omega_n(t)}{\mu - \mu_n}$$

is a solution of

$$\mu U - \mathsf{L}_0[U] = \omega_n, \qquad L_1[U] = L_2[U] = 0.$$

Since the solution is unique, Lemma 8.5.1 gives

$$\int_a^b G(s, t; \mu) \omega_n(s) \, ds = \frac{\omega_n(t)}{\mu - \mu_n}. \quad (8.5.19)$$

This shows that $C_n = 1$ for all n.

We can now form the series

$$R(s, t; \mu) = \sum_{n=0}^{\infty} \frac{\omega_n(s)\omega_n(t)}{\mu - \mu_n}. \quad (8.5.20)$$

Since the sup norm of ω_n is a bounded function of n by (8.4.19) and since $\mu_n = O(n^2)$, the series converges absolutely for $(s, t) \in S$, the square $a \le s, t \le b$, and $\mu \in \mathrm{M}$. Moreover, the convergence is uniform for $(s, t, \mu) \in S \times \mathrm{M}_\delta$ where

$$\mathrm{M}_\delta = [\mu \mid |\mu - \mu_n| > \delta, \forall n].$$

It is clear that $R(s, t; \mu)$ is the canonical partial fraction series of the meromorphic function $G(s, t; \mu)$ so that

$$G(s, t; \mu) = R(s, t; \mu) + E(s, t; \mu) \tag{8.5.21}$$

where $E(s, t; \mu)$ is an entire function of μ which will be shown to be identically zero. This can be done in various ways, none very elementary. We shall base the desired result on the basic facts concerning integral equations with a symmetric kernel. This method seems to require the least preparation.

We start with some notation. Let $K(s, t) = K(t, s)$ be defined as a real, continuous function of (s, t) in S, not identically zero and consider the mapping of $L_2(a, b)$ into itself defined by

$$f \to Kf \equiv \int_a^b K(s, t)f(s)\,ds. \tag{8.5.22}$$

This is a linear bounded transformation and we set

$$\sup_{\|f\|=1} \|Kf\| = M.$$

We recall the definition of the inner product

$$(f, g) = \int_a^b f(s)\overline{g(s)}\,ds$$

and note that

$$(Kf, g) = (f, Kg) \tag{8.5.23}$$

by the symmetry of the kernel.

Lemma 8.5.3. *If* $\sup_{\|f\|=1} |(Kf, f)| = \alpha$, *then* $\alpha = M$.

Proof. Since

$$|(Kf, f)| \le \|Kf\|\,\|f\| \le M \quad \text{if} \quad \|f\| = 1,$$

we have $\alpha \le M$. To prove $\alpha \ge M$ we consider arbitrary elements f and g of L_2 with $\|f\| = \|g\| = 1$ and form

$$(K(f + g), f + g) = (Kf, f) + (Kg, g) + (Kf, g) + (Kg, f).$$

Hence

$$(Kf, f) + (Kg, g) + 2\Re[(Kf, g)] \le \alpha\|f + g\|^2,$$

$$(Kf, f) + (Kg, g) - 2\Re[(Kf, g)] \le \alpha\|f - g\|^2$$

so that

$$4\Re[(Kf, g)] \leq \alpha\|f + g\|^2 + \alpha\|f - g\|^2 = 2\alpha[\|f\|^2 + \|g\|^2] = 4\alpha$$

by the parallelogram law. From

$$\Re[(Kf, g)] \leq \alpha$$

for all f and g it follows that $M \leq \alpha$. For we obtain

$$\|Kf\| \leq \alpha$$

for all f. Hence $M = \alpha$ as asserted. ▌

We come now to the theorem of Erhard Schmidt (1876–1959) according to which every linear integral equation with symmetric kernel has at least one characteristic value.

Lemma 8.5.4. *If $K(s, t) = K(t, s)$ is real and continuous in S and not identically zero, then there exists a real λ and a real continuous function $g(t)$, not identically zero, such that*

$$\int_a^b K(s, t)g(s)\, ds = \lambda g(t). \tag{8.5.24}$$

Proof. Without restricting the generality we may assume that the real numbers (Kf, f) satisfy

$$\sup_{\|f\|=1} (Kf, f) = M.$$

If this is not true, we have instead $\inf_{\|f\|=1} (Kf, f) = -M$ and the necessary modifications of the proof are obvious. By the definition of the supremum we can find a sequence $\{f_n\} \subset L_2(a, b)$ such that $\|f_n\| = 1$ and

$$(Kf_n, f_n) = M_n \uparrow M.$$

Now the functions $(Kf_n)(t)$ are in $C[a, b]$ as well as in $L_2(a, b)$ and they form a uniformly bounded equicontinuous family in $C[a, b]$. This follows from the two inequalities

$$\left|\int_a^b K(s, t)f(s)\, ds\right| \leq \left\{\int_a^b [K(s, t)]^2\, ds\right\}^{1/2}\left\{\int_a^b |f(s)|^2\, ds\right\}^{1/2},$$

$$\left|\int_a^b K(s, t_1)f(s)\, ds - \int_a^b K(s, t_2)f(s)\, ds\right|$$

$$\leq \left\{\int_a^b [K(s, t_1) - K(s, t_2)]^2\, ds\right\}^{1/2}\left\{\int_a^b |f(s)|^2\, ds\right\}^{1/2}.$$

From the theorem of Ascoli it follows that there exists a subsequence which converges uniformly to a continuous limit, $g(t)$ say, and we may assume that

$$\lim_{n\to\infty} (Kf_n)(t) = g(t),$$

i.e. the whole sequence converges. This is convergence in the C-metric which obviously implies convergence also in the L_2-metric. We have now

$$\|Kf_n - Mf_n\|^2 = \|Kf_n\|^2 + M^2\|f_n\|^2 - 2M(Kf_n, f_n)$$
$$\to \|g\|^2 - M^2$$

so that $\|g\| \geq M$ which shows that g cannot be identically 0.

On the other hand, since $\|Kf_n\| \leq M\|f_n\| = M$ it is seen that

$$\lim_{n\to\infty} \|Kf_n - Mf_n\|^2 = M^2 - M^2 = 0.$$

Since K is a linear bounded transformation this implies that

$$\lim \|K(Kf_n) - MKf_n\| = 0$$

or

$$\|Kg - Mg\| = 0.$$

Here g and Kg are continuous functions of t so we get

$$(Kg)(t) = Mg(t),$$

i.e. M is a characteristic value and g is a non-trivial characteristic function. ∎

We use this result to prove

Lemma 8.5.5. $E(s, t; \mu) \equiv 0.$

Proof. We take $K(s, t) = E(s, t; \mu)$ in the notation of Lemma 8.5.4 where μ is fixed real in M. This is a real continuous symmetric kernel and, unless it is identically zero, there exist a real λ and a real continuous function $g(t)$, not identically zero, such that

$$\int_a^b E(s, t; \mu)g(s)\,ds = \lambda g(t). \qquad (8.5.25)$$

Here we substitute what is obtained from formulas (8.5.20) and (8.5.21) to obtain

$$\int_a^b G(s, t; \mu)g(s)\,ds - \sum_{n=0}^{\infty} \frac{g_n}{\mu - \mu_n}\,\omega_n(t) = \lambda g(t) \qquad (8.5.26)$$

where

$$g_n = \int_a^b g(s)\omega_n(s)\,ds$$

and we have integrated termwise in order to evaluate

$$\int_a^b R(s, t; \mu)g(s)\,ds.$$

This is permissible since the series for $R(s, t; \mu)$ is uniformly convergent for $(s, t, \mu) \in S \times M_\delta$. We now multiply by $\omega_k(t)$ on both sides in (8.5.26) and integrate termwise with respect to t from a to b. Again this is permissible. The resulting double integral in the first term on the left is absolutely convergent since the integrand is a continuous function of (s, t) in S. Hence the order of integration may be inverted and we are left with

$$\int_a^b g(s)\left\{\int_a^b G(s, t; \mu)\omega_k(t)\,dt\right\} ds = \frac{g_k}{\mu - \mu_k} - \lambda g_k$$

since all other terms drop out. By (8.5.19) the left member equals

$$\int_a^b g(s)\frac{\omega_k(s)}{\mu - \mu_k}\,ds = \frac{g_k}{\mu - \mu_k}.$$

This implies

$$g_k = 0, \qquad \forall k.$$

Hence (8.5.26) reduces to

$$\int_a^b G(s, t; \mu)g(s)\,ds = \lambda g(t).$$

Now Lemma 8.5.1 comes into play and shows that the integral on the left is $Y(t, \mu; g)$ and hence satisfies

$$\mu Y - \mathsf{L}_0[Y] = g, \qquad L_1[Y] = 0, \qquad L_2[Y] = 0.$$

Here $Y = \lambda g$ so that

$$\mathsf{L}_0[g] = \left(\mu - \frac{1}{\lambda}\right)g, \qquad L_1[g] = 0, \qquad L_2[g] = 0.$$

In other words, the original boundary value problem should admit $\mu - 1/\lambda$ as a characteristic value with g as the corresponding characteristic function. This is impossible, however, for we have already enumerated all the characteristic values $\{\mu_n \mid n = 0, 1, 2, \ldots\}$. It follows that the symmetric kernel $E(s, t; \mu)$ cannot have any characteristic values and hence is identically zero for all real μ. Now $E(s, t; \mu)$ is an entire function of μ for fixed $(s, t) \in S$ and if an analytic function vanishes on the real axis, then it vanishes for all complex values. ∎

Corollary. *We have*

$$Y(t, \mu; f) = \sum_{n=0}^{\infty} \frac{f_n}{\mu - \mu_n}\,\omega_n(t) \tag{8.5.27}$$

where the series is absolutely and uniformly convergent in $S \times M_\delta$.

Proof of Theorem 8.5.1. We have now collected all the results needed for the proof. If the orthonormal set $\{\omega_n\}$ is not complete in $L_2(a, b)$, then there exists an $f \in L_2(a, b)$, f not equivalent to 0, such that

$$f_n = (f, \omega_n) = 0, \qquad \forall n,$$

whence it follows that

$$Y(t, \mu; f) \equiv 0$$

by (8.5.27). Since

$$\mu Y - \mathsf{L}_0[Y] = f$$

we have $f \equiv 0$. This is a contradiction and shows that the orthonormal set $\{\omega_n\}$ is complete in $L_2(a, b)$. ∎

Let us return to the properties of

$$Y(t, \mu; f) = \sum_{n=0}^{\infty} \frac{f_n}{\mu - \mu_n} \omega_n(t).$$

We have $Y \in C[a, b] \cap L_2(a, b)$, more precisely $Y \in X_{1,2}$ in our previous notation. The L_2-norm of Y is

$$\| Y(\cdot, \mu; f)\| = \left\{\sum_{n=0}^{\infty} \frac{|f_n|^2}{|\mu - \mu_n|^2}\right\}^{1/2}.$$

Let $d(\mu)$ be the distance of μ from the spectrum $\{\mu_n\}$. Then

$$\| Y(\cdot, \mu; f)\| \leq \frac{\|f\|}{d(r)} \tag{8.5.28}$$

and this is the best possible estimate for the upper bound is reached if $f = \omega_k$ where k is so chosen that $d(\mu) = |\mu - \mu_k|$. The mapping

$$f \to Y(\cdot, \mu; f)$$

defines a linear bounded transformation on $L_2(a, b)$ into itself, more precisely onto $X_{1,2}$. We write

$$Y(t, \mu; f) = \mathsf{R}(\mu, \mathsf{L}_0)[f](t) \tag{8.5.29}$$

and note that

$$(\mu I - \mathsf{L}_0)\mathsf{R}(\mu, \mathsf{L}_0)f = f. \tag{8.5.30}$$

This was proved in Lemma 8.5.1 for $f \in C[a, b]$ or pointwise almost everywhere. Here the meaning is the following. For any $f \in L_2(a, b)$, the operator $\mathsf{R}(\mu, \mathsf{L}_0)$ maps f into $X_{1,2}$, i.e. the image is an absolutely continuous function g such that $L_1[g] = L_2[g] = 0$ while $\mathsf{L}_0[g]$ exists as an element of $L_2(a, b)$. If now $\mu I - \mathsf{L}_0$ is applied to g the result is a function equivalent to f.

Next, suppose that $f \in X_{1,2}$ and set

$$(\mu I - \mathsf{L}_0)f \equiv h.$$

Then $\mathsf{R}(\mu, \mathsf{L}_0)h$ exists and belongs to $X_{1,2}$. Further, by the identity of Lagrange

$$(\mathsf{L}_0 f, \omega_n) = (f, \mathsf{L}_0\omega_n) = \mu_n(f, \omega_n)$$

so that the Fourier coefficients of f and of h are related by

$$h_n = (\mu - \mu_n)f_n.$$

It follows that

$$\mathsf{R}(\mu, \mathsf{L}_0)h = \sum_{n=0}^{\infty} f_n\omega_n(t) = f(t)$$

since the series is absolutely convergent. Hence

$$\mathsf{R}(\mu, \mathsf{L}_0)(\mu I - \mathsf{L}_0)f = f, \qquad f \in X_{1,2}. \tag{8.5.31}$$

Thus we have proved

Theorem 8.5.2. *The operator* $\mathsf{R}(\mu, \mathsf{L}_0)$, $\mu \in \mathrm{M}$, *is the resolvent of the differential operator* L_0 *restricted to the space* $X_{1,2}$. *It maps* $L_2(a, b)$ *in a* (1, 1) *manner onto* $X_{1,2}$.

We have also the following

Corollary. *The Fourier series of a function* $f \in X_{1,2}$ *is absolutely and uniformly convergent and its sum is* $f(t)$ *for* $a \leq t \leq b$.

In the German literature, such a function

$$f(t) = \int_a^b G(s, t; \alpha)h(s)\,ds \tag{8.5.32}$$

would be said to be "*quellenmässig dargestellt.*"

The following is an important property of Green's function.

Theorem 8.5.3. $G(s, t; \mu) > 0$ *for* μ *real and* $> \mu_0$, $a < s < t < b$.

Proof. To prove this we have to go back to the definition of $G(s, t; \mu)$ by formula (8.5.12) and analyze the three factors $D(\mu)$, $y_1(s, \mu)$, $y_2(t, \mu)$ where $a < s < t < b$. They are entire functions of μ and the zeros of $D(\mu)$ are the real numbers $\{\mu_n\}$ of which μ_0 is the largest. Without restricting the generality we may assume $\mu_0 < 0$ in this discussion. This can always be brought about by a translation of the parameter. It is clear that $D(\mu)$ keeps a constant sign for $\mu > \mu_0$.

For fixed s and t the functions $y_1(s, \mu)$ and $y_2(t, \mu)$ are also entire functions of μ of order $\leq \frac{1}{2}$. The zeros of these solutions *qua* functions of μ are necessarily real. To show this we observe that the two boundary value problems

$$[P(x)y'(x)]' + [g(x) - \mu]y(x) = 0 \tag{8.5.33}$$

with

$$L_1[y_1] = 0, \qquad y_1(s) = 0, \tag{8.5.34}$$

and

$$y_2(t) = 0, \qquad L_2[y_2] = 0, \tag{8.5.35}$$

respectively, have real characteristic values by Theorem 8.2.2. We have here boundary value problems for the intervals (a, s) and (t, b). Prüfer's method applies and gives two sequences of characteristic values, $\{\alpha_n(s)\}$ and $\{\beta_n(t)\}$, where

$$\alpha_0(s) > \alpha_1(s) > \cdots > \alpha_n(s) > \cdots \tag{8.5.36}$$

$$\beta_0(t) > \beta_1(t) > \cdots > \beta_n(t) > \cdots \tag{8.5.37}$$

These are the zeros of $y_1(s, \mu)$ and $y_2(t, \mu)$, respectively.

Now $y_1(x, \mu_0)$ is that solution of (8.5.33) which satisfies

$$L_1[y_1] = 0, \qquad L_2[y_1] = 0$$

and has no zero in the open interval (a, b). On the other hand, $y_1(x, \alpha_0(s))$ satisfies (8.5.33) and (8.5.34) and has no zero in $(0, s)$ while $x = s$ is a zero. We conclude from Theorem 8.3.3 that

$$\alpha_0(s) < \mu_0 \tag{8.5.38}$$

and in the same manner it is shown that

$$\beta_0(t) < \mu_0. \tag{8.5.39}$$

It follows that each of the three functions $D(\mu)$, $y_1(s, \mu)$, $y_2(t, \mu)$ keeps a constant sign for $\mu > \mu_0$. This means that $G(s, t; \mu)$ keeps a constant sign for $\mu > \mu_0$ and since $G(s, s; \mu) > 0$ for such values of μ, it follows that $G(s, t; \mu) > 0$ as asserted. ▮

We shall also need some information concerning the partial derivative of $G(s, t; \mu)$ with respect to s for μ large positive. We restrict ourselves to a special case.

Lemma 8.5.6. *If the boundary conditions are of type* (2, 2) *and* $\mu > \max Q(x)$, $\mu > \mu_0$, *then* $G_s'(s, t; \mu)$ *has the sign of* $t - s$.

Proof. We have

$$[P(x)y_1(x, \mu)y_1'(x, \mu)]_a^s + \int_a^s [Q(x) - \mu][y_1(x, \mu)]^2\, dx = 0.$$

If $\mu > \max Q(x)$, then the integral is negative and

$$P(s)y_1(s, \mu)y_1'(s, \mu) > 0$$

since $y_1'(a, \mu) \equiv 0$. We take $y_1(a, \mu) \equiv 1$ so that $y_1(s, \mu) > 0$ for $\mu > \mu_0$. Hence

$$y_1'(s, \mu) > 0.$$

In the same manner we show that

$$y_2'(s, \mu) < 0.$$

Here $y_2(b, \mu) \equiv 1$, $y_2'(b, \mu) \equiv 0$ so that $y_2(s, \mu) > 0$ for $\mu > \mu_0$ and hence also $D(\mu) > 0$ for $\mu > \mu_0$. We have now

$$G_s'(s, t; \mu) = \begin{cases} [D(\mu)]^{-1} y_1'(s, \mu) y_2(t, \mu), & s < t, \\ [D(\mu)]^{-1} y_2'(s, \mu) y_1(t, \mu), & t < s, \end{cases} \tag{8.5.40}$$

and the assertion follows. ▮

This implies that the partial is discontinuous at $s = t$.

We have seen that $D(\mu)$, $y_1(s, \mu)$, $y_2(t, \mu)$ are entire functions of μ of order $\leq \frac{1}{2}$ whose zeros are real negative. Now entire functions of this class have rather special growth properties which may be used to get the asymptotic behavior of $G(s, t; \mu)$ as $\mu \to \infty$ in the sector $|\arg \mu| \leq \pi - \varepsilon$, $0 < \varepsilon$.

Suppose that $F(z)$ is an entire function of z of order $\frac{1}{2}$ and with real negative zeros $\{-r_n \mid n = 0, 1, 2, \ldots\}$. Such a function is represented by an infinite product of the form

$$F(z) = \prod_{n=0}^{\infty} \left(1 + \frac{z}{r_n}\right),$$

if $F(0) = 1$. The product is absolutely convergent and there are no exponential factors. Let $n(r)$ be the number of points r_n in the interval $(0, r)$. Then, for z in the plane cut from $-\infty$ to $-r_0$ and for the principal value of the logarithm

$$\log F(z) = \int_0^\infty \log\left(1 + \frac{z}{t}\right) dn(t)$$

$$= z \int_{r_0}^\infty \frac{n(t)\, dt}{t(t + z)}, \tag{8.5.41}$$

as is easily verified. The growth properties of $F(z)$ are closely related to those of $n(r)$. This is illustrated by the following lemma which is a special case of results due to G. Pólya and G. Szegö.

Lemma 8.5.8. *If*

$$n(r) = Cr^{1/2} + O(1), \qquad t \to +\infty, \tag{8.5.42}$$

then in the sector $|\arg z| \leq \pi - \varepsilon$, $0 < \varepsilon$,

$$\log F(z) = \pi C z^{1/2} + R(z), \qquad |R(z)| \leq K(\varepsilon) \log |z|. \tag{8.5.43}$$

Proof. We have

$$\log F(z) = Cz \int_{r_0}^\infty \frac{dt}{t^{1/2}(t + z)} + O\left\{|z| \int_{r_0}^\infty \frac{dt}{t|t + z|}\right\}.$$

In the first integral we may replace the lower limit r_0 by 0. This introduces an error term which is uniformly bounded for all large $|z|$. Since

$$z \int_0^\infty \frac{dt}{t^{1/2}(t + z)} = \pi z^{1/2}, \tag{8.5.44}$$

we get

$$\log F(z) = \pi C z^{1/2} + R(z).$$

To estimate the remainder we note that

$$|t + z| = |t + r\, e^{i\theta}| \geq \cos(\tfrac{1}{2}\theta)(t + r)$$

so that $|R(z)|$ is dominated by a constant multiple of

$$\sec(\tfrac{1}{2}\theta) \log\left(1 + \frac{r}{r_0}\right).$$

In the sector $|\arg z| \leq \pi - \varepsilon$ we have $\sec(\tfrac{1}{2}\theta) \leq \operatorname{cosec}(\tfrac{1}{2}\varepsilon)$. This gives (8.4.43). ▮

This estimate can now be applied to the three factors of $G(s, t; \mu)$. We set

$$C(\alpha, \beta) = \frac{1}{\pi}\int_\alpha^\beta [P(u)]^{-1/2}\, du, \qquad a \leq \alpha < \beta \leq b. \tag{8.5.45}$$

Then formula (8.4.8) gives

$$\begin{aligned} |\mu_n|^{1/2} &= [C(a, b)]^{-1}(n + \eta) + O(n^{-1}), \\ |\alpha_n(s)|^{1/2} &= [C(a, s)]^{-1}(n + \eta_1) + O(n^{-1}), \\ |\beta_n(t)|^{1/2} &= [C(t, b)]^{-1}(n + \eta_2) + O(n^{-1}), \end{aligned} \tag{8.5.46}$$

where the η's are $0, \tfrac{1}{2}, 1$ depending upon the type of the boundary conditions. See (8.4.7). Further it is to be observed that, in the last two formulas, the remainder depends upon s and t, respectively, but the estimates hold uniformly with respect to s and t provided $a + \delta \leq s < t \leq b - \delta$ for some fixed $\delta > 0$. If we now denote the corresponding enumerative functions by $n(r)$, $n_1(r)$, and $n_2(r)$, respectively, we obtain

$$\begin{aligned} n(r) &= C(a, b)r^{1/2} + O(1), \\ n_1(r) &= C(a, s)r^{1/2} + O(1), \\ n_2(r) &= C(t, b)r^{1/2} + O(1), \end{aligned} \tag{8.5.47}$$

where again the last two estimates hold uniformly for $a + \delta \leq s < t \leq b - \delta$. It follows that

$$\begin{aligned} \log D(\mu) &= \pi C(a, b)\mu^{1/2} + O(\log|\mu|), \\ \log y_1(s, \mu) &= \pi C(a, s)\mu^{1/2} + O(\log|\mu|), \\ \log y_2(t, \mu) &= \pi C(t, b)\mu^{1/2} + O(\log|\mu|). \end{aligned} \tag{8.5.48}$$

Since

$$C(a, b) = C(a, s) + C(s, t) + C(t, b), \qquad s < t, \tag{8.5.49}$$

we obtain

Theorem 8.5.4. *We have*

$$\log G(s, t; \mu) = -\pi C(s, t)\mu^{1/2} + O(\log |\mu|), \tag{8.5.50}$$

uniformly with respect to (s, t, μ) *in* $a + \delta \le s < t \le b - \delta$, $2 < |\mu|$, $|\arg \mu| \le \pi - \varepsilon$.

These estimates are of no value for $s = t$ and also leave the excluded sector about the negative real axis in doubt. They can be supplemented by the obvious estimate

$$|G(s, t; \mu)| \le A \sum_{n=0}^{\infty} |\mu - \mu_n|^{-1} \tag{8.5.51}$$

which follows from the partial fraction series together with the uniform boundedness of $\omega_n(s)$. Suppose, in particular, that μ is real, $\mu > \mu_0$, and note that $|\mu_n| > (n/c)^2$, $\forall n$, for some choice of c. Then

$$G(s, t; \mu) < A \sum_{n=0}^{\infty} (\mu - \mu_n)^{-1} < A \sum_{n=0}^{\infty} [\mu + (n/c)^2]^{-1}.$$

We can use the well-known integral test to estimate the last member. This gives

$$G(s, t; \mu) < \tfrac{1}{2}\pi c A \mu^{-1/2} + O(\mu^{-1}), \qquad 0 < \mu \to +\infty, \tag{8.5.52}$$

for all $(s, t) \in S$. More generally, if μ is allowed to be complex, one can prove the existence of a sequence of circles $|\mu| = R_n$, $|\mu_n| < R_n < |\mu_{n+1}|$, such that

$$|\mu|^{1/2}|G(s, t; \mu)| \le B, \qquad |\mu| = R_n, \tag{8.5.53}$$

uniformly in (s, t) and n. Note that the maximum of the right-hand member of (8.5.51) on the circle $|\mu| = R_n$ is assumed at $\mu = -R_n$. We do not insist on this point any further.

Instead, we shall see what bearing these results have on the convergence and summability theory of series of the form

$$\sum_{n=0}^{\infty} f_n \omega_n(t), \qquad f_n = \int_a^b f(s)\omega_n(s)\, ds.$$

Such a series may or not converge, but it may be summable to $f(t)$, say at its points of continuity. Our point of departure is the observation that

$$\lim_{\mu \to \infty} \|\mu \mathsf{R}(\mu, \mathsf{L}_0)[f] - f\| = 0 \tag{8.5.54}$$

as is easily verified. This is convergence in the L_2-sense but it suggests posing the question for pointwise convergence.

To avoid lengthy case distinctions we restrict ourselves to boundary conditions of type (2, 2), i.e.

$$y'(a, \mu) = 0, \qquad y'(b, \mu) = 0. \tag{8.5.55}$$

The summability theorem holds in all cases, however. We start with

Lemma 8.5.7. *If the boundary conditions are of type* (2, 2), *then*

$$\sum_{n=0}^{\infty} \omega_n(t) \int_a^b \omega_n(s)\, ds \equiv 1, \tag{8.5.56}$$

the series being absolutely and uniformly convergent in $[a, b]$.

Proof. The functions $\omega_n(t)$ are uniformly bounded. To evaluate the integral we integrate

$$[P(s)\omega_n'(s)]' + [Q(s) - \mu_n]\omega_n(s) = 0$$

between the limits a and b to obtain

$$\mu_n \int_a^b \omega_n(s)\, ds = \int_a^b Q(s)\omega_n(s)\, ds \equiv q_n.$$

The integrated term drops out in the limits by (8.5.55). Hence

$$\int_a^b \omega_n(s)\, ds = \frac{q_n}{\mu_n}, \qquad \sum q_n^2 < \infty. \tag{8.5.57}$$

This shows the absolute and uniform convergence of the series (8.5.56), which is the Fourier series of the function $f(t) \equiv 1$. Since the series is uniformly convergent, it must be the Fourier series of its sum which is a continuous function. Since only equivalent functions can have identical Fourier series, it follows that the sum function is $\equiv 1$ as asserted. ∎

It should be observed that a change in the boundary conditions affects the series (8.5.56) but only at the endpoints. If the conditions had been (1, 1) instead, the most unfavorable case, the series would still converge in $[a, b]$ but not absolutely and its sum at the endpoints would be 0 instead of 1.

Next we observe that

$$\mu \int_a^b G(s, t; \mu)\, ds = \sum_{n=0}^{\infty} \frac{\mu}{\mu - \mu_n} \omega_n(t) \int_a^b \omega_n(s)\, ds,$$

whence it follows that

$$\lim_{\mu \to \infty} \mu \int_a^b G(s, t; \mu)\, ds \equiv 1 \tag{8.5.58}$$

by Problem 4 of Exercise 8.4, which states that the "resolvent method" of summability preserves convergence and limits.

We can now prove

Theorem 8.5.5. *If* $f \in L_2(a, b)$, *if the boundary conditions are of type* (2, 2), *then*

$$\lim_{\mu \to \infty} \sum_{n=0}^{\infty} \frac{\mu}{\mu - \mu_n} f_n \omega_n(t) = f(t) \tag{8.5.59}$$

almost everywhere and, in particular, at all points of continuity of $f(t)$ *in the open interval* (a, b).

Proof. By (8.5.58) it suffices to show that

$$\lim_{\mu \to +\infty} \mu \int_a^b G(s, t; \mu)|f(s) - f(t)|\, ds = 0 \tag{8.5.60}$$

for almost all t. Now by a well-known fact in the Lebesgue theory of integration, the function

$$f(s, t) \equiv \int_t^s |f(u) - f(t)|\, du = o(|t - s|) \tag{8.5.61}$$

for almost all t. We suppose that t belongs to the so-called *Lebesgue set* for which (8.5.61) holds. This set includes all points of continuity of f if any. If $\varepsilon > 0$ is given, we can then find a $\delta > 0$ such that

$$|f(s, t)| < \varepsilon |s - t| \qquad \text{for} \quad |s - t| < \delta.$$

For $a + \delta \leq t \leq b - \delta$ we write

$$\mu \int_a^b = \mu \left\{ \int_a^{t-\delta} + \int_{t-\delta}^{t+\delta} + \int_{t+\delta}^b \right\} \equiv I_1 + I_2 + I_3.$$

In the first interval $(s, t - \delta)$ the kernel $\mu G(s, t; \mu)$ is an increasing function of s by Lemma 8.5.6 so that its largest value is reached for $s = t - \delta$. Formula (8.5.49) shows the existence of two positive numbers h and k such that

$$G(t - \delta, t; \mu) < \mu^k \exp(-h\mu^{1/2}).$$

It follows that

$$I_1 < \mu^{k+1} \exp(-h\mu^{1/2}) \int_a^{t-\delta} |f(s) - f(t)|\, ds$$

$$= \mu^{k+1} \exp(-h\mu^{1/2})[f(t - \delta, t) - f(a, t)] \to 0 \qquad \text{as} \quad \mu \to \infty.$$

Similarly,

$$I_3 < \mu^{k+1} \exp(-h\mu^{1/2})[f(b, t) - f(t + \delta, t)] \to 0 \qquad \text{as} \quad \mu \to \infty.$$

In I_2 we integrate by parts and obtain

$$I_2 = \mu[G(s, t; \mu)f(s, t)]_{s=t-\delta}^{s=t+\delta} - \mu \int_{t-\delta}^{t+\delta} G_s'(s, t; \mu) f(s, t)\, ds$$

which does not exceed

$$\delta\varepsilon\mu[G(t + \delta, t; \mu) + G(t - \delta, t; \mu)] - \varepsilon\mu \int_{t-\delta}^{t+\delta} G_s'(s, t; \mu)(s - t)\, ds.$$

Note that the last term is positive since $G_s'(s, t; \mu)(s - t) < 0$ by Lemma 8.5.8. Integration by parts reduces this upper bound for I_2 to

$$\varepsilon\mu \int_{t-\delta}^{t+\delta} G(s, t; \mu)\, ds \to \varepsilon \qquad \text{as} \quad \mu \to \infty.$$

It follows that the superior limit of the expression in the left member of (8.5.60) is at most ε. Since ε is arbitrary, it follows that the limit exists and is 0 as indicated. ∎

This proves resolvent summability almost everywhere. If the series for f should happen to converge at a point $t = t_0$ in the Lebesgue set of f, then the sum of the series is $f(t_0)$ since it is resolvent summable to this value. Ordinary convergence of these orthogonal series is valid under similar rules that govern convergence of trigonometric Fourier series and, under suitable restrictions on P and Q, it is possible to prove equiconvergence theorems for the two classes of expansions. We shall not pursue these notions any further.

EXERCISE 8.5

In Problems 1–4 the data (a, b), L_0, L_1, L_2 are given. It is required to find the corresponding Green's function and to discuss the characteristic values. They can be found explicitly in Nos. 1–3.

1. $(-\pi, \pi)$, $\mathsf{L}_0[y] = y''$, $L_1[y] = y(-\pi)$, $L_2[y] = y(\pi)$.
2. $(0, \pi)$, $\mathsf{L}_0[y] = y''$, $L_1[y] = y(0)$, $L_2[y] = y'(\pi)$.
3. $(1, 2)$, $\mathsf{L}_0[y] = (x^2y')'$, $L_1[y] = y(1)$, $L_2[y] = y(2)$.
4. $(1, 2)$, $\mathsf{L}_0[y] = y'' + \frac{1}{4}x^{-2}y$, $L_1[y] = y(1)$, $L_2[y] = y(2)$.
5. Take Green's function in Problem 1 and verify that (8.5.49) holds. What estimates are valid for $G(s, t; \mu)$?
6. Give an estimate of the remainder in the first formula under (8.5.47) by going back to (8.4.9).
7. Why does (8.5.38) hold?
8. Verify (8.5.44).
9. Verify (8.5.54).
10. Formulate a (singular) boundary value problem of which the Legendre polynomials are the characteristic functions.
11. Show that Lemma 8.5.8 is valid for any boundary conditions of types (2, 3), (3, 2), and (3, 3). How does this affect the possibility of extending Theorem 8.5.5?
12. Show that in the case (1, 1) the numbers $\omega_n'(a)$ and $\omega_n'(b)$ are $O(n)$ and hence that $\int_a^b \omega_n(s)\,ds = O(n^{-1})$ rather than $O(n^{-2})$. The series (8.5.56) still converges to 1 for $a < t < b$ since f is of bounded variation. Its sum is 0 at the endpoints since all terms are 0.

    Given the quadratic integral form

$$\int_a^b \int_a^b G(s, t; \mu) f(s) f(t)\, ds\, dt,$$

where μ is fixed positive, f real valued, $f \in L_2(a, b)$, $\|f\| = 1$.

13. Show that the maximum value of the form is $(\mu - \mu_0)^{-1}$ which is reached for $f = \omega_0$.
14. Find the maximum value and for what f it is reached if f is supposed to be orthogonal to $\omega_0, \omega_1, \ldots, \omega_n$.

    This device can be used to prove the existence of infinitely many real characteristic values and functions even under more general lateral conditions. [Method of Courant–Hilbert.]
15. Take $P(x) \equiv 1$ and let $w_0(x)$ satisfy

$$w_0'' - \mu w_0 = 0, \qquad L_1[w_0] = 0, \qquad \|w_0\| = 1.$$

Show that the solution $y_1(x, \mu)$ of

$$y_1''(x, \mu) + [Q(x) - \mu]y_1(x, \mu) = 0, \qquad L_1 y_1(\cdot, \mu) = 0$$

satisfies

$$y(x) = w_0(x) - (-\mu)^{-1/2} \int_a^x \sin[(-\mu)^{1/2}(x - s)]Q(s)y(s)\,ds$$

and use this to get the asymptotic behavior of $y_1(x, \mu)$ and of the characteristic values. [*Hint*: Divide by $\exp[-i(-\mu)^{1/2}x]$ for μ in the upper half-plane, follow the pattern of the discussion in Section 7.4, and reduce the problem to an application of Theorem 1.5.7. This is essentially the method of E. C. Titchmarsh (1899–1963).]

16. Show that $G(s, t; \mu)$ satisfies $\mathsf{L}_0[y] = \mu y$ for all $\mu \in \mathrm{M}$ and all $s \neq t$ as well as the boundary conditions. Show that $G_s'(s, t; \mu)$ is continuous except for $s = t$ where there is a jump. Compute the difference between the right- and left-hand limits. Show that Green's function is uniquely determined by these properties.
17. Examine the validity of Lemma 8.5.6 if the type of the boundary condition is changed.
18. If L_1 and L_2 are arbitrary linear functionals on $C^1[a, b]$, i.e. of type (8.2.10), examine the possibility of constructing a corresponding Green's function. The problem is to satisfy (8.5.9).

COLLATERAL READING

The literature on boundary value problems is enormous and steadily growing. Three monographs should be noted:

ATKINSON, F. V., *Discrete and continuous boundary value problems*, Academic Press, New York (1964).

BÔCHER, Maxime, *Leçons sur les méthodes de Sturm dans la théorie des équations différentielles linéaires et leurs développements modernes*, Gauthier-Villars, Paris (1917).

TITCHMARSH, E. C., *Eigenfunction expansions associated with second order differential equations*, Clarendon Press, Oxford (1947).

The first and the third have good bibliographies. Many textbooks contain excellent accounts of the Sturm–Liouville theory and its later generalizations, with more or less extensive references to the literature. We mention in particular the following which represent different modes of attack.

BIEBERBACH, Ludwig, *Einführung in die Theorie der Differentialgleichungen im reellen Gebiet*, Springer-Verlag, Berlin (1956), §4.

CODDINGTON, E. A., and Norman LEVINSON, *Theory of ordinary differential equations*, McGraw-Hill, New York (1955), Chapters 7, 8, 11, 12.

HARTMAN, Philip, *Ordinary differential equations*, Wiley, New York (1964), Chapter 12, Part II.

INCE, E. L., *Ordinary differential equations*, Dover, New York (1944), Chapters 9, 10.

KAMKE, E., *Differentialgleichungen reeller Funktionen*, Akad. Verlagsges., Leipzig (1930), Chapter 8, §27.

YOSIDA, Kôsaku, *Lectures on differential and integral equations*, Interscience, New York (1960), Chapter 2.

Bôcher, followed by Ince, stressed the algebraic theory and based the proof of the existence theorem on Sturm's comparison theorems (Problems 9 and 10 of Exercise 8.1). Coddington and Levinson use operator theory and the Courant–Hilbert method for the characteristic values. Hartman applies fixed point theory to generalized boundary problems. Kamke, followed by Atkinson, applies Prüfer's method to obtain existence and expansion theorems. Bieberbach and Yosida, followed by the present author, use Lemma 8.5.4 to prove the identity of $G(s, t; \mu)$ and $R(s, t; \mu)$ which is the crucial step.

In his discussion Titchmarsh employs asymptotic integration of an equivalent Volterra equation, contour integration, and Fourier analysis. The resolvent method of summability seems to be due to him. Incidentally, contour integration is of long standing in this theory. It was used by Cauchy and was basic in the work of G. D. Birkhoff and J. D. Tamarkin around 1910.

The Pólya-Szegö theorem on entire functions of order < 1 with real negative zeros, which is used above to estimate Green's function, would seem to have applications to equations of higher order and to other differential problems.

For the operator theoretical aspects of boundary value problems, regular and singular, see:

DUNFORD, N., and J. SCHWARTZ, *Linear operators*, II. *Spectral theory*, Interscience, New York (1963), Chapter 13.

NAĬMARK, M. A., *Lineĭnye Differentsial'nye Operatory*, Gosudarstvenoe Izdatel'stvo Tehn. Teor. Literatury, Moscow (1954).

STONE, M. H., *Linear transformations in Hilbert space and their applications to analysis*, Amer. Math. Soc. Coll. Publ. **15**, Chapters 3:3 and 10:2, 3, New York (1932).

The basic papers of Sturm and Liouville appeared in the *Journal de Mathématiques purées et appliquées*, volumes 1 and 2. See, e.g.

STURM, C., "Sur les équations différentielles linéaires du second ordre," *Ibid.*, (1) **1**, 106–186 (1836).

Further references:

LORCH, L., and P. SZEGO, "Higher monotonicity properties of certain Sturm–Liouville functions," *Acta Math.*, **109**, 55–73 (1963).

PRÜFER, H., "Neue Herleitung der Sturm Liouvilleschen Reihenentwicklung stetiger Funktionen," *Math. Annalen*, **95**, 409–518 (1926).

TAMARKIN, J. D., "Sur quelques points de la théorie des équations différentielles," *Rendiconti di Palermo*, **34**, 654–676 (1912).

TAMARKIN, J. D., "Some general problems of the theory of ordinary linear differential equations and expansion of an arbitrary function in series of fundamental functions," *Math. Zeitschrift*, **27**, 1–54 (1927).

For the theory of entire functions used in this chapter, see the author's *Analytic function theory*, vol. II, Chapter 14.

Lemma 8.5.7 is suggested by a problem in

PÓLYA, G., and G. SZEGÖ, *Aufgaben und Lehrsätze aus der Analysis*, vol. II, 3rd edition, Springer-Verlag, Berlin (1964). See p. 9, no. 61.

9 SOLUTIONS ON THE REAL LINE

This chapter is devoted to a study of the properties of solutions of a second order linear differential equation on the interval $[0, \infty)$. Questions of growth, non-oscillation, and oscillation are examined in some detail and kinematical interpretations, for what they are worth, are given when appropriate. The discussion is in some respects complementary to that in Chapter 8 where only a finite interval was considered. It is also preparatory for Chapter 10 where boundary value problems are studied for an infinite interval.

In the first five sections, real-valued solutions are considered, in the last section an extension is made to the case where the solution takes on values in an abstract B-algebra with a star operation analogous to that of transposition in the matrix case. Only the latter seems to have been considered in the literature.

There are six sections: Almost Uniform Motion; Growth Properties; Spiral Motion; Non-oscillation and the Riccati Equation; The Oscillatory Case; Abstract Oscillation Theory.

9.1 ALMOST UNIFORM MOTION

Let us consider the equation

$$y''(t) - G(t)y(t) = 0 \tag{9.1.1}$$

under the assumption that $G(t)$ is continuous and $tG(t) \in L(0, \infty)$. At first sight this would seem to be a fairly trivial case but it has been considered by a number of authors and it plays a role both as an exception and for its applications. The problem is implicitly contained in the work of M. Bôcher (1900) and H. Weyl (1909), and it occurs explicitly in work of A. Wintner (1949) and of the author (1948).

Theorem 9.1.1. *If* $tG(t) \in L(0, \infty)$, *the Eq.* (9.1.1) *has a unique solution* $y_0(t)$ *such that*

$$\lim_{t\to+\infty} y_0(t) = 1, \qquad \lim_{t\to\infty} ty_0'(t) = 0. \tag{9.1.2}$$

If $G(t)$ *is real and ultimately keeps a constant sign, the condition* $tG(t) \in L(0, \infty)$ *is necessary as well as sufficient for the existence of such a solution.*

There is also a solution, non-unique, $y_1(t)$ such that

$$\lim_{t\to+\infty} \frac{y_1(t)}{t} = 1, \qquad \lim_{t\to+\infty} y_1'(t) = 1. \tag{9.1.3}$$

If G satisfies the more stringent condition $t^2G(t) \in L(0, \infty)$, then y_0 satisfies

$$\lim_{t\to+\infty} t[y_0(t) - 1] = 0, \qquad \lim_{t\to+\infty} t^2 y_0'(t) = 0 \tag{9.1.4}$$

and there exists a unique solution $y_2(t)$ such that

$$\lim_{t\to+\infty} [y_2(t) - t] = 0, \qquad \lim_{t\to+\infty} t[y_2'(t) - 1] = 0. \tag{9.1.5}$$

Again, if $G(t)$ keeps a constant sign, the condition $t^2G(t) \in L(0, \infty)$ is necessary as well as sufficient for the existence of such solutions.

Proof. We replace (9.1.1) by the equation

$$y''(t, \lambda) - \lambda G(t) y(t, \lambda) = 0 \tag{9.1.6}$$

which we propose to solve by a power series in λ

$$y_0(t, \lambda) = \sum_{n=0}^{\infty} v_n(t)\lambda^n, \tag{9.1.7}$$

where

$$v_0''(t) = 0, \qquad v_n''(t) = G(t)v_{n-1}(t), \qquad n > 0.$$

We satisfy these conditions by setting

$$v_0(t) \equiv 1, \qquad v_n(t) = \int_t^\infty (s - t)G(s)v_{n-1}(s)\,ds,$$

assuming the integrals to be convergent. This is certainly the case for $n = 1$ for we have

$$|v_1(t)| < g_2(t) \equiv \int_t^\infty sg(s)\,ds, \qquad g(t) \equiv |G(t)|.$$

Suppose it be known that

$$|v_n(t)| \le \frac{1}{n!}[g_2(t)]^n.$$

Then

$$|v_{n+1}(t)| \le \frac{1}{n!}\int_t^\infty (s - t)g(s)[g_2(s)]^n\,ds$$

$$< \frac{1}{n!}\int_t^\infty sg(s)[g_2(s)]^n\,ds = \frac{1}{(n+1)!}[g_2(t)]^{n+1}.$$

It follows that the series (9.1.7) is absolutely convergent for all t and all finite λ. Further

$$|y_0(t, \lambda)| \le \exp[|\lambda| g_2(t)]$$

or

$$|y_0(t, \lambda)| \le \exp\left[|\lambda| \int_t^\infty s|G(s)|\, ds\right]. \tag{9.1.8}$$

Thus $y_0(t, \lambda)$ exists and it has clearly the property

$$\lim_{t\to+\infty} y_0(t, \lambda) = 1$$

for all λ.

As to the derivative, we note first that

$$y_0(t, \lambda) = 1 + \lambda \int_t^\infty (s - t)G(s)y_0(s, \lambda)\, ds, \tag{9.1.9}$$

for the integral converges and twofold differentiation gives (9.1.6). Since

$$y_0'(t, \lambda) = -\lambda \int_t^\infty G(s)y_0(s, \lambda)\, ds, \tag{9.1.10}$$

it follows that for large t

$$\begin{aligned} t|y_0'(t, \lambda)| &\le (1 + \varepsilon)|\lambda| t \int_t^\infty g(s)\, ds \\ &\le (1 + \varepsilon)|\lambda| \int_t^\infty sg(s)\, ds \to 0. \end{aligned}$$

Hence (9.1.2) is satisfied by $y_0(t, \lambda)$ for each fixed λ.

If the stronger condition $t^2G(t) \in L(0, \infty)$ holds, then

$$g_3(t) \equiv \int_t^\infty s^2 g(s)\, ds$$

exists and

$$tg_2(t) < g_3(t).$$

Since

$$\begin{aligned} |y_0(t, \lambda) - 1| &\le \exp[|\lambda| g_2(t)] - 1 \\ &< \exp[|\lambda| t^{-1} g_3(t)] - 1, \end{aligned}$$

we see that the first inequality under (9.1.4) is valid. The second one holds because

$$t^2|y_0'(t, \lambda)| \le (1 + \varepsilon)|\lambda| tg_2(t) < (1 + \varepsilon)|\lambda| g_3(t).$$

If the condition $t^2G(t) \in L(0, \infty)$ applies, then we can obtain a dominant solution $y_2(t, \lambda)$ as a power series in λ

$$y_2(t, \lambda) = t + \sum_{n=1}^{\infty} V_n(t)\lambda^n,$$

where

$$V_n(t) = \int_t^\infty (s - t)G(s)V_{n-1}(s)\, ds, \qquad V_0(t) = t.$$

The series converges absolutely for all finite t and λ and

$$|y_2(t, \lambda) - t| \leq \exp\left[|\lambda| \int_t^\infty s^2|G(s)|\, ds\right] - 1 \tag{9.1.11}$$

and this implies the first inequality under (9.1.5). For the derivative we note that

$$y_2(t, \lambda) = t + \lambda \int_t^\infty (s - t)G(s)y_2(s, \lambda)\, ds, \tag{9.1.12}$$

$$y_2'(t, \lambda) = 1 - \lambda \int_t^\infty G(s)y_2(s, \lambda)\, ds. \tag{9.1.13}$$

For large values of t the second equation gives

$$t|y_2'(t, \lambda) - 1| \leq (1 + \varepsilon)|\lambda| g_3(t)$$

and this implies the second inequality.

In the general case where g_2 exists but not g_3, a different procedure is necessary. We base the argument on the following

Lemma 9.1.1. *If a solution $y_1(t) \not\equiv 0$ is known of the differential equation*

$$p_0(t)y'' + p_1(t)y' + p_2(t)y = 0, \tag{9.1.14}$$

then the general solution is

$$y(t) = C_1y_1(t) \int_a^t \exp\left(-\int_a^s \frac{p_1(u)}{p_0(u)}\, du\right) \frac{ds}{[y_1(s)]^2} + C_2y_1(t). \tag{9.1.15}$$

Proof. Substitute $y = y_1u$ in the equation. The result is a first order equation for u' where the variables are separated. The integration is left to the reader. ∎

Continuation of the proof of Theorem 9.1.1. We apply the lemma to Eq. (9.1.6) for a fixed λ and give a so large a value that $|y_0(t, \lambda) - 1| < \varepsilon$, a preassigned small number, for $a \leq t$. Then a second solution is given by

$$y_1(t, \lambda) = y_0(t, \lambda) \int_a^t \frac{ds}{[y_0(s, \lambda)]^2}\cdot \tag{9.1.16}$$

The integral exists since $|y_0(t, \lambda)| > 1 - \varepsilon$. A simple calculation shows that

$$|y_1(t, \lambda) - t| = o(t),\ t \to \infty \tag{9.1.17}$$

and this proves the first part of (9.1.3). The second part is proved as follows. We have

$$y_1'(t, \lambda) = y_0'(t, \lambda) \int_a^t \frac{ds}{[y_0(s, \lambda)]^2} + \frac{1}{y_0(t, \lambda)}\cdot \tag{9.1.18}$$

Here the first term tends to 0 since $ty_0'(t, \lambda) \to 0$ and the second term tends to 1.

The functions $y_\nu(t)$, $\nu = 0, 1, 2$, mentioned in the theorem are obtained by setting $\lambda = 1$.

It remains to prove the necessity of the integrability conditions, assuming $G(t)$ ultimately real and of constant sign, say $G(t) > 0$ for $t > b$. It is easiest to work with a dominant solution. Suppose that we take a solution $y_1(t)$ satisfying conditions (9.1.3). We take a so large that

$$\tfrac{1}{2}t < y_1(t) < 2t, \qquad a \le t.$$

Then, with $c > \max(a, b)$

$$y_1'(t) - y_1'(c) = \int_c^t G(s) y_1(s)\, ds.$$

Here the right member lies between constant multiples of

$$\int_c^t sG(s)\, ds$$

and is an increasing function of t which tends to the finite limit $1 - y_1'(c)$ as $t \to +\infty$. This shows that $tG(t) \in L(0, \infty)$.

Suppose now that a solution $y_2(t)$ exists with the properties (9.1.5). This shows first that $sG(s) \in L(0, \infty)$ so that

$$1 - y_2'(t) = \int_t^\infty G(s) y_2(s)\, ds.$$

Integrating with respect to t from c to ω, we get

$$\omega - y_2(\omega) - [c - y_2(c)] = \int_c^\omega \int_t^\infty G(s) y_2(s)\, ds\, dt.$$

This is an increasing function of ω which tends to the finite limit $y_2(c) - c$ as $\omega \to +\infty$. This shows the existence of

$$\begin{aligned}\int_c^\infty \int_t^\infty G(s) y_2(s)\, ds\, dt &= \int_c^\infty (s - c) G(s) y_2(s)\, ds \\ &= \int_c^\infty sG(s) y_2(s)\, ds - c\int_c^\infty G(s) y_2(s)\, ds \\ &> \tfrac{1}{2}\int_c^\infty s^2 G(s)\, ds - 2c \int_c^\infty sG(s)\, ds.\end{aligned}$$

Hence $t^2 G(t) \in L(0, \infty)$. ▮

Referring back to the estimates for the solutions $y_0(t, \lambda)$ and $y_2(t, \lambda)$ we see that they are, for fixed t, entire functions of λ of order ≤ 1. This is the first time that we have encountered such a high order of a solution with respect to a parameter that occurs linearly in the equation. We have been used to entire functions of order $\tfrac{1}{2}$ and normal type in connection with solutions of linear second order equations. Here it is the infinite interval that causes the deviation from the familiar pattern. We shall look further into this question. First, however, we shall state and prove a simple inequality.

Theorem 9.1.2. *If $tG(t) \in L(0, \infty)$, if $G(t)$ and λ are real, then*

$$y_0(t, \lambda) < \exp\left[\lambda \int_t^\infty (s - t)G(s)\, ds\right]. \tag{9.1.19}$$

If λ and $G(t)$ are positive, the inequality is valid for all t, otherwise for t greater than the largest positive zero of $y_0(t, \lambda)$ in case such zeros exist.

Proof. Here we shall use the equivalent Riccati equation. We set

$$w_0(t, \lambda) = \frac{y_0'(t, \lambda)}{y_0(t, \lambda)} \tag{9.1.20}$$

and obtain

$$w_0'(t, \lambda) = \lambda G(t) - [w_0(t, \lambda)]^2. \tag{9.1.21}$$

If t exceeds the largest zero of $y_0(t, \lambda)$, then $w_0(t, \lambda)$ is continuous in t and tends to the limit 0 as $t \to +\infty$ by (9.1.2). Hence from

$$w_0'(t, \lambda) < \lambda G(t)$$

one obtains by integration

$$\frac{y_0'(t, \lambda)}{y_0(t, \lambda)} > -\lambda \int_t^\infty G(s)\, ds.$$

A second integration gives (9.1.19). ∎

We can get more information out of the Riccati equation by imposing more restrictions on $G(t)$.

Theorem 9.1.3. *Suppose that $G(t)$ is positive, continuous and decreasing and $tG(t) \in L(0, \infty)$. Then for any β, $0 < t < \beta \le \infty$,*

$$|y_0(t, \lambda)| \le y_0(\beta, |\lambda|) \exp\left\{|\lambda|^{1/2} \int_t^\beta [G(s)]^{1/2}\, ds\right\}. \tag{9.1.22}$$

In particular, if $[G(t)]^{1/2} \in L(0, \infty)$, then

$$|y_0(t, \lambda)| \le \exp\left\{|\lambda|^{1/2} \int_t^\infty [G(s)]^{1/2}\, ds\right\}. \tag{9.1.23}$$

Proof. The power series (9.1.7) has positive coefficients since $G(t) > 0$. It follows that

$$|y_0(t, \lambda)| \le y_0(t, |\lambda|). \tag{9.1.24}$$

Thus we can restrict ourselves to positive real values of λ. We want to show that for positive λ and t

$$w_0'(t, \lambda) = \frac{d^2}{dt^2} \log y_0(t, \lambda) > 0. \tag{9.1.25}$$

To prove this, we consider (9.1.21). Now $y_0(t, \lambda)$ is a positive decreasing function of t since each term of the series (9.1.7) has this property, excepting the first which is a constant. It follows that $w_0(t, \lambda) < 0$. Suppose now that $w_0'(t, \lambda) < 0$ in some interval $0 \le t_1 < t < t_2 \le \infty$. If this interval is finite, we may suppose that $w_0'(t_2, \lambda) = 0$. In this case

$$[\lambda G(t_1)]^{1/2} \le |w_0(t_1, \lambda)| < |w_0(t_2, \lambda)| = [\lambda G(t_2)]^{1/2}$$

and this contradicts the assumption that $G(t)$ is decreasing. On the other hand, if $t_2 = \infty$ then $w_0(t, \lambda)$ would decrease to a negative limit. This contradicts the fact that the limit of $w_0(t, \lambda)$ as $t \to +\infty$ is 0. Thus (9.1.25) must hold for all t. This implies

$$-w_0(s, \lambda) < [\lambda G(s)]^{1/2}$$

and integration over (t, β) gives (9.1.22). We get (9.1.23) if it is permitted to take $\beta = \infty$. Note that $y_0(\infty, \lambda) \equiv 1$. ∎

Corollary 1. *For λ and t positive*

$$y_0(t, \lambda) \le \min_{\beta} \exp\left\{\lambda \int_{\beta}^{\infty} (s - \beta)G(s)\, ds + \lambda^{1/2} \int_t^{\beta} [G(s)]^{1/2}\, ds\right\}. \tag{9.1.26}$$

Proof. Combine (9.1.19) and (9.1.22). ∎

Corollary 2. *Under the assumptions of Theorem* 9.1.3

$$\lim_{\lambda \to +\infty} \frac{1}{\lambda} \log y_0(t, \lambda) = 0, \tag{9.1.27}$$

uniformly in t.

Proof. Set

$$\lambda \int_{\beta}^{\infty} (s - \beta)G(s)\, ds + \lambda^{1/2} \int_0^{\beta} [G(s)]^{1/2}\, ds \equiv E(\lambda, \beta).$$

For fixed λ, β this is the maximum value of the exponent in (9.1.26). Here

$$\left\{\int_0^{\beta} [G(s)]^{1/2}\, ds\right\}^2 \le \int_0^{\beta} \frac{ds}{s + 1} \cdot \int_0^{\beta} (s + 1)G(s)\, ds$$

$$< \log(\beta + 1) \cdot \int_0^{\infty} (s + 1)G(s)\, ds.$$

Now β is at our disposal. For a fixed σ, $0 < \sigma < 1$, we take $\beta = \exp(\lambda^{\sigma})$. It is clear that

$$\min_{\beta} \frac{1}{\lambda} E(\lambda, \beta) \le \frac{1}{\lambda} E(\lambda, e^{\lambda^{\sigma}})$$

and this tends to 0 as $\lambda \to +\infty$. Thus if $G(t)$ is decreasing and if $y_0(0, \lambda) = \max_t y_0(t, \lambda)$ is an entire function of λ of order 1, then it must be of minimal type of this order. ∎

The following lemma is a useful comparison theorem.

Lemma 9.1.1. *Given the two equations*

$$y'' - \lambda g(t)y = 0, \qquad Y'' - \lambda G(t)Y = 0 \tag{9.1.28}$$

where g and G are continuous, $0 < g(t) < G(t)$ *and* $tG(t) \in L(0, \infty)$*. Then for* $\lambda > 0$

$$y_0(t, \lambda) < Y_0(t, \lambda). \tag{9.1.29}$$

Proof. Use the power series (9.1.7). ▮

This lemma indicates a way of getting around the restrictive assumption that $G(t)$ is decreasing. It is sufficient that $G(t)$ admits of a decreasing majorant $G_1(t)$ which satisfies the conditions of Theorem 9.1.3.

Unfortunately there are but few equations where we can either compute $y_0(t, \lambda)$ explicitly or find an accurate estimate, and this scarcity is particularly annoying in the so-called *fringe zone*, the functions $G(t)$ such that

$$tG(t) \in L(0, \infty), \qquad [G(t)]^{1/2} \notin L(0, \infty).$$

Here (9.1.26) or similar inequality is often the only recourse.

The following special case is of some interest in itself and is useful for comparison purposes. The basic interval is $(1, \infty)$ rather than $(0, \infty)$. We take

$$y'' - \lambda t^{-2-\alpha} y = 0 \tag{9.1.30}$$

where to start with α is real positive. Then

$$y_0(t, \lambda, \alpha) = \sum_{n=0}^{\infty} \frac{1}{n!(\alpha + 1)(2\alpha + 1)\cdots(n\alpha + 1)} \left(\frac{\lambda}{\alpha t^{\alpha}}\right)^n \tag{9.1.31}$$

which may be expressed in terms of the Bessel function $I_{1/\alpha}$. The solution is an analytic function of t, λ, α. It is an entire function of $t^{-\alpha}$ and an entire function of λ. The dependence on α is more intricate. The points $\alpha = -1, -\frac{1}{2}, \ldots, -1/n, \ldots$ are simple poles, $\alpha = 0$ is a limit point of poles, while $\alpha = \infty$ is an essential singularity. The principle of permanency of functional equations shows that the series satisfies the differential equation for all non-singular values of t, λ, α. The properties

$$\lim_{t\to\infty} y_0(t, \lambda, \alpha) = 1, \qquad \lim_{t\to\infty} t y_0'(t, \lambda, \alpha) = 0$$

hold only for $\Re(\alpha) > 0$ which is precisely the values for which $tG(t) \in L(1, \infty)$. The study of this equation goes back to Euler.

Finally, we give some explanation of the title of this section. We can give a kinematic interpretation of Eq. (9.1.6). If to start with λ and $G(t)$ are real, then (9.1.6) is the equation of motion of a particle along a line. At the time t its position is given by $y(t)$ and it is moving under the influence of a *central force* given by $\lambda G(t)y(t)$. There are several possible motions, depending upon the initial conditions for $t = 0$. In the typical case $y(t, \lambda)$ is a dominant solution and is approximately proportional to t. In this sense the motion is "almost uniform." We have also an exceptional motion corresponding to (constant multiples of) the subdominant solution. If λ and $G(t)$ have the same sign, the particle simply recedes from $y_0(0, \lambda)$ to 1 while t goes from 0 to ∞, while, if the signs are opposite, the particle may describe a finite number of oscillations before it approaches its position of rest.

The dynamic interpretation is also available if λ is complex and $G(t)$ is complex valued. To simplify, let us take $G(t)$ real positive and set $\lambda = \mu + i\nu$ where $\nu \neq 0$. We set

$$y = r\, e^{i\theta}, \qquad \lambda = \rho\, e^{i\varphi}$$

Then $[r, \theta]$ are the polar coordinates of a particle moving in the plane under the influence of a force of magnitude

$$\rho G(t) r,$$

making the constant angle φ with the radius vector. We can also write the equations of motion under the form

$$r''(t) - r(t)[\theta'(t)]^2 = \mu G(t) r(t), \tag{9.1.32}$$

$$\frac{d}{dt}\{[r(t)]^2\theta'(t)\} = \nu G(t)[r(t)]^2, \tag{9.1.33}$$

where the left sides are the *radial* and *transverse accelerations*, respectively. Thus these accelerations have the signs of μ and ν respectively. From Eq. (9.1.33) we conclude that $\theta(t)$ tends to a finite limit. If $\theta(0) = 0$, $\theta'(0) = 0$, then $\theta(t)$ increases or decreases to its limit according as $\nu > 0$ or <0. If in Eq. (9.1.32) we assume $r(0) = 0$, $r'(0) \geq 0 \mu > 0$, we see that $r(t)$ is increasing and grows as Ct. Again we have an almost uniform motion.

EXERCISE 9.1

1. Equation (9.1.1) may have a solution satisfying $\lim_{t\to\infty} y(t) = 1$ without $tG(t)$ belonging to $L(0, \infty)$, if $G(t)$ can change its sign infinitely often. Verify that this is the case for the equation satisfied by
$$1 - \frac{\sin t}{t}.$$
2. If $G(t) = -e^{-2t}$, verify that $y_0(t) = J_0(e^{-t})$.
3. In (9.1.30) assume $\alpha > 1$ and compute $y_2(t, \lambda, \alpha)$. Express it as a Bessel function. Discuss the singularities of the solution as a function of α.
4. The point $\alpha = -1/n$ is a pole of $y_0(t, \lambda, \alpha)$. We can remove all poles by dividing $y_0(t, \lambda, \alpha)$ by $\Gamma(1 + 1/\alpha)$. The resulting function is a solution also for the excluded values $\{-1/n\}$. What is it equal to for such a value? What multiplier should be used to remove the poles in the case of $y_2(t, \lambda, \alpha)$?

5. Find explicitly the solution $y_0(t, \lambda)$ for Halm's equation
$$(1 + t^2)^2 y'' - \lambda y = 0$$
and find for what values of λ does $y_0(t, \lambda) \in C[-\infty, \infty]$.

6. What estimate is obtainable for $y_0(t, \lambda)$, if $G(t) = \operatorname{sech}^2 t$?

7. In the preceding problem introduce $x = \tanh t$ as a new variable and express $y_0(t, \lambda)$ in terms of the Legendre function $P_a(x)$ of formula (7.2.2). For what values of λ does $y_0(t, \lambda)$ belong to $C[-\infty, +\infty]$?

8. Take $G(t) = [(t + e) \log (t + e)]^{-2}$ and reduce the corresponding equation (9.1.6) to the Bessel equation
$$z^2 \frac{d^2 Y}{dz^2} + z \frac{dY}{dz} + (z^2 - \lambda - \tfrac{1}{4}) Y = 0$$
by setting
$$u = \log (t + e), \qquad y = u^{1/2} e^{u/2}, \qquad u = -2iz.$$
What solution of the Bessel equation should be used to get (a multiple of) $y_0(t, \lambda)$?

9. With $G(t)$ as in the preceding problem, use (9.1.26) to estimate $y_0(t, \lambda)$. It is not required to find the actual minimum.

10. The inequality (9.1.25) states that $y_0(t, \lambda)$ is logarithmically convex in t. Show that if $f(t)$ has this property and $t_1 < t_2$, $0 < \alpha < 1$, then
$$f[\alpha t_1 + (1 - \alpha) t_2] < [f(t_1)]^{\alpha} [f(t_2)]^{1-\alpha}.$$

11. Prove that $t[\theta'(t)]^2 \in L(0, \infty)$. See (9.1.32) and (9.1.33).

12. Prove the assertions made in the text concerning $\theta(t)$.

13. Same question for $r(t)$.

14. If $r(0) = 0$, $r'(0) \geq 0$, $\theta(0) = \theta'(0) = 0$ and $\nu > 0$, show that
$$\theta(t) < \nu \int_0^t (t - s)\, G(s)\, ds.$$

9.2 GROWTH PROPERTIES

In this section a study is made of the equation
$$y'' - G(t) y = 0 \tag{9.2.1}$$
under the assumption that $G(t)$ is positive and continuous in $[0, \infty)$ while $tG(t) \notin L(0, \infty)$. We shall be concerned with the geometric and growth properties of the real solutions.

These solutions are non-oscillatory in $[0, \infty)$ for the identity
$$[y(t) y'(t)]_a^b - \int_a^b [y'(t)]^2\, dt - \int_a^b G(t)[y(t)]^2\, dt = 0 \tag{9.2.2}$$

shows that

$$y(t)y'(t)$$

can vanish at most once in $[0, \infty)$.

This observation leads to a classification of the real solutions according to the shape of their graphs. A fundamental system of solutions $Y_0(t)$ and $Y_1(t)$ is determined by the initial conditions

$$\begin{aligned} Y_0(0) &= 0, \qquad & Y_1(0) &= 1, \\ Y_0'(0) &= 1, \qquad & Y_1'(0) &= 0. \end{aligned} \tag{9.2.3}$$

A simple argument shows that these functions are strictly increasing together with their first order derivatives and, moreover,

$$\lim_{t\to\infty} \frac{Y_j(t)}{t} = +\infty, \qquad j = 0, 1. \tag{9.2.4}$$

We now consider the family of solutions

$$y_\alpha(t) = Y_1(t) + \alpha Y_0(t), \qquad -\infty < \alpha < \infty. \tag{9.2.5}$$

It is clear that, for t fixed, $y_\alpha(t)$ is an increasing and differentiable function of α. For $\alpha > 0$ all functions $y_\alpha(t)$ and $y_\alpha'(t)$ are strictly increasing and become infinite with t. Solutions with a positive minimum are obtainable for α in some interval $(-\beta, 0)$, solutions with a zero for α in some interval $(-\infty, -\gamma)$. We shall prove that $\beta = \gamma$. This is intuitively obvious but it can even be proved.

We start with solutions having zeros. Here $y_\alpha(t)$ will have a zero at $t = a$, its only zero, if

$$\alpha = -\frac{Y_1(a)}{Y_0(a)}. \tag{9.2.6}$$

This defines α as a function of a and

$$\alpha'(a) = \frac{1}{[Y_0(a)]^2} \tag{9.2.7}$$

shows that it is an increasing function of a. As a goes from 0 to $+\infty$, $\alpha(a)$ goes from $-\infty$ to $-\gamma < 0$ where

$$\gamma = -\lim_{t\to+\infty} \frac{Y_1(t)}{Y_0(t)}. \tag{9.2.8}$$

We now consider solutions with a positive minimum, a unique minimum. This will be located at $t = \tau$ if

$$\alpha = \tilde{\alpha} = -\frac{Y_1'(\tau)}{Y_0'(\tau)}. \tag{9.2.9}$$

This defines $\tilde{\alpha}$ as a function of τ over the interval $[0, \infty)$ and it is a decreasing function of τ. Its derivative, $\tilde{\alpha}'(\tau)$, exists and equals

$$\tilde{\alpha}'(\tau) = -\frac{G(\tau)}{[Y_0'(\tau)]^2} < 0 \tag{9.2.10}$$

so that $\tilde{\alpha}(\tau)$ is decreasing. Its limit as $\tau \to +\infty$ is $-\beta$ where

$$\beta = \lim_{t \to +\infty} \frac{Y_1'(t)}{Y_0'(t)}. \tag{9.2.11}$$

Now

$$Y_0(t)Y_1'(t) - Y_0'(t)Y_1(t) \equiv -1$$

whence it follows that

$$\gamma = \beta.$$

We have found two expressions for β, more will turn up later.

The discussion shows that $y_{-\beta}(t)$ is a strictly decreasing positive function. Its limit for $t \to +\infty$ cannot be positive for this would imply $tG(t) \in L(0, \infty)$ since $G(t) > 0$. Hence

$$\lim_{t \to +\infty} y_{-\beta}(t) = 0.$$

This is the exceptional *subdominant solution*. Its graph separates the graphs of the solutions $y_\alpha(t)$, which have minima from those which have zeros.

We can construct a subdominant solution directly using Lemma 9.1.1. Formula (9.1.16) suggests forming

$$y_+(t) \equiv MY_1(t)\int_t^\infty \frac{ds}{[Y_1(s)]^2}, \qquad M^{-1} = \int_0^\infty \frac{ds}{[Y_1(s)]^2}. \tag{9.2.12}$$

The integral exists since $Y_1(s) > 1 + s$ for large s. The multiplier M has been chosen so that

$$y_+(0) = 1.$$

Thus this solution is a member of the family $\{y_\alpha\}$. Further

$$y_+'(t) = M\left\{Y_1'(t)\int_t^\infty \frac{ds}{[Y_1(s)]^2} - \frac{1}{Y_1(t)}\right\}$$

$$< M\left\{\int_t^\infty \frac{Y_1'(s)\,ds}{[Y_1(s)]^2} - \frac{1}{Y_1(t)}\right\} = 0.$$

Thus $y_+(t)$ is positive and strictly decreasing for all t and the only member of the family $\{y_\alpha\}$ with these properties is $y_{-\beta}(t)$. Hence

$$y_+(t) \equiv y_{-\beta}(t). \tag{9.2.13}$$

Since

$$y_+'(0) = -M = -\beta$$

we have a third expression for β.

The subdominant has interesting integrability properties. If in (9.2.2) we set $y = y_\alpha$, $-\beta < \alpha < 0$, $\lambda = 1$, $a = 0$, $b = \tau(\alpha)$, then

$$\alpha + \int_0^{\tau(\alpha)} \{[y'_\alpha(t)]^2 + G(t)[y_\alpha(t)]^2\}\,dt = 0.$$

Here we let α decrease to $-\beta$. Then

$$\tau(\alpha) \to +\infty, \qquad y'_\alpha(t) \downarrow y'_{-\beta}(t), \qquad y_\alpha(t) \downarrow y_{-\beta}(t),$$

the last two holding uniformly on any fixed finite interval. The usual argument shows that

$$[y'_+(t)]^2 \in L(0, \infty), \qquad G(t)[y_+(t)]^2 \in L(0, \infty) \tag{9.2.14}$$

and

$$\int_0^\infty \{[y'_+(t)]^2 + G(t)[y_+(t)]^2\}\,dt = -\beta \tag{9.2.15}$$

which is a fourth expression for β. Property (9.2.14) together with $y_+(0) = 1$ characterize the normalized subdominant completely.

Thus we have proved Lemma 7.6.1 which was stated without proof in Section 7.6. The extension to the whole line is trivial. This completes our discussion of the geometric properties of the real solutions of (9.2.3).

We prove a comparison theorem which implies Lemma 7.6.2.

Theorem 9.2.1. *Consider the equations*

$$y'' - g(t)y = 0, \qquad Y'' - G(t)Y = 0 \tag{9.2.16}$$

where g and G are continuous on $(0, \infty)$, $0 < g(t) < G(t)$, and $tg(t) \notin L(0, \infty)$. Let y_α and Y_α be the solutions of the two equations corresponding to

$$y_\alpha(0) = Y_\alpha(0) = 1, \qquad y'_\alpha(0) = Y'_\alpha(0) = \alpha, \qquad -\infty < \alpha < \infty.$$

Let y_ω and Y_ω be determined by

$$y_\omega(0) = Y_\omega(0) = 0, \qquad y'_\omega(0) = Y'_\omega(0) = 1,$$

and let y_+ and Y_+ be the normalized subdominants. Finally, let β and γ be such that $y_{-\beta} = y_+$, $Y_{-\gamma} = Y_+$. Then $\beta < \gamma$ and

$$y_\alpha(t) < Y_\alpha(t), \qquad 0 < t < \infty, \qquad -\gamma \le \alpha, \tag{9.2.17}$$

$$y_\omega(t) < Y_\omega(t), \tag{9.2.18}$$

$$y_+(t) > Y_+(t). \tag{9.2.19}$$

Proof. We use the identity

$$[y(s)Y'(s) - y'(s)Y(s)]_a^b = \int_a^b [G(s) - g(s)]y(s)Y(s)\,ds. \tag{9.2.20}$$

Let $y(s)$ and $Y(s)$ be corresponding solutions, either with the same subscript α where $\alpha \geq 0$ or the subscript ω and take $a = 0$, $b = t$. Then the right member is positive for all t. The left member is zero in the lower limit. Hence

$$y(t)Y'(t) - y'(t)Y(t) > 0$$

or

$$\frac{d}{dt}\frac{Y(t)}{y(t)} > 0 \quad \text{and} \quad \frac{Y(t)}{y(t)} > 1 \quad \text{for} \quad t > 0.$$

This proves (9.2.17) for $\alpha \geq 0$ and (9.2.18).

Since $y_0(t) < Y_0(t)$ we have

$$-\gamma = -\left\{\int_0^\infty [Y_0(t)]^{-2}\,ds\right\}^{-1} < -\left\{\int_0^\infty [y_0(t)]^{-2}\,ds\right\}^{-1} = -\beta$$

as asserted. This means that (9.2.17) holds at least for $-\beta \leq \alpha < 0$ for again the right member of (9.2.20) is positive. In the remaining interval $-\gamma \leq \alpha < -\beta$, the inequality (9.2.17) is true for $0 < t < a(\alpha)$ where $a(\alpha)$ is the zero of $y_\alpha(t)$. This follows from the same argument. For $a(\alpha) < t$ we have $y_\alpha(t) < 0 < Y_\alpha(t)$ so that (9.2.17) is trivially true.

Finally we take $y = y_+$, $Y = Y_+$, $a = 0$, $b = t$ and obtain

$$y_+(t)Y_+'(t) - y_+'(t)Y_+(t) + \gamma - \beta = \int_0^t [G(s) - g(s)]y_+(s)Y_+(s)\,ds.$$

As $t \to +\infty$ the left member converges to $\gamma - \beta$. Hence

$$[G(t) - g(t)]y_+(t)Y_+(t) \in L(0, \infty). \tag{9.2.21}$$

Using (9.2.20) once more, now with $a = t$, $b = \infty$, we get

$$y_+'(t)Y_+(t) - y_+(t)Y_+'(t) = \int_t^\infty [G(s) - g(s)]y_+(s)Y_+(s)\,ds.$$

Since this is positive

$$\frac{d}{dt}\frac{y_+(t)}{Y_+(t)} > 0$$

and (9.2.19) results. ▮

Corollary. *Lemma* 7.6.2.

For if $g(t) = a^2$, $a > 0$, then $y_+(t) = e^{-at}$.

We can get a useful class of comparison functions by the following construction. Let $f(t)$ be continuous and positive together with its first and second order derivatives and suppose that

$$\limsup_{t\to\infty} f''(t)[f'(t)]^{-2} < 1. \tag{9.2.22}$$

Then

$$\exp\,[f(t)] \tag{9.2.23}$$

is a dominant solution of the equation

$$y'' - \{[f'(t)]^2 + f''(t)\}y = 0. \tag{9.2.24}$$

The subdominant solution is a constant multiple of

$$\exp\,[f(t)] \int_t^\infty \exp\,[-2f(s)]\,ds. \tag{9.2.25}$$

Using a technique familiar from the theory of the probability integral (special case $f(t) = \frac{1}{2}t^2$), we get

$$\begin{aligned}\int_t^\infty \exp\,[-2f(s)]\,ds &= -\tfrac{1}{2}\int_t^\infty [f'(s)]^{-1}\,d\exp\,[-2f(s)]\\ &= \tfrac{1}{2}[f'(t)]^{-1}\exp\,[-2f(t)]\\ &\quad - \tfrac{1}{2}\int_t^\infty \exp\,[-2f(s)]f''(s)[f'(s)]^{-2}\,ds\end{aligned}$$

and the estimate

$$\exp\,[f(t)]\int_t^\infty \exp\,[-2f(s)]\,ds = \theta[f'(t)]^{-1}\exp\,[-f(t)] \tag{9.2.26}$$

where for large values of t

$$\tfrac{1}{3} < \theta < \tfrac{1}{2}.$$

We can use this device to find majorants and minorants for the solutions of (9.2.3). Unfortunately, to do this we have to impose further restrictions on $G(t)$. The simplest choice is

$$f(t) = \int_0^t [G(s)]^{1/2}\,ds. \tag{9.2.27}$$

This choice leads to

Lemma 9.2.1. *Let $G(t)$ be positive, continuous and increasing with $G'(t)$ continuous and* $\limsup G'(t)[G(t)]^{-3/2} < 2$. *Let $y_a(t)$ be the solution of* (9.2.3) *with $y_a(0) = 1$, $y_a'(0) = a = [G(0)]^{1/2}$. Then*

$$y_a(t) < \exp\left\{\int_0^t [G(s)]^{1/2}\,ds\right\}. \tag{9.2.28}$$

If $y_+(t)$ is the normalized subdominant solution of (9.2.3), *then we can find a positive constant C such that*

$$y_+(t) > C[G(t)]^{-1/2}\exp\left\{-\int_0^t [G(s)]^{1/2}\,ds\right\}. \tag{9.2.29}$$

Proof. The reader can verify that (9.2.22) holds and the relation

$$G(t) < [f'(t)]^2 + f''(t).$$

We have chosen a so that $y_a(t)$ has the same initial values as the right member of (9.2.28) so the latter becomes a special case of (9.2.17). For the present choice of $f(t)$ the subdominant (9.2.25) can be normalized by dividing through by

$$M \equiv \int_0^\infty \exp\left\{-2\int_0^t [G(s)]^{1/2}\,ds\right\}dt.$$

Using (9.2.19) and (9.2.26) we get for large values of t

$$y_+(t) > \tfrac{1}{3}M^{-1}[G(t)]^{-1/2}\exp\left\{-\int_0^t [G(s)]^{-1/2}\,ds\right\}$$

and this is (9.2.29). ▮

It is also possible to obtain some results when G is decreasing but we restrict ourselves to indicating the possibility. (See Problem 12 in the Exercise below.)

The estimates in the lemma are rather crude and may be improved at the price of further restrictions on G. Since the inequalities call to mind the Liouville transformation, we shall try

$$f(t) = \int_0^t [G(s)]^{1/2}\,ds - \tfrac{1}{4}\log G(t). \tag{9.2.30}$$

Assuming existence of the necessary derivatives, we get

$$f'(t) = [G(t)]^{1/2} - \frac{1}{4}\frac{G'(t)}{G(t)},$$

$$f''(t) = \frac{1}{2}\frac{G'(t)}{[G(t)]^{1/2}} + \frac{1}{4}\left[\frac{G'(t)}{G(t)}\right]^2 - \frac{1}{4}\frac{G''(t)}{G(t)}$$

and

$$[f'(t)]^2 + f''(t) = G(t) + \frac{5}{16}\left[\frac{G'(t)}{G(t)}\right]^2 - \frac{1}{4}\frac{G''(t)}{G(t)}. \tag{9.2.31}$$

This gives

Theorem 9.2.2. *Let $G(t)$ be positive and continuous and possess continuous first and second order derivatives satisfying*

$$G(t)G''(t) < \tfrac{5}{4}[G'(t)]^2. \tag{9.2.32}$$

Then there exists a dominant solution $y(t)$ of (9.2.3) such that

$$y(t) < [G(t)]^{-1/4}\exp\left\{\int_0^t [G(s)]^{1/2}\,ds\right\}, \tag{9.2.33}$$

and a positive constant C such that

$$y_+(t) > C[G(t)]^{-1/4} \exp\left\{-\int_0^t [G(s)]^{1/2}\, ds\right\}. \tag{9.2.34}$$

Proof. Here (9.2.33) is immediate. The initial values of the right member are

$$Y(0) = [G(0)]^{-1/4}, \qquad Y'(0) = [G(0)]^{1/4} - \tfrac{1}{4}G'(0)[G(0)]^{-5/4}$$

and $y(t)$ is the solution of (9.2.3) with the same initial values. As to $y_+(t)$, it so happens that the integral in the expected minorant can be simplified. We have

$$\int_t^\infty \exp[-2f(s)]\, ds = \int_t^\infty \exp\left\{-2\int_0^s [G(u)]^{1/2}\, du\right\}[G(s)]^{1/2}\, ds$$

$$= \tfrac{1}{2} \exp\left\{-2\int_0^t [G(s)]^{1/2}\, ds\right\}.$$

Hence

$$Y_+(t) = [G(0)]^{1/4}[G(t)]^{-1/4} \exp\left\{-\int_0^t [G(s)]^{1/2}\, ds\right\}, \tag{9.2.35}$$

so the C in formula (9.2.34) is $[G(0)]^{1/4}$. In this argument we have tacitly assumed

$$[G(t)]^{1/2} \notin L(0, \infty). \quad \blacksquare$$

Liouville's transformation can be applied to the growth problem. We encounter no new differentiability conditions beyond those of Theorem 9.2.2. The inequality (9.2.32) has now to be replaced by an integrability condition. We introduce new variables in (9.2.1) setting

$$x = \int_0^t [G(s)]^{1/2}\, ds, \qquad W = [G(t)]^{1/4}\, y. \tag{9.2.36}$$

The result is

$$W'' - [1 + F(x)]W = 0 \tag{9.2.37}$$

with

$$F(x) = \frac{1}{4}\frac{G''(t)}{[G(t)]^2} - \frac{5}{16}\frac{[G'(t)]^2}{[G(t)]^3}. \tag{9.2.38}$$

If

$$F(x) \in L(0, \infty),$$

Eq. (9.2.37) has two solutions of the form

$$W_1(x) = e^x[1 + R_1(x)], \qquad W_+(x) = e^{-x}[1 + R_+(x)] \tag{9.2.39}$$

where

$$|R_+(x)| < \exp\left[\int_x^\infty |F(\xi)|\, d\xi\right] - 1, \qquad 0 < x < \infty, \tag{9.2.40}$$

and $R_1(x)$ is of the same order of magnitude as $R_+(x)$ for large x. Proceeding as in the proof of Theorem 5.4.6 we show that a subdominant solution of (9.2.37) satisfies the equivalent integral equation

$$W_+(x) = e^{-x} - \int_x^\infty \sinh(\xi - x)\, F(\xi) W_+(\xi)\, d\xi.$$

Setting

$$U(x) = W_+(x)\, e^x,$$

one gets

$$U(x) = 1 - \tfrac{1}{2} \int_x^\infty [1 - e^{-2(\xi - x)}] F(\xi) U(\xi)\, d\xi.$$

The estimate for $R_+(x)$ is then obtained in the usual manner. Using Lemma 9.1.1 we then use $W_+(x)$ to construct dominant solutions satisfying the stated conditions. Reverting back to the old variables we see that we have proved:

Theorem 9.2.3. *Let $G(t)$ be positive and continuous in $[0, \infty)$ and possess continuous first and second order derivatives. Set*

$$H(t) = \{\tfrac{5}{16}[G'(t)]^2 - \tfrac{1}{4}G(t)G''(t)\}[G(t)]^{-5/2} \tag{9.2.41}$$

and suppose that

$$H(t) \in L(0, \infty). \tag{9.2.42}$$

Then there exist constants C_1 and C_2 such that

$$y_1(t) = C_1[G(t)]^{-1/4} \exp\left\{\int_0^t [G(s)]^{1/2}\, ds\right\}[1 + R_1^*(t)], \tag{9.2.43}$$

$$y_+(t) = C_2[G(t)]^{-1/4} \exp\left\{-\int_0^t [G(s)]^{1/2}\, ds\right\}[1 + R_+^*(t)], \tag{9.2.44}$$

where

$$|R_+^*(t)| \le \exp\left\{\int_t^\infty |H(s)|\, ds\right\} - 1 \tag{9.2.45}$$

and $|R_1^*(t)| \le C|R_+^*(t)|$.

EXERCISE 9.2

1. In the notation of (9.2.5) let $-\beta < \alpha < 0$ and suppose that $y_\alpha'(\tau) = 0$. Show that $y_\alpha(\tau) = [Y_0'(\tau)]^{-1}$.
2. Suppose instead that $\alpha < -\beta$ and $y_\alpha(a) = 0$. Show that $y_\alpha'(a) = -[Y_0(a)]^{-1}$.
3. The zero a of $y_\alpha(t)$ is a function of α. Show that $a'(\alpha) = [y_\alpha'(a(\alpha))]^{-2}$. [*Hint*: Use (9.2.2), $y = y_\alpha(t)$, $a = 0$, $b = a(\alpha)$, differentiate with respect to α and evaluate the integrals.]

4. Verify (9.2.32) if $G(t)$ is logarithmically concave.
5. Verify (9.2.32) if $G'(t)[G(t)]^{-5/4}$ is decreasing.
6. Suppose that $G(t)$ is positive and bounded away from 0 and that

$$G'(t)[G(t)]^{-5/4} \in BV[0, \infty] \cap L_2(0, \infty).$$

Show that the integrability condition (9.2.42) holds
Verify the integrability condition if $G(t)$ equals

7. $(1 + t)^\alpha$, $\alpha > -2$.
8. $(2 + t)^{-2}[\log (2 + t)]^{2+\varepsilon}$, $\varepsilon > 0$.
9. $\exp (t^n)$, n positive integer.
10. $2 + \sin (t^\alpha)$, $0 < \alpha < \frac{1}{2}$.
11. $1 + t + t^\alpha \sin t$, $0 < \alpha < \frac{1}{2}$.
12. Suppose that for a fixed δ, $0 < \delta < 1$,

$$G'(t) < 0 < G'(t) + (2 - \delta)[G(t)]^{3/2},$$

and define $f(t)$ by (9.2.27). Prove an analogue of Lemma 9.2.1 using the double inequality

$$\tfrac{1}{2}\delta G(t) < [f'(t)]^2 + f''(t) < G(t).$$

13. Let $y(t)$ be any solution of (9.2.1). Prove that

$$C \exp\left\{-\int_0^t [G(s) + 1]\, ds\right\} < [y(t)]^2 + [y'(t)]^2$$

$$< C \exp\left\{\int_0^t [G(s) + 1]\, ds\right\},$$

where C is the initial value of the middle member. [*Hint*: Write the equation as a system for $y_1 = y$, $y_2 = y'$. Find the derivative of the sum of the squares and compare $y_1 y_2$ with $y_1^2 + y_2^2$. The argument goes back to A. M. Lyapunov (1892).]

14. Let $G(t) = G_1(t) + G_2(t)$ where G_1 and G_2 are ≥ 0. Consider the three differential equations and initial conditions

$$u''(t) - G_1(t)u(t) = 0, \quad u(0) = 1, \quad u'(0) = \alpha \geq 0,$$
$$v''(t) - G_2(t)v(t) = 0, \quad v(0) = 1, \quad v'(0) = \beta \geq 0,$$
$$w''(t) - G(t)w(t) = 0, \quad w(0) = 1, \quad w'(0) = \alpha + \beta.$$

Show that

$$w(t) \leq u(t)v(t).$$

[*Hint*: What equation is satisfied by the product?]

15. Let $u_+(t)$, $v_+(t)$, $w_+(t)$ be the normalized subdominant solutions of the preceding equations. Show that

$$w_+(t) \geq u_+(t)v_+(t).$$

16. Use this method to estimate the solutions of

$$w''(t) - (a^2 + 1 + t^2)w(t) = 0, \qquad a > 0.$$

17. Same question for

$$w''(t) - (t + t^3)w(t) = 0.$$

[*Hint*: The "component equations" have solutions expressible in terms of Bessel functions of order $\frac{1}{3}$ and $\frac{1}{5}$, respectively. Use (7.3.29) to estimate the Bessel functions of purely imaginary argument.]

9.3 SPIRAL MOTION

We shall now consider the solutions of

$$w'' - \lambda G(t)w = 0 \tag{9.3.1}$$

where λ is a complex parameter and $G(t)$ satisfies the assumptions made in the preceding section, i.e. $G(t)$ is continuous and positive in $[0, \infty)$ and $tG(t)$ does not belong to $L(0, \infty)$. The results can be given a rather striking formulation in terms of kinematical concepts. We interpret (9.3.1) as the equation of motion in complex form of a particle moving in the plane under a central force. The notation and terminology introduced towards the end of Section 9.1 will be used.

Let $w_0(t, \lambda)$ and $w_1(t, \lambda)$ be a fundamental system of solutions defined by the initial values

$$\begin{aligned} w_0(0, \lambda) &\equiv 0, & w_1(0, \lambda) &\equiv 1, \\ w_0'(0, \lambda) &\equiv 1, & w_1'(0, \lambda) &\equiv 0. \end{aligned} \tag{9.3.2}$$

These solutions exist for $0 \leq t < \infty$ and all finite values of λ. For fixed $t \neq 0$ they are entire functions of λ of order $\leq \frac{1}{2}$. In the following λ will not be allowed to take on real negative values. The remaining part of the λ-plane will be denoted by Λ.

We show first that for $\lambda \in \Lambda$ neither w_0 nor w_1 can have a zero on the open interval $0 < t < \infty$. This follows from the identity

$$[\overline{w(s)}w'(s)]_a^b - \int_a^b |w'(s)|^2 \, ds - \lambda \int_a^b G(s)|w(s)|^2 \, ds = 0 \tag{9.3.3}$$

where we set $w = w_j$, $j = 0, 1$, $a = 0$. If $t = b$ were a zero of

$$w_j(t)w_j'(t)$$

and λ not real negative, a contradiction would arise since either the imaginary or the real part of the left member could not be zero.

Thus $[w_1(t, \lambda)]^{-1}$ exists as a continuous function of t and λ, $(t, \lambda) \in [0, \infty) \times \Lambda$. It will be shown that this function belongs to $L_2(0, \infty)$ as function of t.

Since $G(t) > 0$, the coefficients in the power series

$$w_j(t, \lambda) = \sum_{n=0}^{\infty} w_{n,j}(t)\lambda^n$$

are positive. It follows that

$$|w_j(t, \lambda)| \le w_j(t, |\lambda|). \tag{9.3.4}$$

In the opposite direction we have

$$w_j(t, \mu) < |w_j(t, \mu + i\nu)|, \qquad 0 < t, \quad 0 < \mu. \tag{9.3.5}$$

This follows from formulas (9.1.32) and (9.1.33) together with Theorem 9.2.1.

We set

$$w_j(t, \lambda) = r_j(t, \lambda) \exp [i\theta_j(t, \lambda)] \tag{9.3.6}$$

so that

$$w_j'(t, \lambda) = [r_j'(t, \lambda) + ir_j(t, \lambda)\theta_j'(t, \lambda)] \exp [i\theta_j(t, \lambda)].$$

We need the initial values of r_j and θ_j. If $j = 1$, we get by inspection

$$\begin{aligned} r_1(0, \lambda) &\equiv 1, \qquad \theta_1(0, \lambda) \equiv 0, \\ r_1'(0, \lambda) &\equiv 0, \qquad \theta_1'(0, \lambda) \equiv 0 \end{aligned} \tag{9.3.7}$$

and for $j = 0$ we get directly

$$r_j(0, \lambda) \equiv 0, \qquad r_j'(0, \lambda) \equiv 1, \qquad \theta_j(0, \lambda) \equiv 0. \tag{9.3.8}$$

To get $\theta_0'(0, \lambda)$ we use (9.1.33), i.e.

$$\frac{d}{dt}\{[r_j(t, \lambda)]^2\theta_j'(t, \lambda)\} = \nu G(t)[r_j(t, \lambda)]^2.$$

Integrating and noting initial values we get

$$[r_j(t, \lambda)]^2\theta_j'(t, \lambda) = \nu \int_0^t G(s)[r_j(s, \lambda)]^2 \, ds. \tag{9.3.9}$$

The initial conditions show that $r_0(t, \lambda) = t[1 + o(1)]$ for small t. Hence

$$\begin{aligned} \lim_{t\to 0} \theta_0'(t, \lambda) &= \nu \lim_{t\to 0} [r_0(t, \lambda)]^{-2} \int_0^t G(s)[r_0(s, \lambda)]^2 \, ds \\ &= 0 \end{aligned}$$

or

$$\theta_0'(0, \lambda) = 0. \tag{9.3.10}$$

To prove (9.3.5) we compare $r_j(t, \lambda) = |w_j(t, \lambda)|$ with $w_j(t, \mu)$ using the differential equations satisfied by these functions, i.e.

$$r_j''(t, \lambda) - \{\mu G(t) + [\theta_j'(t)]^2\}r_j(t, \lambda) = 0,$$

$$w_j''(t, \mu) - \mu G(t)w_j(t, \mu) = 0.$$

The conditions of Theorem 9.2.1 are verified for $\mu > 0$ since the initial values are the same and the coefficient of r_j dominates that of w_j. This gives (9.3.5).

It follows that

$$[w_j(t, \mu + i\nu)]^{-1} \in L_2(1, \infty), \qquad 0 < \mu, \tag{9.3.11}$$

since this holds for $\nu = 0$. We shall see in a moment that the inclusion is valid for all λ in Λ. To prove this we go back to formula (9.3.3) which gives

$$\overline{w_j(t, \lambda)} w_j'(t, \lambda) = M_j(t, \lambda) + \lambda N_j(t, \lambda) \tag{9.3.12}$$

where

$$M_j(t, \lambda) = \int_0^t |w_j'(s, \lambda)|^2 \, ds, \tag{9.3.13}$$

$$N_j(t, \lambda) = \int_0^t G(s) |w_j(s, \lambda)|^2 \, ds. \tag{9.3.14}$$

We also set

$$L_j(t, \lambda) = M_j(t, \lambda) + \rho N_j(t, \lambda), \qquad \rho = |\lambda|. \tag{9.3.15}$$

Set

$$\arg \lambda = \varphi = 2\gamma, \qquad |\gamma| < \tfrac{1}{2}\pi.$$

Then (9.3.12) gives

$$\cos \gamma \, L_j(t, \lambda) = \Re[e^{-i\gamma} \overline{w_j(t, \lambda)} w_j'(t, \lambda)]. \tag{9.3.16}$$

This gives the inequality

$$\cos \gamma \, L_j(t, \lambda) \le |w_j(t, \lambda) w_j'(t, \lambda)| \le L_j(t, \lambda). \tag{9.3.17}$$

Now

$$L_j'(t, \lambda) = |w_j'(t, \lambda)|^2 + \rho G(t) |w_j(t, \lambda)|^2 > |w_j'(t, \lambda)|^2$$

and using this together with (9.3.17) we get

$$\frac{\cos^2 \gamma}{|w_j(t, \lambda)|^2} \le \frac{|w_j'(t, \lambda)|^2}{[L_j(t, \lambda)]^2} < \frac{L_j'(t, \lambda)}{[L_j(t, \lambda)]^2},$$

whence

$$\cos^2 \gamma \int_t^\infty \frac{ds}{|w_j(s, \lambda)|^2} < \frac{1}{L_j(t, \lambda)}. \tag{9.3.18}$$

Hence (9.3.11) holds for all $\lambda \in \Lambda$.

In the same manner we obtain

$$\rho \cos^2 \gamma \frac{G(t)}{|w_j'(t, \lambda)|^2} \le \rho \frac{G(t) |w_j(t, \lambda)|^2}{[L_j(t, \lambda)]^2} < \frac{L_j'(t, \lambda)}{[L_j(t, \lambda)]^2}$$

and

$$\rho \cos^2 \gamma \int_t^\infty \frac{G(s) \, ds}{|w_j'(s, \lambda)|^2} < \frac{1}{L_j(t, \lambda)}. \tag{9.3.19}$$

We shall use these inequalities to prove that the three increasing functions $M_j(t, \lambda)$, $N_j(t, \lambda)$, $L_j(t, \lambda)$ all become infinite with t. For this purpose some elementary inequalities will be needed. Since

$$w_j(t, \lambda) = j + \int_0^t w_j'(s, \lambda)\, ds, \qquad j = 0, 1,$$

the Bouniakovski-Schwarz inequality gives

$$|w_j(t, \lambda)| \le j + t^{1/2}[M_j(t, \lambda)]^{1/2}.$$

As we have just seen $|w_j(t, \lambda)|^{-1} \in L_2(1, \infty)$. Hence

$$\{j + t^{1/2}[M_j(t, \lambda)]^{1/2}\}^{-1} \in L_2(1, \infty)$$

and this is not possible if $M_j(t, \lambda)$ is bounded. Thus

$$\lim_{t\to\infty} M_j(t, \lambda) = +\infty, \qquad \lim_{t\to\infty} L_j(t, \lambda) = +\infty. \tag{9.3.20}$$

The function $N_j(t, \lambda)$ presents a tougher problem. We note first that

$$w_j'(t, \lambda) = 1 - j + \lambda \int_0^t G(s) w_j(s, \lambda)\, ds$$

so that

$$|w_j'(t, \lambda)| \le 1 - j + \rho \left\{ \int_0^t G(s)\, ds \cdot \int_0^t G(s) |w_j(s, \lambda)|^2\, ds \right\}^{1/2}$$

$$= 1 - j + \rho [N_j(t, \lambda)]^{1/2} \left[\int_0^t G(s)\, ds \right]^{1/2}.$$

Combining this with (9.3.19) we see that

$$G(t) \left\{ 1 - j + \rho [N_j(t, \lambda)]^{1/2} \left[\int_0^t G(s)\, ds \right]^{1/2} \right\}^{-2} \in L(1, \infty).$$

If now $N_j(t, \lambda)$ were bounded we must have

$$G(t) \left[\int_0^t G(s)\, ds \right]^{-1} \in L(1, \infty)$$

and this is the case iff $G(t) \in L(1, \infty)$. Thus

$$\lim_{t\to\infty} N_j(t, \lambda) = +\infty \tag{9.3.21}$$

at least unless $G(t) \in L(0, \infty)$.

If $\mu > 0$ a simpler argument can be given. In this case $r_j''(t, \lambda) > 0$, $r_j'(t, \lambda)$ is increasing and $r_j(t, \lambda) > Ct$ for large t. But then

$$N_j(t, \lambda) = \int_0^t G(s) [r_j(s, \lambda)]^2\, ds$$

becomes infinite with t since $t^2G(t)$ is not in $L(0, \infty)$. We see that in this case we can assert that

$$N_j(t, \lambda)r^{-1} \to +\infty.$$

We shall return to the excluded case $G(t) \in L(0, \infty)$, $\mu < 0$, when we have proved that $\theta_j(t, \lambda)$ is unbounded. Before proving this, let us observe that the techniquc used in proving (9.3.18) can also be used to get a lower bound for $L_j(t, \lambda)$. This follows from the fact that the geometric mean does not exceed the arithmetic. Hence

$$\begin{aligned} L_j'(t, \lambda) &= |w_j'(t, \lambda)|^2 + \rho G(t)|w_j(t, \lambda)|^2 \\ &\geq 2[\rho G(t)]^{1/2}|w_j(t, \lambda)|\,|w_j'(t, \lambda)| \\ &\geq 2\cos\gamma[\rho G(t)]^{1/2}L_j(t, \lambda) \end{aligned}$$

whence

$$L_j(t, \lambda) \geq L_j(1, \lambda)\exp\left\{2\cos\gamma\rho^{1/2}\int_1^t [G(s)]^{1/2}\,ds\right\}.$$

This formula implies $\lim L_j(t, \lambda) = \infty$ unless $[G(t)]^{1/2} \in L(0, \infty)$. This contingency is not excluded by our assumption $tG(t) \notin L(0\ \infty)$.

We come now to the basic result for the argument $\theta_j(t, \lambda)$.

Theorem 9.3.1. *The functions $\theta_j(t, \gamma)$ are monotone, increasing for $\nu > 0$, decreasing for $\nu < 0$, and become infinite with t.*

Proof. Monotony follows from (9.3.9). Hence the $\theta_j(t, \lambda)$ tend to finite or infinite limits as $t \to +\infty$. We shall show that the first alternative leads to contradictions. Suppose that

$$\lim_{t\to\infty} \theta_j(t, \lambda) = \omega_j,$$

a finite number, and set

$$e^{-i\omega_j}w_j = W_j = U_j + iV_j.$$

To fix the ideas suppose that $\nu > 0$ so that each $\theta_j(t, \lambda)$ is increasing. Then the argument of W_j may be assumed to be negative and to increase to 0. This means that U_j is ultimately positive while V_j is negative and $V_j/U_j \to 0$. It follows that

$$\int_0^t G(s)U_j(s)\,ds \qquad \text{and} \qquad -\int_0^t G(s)V_j(s)\,ds$$

are ultimately increasing and tend to finite or infinite limits as $t \to \infty$. If the first limit is finite, so is the second one. Suppose the finite case is present. Since

$$W_j'(t, \lambda) = (1 - j)e^{-i\omega_j} + \lambda\int_0^t G(s)W_j(s, \lambda)\,ds,$$

it is seen that $W'(t, \lambda) \to l_j$, a finite number, as $t \to +\infty$. Hence

$$W_j(t, \lambda) = l_j t + o(t).$$

If $l_j \neq 0$, this requires $tG(t) \in L(0, \infty)$ which is not the case. Thus $l_j = 0$ and this gives

$$W_j'(t, \lambda) = -\lambda \int_t^\infty G(s) W_j(s, \lambda)\, ds.$$

Now $|W_j(t, \lambda)|^{-2} \in L(1, \infty)$ so that $\limsup U_j = +\infty$. Consider

$$W_j(x, \lambda) - W_j(a, \lambda) = -\lambda \int_a^x \int_t^\infty G(s) W_j(s, \lambda)\, ds\, dt$$

where a is taken so large that $-\varepsilon < \arg W_j(s, \lambda) < 0$ for a given ε and $a \leq s$. The argument of the double integral lies between $-\varepsilon$ and 0 for $a \leq x$. We can find a sequence of values $\{x_n\}$, $x_n \to \infty$, such that $U_j(x_n, \lambda) \to +\infty$. For large values of n, the argument of the left side ultimately lies between $-\varepsilon$ and $+\varepsilon$ while that of the right lies between $2\gamma - \pi - \varepsilon$ and $2\gamma - \pi$ where $2\gamma = \arg \lambda$ and $0 < |\gamma| < \frac{1}{2}\pi$. This again is a contradiction.

Finally suppose that $U_j'(t, \lambda) \to +\infty$. Here

$$W_j(x, \lambda) = W_j(a, \lambda) + (x - a) W_j'(a, \lambda) + \lambda \int_a^x \int_a^t G(s) W_j(s, \lambda)\, ds$$

where a is chosen as above. The dominant term on the right is the double integral which becomes infinite with x and faster than x. Its argument lies between $2\gamma - \varepsilon$ and 2γ while that of the left member lies between $-\varepsilon$ and 0. This contradiction gives

$$\frac{1}{\nu} \lim_{t\to\infty} \theta_j(t, \lambda) = +\infty, \qquad \lambda \in \Lambda, \quad \nu \neq 0. \blacksquare \tag{9.3.22}$$

Corollary. (9.3.21) *holds for all* $\lambda \in \Lambda$.

Proof. If $\nu = 0$, this follows from $w_j(t, \lambda)/t \to \infty$, the definition of $N_j(t, \lambda)$ and the fact that $tG(t) \notin L(0, \infty)$. For $\nu \neq 0$ we observe that

$$\theta_j(t, \lambda) = \nu \int_0^t |w_j(s, \lambda)|^{-2} N_j(s, \lambda)\, ds$$

and that the integral without the factor N_j converges. Hence N_j must become infinite with t. ∎

We can now describe the orbit in the complex plane traced by $w_j(t, \lambda)$ moving under the influence of a central force such that (9.3.1) is the equation of motion.

Theorem 9.3.2. *As t goes from* 0 *to infinity the point* $w_j(t, \lambda)$ *describes a spiral* $S_j(\lambda)$ *in the complex plane from* $w = j$ *to* $w = \infty$. *The polar angle*

$\theta_j(t, \lambda)$ increases from 0 to $+\infty$, if $\nu > 0$, decreases to $-\infty$ if $\nu < 0$. If $\Re(\lambda) = \mu > 0$, the radius vector $r_j(t, \lambda)$ is strictly increasing from $r = j$ to $r = \infty$. In any case $\limsup_{t\to\infty} r_j(t, \lambda) = +\infty$ *and* $[r_j(t, \lambda)]^{-2} \in L(1, \infty)$. *The radius of curvature of $S_j(\lambda)$ is positive and the curve is concave towards the origin. There are no points of inflection.*

Proof. Most of these statements have already been proved, only the curvature remains. For a curve

$$w = w(t)$$

in complex form the radius of curvature is given by

$$R = \frac{|w'(t)|^3}{\Im[\overline{w'(t)}w''(t)]}\cdot \tag{9.3.23}$$

For $S_j(\lambda)$ this reduces to

$$R_j = \frac{|w_j'(t, \lambda)|^3}{\nu G(t) M_j(t, \lambda)}, \qquad \nu > 0. \tag{9.3.24}$$

For $\nu < 0$ the sign should be changed since the curve is now described in the negative sense. There are clearly no points of inflection. ∎

We have carried through the discussion for the solutions of the fundamental system. The results hold, at least for large values of t, for linear combinations of w_0 and w_1 with one striking exception. The subdominant (and its multiples) is exceptional. We define a non-normalized subdominant by the formula

$$w_+(t, \lambda) = w_1(t, \lambda) \int_t^\infty [w_1(s, \lambda)]^{-2}\, ds, \qquad \lambda \in \Lambda. \tag{9.3.25}$$

The integral exists by virtue of (9.3.18). The analytic and geometric properties of the subdominant are summarized in the

Theorem 9.3.3. *For each $\lambda \in \Lambda$*

$$\lim_{t\to\infty} w_+(t, \lambda) w_+'(t, \lambda) = 0, \tag{9.3.26}$$

$$G(t)|w_+(t, \lambda)|^2 + |w_+'(t, \lambda)|^2 \in L(0, \infty). \tag{9.3.27}$$

Further, $|w_+(t, \lambda)|$ is monotone decreasing if $\mu \geq 0$ and tends to 0 if $\mu > 0$. The subdominant describes a spiral $S_+(\lambda)$ as t goes from 0 to ∞, the sense of the rotation being opposite that of $S_j(\lambda)$. The polar angle is such that $-(1/\nu)\theta_+(t, \lambda)$ increases to $+\infty$. The radius of curvature is positive, $S_+(\lambda)$ is concave towards the origin and there are no points of inflection.

Proof. We have

$$w_+'(t, \lambda) = w_1'(t, \lambda) \int_t^\infty [w_1(s, \lambda)]^{-2}\, ds - [w_1(t, \lambda)]^{-1}$$

and this is dominated by

$$\sec^2 \gamma |w_1'(t, \lambda)| [L_1(t, \lambda)]^{-1} + |w_1(t, \lambda)|^{-1},$$

where both summands belong to $L_2(0, \infty)$. Hence $w_+'(t, \lambda)$ has the same property. Further

$$w_+(t, \lambda) w_+'(t, \lambda) = w_1(t, \lambda) w_1'(t, \lambda) \left\{ \int_t^\infty [w_1(s, \lambda)]^{-2} \, ds \right\}^2$$
$$- \int_t^\infty [w_1(s, \lambda)]^{-2} \, ds.$$

This is dominated by

$$(\sec^4 \gamma + \sec^2 \gamma)[L_1(t, \lambda)]^{-1}$$

and hence goes to 0 as $t \to +\infty$. This proves (9.3.26).

To prove (9.3.27) we note that

$$[\overline{w_+(s, \lambda)} w_+'(s, \lambda)]_0^\omega = \int_0^\omega |w_+'(s, \lambda)|^2 \, ds + \lambda \int_0^\omega G(s) |w_+(s, \lambda)|^2 \, ds.$$

As $\omega \to \infty$ the left member goes to a finite limit. Hence also the right member. Here the first term is known to have a finite limit so the second term must also have a finite limit. This proves (9.3.27). If

$$w_+(t, \lambda) = r_+(t, \lambda) \exp [i\theta_+(t, \lambda)]$$

we have

$$r_+''(t, \lambda) = \{\mu G(t) + [\theta_+'(t, \lambda)]^2\} r_+(t, \lambda),$$

$$\frac{d}{dt} \{[r_+(t, \lambda)]^2 \theta_+'(t, \lambda)\} = \nu G(t) [r_+(t, \lambda)]^2.$$

If now $\mu > 0$ the first equation shows that $r_+(t, \lambda)$ is convex and Theorem 9.2.1 gives

$$r_+(t, \mu + i\nu) < C(\lambda) r_+(t, \mu) = C(\lambda) w_+(t, \mu).$$

Here $C(\lambda)$ is the quotient of the two factors needed to normalize $r_+(t, \mu + i\nu)$ and $w_+(t, \mu)$. Since $w_+(t, \mu) \to 0$ as $t \to +\infty$ so does $r_+(t, \lambda)$, $\mu > 0$. For $\mu = 0$, $r_+(t, i\nu)$ is still non-increasing but for $\mu < 0$ the subdominant may very well increase to $+\infty$ in absolute value. Examples illustrating the various possibilities are found in the Exercise below.

It is an easy matter to verify the identity

$$w_0(t, \lambda) = w_+(0, \lambda) w_+(t, \lambda) \int_0^t [w_+(s, \lambda)]^{-2} \, ds. \tag{9.3.28}$$

This relation shows, incidentally, that if $|w_+(t, \lambda)| \to C > 0$, then $w_0(t, \lambda) = O(t)$ and this cannot hold for $\mu > 0$ but may happen for $\mu \leq 0$.

Our main use for formula (9.3.28) is in the discussion of the polar angle.

We have

$$\theta_+(t, \lambda) = \theta_+(0, \lambda) - \nu \int_0^t N_+(s, \lambda)|w_+(s, \lambda)|^{-2}\, ds \tag{9.3.29}$$

where

$$N_+(s, \lambda) = \int_t^\infty G(s)|w_+(s, \lambda)|^2\, ds. \tag{9.3.30}$$

The monotony properties of the argument are obvious. If now $\theta_+(t, \lambda)$ should decrease or increase to a finite limit, $\theta_+(t, \lambda)$ would be bounded and (9.3.28) then shows that $\arg w_0(t, \lambda) = \theta_0(t, \lambda)$ is also bounded and this we know is false. Hence $\theta_+(t, \lambda)$ is unbounded as asserted.

The radius of curvature of $S_+(\lambda)$ is obtained by replacing the subscript j in formula (9.3.24) by $+$. Here

$$M_+(t, \lambda) = \int_t^\infty |w'_+(s, \lambda)|^2\, ds. \;\blacksquare \tag{9.3.31}$$

We also write

$$L_+(t, \lambda) = M_+(t, \lambda) + \rho N_+(t, \lambda) \tag{9.3.32}$$

and note the inequalities

$$\cos \gamma L_+(t, \lambda) \le |w_+(t, \lambda) w'_+(t, \lambda)| \le L_+(t, \lambda) \tag{9.3.33}$$

$$L_+(t, \lambda) \le L_+(0, \lambda) \exp\left\{-2\rho^{1/2} \cos \gamma \int_0^t [G(s)]^{1/2}\, ds\right\}. \tag{9.3.34}$$

These are proved as the corresponding formulas for the dominant solutions.

EXERCISE 9.3

Verify the following formulas

1. (9.3.23) and (9.3.24).
2. (9.3.33) and (9.3.34).
3. Verify (9.3.28) and prove that

$$w_0(t, \lambda) + w_+(t, \lambda) = w_1(t, \lambda) \int_0^\infty [w_1(s, \lambda)]^{-2}\, ds.$$

4. Use the formula of the preceding problem to prove that the following limits exist and are equal. Find the limit!

$$\lim_{t\to\infty} \frac{w_0(t, \lambda)}{w_1(t, \lambda)}, \qquad \lim_{t\to\infty} \frac{w'_0(t, \lambda)}{w'_1(t, \lambda)}.$$

5. Show also that $L_0(t, \lambda)/L_1(t, \lambda)$ is bounded away from 0 and ∞ and that $L_1(t, \lambda)L_+(t, \lambda)$ is bounded above.
6. How should formulas (9.3.18) and (9.3.19) be modified for the subdominant solution?

7. Take $G(t) = (t+1)^{-2}$, $\lambda = -1 + i$, and show that the spiral $S_+(\lambda)$ reduces to a circle described infinitely often. Find its radius.
8. In the case $G(t) = (t+1)^{-2}$ a dominant solution is given by $(1+t)^{\alpha_1 + \beta i}$ and a subdominant by $(1+t)^{\alpha_2 - \beta i}$ where $\alpha_1 > \frac{1}{2}$ and $\alpha_2 < \frac{1}{2}$. Find $\alpha_1, \alpha_2, \beta$. For these solutions compute the functions L, M, N and the radii of curvature of the corresponding spirals.
9. With G as in Problem 8, show that the subdominant tends to 0 as $t \to +\infty$ iff λ is outside the parabola $\nu^2 + \mu + \frac{1}{4} = 0$ and that for such values of λ the area swept by the radius vector of the subdominant as t goes from 0 to ∞ is finite.
10. Show that for λ inside the parabola the absolute value of the subdominant is strictly increasing and goes to ∞ with t.
11. Show that a necessary and sufficient condition that $w_+(t, \lambda)$ have the property of its radius vector sweeping a finite area is that $N_+(t, \lambda) \in L(0, \infty)$ and that if this condition is satisfied then $w_+(t, \lambda) \to 0$ as $t \to \infty$.
12. Suppose that

$$\liminf_{t \to \infty} (\log t)^{-1} \int_0^t [G(s)]^{1/2}\, ds = \alpha,$$

$0 < \alpha \leq \infty$. Show that $w_+(t, \lambda) \to 0$ as $t \to \infty$ if $\lambda = \rho e^{2i\gamma}$ satisfies the condition $4\rho \cos^2 \gamma > \alpha^{-2}$ and interpret the condition geometrically. If $\alpha = \infty$ the condition is to be understood to be satisfied by all λ in Λ. [*Hint*: Show that $L_+(t, \lambda) \in L(0, \infty)$ for such values of λ and compare with Problem 11.]

13. For the case $G(t) = t^n$, the inequality (9.3.5) with $j = 0$ takes the following form. Let

$$w_0(t, 1) = t \sum_{k=0}^{\infty} c_k t^{(n+2)k}$$

where $c_0 = 1$, $c_k > 0$. Then

$$\left| \sum_{k=0}^{\infty} c_k\, e^{ik\varphi} x^k \right| > \sum_{k=0}^{\infty} c_k (\cos \varphi)^k x^k, \qquad 0 < x, \quad |\varphi| < \tfrac{1}{2}\pi.$$

Prove this! [For $n = 0$ this is a well-known property of the exponential function but for $n > 0$ we are dealing with Bessel functions of order $(n+2)^{-1}$ and the inequality may possibly be new.]

9.4 NON-OSCILLATION AND THE RICCATI EQUATION

We shall consider questions of non-oscillation for solutions of the equation

$$y'' + F(t)y = 0 \tag{9.4.1}$$

on the interval $(0, \infty)$. *A real solution of the equation is said to be non-oscillatory in the wide sense in* $(0, \infty)$ *if there exists a finite a such that the solution has no zeros in* $[a, \infty)$. If such a solution exists then all solutions are non-oscillatory in the wide sense and the equation is said to have the same property. Normally we omit the predicate "in the wide sense."

In Section 9.1 it was shown that the equation is non-oscillatory if

$$tF(t) \in L(0, \infty). \tag{9.4.2}$$

Here $F(t)$ is not required to keep a constant sign. In fact $F(t)$ may oscillate infinitely often in $(0, \infty)$, if (9.4.2) holds each solution will have only a finite number of zeros in $[0, \infty)$.

In Section 9.2 the case $F(t) = -G(t)$ with $G(t) > 0$ was studied. Here the equation was *non-oscillatory in the strict sense*: no solution can have more than one zero in $[0, \infty)$.

We shall now consider the case where $F(t) > 0$ and

$$tF(t) \notin L(0, \infty). \tag{9.4.3}$$

Necessary conditions for non-oscillation in the wide sense will be found as well as sufficient conditions. Here it is convenient to consider the associated Riccati equation. (Cf. Appendix C.) If $y(t)$ is a solution of (9.4.1) and $y(t) \neq 0$ for $a \leq t$, then

$$v(t) \equiv \frac{y'(t)}{y(t)} \tag{9.4.4}$$

is continuous in $[a, \infty)$ and satisfies the Riccati equation

$$v'(t) = -F(t) - [v(t)]^2. \tag{9.4.5}$$

Lemma 9.4.1. *If Eq.* (9.4.1) *has a solution* $y(t)$ *such that* $y(t)y'(t) \neq 0$ *for* $a \leq t$, *then*

$$F(t) \in L(0, \infty) \tag{9.4.6}$$

and the corresponding logarithmic derivative $v(t)$ *is positive and strictly decreasing for* $a \leq t$. *Moreover*

$$\limsup_{t \to \infty} tv(t) \leq 1. \tag{9.4.7}$$

Proof. We note first that if $y(t) \neq 0$ for $c \leq t$, then $y'(t)$ can have at most one zero for a value of $t > c$ since otherwise $y''(t)$ and hence also $y(t)$ would have zeros beyond c. Thus the assumption that there is a last zero also implies that there is a last extremum.

It is clear that $v(t) \neq 0$ for $a \leq t$ and $v'(t) < 0$ so that $v(t)$ is decreasing. Since

$$\frac{v'(s)}{[v(s)]^2} + 1 < 0$$

we have

$$\int_a^t \frac{v'(s)\,ds}{[v(s)]^2} + t - a < 0$$

and

$$\frac{1}{v(a)} - \frac{1}{v(t)} + t - a < 0.$$

This shows that $v(t)$ must ultimately be positive and go to 0 as $t \to \infty$. Hence $v(t) > 0$ for $a \le t$ and $v(t)$ decreases to 0 as $t \to \infty$. Further

$$tv(t) < \frac{v(a)t}{v(a)(t - a) + 1}$$

and this implies (9.4.7).

Integrating both sides of (9.4.5) from $t = a$ to $t = b$ gives

$$v(b) - v(a) = -\int_a^b [v(t)]^2\,dt - \int_a^b F(t)\,dt.$$

Here we let $b \to \infty$. Then $v(b) \to 0$ and the first integral on the right has a finite limit since $tv(t)$ is bounded. Thus the second integral has a finite limit and this is (9.4.6). ▮

Thus if F is positive and the equation is non-oscillatory then F must belong to $L(0, \infty)$. We shall find more stringent conditions.

To this end we introduce two integral equations. The proof just given shows that $v(t)$ satisfies

$$v(t) = \int_t^\infty [v(s)]^2\,ds + \int_t^\infty F(s)\,ds. \tag{9.4.8}$$

Here we set

$$tv(t) \equiv u(t), \qquad t\int_t^\infty F(s)\,ds \equiv f(t) \tag{9.4.9}$$

and obtain

$$u(t) = t\int_t^\infty [u(s)]^2 \frac{ds}{s^2} + f(t). \tag{9.4.10}$$

By (9.4.7) the left member is bounded and its superior limit does not exceed 1. It follows that $f(t)$ must have the same property. We can then introduce

$$\lim_{t\to\infty} \begin{matrix}\sup\\ \\ \inf\end{matrix}\; f(t) = \begin{cases} f^* \\ \\ f_* \end{cases}, \tag{9.4.11}$$

$$\lim_{t\to\infty} \begin{matrix}\sup\\ \\ \inf\end{matrix}\; u(t) = \begin{cases} u^* \\ \\ u_* \end{cases}. \tag{9.4.12}$$

We see that (9.4.10) gives

$$\begin{aligned} u^* &\le (u^*)^2 + f^*, \\ u_* &\ge (u_*)^2 + f_*. \end{aligned} \tag{9.4.13}$$

The second inequality yields two important relations, namely

$$\tfrac{1}{2} - (\tfrac{1}{4} - f_*)^{1/2} \le u_* \le \tfrac{1}{2} + (\tfrac{1}{4} - f_*)^{1/2}, \tag{9.4.14}$$

$$f_* \le \tfrac{1}{4}. \tag{9.4.15}$$

This gives

Theorem 9.4.1. *If* $F(t) > 0$, *a necessary condition that the equation* (9.4.1) *be non-oscillatory is that*

$$f_* \le \tfrac{1}{4}, \qquad f^* \le 1. \tag{9.4.16}$$

In the opposite direction we have

Theorem 9.4.2. *A sufficient condition that* (9.4.1) *be non-oscillatory is that* $f^* < \tfrac{1}{4}$.

This is a corollary of

Theorem 9.4.3. *If* $F(t) > 0$ *and if numbers* a *and* ρ *can be found with* $0 \le a < \infty$ *and* $0 \le \rho \le \tfrac{1}{4}$ *such that*

$$f(t) \le \rho, \qquad a \le t, \tag{9.4.17}$$

then (9.4.1) *has a subdominant solution* $y_+(t)$ *which is positive and strictly increasing for* $a \le t$ *and*

$$y_+(t) \le y_+(a)\left(\frac{t}{a}\right)^{\sigma} \quad \text{with} \quad \sigma = \tfrac{1}{2} - (\tfrac{1}{4} - \rho)^{1/2}. \tag{9.4.18}$$

Proof. We construct the logarithmic derivative of the desired solution by solving (9.4.10), using the method of successive approximations setting

$$u_0(t) = f(t), \qquad u_n(t) = t\int_t^\infty [u_{n-1}(s)]^2 \frac{ds}{s^2} + f(t), \qquad a \le t.$$

This sequence is strictly increasing for $f(t) = u_0(t) < u_1(t)$ and

$$u_n(t) - u_{n-1}(t) = t\int_t^\infty \{[u_{n-1}(s)]^2 - [u_{n-2}(s)]^2\}\frac{ds}{s^2},$$

so that $u_{n-2}(t) < u_{n-1}(t)$ implies $u_{n-1}(t) < u_n(t)$. If we apply the same process to the equation

$$U(t) = t\int_t^\infty [U(s)]^2 \frac{ds}{s^2} + \rho, \tag{9.4.19}$$

we obtain a monotone increasing sequence of constants $\{\sigma_n\}$ with

$$\sigma_0 = \rho, \qquad \sigma_n \le \tfrac{1}{2}, \qquad \lim_{n\to\infty} \sigma_n \equiv \sigma = \tfrac{1}{2} - (\tfrac{1}{4} - \rho)^{1/2}.$$

Since $f(t) \le \rho$, we have $u_n(t) \le \sigma_n$ for all n whence

$$\lim_{n\to\infty} u_n(t) \equiv u(t) \le \sigma. \tag{9.4.20}$$

This shows the existence of $v(t)$ and the inequality

$$v(t) \le \frac{\sigma}{t}. \tag{9.4.21}$$

We then set

$$y_+(t) = y_+(a) \exp\left[\int_a^t v(s)\, ds\right].$$

This is a solution of (9.4.1) for $t > a$ and it satisfies (9.4.18). All that remains to prove is that it is a subdominant solution. To this end it is sufficient to show that (9.4.1) has a solution $y_1(t)$ such that $y_1(t)/y_+(t) \to \infty$ with t. We can take

$$y_1(t) = y_+(t) \int_a^t [y_+(s)]^{-2}\, ds.$$

This is a solution. Since $y_+(s)$ is positive, increasing and dominated by Ct^σ we have

$$\frac{y_1(t)}{y_+(t)} = \int_a^t [y_+(s)]^{-2}\, ds$$

$$> C^{-2} \int_a^t s^{-2\sigma}\, ds = \frac{C^{-2}}{1 - 2\sigma}\{t^{1-2\sigma} - a^{1-2\sigma}\},$$

provided $\sigma < \frac{1}{2}$. If $\sigma = \frac{1}{2}$ we obtain instead $C^{-2} \log(t/a)$. In either case the limit of the quotient is infinite with t so the solution obtained is indeed the subdominant. ∎

The principle used in the proof can be generalized and gives the following theorem stated without a proof.

Theorem 9.4.4. *Given the differential equations*

$$\begin{aligned} Y'' + F_1(t)Y = 0, &\qquad f_1(t) = t\int_t^\infty F_1(s)\, ds, \\ y'' + F_2(t)y = 0, &\qquad f_2(t) = t\int_t^\infty F_2(s)\, ds, \end{aligned} \tag{9.4.22}$$

where $0 < f_2(t) < f_1(t)$. *If the first equation is non-oscillatory in the wide sense so is the second.*

Using the same principle again we can prove

Theorem 9.4.5. *If* $f(t) \le \frac{1}{4}$ *and decreasing for* $a \le t$, *then*

$$u(t) \le \tfrac{1}{2} - [\tfrac{1}{4} - f(t)]^{1/2}, \tag{9.4.23}$$

$$y_+(t) \le y_+(a) \exp\left\{\int_a^t (\tfrac{1}{2} - [\tfrac{1}{4} - f(s)]^{1/2}) \frac{ds}{s}\right\}. \tag{9.4.24}$$

Proof. We return to the proof of Theorem 9.4.1. Let $a < b < t$. Then $f(b) > f(t)$ and the solution $u(t)$ of (9.4.10) which is determined by $u_0(t) = f(t)$ is dominated by the solution of

$$U(t) = t\int_t^\infty [U(s)]^2 \frac{ds}{s^2} + f(b) \qquad \text{with} \qquad U_0(t) = f(b).$$

Now $U(t) \equiv \frac{1}{2} - [\frac{1}{4} - f(b)]^{1/2}$, whence (9.4.23) follows. The definition of $y_+(t)$ in terms of $u(t)$ gives (9.4.24). ▮

Since the right member of (9.4.23) does not exceed $2f(t)$ we obtain the

Corollary. *We have*

$$y_+(t) \le y_+(a) \exp\left\{2\int_a^t dx \int_x^\infty F(s)\, ds\right\}. \tag{9.4.25}$$

We have seen that Eq. (9.4.1) is oscillatory if $\frac{1}{4} < f_*$, non-oscillatory if $f^* < \frac{1}{4}$. No conclusion can be drawn if either f_* or f^* equals $\frac{1}{4}$. This will follow from examples below. The inequalities (9.4.16) are the best of their kind. There exist non-oscillatory equations with $f^* = 1$, and oscillatory equations with $f_* = 0$. (See the author's 1948 paper quoted in the Collateral Reading.)

We know that the equation

$$y'' + \rho t^{-2} y = 0 \tag{9.4.26}$$

is oscillatory for $\rho > \frac{1}{4}$ and non-oscillatory for $\rho \le \frac{1}{4}$. Here is a non-oscillatory case with $f_* = f^* = \frac{1}{4}$. The combination of this equation with (9.4.1) and Theorem 9.4.2 gives a slight generalization of a comparison theorem due to Adolf Kneser (1862–1930) in 1893.

Lemma 9.4.2. *Let*

$$\lim\begin{matrix}\sup\\ \inf\end{matrix}\; t^2F(t) = \begin{cases}\gamma^* \\ \gamma_*\end{cases}. \tag{9.4.27}$$

Then (9.4.1) *is non-oscillatory if* $\gamma^* < \frac{1}{4}$, *oscillatory if* $\frac{1}{4} < \gamma_*$, *and no conclusion can be drawn if either* γ_* *or* γ^* *equals* $\frac{1}{4}$.

Take

$$y(t) = t^{1/2}[C_1(\log t)^\alpha + C_2(\log t)^{1-\alpha}] \tag{9.4.28}$$

where α and $1 + \alpha$ are the roots of the quadratic $\xi^2 - \xi + \gamma = 0$. For $\alpha \ne \frac{1}{2}$ this is the general solution of the equation

$$y'' + \left\{\frac{1}{4t^2} + \frac{\gamma}{(t\log t)^2}\right\} y = 0. \tag{9.4.29}$$

Here $f^* = \frac{1}{4}$, the equation is oscillatory for $\gamma > \frac{1}{4}$, non-oscillatory for $\gamma \le \frac{1}{4}$. This gives a comparison theorem, also due to Kneser, which we formulate as follows.

Lemma 9.4.3. *Let*

$$\lim_{\inf}^{\sup} (t \log t)^2 \left(F(t) - \frac{1}{4t^2}\right) = \begin{cases} \gamma^* \\ \gamma_* \end{cases}. \tag{9.4.30}$$

Then (9.4.1) *is non-oscillatory if* $\gamma^* < \frac{1}{4}$, *oscillatory if* $\gamma_* > \frac{1}{4}$, *and no conclusion can be drawn if either* γ_* *or* γ^* *equals* $\frac{1}{4}$.

There is a whole "logarithmic scale" of such comparison theorems due to Kneser, but we desist from further elaboration. At this stage we leave the case $F(t) > 0$ and make some comments on the case where $F(t)$ changes its sign infinitely often in $(0, \infty)$. The following extension of Theorem 9.4.2 is sometimes useful.

Theorem 9.4.6. *Given the differential equations*

$$Y'' + F_1(t)Y = 0, \qquad f_1(t) = t\int_t^\infty F_1(s)\,ds, \tag{9.4.31}$$

$$y'' + F_2(t)y = 0, \qquad f_2(t) = t\int_t^\infty F_2(s)\,ds, \tag{9.4.32}$$

where $0 < F_1(t)$ *and* $|f_2(t)| \le f_1(t)$. *If the first equation is non-oscillatory, so is the second.*

Proof. We use the quadratic integral equation (9.4.10). It is known that there is a function $U(t)$ satisfying

$$U(t) = t\int_t^\infty [U(s)]^2 \frac{ds}{s^2} + f_1(t), \qquad a \le t.$$

This function is obtainable as the limit of a strictly increasing sequence $\{U_n(t)\}$ of successive approximations using $U_0(t) = f_1(t)$. Our object is to show that the equation

$$u(t) = t\int_t^\infty [u(s)]^2 \frac{ds}{s^2} + f_2(t)$$

has a solution $u(t)$ such that

$$|u(t)| \le U(t), \qquad a \le t. \tag{9.4.33}$$

We can construct this solution using the method of successive approximations taking $u_0(t) = f_2(t)$. The existence of the approximations is obvious. The convergence of the sequence $\{u_n(t)\}$ follows from the two inequalities

$$|u_n(t)| \le U_n(t), \tag{9.4.34}$$

$$|u_{n+1}(t) - u_n(t)| \le U_{n+1}(t) - U_n(t) \tag{9.4.35}$$

which to ether imply

$$|[u_{n+1}(t)]^2 - [u_n(t)]^2| \le [U_{n+1}(t)]^2 - [U_n(t)]^2. \tag{9.4.36}$$

Now (9.4.34) is certainly true for $n = 0$. Since

$$u_1(t) - u_0(t) = t \int_t^\infty [u_0(s)]^2 \frac{ds}{s^2}$$

$$\leq t \int_t^\infty [U_0(s)]^2 \frac{ds}{s^2} = U_1(t) - U_0(t),$$

the other two inequalities hold for $n = 0$. We can then use induction on n. If the first inequality holds for $n = k$ then

$$|u_{k+1}(t)| \leq t \int_t^\infty [u_k(s)]^2 \frac{ds}{s^2} + |f_2(t)|$$

$$\leq t \int_t^\infty [U_k(s)]^2 \frac{ds}{s^2} + f_1(t) = U_{k+1}(t),$$

so (9.4.34) holds for all n. Similarly, if (9.4.36) holds for $n = k - 1$ then

$$|u_{k+1}(t) - u_k(t)| \leq t \int_t^\infty |[u_k(s)]^2 - [u_{k-1}(s)]^2| \frac{ds}{s^2}$$

$$\leq t \int_t^\infty \{[U_k(s)]^2 - [U_{k-1}(s)]^2\} \frac{ds}{s^2}$$

$$= U_{k+1}(t) - U_k(t),$$

so the remaining inequalities also hold for all n. These inequalities show the existence of $\lim_{n\to\infty} u_n(t) = u(t)$ and the inequality (9.4.33).

Once $u(t)$ has been constructed, a solution of (9.4.32) is given by

$$y(t) = \exp\left\{\int_a^t u(s) \frac{ds}{s}\right\}. \tag{9.4.37}$$

This solution has no zeros for $a \leq t$, whence it follows that the equation is non-oscillatory. In this case there may conceivably be extrema for $t > a$, since $u(t)$ may have zeros, even infinitely many zeros. ∎

If we know in addition that

$$f_1(t) \leq \rho \leq \tfrac{1}{4}$$

and if

$$\sigma \equiv \tfrac{1}{2} - (\tfrac{1}{4} - \rho)^{1/2},$$

then

$$|u(t)| \leq U(t) \leq \sigma.$$

This gives

$$\left(\frac{a}{t}\right)^\sigma \leq y(t) \leq \left(\frac{t}{a}\right)^\sigma$$

and since $\sigma \leq \frac{1}{2}$, $[y(t)]^{-2}$ cannot be in $L(0, \infty)$, whence it follows that $y(t)$ is the subdominant solution of (9.4.32).

As an example to show the use of Theorem 9.4.6 take

$$F(t) = (1 + t)^{-1-\delta} \sin (1 + t), \qquad 0 < \delta.$$

Here

$$|f(t)| \le 2(1 + t)^{-\delta} \to 0 \tag{9.4.38}$$

and the equation is non-oscillatory. In this case $F(t) \in L(0, \infty)$. But if we take instead

$$F(t) = (1 + t)^{-\delta} \sin (1 + t)^2, \qquad 0 < \delta \le 1,$$

then $F(t) \notin L(0, \infty)$. The improper integral $\lim_{\omega \to \infty} \int_0^\omega$ exists, however, and

$$|f(t)| \le 2(1 + t)^{-\delta} \to 0, \tag{9.4.39}$$

so the corresponding differential equation is also non-oscillatory. These examples illustrate the greater power of the inequality $|f_2(t)| \le f_1(t)$ in proving non-oscillation compared to the more restrictive inequality $|F_2(t)| \le F_1(t)$. With these remarks we end our discussion of the case where $F(t)$ is allowed infinitely many sign changes.

We now return to the equation

$$y'' - G(t)y = 0 \tag{9.4.40}$$

where $G(t)$ is positive and continuous and $tG(t) \notin L(0, \infty)$. We recall the four types of solutions found in Section 9.2:

1) solutions with a zero,
2) solutions with an extremum,
3) dominant solutions with $y(t)y'(t) \neq 0$ for $0 \le t$,
4) subdominant solutions.

Consider the corresponding logarithmic derivative

$$v(t) = \frac{y'(t)}{y(t)} \tag{9.4.41}$$

which satisfies the Riccati equation

$$v'(t) + [v(t)]^2 = G(t). \tag{9.4.42}$$

The integral curves of this equation also fall into four classes, corresponding to the four classes of solutions of (9.4.40). If $y(t)$ belongs to the first class and has its zero at $t = a$, then $v(t)$ has a vertical asymptote for $t = a$. To the left of the asymptote $v(t) < 0$, to the right $v(t) > 0$. If $y(t)$ belongs to the second class and $y'(\tau) = 0$, then $v(t) < 0$ for $t < \tau$, positive for $t > \tau$. For curves of the third class, $v(t) > 0$ for all $t \ge 0$. There is one and only one curve

$$C_0 : v = v_0(t) \tag{9.4.43}$$

corresponding to the subdominant solutions of (9.4.40). This curve lies in the lower half-plane and separates the v-curves of class (2) from curves of class (3). All v-curves below C_0 have asymptotes and escape from the lower half-plane by going to $-\infty$ and then reappearing at the upper end of the asymptote in the upper half-plane. All v-curves between C_0 and the t-axis cross the latter into the upper half-plane.

We shall examine the asymptotic behavior of the solutions of the Riccati equation as $t \to +\infty$ with a view of showing that $v_0(t)$ is approximately $-[G(t)]^{1/2}$ for large t while all other solutions are approximately $+[G(t)]^{1/2}$. To prove this rigorously it is necessary to make restrictive assumptions on $G(t)$. Thus we restrict the discussion to the case where $G(t)$ is piecewise monotone with only a finite number of changes of the monotony in each finite subinterval of $[0, \infty)$. The curves

$$\Gamma^+ : v = [G(t)]^{1/2}. \qquad \Gamma^- : v = -[G(t)]^{1/2} \tag{9.4.44}$$

play a basic role in the discussion. They together with the positive t-axis divide the right half-plane into four regions, counting from below, D_1, D_2, D_3, and D_4. Here $v'(t)$ is positive in D_2 and D_3, negative in D_1 and D_4 and 0 on Γ^+ and Γ^-. If an integral curve C intersects Γ^+, it has a minimum at the point of intersection, if, with increasing values of t, C passes from D_4 to D_3, a maximum if the passage is from D_3 to D_4. (See Figure 9.1.) Similar results hold for intersections with Γ^-. C may have other points in common with Γ^+, but it is only the intersections which are of importance for the following.

We start with some preliminary results.

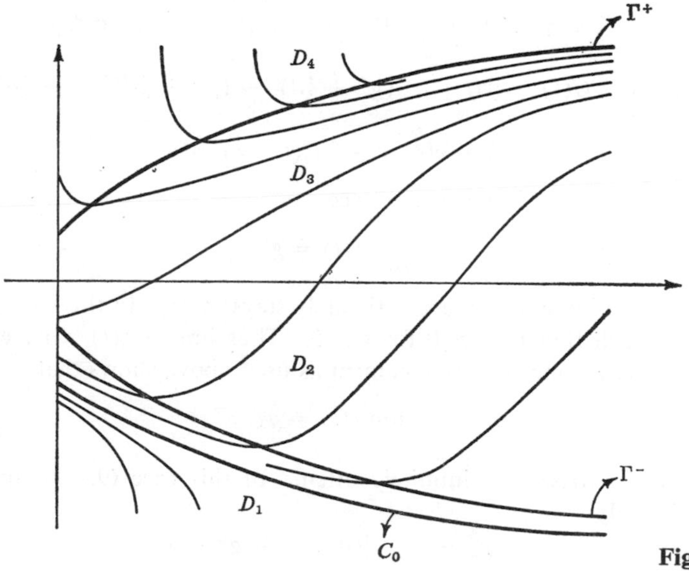

Figure 9.1

Lemma 9.4.4. With $G(t)$ bounded, positive, continuous, and piecewise monotone in $[0, \infty)$, let $v(t)$ be a solution of (9.4.42), positive for $t \geq a \geq 0$. Set

$$\lim_{\sup}^{\inf} [G(t)]^{1/2} = \begin{cases} g_* \\ g^* \end{cases}, \quad \lim_{\sup}^{\inf} v(t) = \begin{cases} v_* \\ v^* \end{cases}. \tag{9.4.45}$$

Then

$$g_* \leq v_* \leq v^* \leq g^*. \tag{9.4.46}$$

Proof. By assumption there is an integral curve

$$C: y = v(t), \qquad a \leq t, \tag{9.4.47}$$

located in the first quadrant. This curve may possibly stay in one of the regions D_3 and D_4 or it may cross the separating curve Γ^+ once or several times, perhaps infinitely often. These crossings are limited by geometric considerations: an entry from D_4 to D_3 is possible only along a rising arc of Γ^+, an exit from D_3 to D_4 only along a falling arc. Thus if $G(t)$ is increasing, C can cross Γ^+ at most once. If it enters D_3, it stays in D_3.

There are several cases and subcases to examine.

1. $(a, v(a)) \in D_4$. Then $v'(a) < 0$ and to start with at least $v(t)$ is decreasing. There are three possibilities.

1(i). C ultimately stays in D_4. Since $v(t)$ is ultimately decreasing, $\lim_{t\to\infty} v(t) \equiv v_\infty = v_* = v^*$ exists and since the distant part of C lies above Γ^+, $v_\infty \geq g^*$. Here equality must hold for if $v_\infty = g^* + d$, $d > 0$. then there is a c, $c > a$, such that

$$g^* + \tfrac{2}{3}d \leq v(t), \qquad [G(t)]^{1/2} \leq g^* + \tfrac{1}{3}d, \qquad c \leq t,$$

and

$$v'(t) = G(t) - [v(t)]^2 \leq (g^* + \tfrac{1}{3}d)^2 - (g^* + \tfrac{2}{3}d)^2 < -\tfrac{1}{3}d^2.$$

Hence

$$v(t) - v(c) < -\tfrac{1}{3}d^2(t - c) \to -\infty$$

as $t \to +\infty$ and this is absurd. Hence

$$\lim_{t\to\infty} v(t) = g^*. \tag{9.4.48}$$

1(ii). The integral curve C ultimately stays in D_3. In this case there is a b, $a < b$, such that $v'(t) > 0$ for $t > b$. Thus $\lim_{t\to\infty} v(t) \equiv v_\infty$ exists and $v_\infty \leq g_*$. The same type of argument as used above shows that

$$\lim_{t\to\infty} v(t) = g_*. \tag{9.4.49}$$

1(iii). C crosses Γ^+ infinitely often. In this case (9.4.46) must hold. For ultimately

$$g_* - \delta < [G(t)]^{1/2} < g^* + \delta$$

and at an entry of C into D_3, say at $t = a_n$,

$$g_* - \delta < v(a_n) = [G(a_n)]^{1/2}$$

and at the next exit, say at $t = b_n$,

$$v(b_n) = [G(b_n)]^{1/2} < g^* + \delta.$$

Since $v(t)$ is increasing in the interval (a_n, b_n)

$$g_* - \delta < v(t) < g^* + \delta, \qquad a_n \leq t \leq b_n.$$

The same inequality holds in (b_n, a_{n+1}) where $v(t)$ is decreasing, hence for all large values of t. Since δ is arbitrary, (9.4.46) follows. This completes the discussion for $(a, v(a)) \in D_4$.

2. $(a, v(a)) \in D_3$. If C, after some crossings of Γ^+, ultimately stays in D_4, then the discussion under 1(i) applies and (9.4.48) holds. On the other hand, if C ultimately stays in D_3 then 1(ii) applies and (9.4.49) holds. Finally, if C crosses Γ^+ infinitely often, then 1(iii) applies and (9.4.46) holds.

Thus in all cases (9.4.46) is valid and, if C does not cross Γ^+ infinitely often, then one of the sharper assertions (9.4.48) or (9.4.49) holds. In particular,

$$\lim_{t\to\infty} v(t) = \lim_{t\to\infty} [G(t)]^{1/2}, \tag{9.4.50}$$

provided the right member exists. ∎

The assumption that $G(t)$ be bounded can be dropped. Suppose

$$\limsup_{t\to\infty} [G(t)]^{1/2} = g^* = +\infty.$$

Then case 1(i) cannot be realized. The integral curve C must enter D_3. It need not stay there but one of the cases 1(ii) or 1(iii) must be present.

Suppose that it is 1(ii). Then $v(t)$ will increase to a limit $v_\infty \leq g_*$. Here again we must have equality. Suppose first that $g_* < \infty$. Then the argument given above applies and shows that the assumption $v_\infty < g_*$ leads to the conclusion $v_\infty = \infty$ which contradicts $g_* < \infty$.

Next, suppose that $g_* = \infty$ and set

$$g_*(c) = \inf\{[G(t)]^{1/2} \mid c \leq t\}, \qquad a \leq c.$$

Then $g_*(c) \to \infty$ with c. Suppose that for some large value of c we have $v(t) < g_*(c) - d$ for all $t \geq c$. Here d is fixed and $< g_*(c)$. Then for $c < t$

$$v'(t) > [g_*(c)]^2 - [g_*(c) - d]^2 > dg_*(c)$$

and

$$v(t) > v(c) + dg_*(c)(t - c)$$

which becomes infinite with t. Hence the assumption that $v(t)$ is bounded is untenable and we conclude that $v(t) \to +\infty$ with t.

Let us now consider case 1(iii). Here we have infinitely many intersections of C and Γ^+. If $g_* < \infty$, we have $v(t) > g_* - \delta$ for $t > t(\delta)$ so $v_* \geq g_*$ while $v^* \leq \infty$. If $g_* = \infty$ so are v_* and v^*.

Case 2 reduces to 1(ii) and 1(iii). Thus we have proved

Lemma 9.4.5. *If* $g_* \leq g^* = \infty$, *then*

$$g_* \leq v_* \leq v^* \leq \infty. \tag{9.4.51}$$

In particular, $\lim_{t\to\infty} v(t) = \lim_{t\to\infty} [G(t)]^{1/2}$ *if the latter limit exists.*

It is clear that the situation becomes much simpler if $G(t)$ is increasing or at least ultimately increasing, for then the troublesome case 1(iii) is excluded. Moreover, if $g_* = g^* = +\infty$, case 1(i) is also excluded. Since $g_* = g^*$ we have always

$$\lim_{t\to\infty} v(t) = \lim_{t\to\infty} [G(t)]^{1/2}.$$

This does not say much if the limit is infinite, but it is possible to make significant statements concerning the difference

$$\Delta(t) \equiv [G(t)]^{1/2} - v(t). \tag{9.4.52}$$

Theorem 9.4.7. *If* $G(t)$ *is positive, continuous and increasing and if* $v(t)$ *is a solution of* (9.4.42), *positive and increasing for* $c < t$, *then*

$$\int_c^t \Delta(s)\, ds < \tfrac{1}{4} \log G(t) - \tfrac{1}{2} \log v(c), \tag{9.4.53}$$

$$\int_c^\infty \Delta(s)[\log G(s)]^{-2}\, ds < \tfrac{1}{8}[\log v(c)]^{-1}, \qquad 1 < v(c), \tag{9.4.54}$$

$$\limsup_{t\to\infty} \Delta(t) \leq \tfrac{1}{2} \limsup_{t\to\infty} \frac{G'(t)}{G(t)}. \tag{9.4.55}$$

Proof. We have

$$v'(t) = G(t) - [v(t)]^2 = \{[G(t)]^{1/2} + v(t)\}\,\Delta(t) > 2v(t)\,\Delta(t)$$

whence

$$\int_c^t \Delta(s)\, ds < \frac{1}{2}\int_c^t \frac{v'(s)}{v(s)}\, ds = \tfrac{1}{2}\log v(t) - \tfrac{1}{2}\log v(c)$$
$$< \tfrac{1}{4}\log G(t) - \tfrac{1}{2}\log v(c)$$

as asserted. On the other hand, if $v(c) > 1$,

$$\frac{1}{\log v(c)} = \int_c^\infty \frac{v'(t)\, dt}{v(t)[\log v(t)]^2} > 2\int_c^\infty \frac{\Delta(t)\, dt}{[\log v(t)]^2} > 8\int_c^\infty \frac{\Delta(t)\, dt}{[\log G(t)]^2},$$

which is the second inequality. The latter is just a special case of inequalities of the following type: if $H(u)$ is a positive decreasing function such that $u^{-1}H(u) \in L(a, \infty)$, then

$$\Delta(t)H\{[G(t)]^{1/2}\} \in L(\omega, \infty) \tag{9.4.56}$$

for some ω.

The third inequality is trivially true if the curve $v = G(t)$ has infinitely many vertical tangents. If $G(t)$ is not differentiable everywhere, $G'(t)$ is to be replaced by the larger of the left- and right-hand derivatives. For the following discussion we assume that $G(t)$ is differentiable everywhere and $G'(t)$ is continuous. Then a simple calculation shows that $\Delta(t)$ satisfies the differential equation

$$\Delta'(t) + 2\,\Delta(t)[G(t)]^{1/2} - [\Delta(t)]^2 = \tfrac{1}{2}G'(t)[G(t)]^{-1/2}. \qquad (9.4.57)$$

Since $0 < v(t) < [G(t)]^{1/2}$, the same inequality is satisfied by $\Delta(t)$. It follows that the left member of (9.4.57) exceeds

$$\Delta'(t) + \Delta(t)[G(t)]^{1/2},$$

so that

$$\Delta'(t) + \Delta(t)[G(t)]^{1/2} < \tfrac{1}{2}G'(t)[G(t)]^{-1/2}.$$

We make the left member into an exact derivative by multiplying by

$$E(t) \equiv \exp\left\{\int_0^t [G(s)]^{1/2}\,ds\right\}.$$

Integration gives

$$\begin{aligned}\Delta(t)E(t) - \Delta(t_0)E(t_0) &< \frac{1}{2}\int_{t_0}^t \frac{G'(u)}{G(u)}\,[G(u)]^{1/2}E(u)\,du \\ &< \frac{1}{2}\left\{\sup_{t_0<u<t}\frac{G'(u)}{G(u)}\right\}\int_{t_0}^t dE(u) \\ &= \frac{1}{2}\left\{\sup\frac{G'(u)}{G(u)}\right\}[E(t) - E(t_0)]\end{aligned}$$

whence

$$\Delta(t) < \Delta(t_0)E(t_0)[E(t)]^{-1} + \frac{1}{2}\left\{\sup\frac{G'(u)}{G(u)}\right\}[1 - E(t_0)[E(t)]^{-1}.$$

If $G'(t)[G(t)]^{-1/2}$ is unbounded this shows that

$$\Delta(t) < \tfrac{1}{2}\sup_{0<u<t}\frac{G'(u)}{G(u)} + o(1), \qquad (9.4.58)$$

while (9.4.55) follows, if the fraction is bounded, since we can take t_0 arbitrarily large. Inequality (9.4.58) is of interest if the fraction is small in comparison with $[G(t)]^{1/2}$ which will be the case as long as the increasing function $G(t)$ is not of too irregular growth. ▌

An interesting conclusion can be drawn from (9.4.53). Since

$$\frac{y'(t)}{y(t)} = v(t) = [G(t)]^{1/2} - \Delta(t),$$

integration gives

$$\log \frac{y(t)}{y(c)} = \int_c^t [G(s)]^{1/2}\, ds - \int_c^t \Delta(s)\, ds$$

$$> \int_c^t [G(s)]^{1/2}\, ds + \tfrac{1}{2} \log v(c) - \tfrac{1}{4} \log G(t)$$

or

$$y(t) > [y(c)y'(c)]^{1/2}[G(t)]^{-1/4} \exp\left\{\int_c^t [G(s)]^{1/2}\, ds\right\}. \tag{9.4.59}$$

This should be compared with the lower bound (9.2.34) derived under more restrictive assumptions.

The exceptional solution is much harder to handle and the best we can do is

Theorem 9.4.8. *If $G(t)$ is increasing, then $v_0(t) < -[G(t)]^{1/2}$ for all t and*

$$1 - \frac{G(t)}{|v_0(t)|^2} \in L(0, \infty). \tag{9.4.60}$$

Proof. Suppose, contrariwise, that $v_0(t) \in D_2$ for some $t = t_0$. It would then stay above Γ^- for $t > t_0$ and would approach a limit $> v_0(t_0)$ as $t \to +\infty$. But if $v_0(t) > -a \geq v_0(t_0)$, then

$$v(t) - v(t_0) > [G(t) - a^2](t - t_0) \to +\infty$$

and this is absurd. Hence the exceptional curve C_0 lies below Γ^- for all t. Set

$$w(t) = -v_0(t)$$

so that

$$w'(t) = [w(t)]^2 - G(t).$$

This gives

$$\int_0^t \frac{w'(s)\, ds}{[w(s)]^2} = \int_0^t \left\{1 - \frac{G(s)}{[w(s)]^2}\right\} ds.$$

Here the left member tends to a finite limit as $t \to +\infty$ and, since the integrand is positive, (9.4.60) follows. This of course shows that

$$\limsup_{t \to \infty} \frac{[G(t)]^{1/2}}{|v_0(t)|} = 1$$

and the total length of the intervals where the fraction is $< 1 - \varepsilon$, $\varepsilon > 0$, fixed, is finite. We can also prove a weak analogue of (9.4.54):

$$\frac{|v_0(t)| - [G(t)]^{1/2}}{[\log |v_0(t)|]^2} \in L(\omega, \infty). \tag{9.4.61}$$

EXERCISE 9.4

1. If (9.4.10) has a solution $u_1(t)$ for $a \le t$ with $\lim_{t\to+\infty} u_1(t) = \alpha$, $\frac{1}{2} < \alpha \le 1$, show that $\lim_{t\to+\infty} f(t)$ exists and is $\alpha - \alpha^2$. Show that if other solutions have limits then the limit is either α or $1 - \alpha$.
2. Let $y_1(t)$ be the corresponding solution of (9.4.1), i.e.
$$y_1(t) = \exp\left[\int_a^t u_1(s)\,\frac{ds}{s}\right].$$
Show that $[y_1(t)]^{-2} \in L(a, \infty)$. Set $y_2(t) = y_1(t)\int_t^\infty [y(s)]^{-2}\,ds$ and $u_2(t) = t(d/dt)\log y_2(t)$. Show that $u_2(t)$ also satisfies (9.4.10) and that it tends to the limit $1 - \alpha$ as $t \to +\infty$.
3. Use the preceding results to show that all solutions of (9.4.10) have limits if one of them does.
4. If $\lim_{t\to\infty} f(t) = \rho$ exists and $\rho < \frac{1}{4}$, show that all solutions of (9.4.10) have limits, namely one of the roots of the equation $\sigma^2 - \sigma + \rho = 0$. [*Hint*: Use Theorem 9.4.4 with a suitably chosen constant $f_1(t)$.]
5. Prove Theorem 9.4.4. [*Hint*: If (9.4.21) is non-oscillatory, then the corresponding equation (9.4.10) has solutions. Let $U(t)$ be a solution defined for $a \le t$. Prove that Eq. (9.4.10) with $f(t)$ replaced by $f_2(t)$ has a solution $u(t)$. Use the method of successive approximations with $U(t)$ as the first approximation. After $u(t)$ has been found, construct $y(t)$.]
6. Prove that the equation with
$$F(t) = \frac{\sin^2 t}{t^2}$$
is oscillatory. [*Hint*: Show that $\lim_{t\to\infty} f(t) = \frac{1}{2}$, first letting $t \to \infty$ through the multiples of π and then without this restriction.]
7. Given $F(t) = (1 + t)^{-\delta}\sin(1 + t)^{1/2}$. For what values of δ does Theorem 9.4.6 give non-oscillation of the equation $y'' + F(t)y = 0$?
8. If $F(t) = c(\sin t/t)$, for what values of the positive constant c does Theorem 9.4.6 ensure oscillation?
9. In the notation of Theorem 9.4.7, show that
$$\lim_{t\to\infty}\frac{[G(t)]^{1/2}}{v(t)} = 1 \quad \text{if} \quad \lim_{t\to\infty}\frac{G'(t)}{[G(t)]^{3/2}} = 0$$
where $G'(t)$ is continuous and ≥ 0.

The following problems are concerned with the equation
$$v'(t) = G(t) - [v(t)]^3$$
where $G(t)$ is a positive increasing unbounded function with a continuous derivative.

10. If a solution exists for $t > a$ but becomes infinite as t decreases to a, show that $v(t)(t - a)^{1/2}$ tends to a limit, and find this limit.
11. Show that each solution is ultimately $< [G(t)]^{1/3}$. Set $v(t) = [G(t)]^{1/3} - \Delta(t)$ and show that $\Delta(t) \in L(\omega, \infty)$ for large ω.

12. Show that

$$\limsup_{t\to\infty} \Delta(t) \le \tfrac{1}{3} \limsup_{t\to\infty} \frac{G'(t)}{[G(t)]^{4/3}}.$$

[*Hint*: If $a > b > 0$, show that $3a^2b - 3ab^2 + b^3 > a^2b$. Imitate the proof of (9.4.55).]

13. This is an addition to Problem 10. Suppose that $v(t)$ is defined in some small interval containing $t = c$ and that $v(c) = -b < 0$ where $c - \frac{1}{2}b^{-2} > 0$. Show that there is an a, $c - \frac{1}{2}b^{-2} < a < c$ such that $v(t) \to -\infty$ as $t \downarrow a$. There is a similar result if $v(c) = b$ and $b^3 > G(a)$. Try to find it.

9.5 THE OSCILLATORY CASE

We return to the equation

$$y'' + F(t)y = 0 \tag{9.5.1}$$

where $F(t)$ is positive and continuous and has a continuous derivative in $(0, \infty)$. Using variants of Prüfer's method (see Sections 8.3 and 8.4), we can get information about the oscillatory properties of the solutions in terms of properties of the function

$$W(t) = F'(t)[F(t)]^{-3/2}. \tag{9.5.2}$$

The prototype of the resulting theorem is due to the Swedish mathematician Anders Wiman (1865–1959) in 1917.

Theorem 9.5.1. *If*

$$\lim_{t\to\infty} W(t) = 0, \tag{9.5.3}$$

then the solutions of (9.5.1) *are oscillatory in* $[0, \infty)$. *The number of zeros of* $y(t)$ *in* $[0, \omega)$ *is*

$$N(\omega, y) = \frac{1}{\pi}\int_0^\omega [F(s)]^{1/2}\, ds + R(\omega, y) \tag{9.5.4}$$

where

$$|R(\omega, y)| \le \frac{1}{4\pi} V_0^\omega[\log F(s)] + O(1) \tag{9.5.5}$$

is of smaller order than the principal term as $t \to +\infty$.

If, in addition, $W(t) \in BV[0, \infty]$, *then the quadratic form*

$$Q(t) = Q(t; F, y) \equiv [F(t)]^{1/2}[y(t)]^2 + [F(t)]^{-1/2}[y'(t)]^2 \tag{9.5.6}$$

is bounded away from 0 *and* ∞ *for* $0 < t < \infty$.

Proof. Set

$$M(t) = \sup\,[|W(s)|\,|t \le s]. \tag{9.5.7}$$

Then $M(t)$ is a monotone decreasing function and $\lim_{t\to\infty} M(t) = 0$ by (9.5.3). This gives

$$|[F(t+h)]^{-1/2} - [F(t)]^{-1/2}| = \left|\tfrac{1}{2}\int_t^{t+h} W(s)\,ds\right| < \tfrac{1}{2}|h|M(t).$$

This implies first that

$$\limsup_{h\to\infty}\,(t+h)^{-1}[F(t+h)]^{-1/2} \le \tfrac{1}{2}M(t)$$

for any $t > 0$. Hence

$$\lim_{t\to\infty} t^{-1}[F(t)]^{-1/2} = 0$$

or

$$\lim_{t\to\infty} t^2F(t) = \infty. \tag{9.5.8}$$

By Lemma 9.4.2 the solutions of (9.5.1) are oscillatory.

Secondly, we note that if

$$|h| < C[F(t)]^{-1/2}, \tag{9.5.9}$$

then

$$\left|\left[\frac{F(t)}{F(t+h)}\right]^{1/2} - 1\right| < \tfrac{1}{2}CM(t). \tag{9.5.10}$$

At this stage we introduce polar coordinates by setting

$$\begin{aligned}[F(t)]^{1/2}y(t) &= R(t)\sin[\theta(t)],\\ y'(t) &= R(t)\cos[\theta(t)].\end{aligned} \tag{9.5.11}$$

This choice is different from (8.3.1) and (8.4.1) but serves our immediate needs better. We have

$$[R(t)]^2 = F(t)[y(t)]^2 + [y'(t)]^2 > 0 \tag{9.5.12}$$

since $y(t)$ and $y'(t)$ cannot vanish simultaneously and $F(t) > 0$. It follows that $y(t) = 0$ iff $\theta(t) = n\pi$ while $y'(t) = 0$ iff $\theta(t) = (n + \tfrac{1}{2})\pi$.

Here R and θ satisfy the differential equations

$$\frac{R'(t)}{R(t)} = \frac{1}{2}\frac{F'(t)}{F(t)}\sin^2[\theta(t)], \tag{9.5.13}$$

$$\theta'(t) = [F(t)]^{1/2} + \frac{1}{4}\frac{F'(t)}{F(t)}\sin[2\theta(t)]. \tag{9.5.14}$$

If $\theta(0)$ is given, the second equation determines $\theta(t)$ uniquely for all $t > 0$. Since $N(\omega, y_1)$ and $N(\omega, y_2)$ differ by one unit at most, we may restrict ourselves to the solution determined by the initial values

$$y_0(0) = 0, \qquad y_0'(0) = 1.$$

Then

$$\theta(t) = \int_0^t [F(s)]^{1/2}\,ds + \frac{1}{4}\int_0^t \frac{F'(s)}{F(s)}\sin[2\theta(s)]\,ds. \tag{9.5.15}$$

Without restricting the generality, we may suppose that $M(t) < 4$ for $t > 0$. Then $\theta'(t) > 0$ and $\theta(t)$ is strictly increasing. The number of zeros of $y_0(t)$ in $[0, \omega)$ is then

$$\left[\frac{\theta(\omega)}{\pi}\right] + 1$$

where $[u]$ denotes the largest integer $\leq u$. The estimate (9.5.5) follows from these formulas. We recall that $V_\alpha^\beta[f]$ denotes the total variation of $f(t)$ on the interval $[\alpha, \beta]$. Since

$$\int_0^t \frac{|F'(s)|}{F(s)}\, ds = \int_0^t |W(s)|[F(s)]^{1/2}\, ds \leq \int_0^t M(s)[F(s)]^{1/2}\, ds$$

$$= o\left\{\int_0^t [F(s)]^{1/2}\, ds\right\},$$

it is seen that the remainder in formula (9.5.4) is indeed of smaller order than the leading term.

Suppose that the zeros of $y_0(t)$ are given by the sequence $\{t_n\}$, $0 = t_0 < t_1 < t_2 < \cdots$ Formula (9.5.15) then gives

$$\pi = \int_{t_n}^{t_{n+1}} [F(s)]^{1/2}\{1 + \tfrac{1}{4}W(s) \sin [2\theta(s)]\}\, ds$$

$$= \int_{t_n}^{t_{n+1}} [F(s)]^{1/2}\, ds + \delta_n,$$

where $\delta_n \to 0$ as $n \to \infty$. This relation implies

$$\lim_{n\to\infty} (t_{n+1} - t_n)[F(t_n)]^{1/2} = \pi. \tag{9.5.16}$$

In fact

$$\pi - \delta_n = (t_{n+1} - t_n)[F(\xi_n)]^{1/2},$$

where $t_n < \xi_n < t_{n+1}$ and (9.5.10) gives

$$1 - \pi M(t_n) < \left[\frac{F(\xi_n)}{F(t_n)}\right]^{1/2} < 1 + \pi M(t_n),$$

if n is so large that $|\delta_n| < \pi$. Combining the last two inequalities and remembering that δ_n and $M(t_n)$ tend to 0 as $n \to \infty$, we obtain (9.5.16). The same relation obviously holds for the zeros of any other solution.

To prove the boundedness of $Q(t)$, we change the polar coordinates using instead the convention of (8.4.1). We set

$$\begin{aligned} [F(t)]^{1/4}y(t) &= r(t) \sin [\theta(t)], \\ [F(t)]^{-1/4}y'(t) &= r(t) \cos [\theta(t)], \end{aligned} \tag{9.5.17}$$

so that

$$Q(t) = [r(t)]^2. \tag{9.5.18}$$

The differential equation for $r(t)$ is

$$\frac{r'(t)}{r(t)} = -\frac{1}{4}\frac{F'(t)}{F(t)}\cos[2\theta(t)], \tag{9.5.19}$$

while $\theta(t)$ is still determined by (9.5.14). We have to prove that $\log r(t)$ is bounded when $W(t) \in BV[0, \infty]$. We may restrict ourselves to the solution $y_0(t)$ for which $r(0) = [F(0)]^{-1/4}$, $\theta(0) = 0$. Set

$$H(t) = V_t^{\infty}[W(s)]. \tag{9.5.20}$$

This is a monotone decreasing function tending to 0 with $1/t$. Hence there exists an a, $0 \le a < \infty$, such that $H(a) < 4$.

Equation (9.5.19) now gives

$$\log r(t) - \log r(a) = -\frac{1}{4}\int_a^t \frac{F'(s)}{F(s)}\cos[2\theta(s)]\,ds$$

$$= -\frac{1}{4}\int_a^t \frac{F'(s)}{F(s)\,\theta'(s)}\cos[2\theta(s)]\,d\theta(s).$$

Combining this with (9.5.14) we see that the last member equals

$$-\tfrac{1}{4}\int_a^t W(s)\{1 + \tfrac{1}{4}W(s)\sin[2\theta(s)]\}^{-1}\cos[2\theta(s)]\,d\theta(s)$$

$$= -\sum_{n=0}^{\infty}(-\tfrac{1}{4})^{n+1}\int_a^t [W(s)]^{n+1}\{\sin[2\theta(s)]\}^n\cos[2\theta(s)]\,d\theta(s) \tag{9.5.21}$$

where, as we shall see in a moment, the series converges absolutely and uniformly for $a \le t < \infty$. Integration by parts shows that the integral in the nth term of the series equals

$$\tfrac{1}{2}(n+1)^{-1}[\{W(s)\sin[2\theta(s)]\}^{n+1}]_a^t - \tfrac{1}{2}\int_a^t [W(s)]^n\{\sin[2\theta(s)]\}^{n+1}\,dW(s).$$

Here

$$|W(s)| \le H(s), \qquad |dW(s)| = -dH(s),$$

so that the integral in question is dominated by

$$\tfrac{1}{2}(n+1)^{-1}\{[H(t)]^{n+1} + [H(a)]^{n+1}\} - \tfrac{1}{2}\int_a^t [H(s)]^n\,dH(s)$$

$$= (n+1)^{-1}[H(a)]^{n+1},$$

uniformly in t. Since $H(a) < 4$ by assumption, the series in (9.5.21) converges absolutely and uniformly for $a \le t < \infty$. Further

$$\left|\log\frac{r(t)}{r(a)}\right| \le \log[1 - \tfrac{1}{4}H(a)]^{-1/4} \tag{9.5.22}$$

for all such t. This estimate shows that $r(t)$ is bounded away from 0 and infinity.

Since the series in (9.5.21) converges uniformly with respect to t in $[a, \infty)$, we can let $t \to \infty$ termwise and see that $\lim \log r(t)$ exists as a finite quantity. This implies that

$$\lim_{t\to\infty} r(t) \equiv r(\infty) \tag{9.5.23}$$

exists and is neither 0 nor ∞.

If in formula (9.5.22) we replace t by ∞ and a by t, we obtain

$$\max\left\{\frac{r(t)}{r(a)}, \frac{r(a)}{r(t)}\right\} < [1 - \tfrac{1}{4}H(t)]^{-1/4}, \qquad a < t, \tag{9.5.24}$$

and finally

$$|r(t) - r(\infty)| < r(\infty)\{[1 - \tfrac{1}{4}H(t)]^{-1/4} - 1\}. \tag{9.5.25}$$

These relations have a number of consequences some of which are listed in the next two theorems. The proofs are omitted since they are immediate consequences of the formulas already established.

Theorem 9.5.2. *If* $\lim_{t\to\infty} W(t) = 0$ *and* $G(t) \in BV[0, \infty)$, *then* (9.5.23) *holds. If* $\{t_n\}$ *and* $\{\tau_n\}$ *are consecutive zeros of* $y_0(t)$ *and* $y_0'(t)$, *respectively, then*

$$\lim_{n\to\infty} [F(\tau_n)]^{1/4}|y_0(\tau_n)| = \lim_{n\to\infty} [F(t_n)]^{-1/4}|y_0'(t_n)| = r(\infty). \tag{9.5.26}$$

Here we can of course replace $y_0(t)$ by any other solution $y(t)$ provided $r(t)$ is changed accordingly. The method unfortunately gives no information about the value of $r(\infty)$ and formula (9.5.26) is only moderately useful for computational purposes.

Theorem 9.5.3. *Under the same assumptions*

$$y_0(t) = [F(t)]^{-1/4}r(\infty)[1 + s_0(t)] \sin [\theta(t)], \tag{9.5.27}$$

$$y_0'(t) = [F(t)]^{1/4}r(\infty)[1 + s_1(t)] \cos [\theta(t)], \tag{9.5.28}$$

where

$$\theta(t) = \int_0^t [F(s)]^{1/2}\, ds + \rho(t), \tag{9.5.29}$$

$$|\rho(t)| \le \tfrac{1}{4}V_0^t[\log F(s)], \tag{9.5.30}$$

$$|s_j(t)| \le [1 - \tfrac{1}{4}H(t)]^{-1/4} - 1, \qquad H(t) < 4, \tag{9.5.31}$$

and

$$H(t) = V_t^\infty[W(s)].$$

Similar formulas hold for any other solution with obvious changes.

We now leave quantitative results and turn to qualitative considerations which generalize to oscillation problems of higher order. Oscillation and non-oscillation are intimately connected with the asymptotic behavior of certain classes of argument functions, associated with solutions and with solution matrices.

We have considerable freedom in choosing such functions, since the only property that matters for oscillation theory is boundedness or non-boundedness. For the solution $y_0(t)$ considered above, $\theta_0(t)$ is a natural choice for $\arg y_0(t)$. It is of course the argument of the complex valued function

$$\begin{aligned} z_0(t) &\equiv [F(t)]^{-1/4}y_0'(t) + i[F(t)]^{1/4}y_0(t) \\ &= r_0(t)\exp[i\theta_0(t)]. \end{aligned} \tag{9.5.32}$$

But we could also choose the function $\vartheta_0(t)$ of Section 8.3. Similarly, if $y_1(t)$ is solution defined by

$$y_1(0) = 1, \qquad y_0'(0) = 0,$$

we define its argument as $\theta_1(t)$, i.e. the solution of (9.5.14) with the initial value $\theta_1(0) = \frac{1}{2}\pi$. These functions differ for all t by an amount less than π in absolute value. Thus, if one is unbounded, so is the other. Hence we see that

$$\lim_{t\to\infty} \theta_0(t) = +\infty \tag{9.5.33}$$

is a necessary and sufficient condition for Eq. (9.5.1) to be oscillatory.

If this is the case, then $z = z_0(t)$ describes a spiral in the complex plane. If (9.5.23) holds, the spiral has the asymptotic circle

$$|z| = r(\infty).$$

Similarly for the other solutions. Thus we have spiral motion and in the same positive direction for all solutions.

Let us introduce the matrix

$$\begin{aligned} \tilde{\mathcal{Y}}(t) &= \begin{pmatrix} [F(t)]^{-1/4}\, y_1'(t) & [F(t)]^{-1/4}\, y_0'(t) \\ [F(t)]^{1/4}\, y_1(t) & [F(t)]^{1/4}\, y_0(t) \end{pmatrix} \\ &= \begin{pmatrix} 0 & [F(t)]^{-1/4} \\ [F(t)]^{1/4} & 0 \end{pmatrix} \mathcal{Y}(t) \end{aligned} \tag{9.5.34}$$

where the matrix

$$\mathcal{Y}(t) = \begin{pmatrix} y_1(t) & y_0(t) \\ y_1'(t) & y_0'(t) \end{pmatrix} \tag{9.5.35}$$

satisfies the equation

$$\mathcal{Y}'(t) = \begin{pmatrix} 0 & 1 \\ -F(t) & 0 \end{pmatrix} \mathcal{Y}(t). \tag{9.5.36}$$

This we can rewrite in the form

$$\mathcal{U}\mathcal{Y}'(t) = \begin{pmatrix} F(t) & 0 \\ 0 & 1 \end{pmatrix} \mathcal{Y}(t). \tag{9.5.37}$$

Here we have attained that the coefficient on the right is a symmetric matrix. $\mathcal{U}$ on the other hand is the constant matrix

$$\mathcal{U} = \begin{pmatrix} 0 & -1 \\ 1 & 0 \end{pmatrix}. \tag{9.5.38}$$

A simple calculation shows that

$$\tilde{\mathfrak{Y}}^*(t)\mathfrak{U}\tilde{\mathfrak{Y}}(t) = \mathfrak{U}. \tag{9.5.39}$$

The matrix $\tilde{\mathfrak{Y}}(t)$ is an example of a 2 by 2 symplectic matrix. Such matrices are real, and satisfy (9.5.39), where the asterisk indicates that the matrix is to be replaced by its transpose.

We come now to the question of interpreting $\tilde{\mathfrak{Y}}(t)$ as a three-dimensional motion and in this connection to define an argument of $\tilde{\mathfrak{Y}}(t)$. There is no difficulty in representing $\tilde{\mathfrak{Y}}(t)$ as an orbit on an ordinary torus T. We recall that a torus is described if a circle of radius r revolves about an axis in the plane of the circle at a distance R from its center, where $r < R$. Position on the torus is measured by two angles, the *meridional angle* α and the *latitude* β, so that a parametric representation of the torus is

$$x_1 = \cos\alpha\ (R + r\cos\beta), \quad x_2 = \sin\alpha\ (R + r\cos\beta), \quad x_3 = r\sin\beta. \tag{9.5.40}$$

T is the Cartesian product of two circles.

The matrix $\tilde{\mathfrak{Y}}(t)$ has two column vectors which we can think of as $z_1(t)$ and $z_0(t)$, respectively, with corresponding arguments $\theta_1(t)$ and $\theta_0(t)$. We can define a path Γ on T by

$$\Gamma\colon \alpha = \theta_0(t), \qquad \beta = \theta_1(t), \qquad 0 \le t < \infty. \tag{9.5.41}$$

In the oscillatory case $|\theta_0(t) - \theta_1(t)| < \pi$, $\lim \theta_0(t) = \lim \theta_1(t) = +\infty$ so that Γ winds infinitely often around T, while, if the Eq. (9.5.1) is non-oscillatory, $\theta_0(t)$ and $\theta_1(t)$ tend to finite limits, there are only a finite number of windings, and Γ has an asymptotic point.

We can assign to $\tilde{\mathfrak{Y}}(t)$ arbitrarily the argument $\theta_0(t)$:

$$\arg \tilde{\mathfrak{Y}}(t) = \theta_0(t) \tag{9.5.42}$$

and the condition

$$\lim_{t\to\infty} \arg \tilde{\mathfrak{Y}}(t) = +\infty \tag{9.5.43}$$

is necessary and sufficient for (9.5.1) to be oscillatory. Alternate definitions of $\arg \tilde{\mathfrak{Y}}(t)$ are possible. One such is furnished by the arc length of Γ, measured from the starting-point, which is finite in the non-oscillatory case and infinite in the oscillatory one. We can also define an argument of $\mathfrak{Y}(t)$ itself by such considerations.

EXERCISE 9.5

1. Let $f(t)$ be a positive twice differentiable function. Show that

$$y(t) = [f(t)]^{-1/4} \sin\left\{\int_0^t [f(s)]^{1/2}\, ds\right\}$$

satisfies a differential equation of type (9.5.1) with

$$F(t) = f(t) + \frac{1}{4}\frac{f''(t)}{f(t)} - \frac{5}{16}\left(\frac{f'(t)}{f(t)}\right)^2.$$

2. With f and y as in the preceding problem, consider the quadratic form

$$Q_0(t, y) \equiv [f(t)]^{1/2}[y(t)]^2 + [f(t)]^{-1/2}[y'(t)]^2.$$

Show that this equals

$$\sin^2 [f_1(t)] + \{\cos [f_1(t)] - w(t) \sin [f_1(t)]\}^2$$

with

$$f_1(t) = \int_0^t [f(s)]^{1/2}\, ds, \qquad w(t) = f'(t)[f(t)]^{-3/2}.$$

Show that $Q_0(t, y)$ is bounded away from 0 and ∞, iff $w(t)$ is bounded and tends to a finite limit, iff $\lim_{t\to\infty} w(t) = 0$. [These conditions are not sufficient to ensure corresponding results for the form $Q(t, y)$ of (9.5.6).]

3. Consider the Euler equation

$$y'' + a(t + 1)^{-2}y = 0$$

which is oscillatory iff $a > \frac{1}{4}$. Show that $W(t) \equiv -2a^{-1/2}$ so that the conditions of Theorem 9.5.1 do not hold. Let $a > \frac{1}{4}$. Compute $N(\omega, y_0)$ explicitly and show that the two terms in the right member of (9.5.4) are of the same order of magnitude with respect to ω.

4. For the same equation show that the form $Q(t, y_0)$ is bounded away from 0 and ∞ but does not tend to a limit as $t \to \infty$. This holds for $a > \frac{1}{4}$. For $a < \frac{1}{4}$ the form becomes infinite with t but the corresponding form for the subdominant tends to 0 instead. Verify!

5. Verify (9.5.39) and show that $\mathcal{U}^2 = -\mathcal{E}$, $\mathcal{U}^*\mathcal{U} = \mathcal{U}\mathcal{U}^* = \mathcal{E}$.

6. Does Γ have an arclength? How is it defined?

7. Is the matrix $\mathcal{Y}(t)$ symplectic?

9.6 ABSTRACT OSCILLATION THEORY

The considerations of the preceding sections admit of wide generalizations to matrix equations and differential equations in abstract spaces.

In Section 9.5 it was shown that the equation

$$y'' + F(t)y = 0$$

is equivalent to the matrix equation

$$\mathcal{U}_1\mathcal{Y}' = \begin{pmatrix} F & 0 \\ 0 & 1 \end{pmatrix}\mathcal{Y}, \qquad \mathcal{U}_1 = \begin{pmatrix} 0 & -1 \\ 1 & 0 \end{pmatrix} \tag{9.6.1}$$

and that certain solution matrices are symplectic. We showed that, under certain assumptions, the oscillatory behavior of $y(t)$ could be described geometrically in terms of path curves in the complex plane winding around the origin, and that of $\mathcal{Y}(t)$ by curves winding on a torus.

Equation (9.6.1) can be generalized to

$$\mathfrak{U}_n \mathfrak{Y}'(t) = \mathfrak{H}(t)\mathfrak{Y}(t), \qquad \mathfrak{U}_n = \begin{pmatrix} 0 & -\mathfrak{E}_n \\ \mathfrak{E}_n & 0 \end{pmatrix}. \tag{9.6.2}$$

Here $\mathfrak{E}_n$ is the unit matrix in $\mathfrak{M}_n$ and $\mathfrak{H}(t)$ is a symmetric positive definite $2n$ by $2n$ matrix. Such an equation arises in dynamics when the equations of motion are brought to the Hamiltonian form

$$\frac{dp_j}{dt} = \frac{\partial H}{\partial q_j} \qquad \frac{dq_j}{dt} = -\frac{\partial H}{\partial p_j}, \qquad j = 1, 2, \ldots, n. \tag{9.6.3}$$

Here H is the Hamiltonian

$$H = \sum_1^n \sum_1^n [a_{jk}(t)p_j p_k + 2b_{jk}(t)p_j q_k + c_{jk}(t)q_j q_k]. \tag{9.6.4}$$

The corresponding matrix equation has a symplectic matrix solution provided the initial matrix is symplectic. This now means that

$$\mathfrak{Y}^*(t)\mathfrak{U}_n\mathfrak{Y}(t) \equiv \mathfrak{U}_n \tag{9.6.5}$$

where the star indicates that the matrix is replaced by its transpose. To show this we differentiate the left member and obtain

$$\mathfrak{Y}^{*\prime}(t)\mathfrak{U}_n\mathfrak{Y}(t) + \mathfrak{Y}^*(t)\mathfrak{U}_n\mathfrak{Y}'(t)$$
$$= -\mathfrak{Y}^*(t)\mathfrak{H}(t)\mathfrak{Y}(t) + \mathfrak{Y}^*(t)\mathfrak{H}(t)\mathfrak{Y}(t) = 0.$$

It follows that the left member of (9.6.5) is a constant, and, if the matrix of initial values is symplectic (e.g. the unit matrix), then the initial value of the left member of (9.6.5) is $\mathfrak{U}_n$.

V. A. Jakubovič has devoted a number of papers, starting in 1958, to a study of the oscillatory properties of Eq. (9.6.2), and has shown that it is possible, in a number of different ways, to introduce an argument function which is bounded iff the equation is non-oscillatory. (Cf. the investigations of W. A. Coppel and A. Howe (1965) which contain a critical examination of these concepts with applications to stability theory.)

There is considerable literature on oscillation theory for matrix equations. It is possible to present some of the results for equations where the unknown takes values in a star algebra $\mathfrak{B}$ with properties analogous to a matrix algebra. We refer to Definition 4.2.3 for the postulated properties of $\mathfrak{B}$. When there is need to refer to an individual postulate, the reference will be of the form 4.2.3:vi.

We note the following consequence of 4.2.3:vii. If $x(t)$ is defined and continuous for $\alpha \leq t \leq \beta$ with values in $\mathfrak{B}$, then

$$\int_\alpha^\beta x(s)\,ds$$

is an element of $\mathfrak{B}$ which is symmetric if $x(s)$ is symmetric, positive if $x(s)$ is positive, $\alpha \leq s \leq \beta$.

After these preliminaries, we proceed to a study of the sines and cosines introduced by J. F. Barrett (1957) in his extension of the Prüfer transformation to the matrix case. Let $q(t)$ be defined for $0 \le t < \infty$ as a continuous function of t with values in $\mathfrak{B}$ and symmetric for all t. Consider the system of first order differential equations

$$\begin{aligned} y'(t) &= q(t)z(t), & y(a) &= 0, \\ z'(t) &= -q(t)y(t), & z(a) &= e, \end{aligned} \qquad 0 \le a < \infty. \tag{9.6.6}$$

This can be written as a matrix equation

$$\mathsf{Y}'(t) = \mathsf{Q}(t)\mathsf{Y}(t) \tag{9.6.7}$$

with

$$\mathsf{Q}(t) = \begin{pmatrix} 0 & q(t) \\ -q(t) & 0 \end{pmatrix}, \qquad \mathsf{Y}(t) = \begin{pmatrix} z(t) & y(t) \\ -y(t) & z(t) \end{pmatrix}, \qquad \mathsf{Y}(a) = \begin{pmatrix} e & 0 \\ 0 & e \end{pmatrix}. \tag{9.6.8}$$

These objects Q and Y are elements of the matrix algebra $\mathfrak{M}_2(\mathfrak{B})$ over $\mathfrak{B}$ where we define the norm of a matrix as the maximum of the sum of the norms of the elements in a row or in a column.

The existence and uniqueness theorems apply to (9.6.7) and lead to a pair of functions

$$y(t) = S(a, t; q), \qquad z(t) = C(a, t; q). \tag{9.6.9}$$

These functions have a number of properties. We note first

$$S^*S + C^*C = e, \qquad S^*C = C^*S. \tag{9.6.10}$$

The four products occurring in these relations commute as is shown by simple computation. To prove (9.6.10), note that

$$(S^*S + C^*C)' = 0, \qquad (S^*C - C^*S)' = 0$$

as follows from the differential equations. We have also the relations

$$SS^* + CC^* = e, \qquad SC^* = CS^* \tag{9.6.11}$$

where again the four products commute. To prove this we set

$$L = SS^* + CC^*, \qquad M = CS^* - SC^*$$

and find that L and M satisfy

$$\begin{aligned} L' &= qM - Mq, & L(a) &= e, \\ M' &= Lq - qL, & M(a) &= 0. \end{aligned} \tag{9.6.12}$$

These equations are obviously satisfied by $L(t) \equiv e$, $M(t) \equiv 0$; since the solution is unique (9.6.11) follows.

Relations (9.6.10) and (9.6.11) imply that

$$(C^* - iS^*)(C + iS) = (C + iS)(C^* - iS^*) = e$$

or

$$(C + iS)^{-1} = (C + iS)^*. \tag{9.6.13}$$

This shows that $C + iS$ is a so-called *unitary element* of the algebra $\mathfrak{B}$, i.e. an x such that $x^* = x^{-1}$. The spectrum of such an element is located on the unit circle. For we can embed e, x, and x^* in a maximal commutative subalgebra $\mathfrak{A}$, which is closed under inversion and conjugation. Then the Gelfand Representation Theorem (Theorem 4.4.3) applies and for any admissible linear multiplicative functional on $\mathfrak{A}$ we have

$$\mu(x^*) = \overline{\mu(x)} \tag{9.6.14}$$

so that, if x is unitary,

$$\mu(x)\mu(x^*) = \mu(x)\overline{\mu(x)} = \mu(e) = 1 \quad \text{and} \quad |\mu(x)| = 1.$$

Since any $\mu(x)$ is a spectral value of x and every spectral value of x is attained for some μ, it follows that

$$\sigma(x) \in (\lambda \mid |\lambda| = 1) \quad \text{if} \quad x^* = x^{-1}.$$

We note that $C - iS$ is also unitary.

It was noted above that the four products C^*C, S^*S, S^*C, C^*S commute. We can then embed them in a commutative subalgebra $\mathfrak{A}_1$ to which the Gelfand Theorem applies. This gives, by (9.6.10),

$$\mu(C^*C) + \mu(S^*S) = 1. \tag{9.6.15}$$

Now C^*C and S^*S have non-negative spectra by 4.2.3:viii, and this relation asserts that these spectra are confined to the interval $[0, 1]$. Moreover, if $\alpha \in \sigma(C^*C)$ then $1 - \alpha \in \sigma(S^*S)$. Further the spectral radii of C^*C and S^*S are both ≤ 1. The same results hold for CC^* and SS^*.

In the n by n matrix case, Barrett proved that

$$\|\mathcal{C}\|^2 + \|\mathcal{S}\|^2 = n \tag{9.6.16}$$

in terms of the Frobenius-Wedderburn norm which assigns the norm $\sqrt{n}$ to the unit matrix. This follows again from (9.6.10) by taking traces noting that $\operatorname{tr}(\mathcal{A}^*\mathcal{A}) = \|\mathcal{A}\|^2$ and $\operatorname{tr}(\mathcal{E}) = n$. If this norm is replaced by any other admissible norm, (9.6.16) implies the existence of a fixed number m, depending upon n and upon the norm, such that

$$\|\mathcal{C}(a, t; q)\| \leq m, \qquad \|\mathcal{S}(a, t; q)\| \leq m \tag{9.6.17}$$

for all a, t, q.

In the general non-matrix case the situation is not clear. We can get fairly precise results if

$$q(s) \textit{ commutes with } q(t) \textit{ for all } s \textit{ and } t. \tag{9.6.18}$$

This implies that

$$q(t) \textit{ commutes with } \int_a^t q(s)\, ds$$

for all a and t. In this case the solution of (9.6.6) turns out to be

$$C(a, t; q) = \cos\left\{\int_a^t q(s)\,ds\right\},$$
$$S(a, t; q) = \sin\left\{\int_a^t q(s)\,ds\right\} \tag{9.6.19}$$

where $\cos x$ and $\sin x$ is defined by the ordinary power series for $x \in \mathfrak{B}$. In this case C and S are symmetric; (9.6.10) becomes

$$C^2 + S^2 = e$$

and (9.6.15) gives

$$[\mu(C)]^2 + [\mu(S)]^2 = 1.$$

In the first of these relations, C^2 and S^2 belong to $\mathfrak{B}^+$, the positive cone of $\mathfrak{B}$, and hence

$$C^2 < e, \qquad S^2 < e.$$

The relation between the spectra asserts that the spectra of C and of S are restricted to the interval $[-1, 1]$. Hence the spectral radii of C and of S do not exceed 1. Moreover, by 4.2.3:v, i.e. $\|xx^*\| = \|x\|^2$, then

$$\|C^*C\| = \|C^2\| = \|C\|^2, \qquad \|S^*S\| = \|S^2\| = \|S\|^2$$

and by (4.2.18), $\|C\| = r(C)$, $\|S\| = r(S)$ so that

$$\|C\| \le 1, \qquad \|S\| \le 1. \tag{9.6.20}$$

We cannot expect this to hold in general, but there is enough evidence available to suggest that (9.6.17) is a reasonable hypothesis, and we shall assume these inequalities in the discussion leading up to the analogue of Barrett's theorem.

We come now to oscillation theory for equations of the form

$$y''(t) + F(t)y(t) = 0 \tag{9.6.21}$$

in a star algebra $\mathfrak{B}$. Here $F(t)$ is continuous and symmetric for all $t \ge 0$. Later this assumption will be strengthened to $F(t)$ being positive. We also assume that (9.6.17) holds in $\mathfrak{B}$.

For the discussion we need a lemma concerning the change in the solution matrix $\mathsf{Y}(t)$ of (9.6.8) brought about by a change in the coefficient matrix $\mathsf{Q}(t)$. Here

$$\mathsf{Y} = \begin{pmatrix} C & S \\ -S & C \end{pmatrix} \quad \text{and} \quad \mathsf{Y}^{-1} = \begin{pmatrix} C^* & -S^* \\ S^* & C^* \end{pmatrix}. \tag{9.6.22}$$

By (9.6.17) and the definition of the norm of a matrix in $\mathfrak{M}_2(\mathfrak{B})$

$$\|\mathsf{Y}(t)\| \le 2m, \qquad \|[\mathsf{Y}(t)]^{-1}\| \le 2m \tag{9.6.23}$$

for all t and all admissible q. From this is obtained:

Lemma 9.6.1. *If* Y_1 *and* Y_2 *are solution matrices* (9.6.22) *corresponding to* $\mathsf{Q} = \mathsf{Q}_1$ *and* Q_2, *respectively, with the same choice of* a, *then*

$$\|\mathsf{Y}_1(t) - \mathsf{Y}_2(t)\| \le 8m^3 \int_a^t \|\mathsf{Q}_1(s) - \mathsf{Q}_2(s)\|\, ds \tag{9.6.24}$$

or, equivalently, with obvious notation,

$$\|C_1(t) - C_2(t)\| + \|S_1(t) - S_2(t)\| \le 8m^3 \int_a^t \|q_1(s) - q_2(s)\|\, ds. \tag{9.6.25}$$

Proof. By assumption

$$\mathsf{Y}_1' = \mathsf{Q}_1\mathsf{Y}_1, \qquad \mathsf{Y}_2' = \mathsf{Q}_2\mathsf{Y}_2, \qquad \mathsf{Y}_1(a) = \mathsf{Y}_2(a) = \begin{pmatrix} e & 0 \\ 0 & e \end{pmatrix}.$$

Hence

$$[\mathsf{Y}_1(t) - \mathsf{Y}_2(t)]' = \mathsf{Q}_2(t)[\mathsf{Y}_1(t) - \mathsf{Y}_2(t)] + [\mathsf{Q}_1(t) - \mathsf{Q}_2(t)]\mathsf{Y}_1(t)$$

with the solution

$$\mathsf{Y}_1(t) - \mathsf{Y}_2(t) = \mathsf{Y}_2(t) \int_a^t [\mathsf{Y}_2(s)]^{-1}[\mathsf{Q}_1(s) - \mathsf{Q}_2(s)]\mathsf{Y}_1(s)\, ds \tag{9.6.26}$$

as may be shown by differentiation. Using (9.6.23) we obtain the desired inequalities. The same estimates hold for the starred differences by 4.2.19:v. ∎

The analogue of Barrett's main theorem for the Prüfer transformation reads:

Theorem 9.6.1. *Suppose that* $F(t)$ *is symmetric and* (9.6.17) *holds in* $\mathfrak{B}$. *If* $y(t)$ *is a solution of* (9.6.21) *with* $y(a) = 0$, $y'(a) = e$, *then there exist two functions* $q(t)$ *and* $r(t)$ *with values in* $\mathfrak{B}$, $q(t)$ *symmetric and* $r(t)$ *nonsingular, such that*

$$y(t) = S^*(a, t; q)r(t), \qquad y'(t) = C^*(a, t; q)r(t). \tag{9.6.27}$$

Proof. Let us first see what relations must be satisfied by q and r if (9.6.27) is to hold. Differentiation yields

$$y' = S^{*\prime}r + S^*r' = C^*r,$$

$$y'' = C^{*\prime}r + C^*r' = -Fy = -FS^*r.$$

Substituting the expressions for the derivatives of S^* and C^*, we get

$$S^*r' = (-C^*q + C^*)r,$$

$$C^*r' = (S^*q - FS^*)r.$$

Using the identities (9.6.11), we obtain

$$r' = (SC^* - CFS^*)r, \tag{9.6.28}$$

$$q = CC^* + SFS^*, \qquad q(a) = e. \tag{9.6.29}$$

Here (9.6.28) has a unique solution if $r(a)$ is given and (9.6.27) implies $r(a) = y'(a) = e$. It follows that $r(t)$ is non-singular. (Cf. Section 6.1.)

To construct the function $q(t)$ and the corresponding functions C and S, we can use the alternating method of Barrett. We start with

$$q_1(t) = q(a) = e$$

and determine

$$S_1(a, t; q_1) = \sin(t - a)e, \qquad C_1(a, t; q_1) = \cos(t - a)e.$$

Then set

$$q_2 = C_1C_1^* + S_1FS_1^*$$

and determine C_2 and S_2, and so on. In general

$$q_n = C_{n-1}C_{n-1}^* + S_{n-1}FS_{n-1}^* \tag{9.6.30}$$

and

$$C_n = C(a, t; q_n), \qquad S_n = S(a, t; q_n). \tag{9.6.31}$$

Each of these functions is well defined for $a \le t$.

To prove convergence of the sequence $\{q_n(t)\}$ we use Lemma 9.6.1. We have

$$\begin{aligned} q_{n+1} - q_n = {} & \tfrac{1}{2}(C_n - C_{n-1})(C_n^* + C_{n-1}^*) + \tfrac{1}{2}(C_n + C_{n-1})(C_n^* - C_{n-1}^*) \\ & + \tfrac{1}{2}(S_n - S_{n-1})F(S_n^* + S_{n-1}^*) + \tfrac{1}{2}(S_n + S_{n-1})F(S_n^* - S_{n-1}^*). \end{aligned}$$

Here we substitute the estimate (9.6.25) and obtain

$$\|q_{n+1}(t) - q_n(t)\| \le 16m^4[1 + \|F(t)\|] \int_a^t \|q_n(s) - q_{n-1}(s)\|\, ds. \tag{9.6.32}$$

We restrict the discussion to an arbitrary finite interval $[a, b]$ and suppose that for such values of t

$$1 + \|F(t)\| \le M.$$

It follows from (9.6.29) that

$$\|q_n(t)\| \le m^2M$$

for all n. We now get in the usual manner

$$\|q_{n+1}(t) - q_n(t)\| \le (M + 1)\frac{1}{n!}[16m^4M(t - a)]^n$$

since $\|q_2(t) - q_1(t)\| \leq M + 1$. This shows the convergence of the sequence $\{q_n(t)\}$, uniformly with respect to t on any bounded interval $[a, b]$. It follows that

$$\lim_{n\to\infty} q_n(t) = q(t)$$

exists. Further

$$\lim_{n\to\infty} C(a, t; q_n) = C(a, t; \lim_{n\to\infty} q_n) = C(a, t; q),$$

and so on. The same type of argument shows that $q(t)$ satisfies (9.6.29). Once we have found C and S we can determine $r(t)$ from (9.6.28). Finally, it is verified by differentiation that (9.6.27) gives the solution of (9.6.21) with the prescribed initial values.

So far there has been some talk about oscillation of solutions of differential equations in B-algebras without any attempt to make this notion precise.

Definition 9.6.1. *A solution of* (9.6.21) *is said to be oscillatory in* $(0, \infty)$ *if* $y^*(t)y'(t)$ *is not identically singular but admits of an algebraic singularity in every interval* (b, ∞). *The solution is non-oscillatory if the product has a last algebraic singularity.*

For the case where $-F(t) \in \mathfrak{B}^+$, see Problem 10, Exercise 9.6.

In the following we restrict ourselves to the case where $F(t) \in \mathfrak{B}^+$ for all t. We need some additional information concerning the properties of positive elements. We recall that a partial ordering is established in $\mathfrak{B}$ by the convention that $x_1 < x_2$ means that $x_2 - x_1 \in \mathfrak{B}^+$, i.e. the difference is non-negative. We leave the proof of the next lemma to the reader.

Lemma 9.6.2. *The unit element e is positive. The inverse of a positive element x is positive and* $\sigma(x^{-1}) = \{\lambda^{-1} | \lambda \in \sigma(x)\}$. *Further, if* $\sigma(x) \subset [\alpha, \beta]$, $0 < \alpha$, *then*

$$\alpha e < x < \beta e, \frac{1}{\beta} e < x^{-1} < \frac{1}{\alpha} e. \tag{9.6.33}$$

Either of these inequalities implies that $\sigma(x) \subset [\alpha, \beta]$. *Moreover, any integral power of a positive element x is positive. In particular,* (9.6.33) *implies that*

$$\alpha^2 e < x^2 < \beta^2 e. \tag{9.6.34}$$

Lemma 9.6.3. *A positive element of* $\mathfrak{B}$ *has a positive square root.*

Proof. If x is positive we define

$$x^{1/2} = \frac{1}{2\pi i} \int_\Gamma \lambda^{1/2} R(\lambda, x)\, d\lambda \tag{9.6.35}$$

where Γ is a simple closed curve surrounding the (positive) spectrum of x leaving $\lambda = 0$ on the outside and $\lambda^{1/2}$ is real positive for λ real positive. Since $x = x^*$ we have $R(\lambda, x) = R(\lambda, x^*)$ and $x^{1/2} = (x^{1/2})^*$. Since x and $x^{1/2}$ commute, $\sigma(x^{1/2}) = \{\alpha^{1/2} | \alpha \in \sigma(x)\}$ and $x^{1/2}$ is positive. ∎

For the results to be proved we also need the basic property of the Wronskian associated with (9.6.21). Let $u(t)$ and $v(t)$ be any solutions of (9.6.21) and form

$$W(u, v) \equiv u^*(t)v'(t) - u^{*\prime}(t)v(t). \tag{9.6.36}$$

Differentiation shows that this expression is independent of t. In particular, if $u(t) = v(t) = y(t)$ and if $y^*(t)y'(t)$ is real anywhere, then it has this property everywhere and

$$W(y, y) \equiv 0. \tag{9.6.37}$$

We shall now prove the analogue of Theorem 9.4.1.

Theorem 9.6.2. *Let $F(t)$ be positive in $[0, \infty)$ and let (9.6.21) have a non-oscillatory solution $y(t)$ such that $y^*(t)y'(t)$ is real. Then*

$$F(t) \in L[(0, \infty); \mathfrak{B}], \tag{9.6.38}$$

$$\lim_{\inf}^{\sup} t \int_t^\infty F(s)\, ds < \begin{cases} e, \\ \frac{1}{4}e. \end{cases} \tag{9.6.39}$$

Proof. We may assume that $y(t)$ and $y'(t)$ are regular for $t \geq b \geq 0$. Since (9.3.37) holds we have

$$y'(t)[y(t)]^{-1} = [y^*(t)]^{-1}\, y^{*\prime}(t).$$

Hence, if we set

$$w(t) = y'(t)[y(t)]^{-1}, \qquad b \leq t, \tag{9.6.40}$$

then $w^*(t) = w(t)$ so $w(t)$ is real. It is also regular. Differentiation leads to the Riccati equation

$$w'(t) = -F(t) - [w(t)]^2. \tag{9.6.41}$$

Here $[w(t)]^2 = w(t)w^*(t)$ is positive, being non-negative and regular. Hence

$$-w't) = F(t) + [w(t)]^2$$

is a positive function and the same is true of its integral. Thus for, $b \leq t \leq \omega$,

$$w(t) - w(\omega) = \int_t^\omega \{F(s) + [w(s)]^2\}\, ds \tag{9.6.42}$$

is positive and increasing. This shows that $w(t)$ is decreasing and should tend to a limit $w(\infty)$ as $t \to \infty$.

It should be shown that $w(t)$ is positive and that $w(\infty) = 0$. Since $w(t)$ is regular for $t > b$, the Riccati equation gives

$$-[w(t)]^{-1}w'(t)[w(t)]^{-1} = e + [w(t)]^{-1}F(t)[w(t)]^{-1}. \tag{9.6.43}$$

The left member is the derivative of $[w(t)]^{-1}$. In the right member $F(t)$ is positive and has a positive square root by Lemma 9.6.3. Hence if we set

$$Q(t) = [F(t)]^{1/2}[w(t)]^{-1}, \tag{9.6.44}$$

then

$$[w(t)]^{-1}F(t)[w(t)]^{-1} = Q^*(s)Q(s)$$

and this is non-negative and regular, hence positive. Integration now gives

$$[w(t)]^{-1} = [w(b)]^{-1} + (t - b)e + \int_b^t Q^*(s)Q(s)\,ds. \tag{9.6.45}$$

Here the first two elements on the right commute so that

$$\sigma\{[w(b)]^{-1} + (t - b)e\} = \sigma\{[w(b)]^{-1}\} + t - b$$

and this is positive for all large t, say for $t \geq c \geq b$. For such values of t the right member in (9.6.45) is positive by Lemma 9.6.2. Replacing b by c in (9.6.45) which is permitted, we get

$$[w(t)]^{-1} = [w(c)]^{-1} + (t - c)e + \int_c^t Q^*(s)Q(s)\,ds, \tag{9.6.46}$$

where the summands are positive for $t > c$. It follows that $w(t)$ is positive for $t > c$.

We have now for $t > c$

$$[(t - c)w(t)]^{-1} > e \tag{9.6.47}$$

so that the spectrum of the left member is real positive and confined to $[1, \infty)$. By Lemma 9.6.2 this means that the spectrum of $(t - c)w(t)$ lies in $(0, 1]$. Hence we have

$$0 < (t - c)w(t) < e \tag{9.6.48}$$

and from this we conclude that

$$\lim_{t\to\infty} w(t) = 0, \qquad \limsup_{t\to\infty} tw(t) < e. \tag{9.6.49}$$

We now return to (9.6.42) where we let $\omega \to \infty$. Since the left member has the finite limit $w(t)$, the right member must also have a finite limit. Since both $F(s)$ and $[w(s)]^2$ are positive this implies (9.6.38) and the integral equation

$$w(t) = \int_t^\infty [w(s)]^2\,ds + \int_t^\infty F(s)\,ds. \tag{9.6.50}$$

Here we set

$$t \int_t^\infty F(s)\, ds \equiv f(t) \tag{9.6.51}$$

and introduce the limits

$$\lim \begin{matrix}\sup \\ \inf\end{matrix} f(t) = \begin{cases} f^* e, \\ f_* e, \end{cases} \tag{9.6.52}$$

$$\lim \begin{matrix}\sup \\ \inf\end{matrix} tw(t) = \begin{cases} u^* e, \\ u_* e. \end{cases} \tag{9.6.53}$$

where f^*, f_*, u^*, u_* are non-negative numbers. We already know that $u^* \leq 1$. Writing (9.6.50) in the equivalent form

$$tw(t) = t \int_t^\infty [w(s)]^2\, ds + f(t),$$

we see that $f^* \leq u^* \leq 1$ which is the first inequality under (9.6.39). The second inequality is obtained as follows.

If $\varepsilon > 0$ is given, there is a T such that $s \geq T$

$$(u_* - \varepsilon)e < sw(s) < (u^* + \varepsilon)e,$$

$$(f_* - \varepsilon)e < f(s) < (f^* + \varepsilon)e,$$

where a negative lower bound is to be replaced by 0. Now Lemma 9.6.2 asserts that if $0 < \alpha e < x < \beta e$, then $\alpha^2 e < x^2 < \beta^2 e$. This observation gives

$$tw(t) > [(u_* - \varepsilon)^2 + f_* - \varepsilon]e, \qquad t \geq T.$$

Since ε is arbitrary this gives

$$u_* \geq (u_*)^2 + f_*.$$

Hence the quadratic equation $u^2 - u + f_* = 0$ must have real roots. This proves the second assertion under (9.6.39) and shows that

$$\tfrac{1}{2} - (\tfrac{1}{4} - f_*)^{1/2} \leq u_* \leq \tfrac{1}{2} + (\tfrac{1}{4} - f_*)^{1/2}. \ \blacksquare \tag{9.6.54}$$

The two conditions (9.6.38) and (9.6.39) are necessary (but not sufficient) for Eq. (9.6.21) to possess a non-oscillatory solution with $y^*(t)y'(t)$ real. If either is violated then oscillatory solutions must occur. A sufficient condition for non-oscillation is given by the following generalization of Theorem 9.4.2.

Theorem 9.6.3. *Let $F(t)$ be continuous in* $[0, \infty)$ *and a positive element of $\mathfrak{B}$ for all t. Let $F(t) \in L[(0, \infty); \mathfrak{B}]$ and suppose that for $t \geq c \geq 0$*

$$\|f(t)\| \leq \rho \leq \tfrac{1}{4}. \tag{9.6.55}$$

Then (9.6.21) *has non-oscillatory solutions.*

Proof. We can imitate the proofs of Theorems 9.4.2 and 9.4.6. We solve the $\mathfrak{B}$-valued integral equation

$$u(t) = t\int_t^{\infty} [u(s)]^2 s^{-2}\, ds + f(t) \tag{9.6.56}$$

and the auxiliary scalar equation

$$U(t) = t\int_t^{\infty} [U(s)]^2 s^{-2}\, ds + \rho \tag{9.6.57}$$

by the method of successive approximations using $u_1(t) = f(t)$, $U_1(t) = \rho$ as first approximations. This leads to a sequence of $\mathfrak{B}$-valued functions $\{u_n(t)\}$ and a sequence of positive numbers $\{\sigma_n\}$. By Lemma 9.6.2 the square of a positive function is positive. Since $u_1(t) = f(t)$ is positive, all functions $u_n(t)$ are positive and $f(t) < u_n(t)$. Further, by alternating induction as in the proof of Theorem 9.4.6 it is shown that for all n

$$\|u_n(t)\| \le \sigma_n,$$

$$\|u_n(t) - u_{n-1}(t)\| \le \sigma_n - \sigma_{n-1},$$

$$\begin{aligned}\|[u_n(s)]^2 - [u_{n-1}(s)]^2\| \\ &= \|u_n(s)[u_n(s) - u_{n-1}(s)] + [u_n(s) - u_{n-1}(s)]u_{n-1}(s)\| \\ &\le \sigma_n^2 - \sigma_{n-1}^2 = \sigma_{n+1} - \sigma_n.\end{aligned}$$

It follows that $u_n(t)$ tends to a limit $u(t)$ and $\|u(t)\| \le \sigma$ so that

$$f(t) < u(t) < \sigma e, \quad \sigma = \tfrac{1}{2} - (\tfrac{1}{4} - \rho)^{1/2}. \tag{9.6.58}$$

We then set

$$w(t) = \frac{1}{t}\, u(t). \tag{9.6.59}$$

Here $w(t)$ satisfies the Riccati equation (9.6.41) and is positive for $t \ge c$. Next, determine $y(t)$ from the first order equation

$$y'(t) = w(t)y(t), \quad y(c) = e. \tag{9.6.60}$$

The solution is unique and is a regular element of $\mathfrak{B}$ for $t \ge c$ by Theorem 6.1.5. Differentiation together with the Riccati equation shows that $y(t)$ is a solution of (9.6.21). Thus the latter has at least one solution such that $y^*(t)y'(t)$ is a regular element of $\mathfrak{B}$ for $t \ge c$. Since

$$y^*(t)y'(t) = y^*(t)w(t)y(t)$$

and $w(t)$ is positive, $y^*(t)y'(t)$ is real for $t \ge c$. Other non-oscillatory solutions may be constructed using the formula

$$z(t) = y(t)\int_a^t [y(s)]^{-1}[y^*(s)]^{-1}\, ds$$

where a is any number $\geq c$. Since algebraic singularities of linearly independent solutions do not necessarily alternate even in the matrix case, it is not clear if the existence of one oscillatory or non-oscillatory solution forces all solutions to have the same property. ∎

Finally we mention that in the matrix case there is an extensive literature on oscillation and non-oscillation to which the reader is referred for further results.

EXERCISE 9.6

1. If $q(t)$ is positive, show that $C(t)$ and $S(t)$ are solutions of
$$\{[q(t)]^{-1}y'(t)\}' + q(t)y(t) = 0.$$
2. Verify (9.6.19) if (9.6.18) holds.
3. Let $\mathfrak{B} = \mathfrak{M}_2$ and
$$q(t) = \mathfrak{Q}(t) = \begin{pmatrix} 1 & 0 \\ 0 & \frac{1}{2} \end{pmatrix}.$$
Show that the matrices $\mathfrak{S}(0, t; \mathfrak{Q})$ and $\mathfrak{C}(0, t; \mathfrak{Q})$ are simultaneously singular, if t is an odd multiple of π (G. J. Etgen).
4. Set $T = SC^{-1}$, the *tangent function*, which is defined wherever C is non-singular. Show that T is symmetric. Assume $q(t)$ positive and show that $T' = q + TqT$. Use this to show that if C is non-singular in an interval (a, b) and $T(a) > 0$, then T is positive in this interval (G. J. Etgen).
5. Prove Lemma 9.6.2.
6. Formula (9.6.33) shows that all positive elements of $\mathfrak{B}$ are "commensurable" with the unit element. They are not necessarily commensurable with each other, however. Give an example of two positive matrices such that neither $\mathfrak{X}_2 - \mathfrak{X}_1$ nor $\mathfrak{X}_1 - \mathfrak{X}_2$ is positive.
7. Give an example of two positive diagonal matrices of the same spectral radius having a non-negative difference.
8. If $0 < \alpha e < x < \beta e$ and if the scalar polynomial
$$P(\lambda) = \gamma_0 + \gamma_1\lambda + \cdots + \gamma_n\lambda^n$$
has non-negative coefficients, prove that
$$P(\alpha)e < P(x) < P(\beta)e.$$
9. Let $y(t)$ be defined by (9.6.60). By analogy with Theorem 9.4.3 this solution $y(t)$ should be "subdominant." How can this notion be defined in the B^*-algebra case? If $y(t)$ is subdominant, exhibit a dominant solution.
10. Let $G(t)$ be continuous and positive in $[0, \infty)$. Suppose that $y(t)$ is a solution of $y''(t) = G(t)y(t)$ such that $y^*(t)y'(t)$ is real. If the product is positive for $t = a$, show that it is positive for all $t \geq a$. [*Hint*: Generalize (9.2.2).]

COLLATERAL READING

As general references for this chapter the following should be mentioned:

BELLMAN, Richard, *A survey of the theory of boundedness, stability, and asymptotic behavior of solutions of linear and non-linear differential and difference equations*, Office of Naval Research, Washington, D.C. (1949).

BELLMAN, Richard, *Stability Theory of Differential Equations*, McGraw-Hill, New York (1953).

CESARI, L., *Asymptotic Behavior and Stability Problems in Ordinary Differential Equations*, 2nd ed. (Ergebnisse der Mathematik, N.F.), Springer, Berlin (1963).

COPPEL, W. A., *Stability and Asymptotic Behavior of Differential Equations*, Heath, Boston (1965).

HARTMAN, P., *Ordinary Differential Equations*, Wiley, New York (1964).

The papers referred to in Section 9.1 are:

BÔCHER, M., "On regular singular points of linear differential equations of the second order whose coefficients are not necessarily analytic," *Trans. Amer. Math. Soc.* **1**, 39–52 (1900).

HILLE, E., "Non-oscillation theorems," *Trans. Amer. Math. Soc.* **64**, 234–252 (1948).

WEYL, H., "Über gewöhnliche Differentialgleichungen mit singulären Stellen und ihre Eigenfunktionen," *Göttinger Nachrichten*, Math.-phys. Klasse (1909), pp. 37–63.

WINTNER, A., "On almost free linear motions," *Amer. J. Math.* **71**, 595–602 (1949).

Sections 9.2–9.4 are largely based on previous work of the author. In addition to the paper quoted above, see

HILLE, E., "Behavior of solutions of linear second order differential equations," *Arkiv. f. Matematik*, **2:2**, 25–41 (1951).

HILLE, E., "On a class of orthonormal functions," *Rendiconti del Seminario Matematico della Università di Padova*, **25**, 214–249 (1956).

Investigations referred to in the text:

KNESER, A., "Untersuchungen über die reellen Nullstellen der Integrale linearer Differentialgleichungen," *Math. Ann.* **42**, 409–435 (1893).

LYAPUNOV, A., "Problème général de la stabilité du mouvement," *Ann. Math. Stu.* **17**, Princeton (1947). (Russian original published in Kharkov 1892).

Section 9.5 is largely based on an unpublished investigation of the author's. Equivalent or better results have been found by P. Hartman and A. Wintner. See, e.g.

HARTMAN, P., and A. WINTNER, "Asymptotic integration of linear differential equations," *Amer. J. Math.* **77**, 45–86, 932 (1955), where reference to earlier work of Hartman's is to be found. See also

WIMAN, A., "Über die reellen Lösungen der linearen Differentialgleichungen zweiter Ordnung," *Arkiv f. Mat., Astr. Fys.* **12:14**, 22 pp. (1917).

WIMAN, A., "Über eine Stabilitätsfrage in der Theorie der linearen Differentialgleichungen," *Acta Math.* **66**, 121–145 (1936).

Oscillation theory for matrix differential equations, to start with from the point of view of calculus of variations, has been developed by many authors. We quote:

BARRETT, J. H., "Matrix systems of second order differential equations," *Portugaliae Mathematica*, **14**, 79–89 (1955).

BARRETT, J. H., "A Prüfer transformation for matrix differential equations," *Proc. Amer. Math. Soc.* **8**, 510–518 (1957).

COPPEL, W. A., and A. HOWE, "On the stability of linear canonical systems with periodic coefficients," *J. Aust. Math. Soc.* **5**, 169–195 (1965).

ETGEN, G. J., "Oscillatory properties of certain non-linear matrix differential systems of second order," *Trans. Amer. Math. Soc.* **122**, 289–310 (1966).

JAKUBOVIČ, V. A., "Oscillatory properties of the solutions of canonical equations," *Mat. Sbornik (N.S.)*, **56** (98), 3–42 (1962) (Amer. Math. Soc. Translations, (2) 42 (1964)).

JAKUBOVIČ, V. A., "Arguments on the group of symplectic matrices," *Mat. Sbornik (N.S.)*, **55** (97), 255–280 (1961). [Russian. See *Math. Reviews*, **26**, No. 5072.]

MORSE, Marston, "Calculus of variations in the large," *Amer. Math. Soc. Coll. Publ.* **18**, New York (1934).

REID, W. T., "A matrix differential equation of the Riccati type," *Amer. J. Math.* **68**, 237–246 (1946).

REID, W. T., "A Prüfer transformation for differential systems," *Pacific J. Math.* **8**, 575–584 (1958).

STERNBERG, R. L., "Variational methods and non-oscillation theorems for systems of differential equations," *Duke Math. J.* **19**, 311–322 (1952).

WHYBURN, W. M., "Existence and oscillation theorems for non-linear differential equations of the second order," *Trans. Amer. Math. Soc.* **30**, 848–854 (1928).

The University of North Carolina dissertation of Etgen, quoted above, contains a detailed discussion of the "trigonometric" matrices $\mathcal{C}$, $\mathcal{S}$, and $\mathcal{T}$.
A detailed discussion of star algebras is found in

RICKART, R. C., *General Theory of Banach Algebras*, Van Nostrand, New York (1960).

10 SINGULAR BOUNDARY VALUE PROBLEMS

In this chapter the study of boundary value problems is extended to the singular case for the interval $[0, \infty)$ where the left endpoint is non-singular. An ordinary boundary condition can be assigned at the origin, but the point at infinity poses a serious problem. The difficulty was resolved by Hermann Weyl in his dissertation of 1909. Differential equations fall into two classes: the *limit-circle* case where all solutions are in $L_2(0, \infty)$ and the *limit-point* case where, for non-real values of the parameter, essentially only one solution is in L_2. The limit-point case is the most interesting and the only one that receives detailed study below.

The solution in L_2 occupies most of our attention. It defines the spectrum of the differential operator which is normally not discrete. Hence, expansions in terms of characteristic functions, familiar in the regular case, are now usually replaced by integral representations. Instead of a mapping of functions in L_2 on to Fourier coefficients in l_2, we now get a mapping on to generalized Fourier transforms. These are special cases of unitary transformations between two L_2-spaces and a study of such transforms is given. We also include a discussion of the Green's function and of the resolvent.

At the end of the chapter are some remarks on extensions to equations with solutions in a star algebra.

There are seven sections: Limit-circle or Limit-point?; The $m(\lambda)$ Functions; On the Nature of the Spectrum; Unitary Transformations; Representation Theorems; The Resolvent; Remarks on Generalizations.

10.1 LIMIT-CIRCLE OR LIMIT-POINT?

Singular boundary-value problems are concerned with intervals which are either infinite or have a singular point of the equation at one of the end-points. Here we shall work mainly with the equation

$$y'' + [\lambda - q(x)]y = 0, \tag{10.1.1}$$

and the interval $[0, \infty)$ where $q(x)$ is defined as a real continuous function. The interval $(-\infty, \infty)$ will be considered occasionally, and, exceptionally, also finite intervals with singular end-points.

In analogy with classical boundary value problems, one could prescribe boundary conditions at the end-points, say

$$y(0) = 0, \qquad \lim_{x\to\infty} y(x) = 0.$$

Such a problem is solvable under certain assumptions on $q(x)$ but in general such a question is not well posed. Both for theoretical and applied problems it turns out that it is desirable to start with an investigation of the existence of solutions belonging to $L_2(0, \infty)$. Here Hermann Weyl made a basic observation.

Theorem 10.1.1. *For every non-real value of* λ *the equation* (10.1.1) *has at least one non-trivial solution in* $L_2(0, \infty)$.

Proof. Let α be given, $0 \leq \alpha < 2\pi$, and let $y_1(x, \lambda)$ and $y_2(x, \lambda)$ be the two solutions of (10.1.1) defined by

$$\begin{aligned} y_1(0, \lambda) &= \sin\alpha, & y_1'(0, \lambda) &= -\cos\alpha, \\ y_2(0, \lambda) &= \cos\alpha, & y_2'(0, \lambda) &= \sin\alpha. \end{aligned} \tag{10.1.2}$$

Since their Wronskian is identically 1, these solutions form a fundamental system. They are defined for all $x \geq 0$ and all λ and for fixed x they are entire functions of λ of order $\leq \frac{1}{2}$.

We now form a linear combination of y_1 and y_2

$$y(x; \lambda, m) = y_1(x, \lambda) + my_2(x, \lambda) \tag{10.1.3}$$

where m is to be determined. It will be assumed that $\lambda = \mu + i\nu$ and $\nu \neq 0$. Let β, $0 \leq \beta < 2\pi$, and b, $0 < b < \infty$, be given and determine m by the condition

$$y(b; \lambda, m)\cos\beta + y'(b; \lambda, m)\sin\beta = 0 \tag{10.1.4}$$

whence

$$m = -\frac{\cot\beta y_1(b, \lambda) + y_1'(b, \lambda)}{\cot\beta y_2(b, \lambda) + y_2'(b, \lambda)}. \tag{10.1.5}$$

We have to make a rather thorough examination of this quantity m which of course depends upon α, β, λ, and b. Here we shall use various consequences of the integral identity

$$[\overline{y(x, \lambda)}y'(x, \lambda)]_{x_1}^{x_2} - \int_{x_1}^{x_2} |y'(x, \lambda)|^2\,dx + \int_{x_1}^{x_2} [\lambda - q(x)]|y(x, \lambda)|^2\,dx = 0 \tag{10.1.6}$$

which holds for every solution $y(x, \lambda)$ of (10.1.1) and any choice of x_1, x_2, $0 \leq x_1 < x_2 < \infty$. We have met this type of identity repeatedly; the first occurrence in (7.6.39), Section 9.3 was built on it, and in Chapter 11 we shall meet it again under the name of the *Green's transform* of the equation.

Our first concern is with the denominator in (10.1.5). We have to show that it cannot be zero for any admissible b and β. We set

$$y(x, \lambda) = y_2(x, \lambda), \qquad x_1 = 0, \qquad x_2 = b$$

in (10.1.6) and take the imaginary part to obtain

$$\Im[\overline{y_2(b, \lambda)}\, y_2'(b, \lambda)] = -\nu \int_0^b |y_2(s, \lambda)|^2 \, ds \neq 0 \quad \text{if} \quad \nu \neq 0. \tag{10.1.7}$$

Since

$$\Im\left(\frac{y_2'(b, \lambda)}{y_2(b, \lambda)}\right) = \frac{\Im[\overline{y_2(b, \lambda)}\, y_2'(b, \lambda)]}{|y_2(b, \lambda)|^2},$$

it is seen that the logarithmic derivative of $y_2(x, \lambda)$ with respect to x cannot be real. Hence the denominator in (10.1.5) is not zero and m is well defined.

The form of (10.1.5) suggests that the elementary properties of fractional linear transformations in the complex plane

$$w = \frac{Az + B}{Cz + D} \tag{10.1.8}$$

may have a bearing on the problem at hand. What is needed here is that such a transformation maps a straight line on to a circle or, exceptionally, a straight line, and that points symmetric with respect to the straight line in the z-plane go into points symmetric with respect to the circle in the w-plane. Here w_1 and w_2 are symmetric with respect to the circle $|w - w_0| = R$ if $\arg(w_0 - w_1) = \arg(w_0 - w_2)$ and $|w_0 - w_1|\,|w_0 - w_2| = R^2$. In this context, w_0 and the point at infinity are considered to be symmetric with respect to the circle.

Formula (10.1.5) defines such a linear transformation if we set

$$\begin{gathered} w = m, \quad z = \cot \beta, \quad A = -y_1(b, \lambda), \quad B = -y_1'(b, \lambda), \\ C = y_2(b, \lambda), \quad D = y_2'(b, \lambda). \end{gathered} \tag{10.1.9}$$

Here we are interested in the mapping of the real axis which is described when β goes from π to 0. Since $w = \infty$ for

$$z = z_\infty = -\frac{y_2'(b, \lambda)}{y_2(b, \lambda)},$$

a non-real quantity as we have seen, the image of the real axis is a circle C_b and not a straight line. To fix the ideas, suppose that $\nu > 0$. Then $\Im[z_\infty] > 0$ by (10.1.7). This means that the upper half of the z-plane corresponds to the exterior of C_b and the lower half to the interior. In particular, the center w_0 of the circle is the image of the conjugate of z_∞,

$$z_0 = \bar{z}_\infty \quad \text{with} \quad \Im[\bar{z}_\infty] < 0.$$

Next we show that the circle C_b lies in the upper w-half-plane if $\nu > 0$. This follows again from (10.1.6). Set

$$y(x, \lambda) = y(x; \lambda, m), \qquad x_1 = 0, \qquad x_2 = b$$

in (10.1.6) and note that by (10.1.4)

$$\overline{y(b; \lambda, m)}\, y'(b; \lambda, m) = -\cot \beta |y(b; \lambda, m)|^2$$

which is real, while

$$\overline{y(0; \lambda, m)}\, y'(0; \lambda, m) = -\tfrac{1}{2} \sin 2\alpha\ (1 - |m|^2) - \cos 2\alpha\ \Re[m] + i\Im(m). \tag{10.1.10}$$

Hence, taking the imaginary part,

$$\Im(m) = \nu \int_0^b |y(s; \lambda, m)|^2\, ds. \tag{10.1.11}$$

This has the same sign as ν so that m lies in the upper half-plane if ν is positive.

We need more properties of the circle C_b. Its radius plays an important role. We note that for $\beta = \frac{1}{2}\pi$

$$w_1 = -\frac{y_1'(b, \lambda)}{y_2'(b, \lambda)}$$

is a point of C_b. Using this, the value of w_0, together with the Wronskian of y_1 and y_2 and formula (10.1.7), we can compute $|w_0 - w_1|$ and find the radius

$$r_b = \left[2|\nu| \int_0^b |y_2(s, \lambda)|^2\, ds\right]^{-1}. \tag{10.1.12}$$

We leave the details to the reader. Since the integral is an increasing function of b, it follows that r_b is strictly decreasing and hence tends to a limit ≥ 0. The two cases with "$=0$" or ">0" are fundamentally distinct.

We are going to show that the circles $\{C_b\}$, $0 < b < \infty$, are nested, i.e. C_{b_1} contains C_{b_2} if $b_1 < b_2$. This makes it important to decide when a point w is interior to C_b. To this end, we have to recognize that the equation of C_b is given by (10.1.11), in an unconventional form to be sure. Set

$$m = u + iv, \qquad S = \int_0^b |y_1(s, \lambda)|^2\, ds, \qquad T = \int_0^b |y_2(s, \lambda)|^2\, ds, \tag{10.1.13}$$

$$U + iV = \int_0^b y_1(s, \lambda)\overline{y_2(s, \lambda)}\, ds.$$

Then (10.1.11) asserts that

$$v = \nu[T(u^2 + v^2) + 2Uu + 2Vv + S] \tag{10.1.14}$$

and this is clearly a circle in the u, v-plane and hence the circle C_b. If $\nu > 0$, the point $w = u + iv$ is interior to the circle if

$$v > \nu[T(u^2 + v^2) + 2Uu + 2Vv + S]$$

and retracing the steps, this shows that w is interior to C_b iff

$$\Im[w] > \nu \int_0^b |y(s; \lambda, w)|^2 \, ds. \tag{10.1.15}$$

Suppose now that $b_1 < b_2$ and consider the corresponding circles C_{b_1} and C_{b_2}. Suppose that w is interior to C_{b_2} so that

$$\Im[w] > \nu \int_0^{b_2} |y(s; \lambda, w)|^2 \, ds > \nu \int_0^{b_1} |y(s; \lambda, w)|^2 \, ds.$$

Hence w is also interior to C_{b_1}. This says that C_{b_2} is interior to C_{b_1} if $b_1 < b_2$.

Hence we have a family of nested circles with decreasing radii. There are two alternatives:

(1) $r_b \downarrow 0$. In this case there is one and only one point $m = m(\lambda)$ which is common to all the closed circular disks bounded by the C_b's, $0 < b < \infty$. This is the *limit-point* case and it occurs iff

$$\int_0^\infty |y_2(s, \lambda)|^2 \, ds = +\infty. \tag{10.1.16}$$

(2) $r_b \downarrow r_\infty > 0$. In this case there is a maximal circular disk contained in all the circles C_b. This is the *limit-circle* case and it occurs iff the integral in the left member of (10.1.16) is convergent, i.e. $y_2(s, \lambda) \in L_2(0, \infty)$.

In the limit-circle case we already have a solution in $L_2(0, \infty)$ and as we shall see later, all solutions belong to $L_2(0, \infty)$. In the limit-point case we still have to exhibit a solution in L_2. It is fairly obvious from the procedure that

$$y_1(x, \lambda) + m(\lambda) y_2(x, \lambda) \in L_2(0, \infty). \tag{10.1.17}$$

To prove this, take a sequence $\{b_n\}$, $0 < b_n < b_{n+1} \to \infty$, and on each circle C_{b_n} a point m_n. We have then

$$\lim m_n = m(\lambda), \qquad \lim y(x; \lambda, m_n) = y(x; \lambda, m(\lambda)),$$

in the second case uniformly for x in any finite interval $(0, \omega)$. The sequence $\{\Im(m_n)\}$ is bounded above, say by y_0. Then for $b_n > \omega$

$$y_0 > \Im(m_n) = \nu \int_0^{b_n} |y(s; \lambda, m_n)|^2 \, ds > \nu \int_0^\omega |y(s; \lambda, m_n)|^2 \, ds,$$

and by the uniform convergence

$$y_0 \geq \nu \int_0^\omega |y(s; \lambda, m(\lambda))|^2 \, ds$$

for all ω. This proves (10.1.17). It also proves the important relation

$$\Im[m(\lambda)] = \nu \int_0^\infty |y(s; \lambda, m(\lambda))|^2 \, ds. \tag{10.1.18}$$

It should be noted that in the limit-point case, the multiples of $y(x; \lambda, m(\lambda))$ are the only solutions in $L_2(0, \infty)$. For if there were a second, linearly independent solution, in $L_2(0, \infty)$, then all solutions would have this property since $L_2(0, \infty)$ is a linear vector space. This contradicts (10.1.16), however.

If we apply the same limiting process in the limit-circle case, choosing the sequence $\{m_n\}$ so that it has a unique limit-point, necessarily on the limit-circle, then the same argument applies and shows that $y(x; \lambda, \lim m_n)$ exists, and is in $L_2(0, \infty)$. In this case $y_2(x, \lambda)$ is a linearly independent solution also in $L_2(0, \infty)$ so all solutions belong to this space. ▌

So far we have considered a fixed value of λ in the upper half-plane. We have to show that the result obtained is independent of the choice of λ as long as $\Im(\lambda) \neq 0$.

Theorem 10.1.2. *If for a particular value of λ equation* (10.1.1) *has two linearly independent solutions in $L_2(0, \infty)$, then this property holds for all values of λ, real or complex.*

Proof. Suppose that the equation has two linearly independent solutions in $L_2(0, \infty)$ for $\lambda = \lambda_0$. Then all solutions have this property, in particular the functions $y_1(x, \lambda_0)$ and $y_2(x, \lambda_0)$. Let us write

$$u_1(x) = y_1(x, \lambda_0), \qquad u_2(x) = y_2(x, \lambda_0).$$

Let $v(x)$ be an arbitrary non-trivial solution of

$$y'' + [\lambda - q(x)]y = 0$$

and let a be a positive number to be disposed of later. Let $u(x)$ be the solution of

$$y'' + [\lambda_0 - q(x)]y = 0$$

with the initial values

$$u(a) = v(a), \qquad u'(a) = v'(a).$$

Now form the integral equation

$$v(x) = u(x) + (\lambda - \lambda_0) \int_a^x [u_1(x)u_2(s) - u_2(x)u_1(s)]v(s) \, ds. \tag{10.1.19}$$

There is a unique solution and a simple calculation shows that it coincides with the solution $v(x)$ of the differential equation. Taking absolute values and using Schwarz's inequality, we get

$$|v(x)| \leq |u(x)| + |\lambda - \lambda_0| \, |u_1(x)| \left[\int_a^x |u_2(s)|^2 \, ds \int_a^x |v(s)|^2 \, ds\right]^{1/2}$$
$$+ |\lambda - \lambda_0| \, |u_2(x)| \left[\int_a^x |u_1(s)|^2 \, ds \int_a^x |v(s)|^2 \, ds\right]^{1/2}.$$

Now if A, B, C are positive numbers then

$$(A + B + C)^2 \le 3(A^2 + B^2 + C^2). \tag{10.1.20}$$

Hence, writing t instead of x,

$$\tfrac{1}{3}|v(t)|^2 \le |u(t)|^2 + |\lambda - \lambda_0|^2\left[|u_1(t)|^2 \int_a^t |u_2(s)|^2\,ds + |u_2(t)|^2 \int_a^t |u_1(s)|^2\,ds\right] \int_a^t |v(s)|^2\,ds.$$

This inequality we integrate with respect to t from a to x obtaining

$$\tfrac{1}{3}\int_a^x |v(t)|^2\,dt \le \int_a^x |u(t)|^2\,dt + |\lambda - \lambda_0|^2 \int_a^x \left\{|u_1(t)|^2 \int_a^t |u_2(s)|^2\,ds + |u_2(t)|^2 \int_a^t |u_1(s)|^2\,ds\right\} \int_a^t |v(s)|^2\,ds\,dt. \tag{10.1.21}$$

To simplify we set

$$B(x) = \max\,[|u_1(x)|, \quad |u_2(x)|], \qquad \int_a^\infty B^2(s)\,ds = J_0,$$

$$\int_a^\infty |u(s)|^2\,ds = J, \qquad \int_a^x |v(s)|^2\,ds = V(x).$$

Then the coefficient of $|\lambda - \lambda_0|^2$ in (10.1.21) is dominated by

$$2V(x)\int_a^x B^2(t) \int_a^t B^2(s)\,ds\,dt = V(x)\left[\int_a^x B^2(t)\,dt\right]^2 < J_0^2 V(x),$$

and the inequality becomes

$$V(x) < 3J + 3|\lambda - \lambda_0|^2 J_0^2 V(x). \tag{10.1.22}$$

Now a, the lower limit of integration, is at our disposal and can be chosen in advance so large that

$$6|\lambda - \lambda_0|^2 J_0^2 < 1.$$

Solving for $V(x)$ in (10.1.22) we obtain

$$V(x) = \int_a^x |v(s)|^2\,ds < 6J$$

for all x, i.e. $v(x) \in L_2(a, \infty)$ and hence also to $L_2(0, \infty)$. Since $v(x)$ was an arbitrary solution of (10.1.1), it is seen that all solutions are in $L_2(0, \infty)$. ▌

Corollary 1. The limit-circle case holds iff the equation

$$y'' - q(x)y = 0 \tag{10.1.23}$$

has two linearly independent solutions in $L_2(0, \infty)$.

Corollary 2. The limit-point case is present either for all non-real values of λ or for no such value.

The first Corollary enables us to bring the results of Chapter 9 to bear on this problem. Thus we obtain:

Theorem 10.1.3. *A sufficient condition for the limit-circle case to hold is that* (i) $q(x) = -F(x)$ *is negative,* (ii) $F(x)$ *has a continuous derivative,* (iii) $W(x) \equiv F'(x)[F(x)]^{-3/2} \in BV(0, \infty)$, (iv) $\lim_{x\to\infty} W(x) = 0$, *and* (v) $[F(x)]^{-1/2} \in L(0, \infty)$.

Proof. Conditions (i)–(iv) are those of Theorem 9.5.3 and imply that the solutions of (10.1.23) are of the form

$$C[F(x)]^{-1/4}[1 + o(1)] \sin [\theta(x)]$$

which is in $L_2(0, \infty)$ by condition (v). ▮

A sufficient condition for the limit-point case is given by

Theorem 10.1.4. *Suppose that $q(x)$ is bounded below. Then the limit-point case holds and the solution $y(x; \lambda, m(\lambda))$ also satisfies the conditions*

i) $\lim_{x\to\infty} y(x)y'(x) = 0$,

ii) $y'(x) \in L_2(0, \infty)$,

iii) $|q(x)|^{1/2}y(x) \in L_2(0, \infty)$.

Proof. Set

$$\inf q(x) = q_0 > -\infty \tag{10.1.24}$$

and let $y(x) = y(x; \lambda, m)$ denote a solution in $L_2(0, \infty)$. Then by (10.1.6)

$$\overline{y(x)}y'(x) = A + \int_0^x |y'(s)|^2\, ds - \int_0^x [\lambda - q(s)]|y(s)|^2\, ds$$

where

$$A = \overline{y(0)}y'(0) = A_1 + iA_2, \qquad A_2 = \Im(m),$$

is given by (10.1.10) and

$$\Im(m) = \nu \int_0^\infty |y(s)|^2\, ds$$

by (10.1.18) which holds if m is on the limit-circle, as we may assume. Since

$$\Im[\overline{y(x)}y'(x)] = A_2 - \nu \int_0^x |y(s)|^2\, ds$$

we see that

$$\lim_{x\to\infty} \Im[\overline{y(x)}y'(x)] = 0. \tag{10.1.25}$$

Taking the real part instead we obtain

$$\Re[\overline{y(x)}y'(x)] = A_1 + \int_0^x |y'(s)|^2\,ds - \int_0^x [\mu - q(s)]|y(s)|^2\,ds. \tag{10.1.26}$$

Here

$$-\int_0^x [\mu - q(s)]|y(s)|^2\,ds \ge (q_0 - \mu)\int_0^x |y(s)|^2\,ds$$

is bounded below as $x \to \infty$. Further

$$2\Re[\overline{y(x)}y'(x)] = \frac{d}{dx}|y(x)|^2.$$

Now, either the second and third terms in the right member of (10.1.26) tend to finite limits as $x \to \infty$ or one or both go to $+\infty$. The second alternative implies that $|y(x)|$ is ultimately increasing and goes to $+\infty$ and this contradicts $y(x) \in L_2(0, \infty)$. This proves assertions (ii) and (iii).

Since the integrals tend to finite limits when $x \to +\infty$, we see that (10.1.26) tends to a finite limit as x goes to infinity. This limit must be 0 again because $y(x) \in L_2(0, \infty)$. Combining this with (10.1.25) we see that (i) holds.

We still have to show that we are in the limit-point case. Now the limit-circle case would be present iff $y_2(x, \lambda) \in L_2(0, \infty)$. Suppose this were the case. Then (10.1.7) shows that

$$\lim_{x\to\infty} \Im[\overline{y_2(x, \lambda)}y_2'(x, \lambda)] \equiv l$$

exists and is not zero. Since $y_2(x, \lambda) \in L_2(0, \infty)$ by assumption, we have $|y_2(x, \lambda)| < \varepsilon$, a pre-assigned small positive number, for all large x outside a set of small measure. This requires that $|y_2'(x, \lambda)| > \frac{1}{2}|l|/\varepsilon$ for such values of x and implies that $y_2'(x, \lambda)$ is not L_2. Going back to (10.1.26) with $y(x)$ replaced by $y_2(x, \lambda)$ and A_1 by $\frac{1}{2}\sin 2\alpha$, we see that the third term on the right is still bounded below while the second goes to $+\infty$ with x. This gives

$$\lim_{x\to\infty} |y_2(x, \lambda)| = \infty$$

and contradicts the assumption that $y_2(x, \lambda) \in L_2(0, \infty)$. Hence the limit-point case is present. ∎

The condition $q(x) \ge q_0 > -\infty$ is sufficient but not necessary for the limit-point case. In fact, a much weaker condition has been found by E. A. Coddington and N. Levinson as follows.

Theorem 10.1.5. *The limit-point case holds if a positive differentiable function $M(x)$ and two positive constants k_1 and k_2 can be found such that for $x \geq a \geq 0$, (1) $q(x) \geq -k_1 M(x)$, (2) $|M'(x)|[M(x)]^{-3/2} \leq k_2$, and (3) $\int_a^\infty [M(x)]^{-1/2}\,dx = +\infty$.*

Proof. The idea of the proof is to show that if $y(x)$ is a real solution in $L_2(0, \infty)$ of

$$y'' - q(x)y = 0$$

and if (1) and (2) hold then

$$\int_a^\infty \frac{[y'(x)]^2}{M(x)}\,dx \tag{10.1.27}$$

is necessarily convergent. Now if there were two linearly independent solutions, $y_1(x)$ and $y_2(x)$ both in $L_2(0, \infty)$, then we may assume their Wronskian to be 1. In the identity

$$y_1(x)\{y_2'(x)[M(x)]^{-1/2}\} - y_2(x)\{y_1'(x)[M(x)]^{-1/2}\} = [M(x)]^{-1/2} \tag{10.1.28}$$

the left member belongs to $L(a, \infty)$ by (10.1.27) and Schwarz's inequality while the right member does not by condition (3) and a contradiction results.

To prove the convergence of (10.1.27) we argue, with the authors quoted, as follows. We have

$$\int_a^x \frac{y(s)y''(s)}{M(s)}\,ds = \int_a^x \frac{q(s)[y(s)]^2}{M(s)}\,ds \geq -k_1 \int_a^x [y(s)]^2\,ds.$$

Integration by parts of the first member gives

$$\left[\frac{y(s)y'(s)}{M(s)}\right]_a^x - \int_a^x \frac{[y'(s)]^2}{M(s)}\,ds + \int_a^x \frac{y(s)y'(s)M'(s)}{[M(s)]^2}\,ds.$$

Applying Schwarz's inequality to the second integral we see that it does not exceed

$$\left\{\int_a^x \frac{[M'(s)]^2}{[M(s)]^3}[y(s)]^2\,ds \int_a^x \frac{[y'(s)]^2}{M(s)}\,ds\right\}^{1/2} \leq k_2\left\{\int_a^\infty [y(s)]^2\,ds\right\}^{1/2}[H(x)]^{1/2}$$

where

$$H(x) = \int_a^x \frac{[y'(s)]^2}{M(s)}\,ds.$$

Hence

$$\frac{y(x)y'(x)}{M(x)} > \frac{y(a)y'(a)}{M(a)} + H(x) - k_2\left\{\int_a^\infty [y(s)]^2\,ds\right\}^{1/2}[H(x)]^{1/2}$$
$$- k_1 \int_a^\infty [y(s)]^2\,ds.$$

If now (10.1.27) should diverge, then $H(x) \to +\infty$ and $y(x)y'(x)$ is ultimately positive. This is not consistent with the assumption that $y(x) \in L_2(0, \infty)$. It follows that $H(x)$ is bounded and (10.1.28) shows that the limit-circle case cannot hold. ▮

As a particular instance, we may take $M(x) = x^2$ which satisfies all the conditions. The choice $q(x) = -x^2$ is extreme in two respects. In the first place, if $q(x) = -x^\gamma$, $0 \le \gamma$, then the limit-point case holds for $0 \le \gamma \le 2$ but not for $2 < \gamma$. Secondly, if $\gamma = 2$ and $y(x, \nu i) \in L_2(0, \infty)$, then $y'(x, \nu i)$ and $|q(x)|^{1/2}y(x, \nu i)$ are in $L_2(0, \infty)$ iff $\nu > 2$. Thus the conclusions (ii) and (iii) under Theorem 10.1.4 do not necessarily hold in the limit-point case without further restrictions on $q(x)$. They do hold, however, for all $\nu > 0$ if $q(x) = -x^\gamma$, $0 < \gamma < 2$, so boundedness below is not a necessary condition for Theorem 10.1.4 to be valid.

EXERCISE 10.1

1. Verify (10.1.12).
2. If S, T, U, V are given by (10.1.13), show that

$$U^2 + V^2 = \left(\frac{1}{\nu} V + S\right)T.$$

[*Hint*: Compute r_b from (10.1.14) and compare with (10.1.12).]

3. Find the equation of the limit circle.
4. Verify (10.1.20) and show that equality holds iff $A = B = C$.
5. Verify that the limit point-case holds if $q(x)$ has one of the following forms:

   a. $\cos x - \sin x$. b. $\cosh x - \sinh x$. c. $ax + b$.

6. If $q(x) = -x^\gamma$, $\gamma \ge 0$, show that the limit-circle case holds for $\gamma > 2$.
7. Use the asymptotic form of the solutions to show that the limit-point case holds for $0 \le \gamma \le 2$.
8. Show that the conclusions of Theorem 10.1.4 hold if $0 < \gamma < 2$. [*Hint:* Use the transformation of Liouville and find the asymptotic behavior of the subdominant solution for $\Im(\lambda) > 0$.]
9. Show that conclusions (ii) and (iii) of Theorem 10.1.4 with $\lambda = \nu i$, $\gamma = 2$, hold iff $\nu > 2$.
10. Show that these conclusions hold for no value of ν if

$$q(x) = -(x + 1)^2[\log (x + 1)]^2.$$

Is this a limit-point case?

11. Let $y_1(x)$ and $y_2(x)$ be the solutions of (10.1.23) defined by (10.1.2) and suppose they are in $L_2(0, \infty)$. The solutions of (10.1.1) with the same initial values have the form

$$y_k(x, \lambda) = \sum_{n=0}^{\infty} y_{k,n}(x)\lambda^n$$

where $y_{k,0}(x) = y_k(x)$ and $y_{k,n}(0) = y'_{k,n}(0) = 0$, $n > 0$. Show that

$$y_{k,n}(x) = \int_x^{\infty} [y_2(x)y_1(s) - y_1(x)y_2(s)]y_{k,n-1}(s)\, ds.$$

Use induction to prove that

$$|y_{k,n}(x)| \leq \frac{2^n}{n!} B(x)\left[\int_x^{\infty} B^2(s)\, ds\right]^n$$

where $B(x) = \max\,[|y_1(x)|, |y_2(x)|]$, and hence that

$$\|y_{k,n}(\cdot)\|_2 \leq \frac{2^n}{n!}\left[\int_0^{\infty} B^2(s)\, ds\right]^{n+1/2}.$$

Show that

$$\sum_{n=0}^{\infty} \|y_{k,n}(\cdot)\|_2\lambda^n$$

is an entire function of order ≤ 1.

10.2 THE $m(\lambda)$ FUNCTIONS

In this section we shall be concerned mainly with the limit-point case and we start with a detailed discussion of the functions $m(\lambda)$. To do this we begin with the function $m = m(\lambda, b, \beta)$ of (10.1.5). This we write

$$m(\lambda, b, \beta) = -\frac{\cos\beta y_1(b, \lambda) + \sin\beta y'_1(b, \lambda)}{\cos\beta y_2(b, \lambda) + \sin\beta y'_2(b, \lambda)}. \tag{10.2.1}$$

In the limit-point case the value of β is immaterial for the existence of the limit as $b \to \infty$. To simplify the discussion we take $\beta = 0$ and write

$$m(\lambda, b) = -\frac{y_1(b, \lambda)}{y_2(b, \lambda)}. \tag{10.2.2}$$

For b fixed, $0 < b < \infty$, this is the quotient of two entire functions each of order $\frac{1}{2}$ and normal type.

Lemma 10.2.1. *The function $m(\lambda, b)$ is a meromorphic function of λ with simple real poles $\{\lambda_n(b)\}$, the zeros of $y_2(b, \lambda)$. The residue at $\lambda = \lambda_n(b)$ is*

$$r_n(b) = -\left\{\int_0^b [y_2(s, \lambda_n(b))]^2\, ds\right\}^{-1}. \tag{10.2.3}$$

For fixed b

$$\lim_{n\to\infty} n^{-2}\lambda_n(b) = \left(\frac{\pi}{b}\right)^2 \tag{10.2.4}$$

and for $\alpha \not\equiv \frac{1}{2}\pi (\mathrm{mod}\ \pi)$ *and* $q(x)$ *continuously differentiable*

$$0 < A(b) < -r_n(b) < B(b) < \infty. \tag{10.2.5}$$

Proof. That the zeros of $y_2(b, \lambda)$ are all real follows from (10.1.7). That (10.2.4) holds follows from the Corollary of Theorem 8.3.4 and formula (8.3.25). To prove that the poles are simple we use (10.1.11), which says that

$$\Im[m(\lambda, b)] = \nu \int_0^b |y_1(s, \lambda) + m(\lambda, b) y_2(s, \lambda)|^2 \, ds. \tag{10.2.6}$$

Here we set

$$\lambda = \lambda_n(b) + i\nu = \lambda_n + i\nu.$$

Suppose that the pole is of order p. Then as $\nu \downarrow 0$ the right member becomes infinite as a constant multiple of ν^{1-2p} while the left member becomes infinite at most as ν^{-p}. This forces p to be 1. We denote the residue by $r_n(b)$. It is necessarily a real number. Multiply both sides of (10.2.6) by ν and let $\nu \downarrow 0$. We get

$$-r_n(b) = [r_n(b)]^2 \int_0^b [y_2(s, \lambda_n)]^2 \, ds$$

and this gives (10.2.3) since $r_n(b) \neq 0$. Finally, for (10.2.5) we use the analogue of (8.4.18) with $\vartheta_a \neq 0$ since $\cos \alpha \neq 0$. We thus obtain (10.2.5) where the bounds presumably depend upon b. Since (8.4.18) is derived under the assumption that $q(x)$ is continuously differentiable, this hypothesis is used in proving (10.2.5). It is presumably superfluous. ▮

We now define a partial fraction series

$$m_0(\lambda, b) = \sum_{n=1}^{\infty} \frac{r_n(b)}{\lambda - \lambda_n(b)} \cdot \tag{10.2.7}$$

By virtue of (10.2.4) and (10.2.5) the series converges for all $\lambda \neq \lambda_n(b)$. If we omit fixed neighborhoods of the poles, the series converges uniformly in the remainder of the λ-plane. This implies

Lemma 10.2.2. *In the sector* $0 < \varepsilon \leq \arg \lambda < 2\pi - \varepsilon$

$$\lim m_0(\lambda, b) = 0. \tag{10.2.8}$$

We now come to the main tool of the discussion, a theorem which describes the asymptotic behavior of $m(\lambda, b)$ in sectors not containing the real axis. The argument does not require differentiability of $q(x)$.

Theorem 10.2.1. *Let* $\alpha \not\equiv \frac{1}{2}\pi(\text{mod } \pi)$ *and let* $\lambda \to \infty$ *in the sector* $0 < \varepsilon \leq \arg \lambda \leq \pi - \varepsilon$. *Then*

$$\lim m(\lambda, b) = -\tan \alpha \qquad (10.2.9)$$

for all b with $b \geq 1$. *Moreover*

$$R(\lambda, b, \alpha) = R(\lambda) \equiv |\lambda|^{1/2}|m(\lambda, b) + \tan \alpha| \qquad (10.2.10)$$

is bounded away from 0 and ∞ *as* $\lambda \to \infty$ *in the sector and this holds uniformly with respect to b. If* $\alpha \equiv \frac{1}{2}\pi$ *(mod* π*), then*

$$S(\lambda, b) \equiv |\lambda|^{-1/2}|m(\lambda, b)| \qquad (10.2.11)$$

is bounded away from 0 and ∞ *as* $\lambda \to \infty$, *again uniformly in b.*

The proof is based on the following two lemmas.

Lemma 10.2.3. *If* $|q(x)| \leq q$ *for* $0 \leq x \leq 1$ *and if* $y(x, \lambda)$ *is the solution of* (10.1.1) *with*

$$y(0, \lambda) = c, \qquad y'(0, \lambda) = d, \qquad (10.2.12)$$

then for $0 \leq x \leq \delta \equiv [2(|\lambda| + q)]^{-1/2}$ *we have*

$$y(x, \lambda) = c(1 + \theta_1) + d(1 + \theta_2)x \qquad (10.2.13)$$

where $|\theta_k| \leq \frac{1}{3}$ *for* $k = 1, 2$, *and* $|\lambda| > 1$.

Lemma 10.2.4. *Under the same assumptions and for* $b \geq \delta$

$$\int_0^b |y(s, \lambda)|^2\, ds > \tfrac{4}{9}\delta[|c|^2 - 4|cd|\delta + \tfrac{1}{3}|d|^2\delta^2]. \qquad (10.2.14)$$

Proof of Lemma 10.2.3. From the obvious integral equation

$$y(x, \lambda) = c + dx - \int_0^x (x - s)[\lambda - q(s)]y(s, \lambda)\, ds, \qquad (10.2.15)$$

setting

$$M(x) \equiv \max_{0 \leq s \leq x} |y(s, \lambda)|, \qquad 0 \leq x \leq 1,$$

we obtain

$$M(x) \leq |c| + |d|x + (|\lambda| + q)\tfrac{1}{2}M(x)x^2.$$

If now x is restricted to the shorter interval $[0, \delta]$ with δ defined above, it is seen that $(|\lambda| + q)x^2 \leq \frac{1}{2}$ and

$$M(x) \leq \tfrac{4}{3}(|c| + |d|x).$$

Using (10.2.15) once more we get

$$\begin{aligned}|y(x, \lambda) - c - dx| &\leq \tfrac{4}{3}(|\lambda| + q)\int_0^x (x - s)(|c| + |d|s)\, ds\\ &= \tfrac{4}{3}(|\lambda| + q)(\tfrac{1}{2}|c|x^2 + \tfrac{1}{3}|d|x^3)\\ &< \tfrac{1}{3}(|c| + |d|x)\end{aligned}$$

which is the desired result. ▮

Proof of Lemma 10.2.4. After some simplification (10.2.13) gives

$$|y(x, \lambda)|^2 = |c(1 + \theta_1) + d(1 + \theta_2)x|^2$$
$$> \tfrac{4}{9}(|c|^2 - 8|cd|x + |d|^2x^2).$$

Integrating this from 0 to δ we get (10.2.14) provided $b \geq \delta$. ∎

Proof of Theorem 10.2.1. We take

$$y(x, \lambda) = y_1(x, \lambda) + m(\lambda, b)y_2(x, \lambda)$$

and use (10.1.11), i.e.

$$\Im[m(\lambda, b)] = \nu \int_0^b |y_1(s, \lambda) + m(\lambda, b)y_2(s, \lambda)|^2\, ds \qquad (10.2.16)$$

where we estimate the right member with (10.2.14). Here

$$c = \sin \alpha + m(\lambda, b) \cos \alpha, \qquad d = -\cos \alpha + m(\lambda, b) \sin \alpha$$

and

$$|m(\lambda, b)| \geq \Im[m(\lambda, b)] > 0.$$

Formula (10.2.14) now gives

$$|m(\lambda, b)| > \tfrac{4}{9}\delta\nu[|\sin \alpha + m(\lambda, b) \cos \alpha|^2 - 4|\sin \alpha + m(\lambda, b) \cos \alpha| \times |\cos \alpha - m(\lambda, b) \sin \alpha|\delta + \tfrac{1}{3}|\cos \alpha - m(\lambda, b) \sin \alpha|^2\, \delta^2]. \qquad (10.2.17)$$

Here we set

$$|m(\lambda, b)| \equiv Q(\lambda), \qquad |\sin \alpha| = \sigma, \qquad |\cos \alpha| = \gamma$$

where to start with $\gamma \neq 0$. We then see that (10.2.17) implies the inequality

$$Q(\lambda) > \tfrac{4}{9}\delta\nu\{[\sigma - \gamma Q(\lambda)]^2 - 4[\sigma + \gamma Q(\lambda)][\gamma + \sigma Q(\lambda)]\delta + \tfrac{1}{3}[\gamma - \sigma Q(\lambda)]^2\delta^2\}. \qquad (10.2.18)$$

Here $\varepsilon \leq \arg \lambda \leq \pi - \varepsilon$ so that $\nu \geq \sin \varepsilon \cdot |\lambda|$ and

$$\delta\nu > \frac{\sin \varepsilon \cdot |\lambda|}{[2(|\lambda| + q)]^{1/2}} \qquad (10.2.19)$$

which goes to infinity with $|\lambda|$. On the other hand

$$2\delta < \frac{1}{\delta\nu} < 4\delta \operatorname{cosec} \varepsilon, \qquad (10.2.20)$$

where the second half holds if $|\lambda| > q$.

Now (10.2.18) asserts that a certain quadratic polynomial

$$AQ^2 - BQ + C \qquad (10.2.21)$$

is negative for a positive value of $Q = Q(\lambda)$. Here

$$A = (\gamma - 2\sigma\delta)^2 - \tfrac{11}{3}(\sigma\delta)^2$$

which is positive for $\gamma > (2 + \sqrt{\frac{11}{3}})\sigma\delta$ or for

$$|\cot \alpha| > (2 + \sqrt{\tfrac{11}{3}})\delta.$$

Since $\delta \to 0$ and $\alpha \not\equiv \frac{1}{2}\pi \pmod{\pi}$, this condition is ultimately satisfied so that $A > 0$ and the quadratic has real roots. This implies that $Q(\lambda)$ lies between these roots. These roots tend to coincidence when $\delta \to 0$ and the quadratic reduces to

$$(\gamma Q - \sigma)^2 = 0.$$

It follows that

$$\lim Q(\lambda) = \lim |m(\lambda, b)| = |\tan \alpha|. \tag{10.2.22}$$

This holds uniformly with respect to b and α provided $b \geq 1$ and α stays outside of small intervals surrounding $\pm\frac{1}{2}\pi$.

We now return to (10.2.17). As $\lambda \to \infty$ in the sector, so does $\delta\nu$ while $Q(\lambda)$ is bounded. This says that

$$\lim |\sin \alpha + m(\lambda, b) \cos \alpha| = 0$$

and this gives (10.2.9) since $\cos \alpha \neq 0$.

To get (10.2.10) we note that

$$|m(\lambda, b) + \tan \alpha| > \Im[m(\lambda, b)].$$

Hence we can replace $|m(\lambda, b)|$ in the left member of (10.2.17) by

$$|m(\lambda, b) + \tan \alpha|.$$

We then introduce the function $R(\lambda)$ of (10.2.10) in the inequality and obtain

$$\begin{aligned} R(\lambda) > \tfrac{4}{3}d(\lambda) \cos^2 \alpha[R(\lambda)]^2 - \tfrac{16}{9}[d(\lambda)]^2|\cos \alpha| M(\lambda) R(\lambda) \\ + \tfrac{4}{27}[d(\lambda)]^3[M(\lambda)]^2. \end{aligned} \tag{10.2.23}$$

Here

$$d(\lambda) = \frac{\nu\delta}{|\lambda|^{1/2}} \to \tfrac{1}{2}\sqrt{2} \sin \theta, \qquad \theta = \arg \lambda,$$

$$M(\lambda) = |\cos \alpha - m(\lambda, b) \sin \alpha| \to |\sec \alpha|,$$

if λ goes radially to infinity.

The corresponding quadratic obviously has real roots and, since the sum and products of the roots are positive, the roots are also positive. In the limit, letting $\lambda \to \infty$ radially in the sector, the quadratic becomes

$$R^2 - \sqrt{2}(2 \sin \theta + \tfrac{9}{4} \operatorname{cosec} \theta) \sec^2 \alpha \; R + \tfrac{1}{6} \sin^2 \theta \sec^4 \alpha = 0. \tag{10.2.24}$$

This equation has positive roots $R_1(\alpha, \theta) < R_2(\alpha, \theta)$ and we conclude that

$$R_1(\alpha, \theta) \leq \liminf R(\lambda) \leq \limsup R(\lambda) \leq R_2(\alpha, \theta). \tag{10.2.25}$$

This completes the proof of the case $\alpha \not\equiv \frac{1}{2}\pi \pmod{\pi}$.

Suppose now that $\gamma = \cos\alpha = 0$ so that $\sigma = 1$ and the inequality (10.2.17) reduces to

$$|m(\lambda, b)| > \tfrac{4}{9}\delta\nu[1 - 4|m(\lambda, b)|\delta + \tfrac{1}{3}|m(\lambda, b)|^2\delta^2]. \tag{10.2.26}$$

Here we use the second half of (10.2.20). We set

$$\delta|m(\lambda, b)| = T(\lambda)$$

and conclude that $T(\lambda)$ must lie between the two positive roots of the equation

$$T^2 - (12 + 27 \operatorname{cosec} \varepsilon)T + 3 = 0$$

and this fact is equivalent to (10.2.11). ∎

Corollary 1. *The same asymptotic behavior holds in the sector*

$$-\pi + \varepsilon < \arg \lambda < -\varepsilon.$$

Corollary 2. *The same asymptotic behavior holds for $m(\lambda)$ in the sectors.* For we have

$$\Im[m(\lambda)] = \nu \int_0^\infty |y_1(s, \lambda) + m(\lambda) y_2(s, \lambda)|^2 \, ds \tag{10.2.27}$$

and Lemma 10.2.4 holds also for $b = \infty$ whenever the integral exists.

We can now derive the analytical representation of $m(\lambda, b)$ by a Cauchy-Stieltjes integral. We shall have to use a number of results of complex function theory for which the reader is referred to the author's *Analytic Function Theory*, Vol. II, especially Section 14.4 and Theorem 18.1.1. We state what is needed as lemmas.

First some notation and terminology. Growth and value distribution properties of entire and meromorphic functions are measured by various so-called *characteristic functions*, of which R. Nevanlinna's is the easiest to handle. If $f(0) \neq 0$, and $f(z)$ is an entire or meromorphic function, set

$$m(r, \infty; f) = \frac{1}{2\pi} \int_0^{2\pi} \log^+ |f(r\, e^{i\theta})| \, d\theta, \tag{10.2.28}$$

$$N(r, \infty; f) = \int_0^r n(s, \infty; f) \frac{ds}{s}, \tag{10.2.29}$$

and define the characteristic function

$$T(r; f) = m(r, \infty; f) + N(r, \infty; f). \tag{10.2.30}$$

Here $\log^+ a = \max(\log a, 0)$ and $n(s, \infty; f)$ is the number of poles, each counted with its proper multiplicity, located in the disk $|z| \leq s$. $T(r, f)$ as defined, measures the average affinity of $f(z)$ for the value infinity, but the average affinity is the same for all values up to a bounded additive function.

$T(r; f)$ is a monotone increasing convex function of $\log r$.

If $f(z)$ is an entire function we have

$$T(r;f) = m(r, \infty; f) \leq \log M(r;f) \tag{10.2.31}$$

where $M(r;f)$ is the *maximum modulus.*

The *order* of a meromorphic function is by definition

$$\sigma[f] = \limsup \frac{\log T(r,f)}{\log r}. \tag{10.2.32}$$

For an entire function $T(r;f)$ is usually replaced by $\log M(r;f)$ in this definition. This substitution does not affect the numerical value of the order. The following lemma shows how characteristic functions behave under elementary algebraic operations.

Lemma 10.2.5. *If f, f_1, f_2 are meromorphic functions, then*

$$T\left(r;\frac{1}{f}\right) = T(r;f) - \log|f(0)|, \tag{10.2.33}$$

$$T(r;f_1f_2) \leq T(r;f_1) + T(r;f_2), \tag{10.2.34}$$

$$T(r;f_1 + f_2) \leq T(r;f_1) + T(r;f_2) + \log 2. \tag{10.2.35}$$

We need also a theorem due to E. Phragmén (1863–1937).

Lemma 10.2.6. *If $f(z)$ is holomorphic in a sector S: $\theta_1 \leq \arg z \leq \theta_2$ where $\theta_2 - \theta_1 = \pi/\gamma$, if $f(z)$ is bounded on the rays bounding S, and if*

$$\log|f(r\,e^{i\theta})| = o(r^\gamma) \tag{10.2.36}$$

in S, then f is also bounded in S.

This is the original Phragmén-Lindelöf theorem. It shows that a function cannot be of too modest a growth in a sector without boundedness on the frontier inducing boundedness in the interior.

We shall now introduce a class of step functions $\rho(t, b)$ which are basic for our problem. We set

$$\begin{aligned} \rho(t, b) &= -\sum_{0<\lambda_n(b)\leq t} r_n(b), \qquad 0 < t, \\ \rho(t, b) &= \sum_{t<\lambda_n(b)\leq 0} r_n(b), \qquad t \leq 0. \end{aligned} \tag{10.2.37}$$

These functions are *non-decreasing* and *right-hand continuous* for all t. We have $\rho(t, b) \leq 0$ for $t \leq 0$, ≥ 0 for $t > 0$. Further,

$$\rho[\lambda_n(b) + 0, b] - \rho[\lambda_n(b) - 0, b] = -r_n(b),$$

$$\rho(0, b) = \rho(0 + 0, b) = 0.$$

These are the *spectral functions* of the boundary value problem

$$\sin \alpha \; y(0, \lambda) - \cos \alpha \; y'(0, \lambda) = 0, \qquad y(b, \lambda) = 0$$

which is satisfied by the function $y_2(x, \lambda_n(b))$.

We can now formulate and prove the representation theorem.

Theorem 10.2.2. *If* $\alpha \not\equiv \frac{1}{2}\pi \pmod{\pi}$ *and* $q(x)$ *is continuously differentiable, then*

$$m(\lambda, b) = \int_{-\infty}^{\infty} \frac{d\rho(t, b)}{t - \lambda} - \tan \alpha. \tag{10.2.38}$$

There exist positive constants C_1 *and* C_2*, independent of* b*, such that for* $b > 1$

$$|\rho(t, b)| \le C_1 + C_2 |t|^{1/2}. \tag{10.2.39}$$

Proof. We compare the integral in (10.2.38) with the series defined by (10.2.7) and see that the integral represents $m_0(\lambda, b)$ by virtue of the definition of $\rho(t, b)$. The integral clearly converges uniformly in λ outside any strip $|\Im(\lambda)| \le \varepsilon$. Now the left member of (10.2.38) is a meromorphic function of λ whose canonical partial fraction expansion is given by $m_0(\lambda, b)$. The Mittag-Leffler theorem on partial fractions then asserts that

$$m(\lambda, b) = m_0(\lambda, b) + E(\lambda, b) \tag{10.2.40}$$

where $E(\lambda, b)$ is an entire function of λ. It is to be shown that this entire function reduces to the constant $-\tan \alpha$. Here is where the function theoretical concepts introduced above are needed.

Formula (10.2.4) shows that

$$N(r, \infty; m_0) = \frac{2b}{\pi} \sqrt{r}\,[1 + o(1)]. \tag{10.2.41}$$

From this we conclude that the same formula also represents $T(r; m_0)$. For the additive component $m(r, \infty; m_0)$ is bounded on a sequence of circles $|\lambda| = r_n \to \infty$ by the uniform convergence of the series (10.2.7) outside small disks around the poles. Further, $T(r; m_0)$ is an increasing function of r, so the oscillations of $m(r, \infty; m_0)$ do not affect the outcome. This shows that

$$\sigma(m_0) = \tfrac{1}{2}.$$

On the other hand,

$$m(\lambda, b) = -\frac{y_1(b, \lambda)}{y_2(b, \lambda)},$$

where $y_1(b, \lambda)$ and $y_2(b, \lambda)$ are entire functions of λ of order $\frac{1}{2}$ and normal type whence it follows that

$$T(r; y_k) \le B_k \sqrt{r}\,[1 + o(1)], \qquad k = 1, 2.$$

By Lemma 10.2.5

$$T(r; m) \leq (B_1 + B_2)\sqrt{r}\,[1 + o(1)]$$

and hence by (10.2.35)

$$T(r; E) = T(r; m - m_0) \leq \left(B_1 + B_2 + \frac{2b}{\pi}\right)\sqrt{r}\,[1 + o(1)].$$

This shows that $E(\lambda, b)$ is an entire function of the order at most $\frac{1}{2}$, and a normal type of its order.

Now we use Theorem 10.2.1 which asserts that

$$\lim m(\lambda, b) = -\tan \alpha,$$

if $\lambda \to \infty$ in the sectors $0 < \varepsilon \leq \arg(\pm\lambda) \leq \pi - \varepsilon$. On the other hand, Lemma 10.2.2 says that

$$\lim m_0(\lambda, b) = 0$$

in the same sectors so it follows that

$$\lim E(\lambda, b) = -\tan \alpha. \tag{10.2.42}$$

Now Lemma 10.2.6 applies: $\log |E(r\,e^{i\theta}, b)| = O(\sqrt{r})$ in two sectors each of angular opening 2ε, and is bounded on the rays bounding the sectors. Hence $E(\lambda, b)$ is bounded also in the remaining sectors and thus bounded in the whole plane. By the Liouville theorem such a function is a constant and (10.2.42) shows that this constant must be $-\tan \alpha$. This completes the proof of (10.2.38).

We still have to get the growth properties of $\rho(t, b)$ as a function of t. Here Theorem 10.2.1 is used once more, more precisely (10.2.10). We set $\lambda = i\nu$ and take the imaginary part of (10.2.38) thus obtaining

$$\Im[m(i\nu, b)] = \nu \int_{-\infty}^{\infty} \frac{d\rho(t, b)}{t^2 + \nu^2}. \tag{10.2.43}$$

This exceeds

$$\nu \int_{-\nu}^{\nu} \frac{d\rho(t, b)}{t^2 + \nu^2} > \frac{1}{2\nu}\,[\rho(\nu, b) - \rho(-\nu, b)].$$

On the other hand, (10.2.38) asserts the existence of positive numbers C and t_0, independent of b, such that

$$\Im[m(i\nu, b)] < |m(i\nu, b) + \tan \alpha| < \tfrac{1}{2}C\nu^{-1/2}, \qquad t_0 \leq \nu.$$

Combining the last two inequalities and replacing ν by t we get

$$\rho(t, b) - \rho(-t, b) < Ct^{1/2}, \qquad t_0 \leq t.$$

Here $\rho(-t, b) \leq 0$ so that

$$|\rho(t, b)| \leq C|t|^{1/2}, \qquad t_0 \leq |t|.$$

Since $\rho(t, b)$ is non-decreasing we have

$$|\rho(t, b)| \leq Ct_0^{1/2}, \qquad |t| \leq t_0.$$

These two inequalities together clearly imply (10.2.39). ∎

The most important property of the family of spectral functions $\{\rho(t, b)\}$ is its *compactness*. (Cf. Section 1.6 for this notion in connection with continuous functions.) In the present case the result is closely related to the so-called Helly Theorem [Eduard Helly, 1884–1943] of 1921, for which the reader may consult D. V. Widder, *The Laplace Transform*, pp. 26–33.

Theorem 10.2.3. *There exists a unique non-decreasing right-continuous function $\rho(t)$ such that for any sequence $\{b_n\}$, $0 < b_n < b_{n+1} \to \infty$,*

$$\lim_{n\to\infty} \rho(t, b_n) = \rho(t) \tag{10.2.44}$$

at all points of continuity of $\rho(t)$ and

$$|\rho(t)| \leq C_1 + C_2|t|^{1/2}. \tag{10.2.45}$$

This is under the assumption that (10.1.1) *belongs to the limit-point case.*

Proof. Up to a point we can imitate the argument used in proving Theorem 1.6.2. We start with a finite interval $[-A, A]$ and let $\{t_n\}$ denote an arrangement of the rational numbers in the interval into a sequence. Let $\{\rho(t, b_n)\}$ be a sequence of spectral functions with $0 < b_n < b_{n+1} \to \infty$. By (10.2.39)

$$|\rho(t, b)| \leq C_1 + C_2A^{1/2}, \qquad -A \leq t \leq A, \tag{10.2.46}$$

so the family is uniformly bounded in $[-A, A]$. In the manner shown in the proof of Theorem 1.6.2 we can find a diagonal subsequence, say $\{\rho(t, \beta_p)\}$, which converges at all points t_n in $[-A, A]$. This defines a limit function $\rho(t)$ on the rational points in $[-A, A]$. Since $t_j < t_k$ implies

$$\rho(t_j, \beta_p) \leq \rho(t_k, \beta_p)$$

for all p, we have also

$$\rho(t_j) \leq \rho(t_k)$$

and $\rho(t_j)$ satisfies (10.2.46).

We can extend this function $\rho(t)$ to irrational numbers as follows. Let τ be irrational, $\{t_{j_k}\}$ a descending sequence of rationals converging to τ. Then $\{\rho(t_{j_k})\}$ is a non-increasing sequence, bounded below, and hence has a limit. We set

$$\rho(\tau) = \lim_{k\to\infty} \rho(t_{j_k}).$$

This definition is unique for if $\{s_m\}$ is another descending sequence of rationals converging to τ, then for every m there is a k such that $t_{j_{k+1}} \leq s_m < t_{j_k}$ whence it follows that

$$\lim_{k\to\infty} \rho(t_{j_k}) = \lim_{m\to\infty} \rho(s_m).$$

Thus $\rho(t)$ is defined for all t in $[-A, A]$ as a non-decreasing function of t satisfying (10.2.46).

Suppose that τ is irrational and a point of continuity of $\rho(t)$. We have to prove that $\lim_{p\to\infty} \rho(\tau, \beta_p) = \rho(\tau)$. Given an $\varepsilon > 0$, we can find a δ such that $|\rho(t) - \rho(\tau)| < \varepsilon$ if $|t - \tau| < \delta$. Next we choose two rational numbers t_1 and t_2 and an integer p_0 such that

$$\tau - \delta < t_1 < \tau < t_2 < \tau + \delta,$$

$$|\rho(t_k, \beta_p) - \rho(t_k)| < \varepsilon \quad \text{for} \quad p \geq p_0, \quad k = 1, 2.$$

We have then

$$\rho(t_1) - \varepsilon \leq \rho(t_1, \beta_p) \leq \rho(\tau, \beta_p) \leq \rho(t_2, \beta_p) \leq \rho(t_2) + \varepsilon,$$

$$\rho(t_1) \leq \rho(\tau) \leq \rho(t_2),$$

whence it follows that

$$|\rho(\tau) - \rho(\tau, \beta_p)| \leq \rho(t_2) - \rho(t_1) + \varepsilon \leq 3\varepsilon.$$

Since ε is arbitrary, $\lim \rho(\tau, \beta_p)$ exists and equals $\rho(\tau)$.

By its definition $\rho(t)$ is right-continuous at all irrational points, but this is not necessarily the case at rational points. If necessary we re-define $\rho(t)$ at such points by setting

$$\rho(t) = \rho(t + 0)$$

for all t. It is clear that $\rho(t)$ is non-decreasing and satisfies (10.2.46).

Thus we have defined a limit function with the desired properties in an arbitrary finite interval $[-A, A]$. We can extend the definition of $\rho(t)$ to $(-\infty, \infty)$ in an obvious manner.

This proves compactness of the family $\{\rho(t, b)\}$, but it does not prove that there is a unique limit for $b \to \infty$, if we normalize by demanding right-hand continuity. Now it is clear that $\rho(t, b)$ is uniquely determined by $m(\lambda, b)$. We need to show that $\lim \rho(t, b)$ is uniquely determined by $\lim m(\lambda, b) = m(\lambda)$ which is unique in the limit-point case.

For this purpose we need another auxiliary lemma, the proof of which is left as an exercise:

Lemma 10.2.7. *If $g(t)$ has finite right- and left-hand limits for all t, and if $g(t)(1 + t^2)^{-1} \in L(-\infty, \infty)$, then*

$$\lim_{y\downarrow 0} \frac{y}{\pi} \int_{-\infty}^{\infty} \frac{g(t)\, dt}{(t - x)^2 + y^2} = \tfrac{1}{2}[g(x + 0) + g(x - 0)] \quad (10.2.47)$$

for all x.

Continuation of the proof of Theorem 10.2.3. We have

$$\Im[m(\mu + i\nu, b)] = \nu \int_{-\infty}^{\infty} \frac{d\rho(t, b)}{(t - \mu)^2 + \nu^2} = 2\nu \int_{-\infty}^{\infty} \frac{(t - \mu)\rho(t, b)\, dt}{[(t - \mu)^2 + \nu^2]^2}, \quad (10.2.48)$$

as is seen by an integration by parts. It follows that

$$\int_{\mu_1}^{\mu_2} \Im[m(\mu + i\nu, b)]\, d\mu = \nu \int_{-\infty}^{\infty} \frac{\rho(t, b)\, dt}{(t - \mu_2)^2 + \nu^2} - \nu \int_{-\infty}^{\infty} \frac{\rho(t, b)\, dt}{(t - \mu_1)^2 + \nu^2}$$

and

$$\lim_{\nu \downarrow 0} \int_{\mu_1}^{\mu_2} \Im[m(\mu + i\nu, b)]\, d\mu = \pi[\rho^*(\mu_2, b) - \rho^*(\mu_1, b)]$$

where

$$\rho^*(t, b) = \tfrac{1}{2}[\rho(t + 0, b) + \rho(t - 0, b)].$$

On the other hand, if we let $b \to \infty$ through the sequence $\{\beta_p\}$, then

$$\lim_{p \to \infty} \rho(t, \beta_p) = \rho(t)$$

boundedly for all bounded t with at most a countable number of exceptions. It follows that

$$\lim_{p \to \infty} 2\nu \int_{-\infty}^{\infty} \frac{(t - \mu)\rho(t, \beta_p)\, dt}{[(t - \mu)^2 + \nu^2]^2} = 2\nu \int_{-\infty}^{\infty} \frac{(t - \mu)\rho(t)\, dt}{[(t - \mu)^2 + \nu^2]^2}.$$

Since

$$\lim_{p \to \infty} m(\lambda, \beta_p) = \lim_{b \to \infty} m(\lambda, b) = m(\lambda),$$

we have

$$\Im[m(\mu + i\nu)] = 2\nu \int_{-\infty}^{\infty} \frac{(t - \mu)\rho(t)\, dt}{[(t - \mu)^2 + \nu^2]^2} \tag{10.2.49}$$

and hence also

$$\Im[m(\mu + i\nu)] = \nu \int_{-\infty}^{\infty} \frac{d\rho(t)}{(t - \mu)^2 + \nu^2}. \tag{10.2.50}$$

Obviously we have now for all μ_1, μ_2

$$\lim_{\nu \downarrow 0} \int_{\mu_1}^{\mu_2} \Im[m(\mu + i\nu)]\, d\mu = \pi[\rho^*(\mu_2) - \rho^*(\mu_1)] \tag{10.2.51}$$

where

$$\rho^*(t) = \tfrac{1}{2}[\rho(t + 0) + \rho(t - 0)].$$

If now there should be a sequence $\{\rho(t, b_r)\}$, $b_n \to \infty$, which converges to a limit $\rho_1(t) \neq \rho(t)$, then we must have

$$\rho_1^*(t_2) - \rho_1^*(t_1) = \rho^*(t_2) - \rho^*(t_1)$$

so that $\rho_1^*(t) = \rho^*(t) + C$. But this constant must be 0. For $\rho_1(0 + 0) = \rho(0 + 0) = 0$ since $\rho(0 + 0, b) = \rho(0, b) = 0$ for all b. If now $\rho_1(0 - 0) \neq \rho(0 - 0)$, then

$$\nu \int_{-\infty}^{\infty} \frac{d\rho_1(t)}{(t - \mu)^2 + \nu^2} \neq \nu \int_{-\infty}^{\infty} \frac{d\rho(t)}{(t - \mu)^2 + \nu^2},$$

which is impossible, since both sides must represent $\Im[m(\mu + i\nu)]$. Hence all sequences $\{\rho(t, b_n)\}$, $b_n \to \infty$, have the same (normalized) limit $\rho(t)$. ∎

We have now the final result for this section

Theorem 10.2.4. *If* $\alpha \not\equiv \frac{1}{2}\pi \pmod{\pi}$ *and if the limit-point case is present, then*

$$m(\lambda) = \int_{-\infty}^{\infty} \frac{d\rho(t)}{t - \lambda} - \tan \alpha. \tag{10.2.52}$$

Proof. Pass to the limit with b in formula (10.2.38). This is permitted by the bounded convergence on finite intervals. ∎

Corollary. *$m(\lambda)$ is holomorphic in each of the two half-planes $\Im(\lambda) > 0$ and $\Im(\lambda) < 0$.*

In general, these functions may not be analytic continuations of each other. We have, however,

$$m(\bar{\lambda}) = \overline{m(\lambda)}. \tag{10.2.53}$$

EXERCISE 10.2

For greater precision, the dependence on the parameter α is indicated, when needed, by adding this letter to the function symbols, like $y_2(x, \lambda, \alpha)$, $m(\lambda, \alpha)$, etc.

According to Theorem 8.5.1 the set $\{y_2(x, \lambda_n(b, \alpha), \alpha)\}$ is complete in $L_2(0, b)$. Keep this in mind in handling Problems 1–3.

1. Let $y(x, \lambda, m)$ be given by (10.1.3) with $m = m(\lambda, b, \alpha)$ defined by (10.2.2). By Green's formula (8.1.8) or otherwise, show that

$$\int_0^b y_2(s, \lambda_n) y(s, \lambda, m)\, ds = -\frac{1}{\lambda - \lambda_n}.$$

2. Show that

$$\int_0^b |y(s, \lambda, m)|^2\, ds = \sum_{n=1}^{\infty} \frac{|r_n(b)|}{|\lambda - \lambda_n(b)|^2}.$$

3. Use this to show that

$$\Im[m(\lambda, b, \alpha)] = \nu \int_{-\infty}^{\infty} \frac{d\rho(t, b, \alpha)}{|t - \lambda|^2}$$

and conclude that

$$\Im[m(\lambda, \alpha)] = \nu \int_{-\infty}^{\infty} \frac{d\rho(t, \alpha)}{|t - \lambda|^2}.$$

4. Try to show by direct estimate of the series (10.2.7) that $\sqrt{\nu}\, \Im[m(i\nu, b, \alpha)]$ is bounded below, $\alpha \not\equiv \frac{1}{2}\pi \pmod{\pi}$.
5. Take $q(x) \equiv 0$ and show that $m(\lambda, b, 0) = -\lambda^{-1/2} \tan(\lambda^{1/2} b)$. Show that $m(\lambda, 0) = (-\lambda)^{-1/2}$ where the λ-plane is cut along the positive real axis and that determination of the square root is taken which is positive when λ is real negative.

6. Under the same assumptions, compute $\rho(t, b, 0)$ and show that its limit $\rho(t, 0) = |\pi^{-1}\sqrt{t}$ for $t > 0$ and 0 for $t \le 0$.
7. Verify the value of A in (10.2.21).
8. Verify (10.2.23) and (10.2.24).
9. How should Theorem 10.2.3 be modified in the limit-circle case? Show that compactness is preserved but not uniqueness.

The remaining problems are devoted to the case $\alpha = \frac{1}{2}\pi$ excluded in the text.

10. Show that $m(\lambda, b, \frac{1}{2}\pi) = -[m(\lambda, b, 0)]^{-1} = -[m_0(\lambda, b, 0)]^{-1}$ by examining the relations holding between $y_k(x, \lambda, 0)$ and $y_k(x, \lambda, \frac{1}{2}\pi)$, $k = 1, 2$. Hence $m(\lambda, \frac{1}{2}\pi) = -[m(\lambda, 0)]^{-1}$.
11. Show that $|\lambda_n(b, \frac{1}{2}\pi)|^{1/2}|r_n(b, \frac{1}{2}\pi)|$ is bounded away from 0 and ∞.
12. It is desired to prove that
$$m(\lambda, b, \tfrac{1}{2}\pi) - m(i, b, \tfrac{1}{2}\pi) = \int_{-\infty}^{\infty} \left(\frac{1}{t - \lambda} - \frac{1}{t - i}\right) d\rho(t, b, \tfrac{1}{2}\pi).$$
Verify that
    i) The right-hand member is essentially the canonical partial fraction expansion of the left member and differs from it by an entire function $E(\lambda, b)$ of order $\le \frac{1}{2}$. Note that $\lambda_n(b, \frac{1}{2}\pi)$ may be 0 while $\lambda_n(b, \frac{1}{2}\pi) - i$ cannot.
    ii) $E(\lambda, b)$ is $O(|\lambda|^{1/2})$ in the sectors $\varepsilon \le \arg(\pm\lambda) \le \pi - \varepsilon$.
    iii) $(\lambda + i)^{-1/2}E(\lambda, b)$ is holomorphic and bounded in the remaining (2ε)-sectors.
    iv) An entire function which is $O(|\lambda|^{1/2})$ for large $|\lambda|$ is a constant.
    v) This constant is 0 since both sides are 0 for $\lambda = i$.
13. Use Problem 3 together with (10.2.11) to show that
$$|\rho(t, b, \tfrac{1}{2}\pi)| \le C_1 + C_2|t|^{3/2}$$
for all b and t and that the same estimate holds for $\rho(t, \frac{1}{2}\pi)$.
14. Verify that
$$m(\lambda, \tfrac{1}{2}\pi) - m(i, \tfrac{1}{2}\pi) = \int_{-\infty}^{\infty} \left(\frac{1}{t - \lambda} - \frac{1}{t - i}\right) d\rho(t, \tfrac{1}{2}\pi)$$
in the limit-point case. What can be said in the limit-circle case?

10.3 ON THE NATURE OF THE SPECTRUM

The spectral functions are non-decreasing. Such a function may have intervals of constancy on $(-\infty, \infty)$. Thus $\rho(t, b, \alpha)$ has infinitely many such intervals separated by the points $\lambda_n(b, \alpha)$, $n = 1, 2, 3, \ldots$, while $\rho(t, \alpha)$ may or may not exhibit intervals of constancy. Let C be the union of the open intervals of constancy of the spectral function under consideration and let S be the complement of C. Here S is the set of points of growth of $\rho(t)$ and will be referred to as the *spectrum*, first of $\rho(t)$, later also of the boundary value problem and the corresponding differential operator.

Lemma 10.3.1. *Suppose that $\rho(t)$ has an interval of constancy (t_1, t_2). Then $m(\lambda)$ is real valued and holomorphic in the interval (t_1, t_2) and the functions $m(\lambda)$ for the upper and the lower half-planes are analytic continuations of each other.*

Proof. If $\alpha \not\equiv \frac{1}{2}\pi \pmod{\pi}$ we have

$$m(\lambda, \alpha) = \int_{-\infty}^{t_1} \frac{d\rho(t, \alpha)}{t - \lambda} + \int_{t_2}^{\infty} \frac{d\rho(t, \alpha)}{t - \lambda} - \tan \alpha. \tag{10.3.1}$$

The first function on the right is holomorphic in the λ-plane cut along the real axis from $-\infty$ to t_1 and the second in the plane cut along $(t_2, +\infty)$. Both are holomorphic on (t_1, t_2) and clearly real there. The case $\alpha \equiv \frac{1}{2}\pi \pmod{\pi}$ is handled in a similar manner. ▮

Lemma 10.3.2. *The spectrum S is a closed, infinite, and unbounded set of real numbers.*

Proof. Reality and closure follow from the definition of S. If S were a finite set, then $\rho(t)$ would be a step function with a finite number of jumps, say at the points $\lambda_1, \lambda_2, \ldots, \lambda_n$. Then

$$m(\lambda, \alpha) = \sum_{k=1}^{n} \frac{r_k}{\lambda - \lambda_k} - \tan \alpha, \qquad \alpha \not\equiv \tfrac{1}{2}\pi \pmod{\pi}.$$

This implies that

$$\lambda[m(\lambda, \alpha) + \tan \alpha]$$

is bounded as $\lambda \to \infty$ contrary to (10.2.10) which asserts that

$$\lambda^{1/2}[m(\lambda, \alpha) + \tan \alpha]$$

is bounded away from 0 and ∞ in two large sectors. This contradiction shows that S must be infinite. The same type of argument shows that S is unbounded: for if S were confined to the finite interval (a, b) we would have

$$m(\lambda, \alpha) + \tan \alpha = \int_a^b \frac{d\rho(t, \alpha)}{t - \lambda}$$

and the same contradiction holds. The case $\alpha \equiv \frac{1}{2}\pi \pmod{\pi}$ is handled in a similar manner. ▮

A point t_0 of S may be isolated or a cluster point of S. In the former case t_0 is common end point of two adjacent intervals of constancy of $\rho(t)$. More precisely, there are two points t_1 and t_2, $t_1 < t_0 < t_2$, such that $\rho(t)$ has the constant value $\rho(t_0 - 0)$ in (t_1, t_0) and the constant value $\rho(t_0)$ in (t_0, t_2).

Theorem 10.3.1. *If t_0 is an isolated point of the spectrum S of $\rho(t)$ and if $\rho(t_0) - \rho(t_0 - 0) = \sigma(t_0)$, then $\lambda = t_0$ is a simple pole of $m(\lambda)$ of residue $-\sigma(t_0)$. Moreover, $y_2(x, t_0)$ is a solution of the boundary value problem*

$$y''(x) + [\lambda - q(x)]y(x) = 0, \qquad \lambda = t_0,$$
$$\sin\alpha\, y(0) - \cos\alpha\, y'(0) = 0, \qquad y(s, \lambda) \in L_2(0, \infty). \tag{10.3.2}$$

Proof. If (t_1, t_0) and (t_0, t_2) are intervals of constancy of $\rho(t)$ and if $\alpha \not\equiv \frac{1}{2}\pi \pmod{\pi}$, then

$$\int_{t_1}^{t_2} \frac{d\rho(t, \alpha)}{t - \lambda} = -\frac{\sigma(t_0)}{\lambda - t_0}$$

while the integrals $\int_{-\infty}^{t_1}$ and $\int_{t_2}^{\infty}$ are holomorphic at $\lambda = t_0$. Hence $m(\lambda, \alpha)$ has a simple pole at $\lambda = t_0$ with residue $-\sigma(t_0)$.

In order to prove (10.3.2) we proceed as in the proof of (10.2.3). We have

$$\Im[m(t_0 + iv)] = v\int_0^\infty |y_1(s, t_0 + iv) + m(t_0 + iv)y_2(s, t_0 + iv)|^2\, ds.$$

Here we multiply both sides by v and let $v \downarrow 0$. The left member tends to $\sigma(t_0)$. Hence the right member must also tend to a finite limit which must be

$$\left[\sigma(t_0)\int_0^\infty |y_2(s, t_0)|^2\, ds\right]^2.$$

Hence the integral exists and $y_2(s, t_0) \in L_2(0, \infty)$. Since

$$\sin\alpha\; y_2(0, \lambda) - \cos\alpha\; y_2'(0, \lambda) = 0$$

for all λ, this holds also for $\lambda = t_0$ and $y_2(x, t_0)$ is a solution of the boundary value problem. ∎

Incidentally, we have proved that

$$\sigma(t_0) = \left[\int_0^\infty |y_2(s, t_0)|^2\, ds\right]^{-1}. \tag{10.3.3}$$

If all points of S are isolated, we speak of a *pure point spectrum*. Such a spectrum is present whenever we are dealing with a non-singular boundary value problem but may be present also in singular cases. An instance is given by the Hermite-Weber equation with $q(x) = x^2$. If $\alpha = 0$ we have $S = \{4n + 1 \mid n = 0, 1, 2, \ldots\}$ and the corresponding characteristic functions form the set

$$\{H_{2n}(x)\, e^{-x^2/2}\}$$

involving the Hermite polynomials of even order. For $\alpha = \frac{1}{2}\pi$ we have instead the Hermite polynomials of odd order and the spectral values $\{4n + 3 \mid n = 0, 1, 2, \ldots\}$.

A pure point spectrum may be regarded as exceptional in the singular case but it is sufficiently important to make it worth our while to give sufficient conditions for its occurrence and, more generally, conditions for the spectrum to be bounded below.

We can simplify the work by noting that the functions $m(\lambda, \alpha)$ are related in a very simple fashion. To this end, we note that the solutions

$$y_1(x, \lambda, \alpha) + m(\lambda, \alpha)y_2(x, \lambda, \alpha),$$
$$y_1(x, \lambda, \beta) + m(\lambda, \beta)y_2(x, \lambda, \beta)$$

are both in $L_2(0, \infty)$. Now in the limit-point case here considered there is essentially only one solution in $L_2(0, \infty)$ so the two solutions must be linearly dependent. In particular, their Wronskian must vanish for $x = 0$. This means

$$\begin{vmatrix} \sin\alpha + m(\lambda, \alpha)\cos\alpha & \sin\beta + m(\lambda, \beta)\cos\beta \\ -\cos\alpha + m(\lambda, \alpha)\sin\alpha & -\cos\beta + m(\lambda, \beta)\sin\beta \end{vmatrix} = 0$$

and this gives the curious relation

$$\tan(\alpha - \beta) = \frac{m(\lambda, \beta) - m(\lambda, \alpha)}{1 + m(\lambda, \alpha)m(\lambda, \beta)}. \tag{10.3.4}$$

This looks like the addition theorem for the tangent function and it reduces to the latter when $\lambda \to \infty$ in sectors not containing the real axis since then

$$\lim m(\lambda, \alpha) = -\tan\alpha.$$

We note in particular that

$$m(\lambda, \alpha + \tfrac{1}{2}\pi) = -[m(\lambda, \alpha)]^{-1} \tag{10.3.5}$$

a special case of which occurred in Exercise 10.2. We note also

$$m(\lambda, \beta) = \frac{m(\lambda, \alpha) + \tan(\alpha - \beta)}{1 - \tan(\alpha - \beta)m(\lambda, \alpha)}. \tag{10.3.6}$$

This relation enables us to prove

Theorem 10.3.2. *If for a particular value of α there is a pure point spectrum, say $S_\alpha = \{\lambda_n(\alpha) \mid n = 1, 2, \ldots\}$ with corresponding residues $-\sigma_n(\alpha)$, then $\sum [\sigma_n(\alpha)/\lambda_n(\alpha)]$ is convergent. Moreover, for any $\beta \neq \alpha$, there is also a pure point spectrum S_β and each interval $(\lambda_n(\alpha), \lambda_{n+1}(\alpha))$ contains one and only one point of S_β. There is at most one point of S_β to the left of $\lambda_1(\alpha)$.*

Proof. Again we may suppose $\alpha \not\equiv \frac{1}{2}\pi \pmod{\pi}$. We have then, by assumption,

$$m(\lambda, \alpha) = -\sum \frac{\sigma_n(\alpha)}{\lambda - \lambda_n(\alpha)} - \tan\alpha, \tag{10.3.7}$$

the series being absolutely convergent for all λ not in S_α. In particular, if 0 is not in S_α, the series $\sum [\sigma_n(\alpha)/\lambda_n(\alpha)]$ is absolutely convergent. If, accidentally, 0 is in S_α, then we have merely to suppress the infinite term. The remaining series is still absolutely convergent.

Next we note that all residues are negative by (10.3.3). This means that in the interval $(\lambda_n(\alpha), \lambda_{n+1}(\alpha))$

$$m'(\lambda, \alpha) = \sum \frac{\sigma_n(\alpha)}{[\lambda - \lambda_n(\alpha)]^2} > 0$$

and $m(\lambda, \alpha)$ is strictly increasing from $-\infty$ to $+\infty$. Thus $m(\lambda, \alpha)$ takes on every real value once and only once in this interval. In particular, for a given β, $\beta \neq \alpha + \pi$, it takes on the value $\cot(\alpha - \beta)$ once and only once in the interval. We now take a look at formula (10.3.6). Here $m(\lambda, \alpha)$ is a meromorphic function of λ with real poles. It is then clear that $m(\lambda, \beta)$ is also meromorphic and its poles are at the points where $m(\lambda, \alpha) = \cot(\alpha - \beta)$ which are necessarily real. We have seen that $m(\lambda, \beta)$ has one and only one simple pole in each interval $(\lambda_n(\alpha), \lambda_{n+1}(\alpha))$. Since $\lim_{\lambda \to -\infty} m(\lambda, \alpha) = -\tan \alpha$, there is a pole of $m(\lambda, \beta)$ in $(-\infty, \lambda_1(\alpha))$ iff

$$-\tan \alpha < \cot(\alpha - \beta). \tag{10.3.8}$$

The discussion of this inequality is left to the reader. ∎

The following theorem gives a sufficient condition for the spectrum to be bounded below.

Theorem 10.3.3. *If $q(x)$ is bounded below,* $\inf q(x) = q_0$, *then $m(\lambda, \alpha)$ is holomorphic in the λ-plane cut along the real axis from q_0 to $+\infty$, save for at most one pole on the real axis to the left of $\lambda = q_0$. There is no such pole if $0 < \alpha < \frac{1}{2}\pi$ or $\pi < \alpha < \frac{3}{2}\pi$.*

Proof. The assumptions are those of Theorem 10.1.4. We have consequently for $\mu > 0$, $\lambda = \mu + \nu i$,

$$\tfrac{1}{2}\sin 2\alpha\ [1 - |m(\lambda, \alpha)|^2] + \cos 2\alpha\ \Re[m(\lambda, \alpha)] - i\Im[m(\lambda, \alpha)]$$

$$= \int_0^\infty |y'(s, \lambda, m(\lambda, \alpha))|^2\, ds$$

$$- \int_0^\infty [\lambda - q(s)]|y(s, \lambda, m(\lambda, \alpha))|^2\, ds \tag{10.3.9}$$

with

$$y(x, \lambda, m(\lambda, \alpha)) = y_1(x, \lambda, \alpha) + m(\lambda, \alpha)y_2(x, \lambda, \alpha),$$

and absolutely convergent integrals. Here we first take the real part of the formula for $\alpha = \frac{1}{4}\pi$. To simplify we write

$$m(\lambda, \tfrac{1}{4}\pi) = M(\lambda), \qquad y(s, \lambda, m(\lambda, \tfrac{1}{4}\pi)) = Y(s, \lambda).$$

Thus we obtain

$$1 - |M(\lambda)|^2 = 2\int_0^\infty |Y'(s, \lambda)|^2\, ds$$

$$- 2\int_0^\infty [\mu - q(s)]|Y(s, \lambda)|^2\, ds. \tag{10.3.10}$$

For $\mu < q_0$, $0 < s$

$$\mu - q(s) < 0$$

whence

$$|M(\lambda)| < 1, \qquad \mu < q_0. \tag{10.3.11}$$

Further,

$$2(q_0 - \mu)\int_0^\infty |Y(s, \lambda)|^2\, ds < 1. \tag{10.3.12}$$

Repeated use will be made of these inequalities.

First, taking the imaginary part of (10.3.9) we get

$$\Im[M(\lambda)] = \nu\int_0^\infty |Y(s, \lambda)|^2\, ds < \frac{\nu}{2(q_0 - \mu)},$$

so that

$$\lim_{\nu \downarrow 0} \Im[M(\mu + \nu i)] = 0, \qquad \mu < q_0,$$

uniformly in μ for $\mu < q_0 - \varepsilon$.

Secondly, we can compute

$$\int_0^\infty y(s, \lambda_1, m)y(s, \lambda_2, m)\, ds = \frac{m(\lambda_1, \alpha) - m(\lambda_2, \alpha)}{\lambda_1 - \lambda_2} \tag{10.3.13}$$

by the classical method of Sturm. (See formula (8.1.8).) Letting $\lambda_2 \to \lambda_1 = \lambda$, we get

$$\int_0^\infty [y(s, \lambda, m)]^2\, ds = \frac{\partial}{\partial\lambda} m(\lambda, \alpha). \tag{10.3.14}$$

In particular

$$\int_0^\infty [Y(s, \lambda)]^2\, ds = M'(\lambda). \tag{10.3.15}$$

Combining this relation with the inequality (10.3.12), we get

$$2(q_0 - \mu)|M'(\lambda)| < 1. \tag{10.3.16}$$

It follows from this formula and (10.3.11) that the functions

$$\left\{M\left(\mu + \frac{i}{n}\right) \middle| n = 1, 2, 3, \ldots\right\}$$

are uniformly bounded and equicontinuous in $(-\infty, q_0 - \varepsilon)$. By Theorem 1.6.2 there is at least one subsequence which converges uniformly to a continuous limit, $M(\mu)$ say. Using (10.3.16) once more, we see that

$$\left|M\left(\mu + i\frac{1}{n}\right) - M(\mu)\right| < \frac{\nu}{2(q_0 - \mu)}.$$

Hence

$$\lim_{n\to\infty} M\left(\mu + i\frac{1}{n}\right) = M(\mu)$$

exists as a real continuous function for $\mu < q_0$ and its absolute value does not exceed 1. Here we have supposed $\nu > 0$. Since $m(\bar{\lambda}) = \overline{m(\lambda)}$, the same limit is obtained for approach from the lower half-plane.

By Schwarz's principle of symmetry it follows that $M(\lambda)$ is holomorphic also on the real axis for $\mu < q_0$ and the estimates (10.3.11) and (10.3.16) hold also in the half-plane $\Re(\lambda) < q_0$. Here (10.3.16) shows that

$$\lim_{\nu\downarrow 0} Y(x, \mu + \nu i) \equiv Y(x, \mu), \qquad \mu < q_0, \tag{10.3.17}$$

exists, uniformly in any finite interval and $Y(x, \mu) \in L_2(0, \infty)$. Further, formulas (10.3.10) and (10.3.15) hold also for real values of λ less than q_0. In particular, $M(\mu)$ is a strictly increasing function of μ.

These results for $M(\lambda) = m(\lambda, \frac{1}{4}\pi)$ can be extended to any value of the parameter β with the aid of (10.3.6). This shows that for $\beta \neq \frac{1}{4}\pi$, the function $m(\lambda, \beta)$ is holomorphic in the half-plane $\Re(\lambda) < q_0$ save for a possible pole on the real axis. Such a pole will occur iff $m(\lambda, \frac{1}{4}\pi)$ takes on the value $\cot(\frac{1}{4}\pi - \beta)$ on the interval $(-\infty, q_0)$. Since $m(\lambda, \frac{1}{4}\pi)$ is restricted to values between -1 and $+1$ there, we can be sure that there is no pole if

$$|\cot(\tfrac{1}{4}\pi - \beta)| > 1,$$

and this gives the excluded intervals stated in the theorem. ∎

Theorem 10.3.4. *If $q(x) \to \infty$ with x, then there is a pure point spectrum with at most one spectral value to the left of $q_0 = \inf q(x)$.*

Proof. The preceding theorem shows that $m(\lambda, \alpha)$ has at most one pole in the half-plane $\Re(\lambda) < q_0$ and, if we choose $\alpha = \frac{1}{4}\pi$ there is no pole and $|m(\lambda, \frac{1}{4}\pi)| < 1$ in the half-plane. The idea of the proof is to apply the same argument to the singular boundary value problem for an interval $(a, +\infty)$ where a is so large that

$$\inf q(x) = Q \qquad \text{for} \quad a \le x$$

and Q is a preassigned arbitrarily large positive number.

The discussion given in this chapter for the interval $(0, \infty)$ applies with trivial changes to any subinterval (a, ∞). We let $u_1(x, \lambda)$ and $u_2(x, \lambda)$ be the solutions of (10.1.1) with the initial conditions

$$u_1(a, \lambda) = \tfrac{1}{2}\sqrt{2}, \qquad u_1'(a, \lambda) = -\tfrac{1}{2}\sqrt{2},$$

$$u_2(a, \lambda) = u_2'(a, \lambda) = \tfrac{1}{2}\sqrt{2},$$

i.e. $\alpha = \frac{1}{4}\pi$ in analogy with the choice in the proof of Theorem 10.3.3. We then know the existence of a function $P(\lambda)$ such that

$$U(x, \lambda) \equiv u_1(x, \lambda) + P(\lambda)u_2(x, \lambda) \in L_2(a, \infty).$$

Here $P(\lambda)$ is holomorphic in the three half-planes

$$\nu > 0, \qquad \nu < 0, \qquad \mu < Q = \inf q(x) \qquad \text{for} \quad a \leq x,$$

and in the last half-plane $|P(\lambda)| < 1$.

Now $U(x, \lambda)$ has a unique extension satisfying the differential equation in $(0, a)$ and the extension belongs to $L_2(0, \infty)$. Thus we have two solutions, $U(x, \lambda)$ and $Y(x, \lambda)$, in $L_2(0, \infty)$ and they must be linearly dependent since we are in the limit-point case. We form the Wronskian of the solutions at $x = a$. Equating this to zero, we obtain a fractional linear representation of $M(\lambda)$ in terms of $P(\lambda)$,

$$M(\lambda) = \frac{A(\lambda)P(\lambda) + B(\lambda)}{C(\lambda)P(\lambda) + D(\lambda)} \tag{10.3.18}$$

where

$$A(\lambda) = y_1' - y_1, \qquad B(\lambda) = y_1 + y_1',$$

$$C(\lambda) = y_2 - y_2', \qquad D(\lambda) = -y_2 - y_2',$$

and

$$y_k = y_k(a, \lambda, \tfrac{1}{4}\pi), \qquad y_k' = y_k'(a, \lambda, \tfrac{1}{4}\pi), \qquad k = 1, 2,$$

are entire functions of λ of order $\frac{1}{2}$. This states that $M(\lambda)$ is the quotient of two functions holomorphic in the half-plane $\Re(\lambda) < Q$. $M(\lambda)$ is consequently meromorphic in this half-plane, and we know *a priori* that any isolated singularity is a simple pole located on the real axis. Here Q is arbitrarily large so we conclude that $M(\lambda)$ is meromorphic in the finite plane. Hence there is a discrete point spectrum. If this holds for $m(\lambda, \frac{1}{4}\pi)$, then the same assertion is valid for all functions $m(\lambda, \alpha)$ by Theorem 10.3.2. ∎

The last two theorems, with completely different proofs, are due to H. Weyl. Using the device employed in the proof of Theorem 10.3.4, we can prove a sharper form of Theorem 10.3.3 which is also due to Weyl.

Theorem 10.3.5. *If* $\liminf q(x) = \kappa < \infty$, *then all functions* $m(\lambda, \alpha)$ *are meromorphic in the half-plane* $\mu < \kappa$. *The point* $\lambda = \kappa$ *may be a cluster point of poles of these functions.*

Proof. We proceed as in the proof of Theorem 10.3.4. Choose an $\varepsilon > 0$ and an a such that

$$\inf q(x) > \kappa - \varepsilon \qquad \text{for} \quad a \leq x.$$

Then the preceding argument shows that $M(\lambda)$ is meromorphic in the half-plane $\mu < \kappa - \varepsilon$. This holds for any $\varepsilon > 0$.

If the poles of $m(\lambda, \frac{1}{4}\pi)$ have $\lambda = \kappa$ as a cluster point, then $\lambda = \kappa$ is a cluster point of poles of $m(\lambda, \alpha)$ for any α since the poles of $m(\lambda, \alpha)$ are interlaced with those of $m(\lambda, \frac{1}{4}\kappa)$. According to Weyl, $\lambda = \kappa$ will be a cluster point of poles iff the equation

$$y''(x) + [\kappa - q(x)]y(x) = 0 \tag{10.3.19}$$

is oscillatory on the interval $(0, \infty)$, i.e. every solution has infinitely many zeros there. A case in point is given by

$$q(x) = -c(x + 1)^{-2}, \qquad c > \tfrac{1}{4}, \qquad \kappa = 0. \; ▮ \tag{10.3.20}$$

The proof just given allows us to state the following

Corollary. *Clusterpoints of point spectra are independent of the parameter* α.

If $\rho(t, \alpha)$ is strictly increasing in the interval (t_1, t_2), we say that this interval belongs to the *continuous spectrum* of $\rho(t, \alpha)$. Here we have an observation made by Weyl:

Theorem 10.3.6. *Continuous spectra are independent of* α.

Proof. Suppose that (t_1, t_2) is part of the continuous spectrum of $\rho(t, \alpha)$. Formula (10.2.51) gives

$$\lim_{\nu \downarrow 0} \int_{\mu_1}^{\mu_2} \Im[m(\mu + \nu i, \alpha)]\, d\mu = \pi[\rho^*(\mu_2, \alpha) - \rho^*(\mu_1, \alpha)] > 0$$

for $t_1 \leq \mu_1 < \mu_2 \leq t_2$. On the other hand,

$$\lim_{\nu \downarrow 0} \int_{\mu_1}^{\mu_2} \Im[m(\mu - \nu i, \alpha)]\, d\mu = -\pi[\rho^*(\mu_2, \alpha) - \rho^*(\mu_1, \alpha)] < 0.$$

These two relations show that $m(\lambda, \alpha)$ cannot be holomorphic in the interval (t_1, t_2), for in that case the two limits would be equal. Note that it is perfectly possible for $m(\lambda, \alpha)$ to have an analytic continuation across (t_1, t_2), say from the upper half-plane to the lower one, but this continuation does not agree with the value of $m(\lambda, \alpha)$ in the lower half-plane. Thus the interval (t_1, t_2) plays the role of a cut. Conversely, if (t_1, t_2) is a cut on the two edges of which $m(\lambda, \alpha)$ has limiting values with imaginary parts of opposite signs, then (t_1, t_2) belongs to the continuous spectrum of $m(\lambda, \alpha)$. We now consider formula (10.3.6). If $m(\lambda, \alpha)$ admits (t_1, t_2) as a cut, then $m(\lambda, \beta)$ must also have (t_1, t_2) as a cut, i.e. (t_1, t_2) belongs to the continuous spectrum of $m(\lambda, \alpha)$ for all α. ▮

The next theorem, also due to Weyl, is related to Theorem 10.3.5. The proof is due to E. C. Titchmarsh and is akin in spirit to proofs of theorems with similar hypothesis occurring elsewhere in this treatise.

Theorem 10.3.7. *If $q(x) \in L(0, \infty)$, then there is a continuous spectrum covering the whole positive real axis and each function $\rho(t, \alpha)$ is differentiable and has a continuous derivative for $t > 0$. There may be a point spectrum on the negative real axis which may have $t = 0$ as cluster point but not $t = -\infty$.*

Proof. To simplify matters, we may suppose that $q(x)$ is bounded below and that $\liminf q(x) = 0$. The statements about the point-spectrum then follow from Theorem 10.3.5. Since the continuous spectrum is independent of α, we are free to choose for α a value which will simplify the formulas, say $\alpha = 0$. Further simplification is attained by setting $\lambda = \gamma^2$, $\gamma = \gamma_1 + \gamma_2 i$. Let $y_1(x)$ be the solution of the differential equation with initial values $y_1(0) = 0$, $y_1'(0) = -1$. In the usual manner, one shows that $y_1(x)$ is the unique solution of the integral equation

$$y_1(x) = -\frac{\sin(\gamma x)}{\gamma} + \frac{1}{\gamma}\int_0^x \sin[\gamma(x - s)]q(s)y_1(s)\,ds. \tag{10.3.21}$$

Similarly, the solution with $y_2(0) = 1$, $y_2'(0) = 0$ satisfies

$$y_2(x) = \cos(\gamma x) + \frac{1}{\gamma}\int_0^x \sin[\gamma(x - s)]q(s)y_2(s)\,ds. \tag{10.3.22}$$

For $\gamma > 0$ Theorem 1.5.7 shows that $y_1(x)$ and $y_2(x)$ are bounded for $0 \le x < \infty$, uniformly in γ for $0 < \delta \le \gamma$. Since

$$\int_0^x = \int_0^\infty - \int_x^\infty$$

and the last integral is $o(1)$ as $x \to \infty$, uniformly in γ, we see that

$$y_k(x) = a_k(\gamma)\cos\gamma x + b_k(\gamma)\sin\gamma x + o(1). \tag{10.3.23}$$

Here

$$a_1(\gamma) = -\frac{1}{\gamma}\int_0^\infty \sin(\gamma s)\; q(s)y_1(s)\,ds,$$

$$b_1(\gamma) = -\frac{1}{\gamma} + \frac{1}{\gamma}\int_0^\infty \cos(\gamma s)\; q(s)y_1(s)\,ds. \tag{10.3.24}$$

If in these formulas we replace y_1 by y_2 and add 1 to the first and $1/\gamma$ to the second, we obtain the expressions for $a_2(\gamma)$ and $b_2(\gamma)$, respectively.

Differentiation of (10.3.21) and (10.3.22) with respect to x gives

$$y_k'(x) = -\gamma a_k(\gamma)\sin(\gamma x) + \gamma b_k(\gamma)\cos(\gamma x) + o(1). \tag{10.3.25}$$

Now the Wronskian of y_1 and y_2 is identically 1. Substituting the values of y_k and y_k' we find that the Wronskian equals

$$\gamma[a_1(\gamma)b_2(\gamma) - a_2(\gamma)b_1(\gamma)] + o(1)$$

whence it follows that

$$\gamma[a_1(\gamma)b_2(\gamma) - a_2(\gamma)b_1(\gamma)] \equiv 1. \tag{10.3.26}$$

This shows, in particular, that $a_k(\gamma)$ and $b_k(\gamma)$ cannot vanish simultaneously.

Let us now consider complex values of γ, $\gamma = \gamma_1 + \gamma_2 i$, $0 < \gamma_2$. We multiply (10.3.21) by $e^{-\gamma_2 x}$ and note that

$$|\sin(\gamma x)|\, e^{-\gamma_2 x} < 1, \qquad |\cos(\gamma x)|\, e^{-\gamma_2 x} < 1.$$

We set

$$v_k(x) = |y_k(x)|\, e^{-\gamma_2 x}, \qquad k = 1, 2.$$

Then

$$v_1(x) \le \frac{1}{|\gamma|} + \frac{1}{|\gamma|}\int_0^x |q(s)| v_1(s)\, ds$$

and by Theorem 1.5.7

$$v_1(x) \le \frac{1}{|\gamma|} \exp\left\{\frac{1}{|\gamma|}\int_0^x |q(s)|\, ds\right\} \tag{10.3.27}$$

which is bounded for all x, uniformly in γ for $0 < \delta \le |\gamma|$. Similarly

$$v_2(x) \le \exp\left\{\frac{1}{|\gamma|}\int_0^x |q(s)|\, ds\right\}. \tag{10.3.28}$$

We return again to (10.3.21) with γ complex, $0 < \gamma_2$. We can write the equation

$$y_1(x) = \frac{1}{2i\gamma} e^{-i\gamma x} - \frac{1}{2i\gamma}\int_0^x e^{-i\gamma(x-s)} q(s) y_1(s)\, ds + R_1(x, \gamma). \tag{10.3.29}$$

Here

$$R_1(x, \gamma) = -\frac{1}{2i\gamma} e^{i\gamma x} + \frac{1}{2i\gamma}\int_0^x e^{i\gamma(x-s)} q(s) y_1(s)\, ds.$$

The first term on the right in $R_1(x, \gamma)$ is

$$O(e^{-\gamma_2 x}).$$

In the second term $y_1(x) = O(e^{\gamma_2 x})$ by (10.3.27) so the second term is

$$O\left\{\int_0^x e^{\gamma_2(2s-x)} |q(s)|\, ds\right\}.$$

Here we bisect the interval of integration. Now

$$\int_0^{x/2} e^{\gamma_2(2s-x)} |q(s)|\, ds < \int_0^{x/2} |q(s)|\, ds$$

and

$$\int_{x/2}^{x} e^{\gamma_2(2s-x)}|q(s)|\,ds < e^{\gamma_2 x}\int_{x/2}^{x}|q(s)|\,ds.$$

Both terms are $o(e^{\gamma_2 x})$ so we have

$$R_1(x, \gamma) = o(e^{\gamma_2 x}).$$

In (10.3.29) we replace $\int_0^x$ by $\int_0^\infty$. This introduces an error term

$$\int_x^\infty e^{-i\gamma(x-s)}q(s)y_1(s)\,ds = O\left[e^{\gamma_2 x}\int_x^\infty |q(s)|\,ds\right] = o(e^{\gamma_2 x}).$$

Thus we have

$$y_1(x) = \frac{1}{2i\gamma}e^{-i\gamma x} - \frac{1}{2i\gamma}\int_0^\infty e^{-i\gamma(x-s)}q(s)y_1(s)\,ds + o(e^{\gamma_2 x})$$

and, finally,

$$y_1(x) = e^{-i\gamma x}[P_1(\gamma) + o(1)] \tag{10.3.30}$$

where

$$P_1(\gamma) = \frac{1}{2i\gamma}\left\{1 - \int_0^\infty e^{i\gamma s}q(s)y_1(s)\,ds\right\}. \tag{10.3.31}$$

Similarly one gets

$$y_2(x) = e^{-i\gamma x}[P_2(\gamma) + o(1)] \tag{10.3.32}$$

with

$$P_2(\gamma) = \frac{1}{2} - \frac{1}{2i\gamma}\int_0^\infty e^{i\gamma s}q(s)y_2(s)\,ds. \tag{10.3.33}$$

Since $y_1(x) + m(\lambda)y_2(x) \in L_2(0, \infty)$ we must have

$$m(\lambda) = -\frac{P_1(\sqrt{\lambda})}{P_2(\sqrt{\lambda})}. \tag{10.3.34}$$

Now as γ approaches a real limit, λ approaches a positive limit and

$$P_k(\gamma) \to \tfrac{1}{2}[a_k(\gamma) + ib_k(\gamma)], \qquad k = 1, 2. \tag{10.3.35}$$

Here $P_k(\gamma) \neq 0$, $k = 1, 2$, by (10.3.26). It follows that

$$\lim_{\nu\downarrow 0} m(\lambda) \equiv m(\mu) = -\frac{a_1(\sqrt{\mu}) + ib_1(\sqrt{\mu})}{a_2(\sqrt{\mu}) + ib_2(\sqrt{\mu})} \tag{10.3.36}$$

and

$$\lim \Im[m(\mu + \nu i)] = \mu^{-1/2}\{[a_2(\sqrt{\mu})]^2 + [b_2(\sqrt{\mu})]^2\}^{-1}. \tag{10.3.37}$$

Hence, for $0 < t$,

$$\rho(t) = \frac{1}{\pi}\int_0^t s^{-1/2}\{[a_2(\sqrt{s})]^2 + [b_2(\sqrt{s})]^2\}^{-1}\,ds \tag{10.3.38}$$

and it is clear that $\rho'(t)$ exists and is continuous for $0 < t$.

We have proved the assertions of the theorem for $m(\lambda, 0)$ and $\rho(t, 0)$. The rest follows from (10.3.6) which gives

$$m(\lambda, \alpha) = \frac{m(\lambda, 0) - \tan\alpha}{1 + \tan\alpha \; m(\lambda, 0)}.$$

If $\lambda = \mu + \nu i$, $0 < \mu$, and $\nu \downarrow 0$, then $m(\lambda, 0)$ goes to the continuous, non-real limit $m(\mu, 0)$. It follows that $m(\mu, \alpha) = \lim_{\nu \downarrow 0} m(\lambda, \alpha)$ also exists as a non-real continuous function of μ and we have

$$\rho(t, \alpha) = \frac{1}{\pi} \int_0^t \Im[m(\mu, \alpha)] \, d\mu \tag{10.3.39}$$

so the assertions hold for all values of α. ∎

The last formula suggests an interesting generalization.

Theorem 10.3.8. *If the function $m(\mu + \nu i, \alpha)$ converges boundedly to a non-real limit $m(\mu, \alpha)$ as $\nu \downarrow 0$ and $t_1 < \mu < t_2$, then $\rho(t, \alpha)$ is absolutely continuous in this interval and*

$$\rho(t, \alpha) - \rho(t_1, \alpha) = \frac{1}{\pi} \int_{t_1}^t \Im[m(\mu, \alpha)] \, d\mu. \tag{10.3.40}$$

Conversely, if $\rho(t, \alpha)$ is absolutely continuous and strictly increasing in (t_1, t_2), then for almost all t in this interval

$$\rho'(t, \alpha) = \frac{1}{\pi} \lim_{\nu \downarrow 0} \Im[m(t + \nu i, \alpha)]. \tag{10.3.41}$$

Proof. The function $m(\mu, \alpha)$ as the limit of an analytic function is measurable and, being bounded, it is integrable over (t_1, t_2). Again by bounded convergence

$$\lim_{\nu \downarrow 0} \int_{t_1}^t \Im[m(\mu + \nu i, \alpha)] \, d\mu = \int_{t_1}^t \Im[m(\mu, \alpha)] \, d\mu.$$

By (10.2.51) the left member is $\pi[\rho^*(t, \alpha) - \rho^*(t_1, \alpha)]$. Now the right member is obviously a continuous function of t which goes to 0 as $t \downarrow t_1$. It follows that the asterisks may be dropped and formula (10.3.40) follows. The integral of a bounded measurable function is by definition an absolutely continuous function of its upper limit.

For the converse we write

$$\Im[m(\lambda, \alpha)] = \nu \int_{-\infty}^{\infty} \frac{d\rho(t, \alpha)}{(t - \mu)^2 + \nu^2}$$

$$= \nu \int_{t_1}^{t_2} \frac{\rho'(t, \alpha)}{(t - \mu)^2 + \nu^2} \, dt + \nu \left\{ \int_{-\infty}^{t_1} + \int_{t_2}^{\infty} \right\} \cdots.$$

Here the last two integrals tend to finite limits as $\nu \downarrow 0$. To the first integral we apply Lemma 10.2.7 which is also true if $g(t)$ is merely a measurable function such that $g(t)(1 + t^2)^{-1} \in L(-\infty, \infty)$. In this case, all we can assert, however, is that the limit exists for almost all x and equals $g(x)$ for almost all such x. This gives the desired result. ∎

If $q(x)$ satisfies other hypotheses, the spectral functions may be studied by first applying a Liouville transformation to (10.1.1) and then applying the technique used in the proof of Theorem 10.3.7 to the resulting perturbed sine equation. We shall not carry through the laborious argument but restrict ourselves to stating a result due to E. C. Titchmarsh, for the proof of which we refer to his treatise, *Eigenfunction Expansions*, Vol. I, pp. 101–103, 106–110.

Theorem 10.3.9. *Let $q(x)$ be negative and twice continuously differentiable. Let $q'(x) < 0$, $q(x) \to -\infty$, $q'(x) = O[|q(x)|^c]$ for a c with $0 < c < \frac{3}{2}$, and let $q''(x)$ be ultimately of one sign. Then if $|q(x)|^{-1/2} \notin L(0, \infty)$ the continuous spectrum covers the whole real axis. On the other hand, if $|q(x)|^{-1/2} \in L(0, \infty)$, then the continuous spectrum covers $(-\infty, 0)$ and there may be a discrete point spectrum on $(0, \infty)$.*

In consulting Titchmarsh's treatise, the reader should observe the difference in notation. In particular, his function $m(\lambda)$ is the reciprocal of our function.

EXERCISE 10.3

1. Prove Lemma 10.3.2 for $\alpha = \frac{1}{2}\pi$.
2. For what values of β is (10.3.8) valid?
3. Show that for $q(x)$ defined by (10.3.20) the solutions of (10.3.19) have infinitely many zeros in $(0, \infty)$.
4. Show that if the differential equation (10.1.1) has no quadratically integrable solution for any real λ, then the continuous spectrum covers the whole real axis [H. Weyl].
5. If $q(x) = -x$, Theorem 10.3.9 asserts the continuous spectrum covers the real axis. Show that the condition of the preceding problem is satisfied. Show that if $y(x)$ is a solution of the differential equation for $\lambda = 0$, then $y(x + \lambda)$ is a solution of the general equation. Here $y(x)$ is expressible in terms of Bessel functions of order $\frac{1}{3}$ and $-\frac{1}{3}$ in the variable $x^{3/2}$. It is enough to show that $y(x)$ cannot be quadratically integrable. Theorem 9.5.3 applies to this situation. One can also use the asymptotic form of Bessel functions for real large values of x.
6. Use the results of Section 9.5 to find a sufficient condition for a continuous spectrum covering the whole real axis. [*Hint*: Theorem 10.1.3 where condition (v) is negated.]

10.4 UNITARY TRANSFORMATIONS

With a boundary value problem, regular or singular, there are associated two L_2-spaces and a mapping of one space on to the other which is of a rather special character. Thus, in the regular case, corresponding to a finite interval $[a, b]$ where $q(x)$ is continuous, one space is $L_2(a, b)$, the other l_2. If the characteristic functions form the orthonormal family $\{\omega_n(x)\}$, if $f \in L_2(a, b)$, and if

$$f_n = \int_a^b f(s)\omega_n(s)\, ds, \qquad n = 0, 1, 2, \ldots, \tag{10.4.1}$$

then this formula defines a mapping T of $L_2(a, b)$ into l_2 such that

$$\int_a^b |f(s)|^2\, ds = \sum_{n=0}^{\infty} |f_n|^2. \tag{10.4.2}$$

More generally, inner products go into inner products:

$$\int_a^b f(s)\overline{g(s)}\, ds = \sum_{n=0}^{\infty} f_n \bar{g}_n \tag{10.4.3}$$

with obvious notation. Conversely, if $\{f_n\} \in l_2$, then there exists an $f \in L_2(a, b)$ such that (10.4.1) holds and this f is uniquely determined (neglecting sets of Lebesgue measure zero).

The mapping T is linear, one-to-one and onto. It is norm preserving and hence takes inner products into inner products. Such a transformation is said to be *unitary*. The two spaces $L_2(a, b)$ and l_2 appear to be of rather different structure. They are both realizations of a Hilbert space and by introducing suitable measure functions we can both eliminate the apparent disparity and formulate the results in a manner suitable for generalization.

As a preparation we need some terminology and notation. Let $\sigma(t)$ be defined on $(-\infty, \infty)$ as a non-decreasing, right-continuous function. Let S be a set on the t-axis, to start with a bounded set. We can cover S by means of open sets G_γ. Let $V(G_\gamma)$ be the total variation of $\sigma(t)$ on G_γ and define the *outer σ-measure* of S as

$$\sigma_0(S) = \inf V(G_\gamma)$$

for all possible coverings of S by open sets. Let S' be the complement of S with respect to an interval (a, b) which covers S. Then S' has an outer measure and we define the *inner σ-measure* of S as

$$\sigma_i(S) = V_a^b[\sigma] - \sigma_0(S')$$

and say that S *is σ-measurable if*

$$\sigma_i(S) = \sigma_0(S).$$

Should the set S be unbounded, we say that it is σ-measurable if $S \cap (-a, a)$ is σ-measurable for all a.

Consider now a real valued function $g(t)$ defined on $(-\infty, \infty)$. We say that $g(t)$ *is σ-measurable if each of the sets* $\{t \mid g(t) > \gamma\}$ *is σ-measurable*, $-\infty < \gamma < \infty$. A complex-valued function is σ-measurable if its real and imaginary parts are σ-measurable. Two functions g_1 and g_2 are *σ-equivalent* if they are σ-measurable and $g_1(t) - g_2(t) \neq 0$ at most in a set of σ-measure 0. The σ-measurable functions form an algebra over the complex numbers.

Finally, we define $L_2(\sigma)$ *as the set of classes of σ-equivalent functions* $g(t)$ *such that* (i) $g(t)$ *is σ-measurable and* (ii) *the integral*

$$\int_{-\infty}^{\infty} |g(t)|^2 \, d\sigma(t) \equiv (\|g\|_\sigma)^2 \tag{10.4.4}$$

exists. This is a linear vector space over the complex field and an *inner product* is defined by

$$(f, g)_\sigma \equiv \int_{-\infty}^{\infty} f(t)\overline{g(t)} \, d\sigma(t). \tag{10.4.5}$$

The inner product is a bilinear form in its two arguments, it is *Hermitian* in the sense that

$$(g, f)_\sigma = \overline{(f, g)_\sigma}.$$

The Bouniakovski-Schwarz inequality holds:

$$|(f, g)_\sigma| \leq \|f\|_\sigma \|g\|_\sigma. \tag{10.4.6}$$

Further, $(f, g)_\sigma$ is a continuous function (in the norm topology) in both arguments. Finally, $L_2(\sigma)$ is complete under the norm defined by (10.4.4), so it is a Banach space.

It will be assumed in the following that the measure functions $\sigma(t)$ are *normalized* so that $\sigma(0) = \sigma(0 + 0) = 0$.

The integrals occurring in formulas (10.4.4) and (10.4.5) as well as those to be found below are Lebesgue-Stieltjes integrals. When the integral involves a finite interval, the latter is supposed to be of type $(a, b]$, i.e. open on the left and closed on the right.

We see now that $L_2(a, b)$ and l_2 are special instances of $L_2(\sigma)$-spaces with $\sigma(t)$ equal to

$$\begin{cases} 0, \ t < a, \\ t - a, \ a \leq t \leq b, \\ b - a, \ b < t \end{cases} \quad \text{and} \quad \begin{cases} -1, \ t < 0, \\ n, \ n \leq t < n + 1, \ n = 0, 1, \ldots, \end{cases}$$

respectively.

We shall consider unitary mappings of an $L_2(\sigma)$ on an $L_2(\rho)$ where σ and ρ may be distinct or coincide.

Definition 10.4.1. *A linear transformation on $L_2(\sigma)$ to $L_2(\rho)$ is said to be unitary if* (i) *the domain of T is $L_2(\sigma)$ and its range is $L_2(\rho)$, and* (ii) *for $f, g \in L_2(\sigma)$*

$$(f, g)_\sigma = (Tf, Tg)_\rho.$$

Such a mapping defines and is defined by a pair of kernels having remarkable properties, as shown by S. Bochner in 1934 for the case when both spaces are $L_2(0, \infty)$, but the extension is routine analysis. It is convenient to use lattice notation: if x and y are real numbers we set

$$x \wedge y = \min(x, y), \qquad x \vee y = \max(x, y).$$

Further we set

$$\tilde{\rho}(x, y) = \begin{cases} \rho(x \wedge y), & \text{if } 0 \le x \wedge y, \\ 0, & \text{if } xy < 0, \\ -\rho(x \vee y), & \text{if } x \vee y < 0, \end{cases} \tag{10.4.7}$$

with similar notation for σ.

Theorem 10.4.1. *Let T be a unitary transformation on $L_2(\sigma)$ to $L_2(\rho)$ and set $Tf = g$, Then there exist two well-defined kernels $K(x, s)$ and $L(y, t)$ such that*

$$(\operatorname{sgn} x) \int_0^x g(t)\, d\rho(t) = \int_{-\infty}^{\infty} \overline{K(x, s)} f(s)\, d\sigma(s), \tag{10.4.8}$$

$$(\operatorname{sgn} y) \int_0^y f(s)\, d\sigma(s) = \int_{-\infty}^{\infty} \overline{L(y, t)} g(t)\, d\rho(t) \tag{10.4.9}$$

for any $f \in L_2(\sigma)$. Here

$$\int_{-\infty}^{\infty} K(x, s)\overline{K(y, s)}\, d\sigma(s) = \tilde{\rho}(x, y), \tag{10.4.10}$$

$$\int_{-\infty}^{\infty} L(x, t)\overline{L(y, t)}\, d\rho(t) = \tilde{\sigma}(x, y), \tag{10.4.11}$$

$$(\operatorname{sgn} y) \int_0^y \overline{K(x, s)}\, d\sigma(s) = (\operatorname{sgn} x) \int_0^x \overline{L(y, t)}\, d\rho(t). \tag{10.4.12}$$

Proof. For any fixed real x let $\chi_x(s)$ be the characteristic function of the open interval with endpoints 0 and x, i.e. $\chi_x(s)$ is 1 or 0 according as s lies in the interval or not. Then $\chi_x(s) \in L_2(\rho) \cap L_2(\sigma)$. Define

$$K(x, t) = T^{-1}[\chi_x(s)]. \tag{10.4.13}$$

This makes sense for χ_x belongs to the range of T and T is one-to-one. Then

$$T[K(x, t)] = \chi_x(s) \in L_2(\sigma).$$

Since T preserves inner products

$$\int_{-\infty}^{\infty} \overline{K(x, s)} f(s)\, d\sigma(s) = \int_{-\infty}^{\infty} \chi_x(t) g(t)\, d\rho(t)$$

where $g = Tf$. Hence for $x > 0$

$$\int_0^x g(t)\, d\rho(t) = \int_{-\infty}^{\infty} \overline{K(x, s)} f(s)\, d\sigma(s),$$

while if $x < 0$ the left member should read

$$\int_x^0 g(t)\, d\rho(t) = (\operatorname{sgn} x) \int_0^x g(t)\, d\rho(t)$$

by definition. This proves (10.4.8).

Next, we define

$$L(y, t) = T[\chi_y(s)]. \tag{10.4.14}$$

This makes sense for any fixed y. Proceeding as above, we get

$$\int_{-\infty}^{\infty} \overline{L(y, t)} g(t)\, d\rho(t) = \int_{-\infty}^{\infty} \chi_y(s) f(s)\, d\sigma(s)$$

and (10.4.9) results.

Again by the definition of the inner products

$$\int_{-\infty}^{\infty} K(x, s)\overline{K(y, s)}\, d\sigma(s) = \int_{-\infty}^{\infty} \chi_x(t)\chi_y(t)\, d\rho(t).$$

Suppose first that $0 < x < y$. Then the right member reduces to

$$\int_0^x d\rho(t) = \rho(x + 0) - \rho(0 + 0) = \rho(x).$$

Note that the integral is extended over the interval $(0, x]$, and that $\rho(t)$ is right continuous and normalized by the condition $\rho(0) = 0$. If $x < 0 < y$, then the integral is 0 while if $x < y < 0$, the integral becomes

$$\int_y^0 d\rho(t) = \rho(0 + 0) - \rho(y + 0) = -\rho(y).$$

In all three cases, the value of the integral equals $\tilde{\rho}(x, y)$ as asserted. The same argument proves (10.4.11). Finally, to get (10.4.12) we observe that $\chi_y(s) \in L_2(\sigma)$, $\chi_x(t) \in L_2(\rho)$, and

$$T[\chi_y(s)] = L(y, t), \qquad T^{-1}[\chi_x(t)] = K(x, s)$$

so that

$$\int_{-\infty}^{\infty} K(x, s)\chi_y(s)\, d\sigma(s) = \int_{-\infty}^{\infty} L(y, t)\chi_x(t)\, d\rho(t).$$

This reduces to (10.4.12).

It remains to prove that the kernels K and L are uniquely determined by T up to sets of measure zero. Suppose that there are two functions $\tilde{K}$ and $\tilde{L}$ which satisfy (10.4.8) to (10.4.12). Then, from (10.4.8), it follows that for all x and for all $f \in L_2(\sigma)$

$$\int_{-\infty}^{\infty} K(x, s)f(s)\, d\sigma(s) = \int_{-\infty}^{\infty} \tilde{K}(x, s)f(s)\, d\sigma(s).$$

This is possible iff $K(x, s) = \tilde{K}(x, s)$ for all s with the possible exception of a set of σ-measure 0. The same argument applies to L. ∎

Corollary. *For each fixed x and y the kernels $K(x, \cdot)$ and $L(y, \cdot)$ belong to $L_2(\sigma)$ and $L_2(\rho)$, respectively.*

The theorem admits of a converse.

Theorem 10.4.2. *Let $K(x, s)$ and $L(y, t)$ be two kernels defined for all real x, y, s, and t, and satisfying conditions* (10.4.10) *to* (10.4.12). *Then the transformation $g = Tf$ defined by* (10.4.8) *and* (10.4.9) *is a unitary mapping on $L_2(\sigma)$ to $L_2(\rho)$.*

Proof. We can define operators U and V on the characteristic functions $\chi_x(s)$ by the formulas

$$U\chi_x(t) = K(x, s), \qquad V\chi_y(s) = L(y, t). \tag{10.4.15}$$

Now formulas (10.4.10) and (10.4.11) show that inner products are preserved by these mappings so that

$$(U\chi_x, U\chi_y)_\sigma = (\chi_x, \chi_y)_\rho, \qquad (V\chi_x, V\chi_y)_\rho = (\chi_x, \chi_y)_\sigma$$

and (10.4.12) gives

$$(\chi_y, U\chi_x)_\sigma = (V\chi_y, \chi_x)_\rho.$$

The first two formulas show that U and V are isometric, and the third formula suggests that V is the inverse of U. The bilinear property of the inner products shows that U and V can be extended to finite linear combinations of functions $\chi_x(s)$. Any step function with a finite number of jumps is such a linear combination and the step functions are dense in $L_2(\rho)$ and in $L_2(\sigma)$. Using Cauchy sequences of step functions we can then extend U and V to all of $L_2(\rho)$ and $L_2(\sigma)$, respectively. We denote these extensions by U^0 and V^0. From the construction it follows that these transformations satisfy

$$(U^0 f, U^0 g)_\sigma = (f, g)_\rho \qquad \text{for } f, g \in L_2(\rho), \tag{10.4.16}$$

$$(V^0 F, V^0 G)_\rho = (F, G)_\sigma \qquad \text{for } F, G \in L_2(\sigma), \tag{10.4.17}$$

$$(U^0 f, G)_\sigma = (f, V^0 G)_\rho \qquad \text{for } f \in L_2(\rho),\ G \in L_2(\sigma). \tag{10.4.18}$$

If in the last equation we set $G = U^0 g$ we obtain

$$(f, V^0 U^0 g)_\rho = (f, g)_\rho$$

for all f and g so that $V^0U^0 = I$ and in the same manner we show that $U^0V^0 = I$ so that $V^0 = (U^0)^{-1}$. Hence V^0 is a unitary mapping on $L_2(\sigma)$ to $L_2(\rho)$. Since the kernels are uniquely determined by the mapping, it follows that $T = V^0$. ∎

Formula (10.4.8) and (10.4.9) define T implicitly. In certain circumstances it may be possible to get more explicit expressions. Suppose that $L_2(\sigma) = L_2(\rho) = L_2(0, \infty)$ and suppose the existence of continuous functions $K_1(x, s)$ and $L_1(y, t)$ such that

$$K(x, s) = \int_0^x K_1(\xi, s)\, d\xi, \qquad L(y, t) = \int_0^y L_1(\eta, t)\, d\eta. \tag{10.4.19}$$

Then

$$g(t) = \lim_{n\to\infty} \int_0^n K_1(t, s) f(s)\, ds, \tag{10.4.20}$$

$$f(s) = \lim_{n\to\infty} \int_0^n L_1(s, t) g(t)\, dt, \tag{10.4.21}$$

where the limits are taken in the L_2-sense. Formally these expressions are obtained from (10.4.8) and (10.4.9) by differentiation under the sign of integration. We shall not attempt a rigorous proof. Other cases occur in Section 10.5.

Besides the notion of unitary transformations we shall need two other observations. First, let us return to the starting-point: the mapping of a function $f(s) \in L_2(a, b)$ on to its Fourier coefficients in l_2. We can also place the set $\{f_n\}$ into another $L_2(\sigma)$-space which has a more natural connection with the boundary value problem. Here we take for $\sigma(t)$ the spectral function $\rho(t, b, \alpha)$, assuming $a = 0$ and the boundary condition at $s = b$ to be

$$y_2(b, \lambda, \alpha) = 0.$$

Let the roots of this equation be $\lambda = \lambda_n(b)$, $n = 0, 1, 2, \ldots$, and set

$$y_2(x, \lambda_n(b), \alpha) = y_{2,n}(x).$$

Then $\rho(t, b, \alpha)$ is a normalized right-continuous step function with $\rho(0, b, \alpha) = 0$ and a jump

$$r_n(b) = \left\{\int_0^b [y_{2,n}(s)]^2\, ds\right\}^{-1}$$

at each of the points $t = \lambda_n(b)$. The normalized characteristic functions are

$$\omega_n(x) = [r_n(b)]^{1/2} y_{1,n}(x)$$

and

$$f_n = [r_n(b)]^{1/2} \int_0^b f(s) y_{2,n}(s)\, ds.$$

Let us introduce

$$g(t, b, \alpha) = \int_0^b f(s) y_2(s, t, \alpha)\, ds \tag{10.4.22}$$

and let Δ be an open interval on the t-axis. Then

$$f(x, \Delta) \equiv \int_\Delta g(t, b, \alpha) y_2(x, t, \alpha)\, d\rho(t, b, \alpha) \tag{10.4.23}$$

reduces to

$$\sum f_n \omega_n(x)$$

where the summation extends over those values of n for which $\lambda_n(b)$ lies in Δ. It follows that

$$\lim_{\Delta \to (-\infty, \infty)} \int_0^b |f(x) - f(x, \Delta)|^2\, dx = 0 \tag{10.4.24}$$

and the closure relation becomes

$$\int_0^b |f(s)|^2\, ds = \int_{-\infty}^{\infty} |g(t, b, \alpha)|^2\, d\rho(t, b, \alpha). \tag{10.4.25}$$

This we can interpret as a unitary mapping of $L_2(0, b)$ onto the space $L_2(\sigma)$ with $\sigma(t) = \rho(t, b, \alpha)$. The mapping is onto, for, if $g(t) \in L_2(\sigma)$, we can define a corresponding $f(x, \Delta)$ with the aid of (10.4.23). This function is in $L_2(0, \infty)$ and converges to a unique $f(x) \in L_2(0, \infty)$ as $\Delta \to (-\infty, \infty)$. This is the first observation.

The second is the Helly Integration Theorem, already referred to in connection with Theorem 10.2.3. There we could by-pass the difficulties by an integration by parts, but here the same device is not always available. What is needed is stated as

Theorem 10.4.3. *Let $[a, b]$ be a finite interval, $\{\sigma_n(t)\}$ a uniformly bounded sequence of non-decreasing functions on $[a, b]$ such that $\lim_{n\to\infty} \sigma_n(t) \equiv \sigma(t)$ exists for $a \le t \le b$. Then, if $f \in C[a, b]$ we have*

$$\lim_{n\to\infty} \int_a^b f(t)\, d\sigma_n(t) = \int_a^b f(t)\, d\sigma(t). \tag{10.4.26}$$

This theorem applies, in particular, to the spectral family $\{\rho(t, b, \alpha)\}$ on any fixed finite interval $[-\omega, \omega]$. Here $\lim_{b\to\infty} \rho(t, b, \alpha) = \rho(t, \alpha)$ and, if $\alpha \not\equiv \frac{1}{2}\pi$, then

$$|\rho(t, b, \alpha)| \le C_1(\alpha) + C_2(\alpha)\omega^{1/2}$$

by (10.2.39). In the exceptional case $\alpha = \pm\frac{1}{2}\pi$, there is a bound $K_1 + K_2\omega^{3/2}$ instead.

EXERCISE 10.4

1. Let T be the transformation on $L_2(a, b)$ to l_2 defined by (10.4.1) and show that the corresponding kernels $K(x, s)$ and $L(y, n)$ are given by

$$K(x, s) = \sum_{n \le x} \omega_n(s), \qquad L(y, n) = \int_a^y \omega_n(s)\, ds.$$

Here $0 \le x, a \le s, y \le b$. Further, $K(x, s) = 0$ outside the stated domain, $L(y, n) = 0$ for $y < a$ and $= L(b, n)$ for $b \le y$.

2. Let T be the unitary mapping of $L_2(0, b)$ onto $L_2(\rho)$ with $\rho(t) = \rho(t, b, \alpha)$. Show that

$$K(x, s) = \int_0^x y_2(s, t, \alpha)\, d\rho(t, b, \alpha), \qquad 0 \le s \le b, \quad -\infty < x < \infty,$$

$$L(y, t) = \int_0^y y_2(s, t, \alpha)\, ds, \qquad 0 \le y \le b, \quad -\infty < t < \infty,$$

and zero outside the stated domains. Verify by direct computation that (10.4.10) to (10.4.12) are satisfied.

3. *The Watson transform.* Given a kernel $k(x)$ such that $k(x)/x \in L_2(0, \infty)$ and

$$\int_0^\infty k(xs)\overline{k(sy)}\, \frac{ds}{s^2} = x \wedge y.$$

Show that the formulas

$$\int_0^x g(t)\, dt = \int_0^\infty \overline{k(xs)} f(s)\, \frac{ds}{s},$$

$$\int_0^y f(s)\, ds = \int_0^\infty k(yt) g(t)\, \frac{dt}{t},$$

define a unitary transformation on $L_2(0, \infty)$ to itself.

The remaining problems involve a form of the Fourier transformation for the interval $(0, \infty)$ as it arises out of the singular boundary value problem for the differential equation $y'' + \lambda y = 0$.

4. In the differential equation take $\alpha = 0$, determine $y_1(x, \lambda, 0)$, $y_2(x, \lambda, 0)$, $m(\lambda, 0)$, $\rho(t, 0)$, and $Y_0(x, \lambda) = y_1 + m y_2$.

5. Verify that for $0 < x \wedge y$

$$\int_0^\infty \sin(xs) \sin(ys)\, \frac{ds}{s^2} = \tfrac{1}{2}\pi (x \wedge y).$$

[*Hint*: $\sin a \sin b = \sin^2 \frac{1}{2}(a + b) - \sin^2 \frac{1}{2}(a - b)$ and $\int_0^\infty \sin^2 u\, (du/u^2) = \frac{1}{2}\pi$.]

6. Two kernels are defined by

$$K(x, s) = \frac{1}{\pi} \frac{\sin(s\sqrt{x})}{s}, \qquad L(y, t) = \frac{\sin(y\sqrt{t})}{\sqrt{t}}$$

for non-negative values of the variables and are 0 in the rest of the (x, s)- and (y, t)-planes. Let

$$\sigma(t) = \begin{cases} 0, & t < 0, \\ t, & 0 \le t, \end{cases} \qquad \text{and} \qquad \rho(t) = \begin{cases} 0, & t < 0, \\ \dfrac{1}{\pi}\sqrt{t}, & 0 \le t. \end{cases}$$

Verify that this choice gives a unitary transformation on $L_2(\sigma)$ to $L_2(\rho)$, $g = T[f]$.

7. If f is of compact support show that

$$g(t) = \int_0^\infty \cos (s\sqrt{t})\, f(s)\, ds.$$

8. If g is of compact support, show that

$$f(s) = \int_0^\infty \cos (s\sqrt{t})\, g(t)\, d\rho(t).$$

9. If $f = Y_0(s, \lambda)$, λ non-real, show that

$$T[f] = (t - \lambda)^{-1}.$$

10. The integral

$$\int_0^\infty \frac{\cos (s\sqrt{t})}{t - \lambda}\, d\rho(t), \qquad \Im(\lambda) \neq 0,$$

is absolutely convergent. Its value should be $Y_0(s, \lambda)$. Prove this, e.g. by using the calculus of residues.

10.5 REPRESENTATION THEOREMS

Following the precepts of D. B. Sears (1954), we shall apply the methods developed in the preceding section to the expansion and inversion problems associated with a singular boundary value problem. Exercise 10.4 contains results bearing on the special case $q(x) \equiv 0$.

The notation will be our usual one except for writing

$$y_1(x, \lambda, \alpha) + m(\lambda, \alpha) y_2(x, \lambda, \alpha) \equiv Y_\alpha(x, \lambda). \tag{10.5.1}$$

The parameter α is often omitted when its actual value is unimportant.

Following the model of Problem 2, Exercise 10.4, we introduce the two kernels

$$K(x, s) = \int_0^x y_2(s, t)\, d\rho(t), \qquad -\infty < x < \infty, \quad 0 \leq s, \tag{10.5.2}$$

$$L(y, t) = \int_0^y y_2(s, t)\, ds, \qquad 0 \leq y, \quad -\infty < t < \infty. \tag{10.5.3}$$

A transformation, $g = T[f]$, is defined implicitly by the equations

$$\int_0^x g(t)\, d\rho(t) = \int_0^\infty K(x, s) f(s)\, ds, \tag{10.5.4}$$

$$\int_0^y f(s)\, ds = \int_{-\infty}^\infty L(y, t) g(t)\, d\rho(t). \tag{10.5.5}$$

Our object is to show that T is unitary on $L_2(0, \infty)$ to $L_2(\rho)$. The proof will be given in several instalments. We start by introducing an auxiliary transformation which later will be identified with T.

Theorem 10.5.1. *Let $f \in L_2(0, \infty)$ and let $L_2(\rho)$ be defined as above, i.e. $\rho(t) = \rho(t, \alpha)$, the spectral function of the problem. Set*

$$g_n(t) = \int_0^n y_2(s, t) f(s)\, ds. \tag{10.5.6}$$

Then $g_n \in L_2(\rho)$ and the sequence $\{g_n\}$ converges in the metric of $L_2(\rho)$ to an element $g(t)$. Further

$$\int_0^\infty |f(s)|^2\, ds = \int_{-\infty}^\infty |g(t)|^2\, d\rho(t). \tag{10.5.7}$$

Proof. We start by proving the existence of $g(t) \equiv U[f]$ and the validity of Bessel's inequality, i.e. (10.5.7), with "=" replaced by "≥". In a second step, the latter is sharpened to the closure relation.

Suppose that $f \in L_2(0, \infty)$ and set

$$f_n(x) = \begin{cases} f(x), & 0 \le x \le n, \\ 0, & n < x. \end{cases}$$

Let

$$g_n(t, b) = \int_0^b f_n(s) y_2(s, t)\, ds.$$

Then for $b > n$

$$g_n(t, b) = \int_0^n f(s) y_2(s, t)\, ds \equiv g_n(t). \tag{10.5.8}$$

This is an entire function of t and hence measurable with respect to any spectral measure. Moreover, by (10.4.25),

$$\int_0^\infty |f_n(s)|^2\, ds = \int_{-\infty}^\infty |g_n(t)|^2\, d\rho(t, b)$$

for any $b > n$. Hence, for any fixed finite ω and $b > n$

$$\int_0^\infty |f_n(s)|^2\, ds > \int_{-\omega}^\omega |g_n(t)|^2\, d\rho(t, b).$$

Here we can pass to the limit with b and by Theorem 10.4.3

$$\int_0^\infty |f_n(s)|^2\, ds \ge \int_{-\omega}^\omega |g_n(t)|^2\, d\rho(t).$$

Since ω is arbitrary, this shows that $g_n(t) \in L_2(\rho)$ and

$$\int_0^\infty |f_n(s)|^2\, ds \ge \int_{-\infty}^\infty |g_n(t)|^2\, d\rho(t). \tag{10.5.9}$$

In the same manner one proves that for $0 < m < n$

$$\int_0^\infty |f_n(s) - f_m(s)|^2\, ds \geq \int_{-\infty}^\infty |g_n(t) - g_m(t)|^2\, d\rho(t).$$

Here the left member is

$$\int_m^n |f(s)|^2\, ds$$

which tends to 0 as $m \to \infty$. It follows that $\{g_n(t)\}$ is a Cauchy sequence in $L_2(\rho)$ and hence has a limit $g(t)$ in this space. We can then let $n \to \infty$ in (10.5.9) to obtain

$$\int_0^\infty |f(s)|^2\, ds \geq \int_{-\infty}^\infty |g(t)|^2\, d\rho(t). \tag{10.5.10}$$

We set

$$g(t) = U[f](t). \tag{10.5.11}$$

This defines a linear bounded transformation of $L_2(0, \infty)$ into $L_2(\rho)$. The mapping is one-to-one and the bound is ≤ 1.

In the second step, we show that equality holds in (10.5.10), so that Bessel's inequality becomes the closure relation. To this end it is enough to show that equality holds for any f in a set dense in $L_2(0, \infty)$. The differential equation suggests how such a set may be found. The differential operator L is defined by

$$\mathsf{L}[y](x) = q(x)y(x) - y''(x) \tag{10.5.12}$$

whenever the right member has a sense. Let S be the set of all functions F defined and of compact support on $(0, \infty)$ which are continuous together with their first and second order derivatives. Such an F vanishes outside an interval (δ, c), $0 < \delta < c < \infty$. It belongs to the domain of the operator L as well as to the space $L_2(0, \infty)$ and the set S is dense in the latter space. Set

$$\mathsf{L}[F](x) = f(x). \tag{10.5.13}$$

Since $F = 0$ outside of (δ, c), Lagrange's identity or a simple calculation shows that

$$\begin{aligned} U[f](t) &= \int_0^\infty \mathsf{L}[F](s) y_2(s, t)\, ds \\ &= \int_0^\infty F(s) \mathsf{L}[y_2](s)\, ds \\ &= t \int_0^\infty F(s) y_2(s, t)\, ds = tU[F](t). \end{aligned}$$

We note the relation

$$U[\mathsf{L}F](t) = tU[F](t) \tag{10.5.14}$$

for later reference.

We have now, for any $b > c$ and any ω,

$$\int_0^\infty |f(s)|^2\, ds = \int_{-\infty}^\infty |U[f](t)|^2\, d\rho(t, b)$$

$$= \int_{-\infty}^\infty t^2 |U[F](t)|^2\, d\rho(t, b)$$

$$> \omega^2 \int_{|t|>\omega} |U[F](t)|^2\, d\rho(t, b). \tag{10.5.15}$$

Hence

$$\int_0^\infty |F(s)|^2\, ds = \int_{-\infty}^\infty |U[F](t)|^2\, d\rho(t, b)$$

$$= \left\{\int_{-\omega}^{\omega} + \int_{|t|>\omega}\right\} |U[F](t)|^2\, d\rho(t, b)$$

$$< \int_{-\omega}^{\omega} |U[F](t)|^2\, d\rho(t, b) + \omega^{-2} \int_0^\infty |f(s)|^2\, ds$$

by (10.5.15). We can now let $b \to \infty$ in the finite integral and use Theorem 10.4.3. This gives

$$\int_0^\infty |F(s)|^2\, ds \le \int_{-\omega}^{\omega} |U[F](t)|^2\, d\rho(t) + \omega^{-2} \int_0^\infty |f(s)|^2\, ds$$

for all $\omega > 0$. We now let $\omega \to \infty$ to obtain

$$\int_0^\infty |F(s)|^2\, ds \le \int_{-\infty}^\infty |U[F](t)|^2\, d\rho(t).$$

Since (10.5.10) gives the opposite inequality, we have

$$\int_0^\infty |F(s)|^2\, ds = \int_{-\infty}^\infty |U[F](t)|^2\, d\rho(t), \tag{10.5.16}$$

for all $F \in S$, a set dense in $L_2(0, \infty)$.

If now $\{F_n\} \subset S$ is a Cauchy sequence in $L_2(0, \infty)$, then

$$\int_0^\infty |F_n(s) - F_m(s)|^2\, ds = \int_{-\infty}^\infty |U[F_n](t) - U[F_m](t)|^2\, d\rho(t)$$

so that $\{U[F_n]\}$ is a Cauchy sequence in $L_2(\rho)$. If $F_n \to F_0$ and $U[F_n] \to G_0$, then, by the continuity of U, $U[F_0] = G_0$ and (10.5.16) holds also for $F = F_0$. Since F_0 is an arbitrary element of $L_2(0, \infty)$, the closure relation holds for all F. We have also shown that U is a unitary transformation of $L_2(0, \infty)$ into $L_2(\sigma)$.

By the same argument one sees that inner products are preserved so that

$$\int_0^\infty F(s)\overline{G(s)}\, ds = \int_{-\infty}^\infty U[F](t)\overline{U[G](t)}\, d\rho(t) \tag{10.5.17}$$

for all $F, G \in L_2(0, \infty)$. ∎

In particular, take

$$F(s) = \chi_x(s), \qquad G(s) = \chi_y(s), \qquad 0 < x, \quad 0 < y,$$

then

$$U[F](t) = L(x, t), \qquad U[G](t) = L(y, t),$$

so that

$$\int_0^\infty L(x, t)\overline{L(y, t)}\, d\rho(t) = x \wedge y. \tag{10.5.18}$$

This is one of the relations that K and L must satisfy for T be be unitary on $L_2(0, \infty)$ to $L_2(\rho)$.

The corresponding relation for K is harder to prove and at this juncture we merely show that $K(x, \cdot) \in L_2(0, \infty)$ and

$$\int_0^\infty |K(x, s)|^2\, ds \le |\rho(x)|. \tag{10.5.19}$$

Equality will follow later. To prove this, note that the transformation T_b on $L_2(0, b)$ to $L_2[\rho(\cdot, b)]$ defined by (10.4.22) is unitary and the corresponding kernels $K_b(x, s)$ and $L_b(y, t)$ are defined in Problem 2, Exercise 10.4. Hence

$$\int_0^b \left[\int_0^x y_2(s, t)\, d\rho(t, b)\right]^2 ds = |\rho(x, b)|.$$

We have now

$$\int_0^x y_2(s, t)\, d\rho(t, b) = y_2(s, x)\rho(x, b) - \int_0^x y'_{2,t}(s, t)\rho(t, b)\, dt$$

the absolute value of which does not exceed

$$C(x)\{|y_2(s, x)| + V_0^x[y_2(s, \cdot)]\} \equiv B(x, s).$$

Here

$$C(x) = C_1(\alpha) + C_2(\alpha)|x|^{1/2} \qquad \text{or} \qquad K_1 + K_2|x|^{3/2} \tag{10.5.20}$$

according as α is not or is congruent to $\frac{1}{2}\pi \pmod{\pi}$. The bound for $K_b(x, s)$ is independent of b and is clearly in $L_2(0, \omega)$ for any finite ω. Hence for $\omega < b$

$$\int_0^\omega [K_b(x, s)]^2\, ds < |\rho(x, b)|, \qquad |K_b(x, s)| \le B(x, s)$$

and

$$\lim_{b \to \infty} K_b(x, s) = K(x, s)$$

by Theorem 10.4.3. Using Lebesgue's theorem on dominated convergence, we can then pass to the limit with b under the sign of integration obtaining

$$\int_0^\omega [K(x, s)]^2\, ds \le |\rho(x)|.$$

Since ω is arbitrary, (10.5.19) follows. Similarly, for any fixed ω

$$\lim_{b\to\infty} \int_0^\omega |K(x, s) - K_b(x, s)|^2 \, ds = 0. \tag{10.5.21}$$

We shall now prove that

$$T = U, \tag{10.5.22}$$

i.e. the mappings of $L_2(0, \infty)$ into $L_2(\rho)$ defined by (10.5.4) and by Theorem 10.5.1 are identical. As above let $f(s) \in L_2(0, \infty)$ and set $f_n(s) = f(s)$ or 0 according as $s \leq n$ or $>n$. Let

$$g_n(t) = \int_0^n y_2(s, t) f(s) \, ds.$$

Then

$$\begin{aligned} \int_0^x g_n(t) \, d\rho(t) &= \int_0^x \left[\int_0^n y_2(s, t) f(s) \, ds\right] d\rho(t) \\ &= \int_0^n \left[\int_0^x y_2(s, t) \, d\rho(t)\right] f(s) \, ds \\ &= \int_0^n K(x, s) f(s) \, ds \\ &= \int_0^\infty K(x, s) f_n(s) \, ds. \end{aligned}$$

As $n \to \infty$

$$f_n(s) \to f(s), \qquad g_n(t) \to g(t)$$

in $L_2(0, \infty)$ and $L_2(\rho)$, respectively. Since $K(x, \cdot) \in L_2(0, \infty)$, it follows that

$$\int_0^x g(t) \, d\rho(t) = \int_0^\infty f(s) K(x, s) \, ds.$$

This is formula (10.5.4). Here

$$g(t) = U[f](t) \in L_2(\rho)$$

and $x > 0$ is arbitrary. If there were another function $g_1 \in L_2(\rho)$ satisfying the same relation, then for all x

$$\int_0^x g(t) \, d\rho(t) = \int_0^x g_1(t) \, d\rho(t)$$

This, however, implies $g(t) = g_1(t)$, neglecting a set of ρ-measure 0. Hence (10.5.22) holds.

We now return to the question of proving

$$\int_0^\infty K(x, s) K(y, s) \, ds = \tilde{\rho}(x, y). \tag{10.5.23}$$

To this end we prove some lemmas which have a bearing on this and related problems. Let us set

$$Y_\alpha(x, \lambda, b) = y_1(x, \lambda, \alpha) + m(\lambda, b, \alpha) y_2(x, \lambda, \alpha) \tag{10.5.24}$$

where for all λ

$$Y_\alpha(b, \lambda, b) = 0.$$

Lemma 10.5.1. *If $\lambda = \mu + i\nu$, $\nu \neq 0$, then the function*

$$I(\mu, \nu, b) \equiv \nu^2 \int_0^b |Y_\alpha(x, \mu + i\nu, b)|^2 \, dx \tag{10.5.25}$$

is bounded for $-\omega < \mu < \omega$, $-1 < \nu < 1$, uniformly in b, and

$$\lim_{\nu \downarrow 0} I(\mu, \nu, b) = \rho(\mu, b, \alpha) - \rho(\mu - 0, b, \alpha). \tag{10.5.26}$$

Proof. By (10.1.11) and (10.2.38)

$$I(\mu, \nu, b) = \nu \Im[m(\lambda, b, \alpha)] = \nu^2 \int_{-\infty}^{\infty} \frac{d\rho(t, b, \alpha)}{(t - \mu)^2 + \nu^2}.$$

An integration by parts followed by the substitution $t = \mu + \nu s$ gives

$$I(\mu, \nu, b) = \int_{-\infty}^{\infty} \frac{2s\rho(\mu + \nu s, b, \alpha)}{(s^2 + 1)^2} \, ds \tag{10.5.27}$$

since the integrated part vanishes in the limits. Here

$$|\rho(\mu + \nu s, b, \alpha)| \leq C(\mu + \nu s),$$

where $C(x)$ is defined by (10.5.20). Now we have

$$C(\mu + \nu s) < 2[C(\mu) + C(\nu s)]$$

where the factor 2 can be omitted unless $\alpha = \pm\frac{1}{2}\pi$. This shows that there exists an absolute constant K such that for all b

$$I(\mu, \nu, b) < K[C(\mu) + C(\nu)].$$

This expression is bounded if μ and ν are bounded.

To prove (10.5.26) we note that it is permitted to pass to the limit under the sign of integration, since the integrand is dominated by

$$\frac{4s[C(\omega) + C(s)]}{(s^2 + 1)^2}$$

for $|\mu| \leq \omega$, $|\nu| \leq 1$, and this function is $L(-\infty, \infty)$. We have then

$$\lim_{\nu \downarrow 0} \int_0^{\infty} \frac{2s\rho(\mu + \nu s, b, \alpha) \, ds}{(s^2 + 1)^2} = \rho(\mu, b, \alpha) \int_0^{\infty} \frac{2s \, ds}{(s^2 + 1)^2},$$

$$\lim_{\nu \downarrow 0} \int_{-\infty}^{0} \frac{2s\rho(\mu + \nu s, b, \alpha) \, ds}{(s^2 + 1)^2} = \rho(\mu - 0, b, \alpha) \int_{-\infty}^{0} \frac{2s \, ds}{(s^2 + 1)^2},$$

and this gives the desired result. If $\nu < 0$ and $\nu \uparrow 0$, we get the negative of (10.5.26) instead. ∎

Lemma 10.5.2. *We have for fixed non-real* λ

$$\lim_{b\to\infty}\int_0^b |Y_\alpha(x,\lambda) - Y_\alpha(x,\lambda,b)|^2\,dx = 0. \tag{10.5.28}$$

Proof. We have

$$Y_\alpha(x,\lambda) - Y_\alpha(x,\lambda,b) = [m(\lambda,\alpha) - m(\lambda,b,\alpha)]y_2(x,\lambda,\alpha),$$

so that the integral equals

$$|m(\lambda,\alpha) - m(\lambda,b,\alpha)|^2\int_0^b |y_2(x,\lambda,\alpha)|^2\,dx.$$

Here by (10.1.12)

$$|m(\lambda,\alpha) - m(\lambda,b,\alpha)| \le 2r_b(\lambda) = \left[|\nu|\int_0^b |y_2(s,\lambda)|^2\,ds\right]^{-1}$$

It follows that

$$\int_0^b |Y_\alpha(x,\lambda) - Y_\alpha(x,\lambda,b)|^2\,dx \le \nu^{-2}\left[\int_0^b |y_2(s,\lambda)|^2\,ds\right]^{-1}.$$

Here $\lambda = \mu + i\nu$ is fixed and in the limit-point case the integral on the right tends to ∞ so the limit of the left member is 0. This is still true in the limit-circle case provided $b \to \infty$ in such a manner that $m(\lambda, b, \alpha) \to m(\lambda, \alpha)$. ∎

Next we introduce the functions

$$K_b(\lambda, s) = \frac{1}{\pi}\int_0^\mu \Im[Y_\alpha(s, t + i\nu, b)]\,dt, \tag{10.5.29}$$

$$K(\lambda, s) = \frac{1}{\pi}\int_0^\mu \Im[Y_\alpha(s, t + i\nu)]\,dt. \tag{10.5.30}$$

Here $\lambda = \mu + i\nu$, $\nu \ne 0$, and the notation is intended to suggest a relationship between $K(x, s)$ and $K(x + i\nu, s)$, etc. In fact, $K(x, \cdot)$ is the L_2-limit of $K(x + i\nu, \cdot)$ as $\nu \to 0$. More precisely we shall prove

Lemma 10.5.3. *For* $\nu \ne 0$, $K(x + i\nu, \cdot) \in L_2(0, \infty)$ *and its norm is bounded on compact subsets of the* (x, ν)*-plane. Further*

$$\|K(x + i\nu, \cdot) - K(x, \cdot)\| \to 0 \tag{10.5.31}$$

as $\nu \downarrow 0$ *at all points* x *of continuity of* $\rho(t)$.

Proof. We start by considering the function

$$K_b(x + i\nu, s) - K_b(x, s), \qquad 0 \le s \le b,$$

which we expand in terms of the associated orthonormal system $\{\omega_n(s)\}$ where $\omega_n(s) = [r_n(b)]^{1/2}y_2(s, \lambda_n(b), \alpha)$ and

$$y_2(b, \lambda_n(b), \alpha) = 0.$$

We have now

$$\int_0^b K_b(x + iv, s)\omega_n(s)\, ds = \frac{1}{\pi}\int_0^b \left\{\int_0^x \Im[Y_\alpha(s, t + iv, b)]\, dt\right\}\omega_n(s)\, ds$$
$$= \Im\left\{\frac{1}{\pi}\int_0^x \left[\int_0^b Y_\alpha(s, t + iv, b)\omega_n(s)\, ds\right] dt\right\}$$
$$= [r_n(b)]^{1/2}\frac{1}{\pi}\Im\left\{\int_0^x \frac{dt}{\lambda_n(b) - t - iv}\right\}$$
$$= [r_n(b)]^{1/2}\frac{v}{\pi}\int_0^x \frac{dt}{[t - \lambda_n(b)]^2 + v^2}\,.$$

We recall that $r_n(b)$ is the jump of $\rho(t, b, \alpha)$ at $t = \lambda_n(b)$. Next

$$\int_0^b K_b(x, s)\omega_n(s)\, ds = \int_0^b \left[\int_0^x y_2(s, t)\, d\rho(t, b)\right]\omega_n(s)\, ds.$$

If $x > 0$, the integral with respect to t equals

$$\sum r_k(b)y_2(s, \lambda_k(b))$$

where the summation extends over those values of k for which $\lambda_k(b)$ lies in $(0, x]$. If n is such a value, then the double integral equals

$$r_n(b)\int_0^b y_2(s, \lambda_n(b))\omega_n(s)\, ds = [r_n(b)]^{1/2}.$$

If not, then the Fourier coefficient is 0. If $x < 0$, the t-integral gives a similar sum extended over the values of k for which $x < \lambda_k(b) < 0$, but now preceded by a minus sign. If now $x < \lambda_n(b) < 0$, the Fourier coefficient is $-[r_n(b)]^{1/2}$, otherwise 0.

To cope with this ambiguous sign, we introduce a function $S(x, t)$. Only the values of $S(x, t)$ for $t = \lambda_n(b)$ are relevant for our problem. Here $S(x, \lambda_n(b))$ has one of the three values $+1$, -1, and 0. It is -1, if $x < \lambda_n(b) < 0$, $+1$ if $0 < \lambda_n(b) \leq x$, and 0 in all other cases. With this notation we see that

$$\int_0^b [K_b(x + vi, s) - K_b(x, s)]\omega_n(s)\, ds$$
$$= \left\{\frac{v}{\pi}\int_0^x \frac{dt}{[t - \lambda_n(b)]^2 + v^2} - S(x, \lambda_n(b))\right\}[r_n(b)]^{1/2}.$$

In order to use the Parseval formula we have to form the sum of the squares of the right members for $n = 0, 1, 2, \ldots$ This sum can be written as a Stieltjes integral and we obtain the identity

$$\int_0^b [K_b(x + vi, s) - K_b(x, s)]^2\, ds$$
$$= \int_{-\infty}^{\infty} \left\{\frac{v}{\pi}\int_0^x \frac{dt}{(t - \tau)^2 + v^2} - S(x, \tau)\right\}^2 d\rho(\tau, b). \quad (10.5.32)$$

As $\nu \downarrow 0$ the integrand in the right member tends to 0 except for $\tau = x$. To minimize the difficulties caused by the discontinuous integrand we shall assume that $\tau = x$ is a point of continuity of all the spectral functions involved. In formula (10.5.32) we are going to let $b \to \infty$ and $\nu \downarrow 0$ in this order. Since the integral in the right member is extended over an infinite interval and Theorem 10.4.3 applies to finite intervals, we start by getting uniform bounds for the infinite ends.

Choose $\omega > 2|x|$. Then for $\tau > \omega$, $S(x, \tau) = 0$ and $|t - \tau| > \frac{1}{2}\tau$. This gives

$$\int_\omega^\infty \left\{\frac{\nu}{\pi}\int_0^x \frac{dt}{(t-\tau)^2 + \nu^2} - S(x, \tau)\right\}^2 d\rho(\tau, b)$$

$$= \left(\frac{\nu}{\pi}\right)^2 \int_\omega^\infty \left\{\int_0^x \frac{dt}{(t-\tau)^2 + \nu^2}\right\}^2 d\rho(\tau, b)$$

$$< \left(\frac{4}{\pi}\nu x\right)^2 \int_\omega^\infty \tau^{-4}\, d\rho(\tau, b) < K(\nu x)^2 \omega^{-5/2}.$$

To justify the last step, integrate by parts and use the estimate

$$|\rho(t, b, \alpha)| < C|t|^{3/2}$$

which holds for all b and α and all sufficiently large values of $|t|$. The same estimate holds for the integral over $(-\infty, -\omega)$.

It follows that for $b > B$

$$\int_0^B [K_b(x + \nu i, s) - K_b(x, s)]^2\, ds$$

$$< \int_{-\omega}^\omega \left\{\frac{\nu}{\pi}\int_0^x \frac{dt}{(t-\tau)^2 + \nu^2} - S(x, \tau)\right\}^2 d\rho(t, b) + 2K(\nu x)^2 \omega^{-5/2}.$$

We can now let $b \to \infty$. Then

$$K_b(x + \nu i, s) \to K(x + \nu i, s), \qquad K_b(x, s) \to K(x, s).$$

Further, $\rho(\tau, b) \to \rho(\tau)$ and, since these functions are continuous at $\tau = x$, the discontinuity of the integrand at this point does not matter and the conclusion of Theorem 10.4.3 remains valid. Hence

$$\int_0^B [K(x + \nu i, s) - K(x, s)]^2\, ds$$

$$\leq \int_{-\omega}^\omega \left\{\frac{\nu}{\pi}\int_0^x \frac{dt}{(t-\tau)^2 + \nu^2} - S(x, \tau)\right\}^2 d\rho(\tau) + 2K(\nu x)^2 \omega^{-5/2}.$$

This, being true for all values of B, will also hold for $B = \infty$. Since $K(x, \cdot) \in L_2(0, \infty)$, it follows that $K(x + i\nu, \cdot)$ has the same property. The last inequality shows that

$$\|K(x + i\nu, \cdot) - K(x, \cdot)\|$$

is bounded if $|x + i\nu| < R$. By (10.5.19) the same holds for $\|K(x, \cdot)\|$ and hence also for

$$\|K(x + i\nu, \cdot)\| \leq \|K(x + i\nu, \cdot) - K(x, \cdot)\| + \|K(x, \cdot)\|.$$

Finally we let $\nu \downarrow 0$ and obtain (10.5.31) as asserted. ∎

Lemma 10.5.4. *We have*

$$\int_0^b K_b(x, s)\, Y_\alpha(s, \lambda, b)\, ds = \int_0^x \frac{d\rho(t, b)}{t - \lambda}, \tag{10.5.33}$$

$$\int_0^b K_b(x, s) K_b(y + i\nu, s)\, ds = \int_0^x \left\{\frac{\nu}{\pi}\int_0^y \frac{du}{(u - t)^2 + \nu^2}\right\} d\rho(t, b). \tag{10.5.34}$$

Proof. The Fourier coefficients of the functions $K_b(x, s)$, $K_b(y + i\nu, s)$ and $Y_\alpha(s, \lambda, b)$ which occur in these inner products can be read off from the above calculations. They are $[r_n(b)]^{1/2}$ multiplied by

$$S(x, \lambda_n(b)), \qquad \frac{\nu}{\pi}\int_0^y \frac{du}{[u - \lambda_n(b)]^2 + \nu^2}, \qquad \text{and} \qquad \frac{1}{\lambda_n(b) - \lambda},$$

respectively. The inner products can then be computed by the closure relations in terms of the Fourier coefficients. The resulting series may be rewritten as Stieltjes integrals, with $\rho(t, b)$ as integrator, and thus the stated formulas are obtained. ∎

The main theorem can now be proved.

Theorem 10.5.2. *The transformation T defined by formulas* (10.5.2) *to* (10.5.5) *is a unitary mapping of $L_2(0, \infty)$ onto $L_2(\rho)$.*

Proof. We have already proved (10.5.18) but (10.5.23) remains. The latter calls for a justification of passing to the limit, $b \to \infty$, $\nu \downarrow 0$, in (10.5.34). We start with (10.5.33) and set

$$\delta(x, \lambda, b) \equiv \int_0^b K_b(x, s)\, Y_\alpha(s, \lambda, b)\, ds - \int_0^b K(x, s)\, Y_\alpha(s, \lambda)\, ds.$$

Then

$$\delta(x, \lambda, b) = \int_0^b K_b(x, s)[Y_\alpha(s, \lambda, b) - Y_\alpha(s, \lambda)]\, ds$$
$$+ \int_0^b Y_\alpha(s, \lambda)[K_b(x, s) - K(x, s)]\, ds.$$

Here the absolute value of the first integral does not exceed

$$\left\{\int_0^b [K_b(x, s)]^2\, ds\right\}^{1/2} \left\{\int_0^b |Y_\alpha(s, \lambda, b) - Y_\alpha(s, \lambda)|^2\, ds\right\}^{1/2}.$$

Since the first factor is dominated by $[C(x)]^{1/2}$ and the second tends to 0 as $b \to \infty$ by Lemma 10.5.2, it follows that the first integral converges to 0. To handle the second integral, we choose ω so large that for α and λ fixed

$$\int_{\omega}^{\infty} |Y_\alpha(s, \lambda)|^2 \, ds < \varepsilon^2.$$

where ε is a given positive number. We split the interval of integration into two parts $(0, \omega)$ and (ω, b). Here

$$\left|\int_0^{\omega}\right|^2 \leq \int_0^{\omega} |Y_\alpha(s, \lambda)|^2 \, ds \cdot \int_0^{\omega} [K_b(x, s) - K(x, s)]^2 \, ds.$$

The first factor is bounded uniformly in ω and the second factor goes to 0 as $b \to \infty$ by (10.5.21). Further

$$\left|\int_{\omega}^{b}\right|^2 \leq \int_{\omega}^{b} |Y_\alpha(s, \lambda)|^2 \, ds \cdot \int_{\omega}^{b} [K_b(x, s) - K(s, x)]^2 \, ds$$
$$\leq 4\varepsilon^2 C(x).$$

Combining these results, we conclude that

$$\lim_{b \to \infty} \delta(x, \lambda, b) = 0.$$

But this asserts that

$$\lim_{b \to \infty} \int_0^b K(x, s) Y_\alpha(s, \lambda) \, ds = \lim_{b \to \infty} \int_0^b K_b(x, s) Y_\alpha(s, \lambda, b) \, ds$$
$$= \lim_{b \to \infty} \int_0^x \frac{d\rho(t, b)}{t - \lambda}$$

by (10.5.33). Since the integral in the first member remains absolutely convergent when $b \to \infty$, we have proved

$$\int_0^{\infty} K(x, s) Y_\alpha(s, \lambda) \, ds = \int_0^x \frac{d\rho(t)}{t - \lambda}. \tag{10.5.35}$$

Here we set $\lambda = u + iv$, take the imaginary part and integrate with respect to u from 0 to y. Thus

$$\int_0^{\infty} K(x, s) \frac{1}{\pi} \int_0^y \Im[Y_\alpha(s, u + iv)] \, du \, ds = \int_0^{\infty} K(x, s) K(y + iv, s) \, ds.$$

Hence

$$\int_0^{\infty} K(x, s) K(y + iv, s) \, ds = \int_0^x \left\{ \frac{v}{\pi} \int_0^y \frac{du}{(u - t)^2 + v^2} \right\} d\rho(t).$$

This shows that it is possible to let $b \to \infty$ in formula (10.5.34). It remains only to let $\nu \to 0$ and to use (10.5.31). Thus

$$\int_0^\infty K(x, s)K(y, s)\,ds = \lim_{\nu \downarrow 0} \int_0^x \left\{\frac{\nu}{\pi}\int_0^y \frac{du}{(u-t)^2+\nu^2}\right\} d\rho(t)$$

at all points y which are points of continuity of $\rho(t)$. The limit is supposed to be $\tilde{\rho}(x, y)$. The limit clearly depends upon the relative position of the points $0, x, y$. Suppose first that $0 < x < y$. Then the limit of the u-integral is 1 for $0 \le t \le x$ and the limit of the right member is $\rho(x)$. If $x < 0 < y$, the u-integral gives the limit 0 and the limit of the right member is also 0. If $x < y < 0$, the u-integral gives the limit -1 and the right member tends to $-\rho(y)$. In all three cases, the limit coincides with $\tilde{\rho}(x, y)$. The remaining possibilities can be handled by symmetry or limit passage $y \to x$. This proves (10.5.23). Since (10.4.12) obviously holds, the unitary character of T is established. ∎

From (10.5.35) we obtain the

Corollary. *The T-transform of $Y_\alpha(s, \lambda)$ is $(t - \lambda)^{-1}$ if $\Im(\lambda) \neq 0$.*

Among the many consequences of this fact we note

Lemma 10.5.5. *For non-real values of λ_1 and λ_2*

$$\int_0^\infty Y_\alpha(s, \lambda_1)Y_\alpha(s, \lambda_2)\,ds = \frac{m(\lambda_1, \alpha) - m(\lambda_2, \alpha)}{\lambda_1 - \lambda_2}$$

$$= \int_{-\infty}^\infty \frac{d\rho(t)}{(t-\lambda_1)(t-\lambda_2)}. \qquad (10.5.36)$$

Proof. Equality between the first and the third members follows from (10.5.17), between the second and the third from (10.2.52) if $\alpha \not\equiv \frac{1}{2}\pi \pmod{\pi}$, and from Problem 14, Exercise 10.2 if $\alpha = \pm\frac{1}{2}\pi$. ∎

We note in particular

$$\int_0^\infty [Y_\alpha(s, \lambda)]^2\,ds = m'(\lambda, \alpha) = \int_{-\infty}^\infty \frac{d\rho(t)}{(t-\lambda)^2}. \qquad (10.5.37)$$

Special cases of these formulas figured (without proof) in (10.3.13) and (10.3.14). In that context, $q(x)$ was assumed to be bounded below, Theorem 10.1.4 holds and a direct proof could be given.

We now prove an analogue of formula (10.4.24) in order to obtain an explicit formula for T^{-1} to supplement (10.5.5).

Theorem 10.5.3. *If $g(t) = T[f](t)$ and if $\Delta = (a, b]$ is a finite t-interval and if*

$$f(s, \Delta) \equiv \int_\Delta y_2(s, t)g(t)\,d\rho(t), \qquad (10.5.38)$$

then for $\Delta \to (-\infty, \infty)$

$$\lim \int_0^\infty |f(s) - f(s, \Delta)|^2 \, ds = 0. \tag{10.5.39}$$

Proof. Set $g(t, \Delta) = g(t)$ or 0 according as $t \in \Delta$ or not. Then $g(t, \Delta) \in L_2(\rho)$ and since T is unitary, there exists a function $f_\Delta(s) \in L_2(0, \infty)$ such that $T[f_\Delta](t) = g(t, \Delta)$ and

$$\int_0^\infty |f_\Delta(s)|^2 \, ds = \int_{-\infty}^\infty |g(t, \Delta)|^2 \, d\rho(t).$$

Moreover, if $\Delta_1 \supset \Delta_2$ are Δ-intervals, then

$$\int_0^\infty |f_{\Delta_1}(s) - f_{\Delta_2}(s)|^2 \, ds = \int_{-\infty}^\infty |g(t, \Delta_1) - g(t, \Delta_2)|^2 \, d\rho(t) \to 0$$

as $\Delta_2 \to (-\infty, \infty)$. It follows that the f_Δ form a Cauchy family and have a limit f_0 in $L_2(0, \infty)$.

On the other hand, by (10.5.5)

$$\begin{aligned}
\int_0^y f_\Delta(s) \, ds &= \int_{-\infty}^\infty L(y, t) g(t, \Delta) \, d\rho(t) \\
&= \int_{-\infty}^\infty \left[\int_0^y y_2(s, t) \, ds\right] g(t, \Delta) \, d\rho(t) \\
&= \int_0^y \int_\Delta y_2(s, t) g(t) \, d\rho(t) \, ds \\
&= \int_0^y f(s, \Delta) \, ds
\end{aligned}$$

so that

$$f_\Delta(s) = f(s, \Delta)$$

for almost all s. Further,

$$\int_{-\infty}^\infty L(y, t) g(t, \Delta) \, d\rho(t) \to \int_{-\infty}^\infty L(y, t) g(t) \, d\rho(t) = \int_0^y f(s) \, ds$$

again by (10.5.5). Hence

$$\int_0^y f(s) \, ds = \lim_{\Delta \to (-\infty, \infty)} \int_0^y f_\Delta(s) \, ds = \int_0^y f_0(s) \, ds.$$

This shows that

$$f_0(s) = f(s)$$

for almost all s and proves the validity of (10.5.39). ∎

Finally, we prove a result due to Titchmarsh, which will be used in the next section. The proof is closely related to that of Lemma 10.5.2.

Lemma 10.5.6. *If* λ_1 *and* λ_2 *are non-real numbers, then*

$$\lim_{x\to\infty} W[Y_\alpha(x, \lambda_1), \quad Y_\alpha(x, \lambda_2)] = 0. \tag{10.5.40}$$

Proof. Here

$$W[f, g] = fg' - gf' \tag{10.5.41}$$

is the Wronskian of f and g in this order. This is a bilinear form in its two arguments. We note that

$$Y_\alpha(x, \lambda, b) \equiv y_1(x, \lambda) + m(\lambda, b) y_2(x, \lambda)$$

satisfies at $x = b$ a boundary condition independent of λ. Hence

$$W[Y_\alpha(b, \lambda_1, b), \quad Y_\alpha(b, \lambda_2, b)] = 0$$

and

$$W\{Y_\alpha(b, \lambda_1) + [m(\lambda_1, b) - m(\lambda_1)]y_2(b, \lambda_1),$$
$$Y_\alpha(b, \lambda_2) + [m(\lambda_2, b) - m(\lambda_2)]y_2(b, \lambda_2)\} = 0.$$

Using bilinearity we see that this gives

$$\begin{aligned} W[Y_\alpha(b, \lambda_1), Y_\alpha(b, \lambda_2)] &+ [m(\lambda_1, b) - m(\lambda_1)]W[y_2(b, \lambda_1), Y_\alpha(b, \lambda_2)] \\ &+ [m(\lambda_2, b) - m(\lambda_2)]W[Y_\alpha(b, \lambda_1), y_2(b, \lambda_2)] \\ &+ [m(\lambda_1, b) - m(\lambda_1)][m(\lambda_2, b) - m(\lambda_2)]W[y_2(b, \lambda_1), y_2(b, \lambda_2)] = 0. \end{aligned} \tag{10.5.42}$$

By the differential equation and Sturm's method

$$\begin{aligned} W[y_2(b, \lambda_1), Y_\alpha(b, \lambda_2)] &= (\lambda_2 - \lambda_1) \int_0^b y_2(s, \lambda_1) Y_\alpha(s, \lambda_2)\, ds \\ &\quad + W[y_2(0, \lambda_1), Y_\alpha(0, \lambda_2)] \\ &= O\left[\int_0^b |y_2(s, \lambda_1)|^2\, ds\right]^{1/2} + O(1) \end{aligned}$$

as $b \to \infty$, λ_1 and λ_2 being fixed. By (10.1.12)

$$|m(\lambda, b) - m(\lambda)| \leq 2r_b(\lambda) = \left[|\nu| \int_0^b |y_2(s, \lambda)|^2\, ds\right]^{-1},$$

so that in the limit-point case

$$\lim_{b\to\infty} [m(\lambda_1, b) - m(\lambda_1)]W[y_2(b, \lambda_1), Y_\alpha(b, \lambda_2)] = 0.$$

This is true also in the limit-circle case provided $b \to \infty$ in such a manner that $m(\lambda, b) \to m(\lambda)$ since then the integral is bounded. The other terms in (10.5.42) are handled in the same manner and (10.5.40) follows. ∎

Taking $\lambda_2 = \bar{\lambda}_1$ we obtain the

Corollary. *For* $\Im(\lambda) \neq 0$

$$\lim_{x \to \infty} \Im[Y_\alpha(x, \bar{\lambda}) Y'_\alpha(x, \lambda)] = 0. \tag{10.5.43}$$

A special case of this formula occurred in (10.1.25) where it was derived under the assumption that $q(x)$ is bounded below.

EXERCISE 10.5

1. Prove that

$$\int_0^b Y_\alpha(s, \lambda_1, b) Y_\alpha(s, \lambda_2, b)\, ds = \int_{-\infty}^{\infty} \frac{d\rho(t, b, \alpha)}{(t - \lambda_1)(t - \lambda_2)} \cdot$$

2. Show that the right member of the preceding formula tends to the third member of (10.5.36) as $b \to \infty$. Infinite interval!
3. Use Lemma 10.5.6 and the Sturm-Liouville theory to give an alternate proof of Lemma 10.5.5.
4. Suppose that $\rho(t)$ is a step function with a jump r_n at $t = \lambda_n$, $n = 0, 1, 2, \ldots$ Discuss the transformation T in this case.
5. Show that, in the preceding case, the functions $\omega_n(s) = \sqrt{r_n}\, y_2(s, \lambda_n)$ form an orthonormal system complete in $L_2(0, \infty)$.
6. Show that the Fourier series of $f(s)$ in terms of the $\omega_n(s)$ may be integrated term-by-term over any finite interval (a, b) and that the resulting series is absolutely convergent.

The remaining problems are concerned with properties of the system

$$\{(t \mp ni)^{-1} \mid n = 1, 2, 3, \ldots\}$$

in $L_2(\rho)$ and the corresponding system $\{Y_\alpha(s, ni)\}$ in $L_2(0, \infty)$. Here the set $\{ni\}$ could be replaced by any set $\{\lambda_n\}$ such that $\sum_{n=1}^{\infty} \Im(\lambda_n^{-1}) = +\infty$. Using the Gram-Schmidt orthogonalization process, we can find a sequence of rational functions

$$R_n(t) \equiv \sum_{k=-n}^{n} a_{k,n}(t - ki)^{-1}, a_{0,n} = 0,$$

which form an orthonormal system in $L_2(\rho)$.

7. Show that

$$Y_n(s) \equiv \sum_{k=-n}^{n} a_{k,n} Y_\alpha(s, ki)$$

is an orthonormal system in $L_2(0, \infty)$.

8. If $f(x) \in L_2(0, \infty)$ and

$$f_n = \int_0^\infty Y_n(s) f(s)\, ds,$$

and if $g(t) = T[f](t)$, show that

$$f_n = \int_{-\infty}^\infty R_n(t) g(t)\, d\rho(t).$$

9. The linear combinations of the functions $(t - ki)^{-1}$ are dense in $L_2(\rho)$. Assume this fact and prove that $\{R_n(t)\}$ and $\{Y_n(s)\}$ are complete orthonormal systems in $L_2(\rho)$ and $L_2(0, \infty)$, respectively.

10. Show that if

$$f(s) \sim \sum_1^\infty f_n Y_n(s), \qquad \text{then} \qquad g(t) \sim \sum_1^\infty f_n R_n(t).$$

11. If the hypothesis of No. 9 were false, we could find a linear bounded functional $x^*[g] = \int_{-\infty}^\infty g(t) h(t)\, d\rho(t)$ which vanishes for $g(t) = (t \mp ki)^{-1}$, $k = 1, 2, 3, \ldots$, while $h(t)$ is an element of $L_2(\rho)$ not ρ-equivalent to 0. This implies that the analytic function

$$H(z) = \int_{-\infty}^\infty \frac{h(t)\, d\rho(t)}{t - z},$$

holomorphic for $y \neq 0$ and bounded for $|y| > \frac{1}{2}$, is zero for $z = \mp ki$. By a classical theorem of function theory (see, e.g. E. Hille, *Analytic Function Theory*, Vol. II, p. 457), this implies that $H(z) \equiv 0$. Assuming all these facts, the reader is requested to show that $h(t)$ is ρ-equivalent to 0 which contradicts the assumption. An integration by parts will introduce the function $\eta(t) = \int_0^t h(u)\, d\rho(u)$; Lemma 10.2.7 plus $\int_a^b \Im[H(s + iy) + H(s - iy)]\, ds \equiv 0$ may be used to show that $\eta(t) \equiv 0$. How does this show that $h(t) \sim 0$?

10.6 THE RESOLVENT

We shall now introduce *Green's function* of the singular boundary value problem and the corresponding *resolvent of the differential operator* L.

We recall that Green's function is constructed with the aid of two solutions of the differential equation

$$y'' + [\lambda - q(x)]y = 0. \qquad (10.6.1)$$

One of these should satisfy the boundary condition at $x = 0$, namely

$$\sin \alpha\ y(0) - \cos \alpha\ y'(0) = 0, \qquad (10.6.2)$$

and the other the boundary condition at infinity, i.e.

$$y(\cdot) \in L_2(0, \infty). \qquad (10.6.3)$$

These two conditions are satisfied by $y_2(x, \lambda, \alpha)$ and $Y_\alpha(x, \lambda)$, respectively. We restrict ourselves to the limit-point case where the solution of (10.6.3) is unique up to a constant multiplier. We now define for $\Im(\lambda) \neq 0$

$$G_\alpha(x, s; \lambda) = \begin{cases} y_2(s, \lambda, \alpha)\, Y_\alpha(x, \lambda), & 0 \le s \le x, \\ y_2(x, \lambda, \alpha)\, Y_\alpha(s, \lambda), & x < s, \end{cases} \tag{10.6.4}$$

as the Green's function. It is symmetric in x and s, continuous in (x, s). Its partial with respect to x is continuous in x for $x \neq s$. At $x = s$ there is a jump of 1 as x increases. For fixed (x, s), G_α is a holomorphic function of λ in the upper as well as in the lower half-plane. These functions are analytic continuations of each other iff $\rho(t, \alpha)$ has an interval of constancy. Further, for fixed (x, λ) we have $G_\alpha(x, \cdot\,; \lambda) \in L_2(0, \infty)$ and for fixed (s, λ) Green's function satisfies (10.6.2) at $x = 0$.

With this kernel and any function $f \in L_2(0, \infty)$ we form

$$R_\alpha(x, \lambda; f) \equiv \int_0^\infty G_\alpha(x, s; \lambda) f(s)\, ds. \tag{10.6.5}$$

The integral exists since both factors are $L_2(0, \infty)$.

Theorem 10.6.1. *For $\Im(\lambda) \neq 0$ formula* (10.6.5) *defines a linear bounded transformation on $L_2(0, \infty)$ into itself such that*

$$\|R_\alpha(\cdot, \mu + i\nu; f)\| \le \frac{1}{|\nu|} \|f\|. \tag{10.6.6}$$

We have

$$\sin \alpha \; R_\alpha(0, \lambda; f) - \cos \alpha \; R'_\alpha(0, \lambda; f) = 0. \tag{10.6.7}$$

Further, R_α satisfies the differential equation

$$\lambda V - \mathsf{L}[V] = f \tag{10.6.8}$$

for almost all x and is the only solution of this equation which is both in $L_2(0, \infty)$ and satisfies the boundary condition (10.6.7).

Proof. Since

$$R_\alpha(0, \lambda; f) = y_2(0, \lambda) \int_0^\infty Y_\alpha(s, \lambda) f(s)\, ds,$$

$$R'_\alpha(0, \lambda; f) = y'_2(0, \lambda) \int_0^\infty Y_\alpha(s, \lambda) f(s)\, ds,$$

we see that (10.6.7) holds. The derivative is the right-hand derivative and the formula holds regardless of the continuity properties of f. More generally, for $x > 0$

$$R'_\alpha(x, \lambda; f) = Y'_\alpha(x, \lambda) \int_0^x y_2(s, \lambda) f(s)\, ds$$

$$+ \; y'_2(x, \lambda) \int_x^\infty Y_\alpha(s, \lambda) f(s)\, ds$$

as is seen by taking the limit of the difference quotient. Next, if f is continuous at $s = x$

$$R''_\alpha(x, \lambda; f) = Y''_\alpha(x, \lambda) \int_0^x y_2(s, \lambda) f(s)\, ds$$

$$+ y''_2(x, \lambda) \int_x^\infty Y_\alpha(s, \lambda) f(s)\, ds$$

$$+ W[y_2(x, \lambda), Y'_\alpha(x, \lambda)] f(x).$$

Since the Wronskian of y_2 and Y_α is $\equiv 1$ we see that

$$R''_\alpha(x, \lambda; f) = [q(x) - \lambda] R_\alpha(x, \lambda; f) + f(x).$$

Thus $R_\alpha(x, \lambda; f)$ satisfies (10.6.8) at all points of continuity of f. If f is not continuous throughout, the second derivative still exists for almost all x and for almost all such values (10.6.8) holds.

It is clear that (10.6.5) defines a linear transformation on $L_2(0, \infty)$, but it is not clear that the range of the transformation lies in $L_2(0, \infty)$ and that (10.6.6) holds. To settle these matters, it is enough to consider functions f in $L_2(0, \infty)$ which are of compact support. Suppose that $f(x) = 0$ for $x > \omega$. Then

$$R_\alpha(x, \lambda; f) = Y_\alpha(x, \lambda) \int_0^\omega y_2(s, \lambda) f(s)\, ds, \qquad \omega < x.$$

This is in $L_2(0, \infty)$ since Y_α has this property. Similarly

$$R'_\alpha(x, \lambda; f) = Y'_\alpha(x, \lambda) \int_0^\omega y_2(s, \lambda) f(s)\, ds, \qquad \omega < x.$$

These two relations, together with the corollary of Lemma 10.5.6, give

$$\lim_{x \to \infty} \Im[R_\alpha(x, \bar\lambda; \bar f) R'_\alpha(x, \lambda; f)] = 0. \tag{10.6.9}$$

We now consider Eq. (10.6.8) where we multiply both sides by $\bar V = R_\alpha(x, \bar\lambda; \bar f)$ and integrate. After an integration by parts the imaginary part of the result is

$$\Im[R_\alpha(x, \bar\lambda; \bar f) R'_\alpha(x, \lambda; f)] + \nu \int_0^x |R_\alpha(s, \lambda; f)|^2\, ds$$

$$= \Im\left[\int_0^x R_\alpha(s, \bar\lambda; \bar f) f(s)\, ds\right].$$

Here the first term on the left goes to 0 as $x \to \infty$ by (10.6.9) and the right member converges to a finite limit since $f = 0$ for $x > \omega$ and both factors are L_2. Hence

$$\nu \int_0^\infty |R_\alpha(s, \lambda; f)|^2\, ds = \Im\left[\int_0^\infty R_\alpha(s, \bar\lambda; \bar f) f(s)\, ds\right]. \tag{10.6.10}$$

Thus $R_\alpha(\cdot, \lambda; f) \in L_2(0, \infty)$ and the inequality

$$|\nu| \int_0^\infty |R_\alpha(s, \lambda; f)|^2\, ds \le \left\{\int_0^\infty |R_\alpha(s, \lambda; f)|^2\, ds\right\}^{1/2} \left\{\int_0^\infty |f(s)|^2\, ds\right\}^{1/2}$$

gives (10.6.6) provided f is of compact support.

Now if f is any element of $L_2(0, \infty)$ and if

$$f_n(x) = \begin{cases} f(x), & 0 \le x \le n, \\ 0, & n < x, \end{cases}$$

then, for $0 < m < n$,

$$|\nu|^2 \int_0^\infty |R_\alpha(s, \lambda; f_m) - R_\alpha(s, \lambda; f_n)|^2\, ds \le \int_0^\infty |f_m(s) - f_n(s)|^2\, ds.$$

Since the right member goes to 0 as $m \to \infty$, $\{R_\alpha(\cdot, \lambda; f_n)\}$ is a Cauchy sequence in L_2. Now

$$\lim_{n \to \infty} R_\alpha(x, \lambda; f_n) = R_\alpha(x, \lambda; f),$$

both as an L_2-limit and in the sense of pointwise convergence, the latter holding uniformly in x on compact sets. This implies that $R_\alpha(\cdot, \lambda; f) \in L_2(0, \infty)$ and (10.6.6) holds for all $f \in L_2$.

The general solution of (10.6.8) is

$$R_\alpha(x, \lambda; f) + C_1 y_2(x, \lambda, \alpha) + C_2 Y_\alpha(x, \lambda).$$

If the solution is to be in $L_2(0, \infty)$, we must have $C_1 = 0$; if the boundary condition is to hold for $x = 0$, it follows that $C_2 = 0$. Thus $R_\alpha(x, \lambda; f)$ is the only solution satisfying both conditions. ▮

The operator $R(\lambda, \mathsf{L}, \alpha)$ defined on $L_2(0, \infty)$ to itself by

$$R(\lambda, \mathsf{L}, \alpha)[f](x) = R_\alpha(x, \lambda; f) \tag{10.6.11}$$

has been shown to map $L_2(0, \infty)$ onto a subset $D[\mathsf{L}]$, the domain of L, the elements V of which are almost everywhere twice differentiable. Further $\mathsf{L}[V] \in L_2(0, \infty)$ and

$$\sin \alpha V(0) - \cos \alpha V'(0) = 0.$$

Equation (10.6.8) states that

$$(\lambda I - \mathsf{L}) R(\lambda, \mathsf{L}, \alpha)[f] = f \tag{10.6.12}$$

for all $f \in L_2(0, \infty)$. This shows that $R(\lambda, \mathsf{L}, \alpha)$ is a right hand inverse of the operator $\lambda I - \mathsf{L}$. But we have also

$$R(\lambda, \mathsf{L}, \alpha)(\lambda I - \mathsf{L})[g] = g, \tag{10.6.13}$$

in this case only for $g \in D[\mathsf{L}]$.

To prove this, suppose that $g \in D[\mathsf{L}]$ and set

$$(\lambda I - \mathsf{L})[g] = f.$$

Then by the definition of the domain of L in L_2 we have $f \in L_2(0, \infty)$ and by Theorem 10.6.1

$$g = R(\lambda, \mathsf{L}, \alpha)[f],$$

since Eq. (10.6.8) has one and only one solution in $L_2(0, \infty)$ which also satisfies the boundary condition at $x = 0$. Combining one gets (10.6.13). The last two numbered formulas justifies calling $R(\lambda, \mathsf{L}, \alpha)$ *the resolvent of* L.

Theorem 10.6.2. *If $\lambda \to \infty$ in one of the sectors $|\arg \lambda \pm \frac{1}{2}\pi| \leq \frac{1}{2}\pi - \varepsilon$, then*

$$\lim_{\lambda \to \infty} \lambda R(\lambda, \mathsf{L}, \alpha)[f] = f, \tag{10.6.14}$$

the limit taken in the L_2-sense.

Proof. In the sectors indicated formula (10.6.6) gives

$$\|\lambda R(\lambda, \mathsf{L}, \alpha)\| \leq \operatorname{cosec} \varepsilon. \tag{10.6.15}$$

Suppose now that $g \in D[\mathsf{L}]$. This set is dense in $L_2(0, \infty)$, in fact the twice continuously differentiable functions of compact support are dense in $L_2(0, \infty)$ and they all belong to $D[\mathsf{L}]$. By (10.6.13)

$$\lambda R(\lambda, \mathsf{L}, \alpha)[g] = g + R(\lambda, \mathsf{L}, \alpha)[\mathsf{L}g]$$

and here, again by (10.6.6),

$$\|R(\lambda, \mathsf{L}, \alpha)[\mathsf{L}g]\| \leq \frac{1}{|\nu|} \|\mathsf{L}g\|.$$

Hence, in the sectors indicated,

$$\lim_{\lambda \to \infty} \|\lambda R(\lambda, \mathsf{L}, \alpha)[g] - g\| = 0, \qquad g \in D[\mathsf{L}].$$

This should now be extended to all of L_2. If $f \in L_2(0, \infty)$ and if $\delta > 0$ is given, then we can find a $g \in D[\mathsf{L}]$ such that $\|f - g\| < \delta$. Then

$$\begin{aligned} \|\lambda R(\lambda, \mathsf{L}, \alpha)[f] - f\| &\leq \|\lambda R(\lambda, \mathsf{L}, \alpha)[f - g]\| \\ &\quad + \|\lambda R(\lambda, \mathsf{L}, \alpha)[g] - g\| + \|f - g\| \\ &\leq \delta(1 + \operatorname{cosec} \varepsilon) + \frac{1}{|\nu|} \|\mathsf{L}g\|, \end{aligned}$$

whence

$$\limsup_{\lambda \to \infty} \|\lambda R(\lambda, \mathsf{L}, \alpha)[f] - f\| \leq \delta(1 + \operatorname{cosec} \varepsilon).$$

Here δ is arbitrary so (10.6.14) must hold. ▮

The latter formula may be regarded as an expansion theorem for $f \in L_2(0, \infty)$. It is analogous to formula (8.5.54) in the regular case.

The transformation theory of the preceding section applies to Green's function and the resolvent, and leads to beautiful formulas. Our presentation follows that of D. B. Sears (1954–55). We start with some preliminaries.

The function

$$G_\alpha(x, s; \lambda, b) = \begin{cases} y_2(s, \lambda, \alpha) Y_\alpha(x, \lambda, b), & 0 \le s \le x, \\ y_2(x, \lambda, \alpha) Y_\alpha(s, \lambda, b), & x < s, \end{cases} \tag{10.6.16}$$

is the Green's function for the regular boundary value problem for the interval $(0, b)$, where (10.6.3) is replaced by

$$y(b) = 0. \tag{10.6.17}$$

Lemma 10.6.1. *We have*

$$\lim_{b \to \infty} \int_0^b |G_\alpha(x, s; \lambda, b) - G_\alpha(x, s; \lambda)|^2 \, ds = 0, \tag{10.6.18}$$

uniformly with respect to x and λ *in compact subsets of* $[0, \infty)$ *and* $\Im(\lambda) > 0$, *respectively.*

Proof. We have

$$G_\alpha(x, s; \lambda) - G_\alpha(x, s; \lambda, b) = [m(\lambda) - m(\lambda, b)] y_2(s, \lambda, \alpha) y_2(x, \lambda, \alpha)$$

for all x, s. Hence, by an often used estimate,

$$\int_0^b |G_\alpha(x, s; \lambda) - G_\alpha(x, s; \lambda, b)|^2 \, ds$$

$$= |m(\lambda) - m(\lambda, b)|^2 |y_2(x, \lambda, \alpha)|^2 \int_0^b |y_2(s, \lambda, b)|^2 \, ds$$

$$\le \nu^{-2} \left[\int_0^b |y_2(s, \lambda, \alpha)|^2 \, ds\right]^{-1} |y_2(x, \lambda, \alpha)|^2.$$

As $b \to \infty$, this expression tends to 0 in the limit-point case and also in the limit-circle case, provided $m(\lambda, b) \to m(\lambda)$. If λ is confined to a rectangle

$$-a \le \mu \le a, \qquad a^{-1} \le \nu \le a,$$

and if $0 \le x \le \omega$, then $y_2(x, \lambda, \alpha)$ is uniformly bounded while the integral is uniformly large if b is large. Hence the convergence is uniform. ∎

Lemma 10.6.2. *We have*

$$\int_0^b G_\alpha(x, s; \lambda, b) K_b(y, s) \, ds = \int_0^y \frac{y_2(x, t)}{\lambda - t} \, d\rho(t, b). \tag{10.6.19}$$

Proof. The Fourier coefficients of $K_b(y, s)$ in the ω_n-system were found to be $[r_n(b)]^{1/2}S(y, \lambda_n(b))$. Since

$$G(x, s; \lambda, b) = \sum_{n=0}^{\infty} \frac{\omega_n(x)\omega_n(s)}{\lambda - \lambda_n(b)},$$

the nth Fourier coefficient is

$$[r_n(b)]^{1/2} \frac{y_2(x, \lambda_n(b))}{\lambda - \lambda_n(b)}.$$

The inner product of the Fourier coefficient vectors can be written as a Stieltjes integral and the result is (10.6.19). ∎

Lemma 10.6.3. *The T-transform of Green's function is*

$$T[G_\alpha(x, \cdot\,; \lambda)](t) = \frac{y_2(x, t)}{\lambda - t}. \tag{10.6.20}$$

Proof. We have to pass to the limit with b in (10.6.19). The argument is analogous to that used in proving (10.5.35). We set

$$\begin{aligned} \delta(x, y, \lambda, b) &= \int_0^b G_\alpha(x, s; \lambda, b)K_b(y, s)\,ds \\ &\quad - \int_0^b G_\alpha(x, s; \lambda)K(y, s)\,ds \\ &= \int_0^b K_b(y, s)[G_\alpha(x, s; \lambda, b) - G_\alpha(x, s; \lambda)]\,ds \\ &\quad + \int_0^b G_\alpha(x, s; \lambda)[K_b(y, s) - K(y, s)]\,ds. \end{aligned}$$

Here the first integral in the third member is dominated by

$$[C(x)]^{1/2}\left\{\int_0^b |G_\alpha(x, s; \lambda, b) - G_\alpha(x, s; \lambda)|^2\,ds\right\}^{1/2}.$$

This tends to 0 as $b \to \infty$ by Lemma 10.6.1. The second integral is dominated by

$$\begin{aligned} &\left\{\int_0^\omega |G_\alpha(x, s; \lambda)|^2\,ds\right\}^{1/2}\left\{\int_0^\omega [K_b(y, s) - K(y, s)]^2\,ds\right\}^{1/2} \\ &\quad + \left\{\int_\omega^b G_\alpha(x, s; \lambda)^2\,ds\right\}^{1/2}\left\{\int_\omega^b [K_b(y, s) - K(y, s)]^2\,ds\right\}^{1/2}. \end{aligned}$$

In the first summand, the first factor is bounded uniformly in ω and for (x, λ) in compact sets, while the second factor goes to 0 as $b \to \infty$ by (10.5.21).

In the second summand, the first factor can be made small by choosing ω large at the outset and the second factor is dominated by $2[C(x)]^{1/2}$. Hence

$$\lim_{b\to\infty} \delta(x, y, \lambda, b) = 0.$$

This shows that

$$\lim_{b\to\infty} \int_0^b G_\alpha(x, s; \lambda, b) K_b(y, s)\, ds = \int_0^\infty G_\alpha(x, s; \lambda) K(y, s)\, ds$$

and by Lemma 10.6.2 the left member equals

$$\lim_{b\to\infty} \int_0^y \frac{y_2(x, t)}{\lambda - t}\, d\rho(t, b) = \int_0^y \frac{y_2(x, t)}{\lambda - t}\, d\rho(t).$$

Hence (10.6.20) holds. ▮

We can now get a representation of the Green's function analogous to the series (8.5.20):

Lemma 10.6.4. *If $\Delta \to (-\infty, \infty)$, then*

$$\lim \int_{-\infty}^{\infty} \left| G_\alpha(x, s; \lambda) - \int_\Delta y_2(x, t) y_2(s, t) \frac{d\rho(t)}{\lambda - t} \right|^2 ds = 0. \qquad (10.6.21)$$

Proof. Combine (10.6.20) with Theorem 10.5.3 taking $f(s) = G_\alpha(x, s; \lambda)$. ▮

Theorem 10.6.3. *Let $f \in L_2(0, \infty)$. Then*

$$R_\alpha(x, \lambda; f) = \int_{-\infty}^{\infty} \frac{y_2(s, t) T[f]}{\lambda - t}\, d\rho(t). \qquad (10.6.22)$$

Proof. By the Parseval relation

$$R_\alpha(x, \lambda; f) = \int_0^\infty G_\alpha(x, s; \lambda) f(s)\, ds = \int_{-\infty}^{\infty} T[G_\alpha](t) T[f](t)\, d\rho(t).$$

Now apply Lemma 10.6.3. ▮

Our next theorem gives a converse of the formula (10.5.14) where $U = T$.

Theorem 10.6.4. *Suppose that $g(t)$ and $tg(t)$ belong to $L_2(\rho)$ and that $g(t) = T[f](t)$, $tg(t) = T[h](t)$. Then $f \in D[\mathsf{L}]$ and $\mathsf{L}[f] = h$.*

Proof. For any fixed λ with $\Im(\lambda) \neq 0$ form

$$R(\lambda, \mathsf{L}, \alpha)[h] = \int_{-\infty}^{\infty} \frac{y_2(s, t) t g(t)}{\lambda - t}\, d\rho(t)$$

$$= -\int_{-\infty}^{\infty} y_2(s, t) g(t)\, d\rho(t) + \lambda \int_{-\infty}^{\infty} \frac{y_2(s, t) g(t)}{\lambda - t}\, d\rho(t).$$

Here all integrals are absolutely convergent. The first integral in the third member must be equal to $f(s)$ for almost all s by Theorem 10.5.3 since the integral over the interval Δ represents $f(s, \Delta)$ which converges in the L_2-sense to $f(s)$ as $\Delta \to (-\infty, \infty)$. Hence

$$f = R(\lambda, \mathsf{L}, \alpha)[\lambda f - h] \in D[\mathsf{L}]$$

and

$$\begin{aligned}\mathsf{L}[f] &= \mathsf{L}R(\lambda, \mathsf{L}, \alpha)[\lambda f - h]\\ &= \lambda R(\lambda, \mathsf{L}, \alpha)[\lambda f - h] - [\lambda f - h]\\ &= \lambda f - [\lambda f - h] = h\end{aligned}$$

as asserted. ▌

We state finally without proof the identity

$$G_\alpha(x, \xi; \lambda) - G_\alpha(x, \xi; \mu) = (\mu - \lambda) \int_0^\infty G_\alpha(x, s; \lambda) G_\alpha(s, \xi; \mu)\, ds. \quad (10.6.23)$$

EXERCISE 10.6

1. Show that for $0 \leq a < b$

$$\nu \int_0^\infty \left| \int_a^b G_\alpha(x, s, \lambda)\, ds \right|^2 dx = \int_a^b \int_a^b \Im[G_\alpha(x, s; \lambda)]\, ds\, dx$$

and use this to prove that

$$\nu \int_0^\infty |G_\alpha(x, a; \lambda)|^2\, dx = \Im[G_\alpha(a, a; \bar{\lambda})]$$

and

$$\operatorname{sgn} \Im[G_\alpha(x, x; \lambda)] = -\operatorname{sgn} \Im(\lambda).$$

The next five problems are based on results due to D. B. Sears. Prove the stated formulas.

2. $\displaystyle\int_0^\infty G_\alpha(x, s; \lambda) G_\alpha(\xi, s; \mu)\, ds = \frac{G_\alpha(x, \xi; \lambda) - G_\alpha(x, \xi; \mu)}{\mu - \lambda}.$

3. $\displaystyle\int_0^\infty g(s) R_\alpha(s, \lambda; f)\, ds = \int_{-\infty}^\infty \frac{T[g]T[f]}{\lambda - t}\, d\rho(t).$

4. $\displaystyle\int_0^\infty R_\alpha(s, \lambda; f) R_\alpha(s, \mu; g)\, ds = \int_{-\infty}^\infty \frac{T[f]T[g]}{(\lambda - t)(\mu - t)}\, d\rho(t).$

5. Show that the T-transform of $(\partial|\partial s)G_\alpha(x, s; \lambda)$ is $y_2'(x, \lambda)/(\lambda - t)$.

6. Derive the second and third formulas in No. 1 from No. 2.

7. If $\rho(t)$ is a step function with jumps r_n at $t = \lambda_n$, show that $R_\alpha(x, \lambda; f)$ is a meromorphic function of λ and find its partial fraction expansion.

8. Suppose that $q(x) \geq q_0$ and take $\alpha = \frac{1}{4}\pi$. Imitate the proof of Theorem 10.3.3 to show that $R_\alpha(x, \lambda; f)$ is holomorphic in the half-plane $\Re(\lambda) < q_0$.

9. Find an estimate of the norm of R_α valid in this half-plane.
10. Suppose that $\rho(t, \alpha)$ has $a < t < b$ as interval of constancy. Show that $R_\alpha(x, \lambda; f)$ is holomorphic on the interval (a, b) of the real axis and can be continued analytically across this interval, the continuation agreeing with the local value of $R_\alpha(x, \lambda; f)$.
11. Prove (10.6.23) and give a similar identity for $R_\alpha(x, \lambda; f)$.

10.7 REMARKS ON GENERALIZATIONS

The theory of singular boundary problems given in the preceding sections admits of many extensions. We have treated exclusively the case of an interval $(0, \infty)$ where the left end-point is regular and the right end-point can be either in the limit-point or in the limit-circle case. The latter was largely neglected. There is also the possibility of an interval where both end-points are singular, say the interval $(-\infty, \infty)$. We shall say a few words about this case.

Consider again the differential equation

$$y'' + [\lambda - q(t)]y = 0 \tag{10.7.1}$$

where $q(t)$ is real and continuous for all real t. Define solutions $y_1(t, \lambda)$ and $y_2(t, \lambda)$ by the initial conditions

$$\begin{aligned} y_1(0) &= 0, & y_1'(0) &= -1, \\ y_2(0) &= 1, & y_2'(0) &= 0. \end{aligned} \tag{10.7.2}$$

The end-points can be either in the limit-point or in the limit-circle case which gives four distinct possibilities. To fix the ideas, suppose that both end-points are in the limit-point case. There are then two uniquely defined functions, $m_-(\lambda)$ and $m_+(\lambda)$, such that

$$\begin{aligned} Y_-(x, \lambda) &= y_1(x, \lambda) + m_-(\lambda)y_2(x, \lambda), \\ Y_+(x, \lambda) &= y_1(x, \lambda) + m_+(\lambda)y_2(x, \lambda), \end{aligned} \tag{10.7.3}$$

are in $L_2(-\infty, 0)$ and $L_2(0, \infty)$, respectively. Here m_- and m_+ are holomorphic functions of λ in the upper and in the lower half-planes and for $\Im(\lambda) > 0$

$$\Im[m_-(\lambda)] < 0, \qquad \Im[m_+(\lambda)] > 0. \tag{10.7.4}$$

These functions have spectral representation. There exist two normalized non-decreasing, right-continuous spectral functions $\rho_-(t)$ and $\rho_+(t)$ with $\rho_-(0) = \rho_+(0) = 0$ such that

$$-m_-(\lambda) = \int_{-\infty}^{\infty} \frac{d\rho_-(t)}{t - \lambda}, \qquad m_+(\lambda) = \int_{-\infty}^{\infty} \frac{d\rho_+(t)}{t - \lambda}. \tag{10.7.5}$$

This follows from the corresponding formulas for the interval $(0, \infty)$, where we take $\alpha = 0$. The estimates for $\rho(t)$ and $m(\lambda)$ apply also to the functions $\rho_-(t)$, $\rho_+(t)$, $m_-(\lambda)$ and $m_+(\lambda)$.

The Green's function is now defined by

$$G(x, s; \lambda) = \frac{Y_-(s, \lambda) Y_+(x, \lambda)}{m_+(\lambda) - m_-(\lambda)}, \qquad s < x, \tag{10.7.6}$$

and $G(s, x; \lambda) = G(x, s; \lambda)$. The denominator is the Wronskian of Y_+ and Y_-.

The case where $q(t)$ is an even function of t is of some interest. Here y_1 is odd and y_2 is even. Hence $y_1 + m_+ y_2 \in L_2(0, \infty)$ while $y_1 - m_+ y_2 \in L_2(-\infty, 0)$ so that

$$m_-(\lambda) = -m_+(\lambda). \tag{10.7.7}$$

With these brief remarks we leave the case $(-\infty, \infty)$.

The Weyl theory for the second order case was extended to equations of order $2m$ by I. M. Glazman and Kunihiko Kodaira, both in 1949–50, working independently of each other and using different methods. For the Glazman theory, the reader can consult the second appendix of the Achiezer-Glazman treatise of 1950.

Boundary value problems for first order matrix equations go back to G. D. Birkhoff and R. E. Langer (1923), and G. A. Bliss (1926) for the regular case. Singular problems are of a much later date. (See Fred Brauer (1960) and F. V. Atkinson (1964).) The presentation of Atkinson has been much simplified by W. A. Coppel (unpublished).

While the present author has no direct contributions to make to the theory of singular boundary value problems for first order matrix equations, he feels bound to observe that at least part of the Weyl theory carries over to second order differential equations whose coefficients and solutions have values in a B*-algebra $\mathfrak{B}$, of the type described in Section 4.2. See also Section 9.6, where oscillation problems for the interval $(0, \infty)$ are considered.

Let $\mathfrak{B}$ be a Banach algebra over the complex field in which there is defined a *Hermitian involution*, $x \to x^*$, subject to the conditions stated in Section 4.2. Reference to these conditions will be by numbers like 4.2.3:vii. In Section 9.6, we were mainly concerned with real symmetric positive elements of $\mathfrak{B}$, and certain features of $\mathfrak{B}$ which now become important were not mentioned in the earlier context. We say that x is Hermitian if $x^* = x$. Every element x of $\mathfrak{B}$ admits of a unique Hermitian decomposition

$$x = h + ik, \qquad h^* = h, \qquad k^* = k. \tag{10.7.8}$$

We call h and k the real and imaginary parts of x, respectively, and write

$$h = \mathfrak{R}(x), \qquad k = \mathfrak{I}(x).$$

Let $q(t)$ be defined and continuous for $0 \leq t < \infty$ and let $q^*(t) = q(t)$ so that $\mathfrak{R}[q(t)] = q(t)$, $\mathfrak{I}[q(t)] = 0$. Let e be the unit element of $\mathfrak{B}$, $\lambda = \mu + i\nu$ a complex parameter, and consider the equation

$$y''(t) + [\lambda e - q(t)]y(t) = 0. \tag{10.7.9}$$

Here $y(t)$ has values in $\mathfrak{B}$. We note that

$$y^*(t)[\mu - q(t)]y(t)$$

is Hermitian so its imaginary part is 0.

This is used as follows. Multiply (10.7.9) on the left by $y^*(t)$ and integrate from 0 to b. After an integration by parts we obtain the identity

$$[y^*(t)y'(t)]_0^b - \int_0^b y^{*\prime}(t)y'(t)\,dt + \int_0^b y^*(t)[\mu - q(t)]y(t)\,dt$$

$$+ i\nu \int_0^b y^*(t)y(t)\,dt = 0. \tag{10.7.10}$$

The imaginary part of this is

$$[y^*(t)y'(t)]_0^b + \nu \int_0^b y^*(t)y(t)\,dt = 0, \qquad 0 < b < \infty. \tag{10.7.11}$$

This is the abstract form of Weyl's identity and is the basis for the following discussion.

For fixed λ the integral

$$\int_0^b y^*(t)y(t)\,dt$$

is an increasing function of b. Since the integrand is Hermitian and non-negative by 4.2.3:viii, it follows that the integral is positive for $0 < b$. It then tends to a finite or infinite limit as $b \to \infty$. In the first case we say that $y(\cdot) \in L_2[(0, \infty); \mathfrak{B}]$. Formula (9.6.27) shows that this will certainly be the case if $\|y(\cdot)\| \in L_2(0, \infty)$.

The analogue of Theorem 10.1.2 applies to this case so that, if all solutions are in $L_2[(0, \infty); \mathfrak{B}]$ for some particular value of λ, this will hold for all λ. We refer to this as the *limit-circle case*. Here we shall consider the *limit-point case* where for each λ there are solutions which are not in $L_2[(0, \infty); \mathfrak{B}]$.

Let two solutions $y_1(t, \lambda)$ and $y_2(t, \lambda)$ be defined by the initial conditions

$$\begin{aligned} y_1(0) &= 0, & y_1'(0) &= -e, \\ y_2(0) &= e, & y_2'(0) &= 0. \end{aligned} \tag{10.7.12}$$

We shall now prove an analogue of Weyl's basic theorem.

Theorem 10.7.1. *If $y_2(\cdot, i) \notin L_2[(0, \infty); \mathfrak{B}]$ and if $\lambda = \mu + i\nu$ with $\nu \neq 0$, then there exists a unique solution of the form*

$$y_1(t, \lambda) + y_2(t, \lambda)m(\lambda) \equiv Y(t, \lambda) \tag{10.7.13}$$

which belongs to $L_2[(0, \infty); \mathfrak{B}]$.

Proof. We consider a finite interval $(0, b)$ and solutions

$$y_1(t, \lambda) + y_2(t, \lambda)m \tag{10.7.14}$$

where m is so chosen that

$$\Im[y^*(b, \lambda)y'(b, \lambda)] = 0. \tag{10.7.15}$$

Such an m is said to be *admissible.* In particular,

$$m = m(\lambda, b) \equiv -[y_2(b, \lambda)]^{-1}y_1(b, \lambda) \tag{10.7.16}$$

is admissible. We shall see in a moment that $[y_2(b, \lambda)]^{-1}$ exists for all non-real values of λ. Assuming this to be so, it is seen $y^*(b, \lambda)$ vanishes for such a choice of m.

Taking $y(t) = y_2(t, \lambda)$ in (10.7.11) we see that

$$\Im[y_2^*(b, \lambda)y_2'(b, \lambda)] < 0 \qquad \text{if} \quad \nu > 0$$

and from this we conclude that none of the factors inside the brackets can be singular. Hence $y_2(b, \lambda)$ is non-singular for non-real λ.

Now let m be admissible and substitute (10.7.14) in (10.7.11). The result can be written

$$\Im(m) = \nu H(m) \tag{10.7.17}$$

where $H(m) = H(m; \lambda, b)$ is a quadratic Hermitian form

$$H(m) = S + W^*m + m^*W + m^*Tm \tag{10.7.18}$$

and

$$S = \int_0^b y_1^*(t)y_1(t)\,dt, \qquad W = \int_0^b y_2^*(t)y_1(t)\,dt,$$
$$T = \int_0^b y_2^*(t)y_2(t)\,dt. \tag{10.7.19}$$

Here S, T, W are functions of b and λ such that S and T are Hermitian positive while W may be expected to be non-real.

For fixed b and λ the admissible values of m form a quadric surface $Q = Q_b = Q_b(\lambda)$ whose equation is given by (10.7.17). Here Q is located in the half-space

$$\Im(m) > 0 \qquad \text{if} \quad \nu > 0.$$

Q_b corresponds to the circle C_b of (10.1.14) and will be shown to be in some sense a sphere. The family of surfaces $\{Q_b(\lambda)\}$ has similar nesting and converging properties as the circles.

The nesting property is elementary. For $\nu > 0$ define "interior" and "exterior" of Q as the sets

$$Q^i\colon \nu H(m) < \Im(m), \qquad Q^e\colon \nu H(m) > \Im(m), \tag{10.7.20}$$

respectively. Suppose that $0 < b < c$ and that for a given λ, $m \in Q_c^i(\lambda)$.

We have then

$$\Im(m) > \nu H(m; c, \lambda) > \nu H(m; b, \lambda)$$

so that m is also interior to $Q_b(\lambda)$. This proves the nesting property.

In the following we shall restrict λ to belong to a bounded domain Δ in the upper half-plane having a positive distance from the real axis. We also take $b > 1$. This means that any admissible m for $\lambda \in \Delta$ and $b > 1$ belongs to

$$D = \bigcup_{\lambda \in \Delta} Q_1^i(\lambda)$$

and here D is a bounded domain in $\Im(m) > 0$. This follows from the fact that the quantities $S(1, \lambda)$, $T(1, \lambda)$, $W(1, \lambda)$, are uniformly bounded continuous functions of λ in Δ.

To prove the existence of a unique limit-point if $T(b, \lambda) \to \infty$ with b, requires a more elaborate argument. For given $b > 1$, $\lambda \in \Delta$, we set

$$m_1 = -T^{-1}W, \qquad H(m_1) = S - W^*T^{-1}W \equiv M, \qquad \Im(m_1) = J,$$
$$m_0 = m_1 - \frac{1}{2\nu i}T^{-1}, \qquad E = \frac{1}{\nu}J - M + \frac{1}{4\nu^2}T^{-1}. \tag{10.7.21}$$

An elementary calculation then gives

$$(m^* - m_0^*)T(m - m_0) = E.$$

Now the Hermitian positive element T has a Hermitian positive square root—by Lemma 9.6.3. If for a moment we write

$$T^{1/2}(m - m_0) = y,$$

we have

$$y^*y = E,$$

so that E is non-negative. This we can strengthen to $E > 0$ for if this were not true then E would be singular and this would require that $m - m_0$ is singular for all admissible m on Q_b and this is clearly absurd. If then E is Hermitian positive, it also has a positive Hermitian square root. Setting

$$T^{1/2}(m - m_0)E^{-1/2} \equiv Z \tag{10.7.22}$$

we see that

$$Z^*Z = e \tag{10.7.23}$$

so that Z is unitary, $Z^{-1} = Z^*$. This gives a one-to-one mapping of Q_b on the unitary sphere and justifies our calling Q_b a sphere. We have now

$$m = m_0 + T^{-1/2}ZE^{1/2}, \qquad Z^* = Z^{-1}. \tag{10.7.24}$$

It remains to show that $E = E(b, \lambda)$ is uniformly bounded for $\lambda \in \Delta$, $b > 1$. This will certainly be the case if M and $(1/\nu)J$ are uniformly bounded. Since 4.2.3:v holds, $r(x) = \|x\|$ for real elements. Hence $0 < \alpha e < x < \beta e$ also means $\alpha \leq \|x\| \leq \beta$. Thus, for positive elements boundedness (convergence) in terms of spectral radii and boundedness (convergence) in terms of norms are equivalent notions. Now

$$H(m_1 + x) = x^*Tx + M$$

where x^*Tx is a positive definite Hermitian form, i.e. $x^*Tx > 0$ for all elements x. Hence $M = \min H(m)$ for all m, not necessarily admissible m's. Since $H(m) > 0$ by definition it follows that $M > 0$. The point $m = m_1 = m_1(\lambda, b)$ is inside, on, or outside $Q_b(\lambda)$ according as $(1/\nu)J$ is $> M$, $= M$ or $< M$, respectively. In the classical case $m_1(\lambda, b)$ lies on the circle C_b (cf. Problem 2, Exercise 10.1), but we cannot prove that this is always true in the abstract case. Now, if $m_1 \in Q_b^e$, then

$$E < (4\nu^2 T)^{-1}$$

and this is bounded for $\lambda \in \Delta$ and $1 < b$. If $m_1 \in Q_b$, the displayed inequality is replaced by equality. Finally, if m_1 is inside Q_b, then $m_1 \in D$ and its imaginary part J is bounded uniformly in b and λ. Since $(1/\nu)J > M$ and ν is bounded below, M is bounded. Thus for any choice of $b > 1$, $\lambda \in \Delta$, the element $E(b, \lambda)$ is bounded. Since $T(b, \lambda) \to \infty$, this says that the sphere $Q_b(\lambda)$ contracts to a point which is interior to or on every $Q_b(\lambda)$, $0 < b$. This shows the existence of

$$m(\lambda) = -\lim_{b \to \infty} [T(\lambda, b)]^{-1} W(\lambda, b)$$

as the limit-point. The argument also applies for $\nu < 0$.

We saw above that the element $m(\lambda, b)$ defined by (10.7.16) is admissible. It follows then that we have also

$$m(\lambda) = \lim_{b \to \infty} m(\lambda, b) = -\lim_{b \to \infty} [y_2(b, \lambda)]^{-1} y_1(b, \lambda), \qquad (10.7.25)$$

uniformly for $\lambda \in \Delta$. Here $m(\lambda, b)$ is a holomorphic function of λ in the upper as well as in the lower half-planes. The uniform convergence shows that $m(\lambda)$ has the same properties. Further

$$\Im[m(\bar{\lambda})] = -\Im[m(\lambda)]. \qquad (10.7.26)$$

Once the existence of $m(\lambda)$ has been shown, it is a simple matter to verify that the function $Y(t, \lambda)$ defined by (10.7.13) belongs to $L_2[(0, \infty); \mathfrak{B}]$ and satisfies

$$\Im[m(\lambda)] = \nu \int_0^\infty Y^*(t, \lambda) Y(t, \lambda)\, dt, \qquad \Im(\lambda) \neq 0. \qquad (10.7.27)$$

There cannot exist a second linearly independent solution in $L_2[(0, \infty); \mathfrak{B}]$. Since $m(\lambda)$ is non-singular, this would imply that $y_2(t, \lambda)$ were in $L_2[0, \infty); \mathfrak{B}]$ contrary to hypothesis. ▌

Theorem 10.2.1 also has an analogue in the abstract case for which a proof can be given based on the formula

$$\Im[m(\lambda, b)] = \nu \int_0^b Y^*(s, \lambda, b) Y(s, \lambda, b)\, ds \tag{10.7.28}$$

where

$$Y(s, \lambda, b) = y_1(s, \lambda) + y_2(s, \lambda) m(\lambda, b) \tag{10.7.29}$$

and $m(\lambda, b)$ is given by (10.7.16). Lemmas 10.2.1 and 10.2.2 are too crude for the present purpose but we can get useful expressions for $y_1(t, \lambda)$ and $y_2(t, \lambda)$ for small t and large complex λ from the integral equation

$$y(t) = y(0) + y'(0)t + \int_0^t (t - s)[q(t) - \lambda] y(s)\, ds$$

and the method of successive approximations.

Suppose that λ is restricted to the region $R^+ : |\arg \lambda - \frac{1}{2}\pi| \le \frac{1}{2}\pi - \varepsilon$, $1 < \nu$ and $0 \le t \le 1$. We can then find a constant $a > 1$ such that $\|q(t) - \lambda\| \le a\nu$. We then get

$$y_1(t, \lambda) = -et + R_1$$

with

$$\|R_1\| \le (a\nu)^{-1/2} \sinh [(a\nu)^{1/2} t] - t$$

which is $O(\nu t^3)$ for sufficiently small values of t. This gives

$$S(t, \lambda) \equiv \int_0^t y_1^*(s, \lambda) y_1(s, \lambda)\, ds = \tfrac{1}{3} t^3 e + S_1$$

with

$$\|S_1\| = O(\nu t^5) \qquad \text{for} \quad 0 < t < (a\nu)^{-1/2}.$$

Similarly we obtain

$$y_2(t, \lambda) = e + R_2$$

with

$$\|R_2\| \le \cosh [(a\nu)^{1/2} t] - 1.$$

For $0 < t \le (a\nu)^{-1/2}$ this gives

$$T(t, \lambda) = et + O(\nu t^3), \qquad W(t, \lambda) = -\tfrac{1}{2} t^2 e + O(\nu t^4).$$

We now choose a number δ such that for $t = \delta(a\nu)^{-1/2}$ we have

$$S(t, \lambda) = \tfrac{1}{3} t^3 S(\lambda), \qquad T(t, \lambda) = t T(\lambda), \qquad W(t, \lambda) = -\tfrac{1}{2} t^2 W(\lambda), \tag{10.7.30}$$

where each of the three quantities $S(\lambda), T(\lambda), W(\lambda)$ differs from e by an amount $< \frac{1}{2}$ in norm. This we can clearly do by virtue of the estimates given above.

We can now state and prove

Theorem 10.7.2. *If $\lambda \in R^+$, $1 < b$, and $p(\lambda, b) = \nu^{1/2}m(\lambda, b)$, then the quantities $p(\lambda, b)$ are confined to a bounded domain in the upper half of the p-space, i.e. $\mathfrak{R}[p(\lambda, b)]$ is bounded and $\mathfrak{J}[p(\lambda, b)]$ is positive and bounded away from 0 and ∞ uniformly in b and λ.*

Proof. If $b > t = \delta(a\nu)^{-1/2}$, in particular for $b > 1$, we have

$$\mathfrak{J}[m(\lambda, b)] > \nu H(m; t, \lambda) = \nu[S(t, \lambda) + m(\lambda, b)W^*(t, \lambda) + W(t, \lambda)m^*(\lambda, b) + m^*(\lambda, b)T(t, \lambda)m(\lambda, b)].$$

Here we substitute $t = \delta(a\nu)^{-1/2}$, $m(\lambda, b) = \nu^{-1/2}p(\lambda, b)$ and the values of S, T, W obtained from (10.7.30) and write

$$\eta = \delta a^{-1/2}.$$

After simplification we obtain

$$\mathfrak{J}[p] > \tfrac{1}{3}\eta^3 S(\lambda) - \tfrac{1}{2}\eta^2[pW^*(\lambda) + W(\lambda)p^*] + p^*T(\lambda)p \quad (10.7.31)$$

where $p = p(\lambda, b)$. This inequality is of a type well known from the discussion above. It says that for a fixed $\lambda \in R^+$ and all $b > 1$ the point $p(\lambda, b)$ is interior to a sphere $Q(\lambda)$ in the upper half-space. The equation of $Q(\lambda)$ may be written

$$(p^* - p_0^*)T(p - p_0) = F \quad (10.7.32)$$

where

$$p_0^* = \tfrac{1}{2}\eta T^{-1}W - \frac{1}{2\eta i}T^{-1}, \qquad F = p_0^*Tp_0 - \tfrac{1}{3}\eta^2 S \quad (10.7.33)$$

and it should be recalled that S, T, W are functions of λ while η is a fixed positive number.

The point $p = 0$ is clearly outside each $Q(\lambda)$. The positive element

$$\tfrac{1}{3}\eta^2 ST^{-1}$$

can be taken as a measure of the "exteriority" of $p = 0$ with respect to $Q(\lambda)$. In the classical case this quantity would be the square of the length of the tangent drawn from the origin to the circle. Since ST^{-1} lies between fixed bounds as λ roams over R^+, we can say that $p = 0$ is exterior to $Q(\lambda)$ uniformly in λ.

Further, the center $p_0 = p_0(\lambda)$ varies continuously with λ over a bounded region in the upper half of the p-space and $F = F(\lambda)$ is a bounded continuous function of λ in R^+. It follows that the points

$$p = p_0(\lambda) + r[T(\lambda)]^{-1/2}Z[F(\lambda)]^{1/2}, \qquad 0 \le r \le 1, \quad Z^* = Z^{-1}, \quad (10.7.34)$$

form a bounded region D in $\mathfrak{J}[x] > 0$ and every $p(\lambda, b) \in D$ for $\lambda \in R^+$, $1 < b$. ∎

It would take us too far afield to attempt to carry the abstract theory any further, but we can allow ourselves a glimpse of the promised land and a look at the difficulties to be overcome.

Green's function and the resolvent of **L** can be formed and their properties appear to follow the classical pattern. The spectral function and the transformation theory lead to more serious difficulties. It is natural to expect the existence of a spectral function $\rho(t)$, normalized to be right-continuous and $\rho(0) = 0$, which is increasing and such that

$$m(\lambda) = \int_{-\infty}^{\infty} \frac{d\rho(t)}{t - \lambda}. \tag{10.7.35}$$

If such a function exists, Theorem 10.7.2 can be made to show that $\|\rho(t)\| \leq A + B|t|^{1/2}$ for all t. A basic problem is the nature of the singularities of $m(\lambda, b)$ for fixed b. They are necessarily real numbers $\{\lambda_n\}$, but are they poles, simple poles? If the algebra $\mathfrak{B}$ contains no nilpotent elements, poles must be simple poles and the residue at $\lambda = \lambda_n$ is $[T(\lambda_n)]^{-1}$. Summing residues, we can then construct $\rho(t, b)$ and prove that $m(\lambda, b)$ is represented by (10.7.35) with $\rho(t)$ replaced by $\rho(t, b)$. The limit passage $\rho(t, b) \to \rho(t)$ should cause no serious difficulties. Again, supposing the boundary value problem for $(0, b)$ to have a discrete spectrum, a transformation theory for mapping of $L_2[(0, b); \mathfrak{B}]$ on to a space $L_2[(0, b); \rho_b]$ appears feasible and the passage from $(0, b)$ to $(0, \infty)$ should be manageable. But enough of these speculations!

EXERCISE 10.7

1. If $x = h + ik$, $h^* = h$, $k^* = k$, and k positive, prove that x is non-singular. The following argument is due to Richard M. Koch. Set $k^{-1} = g^2$, g positive and form $gxg = ghg + ie$. Show that its spectrum lies on the line $\mathfrak{I}(\lambda) = 1$ so that x is non-singular. Fill in the details or give a different proof.
2. If $y(t) = u(t) + iv(t)$ satisfies (10.7.9) show that $u(t)[\mu - q(t)]v(t) = v(t)[\mu - q(t)]u(t)$. If $y^*(t)y'(t)$ is real symmetric, show that $u(t)v(t) - v(t)u(t)$ is a constant.
3. Prove the analogue of Theorem 10.1.2.
4. Carry through the proof of (10.7.27).
5. Verify the estimates of S_1, T_1, W_1.
6. Verify (10.7.31) and (10.7.33).

COLLATERAL READING

We refer to the literature quoted at the end of Chapter 8. The most significant entries for the singular case are the treatises by Coddington-Levinson; Titchmarsh, for differential equations; and Dunford-Schwartz and Stone for operator theory. To the latter should be added

ACHIEZER, N. I., and I. M. GLAZMAN, *Theorie der linearen Operatoren im Hilbert Raum*, Akademie-Verlag, Berlin (1954). (Russian original 1950.)

The basic paper is

WEYL, Hermann, "Über gewöhnliche Differentialgleichungen mit Singularitäten und die zugehörigen Entwicklungen willkürlichen Funktionen," *Math. Annalen*, **68**, 220–269 (1910).

Forty years later, Weyl gave a fascinating Gibbs Lecture:

"Ramifications, old and new, of the Eigenvalue problem," *Bull. Amer. Math. Soc.* **50**, 115–139 (1950).

Theorems 10.1.4 and 10.2.1 are taken from the author's paper,

"Green's transforms and singular boundary value problems," *J. Math. pures et appl.* (9) **42**, 332–349 (1963).

For the theory of unitary transformations, see

BOCHNER, S., and K. CHANDRASEKHARAN, *Fourier transforms*, Princeton Univ. Press, Princeton (1949).

Sections 10.5 and part of 10.6 are built on papers by

SEARS, B. D., "Integral transforms and eigenfunction theory," *Quart. J. Math.* (Oxford II), **5**, 47–58 (1954); **6**, 213–217 (1955).

For Section 10.7, we refer to

ATKINSON, F. V., *Discrete and Continuous Boundary Value Problems*, Academic Press, New York (1964).

This treatise has a very extensive bibliography. The nested circles theorem for matrices is found in Section 9.8.

BIRKHOFF, G. D., and R. E. LANGER, "The boundary problems and developments associated with a system of ordinary linear differential equations of the first order," *Proc. Amer. Acad. Arts Sci.* **58**, 51–128 (1923) (Birkhoff's Collected Works, I, 347–424.)

BLISS, G. A., "A boundary value problem for a system of ordinary differential equations of the first order," *Trans. Amer. Math. Soc.* **28**, 561–584 (1926).

BRAUER, Fred, "Spectral theory for linear systems of differential equations," *Pacif. J. Math.* **10**, 17–34 (1960).

GLAZMAN, I. M., "On the theory of singular differential operators," *Uspechi Mat. Nauk*, **5**, 102–135 (1950). AMS Translations, **4**, 331–372 (1962).

KODAIRA, K., "On ordinary differential equations of any even order and the corresponding eigenfunction expansion," *Amer. J. Math.* **72**, 502–544 (1950).

Further detailed information is to be found in

GEL'FAND, I. M., and B. M. LEVITAN, "On the determination of a differential equation from its spectral function," *Izv. Akad. Nauk S.S.S.R., Ser. Mat.* **15**, 309–360 (1951). AMS Translations, (2) **1**, 253–304 (1955).

MARČENKO, V. A., "Certain questions of the theory of one-dimensional linear differential operators of the second order," *I. Trudy Moskov Mat. Obšč.*, **1**, 327–420 (1952); II. *Ibid.* **2**, 3–83 (1953).

MARČENKO, V. A., "Expansions in eigenfunctions of non-self-adjoint singular differential operators of second order," *Mat. Sbornik* (*N.S.*), **52** (94), 739–788 (1960). AMS Translations (2), **25**, 77–130 (1963).

NAĬMARK, M. A., "Lineĭnye Differentsial'nye Operatory," *Gosudarstvennoe Izdatel'stvo Tehn.-Teor. Literatury*, Moscow (1954).

11 COMPLEX OSCILLATION THEORY

While the oscillatory behavior on the real line of solutions of linear second order equations has been known since the work of Sturm and Liouville in the 1830's, the oscillation problem in the complex plane remained untouched until the end of the nineteenth century. Incidental light was thrown on it through the investigations on the asymptotic behavior of solutions for approach to an irregular singular point of finite rank by J. Horn (1897–1908), G. D. Birkhoff (1908), and R. Garnier (1919). The results are of a local nature.

Investigations directly concerned with the zero-point problem in the complex plane go back to A. Hurwitz's work on Bessel functions in 1889, followed by work on hypergeometric functions by H. Van Vleck (1902), Hurwitz (1907), and P. Schafheitlin (1908). They used argument variation, approximating functions, conformal mapping, and (Schafheitlin) variation of parameters. P. Boutroux (1913–14) examined the distribution of zeros and extrema of solutions of Bessel's equation, via the associated Riccati equation, including their displacements with changes in the initial conditions. In 1918–24, the author re-examined these problems, using Liouville's transformation, Green's transform, and variation of parameters, and applied the methods to Legendre's, Hermite-Weber's, and Mathieu's equations. The Schwarzian derivative and univalence were brought to bear on the problems by Z. Nehari (1949) and his pupils, P. Beesack and B. Schwartz, while C. T. Taam used comparison theorems in 1952.

Here we give a digest of these various methods. There are six sections: Oscillatory Behavior; Some Comparison Theorems; Use of the Green's Transform; Applications to Special Equations; Asymptotic Integration and the Indicatrices; and Variation of Parameters.

11.1 OSCILLATORY BEHAVIOR

This introductory section serves two purposes. On the one hand, we study and obtain some preliminary and local information concerning the frequency and orientation in the plane of zeros of solutions of linear second order differential equations with analytic coefficients. On the other, some of the concepts and tools to be used later are developed. These include *equations of motion*, an integral identity known as the *Green's transform*, and a net of curves called *indicatrices* and *anticlinals*.

The differential equation is taken in the form

$$w''(z) + G(z)w(z) = 0 \tag{11.1.1}$$

where $G(z)$ is holomorphic save for poles in a domain D. Set

$$G(z) = P(z) \exp [iQ(z)], \tag{11.1.2}$$

P non-negative, Q real. The role of these two factors in oscillation theory is roughly that P regulates the frequency of the zeros, while Q governs their orientation in the plane.

The trivial case where

$$G(z) = a,$$

a constant, is instructive. A solution of the corresponding differential equation with a zero at $z = z_0$ is of the form

$$w(z) = C \sin \sqrt{a}\,(z - z_0).$$

The zeros

$$z_n = z_0 + a^{-1/2}n\pi$$

are located on the line

$$\arg (z - z_0) \equiv -\tfrac{1}{2} \arg a \pmod \pi \tag{11.1.3}$$

and the distance between consecutive zeros is

$$|a|^{-1/2}\pi. \tag{11.1.4}$$

This suggests generalizations. Let $w(z)$ be the solution of (11.1.1) with initial conditions

$$w(z_0) = 0, \qquad w'(z_0) = 1.$$

It is assumed that $G(z)$ is holomorphic in some disk $|z - z_0| < R$.

We aim to show that, knowing a bound for $|G(z)|$ in the disk, we can find a lower bound for the distance from $z = z_0$ to the nearest zero z_1 of $w(z)$ and, knowing $\arg G(z)$, we can delimit the direction from z_0 to z_1.

To this end we first interpret (11.1.1) as the equation of motion of a "particle" $w(z)$ in the complex plane. If z moves along a ray $\arg (z - z_0) = \theta$, then $w(z)$ describes an orbit in the w-plane. If the ray should happen to pass through z_1, then the orbit is closed and passes again through the origin of the w-plane. As was done in similar situations in Chapter 9, we find it useful to introduce polar coordinates.

The real valued functions $|w(z)|$ and $\arg w(z)$ are uniquely determined by the differential equation in some neighborhood of $z = z_0$. They will be studied on an arbitrary ray $\arg (z - z_0) = \theta$. Set

$$R(r) = |w(z_0 + r\, e^{i\theta})|, \qquad \Theta(r) = \arg w(z_0 + r\, e^{i\theta}). \tag{11.1.5}$$

We need the initial values of these functions and of their first order derivatives with respect to r. They are found to be

$$R(0) = 0, \qquad R'(0) = 1, \qquad \Theta(0) = \theta, \qquad \Theta'(0) = 0. \qquad (11.1.6)$$

The first initial value is evident; the second and third come from the identity

$$w'(z) = e^{-i\theta}\frac{dw}{dr} = [R'(r) + iR(r)\Theta'(r)] \exp i[\Theta(r) - \theta], \qquad (11.1.7)$$

where the prime indicates differentiation with respect to r. For $r = 0$ the desired relations are obtained. Similarly

$$w''(z) = \{R''(r) - R(r)[\Theta'(r)]^2 + i[2R'(r)\Theta'(r) + R(r)\Theta''(r)]\} \times \exp i[\Theta(r) - 2\theta]. \qquad (11.1.8)$$

Since $w''(z_0) = 0$ it follows that $\Theta'(0) = 0$.

Substituting the values of $w(z)$ and $w''(z)$ in terms of $R(r)$ and $\Theta(r)$, we obtain the equation

$$R''(r) - R(r)[\Theta'(r)]^2 + i[2R'(r)\Theta'(r) + R(r)\Theta''(r)] + g(r) \exp [i\gamma(r) + 2i\theta]R(r) = 0 \qquad (11.1.9)$$

where

$$G(z) = g(r) \exp [i\gamma(r)]. \qquad (11.1.10)$$

Separation of reals and imaginaries gives the *real equations of motion*:

$$R''(r) + \{g(r) \cos [\gamma(r) + 2\theta] - [\Theta'(r)]^2\}R(r) = 0, \qquad (11.1.11)$$

$$\{\Theta'(r)[R(r)]^2\}' + g(r) \sin [\gamma(r) + 2\theta][R(r)]^2 = 0, \qquad (11.1.12)$$

where the imaginary part has been multiplied by $R(r)$ to bring it into self-adjoint form.

There is an interval $(0, r_1)$ in which these equations are satisfied by

$$R(r) = |w(z_0 + r\, e^{i\theta})|, \qquad \Theta(r) = \arg w(z_0 + r\, e^{i\theta}),$$

these functions being continuous together with their first and second order derivatives. For increasing values of r, various contingencies may arise affecting the nature of the differential equations. Let us mark on the ray the points where one of the following events occurs: the point is

i) a zero of $G(z)$,
ii) a singularity of $G(z)$,
iii) a zero of $w(z)$,
iv) a zero of $w'(z)$.

Let $z_1 = z_0 + r_1\, e^{i\theta}$ be the first such point. Our problem is to find a lower bound for r_1. The points of the first two categories may be considered to be known. A zero of $G(z)$ affects $\gamma(r)$, which is discontinuous at such a point, with a jump which is a multiple of π. This does not seriously affect the differential equations. A singularity of course puts an end to further progress along the ray. At a zero of $w(z)$ both $R(r)$ and $\Theta(r)$ are affected. Here $R(r)$ is 0, and changes its sign from plus to minus at the first zero encountered. This means that in some interval (r_1, r_2)

$$R(r) = -|w(z_0 + r\,e^{i\theta})| \qquad \text{instead of} \quad |w(z_0 + r\,e^{i\theta})|.$$

The argument $\Theta(r)$ is not defined at $r = r_1$ but it has left- and right-hand limits and we may take

$$\Theta(r_1 + 0) = \Theta(r_1 - 0) + \pi.$$

Likewise $\Theta'(r)$ has finite left- and right-hand limits and by (11.1.8)

$$\Theta'(r_1 + 0) = \Theta'(r_1 - 0) = 0.$$

A zero of $w'(z)$ presents a different problem. If $z_1 = z_0 + r_1\,e^{i\theta}$ is such a point, then

$$R'(r_1) = \Theta'(r_1) = 0$$

and normally these are simple zeros where the functions R' and Θ' change their signs. Geometrically speaking, this means that the orbit has a cusp for $z = z_1$, with both branches to the same side of the cusp tangent in some neighborhood of $z = z_1$. The differential equations are not affected.

We shall return to the study of the equations of motion in the next section. Here we select merely two consequences of the equations which have a direct bearing on the problem of estimating local frequency and orientation of the zeros. We start with (11.1.11) and note the trivial inequality

$$g(r)\cos[\gamma(r) + 2\theta] - [\Theta'(r)]^2 \le g(r).$$

Applying the Sturmian comparison Theorem 8.1.2, we then obtain

Theorem 11.1.1. *Let $v(r) = v(r, \theta)$ be the solution of*

$$v''(r) + |G(z_0 + r\,e^{i\theta})|v(r) = 0 \tag{11.1.13}$$

with $v(0) = 0$, $v'(0) = 1$. Let the least positive zero of $v(r, \theta)$ be $r_a(\theta)$, then the solution $w(z)$ of (11.1.1) with $w(z_0) = 0$, $w'(z_0) = 1$, has no zero on the open segment $(z_0, z_0 + r_a(\theta)\,e^{i\theta})$.

Corollary. *Let $G(z)$ be holomorphic in the disk $|z - z_0| < R$ and satisfy $|G(z)| \le \pi^2 R^{-2}$, then the solution $w(z)$ specified above has no other zeros in $|z - z_0| < R$.*

Here we have for all θ the comparison equation

$$v''(r) + \left(\frac{\pi}{R}\right)^2 v(r) = 0$$

with

$$v(r) = \sin\left(\frac{\pi}{R} r\right)$$

and the only zero in $(-R, R)$ is $r = 0$. ∎

An alternate formulation of the Corollary is:

If $G(z)$ is holomorphic in $|z - z_0| < R$ and if $|G(z)| \le M$, then $w(z)$ has no zero in the punctured disk

$$0 < |z - z_0| < \min(R, \pi M^{-1/2}). \tag{11.1.14}$$

A similar result holds for the solution with an extremum at $z = z_0$. As could be expected, the zero-free region is smaller.

Theorem 11.1.2. *If $G(z)$ is holomorphic in $|z - z_0| < R$ and if $|G(z)| \le M$ there, then the solution of (11.1.1) with $w(z_0) = 1$, $w'(z_0) = 0$, has no zeros in*

$$|z - z_0| < \min(R, \tfrac{1}{2}\pi M^{-1/2}). \tag{11.1.15}$$

Proof. Here we can also use a Sturmian argument. To abbreviate let us write

$$R'' + h(r, \theta)R = 0$$

where

$$h(r, \theta) = g(r)\cos[\gamma(r) + 2\theta] - [\Theta'(r)]^2$$

and consider the solution with initial conditions $R(0) = 1$, $R'(0) = 0$. Compare this with $v(r) = \cos\sqrt{M}\, r$, the solution of

$$v''(r) + Mv(r) = 0$$

which satisfies the same initial conditions. We have now

$$R(r)v'(r) - R'(r)v(r) + \int_0^r [M - h(s, \theta)]R(s)v(s)\, ds = 0.$$

Suppose that $R(r_1) = 0$ for an $r_1 < \min(\frac{1}{2}\pi M^{-1/2}, R)$ and set $r = r_1$. Then $R'(r_1) < 0$, $v(r_1) > 0$ and the integral is positive. This is a contradiction. ∎

The second important implication of the equations of motion is derived from (11.1.12). For a solution of (11.1.1) with $w(z_0)w'(z_0) = 0$, we have $\Theta'(0)R(0) = 0$ and by integration

$$\Theta'(r)[R(r)]^2 = -\int_0^r g(s)\sin[\gamma(s) + 2\theta][R(s)]^2\, ds. \tag{11.1.16}$$

This shows that the left member cannot be zero as long as $\sin[\gamma(s) + 2\theta]$ keeps a constant sign. Let $z_1 = z_0 + r_0(\theta)\, e^{i\theta}$ be the first point on the ray, $\neq z_0$, where either $G(z)$ is singular or

$$\arg G(z_0 + r\, e^{i\theta}) + 2\theta \equiv 0 \pmod{\pi} \tag{11.1.17}$$

and define

$$\mathbf{S}_0(z_0) = [z \mid z = z_0 + r\, e^{i\theta}, 0 \le r \le r_0(\theta), 0 \le \theta < 2\pi]. \qquad (11.1.18)$$

This construction gives

Theorem 11.1.3. *If* $w(z)$ *is a solution of* (11.1.1) *with* $w(z_0)w'(z_0) = 0$, *then*

$$w(z)w'(z) \neq 0, \qquad z \in \mathbf{S}_0(z_0), \qquad z \neq z_0. \qquad (11.1.19)$$

For neither $R(r)$ nor $\Theta'(r)$ can vanish in this region.

We say that $\mathbf{S}_0(z_0)$ is a *zero-free star* of the solution in question.

Condition (11.1.17) can be given a geometric interpretation which is basic for the later discussion. Consider

$$Z(z) = \int_{z_0}^{z} [G(t)]^{1/2}\, dt \equiv X(z) + iY(z). \qquad (11.1.20)$$

This is in general an infinitely many-valued function. If $G(z)$ has no singularities other than poles, then $Z(z)$ has, in general, algebraic branch points at the zeros of $G(z)$ and algebraic or logarithmic branch points at the poles of $G(z)$. Moreover, all determinations of $Z(z)$ are of the form

$$\pm Z(z) + 2\pi i\alpha$$

where α is a constant depending upon the path leading from z_0 to z. Additive periods occur iff logarithmic branch points are actually present.

We are interested in the curve net

$$X(z) = C_1, \qquad Y(z) = C_2. \qquad (11.1.21)$$

Curves of the first family are referred to as *anticlinals*, those of the second as *indicatrices*, for reasons which will appear later. These curves should be thought of as traced on the Riemann surface on which $Z(z)$ is single-valued. The net is the same in all sheets of the surface, only the labeling of the individual curves varies from one sheet to another, i.e. a curve may be $Y(z) = C$ in one sheet and $Y(z) = C'$ in another. In general there is one and only one curve of each family passing through a given point z_1 in the plane. At zeros and poles of $G(z)$ the situation is different. This will be discussed in more detail in Section 11.5.

We may now formulate condition (11.1.17) as follows:

The ray $\arg(z - z_0) = \theta$ *is tangent to the indicatrix passing through the point* $z_1 = z_0 + r_0(\theta)\, e^{i\theta}$ *at this point.*

To see this, set $z = z_0 + \rho\, e^{i\varphi}$ and note that

$$[G(z)]^{1/2} = Z'(z) = e^{-i\varphi} Z'_\rho = e^{-i\varphi}[X'_\rho + iY'_\rho].$$

Along the curve

$$Y(z) = C$$

we have

$$Y'_\rho \, d\rho + Y'_\varphi \, d\varphi = 0.$$

If the ray $z = z_0 + \rho \, e^{i\theta}$ is to be a tangent of this curve at $\rho = r_1$, then

$$Y'_\rho(r_1) = 0$$

so that

$$[G(z_1)]^{1/2} = e^{-i\theta} X'_\rho(r_1)$$

and

$$\arg \, [G(z_1)]^{1/2} \equiv -\theta \pmod{\pi}.$$

This says that for a suitable determination of arg $G(z)$

$$\tfrac{1}{2} \arg G(z_1) \equiv -\theta \pmod{\pi}$$

and this is condition (11.1.17). Hence we have the

Corollary. *The boundary of* $\mathbf{S}_0(z_0)$ *is the locus of the (nearest) points of tangency between the pencil of straight lines through* $z = z_0$ *and the system of indicatrices plus part of the line through* $z = z_0$ *tangent to the local indicatrix there and possibly, plus parts of the lines beyond the singular points.*

This has to be modified if $z = z_0$ is a zero of $G(z)$ since then there is more than one indicatrix through z_0. See also (11.5.36).

We can derive a slightly stronger result than Theorem 11.1.3, using an alternate method based on the Green's transform of the differential equation which will be used extensively below.

Multiply (11.1.1) by $\overline{w(z)}$ and integrate along an arbitrary rectifiable arc joining two points $z = a$ and $z = b$ in a domain D, where $G(z)$ is holomorphic. Thus

$$\int_a^b \overline{w(z)} w''(z) \, dz + \int_a^b G(z)|w(z)|^2 \, dz = 0.$$

Integrate the first term by parts to obtain

$$\overline{w(z)} w'(z) \Big|_a^b - \int_a^b |w'(z)|^2 \, \overline{dz} + \int_a^b G(z)|w(z)|^2 \, dz = 0. \qquad (11.1.22)$$

Note that the derivative of $\overline{w(z)}$ with respect to z in the direction of the path of integration is $\overline{w'(z)}$ times the directional derivative of $\bar{z}$ with respect to z, hence $\overline{dz}$ and not dz in the first integral. This formula is *Green's transform* of (11.1.1).

Suppose now that $w(z)$ is a solution of (11.1.1) with $w(z_0)w'(z_0) = 0$, $w(z) \not\equiv 0$. Green's transform may be used to construct zero-free regions of

$w(z)$, in particular, a zero-free star. Again we consider rays from z_0 and obtain

$$e^{i\theta}\overline{w(z)}w'(z) = \int_0^r |w'(t)|^2\, ds$$
$$- \int_0^r g(s) \exp\,[i\gamma(s) + 2i\theta]|w(t)|^2\, ds \qquad (11.1.23)$$

where

$$t = z_0 + s\, e^{i\theta}, \qquad z = z_0 + r\, e^{i\theta},$$
$$g(s) = |G(t)|, \qquad \gamma(s) = \arg G(t).$$

The first term on the right is positive; the second integral has an argument which lies between

$$\min_{0 \le s \le r} \gamma(s) + 2\theta \qquad \text{and} \qquad \max_{0 \le s \le r} \gamma(s) + 2\theta,$$

provided the difference between the maximum and the minimum is $<\pi$. This leads to the following construction. On the ray mark the first point where either (i) $G(z)$ is singular or

$$\begin{aligned} &\text{ii) } \arg G(z) + 2\theta \equiv 0 \pmod{2\pi} \quad \text{or} \\ &\text{iii) } \max \arg G(z) - \min \arg G(z) = \pi. \end{aligned} \qquad (11.1.24)$$

Let this point correspond to $s = r(\theta)$ and define

$$\mathbf{S}(z_0) = [z|\ z = z_0 + r\, e^{i\theta}, 0 \le r \le r(\theta), 0 \le \theta < 2\pi]. \qquad (11.1.25)$$

From this construction we read off

Theorem 11.1.4. $w(z)w'(z) \neq 0$ *for* $z \in \mathbf{S}(z_0)$, $z \neq z_0$.

We have $\mathbf{S}_0(z_0) \subset \mathbf{S}(z_0)$ and it may be a proper subset.

Let us return to $\mathbf{S}_0(z_0)$ assuming $G(z_0) \neq 0$. The function $r_0(\theta)$ is discontinuous at

$$\theta = \theta_0 \equiv -\tfrac{1}{2}\arg G(z_0) \qquad \text{and} \qquad \theta = \theta_0 + \pi. \qquad (11.1.26)$$

On one side of these rays, $r_0(\theta)$ normally approaches 0, on the other a positive, possibly infinite, limit. This means that the star $\mathbf{S}_0(z_0)$ consists of two parts with z_0 as the only point in common. See Figure 11.1. There are two horn-angles bounded by the line $z = z_0 \pm r\, e^{i\theta}$ and the tangent locus (see p. 637)

$$\Im\,\{(z - z_0)\,[G(z)]^{1/2}\} = 0.$$

In exceptional but important special cases the tangent locus coincides with the line and the horn-angles reduce to segments of the line.

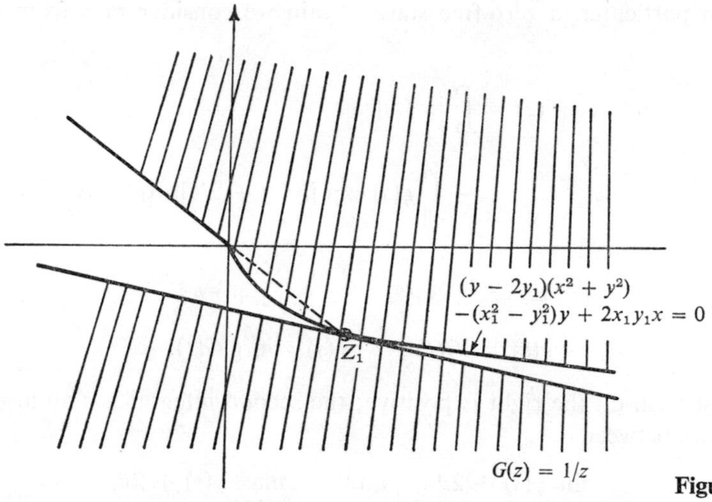

Figure 11.1

The horn-angles do not belong to $\mathbf{S}_0(z_0)$ and may conceivably contain other zeros of $w(z)w'(z)$. The Corollary of Theorem 11.1.1 suggests that for this to be the case, $|G(z)|$ must be fairly large in a neighborhood of $z = z_0$. Now the stars $\mathbf{S}(z_0)$ and $\mathbf{S}_0(z_0)$ are unchanged if $G(z)$ is replaced by $k^2G(z)$, $k > 0$, and it stands to reason that the frequency of oscillation will increase with k. This is indeed the case and we shall prove

Theorem 11.1.5. *Let $G(z)$ be holomorphic in some neighborhood of $z = z_0$, $G(z_0) \neq 0$. Let $w(z, k)$ be the solution of*

$$w''(z) + k^2G(z)w(z) = 0 \tag{11.1.27}$$

with $w(z_0, k) = 0$, $w'(z_0, k) = k^{-1}$. Then $w(z, k)$ has a zero $z_{1,k}$ such that

$$\lim_{k\to\infty} k|z_{1,k} - z_0| = \pi|G(z_0)|^{-1/2}, \tag{11.1.28}$$

$$\lim_{k\to\infty} \arg(z_{1,k} - z_0) \equiv -\tfrac{1}{2}\arg G(z_0) \pmod{\pi}. \tag{11.1.29}$$

Proof. Set

$$z = z_0 + \frac{t}{k}, \qquad G(z) = g\left(\frac{t}{k}\right), \qquad g(0) = a^2 = G(z_0), \qquad w(z) = W(t).$$

This substitution gives

$$\frac{d^2W}{dt^2} + g\left(\frac{t}{k}\right)W = 0, \qquad W(0) = 0, \qquad W'(0) = 1. \tag{11.1.30}$$

This solution is to be compared with

$$\frac{1}{a}\sin at,$$

the solution of

$$\frac{d^2Y}{dt^2} + a^2Y = 0, \qquad Y(0) = 0, \qquad Y'(0) = 1.$$

Here Theorem 3.3.1 will apply after the equations have been written in vector-matrix form

$$\mathbf{w}' = \begin{pmatrix} 0 & 1 \\ -g(t/k) & 0 \end{pmatrix}\mathbf{w}, \qquad \mathbf{y}' = \begin{pmatrix} 0 & 1 \\ -a^2 & 0 \end{pmatrix}\mathbf{y} \tag{11.1.31}$$

with

$$\mathbf{w}(0) = \mathbf{y}(0) = \begin{pmatrix} 0 \\ 1 \end{pmatrix}.$$

Suppose that $G(z)$ is holomorphic in the disk $|z - z_0| < R$ where $|G(z)| \le M$. Then

$$|W(t)|, |Y(t)| \le M^{-1/2} \sinh (M^{1/2}|t|),$$

$$|W'(t)|, |Y'(t)| \le \cosh (M^{1/2}|t|)$$

and these bounds do not exceed a fixed number A, if t is restricted so that $|t| < (2\pi/|a|)$. By Schwarz's Lemma, the inequality

$$|G(z) - G(z_0)| \le 2M, \qquad |z - z_0| < R$$

may be strengthened to

$$|G(z) - G(z_0)| \le \frac{2M}{R}|z - z_0|$$

whence

$$\left|a^2 - g\left(\frac{t}{k}\right)\right| \le \frac{2M}{kR}|t|.$$

To apply Theorem 3.3.1 we need an estimate of the norm of the difference of the right members of the vector equations for $\mathbf{w} = \mathbf{y}$ and also a Lipschitz constant for the approximate equation. Here

$$\left\|\begin{pmatrix} 0 & 0 \\ a^2 - g(t/k) & 0 \end{pmatrix}\mathbf{y}\right\| = |a^2 - g(t/k)|\,|Y(t)|$$

$$< \frac{2AM}{kR}|t| \le \frac{4\pi AM}{|a|kR}, \qquad |t| < \frac{2\pi}{|a|}.$$

This is our ε. For K we take $|a|^2$. Hence

$$|W(t) - Y(t)| \le \|\mathbf{w}(t) - \mathbf{y}(t)\| \le \frac{4\pi AM}{|a|^3kR}[\exp (|a|^2|t|) - 1]. \tag{11.1.32}$$

uniformly in k. The estimates clearly hold for complex values of t, since we can apply Theorem 3.3.1 on any ray $\arg t = \theta$. For large values of k, the last member of (11.1.32) is as small as we please. Now $Y(t) = a^{-1}\sin(at)$ has three zeros inside the circle $|t| = 2\pi/|a|$, one of them at $t = 0$. The theorem of Rouché can be used to prove that, for all large values of k, the function $W(t)$ has zeros in δ-disks about the points $t = \pm\pi/a$, one zero in each disk, and here δ is at our disposal. Going back to the original variables, we see that $w(z, k)$ has a zero in each of the disks

$$\left| z - z_0 \mp \frac{\pi}{ak} \right| < \frac{\delta}{k}$$

for large values of k. This suffices to prove formulas (11.1.28) and (11.1.29). ∎

EXERCISE 11.1

1. Find $\mathbf{S}_0(z_0)$ if $G(z) = a^2$, a not necessarily real.
2. Find $\mathbf{S}_0(0)$ if $G(z) = z$.
3. Find $\mathbf{S}_0(0)$ if $G(z) = 3 - z^2$. Here the odd solution has a single zero while the even solution has infinitely many zeros in each quadrant.
4. For a formally self-adjoint equation
$$[P(z)w'(z)]' + Q(z)w(z) = 0$$
show that the Green's transform is
$$P(z)\overline{w(z)}w'(z)\Big|_{z_1}^{z_2} - \int_{z_1}^{z_2} P(z)|w'(z)|^2\,d\bar{z} + \int_{z_1}^{z_2} Q(z)|w(z)|^2\,dz = 0.$$
5. Consider Legendre's equation, i.e. $P(z) = 1 - z^2$, $Q(z) = a(a + 1)$, $a > 0$. Show that $F(a + 1, -a, 1, \frac{1}{2}(1 - z)) \equiv P_a(z)$ has no complex zeros in the plane cut along the real axis from $-\infty$ to -1, and that real zeros, if any, lie in the interval $(-1, 1)$. If $a = -\frac{1}{2} + i\mu$ instead, show that there are still no complex zeros, but the real zeros lie in $(1, \infty)$. Use $\mathbf{S}(1)$ and justify its use since $z = 1$ is a singular point of the equation.
6. If $a > 0$, show that $P_a(z)$ has no zeros on either border of the cut by discussing the imaginary part. (See Section 7.2.)
7. What is the analogue of the Corollary of Theorem 11.1.1 if
$$|G(z_0 + r\,e^{i\theta})| \le Mr?$$
8. What is the equation of the indicatrices if $G(z) = z$?
9. Let $G(z) = a^2 - z^2$, $a > 0$. Choose $z_0 = 0$ in (11.1.20). Show that the indicatrix $Y(z) = 0$ is made up of five connected arcs meeting at 120° angles at $z = \pm a$, the line segment $(-a, a)$ being one of the arcs. The others have lines parallel to $y = \pm x$ as asymptotes.
10. A description is wanted of the indicatrices for $G(z) = -\tan^2 z$. If $z_0 = 0$, the curve $Y(z) = 1$ intersects itself at all multiples of π forming infinitely many closed regions. The curves $Y(z) = C(< 1)$ consist of infinitely many ovals, one about each of the poles of $\tan z$.

11.2 SOME COMPARISON THEOREMS

After a brief discussion of the remaining aspects of the equations of motion, we shall proceed to consider some comparison theorems. Knowing a majorant Q of $|G|$ or of some linear combination of the real and of the imaginary parts of G and knowing that the majorant equation

$$v'' + Qv = 0$$

has a solution without a zero, we can conclude that certain solutions of (11.1.1) have only one zero in the domain under consideration. Some of these theorems are very strong in the sense that they allow at most one zero for every solution of the equation. In this case the investigation is closely connected with the theory of *univalent analytic functions*. These aspects will be taken up in more detail in Appendix D. Here we shall report on work done by P. R. Beesack, E. Hille, Z. Nehari, V. V. Pokornyi, B. Schwarz, and C. T. Taam.

We return to Eq. (11.1.11). Here the cosine of $\gamma(r) + 2\theta$ comes into play. On the ray $\arg(z - z_0) = \theta$ mark the point nearest to but distinct from z_0 where either $G(z)$ is singular or

$$\arg G(z) + 2\theta \equiv \tfrac{1}{2}\pi \pmod{\pi}. \tag{11.2.1}$$

The corresponding value of r will be denoted by $r_1(\theta)$ if for increasing values of r the cosine goes from minus to plus, otherwise by $r_2(\theta)$. It is convenient to set $r_2(\theta) = 0$ in the first case, and $r_1(\theta) = 0$ in the second. This construction gives rise to two stars $\mathbf{S}_1(z_0)$ and $\mathbf{S}_2(z_0)$. Here

$$\mathbf{S}_j(z_0) = [z \mid z = z_0 + r\,e^{i\theta}, 0 \le r \le r_j(\theta), 0 \le \theta < 2\pi] \tag{11.2.2}$$

with $j = 1, 2$. Only the first of these stars may be claimed to be zero-free, however.

For $z \in \mathbf{S}_1(z_0)$

$$g(r) \cos[\gamma(r) + 2\theta] - [\Theta'(r)]^2 < 0.$$

Formula (9.2.2) applies and shows that no solution of (11.1.1) can admit a zero of $R(r)R'(r)$ on the half-open interval $(0, r_1(\theta)]$ if $R(0)R'(0) = 0$. Hence we get

Theorem 11.2.1. *If* $w(z)$ *is a solution of* (11.1.1) *with* $w(z_0)w'(z_0) = 0$, *then*

$$w(z)w'(z) \neq 0, \qquad z \in \mathbf{S}_1(z_0), \qquad z \neq z_0. \tag{11.2.3}$$

The star $\mathbf{S}_2(z_0)$ presents a different problem. Here the best we can do is to observe that

$$g(r) \cos[\gamma(r) + 2\theta] - [\Theta'(r)]^2 \le g(r) \cos[\gamma(r) + 2\theta] \le g(r).$$

Here we are back to Theorem 11.1.1, which we reformulate in terms of a zero-free star $\mathbf{S}_a(z_0)$ defined by

$$\mathbf{S}_a(z_0) = [z \mid z = z_0 + r\,e^{i\theta}, 0 \le r < r_a(\theta), 0 \le \theta \le 2\pi], \qquad (11.2.4)$$

where $r_a(\theta)$ is defined in Theorem 11.1.1. We then have

Theorem 11.2.2. *The solution $w(z)$ of (11.1.1) with $w(z_0) = 0$, $w'(z_0) = 1$ has no zero in $\mathbf{S}_a(z_0)$ excepting $z = z_0$.*

Theorems 11.1.1 and 11.2.2 are due to Choy-tak Taam (1952). Our next result is also due to Taam (1953), but we prefer to reproduce a proof given by P. R. Beesack (1956). The latter is based on a variant of the Green's transform and a lemma also involving quadratic integral identities.

In (11.1.22) we take $a = z_0$, $b = z_1$, two zeros of the solution $w(z)$ of (11.1.1), and let the path of integration be rectilinear: $z = z_0 + r\,e^{i\theta}$, $0 \le r \le r_1$. This gives

$$\int_0^{r_1} |w'|^2\,dr = \int_0^{r_1} e^{2i\theta}G|w|^2\,dr \equiv \int_0^{r_1} [g_1 + ig_2]|w|^2\,dr,$$

or, separating reals and imaginaries,

$$\int_0^{r_1} g_1|w|^2\,dr = \int_0^{r_1} |w'|^2\,dr, \qquad \int_0^{r_1} g_2|w|^2\,dr = 0.$$

Let λ and μ be real numbers, $\lambda \ge 0$, $\lambda^2 + \mu^2 \ne 0$, multiply the first equation by λ, the second by μ, and add. The result is Beesack's modification of the Green's transform:

$$\int_0^{r_1} (\lambda g_1 + \mu g_2)|w|^2\,dr = \lambda \int_0^{r_1} |w'|^2\,dr. \qquad (11.2.5)$$

This is one of the required identities. The second is expressed in

Lemma 11.2.1. *Let $F(t)$ be real and continuous in the interval (a, b) with $(t-a)^2(b-t)^2\,F(t)$ bounded in (a, b). Suppose that the Riccati equation*

$$Y'(t) = F(t) + [Y(t)]^2 \qquad (11.2.6)$$

has a solution of class C^1 in (a, b) with $(t-a)(b-t)\,Y(t)$ bounded in (a, b). If $y(t)$ is a piecewise smooth function and $y(a) = y(b) = 0$, then

$$\int_a^b \{[y'(t)]^2 - F(t)[y(t)]^2\}\,dt = \int_a^b [y'(t) + Y(t)y(t)]^2\,dt. \qquad (11.2.7)$$

The assumptions imply the existence of the integrals, and to prove the identity one expands the right member, integrates by parts using the boundary conditions for $y(t)$, and simplifies. The important thing here is that the right member is positive, with an exception noted below.

Theorem 11.2.3. *Let $G(z)$ be holomorphic in a domain D containing the line segment $z = z_0 + r\,e^{i\theta}$, $0 \leq r \leq R$. Set*

$$e^{2i\theta}G(z_0 + r\,e^{i\theta}) \equiv g_1(r, \theta) + ig_2(r, \theta). \tag{11.2.8}$$

Let $Q(r)$ be continuous in $(0, R)$ and suppose that the differential equation

$$v''(r) + Q(r)v(r) = 0 \tag{11.2.9}$$

has a solution $v(r)$ with $v(0) = 0$ and no zeros in $(0, R)$. Suppose that real numbers λ, μ can be found, $\lambda \geq 0$, $\lambda^2 + \mu^2 \neq 0$, such that

$$\lambda g_1(r, \theta) + \mu g_2(r, \theta) \leq \lambda Q(r), \qquad 0 \leq r \leq R. \tag{11.2.10}$$

Then any non-trivial solution of (11.1.1) *with $w(z_0) = 0$ is $\neq 0$ on the segment $(z_0, z_0 + R\,e^{i\theta})$ unless $g_2(r, \theta) \equiv 0$. Even if $g_2(r, \theta) \equiv 0$, the conclusion holds, provided $\lambda > 0$. Moreover, if strict inequality holds in* (11.2.10) *for a single point, then $w(z)$ has no zeros in $(z_0, z_0 + R\,e^{i\theta})$.*

Proof. Suppose that $w(z_1) = 0$, $z_1 = z_0 + r_1\,e^{i\theta}$, $0 < r_1 < R$. We go back to (11.2.5) which, together with (11.2.10), gives

$$\lambda \int_0^{r_1} |w'|^2\,dr \leq \lambda \int_0^{r_1} Q(r)|w|^2\,dr.$$

Here we must first dispose of the case $\lambda = 0$ where the inequality gives no information. Now, if $\lambda = 0$, then $\mu \neq 0$, and (11.2.10) shows that either $g_2(r, \theta)$ has a constant sign, opposite that of μ, or else $g_2(r, \theta) \equiv 0$. In the first case, (11.2.5) gives a contradiction, for the left member is negative while the right is zero. It follows that $w(z)$ can have no zero in $(z_0, z_0 + R\,e^{i\theta})$. The second alternative, $g_2(r, \theta) \equiv 0$, is excluded if strict inequality holds in (11.2.10) for at least one point and hence in some interval.

If, however, strict inequality holds nowhere and if $g_2(r, \theta) \equiv 0$, then for $\lambda > 0$ formula (11.2.10) shows that $g_1(r, \theta) = Q(r)$ and the desired conclusion is immediate. If $g_2(r, \theta) \not\equiv 0$, let $\lambda > 0$ and note that

$$\int_0^{r_1} |w'|^2\,dr \leq \int_0^{r_1} Q(r)|w|^2\,dr.$$

Let us write

$$|w(z + r\,e^{i\theta})| = W(r)$$

and note that $W'(r)$ exists for $0 < r < r$. Further

$$|W'(r)| \leq |w'(z)|, \qquad z = z_0 + r\,e^{i\theta},$$

by virtue of (11.1.7) where $W'(r) = R'(r)$. Hence

$$\int_0^{r_1} [W'(t)]^2\,dt \leq \int_0^{r_1} Q(t)[W(t)]^2\,dt. \tag{11.2.11}$$

We now use Lemma 11.2.1 to obtain an opposite inequality and a contradiction. We take

$$a = 0, \quad b = r_1, \quad y(t) = W(t), \quad F(t) = Q(t), \quad Y(t) = -\frac{v'(t)}{v(t)}.$$

Since $v(t)$ has no zeros in $(0, R)$, $Y(t)$ satisfies the Riccati equation

$$Y'(t) = Q(t) + [Y(t)]^2$$

in $(0, R)$ and $t(R - t)\,Y(t)$ is bounded. Further, $W(t)$ is smooth and $W(0) = W(r_1) = 0$. Thus the assumptions of the lemma are satisfied and

$$\begin{aligned}\int_0^{r_1} [W'(t)]^2\,dt &= \int_0^{r_1} Q(t)[W(t)]^2\,dt + \int_0^{r_1} [W'(t) + Y(t)W(t)]^2\,dt \\ &\geq \int_0^{r_1} Q(t)[W(t)]^2\,dt. \qquad (11.2.12)\end{aligned}$$

Here the sign of equality can hold iff

$$W'(t) + Y(t)W(t) \equiv 0,$$

and this implies

$$W(t) \equiv Cv(t).$$

If this should happen, then $W(t) \neq 0$ for $0 < t < R$. Finally, if $W(t) \not\equiv Cv(t)$, then the resulting inequality (11.2.12) contradicts (11.2.11). Hence, in either case $w(z) \neq 0$ on $(z_0, z_0 + R\,e^{i\theta})$. ∎

There are several special cases of interest. We note

i) $Q(r) = \frac{1}{4}\pi^2 R^{-2}$.
ii) $\lambda = 1$, $\mu = 0$, $Q(r) = g_1(r, \theta)$.
iii) $\lambda = 0$, $g_2(r, \theta) \neq 0$ on $0 < r < R$, $\mu = -\operatorname{sgn} g_2$.
iv) $\lambda = 1$, $\mu = 0$, $Q(r) = g_1(r, \theta) < 0$.

Here case (i) is closely related to the Corollary of Theorem 11.1.1 and to Theorem 11.1.2. The result is due to Z. Nehari (1949). We state it as

Theorem 11.2.4. *Let $G(z)$ be holomorphic in the disk $|z - z_0| < R$ and satisfy $|G(z)| \leq \frac{1}{4}\pi^2 R^{-2}$, then no solution of* (11.1.1) *can have more than one zero in the disk.*

For we have $g_1(r, \theta) \leq |e^{2i\theta} G(z_0 + r\,e^{i\theta})| \leq \frac{1}{4}\pi^2 R^{-2}$ so we may take $\lambda = 1$, $\mu = 0$, and the majorant equation

$$v'' + \tfrac{1}{4}\pi^2 R^{-2} v = 0$$

has real solutions with equidistant zeros, the zero-free intervals being equal in length to the diameter of the disk.

Case (ii) is an immediate consequence of (11.1.12), since

$$g(r)\cos[\gamma(r) + 2\theta] - [\Theta'(r)]^2 \leq g_1(r, \theta).$$

This case is essentially covered by Theorems 11.1.1 and 11.2.1. Case (iii) is Theorem 11.1.2 and case (iv) is 11.2.1.

We now turn to a theorem of Beesack based on comparison theorems plus the use of linear fractional transformations.

Theorem 11.2.5. *Let $G(z)$ be holomorphic in $|z| < 1$ and set $M(r) = \max |G(r\, e^{i\theta})|$. Suppose* (i) *that $(1 - r^2)^2 M(r)$ is non-increasing in* (0, 1) *and* (ii) *that the differential equation*

$$v'' + M(r)v = 0 \tag{11.2.13}$$

has a solution without zeros in the interval $(-1, 1)$. *Then no solution of* (11.1.1) *can have more than one zero in* $|z| < 1$.

Proof. Suppose that the solution $w(z)$ of (11.1.1) has two zeros a and b in the disk $|z| < 1$. There is a unique circle Γ passing through $z = a$ and $z = b$ and orthogonal to the unit circle. Without loss of generality we may assume this circle to be symmetric to the imaginary axis, for, if this is not the case at the outset, we use a rotation to achieve this. This changes the differential equation only to the extent that $G(z)$ is replaced by $\omega^2 G(\omega z)$, $|\omega| = 1$, with no change of the maximum modulus and hence no change in the hypotheses.

If accidentally a and b should be real, then the next step is omitted. If not, we use a fractional linear transformation, leaving the unit circle invariant to transform the arc of Γ inside the unit circle into the segment $(-1, 1)$ of the real axis. If Γ intersects the imaginary axis at $z = \beta i$, $-1 < \beta < 1$, $\beta \neq 0$, then

$$\zeta = \frac{z - \beta i}{1 + \beta i z} \tag{11.2.14}$$

will give the desired mapping. We leave verification of this to the reader.

The transformation takes the differential equation into

$$\frac{d^2 Y}{d\zeta^2} - \frac{2\beta i}{1 - \beta\zeta i}\frac{dY}{d\zeta} + \frac{(1 - \beta^2)^2}{(1 - \beta\zeta i)^4} G\left(\frac{\zeta + \beta i}{1 - \beta\zeta i}\right) Y = 0 \tag{11.2.15}$$

where $Y(\zeta) = w(z)$. Here we set $u = (1 - \beta\zeta i)Y$ and obtain

$$u'' + \frac{(1 - \beta^2)^2}{(1 - \beta\zeta i)^4} G\left(\frac{\zeta + \beta i}{1 - \beta\zeta i}\right) u = 0. \tag{11.2.16}$$

It follows that this equation has a solution $u(\zeta)$ with two zeros in the interval $(-1, 1)$. To show that this contradicts the hypotheses we argue as follows. For ζ real, $-1 < \zeta < +1$,

$$|1 - \beta\zeta i|^4 = (1 + \beta^2\zeta^2)^2, \qquad \left|\frac{\beta + \zeta i}{1 - \beta\zeta i}\right| = \left(\frac{\beta^2 + \zeta^2}{1 + \beta^2\zeta^2}\right)^{1/2}.$$

Hence

$$\frac{(1-\beta^2)^2}{|1-\beta\zeta i|^4}\left|G\left(\frac{\beta+\zeta i}{1-\beta\zeta i}\right)\right| \le \frac{(1-\beta^2)^2}{(1+\beta^2\zeta^2)^2} M\left[\left(\frac{\beta^2+\zeta^2}{1+\beta^2\zeta^2}\right)^{1/2}\right].$$

It is to be shown that the right member does not exceed $M(|\zeta|)$.

To this end, set

$$\frac{\beta^2+\zeta^2}{1+\beta^2\zeta^2} = x^2$$

Then $\zeta^2 \le x^2 \le 1$, whence

$$(1-x^2)^2 M(x) \le (1-\zeta^2)^2 M(|\zeta|).$$

Since

$$\frac{1-x^2}{1-\zeta^2} = \frac{1-\beta^2}{1+\beta^2\zeta^2}$$

the assertion follows.

To simplify, let us rewrite (11.2.16) as

$$u'' + H(\zeta)u = 0, \tag{11.2.17}$$

where for $-1 < \zeta < 1$, $|H(\zeta)| \le M(|\zeta|)$. Let ζ_1 and ζ_2 be the two zeros of $u(\zeta)$, $-1 < \zeta_1 < \zeta_2 < 1$. The solution $v(\zeta)$ of

$$v'' + M(|\zeta|)v = 0$$

with $v(\zeta_1) = 0$ has no other zeros in $(-1, 1)$, for, if it did, then every solution of the equation would have a zero in $(-1, 1)$ against the assumption that there is a solution without zeros. Since $|H(\zeta)| \le M(|\zeta|)$, the comparison theorems show that the solution $\omega(\zeta)$ of

$$\omega'' + |H(\zeta)|\omega = 0$$

with $\omega(\zeta_1) = 0$ has no other zeros in $(-1, 1)$. By Theorem 11.1.1 this extends to the solution $u(\zeta)$ of (11.2.17) with $u(\zeta_1) = 0$. It can have no other zero in $(-1, 1)$ and the assumption that (11.1.1) has a solution $w(z)$ with two zeros in the unit disk is found to be untenable. ▮

It remains to give some instances where the assumptions of Theorem 11.2.5 are satisfied. We start with the case

$$M(r) = (1-r^2)^{-2} \tag{11.2.18}$$

studied by Z. Nehari in 1949. Assumption (i) is trivially satisfied. The differential equation

$$v''(z) + a(1-z^2)^{-2}v(z) = 0 \tag{11.2.19}$$

has the general solution

$$C_1(1-z)^\alpha(1+z)^\beta + C_2(1-z)^\beta(1+z)^\alpha$$

where α and β are the two roots of the indicial equation at $z = \pm 1$

$$\rho^2 - \rho + \tfrac{1}{4}a = 0.$$

The roots coincide for $a = 1$ and here the solution is

$$(1 - z^2)^{1/2}\left(C_1 + C_2 \log \frac{1+z}{1-z}\right).$$

In the latter case, a real solution has at most one zero in $(-1, 1)$, and $C_1 = 1$, $C_2 = 0$ gives a solution without zeros in $(-1, 1)$. Hence the comparison equation

$$v'' + (1 - r^2)^{-2} v = 0$$

has the desirable properties and (11.2.18) is an admissible majorant.

Here it should be noted that this is in a way a best possible result since $C(1 - r^2)^{-2}$ is not admissible for any $C > 1$. Take $a = C = 1 + 4\gamma^2$, then the solution

$$(1 - z^2)^{1/2} \sin\left(\gamma \log \frac{1+z}{1-z}\right)$$

has infinitely many zeros in the interval $(-1, 1)$ for any $\gamma > 0$.

Next we take

$$M(r) = (3 - \alpha)(1 - r^2)^{-\alpha}, \qquad 1 \le \alpha \le 2. \tag{11.2.20}$$

Here we observe with Beesack that

$$M(r) \le g(r) \equiv (3 - \alpha)\frac{1 - (2 - \alpha)r^2}{(1 - r^2)^2}$$

since

$$1 - (2 - \alpha)r^2 < (1 - r^2)^{2-\alpha}, \qquad 0 < r < 1,$$

as is seen by expanding the right member in Taylor's series, the remainder after the first two terms being positive. Now

$$u'' + g(r)u = 0$$

has the solution $(1 - r^2)^{(3-\alpha)/2}$ without zeros in $(-1, 1)$. Hence

$$v'' + M(r)v = 0$$

has a solution with the same properties. Indeed, $M(r)$ is an even function of r and the solution with $v(0) = 1$, $v'(0) = 0$ is also even. If it had two zeros in $(-1, 1)$, say $-r_1$ and r_1, then by the comparison theorems $u(r) = (1 - r^2)^{(3-\alpha)/2}$ must have a zero in $(-r_1, r_1)$ which is absurd. It follows that (11.2.20) is also admissible.

The case $\alpha = 1$, i.e. $M(r) = 2(1 - r^2)^{-1}$ was announced by V. V. Pokarnyi in 1951. There are some results due to Nehari (1954) which may be reduced to this case:

Theorem 11.2.6. *Let $G(z)$ be holomorphic in $|z| < 1$ and belong to the Hardy-Lebesgue class $HL(U)$ with norm ≤ 1. Then no solution of* (11.1.1) *can have more than one zero in U.*

Proof. Here U denotes the unit disk, and $HL(U)$ is the class of functions $f(z)$ holomorphic in U such that

$$\|f\| = \sup_r \frac{1}{2\pi}\int_0^{2\pi} |f(r\,e^{i\theta})|\,d\theta < \infty. \tag{11.2.21}$$

This formula defines the norm of f. Suppose that

$$G(z) = \sum_{n=0}^{\infty} a_n z^n.$$

Cauchy's integral then gives

$$a_n r^n = \frac{1}{2\pi}\int_0^{2\pi} G(r\,e^{i\theta})\,e^{-ni\theta}\,d\theta,$$

the absolute value of which does not exceed 1 by assumption. Hence

$$|G(r\,e^{i\theta})| \leq (1 - r)^{-1} < 2(1 - r^2)^{-1}$$

which is an admissible majorant. ▌

It may be shown that

$$M(r) = 2^{3\alpha-2}\pi^{2(1-\alpha)}(1 - r^2)^{-\alpha}, \qquad 0 \leq \alpha \leq 1, \tag{11.2.22}$$

is also an admissible majorant, but here a suitable Sturmian majorant for $M(r)$ is harder to find, and we refer to Beesack's original article for the solution.

Theorem 11.2.5 admits of an important interpretation which should be mentioned here. Let $w_1(z)$ and $w_2(z)$ be two linearly independent solutions of (11.1.1) and form the quotient

$$f(z) = \frac{w_1(z)}{w_2(z)}. \tag{11.2.23}$$

This is a meromorphic function of z in any simply connected domain D in which $G(z)$ is holomorphic. Under the assumptions of Theorem 11.2.5, $f(z)$ is univalent in the unit disk, i.e.

$$f(z_1) \neq f(z_2) \quad \text{if} \quad z_1 \neq z_2, \quad |z_1| < 1, \quad |z_2| < 1. \tag{11.2.24}$$

For if $f(z)$ assumes the value C somewhere in $|z| < 1$, then

$$w_1(z) - Cw_2(z),$$

which is also a solution of (11.1.1), has a zero at such a point, and the theorem asserts that a solution can have at most one zero in the disk. Hence $f(z)$ is univalent. We shall return to the problem of univalency in Appendix D.

Theorem 11.2.5 gives results concerning univalency in the unit disk. Other regions may be studied by conformal mapping of the (simply-connected) domain in question on to the unit disk. The following, a special case of a result due to B. Schwarz (1955), is a sample of what can be attained by such means.

Theorem 11.2.7. *Let $G(z)$ be holomorphic in the right half-plane and suppose that*

$$|G(x + iy)| \leq \tfrac{1}{4}x^{-2}. \tag{11.2.25}$$

Then no solution of (11.1.1) *can have more than one zero in the right half-plane.*

Proof. The transformation

$$t = \frac{1 - z}{1 + z}, \qquad w(z) = (1 + t)^{-1}Y(t)$$

maps the right half-plane on to the unit disk in the t-plane and transforms the differential equation into

$$Y''(t) + 4(1 + t)^{-4}G\left(\frac{1 - t}{1 + t}\right)Y(t) = 0. \tag{11.2.26}$$

If $t = u + iv$, the absolute value of the coefficient of $Y(t)$ does not exceed

$$4\frac{1}{(1 + 2u + |t|^2)^2}\frac{1}{4}\frac{(1 + 2u + |t|^2)^2}{(1 - |t|^2)^2} = \frac{1}{(1 - |t|^2)^2},$$

so we are back to case (11.2.18). The coefficient $\frac{1}{4}$ in (11.2.25) is the best possible, as is shown by the Euler equation

$$w'' + az^{-2}w = 0 \tag{11.2.27}$$

which has real solutions with infinitely many real zeros as soon as $a > \frac{1}{4}$. ∎

The last result of this section is closely connected with Theorem 9.4.1, but has a much less stringent character than its prototype.

Theorem 11.2.8. *Let $G(z)$ be holomorphic in the sector S: $|\arg z| < \alpha < \pi$, let $G(x + iy)$ be integrable out to infinity for fixed y and satisfy*

$$\left|z\int_z^\infty G(t)\,dt\right| \leq \rho < \tfrac{1}{4}, \qquad z \in S, \tag{11.2.28}$$

where the path of integration is parallel to the positive real axis. Then (11.1.1) *has a solution without zeros in S.*

Proof. We note first that the path of integration in (11.2.28) can be replaced by any ray which lies in S and is not parallel to the boundary. This follows from the fact that

$$\lim_{z\to\infty} zG(z) = 0 \tag{11.2.29}$$

if the distance of z from the boundary of S becomes infinite, and this follows from an application of Cauchy's integral. For if

$$F(z) = \int_z^\infty G(t)\,dt, \qquad \text{then} \qquad G(z) = -\frac{1}{2\pi i}\int_\Gamma \frac{F(t)\,dt}{(t-z)^2}$$

where Γ is the circle $|t - z| = \frac{1}{2}\delta(z)$ and $\delta(z)$ is the distance from z to the boundary of S. Since $|F(t)| < \rho[|z| - \frac{1}{2}\delta(z)]^{-1} < 2|z|^{-1}$ on Γ, (11.2.29) is easily deduced.

To construct the desired solution we proceed as in the proof of Theorem 9.4.3. We consider the quadratic integral equation

$$u(z) = f(z) + z\int_z^\infty [u(t)]^2\frac{dt}{t^2}, \qquad f(z) = zF(z), \tag{11.2.30}$$

where, to start with, the path of integration is parallel to the positive real axis. We solve this equation by the method of successive approximations, setting

$$u_1(z) = f(z), \qquad u_n(z) = f(z) + z\int_z^\infty [u_{n-1}(t)]^2\frac{dt}{t^2}.$$

We have to prove that the approximations are uniformly bounded. Here we run into the integral

$$\int_z^\infty |t|^{-2}\,dt = \frac{\theta}{r\sin\theta}, \qquad z = r\,e^{i\theta}. \tag{11.2.31}$$

(See Exercise 7.4, Problem 1.) The factor $\theta(\sin\theta)^{-1}$ is positive and strictly increasing in $(0, \pi)$. It is bounded for $z \in S$. Normally we have to break up S into subsectors to prove the uniform boundedness of $|u_n(z)|$ in S. To this end, let ω be the unique positive root of

$$\frac{\theta}{\sin\theta} = \frac{1}{4\rho}. \tag{11.2.32}$$

If $\alpha \le \omega$, then the following argument applies to all of S; if not, let S_ω be the subsector where $|\arg z| \le \omega$. Let $z \in S_\omega$ and set $\sup|u_n(z)| = \rho_n$ for such values of z. Then $\rho_1 \le \rho$ and

$$\rho_n \le \rho + \frac{\omega}{\sin\omega}\rho_{n-1}^2 = \rho + \frac{1}{4\rho}\rho_{n-1}^2. \tag{11.2.33}$$

From this we see that $\rho_{n-1} < 2\rho$ implies $\rho_n < 2\rho$ and since $\rho_1 \le \rho < 2\rho$, the inequality holds for all n. Hence the sequence $\{u_n(z)\}$ is uniformly bounded in S_ω.

If S_ω does not exhaust S, then consider that part of the sector S where $\omega \le \arg z \le 2\omega$, and use $\arg(t - z) = \omega$ as line of integration in (11.2.30), in the approximations and in (11.2.31). In the latter formula, θ is replaced by $(\theta - \omega)$. This means that the estimates for $u_n(z)$ are unchanged. We still have $|u_n(z)| < 2\rho$ for all n. The same argument applies for $-\omega > \arg z > -2\omega$. If necessary, the argument is repeated for other subsectors until S is exhausted.

We now have a sequence of functions $\{u_n(z)\}$ holomorphic and uniformly bounded in S. We shall show that the sequence converges uniformly on the positive real axis and hence, by the Theorem of Vitali, uniformly on any interior sector. For the convergence proof, note that

$$u_n(x) - u_{n-1}(x) = x \int_x^\infty [u_{n-1}(s) - u_{n-2}(s)][u_{n-1}(s) + u_{n-2}(s)] \frac{ds}{s^2}$$

and here

$$|u_{n-1}(s)| + |u_{n-2}(s)| < 4\rho < 1.$$

Since

$$|u_2(s) - u_1(s)| < \rho^2,$$

complete induction gives

$$|u_n(s) - u_{n-1}(s)| < 4^{n-2}\rho^n$$

and uniform convergence of the sequence $\{u_n(z)\}$ on the real axis as asserted. This implies the existence of

$$\lim_{n\to\infty} u_n(z) \equiv u(z)$$

everywhere in S and the inequality

$$|u(z)| \le 2\rho, \qquad z \in S. \tag{11.2.34}$$

Next we set

$$y(z) = \frac{u(z)}{z}$$

and obtain

$$y(z) = \int_z^\infty G(t)\,dt + \int_z^\infty [y(t)]^2\,dt,$$

whence

$$y'(z) = -G(z) - [y(z)]^2.$$

Here we set

$$y(z) = \frac{w'(z)}{w(z)}$$

and get

$$w''(z) + G(z)w(z) = 0.$$

Thus

$$w(z) = \exp\left\{\int_1^z \frac{u(t)}{t}\,dt\right\} \tag{11.2.35}$$

is a solution of (11.1.1), clearly without zeros in S. ▌

One might think that, under the conditions of Theorem 11.2.8, all solutions have only a small number of zeros in S. This is not necessarily so, however, as shown by an example used by Beesack for a similar purpose. Take

$$w'' + e^{-2z}w = 0 \tag{11.2.36}$$

which is satisfied by any Bessel function of order zero in the variable e^{-z}. The sector S is a proper subset of the right half-plane, but actually $\alpha < \frac{1}{4}\pi$. Now we choose a solution of the equation with a large positive zero x_0. This implies infinitely many zeros $x_0 + 2k\pi i$, $k = 0, \pm 1, \pm 2, \cdots$ of this solution in the right half-plane. The larger x_0, the more zeros are in S. There is no solution with infinitely many zeros in S, but there is no finite upper bound for the number of zeros in S valid for all solutions.

By adding more conditions on $G(z)$ we can attain that 1 is a bound. We quote a theorem due to C. T. Taam (1955). We omit the proof.

Theorem 11.2.9. *Suppose that $G(z)$ is holomorphic in S: $|\arg z| < \frac{1}{4}\pi$ and $\Re[G(z)] \geq 0$ in S. If* (11.2.28) *holds with $\rho \leq \frac{1}{4}$, then no solution can have more than one zero in S.*

EXERCISE 11.2

1. Find $\mathbf{S}_1(0)$ if $G(z) = 3 - z^2$.
2. Find the largest disk with center at $z = 0$ in which $\tan z$ is univalent. Does Theorem 11.2.4 have a bearing on this problem?
3. Verify that $z(1 - z)^{-2}$ is univalent in the unit disk.
4. Given the Euler equation $w'' + az^{-2}w = 0$, show that the solutions have at most one zero in the right half-plane, iff a is interior to or on the cardioid
$$t = -\tfrac{1}{2}e^{i\varphi} - \tfrac{1}{4}e^{2i\varphi}.$$
5. Verify (11.2.14)–(11.2.16).
6. Verify the solution of (11.2.19) and find necessary and sufficient conditions on a in order that no solution shall have more than one zero in the unit disk.
7. Verify the statement concerning the solutions of (11.2.36) and exhibit a solution without zeros in the right half-plane.
8. If $G(z)$ is holomorphic in the strip $-\frac{1}{4}\pi < x < \frac{1}{4}\pi$, $z = x + iy$, and if $G(z) = \frac{1}{3}[1 + f(z)]$ with $|f(z)| \leq 1$, show that no solution has more than one zero in the strip. [*Hint:* Set $t = \tan z$ and reduce to (11.2.18).]

11.3 USE OF THE GREEN'S TRANSFORM

In this section we collect information concerning oscillation and non-oscillation obtainable by a systematic use of the Green's transform in its original form. This will include the construction of zero-free regions, special results for real solutions, structure and configuration of sets of zeros and extrema, discussion of singular points, etc.

The equation to be studied is

$$w''(z) + G(z)w(z) = 0 \tag{11.3.1}$$

with $G(z)$ holomorphic save for poles in the finite plane. The associated Green's transform is

$$[\overline{w(z)}w'(z)]_a^b - \int_a^b |w'(z)|^2 \, \overline{dz} + \int_a^b G(z)|w(z)|^2 \, dz = 0. \tag{11.3.2}$$

Here, to start with, a and b are non-singular points of the equation, and the path of integration C avoids singular points and is a rectifiable arc, which will be taken to be piecewise smooth. The solution $w(z)$ is defined by its initial values, $w(a)$ and $w'(a)$, at $z = a$. We refer to

$$\lambda \equiv \frac{w'(a)}{w(a)} \tag{11.3.3}$$

as the *initial parameter*. It can be any complex number or ∞. If $\lambda \neq 0, \infty$, then $\omega \equiv \arg \lambda$ can be defined, $0 \leq \omega < 2\pi$.

With a given solution $w(z)$ and a given admissible path C there are associated a vector and two vector fields. The vector is the zero vector if $\lambda = 0$ or ∞, otherwise it is the unit vector $e^{i\omega}$. The vector fields belong to the two integrals

$$\int_a^b |w'(z)|^2 \, \overline{dz} \qquad \text{and} \qquad -\int_a^b G(z)|w(z)|^2 \, dz.$$

By assumption C is piecewise smooth. In particular, C has a continuously turning tangent, except for a finite number of points. There is a semi-tangent in the direction of the oriented curve C at all points z, and we denote the slope angle of the semi-tangent by $\theta(z)$. The vector field belonging to the first integral is the set

$$\{\exp[-i\theta(z)] \mid z \in C\},$$

that of the second integral

$$\{\exp i[\arg G(z) - \pi + \theta(z)] \mid z \in C\}.$$

The union of these two fields with the vector $e^{i\omega}$ is the vector field of C with respect to $w(z)$.

Definition 11.3.1. *The path C is called a line of influence (abbreviated an* li) *of the solution $w(z)$ with respect to $z = a$, if an angle ϑ can be found such that*

i) $\vartheta < \omega < \vartheta + \pi$,
ii) $\vartheta < -\theta(z) < \vartheta + \pi, \ z \in C$,
iii) $\vartheta < \arg G(z) - \pi + \theta(z) < \vartheta + \pi, \ z \in C$.

If these conditions hold, the vector field of C is said to be definite. Condition (i) *is omitted if* $\lambda = 0$ *or* ∞.

In certain circumstances, we can replace "$<$" by "$\leq$" in the inequalities. We shall encounter such cases below. If these conditions hold, we still say that the vector field is definite.

Definition 11.3.2. *The totality of points b which are end-points of lines of influence of the solution* $w(z)$ *with respect to* $z = a$ *is called the domain of influence (abbreviated* **DI**) *of the solution* $w(z)$ *with reference to* $z = a$, *denoted by* **DI**(w, a).

Note that if C is an *li* and if $c \in C$, then the arc of C between $z = a$ and $z = c$ is not necessarily an *li* if we allow "$\leq$" instead of "$<$" in Definition 11.3.1.

We now invoke a classical principle: If a set of vectors $V_n = r_n\, e^{i\varphi_n}$ is such that $\vartheta < \varphi_n < \vartheta + \pi$ for all n and a fixed ϑ, then $\sum V_n \neq 0$. Since a definite integral is the limit of certain sums, the principle also extends to integrals of complex-valued functions. This principle leads to

Theorem 11.3.1. *The product* $w(z)w'(z) \neq 0$ *in* **DI**(w, a).

Proof. We have

$$\overline{w(b)}w'(b) = \overline{w(a)}w'(a) + \int_a^b |w'(z)|^2\, dz - \int_a^b G(z)|w(z)|^2\, dz. \qquad (11.3.4)$$

If $b \in$ **DI**(w, a), then there is an *li* leading from $z = a$ to $z = b$ and each of the three terms on the right will have an argument between ϑ and $\vartheta + \pi$ for some choice of ϑ, and hence the sum cannot be zero. ▌

We sometimes know the argument of $\lambda(a)$ all along a certain curve Γ. We then define

$$\mathbf{DI}(w, \Gamma) = \bigcup \mathbf{DI}(w, a), \qquad a \in \Gamma,$$

and we have $w(z)w'(z) \neq 0$ in **DI**(w, Γ). A case in point would be that of a solution which is real along a segment of the real axis where it has neither zeros nor extrema. In this case $\lambda(a)$ is real and keeps a constant sign along the segment.

It is seldom worth the trouble to try to determine the exact shape of a **DI**(w, a), but much information can be gathered even if we put rather severe restrictions on the curves used to build up the *li*'s. In the preceding sections we have considered only the case where C is a ray from $z = a$. The stars $\mathbf{S}_0(a)$ and $\mathbf{S}_1(a)$ are subsets of **DI**(w, a) for the case where $w(a)w'(a) = 0$, but, if $\lambda \neq 0, \infty$, only parts of these stars are likely to qualify.

It is often advantageous to use polygonal lines where the components are parallel to the axes. A simple example will illustrate the technique. Suppose that $G(z) = 3 - z^2$ and that $0 < x_0 < \sqrt{3}$, $0 < y_0$. Then the broken line $[0, x_0, x_0 + iy_0]$ is an *li* for the solutions with $w(0)w'(0) = 0$. The line segment $[0, x_0]$ is not an *li* since there $\theta(z) = 0$,

$$\arg G(z) + \theta(z) - \pi = -\pi,$$

so this portion of the vector field is indefinite. The vertical line segment contributes $-\frac{1}{2}\pi$ from the first integral and vectors in the third quadrant from the second. The resultant of the joint vector fields lies in the lower half-plane and is not zero. Thus the broken line has the stated property. This is also an example of a definite vector field where all vectors lie in $[-\pi, 0]$, both limits being represented. Other applications of this method will be found below.

Another set of curves suitable as lines of integration and linked to the differential equation in a natural manner is the so-called $\mathscr{G}$-net. We set

$$\mathscr{G}(z) = \int_{z_0}^{z} G(t)\, dt \equiv \mathscr{G}_1(z) + i\mathscr{G}_2(z). \tag{11.3.5}$$

The two families

$$\mathscr{G}_1(z) = C_1, \qquad \mathscr{G}_2(z) = C_2 \tag{11.3.6}$$

form the net. If z_1 is any point in the plane which is neither a zero nor a pole of $G(z)$, then there is one and only one curve of each family passing through $z = z_1$, and these curves intersect at right angles. If z_1 is a zero of $G(z)$ of order k, then there are $k + 1$ curves of each family passing through $z = z_1$. Curves of the two systems alternate and make equal angles with each other.

Poles lead to a more complicated picture. If $z = z_1$ is a simple pole with a real or purely imaginary residue, then the curves of one system form closed ovals around z_1, while those of the other pass through $z = z_1$ in such a manner that each straight line through z_1 is tangent to one and only one curve of the system. If the pole is of order $m > 1$, all curves of the net in some neighborhood of $z = z_1$ begin and end at this point. Each system has $2m - 2$ fixed tangents at $z = z_1$ which make equal angles with each other and bisect the angles between the tangents of the other system.

The advantage in using the $\mathscr{G}$-net in the construction of *li*'s lies in the fact that

$$\int_C G(z)|w(z)|^2\, dz$$

equals

$$\int_C |w(z)|^2\, d\mathscr{G}_1(z) \qquad \text{or} \qquad i\int_C |w(z)|^2\, d\mathscr{G}_2(t),$$

according as we integrate along $\mathscr{G}_2(z) = C_4$ or $\mathscr{G}_1(z) = C_3$. It is, of course, also necessary to take into account the variation of $\theta(z)$ along the path which affects the first integral. Here the condition $\max \theta(z) - \min \theta(z) \leq \pi$ is necessary but usually not sufficient. It is also necessary to keep in mind the singular points of the equation. These we neutralize by introducing a suitable system of cuts joining the singular points with each other or with the point of infinity.

A convenient way of standardizing the search for *li*'s is the following. A path starting at $z = a$ is a *standard path*, if

i) it does not encounter a cut except possibly at its end point;
ii) it is made up of a finite number of arcs taken from the two nets $x = C_1$, $y = C_2$ and $\mathcal{G}_1 = C_3$, $\mathcal{G}_2 = C_4$;
iii) along the path, one and the same of the following four pairs of inequalities is satisfied, namely

$$\text{(a)}\ \begin{matrix} dx \geq 0, \\ d\mathcal{G}_1 \leq 0; \end{matrix} \quad \text{(b)}\ \begin{matrix} dx \leq 0, \\ d\mathcal{G}_1 \geq 0; \end{matrix} \quad \text{(c)}\ \begin{matrix} dy \geq 0, \\ d\mathcal{G}_2 \geq 0; \end{matrix} \quad \text{(d)}\ \begin{matrix} dy \leq 0, \\ d\mathcal{G}_2 \leq 0. \end{matrix}$$

A standard path is an li for solutions with $w(a)w'(a) = 0$. This is seen from the equations

$$\Re[\overline{w(z)}w'(z)]_a^b - \int_a^b |w'(z)|^2\, dx + \int_a^b |w(z)|^2\, d\mathcal{G}_1(z) = 0, \qquad (11.3.7)$$

$$\Im[\overline{w(z)}w'(z)]_a^b + \int_a^b |w'(z)|^2\, dy + \int_a^b |w(z)|^2\, d\mathcal{G}_2(z) = 0. \qquad (11.3.8)$$

The anticlinals and indicatrices are also associated with the given differential equation and are possible lines of integration. Here

$$I(C) \equiv \int_C |w'(z)|^2\, \overline{dz} - \int_C G(z)|w(z)|^2\, dz \qquad (11.3.9)$$

becomes

$$I(C) = -i\int_C \{|w'(z)|^2 + |G(z)|\,|w(z)|^2\} \exp\left[\tfrac{1}{2}i \arg G(z)\right] ds, \quad (11.3.10)$$

if C is an anticlinal and s is arc length. If C is an indicatrix instead, the factor $-i$ is to be omitted and minus replaces plus in the last formula. An arc of the anticlinal from $z = a$ is an *li* if $w(a)w'(a) = 0$ provided

$$\max \arg G(z) - \min \arg G(z) < 2\pi$$

along the arc. If an arc of an indicatrix should happen to be rectilinear, it may possibly be used to pass from one anticlinal to another. Usually a horizontal line segment is preferable for such a passage but it is scarcely worth while formulating hard and fast rules in this connection.

So far we have assumed that the initial point $z = a$ is non-singular. The discussion may be extended, however, to singular points and subdominant solutions. We take first the case where the singular point, which we place at $z = 0$, is regular-singular. Suppose that

$$z^2G(z) = \sum_{k=0}^{\infty} c_k z^k \qquad (11.3.11)$$

and that the indicial equation

$$\rho(\rho - 1) + c_0 = 0 \tag{11.3.12}$$

has a root ρ_1 of real part $> \frac{1}{2}$ and let $w_1(z)$ be the corresponding solution. Then $\lim_{z \to 0} \overline{w(z)} w'(z) = 0$ and $|w'(z)|^2$ as well as $|z|^{-2}|w(z)|^2$ are integrable down to 0. It follows that formula (11.3.2) is valid for $w_1(z)$ with $a = 0$ and $w_1(z)w_1'(z) \neq 0$ in $\mathbf{DI}(w_1, 0)$, $z \neq 0$.

As an illustration we may take Bessel's equation in the form

$$z^2 w''(z) + (z^2 + \tfrac{1}{4} - a^2)w(z) = 0 \tag{11.3.13}$$

which is satisfied by $z^{1/2}J_a(z)$. We take a real, positive, and set $z = s\, e^{i\theta}$, $0 \leq s \leq r$, to obtain

$$e^{i\theta}\overline{w(b)}w'(b) = \int_0^r |w'(z)|^2\, ds - \int_0^r \left[e^{2i\theta} - \frac{a^2 - \frac{1}{4}}{s^2}\right] |w(z)|^2\, ds. \tag{11.3.14}$$

The imaginary part of the right member is

$$\sin 2\theta \int_0^r |w(z)|^2\, ds$$

which is 0 iff θ is a multiple of $\frac{1}{2}\pi$. If $a \geq \frac{1}{2}$, the real part is positive for $\theta = \frac{1}{2}\pi$, so that there are no purely imaginary zeros. The power series expansion shows that there can be no purely imaginary zeros so long as $a > -1$. To sum up, we have proved that $J_a(z)$ has only real zeros for $a > 0$ and no purely imaginary zeros for $a > -1$. Actually $J_a(z)$ has only real zeros for $a > -1$ as shown by Adolf Hurwitz (1859–1919) in 1889, one of the earliest results in complex oscillation theory.

We can also handle subdominant solutions at an irregular singular point. To fix the ideas, suppose that $G(z)$ is a polynomial

$$G(z) = a_0 z^n + a_1 z^{n-1} + \cdots + a_n \tag{11.3.15}$$

with real coefficients and $a_0 < 0$. Here the point at infinity is an irregular singular point, and Liouville's transformation as in Section 7.4 gives the asymptotic behavior of the solutions. There are $n + 2$ sectors of opening $2\pi/(n + 2)$ abutting on the point at infinity in each of which there is a subdominant solution which goes to 0 as

$$z^{-n/4} \exp\left\{-2\sqrt{-a_0}\, \frac{z^{(n+2)/2}}{n + 2}\, [1 + o(1)]\right\} \tag{11.3.16}$$

as $z \to \infty$ in the interior of the sector in question. If we let $z \to \infty$ in a direction parallel to the axis of the sector, then it is obvious that the Green's transform remains valid. In particular, for the sector about the positive real axis we have

$$\overline{w(z)}w'(z) = -\int_x^\infty |w'(s + iy)|^2 \, ds + \int_x^\infty [P(s, y) + iQ(s, y)]|w(s + iy)|^2 \, ds. \quad (11.3.17)$$

There will be a region "visible" from $+\infty$, symmetric to the real axis, in which $P(x, y) < 0$. There are also two regions, one on each side of the real axis and symmetric to the latter, in which $Q(x, y) \neq 0$. These three regions are zero-free with respect to the subdominant solution under consideration.

An example will make this clearer. We take

$$G(z) = a^2 - z^2, \qquad a > 0.$$

Here the four sectors are bounded by the singular indicatrix $Y(z) = 0$ of Problem 9, Exercise 11.1, the infinite branches of which make approximately 45° angles with the co-ordinate axes. We have

$$P(x, y) = a^2 - x^2 + y^2, \qquad Q(x, y) = -2xy.$$

We have $P(x, y) < 0$ to the right of the right branch of the hyperbola $x^2 - y^2 = a^2$ and also to the left of the left branch. The right half of this region is visible from $+\infty$. The imaginary part $Q(x, y)$ keeps a constant sign in each of the four quadrants and the first and the fourth quadrants are visible from $+\infty$. This means that this subdominant solution has no zeros in the right half-plane, with the possible exception of real zeros on the interval $[0, a)$. See formulas (7.5.48) and following for this equation (the Hermite-Weber equation).

We shall give some general applications of this method to differential equations in a domain where various limitations are imposed on the argument of $G(z)$. We start with equations which are real on a segment of the real axis.

Theorem 11.3.2. *Suppose that* (i) $G(z)$ *is holomorphic in a domain* D *such that if* $z_1 = x_1 + iy_1 \in D$, *then* $a < x_1 < b$ *and the line segment* $[x_1 - iy_1, x_1 + iy_1] \in D$, (ii) $G(z)$ *is real on the segment* (a, b) *of the real axis,* (iii) $P(x, y) \equiv \Re[G(z)] > 0$ *in* D, *and* (iv) $w(z)$ *is a non-trivial solution of* (11.3.1), *real on* (a, b). *Then* $w(z)w'(z)$ *has only real zeros in* D *if any.*

Proof. Suppose contrariwise that $z_1 = x_1 + iy_1$, $y_1 > 0$, is a zero of $w(z)w'(z)$ in D. Then $z_1 = x_1 - iy_1$ is also a zero and (11.3.2) gives, after simplification,

$$\int_{-y_1}^{y_1} |w'(x_1 + iy)|^2 \, dy + \int_{-y_1}^{y_1} [P(x_1, y) + iQ(x_1, y)]|w(x_1 + iy)|^2 \, dy = 0. \quad (11.3.18)$$

This is a contradiction since $P(x_1, y) > 0$. Since $G(x) = P(x, 0) > 0$, the equation may be oscillatory in (a, b). ▮

As an application consider Eq. (11.3.13), and suppose that a is real, $|a| > \frac{1}{2}$. Then the curve $P(x, y) = 0$ is the lemniscate

$$(x^2 + y^2)^2 - (a^2 - \tfrac{1}{4})(x^2 - y^2) = 0$$

which is confined to the strip $|x| \le (a^2 - \frac{1}{4})^{1/2}$. Here $P > 0$ outside of the lemniscate, and Theorem 11.3.2 shows that a solution of Bessel's equation, which is real on the positive real axis, has no complex zeros in the half-plane $x \ge (a^2 - \frac{1}{4})^{1/2}$.

Similarly, real solutions of the Hermite-Weber equation can have no complex zeros in the strip $-a \le x \le a$. This applies, in particular, to the subdominant solution considered above.

It is possible to obtain a criterion involving the function $Q(x, y)$, the imaginary part of $G(z)$. We can also generalize the whole approach. First some terminology. We say that a domain D in the plane is *vertically convex* if any vertical line which has a non-void intersection with D, intersects D in an open line segment. Similarly, D is *horizontally convex* if horizontal lines which do intersect D, intersect D in an open line segment. Inspection of the proof of Theorem 11.3.2 shows that the following result is valid:

Theorem 11.3.3. *Let $G(z)$ be holomorphic in a vertically convex domain D, let $P(x, y) = \Re[G(z)] > 0$ in D, and let $w(z)$ be a non-trivial solution of* (11.3.1). *Then no two zeros of $w(z)w'(z)$ can be on the same vertical line in D. The same result holds if $Q(x, y) = \Im[G(z)]$ keeps a constant sign in D.*

Proof. Use (11.3.18), replacing y_0 and $-y_0$ by the ordinates of two zeros assumed to be on $x = x_0$. A contradiction results. ▮

We shall give two more vertical line results.

Theorem 11.3.4. *Let $G(z)$ be holomorphic in a vertically convex domain D, symmetric to the real axis, on which $G(z)$ is supposed to be real. Let $Q(x, y)$ keep a constant sign in the upper half of D, the lower boundary of which is the interval (a, b) of the real axis. Let $w(z)$ be a non-trivial solution of* (11.3.1) *such that $w(x)w'(x)$ is real on (a, b) and keeps a constant sign, the same as that of $Q(x, y)$ above the axis. Then $w(z)w'(z)$ has no complex zeros in D.*

Proof. Since complex zeros come in conjugate pairs, there would be a zero $x_0 + iy_0$ in D with $y_0 > 0$, if the theorem were false. This would require the vanishing of

$$w(x_0)w'(x_0) - i\int_0^{y_0} |w'(x_0 + iy)|^2\,dy - i\int_0^{y_0} [P + iQ]|w(x_0 + iy)|^2\,dy$$

The hypotheses imply that the real part cannot vanish, hence the assumption that there are complex zeros leads to a contradiction. ▮

Consider now a vertically convex domain D, in which $G(z)$ is holomorphic and either $P(x, y) > 0$ or $Q(x, y)$ keeps a constant sign. Consider a nontrivial solution $w(z)$, and the set of zeros of $w(z)w'(z)$ in D. Theorem 11.3.3 permits us to order these zeros in a (finite or infinite) sequence according to increasing values of the abscissa.

Instead of using vertical lines in the discussion, we could have used horizontal lines. Thus we get an analogue of Theorem 11.3.3 in which "vertically convex," "$P(x, y) > 0$," and "vertical line" are replaced by "horizontally convex," "$P(x, y) < 0$" and "horizontal line," respectively. The resulting theorem will be referred to as Theorem 11.3.5 in the following. We can also obtain an analogue of Theorem 11.3.4 for solutions real on the imaginary axis. The formulation and proof of the theorem is left to the reader.

What is more important is that in a horizontally convex domain D, where either $P(x, y) < 0$ or $Q(x, y)$ keeps a constant sign, we can order the zeros of $w(z)w'(z)$ according to increasing ordinates. If D is convex and hence both horizontally and vertically convex and if $Q(x, y)$ keeps a constant sign in D, then we have two valid orderings of the zeros of $w(z)w'(z)$ in D, one according to increasing abscissas and one according to increasing ordinates. Are they consistent? The answer is that either the two orders agree or one is the reverse of the other. This follows from the following

Theorem 11.3.6. *Suppose that $G(z)$ is holomorphic in a convex domain D where $\vartheta_1 < \arg G(z) < \vartheta_2$ and $\vartheta_2 - \vartheta_1 \le \pi$. Let $z = a$ and $z = b$ be two zeros of $w(z)w'(z)$ in D. Then either $\arg(a - b)$ or $\arg(b - a)$ lies in the interval $(-\frac{1}{2}\vartheta_2, -\frac{1}{2}\vartheta_1)$.*

Proof. This follows from (11.1.23) where $z_0 = a$, $z = b$, $r = |b - a|$, $\theta = \arg(b - a)$. Then

$$e^{2i\theta} \int_0^r G(a + s\,e^{i\theta})|w(a + s\,e^{i\theta})|^2\,ds$$

is real positive. But the argument of this expression lies between $\vartheta_1 + 2\theta$ and $\vartheta_2 + 2\theta$ so we may assume that

$$\vartheta_1 + 2\theta < 0 < \vartheta_2 + 2\theta$$

whence the assertion follows. ▮

We can now compare the two orderings of the zeros of $w(z)w'(z)$ given above. If $Q(x, y) > 0$ in D, we have

$$\vartheta_1 = 0, \qquad \vartheta_2 = \pi, \qquad \text{and} \qquad -\tfrac{1}{2}\pi < \arg(b - a) < 0.$$

Suppose that the zeros in D have been ordered according to increasing abscissas and let

$$z_k = x_k + iy_k, \qquad z_{k+1} = x_{k+1} + iy_{k+1}$$

be "consecutive" zeros of $w(z)w'(z)$. Then

$$x_k < x_{k+1}, \qquad y_k > y_{k+1}, \tag{11.3.19}$$

by the inequality just proved. In this case, order by increasing ordinates is opposite to the order by increasing abscissas. Suppose instead that $Q(x, y) < 0$. Then $0 < \arg(b - a) < \frac{1}{2}\pi$ and

$$x_k < x_{k+1}, \qquad y_k < y_{k+1}, \tag{11.3.20}$$

so the two orders are consistent.

Our final result is a convexity theorem.

Theorem 11.3.7. *Let D be a convex domain in which $G(z)$ is holomorphic and $\neq 0$. Let $\vartheta_1 < \arg G(z) < \vartheta_2$ where $\vartheta_2 - \vartheta_1 < \pi$. Let no indicatrix have a point of inflection in D. Let $w(z)$ be a non-trivial solution of* (11.3.1) *having a finite number of zeros and extrema in D. Then these points form the vertices of a convex polygon.*

Proof. Without loss of generality we may assume $\vartheta_1 = 0$ so that $Q(x, y) > 0$. For if this is not so at the outset, we use a rotation, $z = \omega t$, $|\omega| = 1$, where $\arg \omega = -\frac{1}{2}\vartheta_1$. This takes (11.3.1) into

$$\frac{d^2w}{dt^2} + G^*(t)w = 0, \qquad G^*(t) = \omega^2 G(\omega t). \tag{11.3.21}$$

Here $Q^* = \Im[G^*] > 0$ and the image of D is convex. Since

$$\Im \int [G^*(t)]^{1/2}\, dt = \Im \int [G(\omega t)]^{1/2} \omega\, dt = \Im \int [G(z)]^{1/2}\, dz,$$

the property of being an indicatrix is invariant under rotation, and so is the property of a curve to be without points of inflection.

Suppose now that we have $Q(x, y) > 0$. Consider the indicatrix through the point $z = z_0 \in D$ and let $T(z_0)$ denote its tangent at z_0. The angle of inclination of $T(z_0)$ is $-\frac{1}{2}\arg G(z_0)$ and hence lies between $-\frac{1}{2}\pi$ and 0. Hence the indicatrices have negative slope in D. Since they have no points of inflection in D, they must form convex arcs and, by the analyticity of $G(z)$, they change continuously, so all arcs are curved the same way. We have two possibilities: the indicatrices are concave upwards or they are concave downwards. To fix the ideas, we assume the first alternative to hold. Thus all indicatrices lie above their tangents.

By assumption $w(z)w'(z)$ has only a finite number of zeros in D, say $z_1, z_2, \ldots, z_n$ where the numbering is such that (11.3.19) holds. Consider the

n tangents $T_j = T(z_j)$, $j = 1, \ldots, n$. It is claimed that all points z_k, $k \neq j$, lie above T_j. This follows from the discussion of the zero-free star $\mathbf{S}_0(z_j)$, given in Section 11.1. All the points of D below T_j belong to $\mathbf{S}_0(z_j)$ for this part of D is swept by a ray $\arg(z - z_j) = \theta$ where θ lies between $-\frac{1}{2}\arg G(z_j) - \pi$ and $-\frac{1}{2}\arg G(z_j)$. On such a ray we may proceed to the boundary of D, unless we should encounter a point where the ray is tangent to the local indicatrix. But the latter turns its concave side toward z_j; hence it is impossible to draw a tangent from $z = z_j$ to any such indicatrix. Thus all of D below T_j is zero-free.

Let us now draw the polygonal line Π joining $z_1, z_2, \ldots, z_n$. Consider the vertex z_j. The two adjacent vertices z_{j-1} and z_{j+1} are both above the tangent T_j, the first to the left, the second to the right of the vertical line through z_j. It follows that the angle at z_j above Π is $<180°$ and the angles of inclination of the consecutive sides increase from left to right. This shows that Π is a convex arc. ∎

The assumption that $w(z)w'(z)$ has only a finite number of zeros in D is obviously immaterial since we can exhaust D by convex sub-regions and pass to the limit. For a suitable enumeration of the zeros the line Π is still convex.

The line Π passes through the "consecutive" zeros and extrema of $w(z)$ in D. *It is natural to ask if zeros alternate with extrema. More generally, does the Theorem of Rolle have a complex analogue valid at least for solutions of second order linear differential equation?* This is an open question. In some cases the method of variation of parameters enables us to settle such questions. (See Section 11.6.)

EXERCISE 11.3

1. If z is fixed, $J_a(zt)$ as a function of t satisfies the differential equation $L_z(u)\colon (tu')' + (z^2t - a^2/t)u = 0$, where primes indicate differentiation with respect to t. Let $\bar{z}$ be the conjugate of z, let $v = J_a(\bar{z}t)$ and $a > -1$. Show the existence of
$$\int_0^1 [uL_{\bar{z}}(v) - vL_z(u)]\,dt$$
and use this to show that $J_a(z) \neq 0$ unless z is real or purely imaginary. The purely imaginary case was disposed of in the text.
2. A solution of Bessel's equation is supposed to be real on the positive imaginary axis where it has a single zero iy_0. Show that this is the only zero in the half-plane $y \geq y_0$.
3. Determine the $\mathcal{G}$-net if $G(z) = a^2 - z^2$, $a > 0$.
4. What is the nature of the $\mathcal{G}$-net in the neighborhood of a simple pole of $G(z)$ where the residue $a + bi$ satisfies $ab \neq 0$?

5. Formulate and prove the analogue of Theorem 11.3.4 for solutions real on the imaginary axis.
6. Consider the equation

$$[K(z)w'(z)]' + G(z)w(z) = 0$$

where G and K are real on the interval (a, b) of the real axis and $K > 0$. Let G and K be holomorphic in a vertically convex domain D contained in the strip $a < x < b$ and containing (a, b). Formulate and prove an analogue of Theorem 11.3.3.
7. Show that if $G(z) = -1/z$, then the indicatrices are parabolas having their focus at $z = 0$ and axis along the negative real axis. Show that Theorem 11.3.7 holds in the upper half-plane and also in the lower half-plane.
8. Suppose that $G(z) = z^{2k}$, k positive integer. Show that the plane can be subdivided in $2k + 2$ equal sectors in each of which Theorem 11.3.7 holds.
9. Generalize the Green's transforms to the B^*-algebra case.
10. Try to extend Theorem 11.3.2 to this case.

11.4 APPLICATIONS TO SPECIAL EQUATIONS

In the present section some results will be listed concerning oscillatory properties of solutions of special second order differential equations. The various equations considered in Chapter 7 are discussed from this point of view.

I. *The hypergeometric equation.* The equation

$$z(1 - z)y'' + [c - (a + b + 1)z]y' - aby = 0 \tag{11.4.1}$$

is not in a form suitable for our discussion and is replaced by the invariant form

$$w'' + \frac{1}{4}\left\{\frac{1 - \alpha_1^2}{z^2} + \frac{1 - \alpha_2^2}{(z - 1)^2} + \frac{\alpha_1^2 + \alpha_2^2 - \alpha_3^2 - 1}{z(z - 1)}\right\}w = 0. \tag{11.4.2}$$

Here

$$w(z) = z^\rho(1 - z)^\sigma y(z), \qquad \rho = \tfrac{1}{2}(1 - \alpha_1), \qquad \sigma = \tfrac{1}{2}(1 - \alpha_2),$$

$$a = \tfrac{1}{2}(1 - \alpha_1 - \alpha_2 + \alpha_3), \qquad b = \tfrac{1}{2}(1 - \alpha_1 - \alpha_2 - \alpha_3), \qquad c = 1 - \alpha_1. \tag{11.4.3}$$

If $c > 1$, i.e. $\alpha_1 < 0$, the discussion in Section 11.3 applies to $F(a, b, c; z)$ at the singular point $z = 0$. The results are not particularly impressive, however. We have, all parameters being real,

$$\Im\{e^{2i\theta}G(r\,e^{i\theta})\} = -\frac{1}{4}\frac{\sin\theta}{r(r^2 - 2r\cos\theta + 1)^2}(Ar^2 - 2Br\cos\theta + C) \tag{11.4.4}$$

where

$$A = \alpha_1^2 - \alpha_2^2 - \alpha_3^2 + 1, \qquad B = \alpha_1^2 - \alpha_3^2, \qquad C = \alpha_1^2 + \alpha_2^2 - \alpha_3^2 - 1.$$

The curve

$$A(x^2 + y^2) - 2Bx + C = 0$$

is a circle through $z = 1$ unless $A = 0$, when it is a vertical straight line. Since $B^2 - AC = (1 - \alpha_2^2)^2 \geq 0$, the circle may degenerate into the point $z = 1$, but it is never imaginary.

Formula (11.4.4) shows that the zero-free star $\mathbf{S}_0(0)$ contains all rays which can be drawn from the origin, distinct from the real axis, and not encountering the circle just mentioned. There are two cases. (i) The origin is outside the circle. Then $\mathbf{S}_0(0)$ contains all non-real points which are not inside the circle or in its "shadow." (ii) The origin is inside the circle. Then $\mathbf{S}_0(0)$ contains all non-real points inside the circle. In the transition case, where the circle passes through the origin, we get the left half-plane less the real axis. In the exceptional case $A = 0$, we get the half-plane bounded by $2Bx = C$ which contains the origin, again excepting the points on the real axis. These results are due to A. Hurwitz (1907) who used a related method.

If the coefficients in (11.4.2) are positive, i.e.

$$1 - \alpha_1^2 > 0, \qquad 1 - \alpha_2^2 > 0, \qquad \alpha_1^2 + \alpha_2^2 - \alpha_3^2 - 1 > 0,$$

then the non-real points in a certain left half-plane $x \leq x_0 < 0$ cannot be zeros or extrema of $F(a, b, c; z)$. Here x_0 is the abscissa of the left vertical double tangent of the curve $P(x, y) = 0$, a sextic with nodes at $z = 0$ and $z = 1$. This follows from Theorem 11.3.2 since in this half-plane $\Re[G(z)] = P(x, y) > 0$ and $F(a, b, c; x)$ is real for $x < 1$.

II. *Legendre's equation.* Here we get more satisfactory results, at least for the solution

$$P_a(z) = F(a + 1, -a, 1, \tfrac{1}{2}(1 - z)), \tag{11.4.5}$$

assuming a real or $a = -\frac{1}{2} + \mu i$. (Cf. Problems 5, 6, Exercise 11.1.) For $w(z) = P_a(z)$ we have

$$(1 - z^2)\overline{w(z)}w'(z) = \int_1^z (1 - t^2)|w'(t)|^2 \, \overline{dt}$$

$$- a(a + 1) \int_1^z |w(t)|^2 \, dt.$$

Here we set $t = 1 + s\, e^{i\theta}$, $z = 1 + r\, e^{i\theta}$, and divide both sides by $e^{i\theta}$ to obtain

$$-r(2 + r\, e^{i\theta})\overline{w}(1 + r\, e^{i\theta})w'(1 + r\, e^{i\theta})$$

$$= -\int_0^r s(2\, e^{-i\theta} + s)|w'(1 + s\, e^{i\theta})|^2 \, ds - a(a + 1) \int_0^r |w(1 + s\, e^{i\theta})|^2 \, ds.$$

The imaginary part of the right member is

$$2 \sin \theta \int_0^r s|w'(\cdots)|^2\, ds$$

which is 0 iff $\theta \equiv 0 \pmod{\pi}$. This says that $P_a(z)$ has no complex zeros in the plane cut along the real axis from $-\infty$ to -1. The real part is

$$-\int_0^r s(2\cos\theta + s)|w'(\cdots)|^2\, ds - a(a+1)\int_0^r |w(\cdots)|^2\, ds.$$

If $\theta = 0$ and $a \geq 0$, this expression cannot be 0, i.e. $P_a(x)P_a'(x) \neq 0$ for $x \geq +1$ if $a \geq 0$. If $\theta = \pi$ and either $-\frac{1}{2} \leq a \leq 0$ or $a = -\frac{1}{2} + i\mu$, then $P_a(x)P_a'(x) \neq 0$ in $(-1, 1)$.

We now turn to the second important solution

$$Q_a(z) = \frac{\Gamma(\frac{1}{2})\Gamma(1+a)}{\Gamma(a+\frac{3}{2})}(2z)^{-1-a}F(\tfrac{1}{2}a + \tfrac{1}{2}, \tfrac{1}{2}a + 1, a + \tfrac{3}{2}; z^{-2}) \tag{11.4.6}$$

and assume a real and $> -\frac{1}{2}$. If this is the case, we can use the Green's transform integrating along a ray $\arg t = \arg z$ out to infinity. For $Q_a(r\, e^{i\theta}) \in L_2(2, \infty)$, so does $rQ_a'(r\, e^{i\theta})$ and $(1 - z^2)\overline{Q_a(z)}Q_a'(z) \to 0$ as $z \to \infty$ uniformly in $|\arg z| \leq \pi$. Hence we have

$$\begin{aligned} -(1 - r^2\, e^{2i\theta})\, e^{-i\theta}\overline{Q_a}(r\, e^{i\theta})Q_a'(r\, e^{i\theta}) \qquad (11.4.7) \\ = \int_r^\infty (e^{-2i\theta} - s^2)|Q_a'(s\, e^{i\theta})|^2\, ds - a(a+1)\int_r^\infty |Q_a(s\, e^{i\theta})|^2\, ds. \end{aligned}$$

The imaginary part of the right member is

$$-2\sin 2\theta \int_r^\infty |Q_a'(\cdots)|^2\, ds$$

and this is 0 iff θ is a multiple of $\frac{1}{2}\pi$. Now, if $\theta = 0$, we must take $r > 1$ and the real part is

$$\int_r^\infty (1 - s^2)|Q_a'(\cdots)|^2\, ds - a(a+1)\int_r^\infty |Q_a(\cdots)|^2\, ds < 0$$

if $a \geq 0$. Since the coefficients of the series (11.4.6) are >0 for $-\frac{1}{2} < a < 0$, we see that $Q_a(z)$ can have no real zeros >1 or <-1 for $-\frac{1}{2} < a$. Likewise there are no purely imaginary zeros at least for $a \geq 0$ as is seen by setting $\theta = \frac{1}{2}\pi$ and taking the real part of (11.4.7). Thus $Q_a(z)$ has no zeros, real or complex, in the plane cut along the segment $[-1, +1]$ of the real axis. With these remarks we leave Legendre's equation.

III. *Bessel's equation.* Various results concerning this equation are scattered in the preceding section. Here we shall collect information already obtained and fill out the picture in some directions. We take the equation

$$w''(z) + \left(1 - \frac{a^2 - \frac{1}{4}}{z^2}\right)w(z) = 0, \tag{11.4.8}$$

satisfied by $z^{1/2}J_a(z)$, and assume a real ≥ 0. We have seen that $J_a(z)$ has no complex zeros for $a > -1$. On the other hand, there are infinitely many real positive zeros which are distributed in a very regular manner. If $x_n(a)$ is the nth positive zero of $J_a(z)$, we recall that

$$x_{n+1}(a) - x_n(a) < x_{n+2}(a) - x_{n+1}(a) < \pi$$

for $a < \frac{1}{2}$. See Theorem 8.1.7 and applications there given. For $\frac{1}{2} < a$, the inequalities are reversed. In either case

$$\lim_{n\to\infty} [x_{n+1}(a) - x_n(a)] = \pi.$$

Consider next $H_a^{(1)}(z)$, the Hankel-Bessel function which goes exponentially to 0 along the positive imaginary axis. Here the analogue of (11.3.17) applies with the difference that we integrate along vertical lines rather than horizontal. We get

$$\overline{w(z)}w'(z) = i\int_y^\infty |w'(x + it)|^2\,dt$$
$$+ i\int_y^\infty [P(x, t) + iQ(x, t)]|w(x + it)|^2\,dt$$

where

$$w(z) = z^{1/2}H_a^{(1)}(z), \qquad P(x, y) = 1 - (a^2 - \tfrac{1}{4})\frac{x^2 - y^2}{(x^2 + y^2)^2},$$
$$Q(x, y) = (a^2 - \tfrac{1}{4})\frac{2xy}{(x^2 + y^2)^2}.$$

This shows that there can be no zeros in the upper half-plane including the axes. If $a > \frac{1}{2}$, set

$$a^2 - \tfrac{1}{4} \equiv b^2, \qquad b > 0.$$

Then $P(x, y) > 0$ for $|x| \geq b$, so there are no zeros in the half-planes $|x| \geq b$. These results complete those of Section 7.4, where it was shown that $H_a^{(1)}(z) \neq 0$ in that part of the sector

$$-\pi \leq \arg z \leq 2\pi$$

whose distance from the boundary exceeds $b^2\pi/(\log 2)$.

Now consider an arbitrary solution $w(z)$ which we specify by its initial parameter at some point x_0 on the positive real axis. The choice of x_0 is governed by the geometry of the curve $P(x, y) = 0$ which is a lemniscate. The right vertical tangent of this curve is taken as $x = x_0$. This gives

$$x_0 = b \text{ if } a > \tfrac{1}{2}, \qquad x_0 = \tfrac{1}{4}\sqrt{2}\,|b| \text{ if } 0 \leq a \leq \tfrac{1}{2}.$$

Set

$$\lambda(x_0) = \frac{w'(x_0)}{w(x_0)}, \qquad \arg \lambda(x_0) = \omega, \qquad -\pi < \omega \leq +\pi. \qquad (11.4.9)$$

Consider the polygonal line with vertices at x_0, x_1, $x_1 + iy_1$, $x_0 \le x_1$, and where $y_1 > 0$ if $-\pi < \omega \le 0$, otherwise $y_1 < 0$. A simple discussion of the vector fields involved shows that this path is an *li* with respect to the solution $w(z)$ determined by (11.4.9) up to an arbitrary constant multiplier. Thus in the first case $w(z)w'(z) \neq 0$ in the sector $x_0 \le x$, $0 < y$, while in the second case $x_0 \le x$, $y < 0$ is zero-free. If $\omega = 0$ or π, there are no complex zeros in the half-plane $x_0 \le x$.

If $w(z)$ is not a constant multiple of either $z^{1/2}H_a^{(1)}(z)$ or $z^{1/2}H_a^{(2)}(z)$, then $w(z)$ must have infinitely many zeros in the right half-plane. The discussion in Section 7.4 shows the existence of a z_0 such that

$$z_n - z_0 - n\pi \to 0 \qquad \text{as} \quad n \to \infty.$$

If $-\pi < \omega < 0$, it was just found that such a set of zeros cannot be located in the first quadrant. Hence they must lie in the fourth quadrant. If $a > \frac{1}{2}$, then $Q(x, y) < 0$ in the fourth quadrant and if $z_n = x_n + iy_n$

$$x_n < x_{n+1}, \qquad y_n < y_{n+1}$$

where y_n increases to a negative limit while $x_{n+1} - x_n \to \pi$. If $0 \le a < \frac{1}{2}$, we have $Q(x, y) > 0$ instead and

$$y_n > y_{n+1}$$

so that y_n decreases to a negative limit.

If we assume instead that $0 < \omega < \pi$, then the roles of the two quadrants are interchanged: there are infinitely many zeros in the first quadrant and at most a finite number in the fourth. Similarly

$$\Im[\lambda(-x_0)] < 0 \qquad \text{implies no zeros in} \quad x \le -x_0, \quad 0 < y,$$

$$\Im[\lambda(-x_0)] > 0 \qquad \text{implies no zeros in} \quad x \le -x_0, \quad y < 0.$$

It should be noted, however, that if the solution $w(z)$ is defined by the initial parameter $\lambda(x_0)$, then the value of $\lambda(-x_0)$ will depend upon the path described by z in going from x_0 to $-x_0$. In particular, if $\lambda(x_0)$ is real, then the values obtained for $\lambda(-x_0)$, after describing a semicircle in the upper half-plane or in the lower half-plane, will be conjugate imaginary. Hence one of the continuations of $w(z)$ has infinitely many zeros in the upper and the other in the lower half-plane, in the second or third quadrants, respectively.

IV. *The Hermite-Weber equation.* Consider

$$w'' + (a^2 - z^2)w = 0, \qquad 0 < a. \tag{11.4.10}$$

The solutions of this equation which are most important are those for which $w(z)w'(z)$ either vanishes at $z = 0$ or tends exponentially to 0 as $z \to \infty$ along one of the axes. These conditions in general determine six distinct solutions up to constant multipliers, but for special values of a the number may reduce to four. This happens when a^2 is an odd integer and leads to the solution of the singular boundary value problem: Find for what values of a the Eq. (11.4.10) has a non-trivial solution in $L_2(-\infty, +\infty)$. Such a solution exists if $a^2 = 2n + 1$, it goes exponentially to 0 at both ends of the real axis and it is even or odd as a function of z according as n is even or odd.

We return to the general case and assume that $w(0)w'(0) = 0$. If $w(0) = 0$, $w(z)$ is odd, if $w'(0) = 0$, $w(z)$ is even. By constructing the zero-free star at $z = 0$, we see that $w(z)w'(z) \neq 0$ for non-real values of z between the two branches of the hyperbola

$$x^2 - y^2 = \tfrac{1}{2}a^2. \tag{11.4.11}$$

Next we note that for any solution which is real on the real axis the product $w(z)w'(z)$ can vanish at most once on the interval $(a, +\infty)$. In particular, this holds for the even and the odd solutions. Suppose that a real valued solution $w(z)$ is such that $w(z)w'(z) = 0$ for $z = b \geq a$. Setting $t = b + s\,e^{i\theta}$, $z = b + r\,e^{i\theta}$, we get

$$\overline{w(z)}w'(z)\,e^{i\theta} = \int_0^r |w'(\cdots)|^2\,ds$$
$$+ \int_0^r [(b^2 - a^2)\,e^{2i\theta} + 2bs\,e^{3i\theta} + s^2\,e^{4i\theta}]|w(\cdots)|^2\,ds \tag{11.4.12}$$

the imaginary part of which is positive for $0 < \theta \leq \frac{1}{4}\pi$. Hence there are no zeros of $w(z)w'(z)$ in the sector $|\arg(z - b)| \leq \frac{1}{4}\pi$. In addition we can show that $w(z)w'(z) \neq 0$ in the strip

$$-a \leq x \leq b$$

except for real zeros. Here the strip $-a \leq x \leq a$ is excluded by Theorem 11.3.2 since $P(x, y) > 0$ and the solution is real on the real axis. The rest of the strip is excluded because the broken line with vertices at b, x_0, $x_0 + iy_0$, $a \leq x_0 \leq b$, $0 < y_0$, is an *li* for the solution under consideration.

If $w(x)w'(x) \neq 0$ for $a \leq x$, then we can replace b by a in this discussion. This would introduce an additional term $w(a)w'(a)\,e^{i\theta}$ in the right member of (11.4.12). If $w(z)$ is not a constant multiple of the subdominant solution in the sector $|\arg z| \leq \frac{1}{4}\pi$, we have $w(a)w'(a) > 0$ so the additional term has positive imaginary part for $0 < \theta \leq \frac{1}{4}\pi$. Hence $w(z)w'(z) \neq 0$ in the sector $|\arg(z - a)| \leq \frac{1}{4}\pi$, if $w(x)w'(x) \neq 0$ in $[a, \infty)$. As shown by (11.3.17), this holds also for the subdominant solution.

Summing up, we see that the even and the odd solutions of (11.4.10) have all their complex zeros and extrema confined to the two unbounded domains bounded by the hyperbola (11.4.11) and the four rays

$$z = \pm(b + r\,e^{\pm\pi i/4})$$

from which we can exclude the strip

$$-b \leq x \leq b.$$

This is in agreement with the results that may be read off from the discussion in Sections 7.4 and 7.5, according to which the zeros are asymptotically of the form

$$\pm(2k\pi i + C)^{1/2}$$

for large values of $|k|$. Since $Q(x, y) = -2xy$ keeps a constant sign in each quadrant, the corresponding four strings of zeros and extrema form monotone ultimately convex point-sets, as indicated by Theorem 11.3.7.

The subdominant solution for the sector $|\arg z| < \frac{1}{4}\pi$ was discussed in Section 11.3 where it was found that the only zeros and extrema in the closed right half-plane are located in the segment $[0, a)$ of the real axis. Similar results hold for the other three subdominants corresponding to the sectors

$$\tfrac{1}{4}\pi < \arg z < \tfrac{3}{4}\pi, \qquad \tfrac{3}{4}\pi < \arg z < \tfrac{5}{4}\pi, \qquad \tfrac{5}{4}\pi < \arg z < \tfrac{7}{4}\pi.$$

Here $w(z)w'(z) \neq 0$ in the upper half-plane, the left half-plane excepting $(-a, 0]$, and the lower half-plane, respectively.

In particular, if the subdominant for the sector $|\arg z| < \frac{1}{4}\pi$ is also even or odd, i.e. if $a^2 = 2n + 1$, then it also becomes subdominant in the opposite sector and all its zeros and extrema are confined to the real interval $(-a, a)$. The subdominant in question is

$$\exp(-\tfrac{1}{2}z^2)H_n(z)$$

where $H_n(z)$ is the nth Hermite polynomial. This function has n zeros and $n + 1$ extrema in the interval $(-a, a)$. Thus all the complex zeros have disappeared.

The mechanism governing the motions of the zeros and extrema for varying a is of some interest. To fix the ideas, consider the even solution $E(z, a)$ normalized so that $E(0, a) \equiv 1$, $E'(0, a) \equiv 0$. The zeros and extrema of this function are analytic functions of a. Here we restrict ourselves to real variables where the main properties can be obtained by the classical method of Sturm. The differential equation gives

$$E(x, a)E'_x(x, c) - E(x, c)E'_x(x, a)$$
$$= (a^2 - c^2)\int_0^x E(s, a)E(s, c)\,ds.$$

Let $x = x_0 = x_0(a)$ be chosen as a positive zero of $E(x, a)$. Then for small values of $|c - a|$

$$E(x_0, c) = E(x_0, a) + (c - a)E'_a(x_0, a) + o(|c - a|)$$

and, differentiating with respect to a,

$$E'_x(x_0, a)x'_0(a) + E'_a(x_0, a) = 0.$$

Hence

$$E(x_0, c) = -(c - a)E'_x(x_0, a)x'_0(a) + o(|c - a|)$$

and finally

$$[E_x'(x_0, a)]^2 x_0'(a) = -2a \int_0^{x_0} [E(s, a)]^2 \, ds. \tag{11.4.13}$$

It follows that

$$x_0'(a) < 0. \tag{11.4.14}$$

If $x_0(a) < 0$, we have $x_0'(a) > 0$ instead. Thus the zeros of $E(x, a)$ move toward the origin for increasing values of a.

In a similar manner one shows that if $x = \xi = \xi(a)$ is a real extremum of $E(x, a)$, then

$$(\xi^2 - a^2)[E(\xi, a)]^2 \xi'(a) = 2a \int_0^{\xi} [E(s, a)]^2 \, ds. \tag{11.4.15}$$

This shows that the real extrema move away from the points $x = \pm a$ toward the origin or toward infinity according as $|\xi(a)| < a$ or $> a$.

These relations give the key to the mechanism which governs the exchange of zeros and extrema between the real axis and the complex plane. Consider real values of a and start with $a = 0$. $E(z, 0)$ is a Bessel function

$$E(z, 0) = (\tfrac{1}{4}i)^{1/4}\Gamma(\tfrac{3}{4})z^{1/2}J_{-1/4}(\tfrac{1}{2}iz^2)$$

having a triple extremum at $z = 0$ and no real zeros. The complex zeros and extrema are located on the lines $y = \pm x$. The configuration is symmetric with respect to the origin. Further, zeros and extremas alternate on the lines with zeros nearest the origin. For small positive values of a the triple extremum is dissolved into three real distinct extrema: one stays at the origin for all a, one $\xi_+(a) > a$, and one $\xi_-(a) < -a$. As a increases to 1, the two movable extrema recede to $\pm\infty$ and simultaneously the complex zeros and extrema move off to infinity, since there can be no complex zeros of $E(z, a)E'(z, a)$ in the strip $|x| \le \xi_+(a)$. In moving, the complex zeros and extrema preserve their mutual order, i.e. if they are ordered according to increasing abscissas in the first quadrant, then this is also an ordering by increasing ordinates. If zeros are denoted by Z and extrema by E, then the pattern is $Z - E - Z -$, etc., and is symmetric in the other quadrants. We have $E(z, 1) = \exp(-\tfrac{1}{2}z^2)$.

When a passes $+1$ two real zeros appear, one at $+\infty$ and the other at $-\infty$, and for increasing values of a they approach and pass $\pm a$. These zeros then stay in $(-a, a)$ for all a. The net result of this operation is the loss of four complex zeros and the gain of two real zeros. The strings of zeros and extrema are reconstituted and in the first quadrant the pattern is $E - Z - E -$, etc. That zeros and extrema still alternate can be seen by letting a describe a small semi-circle above the point 1 in the a-plane, instead of pushing through the singular point $a = 1$. There is a critical value a_1, $1 < a_1 < \sqrt{5}$ for which the extrema nearest to the real axis coalesce on the axis, one pair at $z = a_1$, the other at $z = -a_1$. For $a > a_1$, these real double extrema separate; two get inside the interval $(-a, a)$ and stay there, the others move to $\pm\infty$ as $a \to \sqrt{5}$. The net result of this exchange is the loss of four complex extrema and the gain of two real ones. We have

$$E(z, \sqrt{5}) = [H_2(0)]^{-1}H_2(z) \exp(-\tfrac{1}{2}z^2).$$

The complex zeros and extrema reappear when a passes $\sqrt{5}$, the order in the first quadrant being $E - Z - E -$, etc. (order with respect to increasing abscissas and ordinates), two real zeros are fed into the real axis, and the process is repeated. Similar considerations apply to the subdominant solutions, but we desist from further details.

V. *Titchmarsh's equation.* We give this name to

$$w''(z) + (\lambda - z^{2n})w(z) = 0 \tag{11.4.16}$$

where $n > 1$ is a positive integer. Titchmarsh studied the corresponding singular boundary value problem: Find the values of λ for which the equation has a non-trivial solution in $L_2(-\infty, \infty)$. He showed that the corresponding characteristic functions are either even or odd, as well as being subdominant at both ends of the real axis. He also raised the question of the distribution of the zeros of these functions. For $n = 2$ he conjectured that the zeros are real or purely imaginary but could not settle the question completely. Here we shall prove Titchmarsh's conjecture.

Let $\{T_m(z)\} = \{T(z, \lambda_m)\}$ be the set of Titchmarsh functions, i.e. solutions of

$$w''(z) + (\lambda - z^4)w(z) = 0, \qquad \lambda = \lambda_m > 0, \tag{11.4.17}$$

where

$$T_m(\cdot) \in L_2(-\infty, \infty), \qquad T_m(-z) = \pm T_m(z).$$

For a general value of λ there are six subdominant solutions, corresponding to the sectors S_1 to S_6, where

$$S_j\colon \tfrac{1}{6}(2j - 3)\pi < \arg z < \tfrac{1}{6}(2j - 1)\pi.$$

The subdominant in S_1 goes to zero as

$$z^{-1} \exp(-\tfrac{1}{3}z^3) \quad \text{as} \quad z \to \infty$$

in the sector.

With our usual notation

$$P(x, y) = \lambda - x^4 + 6x^2y^2 - y^4, \qquad Q(x, y) = -4xy(x^2 - y^2).$$

Since $Q(x, y)$ keeps a constant sign in each of the octants determined by the co-ordinate axes and the lines $y = \pm x$, formula (11.3.17) applies and shows that, if $w(z)$ is the subdominant solution in S_1, then $w(z)w'(z) \neq 0$ in the sector $|\arg z| \leq \tfrac{1}{4}\pi$ except possibly for points on the interval $[0, \lambda^{1/4})$. On the segment $(\lambda^{1/4}, +\infty)$ we have $P(x, y) < 0$, so this interval is zero-free.

If $\lambda = \lambda_m$ and $w(z) = T_m(z)$, this result implies that the only zeros and extrema in the double sector $|\arg(\pm z)| \le \frac{1}{4}\pi$ are on the real axis between $-\lambda^{1/4}$ and $\lambda^{1/4}$. The function $T_m(z)$ is real on the real axis. This excludes complex zeros and extrema in the domain

$$|x| \le \lambda^{1/4}, \qquad P(x, y) > 0.$$

The curve $P(x, y) = 0$, i.e.

$$x^4 - 6x^2y^2 + y^4 = \lambda \quad (>0),$$

is a quartic symmetric with respect to the axes and to the lines $y = \pm x$. It consists of four separate branches with asymptotes bisecting the octants mentioned above. In particular, there is a branch passing through the point $z = i\lambda^{1/4}$. This branch bounds a horizontally convex domain in which $P(x, y) < 0$. Since $T_m(iy)$ is either real or purely imaginary, Theorem 11.3.5 applies and shows that $T_m(z)$ has neither zeros nor extrema in the two regions surrounding the imaginary axis where $P(x, y) < 0$, except possibly for points on the axis.

The remaining parts of the plane we can reach by forming the zero-free star at $z = 0$. Note that $T_m(0)T_m'(0) = 0$. This means using the identity

$$\overline{w(z)}w'(z)\, e^{i\theta} = \int_0^r |w'(\cdot)|^2\, ds$$

$$- \int_0^r [\lambda\, e^{2i\theta} - s^4\, e^{6i\theta}]|w(\cdot)|^2\, ds.$$

Here the problem is to decide when the second term on the right has a positive real part. Now

$$-\Re[\lambda z^2 - z^6] = (y^2 - x^2)[\lambda - x^4 + 14x^2y^2 - y^4]$$

and, if $y^2 > x^2$, the right member exceeds

$$(y^2 - x^2)[\lambda - x^4 + 6x^2y^2 - y^4] = (y^2 - x^2)P(x, y).$$

This shows that the real part is positive for any z in that part of the plane where $y^2 \ge x^2$ and $P(x, y) \ge 0$. This more than covers the parts of the plane where we previously lacked information.

This proves Titchmarsh's conjecture and shows that the functions $T_m(z)$ have all their zeros and extrema on the intervals $(-\lambda^{1/4}, \lambda^{1/4})$, $(\lambda^{1/4}i, \infty i)$, and $(-\infty i, -\lambda^{1/4}i)$ on the axes. Each function $T_m(z)$ is an entire function for which the value 0 is taken on with less than normal frequency. Of the six strings of zeros normally possessed by a solution of (11.4.16), only two are left. Here 0 is the only defective value of $T_m(z)$ and, in the terminology due to R. Nevanlinna, we would say that $w = 0$ has the *defect* $\frac{2}{3}$. For the solutions of the Hermite-Weber equation ($n = 1$) satisfying the singular boundary value problem, the defect of $w = 0$ is 1. For the case of Eq. (11.4.16) with $n > 1$, the defect of $w = 0$ is $2/(n + 1)$ for the singular solutions.

The method used above applies in principle also to the case $n > 2$, but the situation becomes increasingly more complicated and the results correspondingly more meagre. For the Titchmarsh functions of order 3 it may be proved that the complex zeros and extrema form four strings, one in each quadrant. The one in the first quadrant is located in the sector $\frac{5}{16}\pi < \arg z < \frac{3}{8}\pi$.

VI. *The confluent hypergeometric equation.* We recall that the Bessel and the Hermite-Weber equations are reducible to the confluent hypergeometric form. Here we shall consider the function

$$ {}_1F_1(a, c; z) = \sum_{n=0}^{\infty} \frac{a(a+1)\cdots(a+n-1)}{n!c(c+1)\cdots(c+n-1)} z^n \tag{11.4.18} $$

which satisfies the equation

$$ zw'' + (c - z)w' - aw = 0. \tag{11.4.19} $$

The substitution

$$ w = z^{-c/2} e^{z/2} u $$

leads to the equation

$$ u'' - \left\{\frac{1}{4} - \frac{c - 2a}{2z} + \frac{c^2 - 2c}{4z^2}\right\} u = 0 \tag{11.4.20} $$

which is equivalent to the Whittaker equation

$$ U'' - \left\{\frac{1}{4} - \frac{k}{z} + \frac{m^2 - \frac{1}{4}}{z^2}\right\} U = 0. \tag{11.4.21} $$

We shall consider only the solution

$$ z^{c/2} e^{-z/2} {}_1F_1(a, c; z) \equiv u(z) $$

of (11.4.20). We assume a and c to be real positive.

This implies that $u(z)$ can have neither positive zeros not extrema. If $c > 1$, we can use $z = 0$ as lower limit of integration in Green's transform. This leads to the identity

$$ \overline{u(z)}u'(z)\, e^{i\theta} = \int_0^r |u'(\cdot)|^2\, ds $$

$$ + \int_0^r \left[\frac{1}{4} e^{2i\theta} - \frac{c - 2a}{2s} e^{i\theta} + \frac{c^2 - 2c}{4s^2}\right] |u(\cdot)|^2\, ds. $$

The imaginary part of the right-hand side is

$$ \tfrac{1}{2} \sin\theta \int_0^r \left[\cos\theta - \frac{c - 2a}{s}\right] |u(\cdot)|^2\, ds. $$

Here there are three possibilities according as $c \gtreqless 2a$.

Suppose first that $c = 2a$. Then the imaginary part is different from 0 provided z is not on either of the axes. This means that all complex zeros and extrema are purely imaginary, and, setting $z = iy$, we see that there are indeed infinitely many such points on the imaginary axis. This is not surprising since in this case $u(z)$ is a constant multiple of

$$z^{1/2}J_{(c-1)/2}\left(\frac{z}{2i}\right).$$

From this formula it also follows that there are no real zeros of $u(z)$ since $c > 1$.

If $c > 2a$, it is seen that there are no complex zeros or extrema in the half-plane

$$x \leq c - 2a,$$

while, if $c < 2a$, the half-plane

$$x \geq c - 2a$$

is zero-free. In these cases it is difficult to obtain further limitations on the zeros. We can only add some general remarks.

Suppose that $c > 2a$. Then the curve $Q = 0$ consists of the real axis plus the circle

$$(c - 2a)(x^2 + y^2) = (c^2 - 2c)x,$$

which is in the right half-plane if $c > 2$. In the first quadrant outside the circle $Q(x, y) < 0$. This means that the zeros and extrema of $u(z)$ in this domain can be ordered according to strictly increasing ordinates and this ordering is also one by strictly increasing abscissas. That there are infinitely many zeros as well as extrema may be shown by a continuity argument. We know the situation for $c = 2a$ when all the points in question are on the imaginary axis. We keep a fixed and let c increase. The zeros and extrema are analytic functions of c, and when c increases they describe paths in the right half-plane, keeping to the right of the line $x = c - 2a$ and moving in such a manner that no two points are simultaneously on the same horizontal or vertical line. The distance between consecutive zeros remains approximately 2π, the argument $\frac{1}{2}\pi$, with an error $O(1/n)$ at the nth zero in both cases. This gives $x_n = O(\log n)$, $y_n = 2n\pi + O(\log n)$. The asymptotic formula for $u(z)$, known from Whittaker's investigations, shows that $O(\log n)$ is the right order of magnitude. We shall not push this argument any further but turn to the last example.

VII. *Mathieu's equation.* We have

$$w''(z) + (a + b\cos 2z)w(z) = 0. \tag{11.4.22}$$

A detailed discussion of the complex oscillation theory of this equation was published by the author in 1923, and the reader is referred to this paper for further explications. Here we give a brief outline of some of the main results.

We assume $a > b > 0$. With $a + b \cos 2z = P + iQ$, we have

$$P(x, y) = a + b \cos 2x \cosh 2y, \qquad Q(x, y) = -b \sin 2x \sinh 2y.$$

Here $Q = 0$ if either $y = 0$ or x is a multiple of $\frac{1}{2}\pi$. The curve $P = 0$ consists of infinitely many arcs symmetric with respect to the real axis and all the lines $x = \frac{1}{2}k\pi$. The lines $y = 0$ and $x = k\pi$ divide the plane into infinitely many half-strips, each of which contains a branch of $P = 0$. The branch in the half-strip $0 < x < \pi$, $0 < y$ is typical. It is located between the lines $x = \frac{1}{4}\pi$ and $x = \frac{3}{4}\pi$ which are vertical asymptotes. It is symmetric with respect to $x = \frac{1}{2}\pi$ and its lowest point $\frac{1}{2}\pi + iy_0$ is a zero of $a + b \cos 2z$. (See Figure 11.2.)

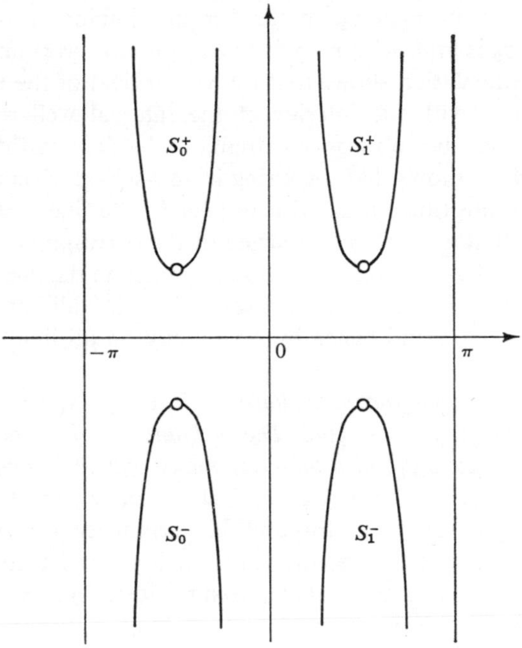

Figure 11.2

The open set $P(x, y) > 0$ is an unbounded domain containing the real axis and all lines $x = k\pi$. On the other hand, the open set $P(x, y) < 0$ consists of infinitely many disjoint pieces, one in each of the half-strips mentioned above. We number these pieces S_n^+ and S_n^-, where S_n^+ lies in the half-strip $(n - 1)\pi < x < n\pi$, $0 < y$, and S_n^- is symmetrically located with respect to the real axis. Theorem 11.3.2 gives:

A solution of (11.4.22) *which is real on the real axis has no complex zeros and extrema in the region* $P(x, y) \geq 0$.

Since $\min\,[a + b \cos 2x] = a - b > 0$, such a solution will have infinitely many real zeros and extrema. Its complex zeros and extrema are located in the domains S_n^+ and S_n^-, and in general there is an infinite string of zeros and extrema in each of these domains. Consider a string in S_n^+ corresponding to a solution $w(z)$ which, at this juncture, need not be real on the real axis. Strings are of three different types, denoted by the prefix *d*-, *r*-, or *l*- (*dexter*, *rectus*, and *laevus*) according as the string is to the right of the line $x = (n - \frac{1}{2})\pi$, on it, or to the left of it. The character of the string is determined by the position of its lowest point, z_1 say. If the latter is to the right of the line or on the line or to the left of it, all points on the string have the same relative position with respect to the line, and the string is *d*-, *r*-, or *l*-, as the case may be.

To fix the ideas, consider the string in S_n^+ and suppose that its lowest point is $z_1 = x_1 + iy_1$ with $x_1 < (n - \frac{1}{2})\pi$ and $y_0 < y_1$. Then if $z_2 = x_2 + iy_2 \in S_n^+$ and $(n - \frac{1}{2})\pi \leq x_2$, $y_1 \leq y_2$, the broken line joining z_1, $(n - \frac{1}{2})\pi + iy_1$, $(n - \frac{1}{2})\pi + iy_2$, z_2 is an *li* with respect to the solution $w(z)$ under consideration. A simple calculation shows that the vector field of the path lies in the interval $[-\frac{1}{2}\pi, \frac{1}{2}\pi]$, with the interior of the interval well represented. It follows that there can be no zeros or extrema in the right half of S_n^+ including the boundary. This shows that the string is an *l*-string. A similar argument applies for other positions of z_1 with respect to the line $x = (n - \frac{1}{2})\pi$. It should be noted that a string is an *r*-string iff the corresponding solution is a constant multiple of a function which is real valued on the line $x = (n - \frac{1}{2})\pi$.

The special Mathieu functions, $\mathrm{ce}_k(z)$ and $\mathrm{se}_k(z)$, all have this property on the lines $x = \pm\frac{1}{2}\pi$, and hence by periodicity on all lines $x = (n - \frac{1}{2})\pi$. Hence we have:

The special Mathieu functions have their complex zeros and extrema located on the lines $x = (n - \frac{1}{2})\pi$. The ordinates of these points exceed y_0 in absolute value. There are also infinitely many real zeros and extrema.

The point $z = \frac{1}{2}\pi$ is a zero of $\mathrm{ce}_{2k+1}(z)$ and of $\mathrm{se}_{2k}(z)$, an extremum of $\mathrm{ce}_{2k}(z)$ and of $\mathrm{se}_{2k+1}(z)$. From this and the periodicity, we conclude that all strings have the same structure, they are *r*-strings, and zeros and extrema alternate, the point nearest the real axis being an extremum or a zero according as $\frac{1}{2}\pi$ is a zero or an extremum of the function.

If the string in S_n^+ is a *d*-string and if $w(z)$ is real on the real axis, then the string in S_n^- is also a *d*-string. But in general nothing seems to be known about what relations hold between the types of the strings in different domains $S_m^\pm$ and $S_n^\pm$ when $a > b > 0$. Complete information is available for $a < b < 0$.

EXERCISE 11.4

1. If $a = -\frac{1}{2} + \mu i$, the solution $P_a(z)$ of Legendre's equation has infinitely many zeros on $(1, \infty)$. Show that the number of zeros in $(1, R)$ is

$$\pi^{-1}(\tfrac{1}{4} + \mu^2)^{1/2} \log [R + (R^2 - 1)^{1/2}] + O(1).$$

2. Can Legendre's equation be oscillatory on the imaginary axis for real values of $a(a + 1)$?
3. How do the positive zeros of $J_a(z)$ move when a increases?
4. If $a = ic$, $c > 0$, Eq. (11.4.8) has solutions real on the positive real axis. Discuss the zeros of such a solution. Show that there are infinitely many zeros in $(0, 1)$ and also in $(1, \infty)$ and compare the frequencies. Show that there are no complex zeros in the right half-plane.
5. Verify (11.4.15).
6. Consider the subdominant solution of (11.4.10) in the sector S: $|\arg z| < \frac{1}{4}\pi$ and determine how its real zeros move when a increases. Find analogues of (11.4.13) and (11.4.15).
7. Prove the assertions made in the text concerning the complex zeros and extrema of the Titchmarsh functions of order 3 ($n = 3$ in (11.4.16)). Show that the points of the string in the first quadrant approach the line $\arg z = \frac{3}{8}\pi$ and that there are no points of the string on the line.
8. If $L_n^{(\alpha)}(z)$ is the nth Laguerre polynomial of order α, then $e^{-z/2}z^{(\alpha+1)/2}L_n^{(\alpha)}(z)$ satisfies (11.4.20) with $a = -n$, $c = \alpha + 1$. With the aid of (11.3.17) or otherwise, show that the positive zeros of $L_n^{(\alpha)}(z)$, $\alpha \geq 1$, do not exceed $4n + 2(\alpha + 1)$ and that any complex zero $z_1 = x_1 + iy_1$ with $0 \leq x_1$, $0 < y_1$, must satisfy $x_1 < 2\gamma$, $y_1 < \gamma$ where $\gamma = \frac{1}{4}(\alpha^2 - 1)[n + \frac{1}{2}(\alpha + 1)]^{-1}$.
9. If $\alpha = -\beta < 0$ and $[\beta]$ is odd, show that no complex zero of $L_n^{(-\beta)}(z)$ can be to the left of the line $x = x_0$ where x_0 is the only negative zero of $L_n^{(-\beta)}(z)$. [Hille-Szegö, 1943.]
10. Suppose that $a < b < 0$ and that $w(z)$ is a solution of (11.4.22). Suppose that the zeros and extrema of $w(z)$ in the half-strip $(n - 1)\pi < x < n\pi$, $0 < y$, form a d-string. Show that all strings in the half-strips $(k - 1)\pi < x < k\pi$, $0 < y$ or $y < 0$, with $k \leq n$ are d-strings. What is the corresponding result if the given string is an l-string instead?
11. Under the same assumption on a, b, there exists a solution of the form $e^{-\mu z}F(z)$ where $\mu > 0$ and $F(z)$ is periodic of period π. Show that the zeros and extrema form infinitely many strings, one for each half-strip, all of the l-type, and that there are no real zeros or extrema. (Cf. Section 7.6.)
12. The following problem illustrates a different technique, that of argument variation, which is useful in discussion of zeros. The function $P_a(z)$ defined by (11.4.5) was found to have no complex zeros in the upper half-plane if $a > -\frac{1}{2}$ and its real zeros lie in the interval $(-1, 1)$. The number of such zeros is $E(a) + 1$ where $E(a)$ is the largest integer $< a$. This can be shown by following the variation of $\arg P_a(z)$ if z describes this path: Start at $z = 1$ and go to $z = R$ (large positive number), describe the semi-circle $z = R\, e^{i\theta}$, $0 \leq \theta \leq \pi$, where the variation is close to $a\pi$, go from $-R$ to $-1 - \varepsilon$ and note that the sign of the imaginary part of $P_a(z)$ is that of $\sin \pi a$, describe the semi-circle $z = -1 + \varepsilon\, e^{i\theta}$, $\pi \geq \theta \geq 0$, note that the sign of $P_a(-1 + \varepsilon)$ is opposite that of $\sin \pi a$, and go from $-1 + \varepsilon$ to $z = 1$, avoiding the real zeros by semi-circles in the upper half-plane. Show that the number of such semi-circles must be $E(a) + 1$ to make the total variation 0 as it should be.

11.5 ASYMPTOTIC INTEGRATION AND THE INDICATRICES

Let $G(z)$ be holomorphic, save for poles in the finite plane, and consider the differential equation

$$w''(z) + G(z)w(z) = 0. \tag{11.5.1}$$

In Section 7.4, we carried this equation into a perturbed sine equation

$$W''(Z) + [1 - F(Z)]W(Z) = 0 \tag{11.5.2}$$

using the Liouville transformation

$$Z(z) = \int_{z_0}^{z} [G(t)]^{1/2}\,dt, \qquad W(Z) = [G(z)]^{1/4}w(z), \tag{11.5.3}$$

and

$$F(Z) = \frac{H''(Z)}{H(Z)}, \qquad H(Z) = [G(z)]^{1/4}. \tag{11.5.4}$$

As indicated earlier, the study of the transformed equation presupposes a study of the function

$$Z(z) = X(z) + iY(z) \tag{11.5.5}$$

and of the geometrical properties of the curve net

$$X(z) = C_1, \qquad Y(z) = C_2. \tag{11.5.6}$$

We recognize the anticlinals and indicatrices introduced in Section 11.1, which also play a basic role in the discussion of zero-free regions. The two problems can be studied in the main simultaneously.

The family of indicatrices is given by

$$\Im\left\{\int_{z_0}^{z} [G(t)]^{1/2}\,dt\right\} = C_2$$

and hence satisfies the differential equation

$$\Im\{[G(z)]^{1/2}\,dz\} = 0 \tag{11.5.7}$$

or in real form

$$U(x, y)\,dy + V(x, y)\,dx = 0 \tag{11.5.8}$$

where

$$U(x, y) + iV(x, y) = [G(x + iy)]^{1/2}. \tag{11.5.9}$$

The existence theorems for differential equations assert that, if $z_1 = x_1 + iy_1$ is neither a zero nor a pole of $G(z)$, then there is one and only one integral curve

$$Y(z) = Y(z_1)$$

of (11.5.8) that passes through $z = z_1$. Hence there is one and only one indicatrix passing through $z = z_1$. If $Z(z)$ should happen to be many-valued, then this assertion holds for each sheet of the Riemann surface on which $Z(z)$ is single-valued.

Similarly, there is one and only one anticlinal through $z = z_1$, for the anticlinals satisfy the equation

$$U(x, y)\,dx - V(x, y)\,dy = 0. \tag{11.5.10}$$

The situation is different at a zero or pole of $G(z)$. Suppose that $z = a$ is a k-fold zero of $G(z)$, so that in some neighborhood of $z = a$ there is a convergent expansion

$$G(z) = \sum_{n=k}^{\infty} g_n(z - a)^n, \qquad g_k \neq 0.$$

Then there is also an expansion

$$[G(z)]^{1/2} = \sum_{m=0}^{\infty} \gamma_m(z - a)^{k/2+m}, \qquad \gamma_0 = [g_k]^{1/2}, \tag{11.5.11}$$

valid possibly in a smaller neighborhood, and hence

$$Z(z) = Z(a) + \sum_{m=0}^{\infty} (m + 1 + \tfrac{1}{2}k)^{-1}\gamma_m(z - a)^{k/2+m-1}. \tag{11.5.12}$$

If k is even, $Z(z)$ is holomorphic at $z = a$; if k is odd, there is an algebraic singularity where two branches are permuted.

The two curve nets have a singularity at $z = a$ regardless of the parity of k. We obtain $X(z)$ and $Y(z)$ by separating reals and imaginaries in (11.5.12). Using polar co-ordinates

$$z = a + r\,e^{i\theta}, \qquad \arg \gamma_m = \theta_m,$$

we find a typical indicatrix represented by an equation of the form

$$\sum_{m=0}^{\infty} \alpha_m r^{m+1+k/2} \sin\,[(m + 1 + \tfrac{1}{2}k)\theta + \theta_m] = C.$$

In particular, if $C = 0$ the equation is of the form

$$\sin\,[(\tfrac{1}{2}k + 1)\theta + \theta_0] + O(r) = 0.$$

for small values of r. This shows that this curve consists of $k + 2$ branches, so-called *semi-characteristics*, ending at $z = a$, where they make equal angles with each other. These semi-characteristics divide the interior of a small disk $|z - a| \leq \rho$ into $m + 2$ sectors, referred to as *hyperbolic regions*. Each integral curve $Y = C$ of (11.5.8) which enters such a region across the circular arc (and there is no other possibility) also leaves it across the arc. We call the point $z = a$ a *saddle-point* of order $k + 2$ of the family $Y = C$. (See Figure 11.3.)

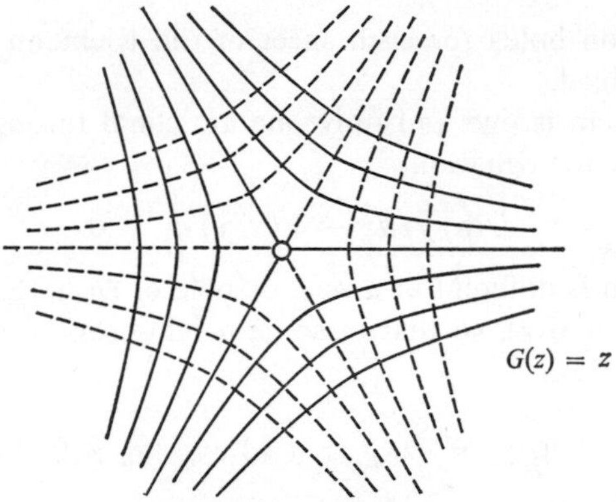

Figure 11.3

The same results hold for the anticlinals which also have a saddle-point of order $k + 2$ at $z = a$. There are $m + 2$ semi-characteristics ending at $z = a$ where their tangents bisect the angles between the tangents of the arcs $Y(z) = Y(a)$.

Suppose now that $z = a$ is instead a pole of order p. Formula (11.5.11) is still valid if we replace k by $-p$, but (11.5.12) may have to be modified in a more radical manner. There are essentially three different cases.

1. $p = 1$. Here formula (11.5.12) is still valid if we set $k = -1$. The point $z = a$ is still an algebraic singularity where two branches permute. There is a single semi-characteristic ending at $z = a$ for each of the systems and a single hyperbolic region. In the simplest case, $G(z) = (z - a)^{-1}$, the curves are actually confocal parabolas. The point $z = a$ will be designated as a *saddle-point of order one*, undoubtedly a misnomer, but consistent with the terminology used above. For the differential equation (11.5.1) this is a regular singular point with one holomorphic and one logarithmic solution.

2. $p = 2$. This is a regular singular point where the roots of the indicial equation have the sum 1. The nature of the roots is partly reflected in the geometry of the X, Y net. We have

$$Z(z) = (g_{-2})^{1/2} \log z + \sum_{m=0}^{\infty} b_n(z - a)^n \qquad (11.5.13)$$

where the coefficients b_n can be read off from (11.5.12) but are of no importance for the following. Here $z = a$ is a logarithmic branch-point of $Z(z)$. For the X, Y net, we have to distinguish between three sub-cases.

2:i. $g_{-2} > 0$. Here $z = a$ is a *vortex* for the family $X = C$ and a *star-point* for $Y = C$. In a small neighborhood of $z = a$, the anticlinals are simple closed curves surrounding $z = a$, while the indicatrices, being orthogonal trajectories of the anticlinals, are semi-characteristics ending at $z = a$, every tangent direction being represented once and only once at that point. The neighborhood is a *vortical region* with respect to the anticlinals, a *radial* region for the indicatrices.

2:ii. $g_{-2} < 0$. Interchange the roles of the two systems in case 2:i.

2:iii. g_{-2} complex. Here for both systems the curves approach the point $z = a$ in the manner of a logarithmic spiral. The point $z = a$ is a *focal point*, or *focus*, for both systems and the neighborhood is a *focal region*.

3. $p > 2$. If p is odd, then $Z(z)$ is represented by (11.5.12) with $k = -p$. The singularity is algebraic, two branches are permuted, and $(z - a)^{p/2-1}Z(z)$ is bounded away from 0 and ∞ as $z \to a$. If p is even and if the expansion (11.5.11) with $k = -p$ contains no term in $(z - a)^{-1}$, then $z = a$ is a pole of $Z(z)$ of order $\frac{1}{2}p - 1$. If, however, there is a term in $(z - a)^{-1}$, then $Z(z)$ has an additional term in $\log(z - a)$, so the pole is combined with a logarithmic branch-point. The latter does not materially affect the shape of the X, Y net.

All arcs of the net in some neighborhood of $z = a$ are closed, and begin and end at $z = a$ where they have definite tangents. For the X-curves, there are $p - 2$ tangent directions at $z = a$ which make equal angles with each other, and these angles are bisected by the tangents of the Y-curves at the singular point. We call $z = a$ a *node* of order $p - 2$ for each family. Let Γ be an arc of the X-family which begins and ends at $z = a$ and does not pass through or enclose any other singular point of the net. Then Γ bounds an *elliptical region* with respect to the X-family and a *cuspidal* with respect to the Y-family.

Each family has $p - 2$ elliptical regions and $p - 2$ cuspidal regions, which, of course, overlap.

See Figures 11.4 to 11.8 for the five types here described.

If $G(z)$ has at most a pole at $z = \infty$, the preceding discussion can be adapted to this case. This means that if $G(z)$ is a rational function, the global structure of the X, Y net can be obtained by patching together the local results listed above.

Suppose that the anticlinals and the indicatrices have been traced in the plane. If the solutions of (11.5.1) are multiple-valued, construct the corresponding Riemann surface on which the solutions are single-valued and trace the net on each sheet of the surface. Each sheet gets the same net, only the labeling of the curves may differ from one sheet to another if $Z(z)$ is not single-valued.

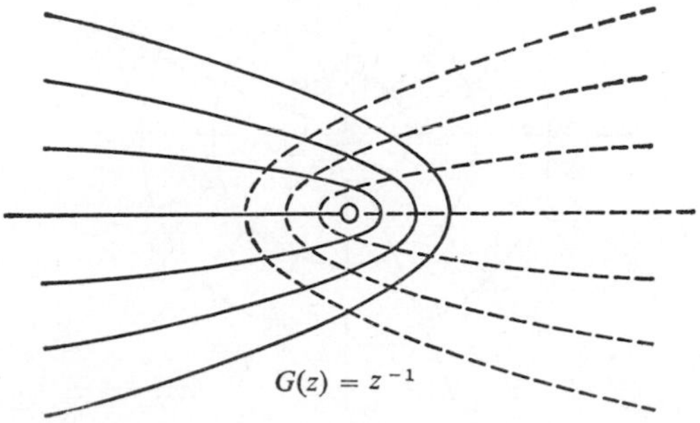

Figure 11.4

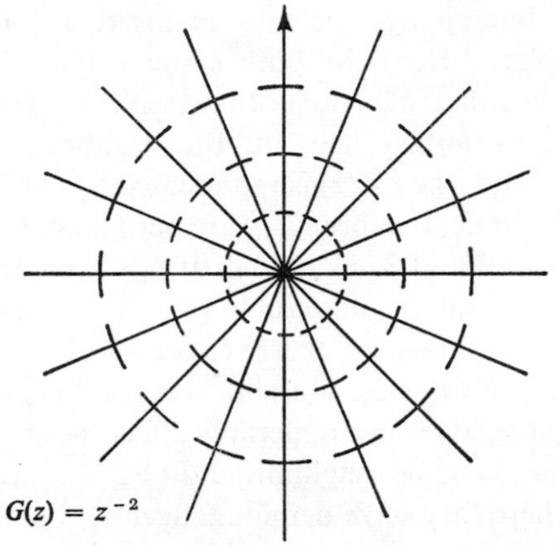

Figure 11.5

In each leaf we mark the singular points of the curves. We note the different regions for the Y-family: cuspidal, elliptic, focal, etc. To simplify matters, suppose there are no focal regions. We assume the possibility of dissecting the plane (or the Riemann surface) into so-called *principal regions* having the following properties. Each principal region has one and only one singular point of $G(z)$ in its interior or on the boundary. Double poles of $G(z)$ are interior points. The surrounding radial or vertical region of the Y-family constitutes the corresponding principal region. A pole of order higher than 2 is a boundary point of one or more principal regions, each containing a single cuspidal region of the Y-family. Saddle-points are boundary points of one or more principal regions and this extends to simple poles of $G(z)$ which give rise to saddle-points of order 1.

The idea of the subdivision is to obtain regions which are mapped conformally by

$$Z = Z(z)$$

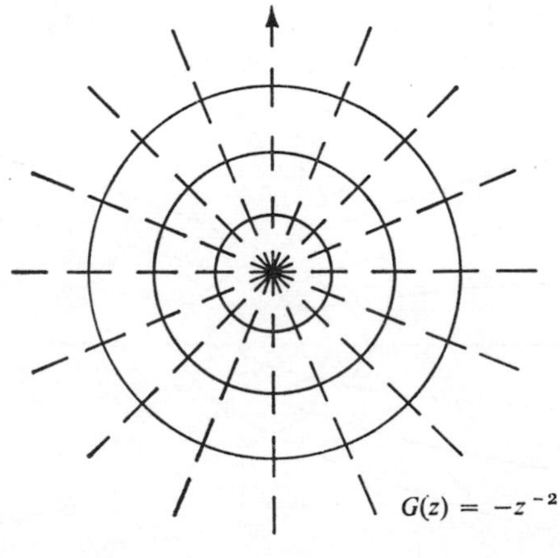

Figure 11.6

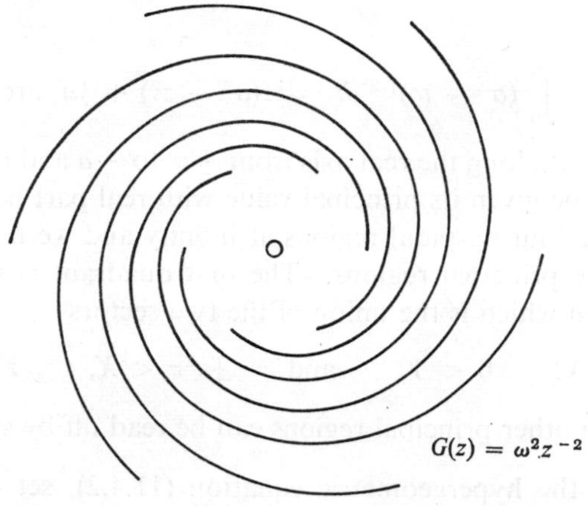

Figure 11.7. Only the anticlinals are shown

on to regions extending to infinity in the Z-plane in which the perturbation term in the transformed equation (11.5.3) behaves in such a manner that a method of asymptotic integration applies. It is usually inevitable that the image region partly overlaps itself, but we may reduce the overlapping to one of finite area. Let us start by giving some examples of sub-division into principal regions.

Example 1. We take the Hermite-Weber equation with

$$G(z) = a^2 - z^2, \qquad a > 0,$$

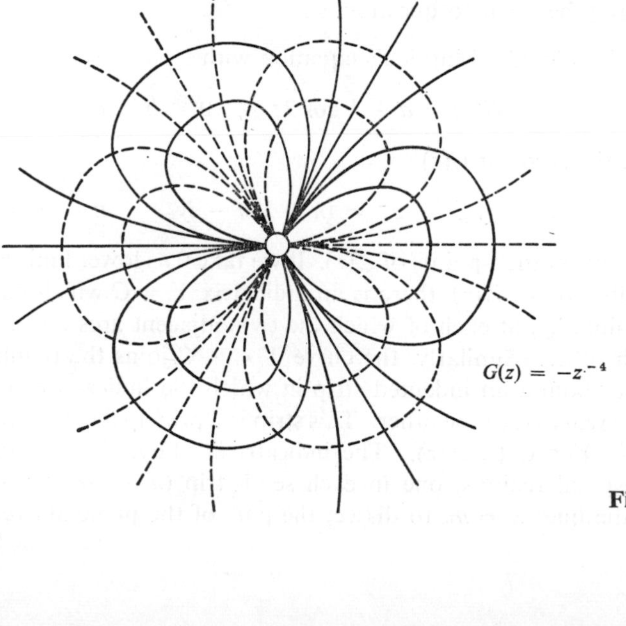

Figure 11.8

and

$$Z(z) = \int_0^z (a^2 - t^2)^{1/2}\, dt = \tfrac{1}{2}z(a^2 - z^2) + \tfrac{1}{2}a^2 \arcsin \frac{z}{a} \cdot$$

If the z-plane is cut along the real axis from $-\infty$ to $-a$ and from $+a$ to $+\infty$ the arcsine may be given its principal value with real part between $-\frac{1}{2}\pi$ and $+\frac{1}{2}\pi$. There are four cuspidal regions at infinity and we may take the four quadrants as the principal regions. The first quadrant is mapped by $Z(z)$ on to the domain which is the union of the two sectors

$$0 < X, \quad 0 < Y, \quad \text{and} \quad \tfrac{1}{4}a^2\pi < X, \quad Y \le 0.$$

The maps of the other principal regions can be read off by symmetry.

Example 2. In the hypergeometric equation (11.4.2), set $\alpha_1 = \alpha_2 = \frac{1}{2}\sqrt{2}$, $\alpha_3 = 0$ to obtain

$$w'' + \tfrac{1}{8}[z^{-2} + (z - 1)^{-2}]w = 0.$$

The neighborhoods of the three singular points, 0, 1, ∞, are radial regions for the Y-curves. If

$$Z(z) = \int_{1/2}^z [G(t)]^{1/2}\, dt,$$

the curve $X = 0$ can be taken as the boundary separating the three principal regions. It consists of three arcs joining the two branch-points $z = \frac{1}{2}(1 \pm i)$ where they make 120° angles with each other. One arc is the line segment, the second goes to the left of $z = 0$, the third to the right of $z = 1$.

The two remaining examples involve equations where the singularity at infinity is of infinite order and where, *a priori*, the applicability of the method may be open to question.

Example 3. We take Mathieu's equation with

$$G(z) = a + b \cos 2z, \qquad 0 < b < a.$$

We mark the zeros of $G(z)$

$$z_n^+ = (n + \tfrac{1}{2})\pi + iy_0, \qquad z_n^- = (n + \tfrac{1}{2})\pi - iy_0, \qquad n = 0, \pm 1, \pm 2, \ldots$$

which are the branch-points of $Z(z)$. If we take 0 as lower limit of integration in the definition of $Z(z)$, there is an indicatrix $Y = C$ which passes through all the points z_n^+, at each of which the two adjacent arcs make a 120° angle with each other. Similarly, the curve $Y = -C$ joins the points z_n^-. These two curves bound an indented strip in which the indicatrices run from one end of the real axis to the other. This strip is a principal region and is mapped on $-C < Y < C$ by $Z(z)$. The indicatrices above $Y = C$ form infinitely many cuspidal regions, one in each semi-strip $(n - 1)\pi < x < n\pi$, $0 < y$. We use the lines $x = n\pi$ to dissect the part of the plane above $Y = C$ into principal regions. We do the same in the part of the plane below $Y = -C$.

Example 4. The equation

$$w'' - \frac{1}{a^2} \tan^2 z \; w = 0, \qquad a > 0, \tag{11.5.14}$$

has regular singular points at the poles of the tangent. The point at infinity is a cluster point of poles. We take

$$Z(z) = \frac{i}{a} \log \cos z.$$

The curve Γ: $|\cos z| = 1$ intersects itself at right angles at all multiples of π and divides the plane into infinitely many principal regions. The bounded ovals are vortical regions for Y, and the two infinite domains above and below Γ are cuspidal but of a different type from those encountered before. They are mapped by $Z(z)$ on to upper and lower half-planes, instead of right and left, and the behavior of the perturbation term $F(Z)$ in the corresponding equation (11.5.3) also differs from the normal.

After this survey of different types of principal regions, let us see how the method of asymptotic integration applies to the different types encountered.

I. *Cuspidal domain of the first kind.* A cuspidal domain D for the indicatrices abuts on a finite or infinite singular point P of (11.5.1), where all the curves of the system have a common tangent or asymptote or asymptotic direction. The region is of the *first kind,* if, in a sufficiently small neighborhood of P, the principal regions which have at least two boundary points in common with D are also cuspidal. The principal cuspidal regions abutting on an irregular singular point of finite rank satisfy this condition and so do the cuspidal regions of Mathieu's equation described above. On the other hand, the two cuspidal regions of Eq. (11.5.14) do not satisfy the criterion and will be said to be of the *second kind.*

Let us now have a closer look at a principal cuspidal region at an irregular singular point where $G(z)$ has a pole of order $p > 2$. To simplify, we place the pole at $z = 0$ and assume that in the local expansion of $Z(z)$ there is no logarithmic term. Thus

$$Z(z) = z^{-(p-2)/2} \sum_{n=0}^{\infty} b_n z^n, \qquad b_0 \neq 0.$$

Conversely, we have an expansion for z in ascending powers of $Z^{-2/(p-2)}$ valid for large values of $|Z|$. It follows that

$$\begin{aligned} [G(z)]^{1/4} &= z^{-p/4} \sum_{n=0}^{\infty} \alpha_n z^n \\ &= Z^{p/[2(p-2)]} \sum_{n=0}^{\infty} h_n Z^{-2n/(p-2)} \equiv H(Z) \qquad (h_0 \neq 0) \end{aligned}$$

whence

$$F(z) = \frac{H''(Z)}{H(Z)} = Z^{-2} \sum_{0}^{\infty} f_n Z^{-2n/(p-2)}, \qquad f_0 = -\frac{p(p-4)}{4(p-2)^2} \cdot \tag{11.5.15}$$

This shows that the method of integration developed in Section 7.4 applies to the present case. The domain D is bounded by a finite number of arcs $X = C_{1,j}$, $Y = C_{2,j}$, and, for a suitable choice of the sign of b_0, the function $Z(z)$ maps D conformally on to a domain Δ containing the half-plane $X > \max C_{1,j}$, where $F(z)$ is holomorphic and satisfies (11.5.15). To each solution $W(Z)$ of (11.5.15) in Δ there is a solution $W_0(Z)$ of

$$W_0''(Z) + W_0(Z) = 0 \tag{11.5.16}$$

to which $W(Z)$ is asymptotic in the sense described in Section 7.4. In applying the theorems of this section it should be noted that we have at our disposal, at least to start with, only a right half-plane, and larger sectors may not be available. This requires an examination of the adjacent cuspidal regions, if any. The discussion at the end of Section 7.4 shows what can be done along such lines.

Formula (7.6.47) shows that this method of asymptotic integration applies also to each principal cuspidal region for the equation of Mathieu.

II. *Cuspidal domain of the second kind.* An example is furnished by Eq. (11.5.14) and we shall discuss this case briefly. The part of the z-plane above the curve Γ is mapped conformally on the upper half, $Y > 0$, of the Z-plane. The corresponding function

$$F(Z) = -a^2(\tfrac{1}{4} e^{2iaZ} - 1)(e^{2iaZ} - 1)^{-2} e^{2iaZ}, \tag{11.5.17}$$

the absolute value of which is less than

$$2a^2 e^{-2aY} \qquad \text{for} \qquad aY > \log 2.$$

Proceeding as in the proof of (7.4.7), we show first that

$$|W(Z)| \le C e^{Y}$$

for a suitable constant C and hence, for $a > 1$, that $W(Z)$ satisfies the singular integral equation

$$W(Z) = W_0(Z) + \int_Z^{Z+i\infty} \sin(T - Z)F(T)W(T)\,dt \tag{11.5.18}$$

with a unique choice of $W_0(Z)$ among the solutions of (11.5.16). Conversely, for every such choice of $W_0(Z)$ (11.5.18) gives a solution of the corresponding equation (11.5.3). Note that the integral converges since $a > 1$.

With

$$U(Z) = e^{iZ} W(Z), \qquad U_0(Z) = e^{iZ} W_0(Z)$$

we obtain the inequality

$$|U(X + iY)| \le |U_0(X + iY)| + 2a^2 \int_Y^\infty \exp[2(S - Y) - 2aS]|U(X + iS)|\, dS. \quad (11.5.19)$$

Now, for fixed a and fixed $g(t)$, the transformation

$$T: f(t) \to g(t) + 2a^2 \int_t^\infty \exp[2(s - t) - 2as] f(s)\, ds \quad (11.5.20)$$

is a contraction on the space of functions continuous and bounded on the interval (ω, ∞) if

$$\omega > \frac{1}{2a} \log \frac{a^2}{a - 1},$$

and some power of T is a contraction on $(\log 2, \infty)$. Hence there is a unique fixed point, and Theorem 1.5.1 applies. In particular, if

$$|U_0(X + iY)| \le M, \qquad \log 2 \le Y,$$

then

$$|U(X + iY)| \le M E_a(a^2 e^{-2aY}) \quad (11.5.21)$$

where

$$E_a(q) = \sum_{n=0}^{\infty} \frac{q^n}{(a - 1)(2a - 1)\cdots(na - 1)} \quad (11.5.22)$$

is an entire function. Moreover,

$$|U(X + iY) - U_0(X + iY)| \le M[E_a(a^2 e^{-2aY}) - 1]$$

and this gives the desired inequality

$$|W(Z) - W_0(Z)| \le M\, e^Y[E_a(a^2 e^{-2aY}) - 1]. \quad (11.5.23)$$

This can be used for a study of the zeros of $W(Z)$. If $W_0(Z) = \sin(Z - Z_0)$, $Z_0 = X_0 + iY_0$, and Y_0 is large, then the Theorem of Rouché can be applied by virtue of (11.5.23) and shows that there is one and only one zero of $W(Z)$ in each disk

$$|Z - X_0 - n\pi - iY_0| < \tfrac{1}{6}\pi,$$

and that there are no other zeros above the line $Y = Y_0$.

In proving these results we have had to assume $a > 1$. This is probably a true indication of the limits of applicability of the method. It is likely that for $a \le 1$ the distribution of the zeros of $W(Z)$ is no longer governed by the asymptotic sine equation. This is strongly suggested by Theorem 11.1.5, according to which the frequency of the oscillation becomes infinite as a decreases to 0.

III. *Radial region.* Such a region corresponds to $G(z)$ having a double pole with positive leading coefficient. If

$$G(z) = z^{-2} \sum_{n=0}^{\infty} g_n z^n, \qquad g_0 = a^2, \quad a > 0,$$

then

$$Z(z) = a \log z + \sum_{n=0}^{\infty} a_n z^n.$$

Conversely,

$$z = \sum_{n=1}^{\infty} c_n \, e^{(nZ/a)}$$

in some left half-plane. We may assume that the boundary of the radial domain D under consideration is the curve $X = C$. Consider the Riemann surface of $\log z$ and keep only that part of the surface which lies over D. This is known as the *universal covering surface* of D. In the present case, $Z(z)$ maps the universal covering surface of D conformally on to the half-plane Δ: $X < C$. Calculating $H(Z)$ and $H''(Z)$, we see that

$$F(Z) = \frac{1}{4a^2} + \sum_{n=1}^{\infty} f_n \, e^{(nZ/a)}.$$

Hence, in this case, the transformed equation is

$$W''(Z) + [b^2 - F_1(Z)]W(Z) = 0 \tag{11.5.24}$$

where

$$b^2 = 1 - \frac{1}{4a^2}, \qquad F_1(Z) = \sum_{n=1}^{\infty} f_n \, e^{(nZ/a)}$$

and

$$|F_1(X + iY)| \leq A \, e^{(X/a)}, \qquad X < C. \tag{11.5.25}$$

Here we assume $a > \frac{1}{4}$ so that b is real positive.

Letting $W_0(Z, b)$ denote a non-trivial solution of

$$W'' + b^2 W = 0,$$

it is seen that $W(Z)$ satisfies

$$W(Z) = W_0(Z, b) + \frac{1}{b} \int_{-\infty}^{Z} \sin b(Z - T) F_1(T) W(T) \, dT. \tag{11.5.26}$$

The usual argument gives

$$|W(Z) - W_0(Z, b)| \leq M(Y) \left\{ \exp \left[\frac{a}{b} A \, e^{(X/a)} \right] - 1 \right\} \tag{11.5.27}$$

where

$$M(Y) = \max |W_0(X + iY, b)|.$$

If

$$W_0(Z, b) = \sin b(Z - Z_0),$$

it is seen that $W(Z)$ is oscillatory in Δ and there is a string of zeros asymptotic to

$$Z_0 - \frac{n}{b}\pi \quad \text{as} \quad n \to \infty.$$

If $0 < a \leq \frac{1}{4}$, the equation is no longer oscillatory in Δ and asymptotic integration is of little interest.

IV. *Vortical region.* The formulas under III are valid if we replace a^2 by $-a^2$. The boundary of the domain D is now a curve $Y = C$ and $Z(z)$ will, for an appropriate choice of the square root, map the universal covering surface of D on to an upper half-plane, $Y > C$. Formula (11.5.24) remains valid if we replace a by $-ia$ but (11.5.25) needs more substantial changes. To apply the method of asymptotic integration at least for small values of a, we need to assume $f_1 = 0$, which is the case if $g_1 = 0$, i.e. the residue of the pole is taken to be zero. Then

$$|F_1(X + iY)| \leq A\, e^{-(2Y/a)}. \tag{11.5.28}$$

We have

$$|W(X + iY)| \leq B\, e^{bY}$$

for some finite B. If now $0 < a < \frac{1}{2}\sqrt{5}$, we have $ab < 1$ and the singular integral equation

$$W(Z) = W_0(Z, b) + \frac{1}{b}\int_Z^{Z+i\infty} \sin b(T - Z)F_1(T)W(T)\, dT \tag{11.5.29}$$

makes sense and has a unique solution for any given $W_0(Z, b)$ satisfying

$$W'' + b^2 W = 0.$$

The integral equation is analogous to (11.5.18) and leads to similar considerations. Here (11.5.20) is replaced by

$$S: f(t) \to g(t) + \frac{A}{b}\int_t^{\infty} \exp\,[2b(s - t) - (2s/a)]f(s)\, ds. \tag{11.5.30}$$

This is also a contraction and, if $g(t) \equiv 1$, the fixed element is of the form

$$E\left[\frac{A}{2b}\, e^{-(2Y/a)}\right]$$

where $E(q)$ is an entire function. Hence

$$|W(Z) - W_0(Z, b)| \leq M\, e^{bY}\left\{E\left[\frac{A}{2b}\, e^{-(2Y/a)}\right] - 1\right\} \tag{11.5.31}$$

which can be used for a discussion of the asymptotic distribution of the zeros. Thus the vortical case is to some extent analogous to the cuspidal case of the second kind. With these remarks we leave the examination of asymptotic integration in principal domains.

Finally, we take up two geometrical questions concerning the indicatrices, mentioned but not solved in earlier sections of this chapter.

In Theorem 11.3.7 figures the assumption that the indicatrices have no points of inflection in a certain domain D. How does one verify such a condition? More generally, given a function $F(z)$ holomorphic in some domain D in the complex plane, *how does one determine the locus of the points of inflection of the curves*

$$\Im[F(z)] = C? \tag{11.5.32}$$

If this is not a family of straight lines, the locus is

$$\Im\left\{\frac{F''(z)}{[F'(z)]^2}\right\} = 0. \tag{11.5.33}$$

To verify this, note that the system (11.5.32) satisfies the differential equation

$$\Im[F'(z)\,dz] = 0 \qquad \text{or} \qquad U(x, y)\,dy + V(x, y)\,dx = 0,$$

if $F'(x + iy) = U(x, y) + iV(x, y)$. As long as $U \neq 0$, we have $y' = -(V/U)$ and total differentiation with respect to x gives

$$Uy'' + [U'_x + U'_y y']y' + V'_x + V'_y y' = 0.$$

Here we use the expression for y' together with the Cauchy-Riemann equations

$$U'_x = V'_y, \qquad U'_y = -V'_x$$

to obtain

$$U^3 y'' + (U^2 - V^2)V'_x - 2UVU'_x = 0.$$

At a point of inflection $y'' = 0$, so that

$$(U^2 - V^2)V'_x - 2UVU'_x = \Im[(U - iV)^2(U'_x + iV'_x)] = 0.$$

Since $U - iV$ is the conjugate of $F'(z)$ and $U'_x + iV'_x = F''(z)$, we have a relation equivalent to (11.5.33). The resulting set may be void.

For the indicatrices

$$F(z) = \int_{z_0}^{z} [G(t)]^{1/2}\,dt$$

so that their *inflection locus is*

$$\Im\{G'(z)[G(z)]^{-3/2}\} = 0. \tag{11.5.34}$$

This implies that the derivative of $[G(z)]^{-1/2}$ is real along the locus. It is worth noting that

$$\Im(w^2) = 2uv, \qquad w = u + iv.$$

Hence (11.5.34) is a part of

$$\Im\{[G'(z)]^2[G(z)]^{-3}\} = 0, \tag{11.5.35}$$

the other part being the inflection locus of the anticlinals. We refer to (11.5.35) as the *joint inflection locus.*

The second problem goes back to the discussion of the boundary of the zero-free star $\mathbf{S}_0(z_0)$, the Corollary of Theorem 11.1.3. Here there is the question of the *locus of tangency* of the pencil of straight lines through $z = z_0$ with the family of indicatrices. This locus can be described analytically by the equation

$$\Im\{[G(z)]^{1/2}(z - z_0)\} = 0 \tag{11.5.36}$$

which is a part of the locus

$$\Im[G(z)(z - z_0)^2] = 0, \tag{11.5.37}$$

the remaining part being the locus of tangency of the pencil with the anticlinals.

EXERCISE 11.5

1. Determine principal regions for Titchmarsh's equation with $G(z) = \lambda - z^4$, $\lambda > 0$.
2. Verify (11.5.17) and the following estimate.
3. Verify (11.5.27).
4. In formula (11.5.4) take $a = \frac{1}{4}$, $b = 0$, and carry through the asymptotic integration. Note that now $W_0(Z, b)$ is a linear function and that the kernel $(1/b) \sin b(Z - T)$ is to be replaced by its limit as $b \to 0$. Take $W_0(z, b) \equiv 1$ and find the analogue of (11.5.27).
5. For Mathieu's equation with $0 < b < a$, let 0 be the lower limit of integration in $Z(z)$. Show that for the principal determination
$$Z(\tfrac{1}{2}\pi) = \tfrac{1}{2}\pi a^{1/2} F(\tfrac{1}{4}, -\tfrac{1}{4}, 1; -(b/a)^2).$$
6. Determine the entire function $E(q)$ of (11.5.31).
7. Let $G(z)$ be a rational function of degree m (= maximum of degrees of numerator and of denominator). Show that the joint inflection locus is an algebraic curve of degree not exceeding $8m - 2$.
8. Show that the joint inflection locus passes through all zeros, extrema, and poles of $G(z)$ with the possible exception of the double poles. Which of these points are multiple points of the locus?
9. If $G(z) = a^2 - z^2$, find the joint inflection locus and determine what parts of the curve correspond to the indicatrices.
10. With the same $G(z)$ and with $z_0 = i$, find the tangent locus and determine what part corresponds to the indicatrices.

11. Show that the curvature of the curve of the family (11.5.32) passing through the point z is

$$-\Im\left\{F''(z)\,\frac{|F'(z)|}{[F'(z)]^2}\right\}.$$

11.6 VARIATION OF PARAMETERS

This powerful method has been basic in one form or another for several investigations on the distribution and enumeration of zeros and extrema of solutions of linear second order differential equations. Early instances are furnished by the work of Paul Schafheitlin (1908) on the zeros of hypergeometric functions and by that of Pierre Boutroux (1913–14) on Bessel's equation, in connection with his monumental memoir on the transcendents of Painlevé. This was followed in the early 1920's by investigations of the present author on, in particular, the Hermite-Weber and Mathieu equations. Some results for the latter equations obtained by this method have already been noted in Section 11.4. Here we shall merely sketch the underlying ideas and the analytical basis of the method.

The solutions of a second order equation

$$w'' + G(z)w = 0 \tag{11.6.1}$$

depend upon various parameters. *External parameters* enter explicitly in the equation, such as the quantities α_1, α_2, α_3 of the hypergeometric equation (11.4.2), the quantity a in Bessel's equation (11.4.8), or in the Hermite-Weber equation (11.4.10) and so on. There are also *internal parameters* such as the *initial parameter*

$$\lambda(z_0) = \frac{w'(z_0)}{w(z_0)}, \tag{11.6.2}$$

the various *asymptotic parameters* Z_0 associated with the method of asymptotic integration applied to a principal domain, etc. All these parameters enter explicitly or implicitly in the definition of the particular solution under consideration. Moreover, they enter analytically in the sense that the solution is an analytic function of the parameter as well as of the variable z.

This is obvious for external parameters which in the commonly considered cases enter linearly in the equation. We have seen on a number of occasions that the solutions will be entire or meromorphic functions of such parameters. The initial parameter enters linearly, and hence analytically, in the solution. The situation is less obvious for asymptotic parameters. Suppose, however, that asymptotic integration in a principal region leads to an approximate solution $C \sin(Z - Z_0)$. Then

$$W(Z) = C \sin(Z - Z_0) + \int_Z^\infty \sin(T - Z)F(T)W(T)\,dT$$

and the solution of this equation is obtained by the method of successive approximations, taking $C \sin (Z - Z_0)$ as the first approximation. This leads to a sequence of approximations $\{W_n(Z, Z_0)\}$ holomorphic functions of Z and Z_0 in appropriate half-planes. There is convergence on compact sub-sets, uniformly in Z as well as in Z_0, whence it follows that the limit $W(Z) = W(Z, Z_0)$ is holomorphic in both variables. Transition to the old variables z and w via the inverse of the Liouville transformation, shows that $w(z)$ is analytic in Z_0.

Suppose now that p is an analytic parameter, external or internal, $w(z, p)$ a solution of (11.6.1) holomorphic in (z, p) for z in some domain D and p in some domain Δ. Let $z_0 \in D$, $p_0 \in \Delta$ be such that

$$w(z_0, p_0) = 0.$$

Here $w'_z(z_0, p_0) \neq 0$, if we exclude trivial null solutions. The implicit function theorem shows the existence of a unique function $z(p)$ such that (i) $z(p_0) = z_0$, (ii) $z(p)$ is holomorphic in some disk $|p - p_0| < \rho$, and there (iii) $w[z(p), p] \equiv 0$. Thus *the zeros of* $w(z, p)$ *are analytic functions of* p.

Similar considerations apply to the extrema. Suppose that $e_0 \in D$, $p_0 \in \Delta$ are such that

$$(\alpha)\ w'_z(e_0, p_0) = 0, \qquad (\beta)\ G(e_0) \neq 0.$$

Then $w''_{zz}(e_0, p_0) \neq 0$ and the implicit function theorem shows the existence of a unique function $e(p)$ such that (i) $e(p_0) = e_0$, (ii) $e(p)$ is holomorphic in $|p - p_0| < \sigma$, and there (iii) $w'_z[e(p), p] \equiv 0$.

Here condition (β) is essential. If it is violated and $z = e_0$ is a zero of order k of $G(z)$, then the partial derivatives of $w(z, p)$ with respect to z vanish up to and including the $(k + 1)^{\text{th}}$ order for $z = e_0$, $p = p_0$. The implicit function theorem in this case asserts the existence of $(k + 1)$ functions $e_j(p)$ such that (i) $e_j(p_0) = e_0$, $j = 1, 2, \ldots, k + 1$, (ii) the symmetric functions of $e_1, \ldots, e_{k+1}$ are holomorphic in a disk $|p - p_0| < \sigma$, while the e_j's have a branch-point at $p = p_0$ about which they are permuted cyclically, and (iii) $w'_z[e_j(p), p] \equiv 0$. Thus we see that *the extrema are also analytic functions of the parameter* p.

For a given solution $w(z, p)$, we have thus a number of *zero functions* $z_n(p)$ and *extremum functions* $e_m(p)$, each locally holomorphic. Let us consider the analytic continuation of these *ZE*-functions. We start with a *Z*-function $z(p)$, which we continue analytically along a path leading from $p = p_0$. As $p \to p_1$ on this path, various possibilities arise.

1) $z(p)$ tends to a finite limit z_1 and $w(z, p)$ is holomorphic for (z, p) in a neighborhood of (z_1, p_1). It is then seen that $z(p)$ is holomorphic at $p = p_1$ and z_1 is one of the roots of the equation $w(z, p_1) = 0$.

2) p_1 is one of the fixed singular points of $w(z, p)$. If $z(p) \to z_1$, a non-singular point of the equation, $p = p_1$ may still be a singularity of $z(p)$.

3) $z(p)$ tends to a finite value a which is a singularity of $G(z)$ and thus of the equation. In this case $p = p_1$ may still be a regular point of $z(p)$ but usually it is a singular point of more than one of the Z-functions.

4) $z(p)$ tends to infinity. Then $p = p_1$ is always a singular point of $z(p)$.

5) $z(p)$ tends to no limit as $p \to p_1$. Again $p = p_1$ is a singular point of $z(p)$.

The same different cases present themselves if $p \to \infty$.

Here are some examples to illustrate the possibilities.

Ad case (2): The following is a somewhat artificial example of this possibility. Take

$$w'' + w = 0, \qquad w(z, p) = \sin(z - \sqrt{p}).$$

Here $z_n(p) = \sqrt{p} + n\pi$, $p = 0$ is a fixed singular point of $w(z, p)$ and of each $z_n(p)$. When $p \to 0$, $z_n(p) \to n\pi$ which is a regular point of the equation.

Ad case (3). Take

$$w'' + \tfrac{2}{9}z^{-2}w = 0, \qquad w(z, p) = z^{2/3} - pz^{1/3}.$$

There is a movable zero, $z(p) = p^3$, which tends to 0 with p. Now $z = 0$ is a singular point of the equation but $p = 0$ is not a singularity of $z(p)$.

Ad case (4). Take

$$w'' + w = 0, \qquad w(z, p) = \cos z - p \sin z.$$

Here $p = \pm i$ are the singular points and

$$z_n(p) = \operatorname{arc\,cot} p + n\pi$$

which becomes infinite as $p \to \pm i$ for all n. Note that in this case the $z_n(p)$ are simply the various determinations of the inverse function of the cotangent and these determinations are permuted when p makes a circuit around $+i$ or $-i$.

Ad case (5). Take

$$w'' + \tfrac{5}{4}z^{-2}w = 0, \qquad w(z, p) = z^{1/2+i} - pz^{1/2-i}.$$

Here

$$z_n(p) = \exp\left[\tfrac{1}{2}\arg p + n\pi - \tfrac{1}{2}i \log|p|\right]$$

which tends to no limit, if p tends radially to either 0 or ∞.

The discussion of the singularities of $e(p)$ follows the same lines, except that under case (1) we have two alternatives according as $G(e_0) \neq 0$ or not. In the first case, $e(p)$ is holomorphic at $z = e_0$; in the second case, there is an algebraic branch-point at $z = e_0$ and several extrema functions coalesce there.

We have found that the zeros and extrema are analytic functions of the parameter p. This implies among other things that the set $S(p) \equiv \{z_n(p), e_m(p)\}$ is deformed in a continuous manner if p is varied continuously, avoiding any of the singular points. Now we know from the discussion in Section 11.3 that with each point in the set there is associated a domain of influence variable with the point in question. Hence we obtain the

Principle of Variation: *Let the parameter p in $w(z, p)$ be varied continuously, avoiding the singular points of the functions $z_n(p)$ and $e_m(p)$. Then the set $S(p)$ is deformed continuously. Every point in the set moves in such a manner that it respects and avoids the domains of influence of all other members of the set.*

This is a handy tool for studying the variation of zeros and extrema with the parameters, especially if the equation admits of solutions which are of real character on some line-segments. Samples of such discussions were given above in Section 11.4.

One more observation is pertinent. Consider a domain D in the plane or on the Riemann surface of the solution $w(z, p)$. For a given value p_0 of p the domain D contains a subset of $S(p_0)$. How does this subset vary with p? If D contains no singular points of the differential equation, then we can loose or gain points of $S(p)$ only through passage across the boundary of D. It is impossible for a zero or an extremum to be generated or annihilated at a regular point. On the other hand, if the domain contains a singular point, the situation may be different. As an illustration we may take

$$w'' + az^{-2}w = 0, \qquad w(z, a) = z^{\rho_1} - z^{\rho_2}, \qquad \rho_1, \rho_2 = \tfrac{1}{2} \pm (\tfrac{1}{4} - a)^{1/2}.$$

Suppose a is real, $a > \frac{1}{4}$. Then

$$z_n(a) = \exp[(a - \tfrac{1}{4})^{-1/2} n\pi], \qquad n = 0, \pm 1, \pm 2, \ldots$$

As a decreases to $\frac{1}{4}$, $z_0(a)$ stays put, the zeros with positive subscript go to $+\infty$, those with negative subscript to 0, and for $a < \frac{1}{4}$ only the zero $z_0(a) \equiv 1$ remains, all the others having been engulfed by the singular points. Here the singular points serve as sinks, but, if we reverse the process and let a increase through $a = \frac{1}{4}$, the singular points are sources instead. This is the picture obtained if we restrict ourselves to positive real values of z and of a, and this choice is often made in the applications. The picture is different if $w(z, a)$ is considered on the Riemann surface of $\log z$ and a is taken as a complex variable on a two-sheeted surface. We shall not stress this point any further.

EXERCISE 11.6

1. At what points in the plane may a solution of the differential equation (11.6.1) possibly have a multiple zero? Give a concrete instance!
2. Take $w'' - w = 0$, $w(z, p) = e^z - p\,e^{-z}$. Determine the singular points of $z_n(p)$ and their nature. What happens when p makes a positive circuit about one of the singularities?

3. Take $a = -2$ in (11.4.20) and consider the solution
$$u(z, c) = z^{c/2} e^{-z/2} {}_1F_1(-2; c; z).$$
The last factor is a quadratic polynomial in z. Determine its zeros, the singularities of the zeros *qua* functions of c, and compare with the fixed singularities of $u(z, c)$. What bearing do the results have on cases (2) and (3) above?
4. Take $w'' - (1 + z^2)w = 0$, $w(z, p) = e^{z^2/2}(1 - p \int_z^\infty e^{-s^2} ds)$. Make plausible that $p = 0$, $\pi^{-1/2}$ and ∞ are the singularities of the zeros of $w(z, p)$. What happens to the zeros when p approaches one of the stated values?
5. The Legendre function $P_a(z)$ normally has a singularity at $z = -1$ where (7.2.11) is valid. The representation changes when a is a positive integer or 0 and the logarithmic term disappears. Set $a = k + \varepsilon$, ε small >0, and show that $P_a(z)$ has a zero at approximately $z = -1 + \exp(-1/\varepsilon)$. [The number of zeros of $P_a(z)$ in $(-1, +1)$ is k if $k - 1 < a \leq k$. The singular point $z = -1$ may be regarded as the source of the new zero which appears when a increasing passes through the value k.]
6. Divide the z-plane into regions where every solution of $w'' + w = 0$ has one and only one zero, multiples of e^{iz} and e^{-iz} excepted.
7. Given $w'' + zw = 0$ and $w(z, p) = w_0(z) + pw_1(z)$ where $w_0(0) = 0$, $w_0'(0) = 1$, $w_1(0) = 1$, $w_1'(0) = 0$, describe the location of the zeros of $w_0(z)$. There exists a $p_0 > 0$ such that $w(z, p_0)$ is subdominant in a 120° sector symmetric with respect to the negative real axis. As p increases to p_0, the complex zeros of $w(z, p)$ go to infinity. Show that the orbits described by these zeros have the negative real axis as common asymptotes. Prove that ωp_0 and $\omega^2 p_0$, $\omega = \frac{1}{2}(-1 + 1\sqrt{3})$, are also singular points of Z-functions. Which Z-functions?

COLLATERAL READING

The only textbook that devotes space to complex oscillation theory is

INCE, E. L., *Ordinary Differential Equations*, Dover reprint (1944), Chapter 21.

This fact makes it necessary to give more detailed references to the periodicals than would otherwise be justified. We quote:

BEESACK, P. E., "Non-oscillation and disconjugacy in the complex domain," *Trans. Amer. Math. Soc.* **81**, 211–242 (1956).

BEESACK, P. E., and B. SCHWARZ, "On the zeros of solutions of second-order linear differential equations," *Canadian J. Math.* **9**, 504–515 (1956).

BOUTROUX, P., "Recherches sur les transcendantes de M. Painlevé et l'étude asymptotique des équations différentielles du second ordre," *Annales de l'École Normale Supérieure*, (3) **30**, 255–375 (1913); *ibid.* **31**, 99–159 (1914).

HILLE, E., "Some problems concerning spherical harmonics," *Arkiv f. Mat., Astr. o. Fysik.* **13:17**, 1–76 (1918).

HILLE, E., "An integral equality and its applications," *Proc. Nat. Acad. Sci.* **7**, 303–305 (1921).

HILLE, E., "Oscillation theorems in the complex domain," *Trans. Amer. Math. Soc.* **23**, 350–385 (1922).

HILLE, E., "On the zeros of Sturm-Liouville functions," *Arkiv f. Mat., Astr. o. Fysik*, **16:17**, 1–20 (1922).

HILLE, E., "Convex distribution of the zeros of Sturm-Liouville functions," *Bull. Amer. Math. Soc.* **28**, 261–265, 462 (1922).

HILLE, E., "On the zeros of Legendre functions," *Arkiv f. Mat., Astr. o. Fysik*, **17:22**, 1–16 (1923).

HILLE, E., "On the zeros of Mathieu functions," *Proc. London Math. Soc.*, (2) **23**, 185–237 (1924).

HILLE, E., "On the zeros of the functions of the parabolic cylinder," *Arkiv f. Mat., Astr. o. Fysik*, **18:26**, 1–56 (1924).

HILLE, E., "An existence theorem," *Trans. Amer. Math. Soc.* **26**, 241–248 (1924).

HILLE, E., "A note on regular singular points," *Arkiv f. Mat., Astr. o. Fysik*, **19A:2**, 1–21 (1925).

HILLE, E., "On the zeros of the functions defined by linear differential equations of the second order," *Proc. Internat. Math. Congress*, Vol. I, Toronto (1924), 511–519.

HILLE, E., "A general type of singular point," *Proc. Nat. Acad. Sci.* **10**, 488–493 (1924).

HILLE, E., "Zero point problems for linear differential equations of the second order," *Matematisk Tidsskrift*, B, 25–44 (1927).

HILLE, E., "Non-oscillation theorems," *Trans. Amer. Math. Soc.* **64**, 234–252 (1948).

HILLE, E., "Remarks on a paper by Zeev Nehari," *Bull. Amer. Math. Soc.* **55**, 552–553 (1949).

HILLE, E., and G. SZEGÖ, "On the complex zeros of Bessel functions," *Bull. Amer. Math. Soc.* **49**, 605–610 (1943).

HURWITZ, A., "Über die Nullstellen der Bessel'schen Funktion," *Math. Annalen*, **33**, 246–266 (1889); *Math. Werke*, Vol. I, 266–286.

HURWITZ, A., "Über die Nullstellen der hypergeometrischen Funktion," *Math. Annalen*, **64**, 517–560 (1907); *Math. Werke*, Vol. I, 660–705.

KLEIN, F., "Vorlesungen über die hypergeometrische Funktion," *Grundlehren der Math. Wissenschaften*, Vol. 39, Springer Verlag, Berlin (1933).

NEHARI, Z., "The Schwarzian derivative and schlicht functions," *Bull. Amer. Math. Soc.* **55**, 545–551 (1949).

NEHARI, Z., "On the zeros of solutions of second-order linear differential equations," *Amer. J. Math.* **76**, 689–697 (1954).

NEHARI, Z., "Some criteria of univalence," *Proc. Amer. Math. Soc.* **5**, 700–704 (1954).

NEHARI, Z., "Univalent functions and linear differential equations," *Lectures on Functions of a Complex Variable*, Univ. of Michigan Press, Ann Arbor (1955), 148–151.

POKARNYI, V. V., "On some sufficient conditions for univalence," *Doklady Akademii Nauk SSSR*, (*N.S.*), **79**, 743–746 (1951).

SCHAFHEITLIN, P., "Über die Nullstellen der hypergeometrischen Funktion," *Sitzungsberichte d. Berliner Math. Gesellschaft*, **7**, 19–28 (1908).

SCHWARZ, B., "Complex non-oscillation theorems and criteria of univalence," *Trans. Amer. Math. Soc.* **80**, 159–186 (1955).

TAAM, Choy-Tak, "Oscillation theorems," *Amer. J. Math.* **74**, 317–324 (1952).

TAAM, Choy-Tak, "On the complex zeros of functions of Sturm-Liouville type," *Pacific J. Math.* **3**, 837–843 (1953).

TAAM, Choy-Tak, "Schlicht functions and linear differential equations of second order," *J. Rat. Mech. Anal.* **4**, 467–480 (1955).

TAAM, Choy-Tak, "On the solutions of second-order linear differential equations," *Proc. Amer. Math. Soc.* **4**, 876–879 (1953).

VAN VLECK, E. B., "A determination of the number of real and imaginary roots of the hypergeometric series," *Trans. Amer. Math. Soc.* **3**, 110–131 (1902).

Much of the material in the later sections of the chapter is taken from an unpublished memoir of the author written in 1924.

PART III

Non-linear Equations

Appendix D
THE SCHWARZIAN

This brief appendix is devoted to the Schwarzian derivative. Schwarz, who was working on conformal mapping of circular polygons, wanted a differential expression invariant under fractional linear transformations applied to the dependent variable. He found

$$\frac{d^2}{dz^2}\left[\log \frac{dw}{dz}\right] - \frac{1}{2}\left\{\frac{d}{dz}\left[\log \frac{dw}{dz}\right]\right\}^2$$

by eliminating the arbitrary constants entering in the fractional linear transformation.

Many applications have been found for the Schwarzian and a few of these are discussed in the following.

There are four sections: The Schwarzian Derivative; Applications to Conformal Mapping; The Schwarzian and Univalence; Univalent Solutions of $y'' + Py = 0$.

D.1 THE SCHWARZIAN DERIVATIVE

In 1869, Hermann Amandus Schwarz introduced a differential operator which later became known as the *Schwarzian derivative*, or *differential parameter*, or, simply, the *Schwarzian*. Its importance soon became manifest: it occurs in the invariant theory of differential equations, in conformal mapping, and in the theory of univalence of analytic functions, to mention only the most outstanding applications.

We shall denote the Schwarzian of w with respect to z by $\{w, z\}$. It is defined by

$$\{w, z\} = \left\{\frac{w''}{w'}\right\}' - \frac{1}{2}\left(\frac{w''}{w'}\right)^2 \tag{D.1.1}$$

which may be written

$$\frac{w'''}{w'} - \frac{3}{2}\left(\frac{w''}{w'}\right)^2.$$

Here the primes denote differentiation with respect to z. There are several ways of introducing this object. From the point of view of the theory of second-order differential equations, the most natural is furnished by

Theorem D.1.1. *Let y_1 and y_2 be two linearly independent solutions of the equation*

$$y''(z) + Q(z)y(z) = 0 \tag{D.1.2}$$

defined and holomorphic in some simply-connected domain D of the complex plane. Then

$$w(z) \equiv \frac{y_1(z)}{y_2(z)} \tag{D.1.3}$$

satisfies the equation

$$\{w, z\} = 2Q(z) \tag{D.1.4}$$

at all points of D where $y_2(z) \neq 0$. Conversely, if $w(z)$ is a solution of (D.1.4), *holomorphic in some neighborhood of $z = z_0 \in D$, then there are two linearly independent solutions $u(z)$ and $v(z)$ of* (D.1.2) *defined in D such that*

$$w(z) = \frac{u(z)}{v(z)}. \tag{D.1.5}$$

Here u and v are uniquely determined if $v(z_0) = 1$.

Proof. This is essentially a matter of computation. We may assume that the Wronskian of y_2 and y_1

$$W[y_2, y_1] \equiv 1.$$

Then

$$w'(z) = [y_2(z)]^{-2} \tag{D.1.6}$$

so that

$$\frac{w''(z)}{w'(z)} = -2\frac{y_2'(z)}{y_2(z)}$$

and

$$\left(\frac{w''(z)}{w'(z)}\right)' = -2\frac{y_2''(z)}{y_2(z)} + 2\left(\frac{y_2'(z)}{y_2(z)}\right)^2$$

$$= 2Q(z) + \frac{1}{2}\frac{w''(z)}{w'(z)}.$$

This proves the first assertion.

Suppose that $w(z)$ is a solution of (D.1.4) given by its initial values

$$w(z_0), \qquad w'(z_0), \qquad w''(z_0).$$

Here $w'(z_0) \neq 0$ since otherwise $Q(z)$ would not be holomorphic at $z = z_0$. We now choose u and v as solutions of (D.1.2) subject to the initial conditions

$$u(z_0) = w(z_0), \qquad u'(z_0) = \frac{2[w'(z_0)]^2 - w(z_0)w''(z_0)}{2w'(z_0)},$$

$$v(z_0) = 1, \qquad v'(z_0) = -\frac{w''(z_0)}{2w'(z_0)}.$$

This is possible and, as we have just seen,

$$\frac{u(z)}{v(z)} \equiv w_1(z) \tag{D.1.7}$$

is a solution of (D.1.4). A simple calculation shows that $w(z)$ and $w_1(z)$ have the same initial values at $z = z_0$. Hence they are identical in their common domain of existence. Here $w_1(z)$ is a meromorphic function of z in D, hence $w(z)$ exists in D and is represented there by (D1.7). ∎

With y_1 and y_2 as in the preceding theorem, let us write

$$\eta(z) = \frac{y_1(z)}{y_2(z)}. \tag{D.1.8}$$

Then $\eta(z)$ is a solution of (D.1.4). The general solution is

$$\frac{a\eta(z) + b}{a\eta(z) + a}, \qquad ad - bc = 1, \tag{D.1.9}$$

involving three arbitrary constants. For the general solution is the quotient of two linearly independent solutions of (D.1.2), i.e. of the form

$$\frac{ay_1 + by_2}{cy_1 + dy_2} = \frac{a\eta + b}{c\eta + d}.$$

This suggests

Theorem D.1.2. *The Schwarzian is invariant under linear fractional transformations acting on its first argument*

$$\left\{\frac{aw + b}{cw + d}, z\right\} = \{w, z\}. \tag{D.1.10}$$

The proof is left to the reader.

One way of expressing this is to say that *the Schwarzian is a differential invariant of the group of linear fractional transformations,* known also as the *projective group.*

We may apply a fractional linear transformation to the second argument instead. We state the result without proof

$$\left\{w, \frac{az + b}{cz + d}\right\} \frac{(ad - bc)^2}{(cz + d)^4} = \{w, z\}. \tag{D.1.11}$$

The reader will recognize the second factor on the left as the square of the derivative of $(az + b)(cz + d)^{-1}$ with respect to z.

EXERCISE D.1

1. If $\{w, z\} \equiv 0$ show that $w = (az + b)(cz + d)^{-1}$ with $ad - bc = 1$.
2. If $f(z)$ is holomorphic at infinity, show that $z^4\{f, z\}$ is holomorphic there.

3. If $f(z) = 4z(1 + z)^{-2}$, show that $\{f, z\} = -6(1 - z^2)^{-2}$ and that f is univalent in the unit circle, i.e. $z_1 \neq z_2$ implies that $f(z_1) \neq f(z_2)$.
4. If $f(z) = \log[(z - a)/(z - b)]$, $a \neq b$, show that

$$\{f, z\} = \frac{1}{2}\frac{(a - b)^2}{(z - a)^2(z - b)^2} \equiv 2Q(z).$$

What is the general solution of $y'' + Q(z)y = 0$?
5. If $Z = \int_a^z [Q(t)]^{1/2}\, dt$, find $\{Z, z\}$. Compare the result with the formulas for the Liouville transformation.
6. Verify (D.1.10).
7. Verify (D.1.11).
8. If $w(z)$ is a solution of (D.1.4), show that the general solution of (D.1.2) is

$$[w'(z)]^{-1/2}[A + Bw(z)].$$

9. If $y'' + 2P(z)y' + Q(z)y = 0$, determine U such that, if $y = Uv$, then v satisfies

$$v'' + [Q - P' - P^2]v = 0.$$

10. Show that it is possible to reduce the equation still further to the form

$$\frac{d^2w}{d\eta^2} = 0$$

by taking the quotient of two independent solutions of the v-equation as new independent variable η and setting $w = v[\eta'(z)]^{1/2}$.
11. Show that

$$\{w, z\} = -\{z, w\}\left(\frac{dw}{dz}\right)^2.$$

12. Show that

$$\{w, z\} = \{w, u\}\left(\frac{du}{dz}\right)^2 + \{u, z\}.$$

D.2 APPLICATIONS TO CONFORMAL MAPPING

Schwarz introduced his differential parameter in a study of the problem of mapping the upper half-plane conformally on to a circular polygon. This problem turned out to be intimately connected with the theory of second-order differential equations of the Fuchsian class. Moreover, the problem triggered off a chain-reaction which, in the 1880's, led Henri Poincaré and Felix Klein to the theory of *automorphic functions*, i.e. analytic functions $F(z)$ such that

$$F(Sz) = F(z) \tag{D.2.1}$$

where S belongs to a given group $\mathfrak{G}$ of fractional linear transformations on z. Under suitable assumptions on $\mathfrak{G}$, there exists a circular polygon Π, the interior of which acts as a fundamental region of the group, in the sense that the images of this region under the group cover without overlapping the domain of existence of the function F. Furthermore, the inverse of the mapping function of the fundamental region is an automorphic function of the group.

It would take us too far afield to unravel these deep connections and we shall restrict ourselves to bringing out the relation between the mapping problem and the Fuchsian class.

Let there be given a simple closed circular polygon Π in the finite w-plane. Its vertices shall be $A_1, A_2, \ldots, A_n$, enumerated in such a way that the interior of Π lies to the left of the arc A_j, A_{j+1} (with $A_{n+1} = A_1$) for each j. The sides are circular arcs or, possibly, straight line segments. At A_j the two adjacent sides shall make an angle of $\pi\alpha_j$ with each other in the interior of Π where $0 < \alpha_j < 2$ and $\alpha_j \neq 1$.

The Riemann mapping theorem asserts that it is possible to map the upper half of the z-plane conformally on the interior of Π. The mapping function is unique up to a linear fractional transformation which leaves the upper half-plane invariant. Here the boundaries are in one-to-one correspondence. In particular, the vertex A_j corresponds to a point a_j on the real axis, and we may suppose that

$$a_1 < a_2 < a_3 < \cdots < a_n.$$

Actually we can fix three of these points, say the first three, at pre-assigned points by a suitable choice of the mapping function. The remaining points a_j are then uniquely determined. We call this mapping function $f(z)$.

This function $f(z)$ is fairly complicated but $\{f, z\}$ is a simple rational function with double poles at $z = a_j, j = 1, 2, \ldots, n$, which vanishes at least to the third order at infinity. This implies that $f(z)$ is the quotient of two linearly independent solutions of a second-order linear differential equation of the Fuchsian class. More precisely we shall sketch a proof of the following

Theorem D.2.1. *If the a's and the α's satisfy the restrictions stated above, then there exist real numbers β_j such that*

$$\{f, z\} = \sum_{j=1}^{n} \left[\frac{1}{2}\frac{1 - \alpha_j^2}{(z - a_j)^2} + \frac{\beta_j}{z - a_j}\right] \tag{D.2.2}$$

where

$$\sum_1^n \beta_j = 0, \quad \sum_1^n [2\beta_j a_j + 1 - \alpha_j^2] = 0, \quad \sum_1^n [\beta_j a_j^2 + (1 - \alpha_j^2)a_j] = 0. \tag{D.2.3}$$

Proof. The mapping of the upper half-plane on to the interior of Π is one-to-one, so $f'(z) \neq 0$ for $\Im(z) > 0$. This means that $\{f, z\}$ exists and is holomorphic for $\Im(z) > 0$. On the open interval (a_j, a_{j+1}) we see that $f(z)$ is continuous and its values fill out the arc (A_j, A_{j+1}). By the extended form of the principle of symmetry, also first observed by Schwarz, $f(z)$ can be continued analytically across the interval (a_j, a_{j+1}). The continuation is holomorphic in the lower half-plane and its value at $\bar{z}$ is obtained from its value at z by a reciprocation in the circular arc (A_j, A_{j+1}). Thus, if the center of the circle is at $w = b$ and its radius is R, then

$$f(\bar{z}) = b + \frac{R^2}{\overline{f(z)} - \bar{b}}.$$

The values of $f(z)$ in the lower half-plane fill out the interior of a polygon Π_j similar to Π and obtained from Π_j by reciprocation in the arc (A_j, A_{j+1}). Analytic continuation is possible across each of the arcs (A_j, A_{j+1}) including (A_n, A_1), and gives rise to a system of n polygons attached to Π, all of which are conformal images of the lower half-plane under the various determinations of $f(z)$ obtained by analytic continuation across the real axis. Again, $f'(z) \neq 0$ on each interval (a_j, a_{j+1}) as well as in the lower half-plane. This means that $\{f, z\}$ is holomorphic for each continuation. We can now get back to the upper half-plane by crossing one of the segments (a_k, a_{k+1}). This corresponds to crossing one of the arcs bounding one of the polygons Π_j and applying a reciprocation with respect to such an arc to get the relation between the values of f at conjugate points. If z is made to describe a closed path in the plane surrounding one or more of the points a_j, then f will normally not return to its initial value, but the function is locally holomorphic and so is its Schwarzian. As we shall see below, $\{f, z\}$ is actually single-valued. In any case, the points $a_1, a_2, \ldots, a_n$ are the only singularities of f and of $\{f, z\}$ in the finite plane.

Now the point at infinity is not singular for any determination of f. In the conformal mapping $z = \infty$ corresponds to an interior point of an arc forming part of the boundary of the polygon under consideration, an interior point of (A_n, A_1) in the original polygon Π. This means that a full neighborhood of the point in question is in one-to-one correspondence with a full neighborhood of $z = \infty$ and this implies that $z = \infty$ is not singular. Since f is not singular at $z = \infty$, the Schwarzian has the same property and, by Problem 2, Exercise D.1, $z^4\{f, z\}$ is holomorphic at ∞.

We note in passing that $\{f, z\}$ is real on each of the intervals (a_j, a_{j+1}) of the real axis, regardless of what determination is chosen for f. For we can find constants a, b, c, d with $ad - bc = 1$, such that

$$F(z) = \frac{af(z) + b}{cf(z) + d} \tag{D.2.4}$$

is real on this interval. Indeed, the values of f are located on a circular arc in the w-plane and all we need to do is to choose the constants so that this arc is mapped on to a segment of the real axis. But if F is real on (a_j, a_{j+1}), so are its derivatives and so is $\{F, z\}$, which equals $\{f, z\}$ by Theorem D.1.2.

We can use the same device for the discussion of $\{f, z\}$ at one of the singular points $z = a_j$. For the given determination of f, this point corresponds to a vertex w_0 of one of the polygons arising during the iterated reflection process. At $w = w_0$ two circular arcs intersect, making an angle $\alpha_j \pi$ with each other. Let w_1 be the second point of intersection of these arcs extended. Then the transformation

$$w^* = e^{i\omega} \frac{w - w_0}{w - w_1}$$

maps the circles on to two straight lines through the origin of the w^*-plane and, if ω is properly chosen, one of the arcs ending at w_0 is mapped on a segment $(0, A)$ of the positive real axis. The corresponding function

$$F(z) = e^{i\omega} \frac{f(z) - w_0}{f(z) - w_1}$$

is then of the form

$$F(z) = (z - a_j)^{\alpha_j} H_j(z)$$

where $H_j(z)$ is a power series in $z - a_j$ with real coefficients and $H_j(a_j) \neq 0$. A simple calculation then gives

$$\{f, z\} = \{F, z\} = \frac{1}{2} \frac{1 - \alpha_j^2}{(z - a_j)^2} + \frac{\beta_j}{z - a_j} + h_j(z)$$

where $h_j(z)$ is holomorphic at $z = a_j$. Further β_j is real.

We now form

$$\Delta(z) = \{f, z\} - \frac{1}{2} \sum_{j=1}^{n} \frac{1 - \alpha_j^2}{(z - a_j)^2} - \sum_{j=1}^{n} \frac{\beta_j}{z - a_j}. \qquad \text{(D.2.5)}$$

No matter what determination we choose for f, the difference $\Delta(z)$ is holomorphic at each of the points a_j and hence locally holomorphic in the finite plane. This means that, starting anywhere in the plane, we can continue $\Delta(z)$ analytically along any path in the finite plane without encountering any singularity of the function. Such a function is necessarily holomorphic in the finite plane, in particular single-valued. Now at infinity $\Delta(z)$ is also holomorphic since each of the components has this property. By the theorem of Liouville, $\Delta(z)$ is a constant and, since $\Delta(z) = 0$ at $z = \infty$, we have $\Delta(z) \equiv 0$. This proves (D.2.2). Since f is holomorphic at infinity, we know that $z^4\{f, z\}$ is also holomorphic at infinity. This implies certain relations between the constants a_j, α_k, β_l, namely those given by (D.2.3). ∎

If $\{f, z\}$ is given by (D.2.2) then the equation

$$y''(z) + \tfrac{1}{2}\{f, z\} y(z) = 0 \qquad \text{(D.2.6)}$$

is clearly of the Fuchsian class. For each of the points $z = a_j$ is a regular singular point, the roots of the indicial equation being $\frac{1}{2} \pm \frac{1}{2}\alpha_j$. The point $z = \infty$ is not singular since $z^3\{f, z\} = 0$ at $z = \infty$.

EXERCISE D.2

1. Verify (D.2.3).
2. Construct a mapping function for a lens-shaped region bounded by two circular arcs with vertices at $z = \pm 1$.
3. The cases $\alpha_j = 0$ and 2 excluded above correspond to interior or exterior horn angles, and the corresponding circular polygons may be degenerate or improper. Problem 4, Exercise D.1, gives an example with $\alpha_1 = \alpha_2 = 0$. Take $a = -1$, $b = +1$, and show that there are linear fractional transforms of the given f which map the upper half-plane on to a domain bounded by two circles tangent to each other either internally or externally. Take the point of tangency to be $w = 0$ and the real axis as the common tangent. The domain is outside of both circles for external tangency, otherwise inside of one and outside of the other.
4. Problem 3, Exercise D.1, gives a case with $\alpha_1 = \alpha_2 = 2$. Show that $2z(1 + z^2)^{-1}$ belongs to the family of mapping functions and that this function maps the upper half-plane on the whole w-plane cut along the segment $[-1, 1]$. The latter taken as a double line is the degenerate polygon with two (2π)-angles.
5. Consider the invariant form of the hypergeometric equation

$$y'' + \frac{1}{4}\left\{\frac{1-\alpha_1^2}{z^2} + \frac{1-\alpha_2^2}{(z-1)^2} + \frac{\alpha_1^2+\alpha_2^2-\alpha_3^2-1}{z(z-1)}\right\}y = 0.$$

This is of type (D.2.6), but the third singular point is at ∞. Take

$$f(z) = y_{02}(z)[y_{01}(z)]^{-1}$$

where y_{01} and y_{02} form the fundamental system at $z = 0$ defined by (7.1.5) and (7.1.8), and the relations between a, b, c and α_1, α_2, α_3 are read off from (11.4.3). Show that f maps the upper half-plane on the interior of a triangle OPQ with angles $\alpha_1\pi$, $\alpha_2\pi$, $\alpha_3\pi$. Take $0 < \alpha_1$, $0 < \alpha_2$, $0 < \alpha_3$, $\alpha_1 + \alpha_2 + \alpha_3 < 1$. Here O is the origin, P lies on the positive real axis, OP and OQ are straight line segments and PQ is a circular arc.

D.3 THE SCHWARZIAN AND UNIVALENCE

Let $f(z)$ be holomorphic in a domain D. We say that $f(z)$ is *univalent* in D if $z_1 \neq z_2$ implies $f(z_1) \neq f(z_2)$ for z_1 and z_2 in D. A necessary condition for univalency in D is that $f'(z) \neq 0$ in D. Hence, if f is holomorphic and univalent in D, then the Schwarzian $\{f, z\}$ is holomorphic in D. It is natural to ask if $\{f, z\}$ has other more specific properties in D. For special choices of D, it is possible to give other necessary conditions for univalency.

The two domains which are usually considered in this connection are the interior K and the exterior Y of the unit circle. We denote by **S** the class of functions

$$f(z) = z + a_2 z^2 + a_3 z^3 + \cdots \tag{D.3.1}$$

which are univalent in K, and by **U** the class of functions

$$F(z) = z + \alpha_0 + \alpha_1 z^{-1} + \alpha_2 z^{-2} + \cdots \tag{D.3.2}$$

which are univalent in Y. The elements of the two classes are in one-to-one correspondence, if

$$f(z) \in \mathbf{S} \qquad \text{then} \qquad [f(\tfrac{1}{z})]^{-1} \in \mathbf{U} \tag{D.3.3}$$

and vice versa. If $F(z) = [f(\frac{1}{z})]^{-1}$, then

$$\alpha_1 = a_2^2 - a_3, \tag{D.3.4}$$

a relation which will be used below. We shall also need

Lemma D.3.1. *If* $F(z) \in \mathbf{U}$, *then* $|\alpha_1| \leq 1$.

This is a consequence of Gronwall's area theorem

$$\sum_1^\infty n|\alpha_n|^2 \leq 1 \tag{D.3.5}$$

which also shows that the inequality is the best possible since

$$z + \alpha_0 + e^{i\theta} z^{-1} \in \mathbf{U}$$

for any choice of the arc θ. Some indications of the proof of (D.3.5) are given in the Exercise below.

We shall now prove a result due to Zeev Nehari (1949).

Theorem D.3.1. *If* $f(z)$ *is univalent in* K, *then*

$$|\{f, z\}| \leq 6(1 - |z|^2)^{-2} \tag{D.3.6}$$

and 6 *is the best possible constant.*

Proof. Let a be an arbitrary point in K. Then

$$Z = \frac{z + a}{1 + \bar{a}z} = a + (1 - |a|^2)(z - \bar{a}z^2 + \bar{a}^2 z^3 - \cdots) \equiv a + w \tag{D.3.7}$$

maps K in a one-to-one manner on to itself. It follows that $f(Z)$ is a univalent function of z in K. It does not belong to **S** but

$$g(z) \equiv \frac{f(Z) - f(a)}{f'(a)(1 - |a|^2)} \equiv z + a_2 z^2 + a_3 z^3 + \cdots \tag{D.3.8}$$

does. We must compute a_2 and a_3. To do so, we note that

$$f(a + w) = f(a) + f'(a)w + \tfrac{1}{2}f''(a)w^2 + \tfrac{1}{6}f'''(a)w^3 + \cdots$$

Here we substitute the power series for w, expand the powers of w, and collect terms. By the Weierstrass double series theorem this is permitted for small values of $|z|$. The result is

$$a_2 = -\bar{a} + \frac{1}{2}\frac{f''(a)}{f'(a)}(1 - |a|^2),$$

$$a_3 = \bar{a}^2 - \bar{a}\frac{f''(a)}{f'(a)}(1 - |a|^2) + \frac{1}{6}\frac{f'''(a)}{f'(a)}(1 - |a|^2)^2. \tag{D.3.9}$$

This gives

$$a_2^2 - a_3 = -\tfrac{1}{6}(1 - |a|^2)^2\left[\frac{f'''(a)}{f'(a)} - \frac{3}{2}\left(\frac{f''(a)}{f'(a)}\right)^2\right]$$

$$= -\tfrac{1}{6}(1 - |a|^2)^2\{f, a\}.$$

By (D.3.4) and Lemma D.3.1 this expression is at most 1 in absolute value. Since a is arbitrary, (D.3.6) follows.

To see that no smaller constant than 6 will do, we refer to Problem 3, Exercise D.1, which exhibits a function univalent in K for which $\{f, z\} = -6(1 - z^2)^{-2}$. ∎

In the preceding section we considered functions univalent in the upper half-plane. Using Problem 11, Exercise D.1, we see that the condition now takes the form

Corollary. *If $f(z)$ is univalent in the upper half-plane, $y > 0$, then*

$$|\{f, z\}| \le \tfrac{3}{2}y^{-2}, \qquad z = x + iy. \tag{D.3.10}$$

The constant is the best possible.

The function $f = z^2$ is univalent in the upper half-plane and $\{z^2, z\} = -\frac{3}{2}z^{-2}$.

Incidentally, it is known that if $g(z) \in \mathbf{S}$, then $|a_2| \le 2$. It follows that

$$\left|-\bar{a} + \tfrac{1}{2}(1 - |a|^2)\frac{f''(a)}{f'(a)}\right| \le 2$$

and hence

$$\left|\frac{f''(z)}{f'(z)}\right| \le \frac{6}{1 - |z|^2}. \tag{D.3.11}$$

Again, no smaller constant will do, since, if

$$f(z) = \frac{z}{(1 + z)^2}, \qquad \text{then} \qquad \frac{f''(z)}{f'(z)} = 2\frac{z - 2}{1 - z^2}$$

and $2z - 4 \to -6$ as $z \to -1$.

These conditions are necessary. As proved in Section 11.2, sufficient conditions for univalency in K are obtained by lowering the constants, in (D.3.6) from 6 to 2, in (D.3.10) from $\frac{3}{2}$ to $\frac{1}{2}$. Cf. formulas (11.2.18) and (11.2.25) and remember that $\{f, z\} = 2Q(z)$ in comparing results.

We have further sufficient conditions in Section 11.2. Formula (11.2.20) shows that

$$|\{f, z\}| \le 2(3 - \alpha)(1 - |z|^2)^{-\alpha}, \qquad 1 \le \alpha \le 2, \tag{D.3.12}$$

implies that $f(z)$ is univalent in K (V. V. Pokornyi, 1951, P. R. Beesack, 1956; see also (11.2.22)). Theorem 11.2.4 (Nehari, 1949) gives

$$|\{f, z\}| \le \tfrac{1}{2}\pi^2 \tag{D.3.13}$$

as a sufficient condition for univalence in K.

As a further instance of relations between the Schwarzian and univalence, we cite an investigation of R. Nevanlinna (1932) where the following problem is posed and solved.

Given q (≥ 2) points $a_1, \ldots, a_q$ and q positive integers $\mu_1, \ldots, \mu_q$, $\sum \mu_j = p$. Find all analytic functions $z(w)$ with the following properties:

1) *The function $z(w)$ is meromorphic in the w-plane punctured at $a_1, \ldots, a_q$.*
2) *$z(w)$ is univalent,*
3) *Over each of the points a_j there are μ_j distinct logarithmic elements of $z(w)$ and possibly also regular elements.*
4) *The range of $z(w)$ is a simply-connected domain D.*

In the case $q = 2$ we must have $\mu_1 = \mu_2 = 1$, $p = 2$, and

$$z(w) = \alpha \log \frac{w - a_1}{w - a_2} + \beta \tag{D.3.14}$$

with arbitrary constants α and β. For $q \ge 3$ the problem is solvable iff $2\mu_j \le p$ for each j. The range of $z(w)$ is then always the finite plane so that there is a unique single-valued inverse function $w(z)$ defined in the finite plane. Moreover, there exists a polynomial $P(z)$ of degree $p - 2$ such that

$$\{w, z\} = 2P(z). \tag{D.3.15}$$

Conversely, any choice of the polynomial $P(z)$ of degree $p - 2$ leads to functions $z(w)$ with the desired properties.

It follows that

$$w(z) = \frac{y_1(z)}{y_2(z)} \tag{D.3.16}$$

where y_1 and y_2 are linearly independent solutions of the equation

$$y''(z) + P(z)y(z) = 0. \tag{D.3.17}$$

The discussion in Section 7.4 shows that y_1 and y_2 are entire functions of order $\frac{1}{2}p$ (and normal type of this order) and $w(z)$ is a meromorphic function of the same order.

Any choice of y_1 and y_2 subject to the stated conditions is admissible and leads to a corresponding function $z(w)$ with the stated properties. The numbers a_j are simply those values of C for which the solution

$$y_1 - Cy_2$$

is subdominant in one of the p sectors surrounding the point at infinity. (Cf. Section 7.4.) If for $C = a_j$ the solution is subdominant in μ_j sectors, then the inverse function $z(w)$ has μ_j distinct logarithmic elements over $w = a_j$. There are, in addition, always infinitely many regular elements if $p > 2$. The condition $2\mu_j \le p$ says that $\mu_j \le [\frac{1}{2}p]$, i.e. the given solution can be subdominant in at most half of the sectors. That this bound can be reached is shown by the equation (7.4.39).

The value of $q \le p$ and of the integers μ_j is uniquely determined by the coefficients of $P(z)$. On the other hand, the position of $a_1, \ldots, a_q$ depends upon the choice of y_1 and y_2. Passing from one fundamental system to another amounts to a fractional linear transformation of the w-plane and a corresponding transformation of the critical points a_j. If $p = q = 3$ the a_j's can be given three assigned distinct values and the corresponding polynomial $P(z)$ can be chosen as $-z$. If $p = 4$, we have $q = 3$ or 4. The equation (D.3.17) can be reduced to the Hermite-Weber equation involving a single parameter. (See (7.5.48).) The exceptional case $q = 3$ arises iff γ is an odd integer. For other values of γ, the cross-ratio of the four critical points is a simple function of γ.

For further details we must refer to Nevanlinna's paper.

EXERCISE D.3

1. If $F(z) \in \mathbf{U}$ and $r > 1$, then the circle $|z| = r$ is mapped by F on a simple closed analytic curve Γ_r. The area enclosed by Γ_r is

$$A(r) = \frac{1}{2}\int_0^{2\pi}\left\{U\frac{\partial V}{\partial\theta} - V\frac{\partial U}{\partial\theta}\right\} d\theta, \qquad F(z) = U(r\,e^{i\theta}) + iV(r\,e^{i\theta}).$$

Show that the integral equals the imaginary part of

$$\tfrac{1}{2}\int_{|z|=r} \overline{F(z)}F'(z)\,dz.$$

2. Show that

$$A(r) = \pi\left[r^2 - \sum_{n=1}^{\infty} n|\alpha_n|^2 r^{-2n}\right] > 0$$

for all $r > 1$ and derive (D.3.5) from this result.

3. Verify (D.3.9).

4. Verify the Corollary.

5. Show that $f(z)$ is univalent for $y > 0$, $z = x + iy$, if

$$[x^2 + (y + 1)^2]^2 |\{f, z\}| \leq 2\pi^2.$$

6. Show that another sufficient condition for univalence in $y > 0$ is

$$y[x^2 + (y + 1)^2] |\{f, z\}| \leq 4.$$

7. Suppose that $z(w)$ is given by (D.3.14). Find the corresponding equation (D.3.17). Show that $P(z) = -\frac{1}{4}\alpha^{-2}$, independent of a_1, a_2, and β. Determine these quantities if $y_1 = \sinh(z/2\alpha)$, $y = \cosh(z/2\alpha)$. What happens if we take $y_1, y_2 = \exp(\pm z/2\alpha)$ instead?
8. Suppose that f and $\{f, z\}$ are holomorphic in K and

$$\sup_{z \in K} |\{f, z\}| = A.$$

What is the least upper bound $\bar{A}$ ($\geq \frac{1}{2}\pi^2$) of the values of A for which there exists a function f univalent in K satisfying this condition?

9. Answer the same question if the condition reads

$$\sup_{z \in K} (1 - |z|^2) |\{f, z\}| = A \qquad (\bar{A} \geq 4).$$

D.4 UNIVALENT SOLUTIONS OF $y'' + Py = 0$

In the preceding section, bounds were found for the Schwarzian $\{f, z\}$ sufficient to make f univalent in $K = (z \mid |z| < 1)$. If $2P(z)$ satisfies such a condition in K, then the quotient of any two linearly independent solutions of

$$y'' + P(z)y = 0 \tag{D.4.1}$$

is univalent in K. In general these criteria fail to give any information about univalency of the solutions themselves. A long step toward filling this gap in our knowledge was taken by M. S. Robertson in 1954.

He is mainly concerned with the case where $z = 0$ is a regular singular point of the equation. If for $|z| < 1$

$$z^2 P(z) = \sum_{n=0}^{\infty} p_n z^n,$$

the indicial equation

$$\rho(\rho - 1) + p_0 = 0$$

has two roots α and β with $\Re(\alpha) \geq \frac{1}{2} \geq \Re(\beta)$. Corresponding to $\rho = \alpha$, there is a unique solution

$$y_1(z) = z^{\alpha}\left[1 + \sum_{n=1}^{\infty} a_n z^n\right], \qquad |z| < 1. \tag{D.4.2}$$

Here

$$f(z) = [y_1(z)]^{1/\alpha} = z + \cdots \tag{D.4.3}$$

is holomorphic and univalent if $|z| < R$ where $0 < R \leq 1$. Under what conditions on $P(z)$ will $R = 1$, i.e. will $f \in \mathbf{S}$, the class of univalent functions considered in the preceding section? More especially, we may ask, with Robertson, under what assumptions will

$$\Re\left[z\frac{f'(z)}{f(z)}\right] \geq 0, \qquad z \in K? \tag{D.4.4}$$

Then f is said to be *star-like*, for f maps K conformally on a domain D which is a star domain with respect to the origin, i.e. if $z_0 \in D$, so does the line segment joining 0 and z_0. More generally, does there exist a real γ, $|\gamma| \leq \frac{1}{2}\pi$, such that

$$\Re\left\{e^{i\gamma}z\frac{f'(z)}{f(z)}\right\} \geq 0, \qquad z \in K? \tag{D.4.5}$$

If $f(0) = 0$, $f'(0) = 1$ and either (D.4.4) or (D.4.5) is satisfied, then $f \in \mathbf{S}$.

A basic tool in the discussion of this problem is a modified version of the Green's transform

$$|y(z)|^2\Re\left[e^{i\gamma}z\frac{y'(z)}{y(z)}\right] = r\cos\gamma\int_0^r |y'(\rho\, e^{i\theta})|^2\, d\rho$$
$$- r\int_0^r \Re[e^{i\gamma}(\rho\, e^{i\theta})^2 P(\rho\, e^{i\theta})]|y(\rho\, e^{i\theta})|^2\frac{d\rho}{\rho^2}, \tag{D.4.6}$$

which is valid for $y = y_1$. This is combined with a majorant method which gives a class of functions $P(z)$ for which (D.4.5) is satisfied by the $f(z)$ defined by (D.4.3). The statement of Robertson's main theorem is lengthy and involves a number of preliminary steps. Instead of describing these we shall restrict ourselves to stating some of his results relating to the case where $zP(z)$ is holomorphic at the origin, so that $\alpha = 1$ and $\beta = 0$.

Theorem D.4.1. *Let $zP(z)$ be holomorphic in K and satisfy a condition of the form*

$$\Re[z^2P(z)] \leq A + B|z| + C|z|^2, \qquad |z| < 1. \tag{D.4.7}$$

Then the solution of (D.4.1) *with $y(0) = 0$, $y'(0) = 1$ is univalent and star-like in K if one of the following conditions holds:*

i) $A = B = 0$, $C = \frac{1}{4}\pi^2$.
ii) $A = C = 0$, $B = \frac{1}{4}X_1^2$ ($\sim$ 1.446) *where X_1 is the least positive zero of the Bessel function $J_0(X)$.*
iii) $B = C = 0$, $A = \frac{1}{2}s_1^2 + \frac{1}{8}$ *where s_1 is the least positive zero of the function*

$$\int_0^\infty [3 + \cosh t]^{-1/2}\cos(st)\, dt, \qquad 1.3 < s_1 < 1.4.$$

In all three cases the constants cannot be replaced by larger numbers. For further details we refer to the original paper.

EXERCISE D.4

1. If in (D.4.7) $A = B = 0$, show that $\frac{1}{4}\pi^2$ is the largest possible value for C.
2. The equation

$$zy'' + by = 0, \qquad |b| \leq \tfrac{1}{4}X_1^2,$$

satisfies condition (ii) of the above theorem. The solution which is holomorphic at the origin is expressible in terms of the Bessel function J_1 (not J_0). What property of this function is implied by the theorem?

3. Verify (D.4.6).

COLLATERAL READING

Reference is made to the following items:

BEESACK, P. R., "Non-oscillation and disconjugacy in the complex domain," *Trans. Amer. Math. Soc.* **81**, 211–242 (1956).

HILLE, E., "Remarks on a paper by Zeev Nehari," *Bull. Amer. Math. Soc.* **55**, 552–553 (1949).

HILLE, E., *Analytic Function Theory*, **2**, Section 17.6. Ginn and Co., Boston (1962).

NEHARI, Z., "The Schwarzian derivative and schlicht functions," *Bull. Amer. Math. Soc.* **55**, 545–551 (1949).

NEVANLINNA, R., "Über Riemannsche Flächen mit endlich vielen Windungspunkten," *Acta Math.* **58**, 295–373 (1932).

POKARNYI, V. V., "On some sufficient conditions for univalence." (Russian), *Doklady Akad. Nauk SSSR, N.S.* **79**, 743–746 (1951).

ROBERTSON, M. S., "Schlicht solutions of $W'' + pW = 0$," *Trans. Amer. Math. Soc.* **76**, 254–274 (1954).

SCHWARZ, H. A., "Über einige Abbildungsaufgaben," *J. reine u. angew. Math.* **70**, 105–120 (1869); *Gesammelte Math. Abhandlungen*, **2**, 65–83 (1890).

12 NON-LINEAR DIFFERENTIAL EQUATIONS IN THE COMPLEX DOMAIN

In this last chapter we give a brief account of a few aspects of the theory of non-linear differential equations in the complex plane. While a linear differential equation has fixed singular points, namely those of the coefficients plus, as a rule, the point at ∞, this is no longer the case for non-linear equations. Here one can usually place a singularity at any desired point. While the position is arbitrary, the nature of the singularity is not.

For the case of a first-order equation of the form

$$w' = R(z, w),$$

R rational in w, the movable singularities are necessarily algebraic as proved by P. Painlevé. If the movable singularities are to be poles, the equation must be of the Riccati type, i.e. R is a polynomial in w of degree 2. For second-order equations we may have movable transcendental critical points as well as movable essential singularities. For third-order equations movable natural boundaries may arise.

The main problem in the chapter is to determine the equations with fixed critical points. If both degree and order are one, the Riccati equations furnish the answer. We also discuss first-order equations of higher degree of the two special types

$$(w')^2 = R(z, w) \qquad \text{and} \qquad (w')^m = P(w)$$

where R is rational and P a polynomial. Finally we give a condensed account of the results of P. Painlevé and P. Boutroux for the second-order case.

There are four sections: Equations of the First Order and the First Degree; Binomial Equations; The Equations of Briot and Bouquet; and The Transcendents of Painlevé.

12.1 EQUATIONS OF THE FIRST ORDER AND THE FIRST DEGREE

In this chapter we are concerned with non-linear differential equations mostly of the first order. We start with the case where the derivative of w with respect to z is a known analytic function of z and w, say

$$w'(z) = f(z, w). \tag{12.1.1}$$

Here $f(z, w)$ is supposed to be holomorphic for (z, w) in some domain D in the space C^2 of two complex variables.

The existence theorems, say Theorem 2.5.1, show that given $(z_0, w_0) \in D$, there is a unique function

$$w(z; z_0, w_0),$$

holomorphic together with $f(z, w(z; z_0, w_0))$ in some disk $\Delta: |z - z_0| < r$, such that

$$w(z_0; z_0, w_0) = w_0, \qquad w'(z; z_0, w_0) = f(z, w(z; z_0, w_0))$$

for all z in Δ.

Formulas (2.5.5) and (2.5.21) give lower bounds for r. It is of some importance for us to have uniform bounds. Let $\eta > 0$ and let $D(\eta) \subset D$ be a bounded domain of distance $\geq \eta$ from the complement of D. Distance here means Euclidean distance in C^2. We take two values of η, $\eta = \delta$ and $\eta = 2\delta$, and suppose that $D(2\delta) \subset D(\delta)$ and that the distance from $D(2\delta)$ to the complement of $D(\delta)$ is δ. We can then find a constant $B = B_\delta$ such that

$$|f(z, w)| \leq B\left[1 - \frac{1}{\delta}|z - z_0|\right]^{-1}\left[1 - \frac{1}{\delta}|w - w_0|\right]^{-1} \tag{12.1.2}$$

for

$$(z_0, w_0) \in D(2\delta), \qquad (z, w) \in D(\delta), \qquad |z - z_0| < \delta, \qquad |w - w_0| < \delta.$$

From Eq. (2.5.19) with z, w, z_0, w_0 replaced by $z - z_0$, $w - w_0$, δ, δ, respectively, we conclude that the radius of holomorphism of $w(z; z_0, w_0)$ satisfies

$$r \geq r_0 \equiv \delta\{1 - \exp[-(2B)^{-1}]\}, \tag{12.1.3}$$

a fixed positive number.

The solution $w(z; z_0, w_0)$ normally exists in a larger domain than the disk Δ. Suppose that we can continue $w(z; z_0, w_0)$ along a path Γ in the z-plane leading from $z = z_0$ to $z = z_1$. If $\zeta \in \Gamma$, set $\omega = w(\zeta; z_0, w_0)$ and suppose that $f(z, w)$ is holomorphic at each point (ζ, ω) for $\zeta \in \Gamma$, $\zeta \neq z_1$. Then the continuation of $w(z; z_0, w_0)$ along Γ is a solution of (12.1.1).

It should be noted that it is not sufficient for our purposes that $w(z; z_0, w_0)$ and $f(z, w(z; z_0, w_0))$ are holomorphic at each point of a curve Γ leading from z_0. This is illustrated by the equation

$$w'(z) = 1 + (w - z)g(w), \tag{12.1.4}$$

where $g(w)$ is holomorphic in $|w| < 1$ and has $|w| = 1$ as its natural boundary. Here $w(z) = z$ is a solution of the equation for $|z| < 1$ and $f(z, w(z)) \equiv 1$. Both functions can be continued analytically outside the unit disk, but $f(z, w)$ does not exist in any neighborhood of a point (z_1, z_1) with $|z_1| > 1$, so the analytic continuation of the solution is not a solution outside the unit disk.

Let us return to the path Γ and examine the various possibilities which may arise as $z \to z_1$. We shall distinguish between six cases. The discussion goes back to Painlevé's Stockholm Lectures of 1895.

Case 1. *$w(z; z_0, w_0) \to w_1$ as $z \to z_1$ along Γ and $f(z, w)$ is holomorphic at (z_1, w_1). Assertion (known as the "Theorem of Painlevé"):*

The continuation of $w(z; z_0, w_0)$ along Γ is holomorphic at $z = z_1$ and in some neighborhood of this point it coincides with $w(z; z_1, w_1)$.

Proof. A curve Γ^* is defined parametrically in C^2 by

$$z = \zeta, \qquad w = \omega = w(\zeta; z_0, w_0) \tag{12.1.5}$$

for $\zeta \in \Gamma$, $\zeta \neq z_1$. We complete the definition by adding the limit-point (z_1, w_1) to Γ^*. Since $f(z, w)$ is holomorphic at each point (ζ, ω) of the closed set Γ^*, we can find domains $D(\delta)$ and $D(2\delta)$ in C^2, with properties as stated above, such that

$$\Gamma^* \subset D(2\delta) \subset D(\delta).$$

It follows that each of the solutions $w(z; \zeta, \omega)$ is holomorphic in a disk $|z - \zeta| < r_0$ with r_0 defined by (12.1.3). We can now select a finite subset of points (ζ_j, ω_j) on Γ^*

$$(\zeta_0, \omega_0) = (z_0, w_0), (\zeta_1, \omega_1), \ldots, (\zeta_n, \omega_n) = (z_1, w_1)$$

such that for each $j > 0$ we have $|\zeta_j - \zeta_{j-1}| \leq \frac{1}{2}r_0$. Now the power series

$$w(z; \zeta_0, \omega_0) = \sum a_{k,0}(z - \zeta_0)^k$$

converges at least in the disk $|z - \zeta_0| < r_0$. Since ζ_1 lies in this disk we can rearrange the given power series into a power series in $z - \zeta_1$, and this series has a radius of convergence at least equal to $r_0 - |\zeta_0 - \zeta_1| > \frac{1}{2}r_0$. There is then a disk centered on ζ_1 in which the rearranged series coincides with $w(z; z_0, w_0)$ and is a solution of (12.1.1). At $z = \zeta_1$ its value is

$$w(\zeta_1; \zeta_0, \omega_0) = \omega_1.$$

But the equation has the solution $w(z; \zeta_1, \omega_1)$, holomorphic in the disk $|z - \zeta_1| < r_0$ which also takes on the value ω_1 at $z = \zeta_1$. By the uniqueness theorem, these two solutions must be identical. It follows that the solution $w(z; \zeta_1, \omega_1)$ is obtained by direct rearrangement of $w(z; z_0, w_0)$.

We can apply the same argument to $w(z; \zeta_1, \omega_1)$ and $w(z; \zeta_2, \omega_2)$ and by complete induction we show that each solution $w(z; \zeta_j, \omega_j)$ is obtained by direct rearrangement of its predecessor $w(z; \zeta_{j-1}, \omega_{j-1})$ for $j = 1, 2, \ldots, n$. It follows that each $w(z; \zeta_j, \omega_j)$ is obtained by at most j successive rearrangements of $w(z; z_0, w_0)$. This holds also for $j = n$, i.e. $w(z; z_1, w_1)$ is obtainable by analytic continuation of $w(z; z_0, w_0)$ along Γ. ▮

Case 2. $w(z; z_0, w_0) \to w_1$ *as* $z \to z_1$ *along* Γ. *Here* $f(z, w)$ *is not holomorphic at* (z_1, w_1) *but* $[f(z, w)]^{-1}$ *is supposed to have this property and* $[f(z_1, w)]^{-1} \not\equiv 0$. *Assertion:*

The point $z = z_1$ *is an algebraic branch-point of* $w(z; z_0, w_0)$ *where a finite number of branches are permuted when* z *makes a circuit about* $z = z_1$.

Proof. We set

$$[f(z, w)]^{-1} \equiv g(z, w) = \sum_{n=0}^{\infty} g_n(w)(z - z_1)^n.$$

For $z = z_1$ this reduces to $g_0(w)$ and

$$g_0(w) = \sum_{m=k}^{\infty} g_{m0}(w - w_1)^m, \qquad k \geq 1.$$

By assumption, not every $g_{m0} = 0$ and we may suppose that $g_{k0} \neq 0$. Let us now consider the differential equation

$$z'(w) = g(z, w) \tag{12.1.6}$$

at $w = w_1$, $z = z_1$. The existence theorem gives a unique solution

$$z(w; w_1, z_1) = z_1 + \sum_{m=p}^{\infty} c_m(w - w_1)^m$$

where p is to be determined. We note that

$$\sum_{m=p}^{\infty} mc_m(w - w_1)^{m-1} = \sum_{n=0}^{\infty} g_n(w)\left[\sum_{m=p}^{\infty} c_m(w - w_1)^m\right]^n.$$

Here the exponent of the lowest power of $w - w_1$ is $p - 1$ on the left and k on the right. Hence

$$\begin{gathered} p = k + 1, \qquad (k + 1)c_{k+1} = g_{k,0}, \\ z - z_1 = (w - w_1)^{k+1} \sum_{m=0}^{\infty} c_{k+1+m}(w - w_1)^m. \end{gathered} \tag{12.1.7}$$

By inversion one obtains

$$w - w_1 = \sum_{j=1}^{\infty} b_j(z - z_1)^{j/(k+1)}, \qquad b_1 \neq 0. \tag{12.1.8}$$

This means that $w(z; z_0, w_0)$ has a branch-point of order k at $z = z_1$ where $k + 1$ branches are permuted cyclically.

Such a singularity is movable in the sense that the position of the branch-point varies with the solution. As an example, take

$$w' = \frac{w - 2z}{w - z}$$

satisfied by

$$w = z + (c^2 - z^2)^{1/2}$$

which clearly has simple branch-points at $z = \pm c$. If $z \to c, w \to c, w - z \to 0$ but $w - c \not\equiv 0$, so the point (c, c) falls under Case 2.

Case 3. *$w(z; z_0, w_0) \to w_1$ as $z \to z_1$ along Γ, $f(z, w)$ is not holomorphic at (z_1, w_1) and $[f(z_1, w)]^{-1} \equiv 0$.*

No general statement can be made in this case for the only holomorphic solution of Eq. (12.1.6) is

$$z(w) \equiv z_1$$

and this gives no information concerning $w(z; z_0, w_0)$.

Normally $z = z_1$ is a fixed singularity of the equation, since the values of z for which

$$[f(z_1, w)]^{-1} \equiv 0$$

may be expected to be isolated and capable of algebraic or analytic determination without the use of any knowledge of the solutions. The point $z = z_1$ is normally a singular point of the equation and of the solutions, but the nature of the singularity is unpredictable. Thus the equation

$$w' = \lambda \frac{w}{z}$$

belongs to Case 3 at (0, 0). The solution is

$$w = Cz^\lambda.$$

Here $z = 0$ is no singularity, a pole, an algebraic branch-point, or a transcendental critical point, according as λ is a positive integer, negative integer, non-integral rational number, or an irrational or complex number, respectively. In the last case, a positive circuit about $z = 0$ multiplies the solution by $e^{2\pi i\lambda}$ and there are countably infinitely many branches.

Case 4. *$w(z; z_0, w_0) \to w_1$ as $z \to z_1$ along Γ and neither $f(z, w)$ nor $[f(z, w)]^{-1}$ is holomorphic at (z_1, w_1).*

Again, $z = z_1$ may or may not be a singularity of the solution. Thus for the two Riccati equations

$$u' = 1 + z^{3/2}u - z^{1/2}u^2,$$

$$v' = \tfrac{3}{2}z^{1/2} + z^{3/2}v - v^2,$$

the point $z = 0$ is a fixed singularity. At (0, 0) neither f nor $1/f$ is holomorphic. The corresponding solutions are $u = z$ and $v = z^{3/2}$, of which the first is regular and the second singular at $z = 0$.

Case 5. *$w(z; z_0, w_0) \to \infty$ as $z \to z_1$.*

Here $z = z_1$ is a singular point of the solution. To discuss its nature we set $w = v^{-1}$ and obtain

$$v' = -v^2 f(z, v^{-1}). \tag{12.1.9}$$

We have now $v \to 0$ as $z \to z_1$ and the discussion is reduced to one of the preceding cases. If the right member of (12.1.9) is holomorphic at $(z_1, 0)$, we conclude that v is holomorphic at $z = z_1$ and has a zero there. Hence w has a pole at $z = z_1$. Similarly, if the transformed equation presents Case 2 at $(z_1, 0)$, then w has an algebraic branch-point at $z = z_1$, where w becomes infinite.

Case 6. When $z \to z_1$, w does not tend to any limit.

This can happen when z_1 is a singular point of $f(z, w)$. Thus, in the case of the equation

$$w' = \frac{w}{z^2} \qquad \text{with} \quad w = C \exp\left(-\frac{1}{z}\right)$$

the solution tends to no limit if the origin is approached along the imaginary axis. It may, however, arise for particular integrals at an arbitrarily pre-assigned point. This is shown by

$$w' = -w(\log w)^2 \qquad \text{with} \quad w = \exp \frac{1}{z - a},$$

a arbitrary. This solution tends to no limit if z tends to a along a vertical line. It was proved by Painlevé that if $f(z, w)$ is a rational function of w, then Case 6 can arise only at fixed singular points.

Theorem 12.1.1. *If $f(z, w)$ is a rational function of w, then the movable singularities of the solutions are poles and/or algebraic branch-points.*

Proof. By assumption

$$w'(z) = \frac{P(z, w)}{Q(z, w)}, \tag{12.1.10}$$

where $P(z, w)$ and $Q(z, w)$ are polynomials in w with coefficients which are analytic functions of z.

Let us first decide which are the fixed singularities. It is clear that the point at infinity is in general a singular point of the solutions. To decide if this is so we have to set $z = 1/t$ and discuss the transformed equation at $t = 0$. Next we have the set of singularities of the coefficients of $P(z, w)$ and $Q(z, w)$. To simplify matters, we suppose that the coefficients are single-valued functions having only a finite number of singular points, say $s_1, s_2, \ldots, s_m$. We set

$$P(z, w) = \sum_{j=1}^{p} P_j(z) w^j, \qquad Q(z, w) = \sum_{k=1}^{q} Q_k(z) w^k. \tag{12.1.11}$$

Thus each point s_μ is a singular point of at least one of the functions P_j, Q_k and these functions have no other singularities.

Further we have to find the values of z for which

$$Q(z, w) \equiv 0.$$

These are the values of z for which Case 3 presents itself. They are obviously the common roots of the equations

$$Q_0(z) = 0, \; Q_1(z) = 0, \ldots, Q_q(z) = 0. \tag{12.1.12}$$

"Ordinarily" these equations have no roots in common, but accidentally there could be infinitely many such roots. Again, to simplify, we suppose that the number is finite and the roots are $r_1, r_2, \ldots, r_n$.

Next we have the roots of the simultaneous equations

$$P(z, w) = 0, \qquad Q(z, w) = 0. \tag{12.1.13}$$

These are algebraic equations in w with analytic coefficients. Elimination of w between these equations leads to a determinant of $p + q$ rows and columns in the coefficients P_j and Q_k. The common roots are the roots of this determinant equated to 0. We suppose that this leads to a finite number of points, say $e_1, e_2, \ldots, e_k$.

This does not exhaust the possibilities, however. We must also take into account the situation which arises when the substitution $w = 1/v$ is made for the study of possible infinitudes of the solutions. This leads to the equation

$$v'(z) = -v^2 \frac{P(z, v^{-1})}{Q(z, v^{-1})} \equiv \frac{P_1(z, v)}{Q_1(z, v)}, \tag{12.1.14}$$

where $P_1(z, v)$ and $Q_1(z, v)$ are polynomials in v. The points $\{s_\mu\}$ and $\{r_\nu\}$ are still singularities of (12.1.14), but the result of eliminating v between $P_1 = 0$, $Q_1 = 0$ is not necessarily the same as that for $P = 0$, $Q = 0$. Thus we have a new set of singular points, $i_1, i_2, \ldots, i_j$ say.

The totality S of points obtained in this way

$$S\colon \infty, s_1, \ldots, s_m; r_1, \ldots, r_n; e_1, \ldots, e_k; i_1, \ldots, i_j$$

constitutes the fixed singular points of the equation. Let us mark them in the complex plane and join the finite points with ∞ by a system of non-intersecting cuts. Let D be the remaining part of the plane. Suppose now that we take a pair of complex numbers (z_0, w_0) where $z_0 \in D$ and $Q(z_0, w_0) \neq 0$. Then there exists a uniquely defined solution $w(z; z_0, w_0)$ holomorphic in some neighborhood of z_0 where it takes the value w_0. It is claimed that this solution can be continued everywhere in D without encountering other than algebraic singularities. In other words, if $w(z; z_0, w_0)$ is continued analytically along some path to a point $z_1 \in D$, then there exist two integers μ, ν and a series expansion

$$w(z; z_0, w_0) = (z - z_1)^{\mu/\nu} \sum_{\alpha=0}^{\infty} c_\alpha (z - z_1)^{\alpha/\nu} \tag{12.1.15}$$

convergent in some punctured neighborhood of z_1. Here $\nu \geq 1$, $-\infty < \mu < \infty$, and the exponents as well as the coefficients of the series will in general depend upon the path Γ.

To see this, let us consider the various possibilities in the light of our preceding discussion. We know that, if we arrive at $z = z_1$ with the limit w_1 and if $f(z, w)$ is holomorphic at (z_1, w_1), then $w(z; z_0, w_0)$ is holomorphic at $z = z_1$ and coincides with $w(z; z_1, w_1)$ in some neighborhood of $z = z_1$. In this case $\mu = 0$, $\nu = 1$. Since $z_1 \in D$ this case will arise iff $Q(z_1, w_1) \neq 0$. On the other hand, if $Q(z_1, w_1) = 0$, we must have $P(z_1, w_1) \neq 0$, since z_1 is not an e_κ. At such a point we have an algebraic branch-point, $\mu = 1, \nu > 1$.

Next we have the possibility that $w \to \infty$ when $z \to z_1$. We then set $w = 1/v$ and obtain the transformed equation (12.1.14). If now $Q_1(z_1, 0) \neq 0$, we see that $v(z)$ has a zero at $z = z_1$, of order β, say, the order being one unit higher than the order of the zero of $P_1(z, 0)$ at $z = z_1$. Here $w(z)$ will have a pole of order β at $z = z_1$ so $\mu = -\beta, \nu = 1$. On the other hand, if $Q_1(z_1, 0) = 0$, then $P_1(z_1, 0) \neq 0$ since z_1 is not an i_j. Here we consider the reciprocal equation for $z(v)$ and find that $z(v) - z_1$ has a multiple zero at $v = 0$. From this we conclude that (12.1.15) holds with $\mu = -1$, $\nu = k + 1$.

It follows that, if w tends to a definite limit, finite or infinite, when $z \to z_1$, then $w(z)$ is holomorphic at $z = z_1$ or has an algebraic branch-point, or a pole, or an algebraic infinitude. It remains to prove that w must tend to a definite limit when $z \to z_1$, $z_1 \in D$. To this end, we mark in the w-plane the q roots $\omega_1, \ldots, \omega_q$ of the algebraic equation

$$Q(z_1, w) = 0$$

and the point at ∞. Let $\delta > 0$ be given and draw circles

$$C\colon |w| = \frac{1}{\delta}, \qquad C_i\colon |w - \omega_i| = \delta, \qquad i = 1, 2, \ldots, q,$$

and let Δ_δ be the part of the plane inside C and outside all C_i's. Let $\tilde{\Delta}_\delta$ be the complement of Δ_δ. Now, as z describes Γ, it may happen that w ultimately stays in $\tilde{\Delta}_\delta$. Since w changes continuously, this means that ultimately only one of the inequalities $|w - w_i| < \delta$, $i = 1, \ldots, q$, or $|w| > 1/\delta$ holds. In this case w tends to a definite limit ω_i or ∞ as $z \to z_1$.

The alternative is that there are points z on Γ in any neighborhood of z_1 such that the corresponding values w are in Δ_δ. Moreover, this can obviously be sharpened to $w \in \Delta_{2\delta}$ since otherwise the preceding argument would apply. Now, for z in some fixed d-neighborhood of z_1 and $w \in \Delta_\delta$, the functions $P(z, w)$ and $Q(z, w)$ are bounded away from ∞ and 0, respectively, and their quotient is bounded, say

$$|f(z, w)| = \left|\frac{P(z, w)}{Q(z, w)}\right| \leq M, \qquad |z - z_1| < d, \qquad w \in \Delta_\delta. \tag{12.1.16}$$

For $|z_2 - z_1| = \varepsilon < \frac{1}{2}d$ and $w_2 \in \Delta_{2\delta}$, $|z - z_2| < \frac{1}{2}d$, $|w - w_2| < \delta$,

$$M\left\{1 - 2\frac{z - z_2}{d}\right\}^{-1}\left\{1 - \frac{w - w_2}{\delta}\right\}^{-1}$$

is an acceptable majorant for $f(z, w)$. It follows that the solution $w(z; z_2, w_2)$ is holomorphic in a disk $|z - z_2| < r$ where

$$r = \tfrac{1}{2}d\left\{1 - \exp\left(-\frac{d}{\delta M}\right)\right\}.$$

Now, by assumption, we can find points z_2 on Γ in any neighborhood of $z = z_1$ such that the corresponding value $w_2 \in \Delta_{2\delta}$. If $|z_1 - z_2| < r$, $w(z; z_2, w_2)$ is holomorphic at $z = z_1$ and coincides with $w(z; z_1, w_1)$ in some neighborhood of $z = z_1$. It follows that the assumption that $w(z; z_0, z_0)$ tends to no limit as $z \to z_1$ leads to a contradiction. ∎

That there are movable poles even in the simplest cases is shown by the equation

$$w' = 1 + w^2 \tag{12.1.17}$$

with the solution

$$w(z) = \tan(z - a)$$

where a is arbitrary and the poles are located at $z = a + (k + \frac{1}{2})\pi$, $k = 0, \pm 1, \pm 2, \ldots$ As an example of movable branch-points we may take

$$w' = -\frac{1}{n}w^{n+1} \quad \text{with} \quad w(z) = (z - a)^{-1/n}, \qquad n > 1. \tag{12.1.18}$$

Equation (12.1.17) is a special case of Riccati's equation

$$w'(z) = P_0(z) + P_1(z)w + P_2(z)w^2 \tag{12.1.19}$$

and we saw in Section C.1 that, given any a, not a singular point of the coefficients or a zero of $P_2(z)$, there is a solution having a simple pole at $z = a$. A simple calculation shows that if $z = a$ is a zero of order k of $P_2(z)$, then there exists a solution with a pole of order $k + 1$ at $z = a$.

Theorem 12.1.2. *Let $R(z, w)$ be a rational function of w. If no solution of the equation*

$$w' = R(z, w)$$

can have a branch point at a non-singular point of the equation, then $R(z, w)$ is a quadratic polynomial in w, i.e. the equation is a Riccati equation.

Proof. Suppose that

$$R(z, w) = \frac{P(z, w)}{Q(z, w)}$$

as above. We note first that $Q(z, w)$ must be of degree 0 with respect to w. If this were not the case, then setting $z = z_0$, a non-singular value, then the equation $Q(z_0, w) = 0$ has q roots. If w_0 is one of these roots, then there exists a solution taking on the value w_0 at $z = z_0$ and this solution has a branch-point there. Hence we must have $q = 0$. We may then assume $Q(z, w) \equiv 1$ so the equation reduces to

$$w' = P(z, w) = \sum_{j=0}^{p} P_j(z)w^j.$$

If now $p > 2$, we set $w = 1/v$ to obtain

$$v'(z) = -[P_0(z)v^p + P_1(z)v^{p-1} + \cdots + P_p(z)]v^{2-p}. \qquad (12.1.20)$$

Here $Q_1(z, v) = v^{p-2}$ which vanishes for $v = 0$ no matter what value z has. Taking a non-singular value z_0 for z, we have $P_p(z_0) \neq 0$ and (12.1.20) has a solution which vanishes at $z = z_0$ and has a branch-point there. Since $w(z) = [v(z)]^{-1}$, the solution $w(z)$ has a branch-point at a non-singular point z_0 against the assumption. Hence we have $p \leq 2$. ∎

The following result is elementary:

Theorem 12.1.3. *Let z_0 be a non-singular point of the Riccati equation* (12.1.19). *Then the solution $w(z; z_0, w_0)$ is a linear fractional function of w_0.*

Proof. Consider four solutions w, w_1, w_2, w_3 with initial values $w_0, 0, 1, \infty$ at $z = z_0$. By (C.1.11) the cross-ratio of the four solutions is a constant

$$R(w, w_1, w_2, w_3) = R(w_0, 0, 1, \infty) = \frac{w_0}{w_0 - 1}.$$

Solving this for $w(z)$, we obtain an expression which is fractional linear in w_0 with coefficients expressed in terms of w_1, w_2, w_3, which are independent of w_0. ∎

Painlevé has emphasized the importance of studying the global properties of the solution as function of the initial value or of some other constant of integration. The solution of the Riccati equation is obviously a much simpler function of w_0 than of z.

The Riccati equation has other extremal properties. The following beautiful theorem is due to Johannes Malmquist (1888–1952).

Theorem 12.1.4. *If $R(z, w)$ is a rational function of z and of w and if the equation*

$$w' = R(z, w) \qquad (12.1.21)$$

has a solution $w(z)$ single-valued in its domain of existence, then either $w(z)$ is a rational function or (12.1.21) *is a Riccati equation.*

A proof based on R. Nevanlinna's theory of meromorphic functions was found by Kôsaku Yosida in 1932. It is reproduced in L. Bieberbach's treatise *Theorie der gewöhnlichen Differentialgleichungen*, 1953, pp. 88–99.

The remainder of this section will be occupied by an account of some results due to Pierre Boutroux (1908) concerning the asymptotic behavior of the solutions of (12.1.21) for large values of z. It is assumed that

$$R(z, w) = \frac{P(z, w)}{Q(z, w)}$$

where P and Q are polynomials in z as well as in w. P shall be of degree σ_1 in z and of degree p in w. Q shall be of degree σ_2 in z and of degree q in w. We set $\sigma = \max(\sigma_1, \sigma_2)$. In the notation of (12.1.11) we assume

$$P_p(z) = az^m + \cdots, \qquad Q_q(z) = bz^n + \cdots$$

where only the terms of highest order are shown. We set

$$\mu = m - n.$$

A preliminary result of basic importance in the discussion is

Lemma 12.1.1. *If $p \le q + 1$, then no solution can become infinite in the finite plane.*

Proof. If $w(z) = \infty$ for $z = z_0$, we set $w = v^{-1}$ and obtain

$$v' = -v^{q-p+2}\, \frac{P_0 v^p + \cdots + P_p}{Q_0 v^q + \cdots + Q_q}.$$

If $p \le q + 1$, there is a unique solution $v(z)$ of this equation which is 0 for $z = z_0$ and it is $v(z) \equiv 0$. Hence no solution of (12.1.21) can become infinite at $z = z_0$. ∎

It now turns out that the asymptotic behavior of $w(z)$ depends upon the value of the integer $p - q - 1$. If this integer is 0, then the solution becomes infinite as an exponential function. In all other cases it grows as a power of z.

For the first case, Boutroux showed

Theorem 12.1.5. *Let $p = q + 1$ and let μ be defined as above, $\mu \ge 0$. Set*

$$E(z) = \frac{a}{b(\mu + 1)}\, z^{\mu+1}. \tag{12.1.22}$$

Then there are $\mu + 1$ sectors where $\Re[E] > 0$ and they alternate with $\mu + 1$ sectors where $\Re[E] < 0$. Let S be a sector strictly interior to one of the sectors of the first kind and $w(z)$ a solution defined at a point $z_0 \in S$ where $|w(z_0)|$ exceeds a lower bound depending upon $|z_0|$. Then there are two positive constants A and B such that for $z \in S$

$$\exp[A|E(z)|] < |w(z)| < \exp[B|E(z)|]. \tag{12.1.23}$$

The proof is omitted except for mentioning that, if $|z|$ is large and $|w(z)| > C|z|^\sigma$, then

$$w'(z) = E'(z)[1 + \delta(z)]w(z) \tag{12.1.24}$$

where $\delta(z) \to 0$ as $z \to \infty$. This is under the assumption that $\mu \geq 0$. If $\mu < 0$ instead, the solution may be bounded at ∞.

In the second case, Boutroux showed:

Theorem 12.1.6. *Let $p \neq q + 1$ and let σ be defined as above. If $w(z)$ is a solution of* (12.1.21), *then*

$$|w(z)| < |z|^{\sigma+3}. \tag{12.1.25}$$

If $p < q + 1$, this holds for all large values of $|z|$ and for all solutions. If $p > q + 1$, it is necessary to exclude for each solution a countable number of non-overlapping circular disks from the Riemann surface on which the solution is single-valued. Each disk contains one and only one infinitude z_n which is also a branch-point where $p - q - 1$ branches are permuted if this number is >1. Here $|z_n| \to \infty$ and the radius of the disk goes to 0 at $n \to \infty$.

Again we omit the proof.

EXERCISE 12.1

1. If the coefficients of (12.1.19) are polynomials in z or, more generally, entire functions, show that all solutions are single-valued.
2. To what extent are the coefficients of a Riccati equation restricted, if it be assumed that all solutions are rational functions of z?
3. Consider $w' = z^2 + w^2$. Show that there are two solutions having only real or purely imaginary poles. What can be said of the distribution of poles for other solutions?
4. A solution of the Riccati equation (12.1.19) is supposed to have a pole of order $m > 1$ at $z = a$. What restrictions does this impose on the coefficients?
5. Suppose that a rational function $w(z)$ satisfies (12.1.21) where $p \leq q + 1$. Show that $w(z)$ is a constant and give necessary and sufficient conditions for the existence of constant solutions.
6. Suppose that $w(z)$ is an entire function satisfying
$$w' = P(w)$$
where $P(w)$ is a polynomial in w of degree $p \geq 2$ having constant coefficients. Show that $w(z)$ is a constant and specify the possible values of this constant.
7. Show that the finite singularities of the solutions of
$$w' = z^3 - w^3$$
are algebraic branch-points where $(z - z_0)^{1/2}w(z) \to \pm \frac{1}{2}\sqrt{2}$ as $z \to z_0$.

8. The preceding problem has a solution which tends to $+\infty$ as $z \downarrow 0$. Show that the solution is real positive for $z = x > 0$, has a single positive minimum and becomes infinite with x.

9. More precisely, show that $w(x) = x - \frac{1}{3}x^{-2} + O(x^{-5})$ as $x \to \infty$.

10. The equation

$$w' = \frac{1 + (zw)^2}{2zw}$$

is of Boutroux's exponential type. According to his theory, there is a solution which is $\sim \exp(\frac{1}{4}z^2)$ in the sectors $|\arg(\pm z)| < \frac{1}{4}\pi$. Verify this by integrating the equation explicitly. What is the asymptotic form of this solution in the complementary sectors?

11. The equation $w' = z^2w - w^3$ is of Boutroux's power type. This is a Bernoulli equation, and the solution with $w(0) = 1$ is

$$w(z) = \exp(\tfrac{1}{3}z^3)\left(1 + 2\int_0^z \exp(\tfrac{2}{3}t^3)\,dt\right)^{-1/2}$$

The branch-points are the infinitely many roots of the equation

$$\int_0^z \exp(\tfrac{2}{3}t^3)\,dt = -\tfrac{1}{2}.$$

Define the sectors S_k: $\{z \mid \frac{1}{6}(2k - 3)\pi < \arg z < \frac{1}{6}(2k - 1)\pi\}$, $k = 1, 2, \ldots, 6$. Show that the branch-points lie in distant S_1, S_3, S_5 and they approach the boundary lines of the sectors. Show that $w(z)$ goes to zero exponentially in the interior of the sectors S_2, S_4, S_6 and $w(z)/z \to 1$ in the interior of S_1, S_3, S_5, small neighborhoods of the branch-points excepted.

12. Let n be a positive integer, a real or complex. Show that if $a \neq n$ the equation

$$zw' = aw + z^n$$

has a unique solution which is holomorphic at $z = 0$. What happens if $a = n$?

13. Equations of the form

$$zw' = aw + zF(z, w), \qquad F(z, w) = \sum_{j,k} F_{jk}z^jw^k,$$

were studied by Briot and Bouquet in 1856. If a is not a positive integer, the equation has at least one solution which is holomorphic and vanishes at $z = 0$. Assuming $a < 1$, show that such a solution can be found by substituting a power series. If $M(z, w)$ is a majorant of $F(z, w)$ and if $W(z)$ is the solution of

$$(1 - a)W(z) = zM(z, W(z)), \qquad W(0) = 0,$$

show that $W(z)$ is a majorant of $w(z)$. Using the Cauchy majorant, $M(1 - z/\alpha)^{-1}(1 - w/\beta)^{-1} = M(z, w)$, determine $W(z)$ and the radius of convergence of its Maclaurin series.

12.2 BINOMIAL EQUATIONS

This name is given to equations of the form

$$[w'(z)]^m = f(z, w) \tag{12.2.1}$$

where m is a positive integer, $m > 1$, and $f(z, w)$ is analytic in z and w. We start with the case $m = 2$ and

$$f(z, w) = R(z, w) = \frac{P(z, w)}{Q(z, w)} \tag{12.2.2}$$

where P and Q are polynomials in z and w. It is assumed that $R(z, w)$ is not the square of a rational function; in other words the equation

$$[w'(z)]^2 = R(z, w) \tag{12.2.3}$$

is irreducible over the field of rational functions. We have

$$\begin{aligned} P(z, w) &= P_0(z) \prod_{\mu=1}^{p} [w - \eta_\mu(z)], \\ Q(z, w) &= Q_0(z) \prod_{\nu=1}^{q} [w - \zeta_\nu(z)]. \end{aligned} \tag{12.2.4}$$

Here $P_0(z)$ and $Q_0(z)$ are polynomials in z, the $\eta_\mu(z)$ are normally the p branches of an algebraic function $\eta(z)$, while the $\zeta_\nu(z)$ are the q branches of an algebraic function $\zeta(z)$. Since R may be reducible without being a perfect square, the relationship between the various η's and ζ's may be fairly complicated.

The Eq. (12.2.3) has a certain number of fixed singular points. We enumerate the following types.

i) $z = \infty$.
ii) The roots of $P_0(z) = 0$ and of $Q_0(z) = 0$.
iii) Values of z for which the algebraic equations in w

$$P(z, w) = 0, \qquad Q(z, w) = 0$$

have common roots.

iv) Values of z for which

$$P_1(z, v) = 0, \qquad Q_1(z, v) = 0$$

have common roots where $v = 1/w$ and

$$v'(z) = \frac{P_1(z, v)}{Q_1(z, v)}. \tag{12.2.5}$$

v) Singularities of $\eta_\mu(z)$ and $\zeta_\nu(z)$ not already included under (i) and (ii).

The movable singularities are associated with the varieties

$$\mathrm{H}: w = \eta(z), \qquad \mathrm{Z}: w = \zeta(z). \tag{12.2.6}$$

Here $\eta(z)$ stands for any one of the functions $\eta_\mu(z)$ and the notation is not intended to suggest any functional relationships.

We start with a point (z_0, w_0) which is not a fixed singularity nor located on either H or Z. In other words, $P(z_0, w_0) \neq 0$, $Q(z_0, w_0) \neq 0$, and $R(z, w)$ is holomorphic in some neighborhood of (z_0, w_0) and its square root $[R(z, w)]^{1/2}$ is holomorphic and can be uniquely defined in some neighborhood of (z_0, w_0). We have then two equations

$$w'(z) = +[R(z, w)]^{1/2}, \qquad w'(z) = -[R(z, w)]^{1/2}, \tag{12.2.7}$$

each of which has a solution holomorphic at $z = z_0$ where it takes on the value w_0.

Suppose now instead that $(z_0, w_0) \in \mathrm{H}$ but not to Z. Here $Q(z, w)$ is holomorphic and $\neq 0$ at (z_0, w_0) while $P(z, w)$ is holomorphic but vanishes at (z_0, w_0). The square root $[R(z, w)]^{1/2}$ is not holomorphic at (z_0, w_0). By assumption, there exists a determination of $\eta(z)$, say $\eta_1(z)$, such that

$$w_0 = \eta_1(z_0).$$

We assume to start with that w_0 is a simple root of $P(z_0, w) = 0$. This implies that

$$P'_w(z, w) \neq 0 \quad \text{at} \quad (z_0, w_0).$$

Hence in the expansion

$$R(z, w) = c_{10}(z - z_0) + c_{01}(w - w_0) + \sum_{j+k>1} c_{jk}(z - z_0)^j(w - w_0)^k \tag{12.2.8}$$

we have

$$c_{01} \neq 0.$$

We can now find positive numbers ρ and M such that

$$|R(z, w)| \leq Mr, \qquad |z - z_0| \leq r, \qquad |w - w_0| \leq r, \qquad r < \rho. \tag{12.2.9}$$

Thus

$$|R(z, w)|^{1/2} \leq M^{1/2}r^{1/2}$$

in some neighborhood of (z_0, w_0). On the other hand,

$$\frac{d}{dr}|w(z)| \leq |w'(z)|$$

so that

$$\frac{d}{dr}|w(z)| \leq M^{1/2}r^{1/2}$$

and

$$||w(z)| - |w_0|| \leq \tfrac{2}{3}M^{1/2}|z - z_0|^{3/2}.$$

This suggests the possibility of an expansion

$$w(z) - w_0 = \sum_{n=0}^{\infty} a_n(z - z_0)^{(n+3)/2}. \tag{12.2.10}$$

Substitution in (12.2.3) and (12.2.8) gives

$$\left[\frac{1}{2}\sum_{0}^{\infty}(n+3)a_n(z-z_0)^{(n+1)/2}\right]^2$$

$$= c_{10}(z - z_0) + c_{01}\sum_{0}^{\infty} a_n(z - z_0)^{(n+3)/2}$$

$$+ \sum\sum c_{jk}(z - z_0)^j\left[\sum_{0}^{\infty} a_n(z - z_0)^{(n+3)/2}\right]^k.$$

This implies the recurrence formulas

$$\tfrac{9}{4}a_0^2 = c_{10}, \qquad 6a_0a_1 = c_{01}a_0, \ldots$$

$$\tfrac{3}{2}(n + 3)a_0a_n + \tfrac{5}{2}(n + 2)a_1a_{n-1} + \cdots = c_{01}a_{n-1} + \cdots$$

If now $c_{10} \neq 0$, we get

$$a_0 = \pm\tfrac{2}{3}(c_{10})^{1/2}$$

and all coefficients can be determined uniquely. In this case, there is definitely a term in $(z - z_0)^{3/2}$ so the point z_0 is a movable branch-point.

If, however, $c_{10} = 0$, this term is missing and the assumption $c_{01} \neq 0$ implies the presence of a term in $(z - z_0)^2$. In general the expansion involves fractional powers of $(z - z_0)$. In exceptional cases all such terms may be missing. This is shown by the trivial example

$$(w')^2 = w \qquad \text{with} \qquad w - w_0 = \tfrac{1}{4}(z - z_0)^2.$$

Here H is the variety $w = 0$ and, if $w_0 = 0$, we have also the singular solution $w(z) \equiv 0$.

Since we ultimately want to find necessary and sufficient conditions for the absence of movable singularities we have to go more fully into this question and also admit the possibility that w_0 is a multiple root of

$$P(z_0, w) = 0.$$

For special cases, this problem was considered by the collaborating French mathematicians A. A. Briot (1817–82) and J. C. Bouquet (1819–85) in 1856, and, for the general case of algebraic differential equations, by L. Fuchs in 1884. The classical method proceeds as follows.

We consider again the equation in w

$$P(z, w) = 0 \tag{12.2.11}$$

which plays the role of *discriminant equation* of (12.2.3). This equation is satisfied by the functions $\eta_j(z)$. Take a particular function denoted by $\eta(z)$. Suppose that $\eta(z)$ is holomorphic in some domain D containing the point $z = z_0$ considered above. Then

$$P(z, \eta(z)) \equiv 0, \qquad z \in D.$$

We assume

$$Q(z, \eta(z)) \not\equiv 0 \tag{12.2.12}$$

and any point z^* where

$$Q(z, \eta(z)) = 0$$

is to be excluded in the following consideration. The algebraic equation in p

$$Q(z, \eta(z))p^2 - P(z, \eta(z)) = 0$$

is satisfied by

$$p = p_0 \equiv 0 \tag{12.2.13}$$

and this is a double root. On the other hand,

$$Q(z, w)p^2 - P(z, w) = 0$$

is satisfied by

$$p(z, w) = [R(z, w)]^{1/2}, \tag{12.2.14}$$

an algebraic function of w (and of z). If $w - \eta(z)$ is a factor of $P(z, w)$ of even multiplicity, then $p(z, w)$ is single-valued in a neighborhood of $w = \eta(z)$. If, however, the multiplicity is odd, then $p(z, w)$ is a two-valued function which admits of an expansion

$$p(z, w) = f_0(z)[w - \eta(z)]^{k/2} + f_1(z)[w - \eta(z)]^{(k+1)/2} + \cdots \tag{12.2.15}$$

Here k is an odd integer ≥ 1 and $f_0(z) \not\equiv 0$. Moreover, the coefficients $f_j(z)$ are holomorphic in D. We exclude from D values z^* for which $f_0(z^*) = 0$.

From the last equation we deduce a differential equation for $w - \eta(z)$, namely

$$\frac{d}{dz}[w(z) - \eta(z)] = -\eta'(z) + \sum_{j=0}^{\infty} f_j(z)[w(z) - \eta(z)]^{(j+k)/2}, \tag{12.2.16}$$

valid in D. At this stage various possibilities arise. It may happen that $w = \eta(z)$, the solution of (12.2.11) under consideration, also satisfies the original differential equation (12.2.3). By (12.2.16) this requires that

$$\eta'(z) \equiv 0, \qquad \eta(z) \equiv \eta, \quad \text{a constant.} \tag{12.2.17}$$

This is now a singular solution of (12.2.3). It corresponds to the case where $P(z, w)$ in the factorization (12.2.4) has a factor $w - \eta(z)$ independent of z. If $\eta(z) \equiv \eta$, then $w = \eta$ is clearly a solution of (12.2.3).

We return to this case later. Let now

$$\eta'(z) \not\equiv 0.$$

The values of z for which $\eta'(z) = 0$, $z \in D$, are excluded in the following. We now set

$$w - \eta = u^2$$

and find for u the differential equation

$$2uu' = -\eta' + \sum_0^\infty f_j u^{j+k}, \tag{12.2.18}$$

where η and the f_j's are holomorphic in D. This gives

$$z'(u) = 2u\left[-\eta' + \sum_0^\infty f_j u^{j+k}\right]^{-1}. \tag{12.2.19}$$

We now take a value $z = z_0 \in D$ where $f_0(z_0) \neq 0$, $\eta'(z_0) \neq 0$. Then (12.2.19) has a unique solution

$$z(u) - z_0 = \sum_0^\infty \beta_j u^{j+2}, \qquad \beta_0 = -[\eta'(z_0)]^{-1} \tag{12.2.20}$$

and, by inversion of the power series, we get

$$u = \beta_0^{-1/2}(z - z_0)^{1/2} + \sum_1^\infty \gamma_j (z - z_0)^{(j+1)/2}.$$

Hence

$$u^2 = w(z) - \eta(z) = \beta_0^{-1}(z - z_0) + \sum_1^\infty \delta_j (z - z_0)^{(j+2)/2}. \tag{12.2.21}$$

This shows that, if $z = z_0$ is an arbitrary non-excluded point on H, more precisely on $w = \eta(z)$, then the equation (12.2.3) admits of a solution $w(z)$ such that $w(z) - \eta(z)$ has the expansion (12.2.21) and $z = z_0$ is a branch-point of the solution through $(z_0, \eta(z_0))$.

This was derived under the assumption that $w - \eta(z)$ is a factor of odd multiplicity of $P(z, w)$. If the multiplicity is even instead, (12.2.16) is replaced by

$$\frac{d}{dz}[w(z) - \eta(z)] = -\eta'(z) + \sum_{j=0}^\infty f_j(z)[w(z) - \eta(z)]^{j+k} \tag{12.2.22}$$

and (12.2.18) now becomes

$$u' = -\eta'(z) + \sum_{0}^{\infty} f_j(z)u^{j+k}. \tag{12.2.23}$$

For small values of $z - z_0$ this equation has a unique solution $u(z)$ with $u(0) = 0$. Since $k \geq 1$, we have $u(z) \equiv 0$ iff $\eta'(z) \equiv 0$, i.e. iff $\eta(z) \equiv \eta$, a constant. If $\eta(z) \equiv \eta$, then

$$w(z) \equiv \eta$$

is the only solution with a value on $w = \eta$, this being the singular solution. On the other hand, if $\eta'(z) \not\equiv 0$, then

$$w(z) = \eta(z) + u(z)$$

is a solution passing through $(z_0, \eta(z_0))$. It is the only solution and it is holomorphic in some neighborhood of $z = z_0$.

Let us return to the case $\eta'(z) \equiv 0$, excluded in the discussion of (12.2.18). We have then

$$2u' = f_0 u^{k-1} + f_1 u^k + \cdots \tag{12.2.24}$$

If $k > 1$, then the equation has one and only one solution holomorphic at $z = z_0$ and this is

$$u(z) \equiv 0.$$

Hence

$$w(z) \equiv \eta$$

is the only solution through (z_0, η) and this is a singular solution. On the other hand, if $k = 1$, then there is a non-trivial holomorphic solution $u(z)$ with $u(0) = 0$, $u'(0) = \frac{1}{2}f_0(z_0) \neq 0$. This means that

$$w(z) = \eta + [u(z)]^2$$

is also a solution through (z_0, η) and this solution is holomorphic at $z = z_0$.

The results obtained in this discussion may be summarized as

Theorem 12.2.1. *Let $w - \eta(z)$ be a factor of $P(z, w)$ which is not also a factor of $Q(z, w) = 0$. Then the equation* (12.2.3) *has a solution passing through $(z_0, \eta(z_0))$ and this solution has a simple branch-point there unless either $w - \eta(z)$ is a factor of even multiplicity or $\eta'(z) \equiv 0$, $\eta(z) \equiv \eta$. In the first exceptional case there is a unique holomorphic solution which reduces to $w(z) \equiv \eta$ if, in addition $\eta(z) \equiv \eta$. If in the second case $w - \eta$ is a simple factor, then there are two holomorphic solutions one of which is $w(z) \equiv \eta$. If the multiplicity is odd and >1, only the singular solution $w(z) \equiv \eta$ passes through (z_0, η).*

It is now a simple matter to discuss the behavior of the solution $w(z)$ if $(z_0, w_0) \in Z$. More precisely, we suppose that $w - \zeta(z)$ is a factor of $Q(z, w)$, so that

$$Q(z, \zeta(z)) \equiv 0$$

for $z \in D$, a domain in which $\zeta(z)$ is holomorphic. It is assumed that

$$P(z, \zeta(z)) \not\equiv 0,$$

and any point of D where $P(z, \zeta(z)) = 0$ is omitted. We now consider the properties of the solution of (12.2.3) which passes through $(z_0, \zeta(z_0))$.

In some neighborhood of $w = \zeta(z)$, we have

$$[R(z, w)]^{1/2} = \sum_{j=0}^{\infty} g_j(z)[w - \zeta(z)]^{(j-k)/\alpha} \tag{12.2.25}$$

where $\alpha = 1$ or 2, k is a positive integer, and $g_0(z) \not\equiv 0$. This gives the differential equation

$$\frac{d}{dz}[w(z) - \zeta(z)] = -\zeta'(z) + \sum_{j=0}^{\infty} g_j(z)[w - \zeta(z)]^{(j-k)/\alpha}. \tag{12.2.26}$$

Here we introduce a new dependent variable u by setting

$$w - \zeta(z) = u^{\alpha}$$

and obtain

$$\alpha u^{\alpha-1}u' = -\zeta'(z) + \sum_{0}^{\infty} g_j(z)u^{j-k}. \tag{12.2.27}$$

Suppose first that $\alpha = 1$, then let $z_0 \in D$ and $g_0(z_0) \neq 0$. Then the equation gives

$$\frac{du}{dz} = g_0(z)u^{-k}\left[1 + \sum_{1}^{\infty} h_n(z)u^n\right]$$

with obvious notation. Hence

$$z'(u) = [g_0(z)]^{-1}u^k\left[1 + \sum_{1}^{\infty} h_n(z)u^n\right]^{-1} \tag{12.2.28}$$

and we obtain

$$z(u) - z_0 = u^{k+1}\sum_{0}^{\infty} \gamma_n u^n, \qquad \gamma_0 \neq 0,$$

and by inversion

$$u(z) = \sum_{1}^{\infty} \delta_n(z - z_0)^{n/(k+1)}, \qquad \delta_1 \neq 0. \tag{12.2.29}$$

Hence

$$w(z) = \zeta(z) + \sum_{1}^{\infty} \delta_n(z - z_0)^{n/(k+1)} \tag{12.2.30}$$

is the solution passing through $(z_0, \zeta(z_0))$ and it has a branch-point at $z = z_0$.

If $\alpha = 2$ instead, we get

$$z(u) - z_0 = u^{k+2} \sum_0^\infty \gamma_n u^n, \qquad \gamma_0 \neq 0,$$

and

$$u(z) = \sum_1^\infty \delta_n (z - z_0)^{n/(k+2)}, \qquad \delta_1 \neq 0.$$

Finally,

$$w(z) = \zeta(z) + \left[\sum_1^\infty \delta_n (z - z_0)^{n/(k+2)}\right]^2 \tag{12.2.31}$$

and again $z = z_0$ is a branch-point.

This leads to

Theorem 12.2.2. *A necessary condition for the absence of movable branch-points is that $Q(z, w)$ be independent of w, i.e. that $R(z, w)$ is a polynomial in w.*

We have now to consider if infinite initial values can give rise to movable branch-points. The canonical substitution

$$w = \frac{1}{v}$$

transforms the equation into

$$(v')^2 = v^4 \frac{P(z, 1/v)}{Q(z, 1/v)} \equiv \frac{P_1(z, v)}{Q_1(z, v)}.$$

If

$$P(z, w) = \sum_{j=0}^p P_j(z) w^{p-j}, \qquad Q(z, w) = \sum_{k=0}^q Q_k(z) w^{q-k},$$

then

$$P_1(z, v) = v^{q+4-p} \sum_0^p P_j(z) v^j \qquad \text{or} \qquad \sum_0^p P_j(z) v^j,$$

$$Q_1(z, v) = \sum_0^q Q_k(z) v^k \qquad \text{or} \qquad v^{p-4-q} \sum_0^q Q_k(z) v^k,$$

according as the integer $q + 4 - p$ is ≥ 0 or < 0. Since a necessary condition for the absence of movable branch-points is that $Q_1(z, v)$ be independent of v, we obtain

Theorem 12.2.3. *A necessary condition for the absence of movable branch-points in* (12.2.3) *is that $R(z, w)$ be a polynomial in w of degree ≤ 4.*

Thus we have reduced $R(z, w)$ to a polynomial $P(z, w)$ of degree ≤ 4. For the absence of branch-points on the variety H, the factors of $P(z, w)$ must satisfy severe restrictions which can be read off from Theorem 12.2.1. An examination of the various possibilities leads to the following result, to be verified by the reader.

Theorem 12.2.4. *Let $P(z, w)$ be a polynomial in w and z which is of degree ≤ 4 in w and not a perfect square. In order that*

$$(w')^2 = P(z, w) \tag{12.2.32}$$

be without movable branch-points, it is necessary and sufficient that $P(z, w)$ be of the form a polynomial $P_0(z)$ times one of the nine following expressions:

i) $w - a$,
ii) $(w - a)(w - b)$,
iii) $(w - a)^3$,
iv) $(w - a)^2(w - b)$,
v) $(w - a)(w - b)(w - c)$,
vi) $(w - a)^2(w - b)(w - c)$,
vii) $(w - a)(w - b)(w - c)(w - d)$,
viii) $[w - \eta(z)]^2(w - b)$,
ix) $[w - \eta(z)]^2(w - b)(w - c)$.

Here $\eta(z)$ is a polynomial and the letters a, b, c, d denote distinct constants.

It should be added that the Theorem of Painlevé holds also for equations of type (12.2.3) and the proof given for Theorem 12.1.1 extends with minor modifications to the present case. As a matter of fact, the theorem holds for the more general case

$$F(z, w, w') = 0 \tag{12.2.33}$$

where F is a polynomial in w and w'. The only movable singularities are algebraic branch-points and, when z approaches such a point, $w(z)$ tends to a finite or infinite limit.

EXERCISE 12.2

1. Find the solution through (0, 0) of $(w')^2 = z - \frac{1}{2}z^2 + 3w$.
2. Prove Painlevé's theorem for Eq. (12.2.3).
3. Verify Theorem 12.2.4.

Take $P_0(z) \equiv 1$ in the following problems.

4. Show that types (i) and (iii) lead to rational functions.
5. Show that the solutions for type (ii) are finite in the finite plane. Express the solutions in terms of e^z. Study the equations $w(z) = a$ (or b).

6. Show that the solutions for type (iv) have infinitely many double poles and are expressible in terms of e^z. Show that $\lim w(z) = a$, if $z \to \infty$ in such a manner as to avoid the poles.
7. Show that the solutions for type (vi) have simple poles and that $w(z)$ is an elementary function of e^z. Discuss the equations $w = a, b$, or c.
8. Equations of type (v) are integrable in terms of elliptic functions. Show that the solutions have double poles and discuss the equations $w = a, b$, or c.
9. Equations of type (vii) are also integrable in terms of elliptic functions. (Cf. Section A.2.) Show that the solutions have simple poles.
10. Show that equations of type (ix) can be reduced to a Riccati equation by setting $(w - b)(w - c)^{-1} = W^2$.
11. Carry out a similar reduction for type (viii).
12. The following equations

$$(w')^6 = (w - a)^5(w - b)^4(w - c)^3 \quad \text{and} \quad (W')^6 = (W - A)^5(W - B)^4$$

are known to be free of movable branch-points. Show that $w(z)$ has simple poles while those of $W(z)$ are triple.

12.3 THE EQUATIONS OF BRIOT AND BOUQUET

In 1855–56 these authors examined equations of the type

$$F(w, w') = 0 \tag{12.3.1}$$

where F is a polynomial in the two arguments w and w' with constant coefficients. Here $z = \infty$ is the only fixed singularity and, if there are no movable branch-points, then the solutions are single-valued and meromorphic in the finite plane. If $w(z)$ is a solution, so is $w(z + C)$ for any choice of the constant C. This then is the general solution of the equation.

Briot and Bouquet were engaged in writing a treatise on elliptic functions (this, the first of its kind, appeared in 1859), and they were interested in finding those equations of type (12.3.1) which are satisfied by doubly-periodic functions or their simply-periodic or rational degeneracies. Now the problem of finding these cases is the same as that of finding when such an equation has no movable branch-points. We recall that seven of the nine equations under Theorem 12.2.4 are of the form

$$(w')^2 = P(w) \tag{12.3.2}$$

where $P(w)$ is a polynomial of degree ≤ 4. Two equations led to rational functions, three to simply periodic functions; and types (v) and (vii) will lead to doubly-periodic functions.

Here we shall consider the binomial case

$$(w')^m = R(w) \tag{12.3.3}$$

where $R(w)$ is a rational function of w and m is a positive integer.

Theorem 12.3.1. *A necessary condition that the solutions of* (12.3.3) *have no movable branch-points is that* $R(w) = P(w)$, *a polynomial of degree* $\leq 2m$.

Proof. Set

$$R(w) = \frac{P(w)}{Q(w)}$$

and suppose that

$$Q(w) = (w - c)^k Q_1(w), \qquad Q_1(c) \neq 0,$$

where k is a positive integer. Then for small values of $|w - c|$

$$w' = (w - c)^{-k/m} \sum_{j=0}^{\infty} a_j (w - c)^j$$

or

$$\sum_{j=0}^{\infty} b_j (w - c)^{j+k/m} w' = 1$$

whence

$$\sum_{j=0}^{\infty} \frac{m b_j}{k + (j + 1)m} (w - c)^{j+1+k/m} = z - z_0.$$

By inversion

$$w - c = \sum_{j=1}^{\infty} \gamma_j (z - z_0)^{mj/(k+m)}.$$

Thus, if $Q(w)$ is not identically constant, there are solutions with arbitrary branch-points.

Suppose now that $Q(w) \equiv 1$ and that we make the transformation

$$w = \frac{1}{v}$$

to obtain

$$(-v')^m = v^{2m} P\left(\frac{1}{v}\right).$$

Here the right member must be a polynomial in v, and this is the case iff $\deg(P) \leq 2m$. ▮

The factors of $P(w)$ are also subject to severe restrictions as we may expect by analogy with the case $m = 2$ and Theorem 12.2.1. Suppose that $(w - a)^k$ is a factor of $P(w)$,

$$P(w) = (w - a)^k P_1(w), \qquad P_1(a) \neq 0.$$

Then for small values of $|w - a|$

$$\frac{d}{dz}(w - a) = (w - a)^{k/m} \sum_{j=0}^{\infty} c_j(w - a)^j, \qquad c_0 \neq 0.$$

Here we set

$$w - a = u^m$$

and obtain

$$mu^{m-1}u' = \sum_{j=0}^{\infty} c_j u^{k+jm}. \tag{12.3.4}$$

There are three possibilities. First we may have $k = m - 1$, in which case

$$mu'(z) = c_0 + \sum_{j=1}^{\infty} c_j u^{jm}, \qquad c_0 \neq 0.$$

This gives

$$u(z) = \sum_{j=1}^{\infty} b_j(z - z_0)^j, \qquad w(z) = a + [u(z)]^m,$$

holomorphic functions of z in some neighborhood of $z = z_0$ where $u(z_0) = 0$.
Secondly, if $k \geq m$, then

$$mu'(z) = \sum_{j=0}^{\infty} c_j u^{k+1+(j-1)m}$$

and the unique holomorphic solution is

$$u(z) \equiv 0, \qquad w(z) \equiv a.$$

Finally, we have $k < m - 1$. This gives

$$b_0 u^{m-k-1} + b_1 u^{2m-k-1} + \cdots = z'(u), \qquad b_0 \neq 0,$$

so that

$$z - z_0 = u^{m-k}\left\{\frac{b_0}{m - k} + \frac{b_1}{2m - k}u^m + \cdots\right\}$$

or

$$(z - z_0)^{1/(m-k)} = u[\alpha_0 + \alpha_1 u^m + \cdots], \qquad \alpha_0 \neq 0.$$

Hence

$$u(z) = \alpha_0^{-1}(z - z_0)^{1/(m-k)}\left[1 + \sum_{n=1}^{\infty} \beta_n(z - z_0)^{nm/(m-k)}\right] \tag{12.3.5}$$

and

$$w(z) = a + \alpha_0^{-m}(z - z_0)^{m/(m-k)}\left[1 + \sum_{n=1}^{\infty} \gamma_n(z - z_0)^{mn/(m-k)}\right]. \tag{12.3.6}$$

This solution has a branch point at $z = z_0$ unless

$$\frac{m}{m-k} = \mu$$

is an integer ≥ 2. This gives

$$k = \frac{\mu - 1}{\mu} m \geq \tfrac{1}{2}m \tag{12.3.7}$$

where μ is a divisor of m. We can summarize this part of the discussion as

Theorem 12.3.2. *A factor $(w - a)^k$ of $P(w)$ will give rise to solutions with movable branch-points unless either $k \geq m - 1$ or else $k = [(\mu - 1)/\mu]m$ where $\mu \geq 2$ is a divisor of m.*

Let us first suppose that $\deg(P) = 2m$ exactly and let $(w - a)^k$ be a factor of $P(w)$ where $k > m$. This leaves room for only one additional factor

$$(w - b)^{2m-k}$$

since the exponent must be $\geq \frac{1}{2}m$ by (12.3.7). This in turn gives

$$2m - k = m - 1, \qquad k = m + 1$$

and the corresponding differential equation is

$$(w')^m = C(w - a)^{m+1}(w - b)^{m-1} \tag{12.3.8}$$

where $a \neq b$ and C is an arbitrary constant, while m is any integer >0.

Suppose instead that $k = m$. The remaining factors would then be either

$$(w - b)^m \qquad \text{or} \qquad (w - b)^{m/2}(w - c)^{m/2}.$$

The first choice is possible iff $m = 1$ and leads to the equation

$$w' = C(w - a)(w - b). \tag{12.3.9}$$

The case $m > 1$ is excluded since it would lead to reducible equations. The second choice is admissible iff $m = 2$ and leads to

$$(w')^2 = C(w - a)^2(w - b)(w - c), \tag{12.3.10}$$

i.e. type (vi) under Theorem 12.2.4.

We have now left the possibility that all exponents k are $\leq m - 1$, and hence of the form $[(\mu - 1)/\mu]m$ where $\mu \geq 2$ is a divisor of m. This leads to the problem of finding positive fractions of the type $(\mu - 1)/\mu$ which add up to 2. There are only four possible choices

$$\tfrac{1}{2}, \tfrac{1}{2}, \tfrac{1}{2}, \tfrac{1}{2}, m = 2; \qquad \tfrac{2}{3}, \tfrac{2}{3}, \tfrac{2}{3}, m = 3;$$

$$\tfrac{3}{4}, \tfrac{3}{4}, \tfrac{1}{2}, m = 4; \qquad \tfrac{5}{6}, \tfrac{2}{3}, \tfrac{1}{2}, m = 6;$$

with the corresponding equations

$$(w')^2 = C(w - a)(w - b)(w - c)(w - d), \tag{12.3.11}$$

$$(w')^3 = C(w - a)^2(w - b)^2(w - c)^2, \tag{12.3.12}$$

$$(w')^4 = C(w - a)^3(w - b)^3(w - c)^2, \tag{12.3.13}$$

$$(w')^6 = C(w - a)^5(w - b)^4(w - c)^3. \tag{12.3.14}$$

This exhausts the list of equations $(w')^m = P(w)$ with $\deg(P) = 2m$ and without movable branch-points. There are seven types given by formulas (12.3.8) to (12.3.14).

But there are also admissible equations with $\deg(P) < 2m$. All these equations are obtained by omitting one of the factors in the right members of (12.3.8) to (12.3.14). Thus, e.g. Eq. (12.3.14) leads to three new equations according as we omit $(w - a)^5$ or $(w - b)^4$ or $(w - c)^3$. That this crude procedure actually leads to admissible equations is easy to verify. In fact, take any one of the seven equations. To fix the ideas, suppose the equation is of the form

$$(w')^m = c_0(w - a)^\alpha(w - b)^\beta(w - c)^\gamma, \qquad \alpha + \beta + \gamma = 2m \tag{12.3.15}$$

and set

$$W = (w - a)^{-1}.$$

The result is

$$(W')^m = K(W - B)^\beta(W - C)^\gamma,$$

$$K = (-1)^m C_0(a - b)^\beta(a - c)^\gamma, \qquad B = \frac{1}{b - a}, \qquad C = \frac{1}{c - a}. \tag{12.3.16}$$

It follows that (12.3.16) is admissible whenever (12.3.15) is. The method applies also if there are two or four factors.

In general, the equations under consideration are formally invariant under a fractional linear transformation applied to w. This may be used to reduce the equations to various normal forms.

For the theory of elliptic functions, the important normal forms are that of Jacobi,

$$(w')^2 = (1 - w^2)(1 - k^2w^2) \tag{12.3.17}$$

where k is an arbitrary parameter, $k \neq \pm 1$; and that of K. Weierstrass

$$(w')^2 = 4(w - e_1)(w - e_2)(w - e_3) \tag{12.3.18}$$

$$= 4w^3 - g_2w - g_3; \qquad e_1 + e_2 + e_3 = 0.$$

For the former, see Eq. (A.2.11). We know from the discussion in Section A.2 that the solution of (12.3.17) with $w(0) = 0$ is the Jacobi *sine amplitude* function

$$\sin \operatorname{am} z \qquad \text{or} \qquad \operatorname{sn} z \qquad \text{or} \qquad \operatorname{sn}(z, k).$$

It is a doubly-periodic function of z with primitive periods

$$4K \quad \text{and} \quad 2iK'$$

where

$$K = \int_0^1 (1 - w^2)^{-1/2}(1 - k^2w^2)^{-1/2}\,dw = \tfrac{1}{2}\pi F(\tfrac{1}{2}, \tfrac{1}{2}, 1; k^2)$$
$$K' = \tfrac{1}{2}\pi F(\tfrac{1}{2}, \tfrac{1}{2}, 1; 1 - k^2). \tag{12.3.19}$$

(See also Problems 7 and 8 of Exercise 7.1.) It was shown in Section A.2 that sn z has simple poles at the points

$$4mK + (2n + 1)iK', \qquad m, n = 0, \pm 1, \pm 2, \ldots$$

We know in advance (Problem 9, Exercise 12.2) that the solutions of (12.3.17) have simple poles if any.

Similarly, *a priori* considerations show that the solutions of (12.3.18) must have double poles. An elementary but tedious calculation shows that if a pole is located at the origin, then for $0 < |z| < \varepsilon$

$$w(z) = \frac{1}{z^2} + \frac{1}{20} g_2 z^2 + \frac{1}{28} g_3 z^4 + \cdots \tag{12.3.20}$$

This solution is the Weierstrass $\wp$-function

$$\wp(z) \quad \text{or} \quad \wp(z; \omega_1, \omega_3) \quad \text{or} \quad \wp(z \mid g_2, g_3),$$

where $2\omega_1$ and $2\omega_3$ are the primitive periods defined by

$$\omega_1 = \int_{e_1}^{\infty} [4(s - e_1)(s - e_2)(s - e_3)]^{-1/2}\,ds,$$
$$\omega_3 = \int_{-\infty}^{e_3} [4(s - e_1)(s - e_2)(s - e_3)]^{-1/2}\,ds. \tag{12.3.21}$$

To fix the ideas, suppose that the e_j's are real, $e_3 < e_2 < e_1$, and consider the cubic

$$t^2 = 4(s - e_1)(s - e_2)(s - e_3). \tag{12.3.22}$$

Cut the s-plane along the real axis from $-\infty$ to e_1 and take that determination of t which is positive for $s > e_1$. For w in the cut plane, the integral

$$z(w) = -\int_w^{\infty} t^{-1}\,ds \tag{12.3.23}$$

is well defined and is finite everywhere. The integral is the (only) *Abelian integral of the first kind* associated with the cubic. If w describes an arbitrary closed path on the Riemann surface associated with the cubic, $z(w)$ does not necessarily return to its initial value, but the new value is of the form

$$\pm z(w) + 2m\omega_1 + 2n\omega_3 \tag{12.3.24}$$

where m and n are integers. Inversion then gives

$$\wp(\pm z + 2m\omega_1 + 2n\omega_3) = \wp(z) \tag{12.3.25}$$

so that $\wp(z)$ is an even doubly-periodic function with the stated periods.

The argument just given is basic for the understanding of the nature of elliptic functions and of the inversion problem for elliptic integrals, which was solved by N. H. Abel and Jacobi in 1827. But, if we merely want to prove that $\wp(z)$ is doubly-periodic, then we can use the known result for sn z together with simple algebra. The periodic properties of sn z were proved in Section A.2 by repeated use of quadratic transformations applied to the Jacobi system of equations. We can use the same device to pass from the Jacobi to the Weierstrass normal form.

To begin with, we note that, if a is a constant, then sn (az, k) satisfies

$$(w')^2 = a^2(1 - w^2)(1 - k^2w^2).$$

We now set

$$W = A + Bw^{-2}$$

where A and B are constants to be chosen. This leads to

$$(W')^2 = 4a^2B^{-1}(W - A)(W - A - B)(W - A - k^2B)$$

and this is to be identified with

$$(W')^2 = 4(W - e_1)(W - e_2)(W - e_3).$$

Hence we take

$$A = e_1, \qquad B = e_2 - e_1, \qquad a = (B)^{1/2}, \qquad k^2 = \frac{e_3 - e_1}{e_2 - e_1},$$

so that

$$\wp(z; \omega_1, \omega_3) = e_1 + (e_2 - e_1)\left\{\text{sn}\left[(e_2 - e_1)^{1/2}z, \left(\frac{e_3 - e_1}{e_2 - e_1}\right)^{1/2}\right]\right\}^{-2}. \tag{12.3.26}$$

Since sn u is doubly-periodic, so is $\wp(z)$ and we can express its periods in terms of the Jacobi periods which are easier to handle, both in theory and in practice.

The $\wp$-function is clearly a solution of the second-order non-linear differential equation

$$w'' = 6w^2 - \tfrac{1}{2}g_2 \tag{12.3.27}$$

which will play a role in the next section. Suppose in particular that $g_2 = 0$, the so-called *equiharmonic* case. Here the e_j's form the vertices of an equilateral triangle and so do the points $0, 2\omega_1, 2\omega_3$. If now we eliminate $\wp$ between

$$(\wp')^2 = 4\wp^3 - g_3 \qquad \text{and} \qquad \wp'' = 6\wp^2,$$

we get

$$(\wp'')^3 = \tfrac{27}{2}[(\wp')^2 + g_3]^2.$$

It follows that $w = \wp'(z; \omega_1, \eta\omega_1)$, $\eta = e^{(2/3)\pi i}$ is a solution of

$$(w')^3 = \tfrac{27}{2}[w^2 + g_3]^2. \tag{12.3.28}$$

This is a special case of

$$(W')^3 = C(W - A)^2(W - B)^2. \tag{12.3.29}$$

It follows that the general solution of the latter equation is

$$\alpha\wp'(z + k \mid 0, g_3) + \tfrac{1}{2}(A + B), \qquad \alpha = \frac{27}{2C}, \qquad \alpha^2 g_3 = -\tfrac{1}{4}(A - B)^2,$$

where we have stated the parameters $g_2 = 0$ and g_3 rather than the periods. We can now solve (12.3.12) in terms of elliptic functions using the substitution

$$w = c + \frac{1}{W},$$

which reduces the equation to one of type (12.3.29).

The same procedure can be used to solve the other equations in the list. In other words, we use a transformation

$$W = (w - a)^{-1}$$

to obtain a reduced equation which is either elementary or easily transformed, say to the Weierstrass normal form. An example will provide a further illustration of the method. Thus

$$(W')^6 = (W - B)^4(W - C)^3$$

is a reduced form of (12.3.14). Here we set

$$W = B + U^3$$

and obtain, after simplification,

$$(U')^2 = \tfrac{1}{9}(U^3 - C + B).$$

A trivial change of the independent variable carries this into (12.3.18) so that W is B plus the cube of an equiharmonic $\wp$-function. The solution has sextuple poles in agreement with the *a priori* test for infinitudes.

Finally, we state a result due to Briot and Bouquet.

Theorem 12.3.3. *Every elliptic, i.e. doubly-periodic meromorphic function satisfies a differential equation of type* (12.3.1).

This follows from a general theorem in the theory of elliptic functions which asserts that *any pair of such functions which have the same periods are algebraically dependent*, i.e. there exists a polynomial $F(s, t)$ with constant coefficients such that

$$F[g(z), h(z)] \equiv 0.$$

Since $w(z)$ and $w'(z)$ is such a pair, the assertion follows.

The Eq. (12.3.1) is now of the form

$$[w'(z)]^m + \sum_{k=1}^{m} P_k(w)[w'(z)]^{m-k} = 0. \qquad (12.3.30)$$

Here the integer m equals the *order* of the elliptic function, i.e. the number of roots in the period parallelogram of the equation

$$w(z) = a.$$

This number is independent of a, and it is customary to count the number of poles, i.e. to take $a = \infty$. Using the methods developed above for securing the absence of movable branch-points, it is a fairly easy matter to show that each $P_k(w)$ is a polynomial in w of a degree not exceeding $2k$. It may also be proved that $P_{m-1}(w) \equiv 0$.

EXERCISE 12.3

1. The equations

$$(W')^m = C(W - A)^{m+1} \quad \text{and} \quad (W')^m = C(W - B)^{m-1}$$

have elementary solutions. Find them and integrate (12.3.8).

2. Suppose that $w(z)$ is a solution of (12.3.18) and not identically constant. Suppose that $w(z_0) = e_1$. Show that $[w(z) - e_1]^{1/2}$ is holomorphic in some neighborhood of $z = z_0$.

3. The solutions of

$$(W')^4 = (W - B)^3(W - C)^2$$

have quadruple poles. So does $[\mathrm{sn}\,(az, k)]^4$. Choose a, b, and k so that $B + b[\mathrm{sn}\,(az, k)]^4$ is a solution. What is the general solution? Find the singular solutions.

4. Verify (12.3.20).

5. What expressions can be found from formulas (12.3.19) and (12.3.26) for the periods of $\wp(z)$? Observe that the primitive periods of $\mathrm{sn}^2\, u$ are one half of those of $\mathrm{sn}\, u$.

6. If (12.3.30) is satisfied by an elliptic function, there can be no movable branch-points. Use this observation and the methods developed above to show that the coefficient of $(w')^m$ must be a constant, which may be taken to be 1, and that $\deg(P_k) \leq 2k$.

7. The restrictions on the degrees in (12.3.30) can be interpreted as follows. Assign to w the *weight* 1, to w' the weight 2, in general to $w^{(n)}$ the weight $n + 1$. The weight of a product is the sum of the weights. The weight of a sum is $\leq$ the highest weight of any of the summands with equality, if there is a single highest term. The condition $\deg(P_k) \leq 2k$ then expresses the fact that no term of the equation can have a higher weight than that of the leading

term $(w')^m$. This is a special case of a theorem due to Jean Chazy for differential equations with fixed critical points.

8. If the order of an elliptic function is p, show that the order of $[w(z)]^n$ is np and that the order of $w'(z)$ lies between $p + 1$ and $2p$, limits included.

12.4 THE TRANSCENDENTS OF PAINLEVE

In the preceding sections we have studied non-linear first-order differential equations

$$F(z, w, w') = 0 \tag{12.4.1}$$

where F is a polynomial in w and w', with coefficients which are analytic functions of z. These equations may have movable branch-points but, by the theorem of Painlevé, such points are algebraic. We have given criteria for the absence of movable branch-points in simple cases. In principle, the method extends to all equations of type (12.4.1).

Before passing over to the second-order case, let us make some remarks concerning the integration problem and the analytic nature of the solutions when all branch-points are fixed. This is supplementary to the comments made above in the various special cases. L. Fuchs (1884) and H. Poincaré (1885) have emphasized the importance of the *genus* p of the algebraic curve

$$F(z, s, t) = 0 \tag{12.4.2}$$

for the integration problem. Here z is regarded as a parameter. The genus, also called the *deficiency*, of an algebraic curve of order n is the difference between $\frac{1}{2}(n - 1)(n - 2)$, which is the maximal number of double points and the actual number present. A cubic is of genus 0 or 1 according as it has one or no double point.

If F is of genus 0 for fixed z, a rational transformation can be found to reduce the equation to a Riccati equation. Type (viii) under Theorem 12.2.5 is a case in point. The solution of the Riccati equation in its turn is the quotient of two solutions of a linear second-order equation and, if the coefficients of (12.4.1) are rational functions of z, the coefficients of the second-order equation will have the same property. If $p = 1$, the general solution of (12.4.1) depends upon an elliptic function whose parameters (k or g_2 and g_3) are constants determined algebraically from the coefficients of (12.4.1). In addition a quadrature may be needed. Note that the cubic (12.3.22) is of genus 1. Finally, if $p > 1$ the general solution is obtained by algebraic operations on the coefficients. If the latter are algebraic in z, so is the solution. In all these cases, the basic assumption is the absence of movable branch-points.

The third case cannot occur for Briot-Bouquet equations. If such an equation lacks branch-points, then the genus of F is 0 or 1. If $p = 0$, then the solution is a rational function of z or e^{az}, if $p = 1$ a rational function of $\wp(az)$ and $\wp'(az)$ for some a.

We turn now to equations of higher order and ask for the nature of movable singularities. Painlevé's theorem breaks down already in the second-order case. Here we can have *movable essential singularities* as well as *movable transcendental critical points.* Thus the equation

$$[ww'' - (w')^2]^2 + 4w(w')^3 = 0$$

has the general solution

$$w = C_1 \exp (z - C_2)^{-1}$$

with a movable essential singularity at $z = C_2$ while

$$ww'' = \alpha(w')^2, \qquad \alpha \neq 1,$$

with the general solution

$$w = C_1(z - C_2)^{1/(1-\alpha)},$$

has a movable transcendental critical point unless α is rational. Similarly

$$w'' = \frac{2w - 1}{w^2 + 1} (w')^2$$

with the solution

$$w = \tan \log (C_1 z - C_2)$$

admits $z = C_2/C_1$ as a logarithmic branch-point as well as a cluster point of poles.

For third-order equations further complications arise. There may be *movable natural boundaries.* An example is furnished by the modular function. (For the following see the discussion in Section D.2.) The reader is now asked to interchange the roles of z and w in the discussion and to admit zero angles. With this understanding the reader will grant the existence of a function $z(w)$ which maps the upper w-half-plane conformally on a domain D in the z-plane bounded by $\Re(z) = 0$; $\Re(z) = 1$; $|z - \frac{1}{2}| = \frac{1}{2}$, $\Im(z) > 0$. The three angles of D are all 0. We may assume that $w = 0, 1, \infty$ go into $z = 0, 1, \infty$. By repeated reflection in the boundary lines and use of Schwarz's principle of symmetry, we can extend the definition of $z(w)$ so that it maps the universal covering surface over the w-plane with branch points at 0, 1, ∞ on to the upper half of the z-plane. The inverse function $w(z)$ is the so-called *modular function.* We know that $z(w)$ satisfies

$$\{z, w\} = R(w) \tag{12.4.3}$$

where $\{z, w\}$ is the Schwarzian of z with respect to w, and $R(w)$ is a rational function of w with poles at $w = 0$ and $w = 1$.

Now a basic property of the Schwarzian is that it is invariant with respect to fractional linear transformations applied to its first argument. Hence for any choice of constants a, b, c, d with $ad - bc = 1$ the function

$$Z(w) = \frac{az(w) + b}{cz(w) + d} \tag{12.4.4}$$

is a solution of (12.4.3). Since $\Im[z(w)] > 0$, the values of $Z(w)$ are confined to a circular domain Δ in the z-plane which is in a (1, 1) correspondence with the upper half-plane under the mapping (12.4.4) which maps the real axis on to a circle Γ. Here Δ is the interior of the circle or the exterior according as $\Im(d/c)$ is >0 or <0. Since a, b, c, d are at our disposal, Γ is an arbitrary circle in the z-plane. By Problem 1, Exercise D.1, we have

$$\{w, z\} = -R(w)(w')^2. \tag{12.4.5}$$

This is a third-order differential equation for w in terms of z, and, by the preceding discussion, it is satisfied by

$$w(Z) = w\left(\frac{az + b}{cz + d}\right)$$

for any choice of a, b, c, d with $ad - bc = 1$. The domain of existence of $w(Z)$ has the circle Γ as its natural boundary, i.e. the domain of existence of the general solution varies with the three essential constants of integration.

We now return to the second-order case. We consider

$$w'' = F(z, w, w') \tag{12.4.6}$$

where F is rational in w and w', and analytic in z. The problem is to characterize the equations which have fixed critical points. Here "critical points" is used as a covering term for branch-points and essential singular points.

The problem was first attacked by E. Picard in 1887 and solved by P. Painlevé in a series of papers starting in 1893. Important contributions were also made by B. Gambier (1906–10). The general method is the creation of Painlevé. Briefly put, it amounts to finding essentially two necessary conditions, enumerating all equations satisfying these conditions, fifty types in all, and then verifying that the necessary conditions are also sufficient. In all but six of these cases the verification could be given by carrying out the integration explicitly or by reduction to simpler equations. In six cases, rather elaborate proofs had to be constructed to show the absence of movable critical points. These equations define new transcendental functions, known as the *Painlevé transcendents.*

The finding of necessary conditions is relatively easy and the method extends to higher-order equations with little additional burden. On the other hand, the sufficiency proof is very laborious and the labor increases heavily with the order of the equation. The third-order case is completely settled, thanks to the work of J. Chazy and R. Garnier. It is also possible to handle the second-order case where F is merely algebraic in w, while remaining rational in w' and analytic in z. Some additional admissible types are encountered, but these equations appear to be of secondary interest compared with those for the Painlevé transcendents.

Painlevé made skilled use of his *α-method* in deriving the necessary conditions. An auxiliary parameter α is introduced in the equation in such a manner that, for $\alpha = 0$, a simpler equation results where the absence or presence of movable critical points can be read off by inspection. If now the equation has single-valued solutions for small $|\alpha|$ except possibly for $\alpha = 0$, then one proves that $\alpha = 0$ can be no exception.

Using this device, Painlevé first showed that F, by assumption rational in w' (and in w), must actually be a polynomial in w' of degree ≤ 2. Hence (12.4.6) reduces to

$$w'' = L(z, w)(w')^2 + M(z, w)w' + N(z, w) \tag{12.4.7}$$

where L, M, N are rational in w. Next it is shown that for any c, not a fixed singular point, the equation

$$W'' = L(c, W)(W')^2$$

must have fixed critical points. This requirement is satisfied if $L(z, w) \equiv 0$. But there are other alternatives which may be described as follows. The equation

$$w'' = L(z, w)(w')^2 \tag{12.4.8}$$

is obtained by applying the process of logarithmic differentiation to any one of the five equations (12.3.8), (12.3.11) to (12.3.14) where, in the result, the constants a, b, c, d are replaced by functions of z. Thus, taking (12.3.8), we see that

$$\frac{m+1}{m}\,\frac{1}{w - a(z)} + \frac{m-1}{m}\,\frac{1}{w - b(z)}$$

is one of the possible functions $L(z, w)$. These six choices exhaust the list of admissible $L(z, w)$.

We still have conditions on M and N. If $L = 0$, then M must be linear in w while N is a polynomial in w of degree ≤ 3. If $L \not\equiv 0$, let $D(z, w)$ be the least common denominator of the partial fractions in $L(z, w)$ and of degree δ, $2 \leq \delta \leq 4$, in w. Then

$$M(z, w) = \frac{\mu(z, w)}{D(z, w)}, \qquad N(z, w) = \frac{\nu(z, w)}{D(z, w)} \tag{12.4.9}$$

where μ and ν are polynomials in w of degree $\leq \delta + 1$ and $\leq \delta + 3$, respectively.

This exhausts the set of necessary conditions and leads to fifty possible types. We shall not enumerate these types. The interested reader is referred to the masterly account given by E. L. Ince in his treatise on *Ordinary Differential Equations*, Chapter 14. We shall, however, list the six equations which give the Painlevé transcendents. They are

i) $w'' = 6w^2 + z,$

ii) $w'' = 2w^3 + zw + \alpha,$

iii) $w'' = \dfrac{1}{w}(w')^2 - \dfrac{1}{z}w' + \dfrac{1}{z}(\alpha w^2 + \beta) + \gamma w^3 + \dfrac{\delta}{w},$

iv) $w'' = \dfrac{1}{2w}(w')^2 + \tfrac{3}{2}w^3 + 4zw^2 + 2(z^2 - \alpha)w + \dfrac{\beta}{w},$

v) $$w'' = \left\{\frac{1}{2w} + \frac{1}{w-1}\right\}(w')^2 - \frac{1}{z}w' + \frac{(w-1)^2}{z^2}\left\{\alpha w + \frac{\beta}{w}\right\} + \gamma\frac{w}{z} + \delta\frac{w(w+1)}{w-1},$$

vi) $$w'' = \frac{1}{2}\left\{\frac{1}{w} + \frac{1}{w-1} + \frac{1}{w-z}\right\}(w')^2 - \left\{\frac{1}{z} + \frac{1}{z-1} + \frac{1}{w-z}\right\}w' + \frac{w(w-1)(w-z)}{z^2(z-1)^2}\left\{\alpha + \frac{\beta z}{w^2} + \frac{\gamma(z-1)}{(w-1)^2} + \frac{\delta z(z-1)}{(w-z)^2}\right\}.$$

There are no critical points at all in the first three cases. If in (iv) and (v) we set $z = e^t$, the solutions become single-valued functions of t. In type (vi), 0, 1, ∞ are critical points. Only the first three equations were actually noted by Painlevé, (iv) and (v) were added by Gambier, and the general form of (vi) is due to R. Fuchs. Here (vi) may be regarded as the prototype; all other equations are obtainable from it by passage to the limit and coalescence.

In the following we shall treat type (i) in some detail. It is the simplest of the equations and in some respects the most fascinating of them all. In particular, the asymptotic properties of the solutions show a high degree of symmetry and elegance.

The first step in the discussion of

$$w'' = 6w^2 + z \tag{12.4.10}$$

is to show that the only algebraic singularities are double poles. In fact, we can find a solution having a double pole at a pre-assigned point $z = z_0$, even a continuum of such solutions depending upon an arbitrary parameter. We note first that if $w(z_0) = w_0$ and $w'(z_0) = w_1$ are finite; then there is a unique solution $w(z; z_0, w_0, w_1)$, holomorphic in some neighborhood of z_0 and having these initial values. If the point $z = z_0$ is to be an algebraic singularity, we see that at least one of the limits $\lim_{z \to z_0} w(z)$ and $\lim_{z \to z_0} w'(z)$ must be infinite. If the second one is infinite, so is $\lim w''(z)$ and then the equation shows that $\lim w(z) = \infty$. Thus in any case $\lim_{z \to z_0} w(z) = \infty$, and $\lim_{z \to z_0} w'(z) = \infty$.

We may now assume the existence of an expansion of the form

$$w(z) = \sum_{n=0}^{\infty} a_n(z - z_0)^{\alpha_n} \tag{12.4.11}$$

where $\alpha_0 < \alpha_1 < \cdots < \alpha_n < \cdots$ and $\alpha_0 < 0$. We may also assume $a_n \neq 0$ for all n. If the point is an algebraic singularity, we certainly have such an expansion where the α's are rational numbers having a common denominator. The argument will show that the α's are integers. Substitution in the equation gives

$$\sum_{n=0}^{\infty} \alpha_n(\alpha_n - 1)a_n(z - z_0)^{\alpha_n - 2} = 6\left[\sum_{n=0}^{\infty} a_n(z - z_0)^{\alpha_n}\right]^2$$
$$+ z_0 + (z - z_0).$$

Here the terms of lowest order must cancel. This gives

$$\alpha_0(\alpha_0 - 1)a_0(z - z_0)^{\alpha_0 - 2} = 6a^2{}_0(z - z_0)^{2\alpha_0}$$

or

$$\alpha_0 = -2, \qquad a_0 = 1.$$

After these terms have been cancelled, the lowest term on the left is

$$\alpha_1(\alpha_1 - 1)a_1(z - z_0)^{\alpha_1 - 2}, \qquad \alpha_1 > -2.$$

On the right, we have the two terms

$$12a_1(z - z_0)^{\alpha_1 - 2} + z_0.$$

Suppose $z_0 \neq 0$. Then the two terms on the right are of the same order iff $\alpha_1 = 2$, and for this value the term of the left is also constant. It is easy to see that cancellation can occur iff

$$\alpha_1 = 2, \qquad a_1 = -\tfrac{1}{10}z_0,$$

and this is true also if $z_0 = 0$.

At the next stage we have to balance

$$\alpha_2(\alpha_2 - 1)a_2(z - z_0)^{\alpha_2 - 2}, \qquad \alpha_2 > 2,$$

against

$$12a_0(z - z_0)^{\alpha_2 - 2} + (z - z_0).$$

This requires

$$\alpha_2 = 3, \qquad a_2 = -\tfrac{1}{6}.$$

For $n = 3$ there are only two terms to balance:

$$\alpha_3(\alpha_3 - 1)a_3(z - z_0)^{\alpha_3 - 2} \quad \text{and} \quad 12a_3(z - z_0)^{\alpha_3 - 2},$$

and this gives

$$\alpha_3 = 4, \qquad a_3 = h,$$

an arbitrary constant. In this manner one proves successively that all exponents are integers. The expansion of $w(z)$ starts out with

$$\begin{aligned} w(z) = (z - z_0)^{-2} - \tfrac{1}{10}z_0(z - z_0)^2 - \tfrac{1}{6}(z - z_0)^3 \\ + h(z - z_0)^4 + \tfrac{1}{300}z_0^2(z - z_0)^6 + \tfrac{1}{150}z_0(z - z_0)^7 + \cdots \end{aligned} \tag{12.4.12}$$

As it stands this is only a formal solution, since we have not given a convergence proof. Such a proof is easy to give. To this end choose a number M such that

$$1 < M, \qquad |z_0| < 10M, \qquad |h| < M^3. \tag{12.4.13}$$

We have then clearly

$$|a_k| < M^k, \qquad 0 \leq k < 6, \tag{12.4.14}$$

i.e. as far as we have computed the coefficients. Now the recurrence relation giving a_n is of the form

$$[\alpha_n(\alpha_n - 1) - 12]a_n = 6 \sum a_j a_k. \tag{12.4.15}$$

Here j and k are positive integers $<n$ whose sum $j + k \leq n$. If $a_j a_k$ occurs in the sum, so does $a_k a_j$ but, for a given integer j, $1 \leq j \leq n - 1$, there is at most one integer k in the same range such that $a_j a_k$ is actually present in the sum. Thus the sum contains at most $n - 1$ terms. If now (12.4.14) is valid for the integers j and k under consideration, we see that

$$|a_n| \leq \frac{6(n - 1)}{(n - 3)(n + 4)} M^n \leq M^n, \qquad 6 \leq n.$$

Here we have used the fact that $\alpha_n \geq n + 1$. Since (12.2.14) is true for $n < 6$, it is valid for all n. This shows that the formal series (12.4.12) converges for

$$0 < |z - z_0| < M^{-1}.$$

Hence the series is an actual solution of (12.4.10) and we have constructed a one parameter family of solutions having a double pole at $z = z_0$.

In order to prove that the solutions of (12.4.10) are meromorphic in the finite plane, Painlevé had to introduce a number of auxiliary functions related to $w(z)$. We start with the pair $u(z)$, $v(z)$ defined by

$$\begin{aligned} w &= v^{-2}, \\ w' &= -2v^{-3} - \tfrac{1}{2}zv - \tfrac{1}{2}v^2 + uv^3. \end{aligned} \tag{12.4.16}$$

These functions satisfy a system of first-order equations

$$\begin{aligned} u' &= \tfrac{1}{8}z^2v + \tfrac{3}{8}zv^2 + \tfrac{1}{4}v^3 - zuv^3 - \tfrac{5}{4}uv^4 + \tfrac{3}{2}u^2v^5, \\ v' &= 1 + \tfrac{1}{4}zv^4 + \tfrac{1}{4}v^5 - \tfrac{1}{2}uv^6. \end{aligned} \tag{12.4.17}$$

Since the right members are holomorphic functions of z, u, v for all finite values of the variables, the equations have unique solutions which at a given point $z = z_0$ assume pre-assigned values u_0 and v_0. In particular, this is the case if $v_0 = 0$. The corresponding solution of (12.4.10) has a double pole at $z = z_0$ and an elementary but laborious calculation shows that the corresponding auxiliary parameter h is

$$h = \tfrac{1}{7}u_0.$$

This gives a second proof of the existence of a solution $w(z)$ of (12.4.10) with a double pole at $z = z_0$ and auxiliary parameter h.

The system (12.4.17) has movable branch-points. For if at $z = z_1$, $w(z_1) = 0$, $w'(z_1) \neq 0$, then $v(z)$ becomes infinite as $C_1(z - z_1)^{-1/2}$ while $u(z) \to 0$ as $C_2(z - z_1)^{1/2}$ where $C_1C_2 = \tfrac{1}{2}$.

The second equation (12.4.16) gives

$$u = w^{3/2}(w' + \tfrac{1}{2}w^{-1}) + 2w^3 + \tfrac{1}{2}zw \tag{12.4.18}$$

so $u(z)$ is not a single-valued function. If $z = z_1$ is a double pole of $w(z)$ and if we choose the square root so that

$$[w(z)]^{3/2} = (z - z_1)^{-3} + \cdots,$$

then $u(z)$ is holomorphic at $z = z_1$ and its Taylor series there starts with the constant term $7h$, in agreement with the observation made above that $u_0 = 7h$. The function

$$V \equiv (w')^2 - 4w^3 - 2zw + \frac{w'}{w} + z \tag{12.4.19}$$

is also holomorphic at a pole of $w(z)$ and its Taylor series starts with the constant term $-28h + z_0$.

We shall also have occasion to use the function

$$W \equiv \frac{V'}{V} = \frac{4w^3 - (w')^2 + w^2 + zw}{w[w(w')^2 - 4w^4 + w' - 2zw^2 + zw]}. \tag{12.4.20}$$

We can now start proving the absence of critical points. Take an arbitrary point $z = z_0$ and finite initial values w_0, w_1. The corresponding solution $w(z)$ of (12.4.10) is holomorphic in a disk $|z - z_0| < \rho$ where ρ depends upon the initial values. If $w(z)$ is not meromorphic in the finite plane, there exists a disk $|z - z_0| < R$ in which $w(z)$ is meromorphic and a point $z = a$ on the circumference of the disk which is a non-algebraic critical point. We note that some types of critical points are excluded by the discussion of the series

(12.4.11), but there are many other possibilities which are not excluded by results obtained so far.

We join z_0 and a by a curve C of finite length such that C avoids the zeros and poles of $w(z)$. This implies that $w(z)$, $u(z)$, $v(z)$, and $V(z)$ are holomorphic along C except at $z = a$. Various contingencies may arise as we approach a along C and it is our object to show that the unfavorable ones are excluded and that $z = a$ is either a regular point or a pole of $w(z)$.

Case I. We note first that, if either $|w(z)|$ or $|w'(z)|$ is bounded along C, then $w(z)$ is regular at $z = a$ and the latter cannot be a critical point. The relations

$$w(z) = w(z_0) + \int_{z_0}^{z} w'(t)\,dt,$$

$$w'(z) = w'(z_0) + 6\int_{z_0}^{z} [w(t)]^2\,dt + \tfrac{1}{2}(z^2 - z_0^2),$$

where the integrals are taken along C, show that boundedness on C of one of the functions $w(z)$ and $w'(z)$ implies that of the other. Now, if $|w(z)| < A$, $|w'(z)| < A$ on C, then at every point $z_1 \in C$ there is a disk $|z - z_1| < \rho$ in which $w(z)$ is holomorphic and, since $|z_1| < R$, the number ρ has a positive lower bound r. Now if $|z_1 - a| < r$, then $w(z)$ is holomorphic at $z = a$ as asserted.

Case II. Next we observe that, if $|w(z)|$ is unbounded on C while $|u(z)|$ stays bounded, then $z = a$ is a pole of $w(z)$. For this means that there are points z_1 on C in any neighborhood of $z = a$ where $|u(z_1)| < A$, $|v(z_1)| < \varepsilon$, $\varepsilon > 0$ pre-assigned. At such a point z_1, the system (12.4.17) has a solution $u(z)$, $v(z)$ which takes on pre-assigned values $u(z_1)$, $v(z_1)$ at $z = z_1$ such that the functions $u(z)$, $v(z)$ are holomorphic in a disk $|z - z_1| < r$, where r has a positive lower bound for $z_1 \in C$, $|u(z_1)| < A$, $|v(z_1)| < \varepsilon$. If $|z_1 - a| < r$, then $u(z)$ and $v(z)$ are holomorphic at $z = a$. Since $\liminf v(z) = 0$ for approach along C and $\lim v(z)$ exists, it follows that $v(a) = 0$ and $w(z)$ has a double pole at $z = a$.

Case III. The same conclusion holds if $|w(z)|$ is unbounded on C while $|V(z)|$ is bounded. For we have then a sequence of points $\{z_n\}$ on C where $z_n \to a$, $|w(z_n)| \to \infty$, $|V(z_n)| < A$. Substituting such a value of z in (12.4.19) and solving for w', we find that one of the roots is

$$w' = -\frac{1}{2w} - 2w^{3/2}\left\{1 + \frac{z}{2w^2} + \frac{V - z}{4w^3} + \frac{1}{16w^5}\right\}^{1/2}$$

$$= -\frac{1}{2w} - 2w^{3/2}\left\{1 + \frac{z}{4w^2} + \frac{V - z}{8w^3} + O(w^{-4})\right\}.$$

Substituting this value for w' in (12.4.18), we obtain

$$u(z) = -\tfrac{1}{4}[V(z) - z] + O(w^{-1}).$$

In other words, we have $|u(z_n)| \leq M$, $v(z_n) \to 0$, and the argument used in case II shows that $z = a$ is a pole of $w(z)$.

Case IV. The only remaining possibility is now that both $|w(z)|$ and $|V(z)|$ are unbounded on C. We split this case into two sub-cases. We first assume that $|w(z)| \geq \varepsilon > 0$ on C and, under this assumption, we show the existence of a sequence $\{z_n\}$ on C such that $z_n \to a$, $|w(z_n)| \to \infty$, $|V(z_n)| \to 0$. Hence this sub-case is reducible to case III.

Now if $|V(z)|$ is unbounded on C, the function $W(z)$ of (12.4.20) must also be unbounded since

$$V(z) = V(z_0) \exp \left[\int_{z_0}^{z} W(t)\, dt\right].$$

Hence there is a sequence $\{z_n\}$ on C with $z_n \to a$ and $|W(z_n)| \to \infty$. Let us now examine the two sequences $\{w(z_n)\}$ and $\{w'(z_n)\}$. They cannot both be bounded because then the argument under case I would apply, $w(z)$ would be holomorphic at $z = a$, which contradicts the assumption that $w(z)$ is unbounded on C. If now $\{w(z_n)\}$ were bounded, $\{w'(z_n)\}$ must be unbounded and we may assume that $\lim |w'(z_n)| = \infty$. Then (12.4.20) gives

$$\limsup |W(z_n)| \leq [\liminf |w(z_n)|]^{-2}$$

and this is finite by assumption. This contradicts the assumption that $|W(z_n)| \to \infty$.

It follows that $\{|w(z_n)|\}$ is an unbounded sequence. Again, we may assume that, after suitable weeding-out and renumbering of the elements, we have a sequence $\{z_n\}$ such that

$$|w(z_n)| \to \infty, \qquad |W(z_n)| \to \infty.$$

We can now eliminate w' between (12.4.19) and (12.4.20) and obtain an expression of the form

$$VW = A + CV + (B + DV)^{1/2} \tag{12.4.21}$$

where

$$\begin{aligned} A &= 1 + z(1 - w)w^{-2} - \tfrac{1}{2}w^{-4}, & C &= -w^{-2}, \\ B &= 4w^{-3} + 2zw^{-5} - zw^{-6} + \tfrac{1}{4}w^{-8}, & D &= w^{-6}. \end{aligned} \tag{12.4.22}$$

It follows that V is a root of the quadratic equation

$$(W - C)^2V^2 - [2A(W - C) + D]V + A^2 - B = 0. \tag{12.4.23}$$

As $z = z_n \to a$

$$A \to 1,\ B \to 0,\ C \to 0,\ D \to 0,\ W \to \infty,$$

and it follows that both roots of the quadratic go to 0, i.e.

$$\lim V(z_n) = 0.$$

We are then back in case III and know that $z = a$ is a pole.

Case V. In the second sub-case, $V(z)$ and $w(z)$ are unbounded on C but $\liminf |w(z)| = 0$. The only properties of C that matter are that C is of finite length and avoids the zeros and poles of $w(z)$. We are free to modify C as long as these properties are preserved and we can reduce the second sub-case to the first, if it is possible to find an admissible curve C on which $\liminf |w(z)| > 0$. This is indeed possible. Intuitively this is at least plausible, but the proof is far from elementary.

Let $\varepsilon > 0$ be a fixed small positive number. There is then by assumption a sequence of points $\{z_n\}$ on C such that $|w(z)| < \varepsilon$ for $z \in C_k$, the arc of C joining z_{2k-1} with z_{2k}, $k = 1, 2, 3, \ldots$, while $|w(z)| \geq \varepsilon$ on the remaining arcs. Consider now the sequence $\{|w'(z_n)|\}$. None of its infinite subsequences can be bounded, for, if there were a bounded subsequence, then the method under case I would apply and $w(z)$ would be holomorphic at $z = a$, which contradicts the assumption that $|w(z)|$ is unbounded on C. Hence, given any small $\eta > 0$, we may assume

$$|w'(z_n)| > 1/\eta \qquad \text{for} \qquad n > N.$$

We set $w(z_n) = w_n$, $w'(z_n) = (\zeta_n)^{-1}$ and consider the differential equation for z in terms of w

$$\frac{d^2z}{dw^2} = -(6w^2 + z)\left(\frac{dz}{dw}\right)^3 \tag{12.4.24}$$

at $w = w_{2k-1}$ with

$$z(w_{2k-1}) = z_{2k-1}, \qquad z'(w_{2k-1}) = \zeta_{2k-1}.$$

There is a unique solution having these initial values, say $z(w)$, and it is holomorphic in a disk $|w - w_{2k-1}| < r_k$ where in fact $r_k \to \infty$ with k. Since $|w_{2k-1}| = \varepsilon$, we are sure that the disk Δ_ε: $|w| \leq \varepsilon$ belongs to the domain of holomorphism of $z(w)$. Moreover, we have for large k

$$z'(w) = \zeta_{2k-1}[1 + \delta(w)], \qquad |w| \leq \varepsilon, \tag{12.4.25}$$

where $\delta(w)$ is holomorphic and

$$|\delta(w)| < \tfrac{1}{2}, \qquad |w| \leq \varepsilon.$$

Further, if w and w_0 are in Δ_ε, then

$$\tfrac{3}{2}|\zeta_{2k-1}|\,|w - w_0| \geq |z(w) - z(w_0)| \geq \tfrac{1}{2}|\zeta_{2k-1}|\,|w - w_0|,$$

so $z(w)$ maps Δ_ε in a one-to-one manner on to a domain D_k in the z-plane. The latter contains the arc C_k joining z_{2k-1} with z_{2k}, and $l(C_k)$, the length of C_k, is at least

$$|z_{2k} - z_{2k-1}| \geq \tfrac{1}{2}|\zeta_{2k-1}|\,|w_{2k} - w_{2k-1}|.$$

In the w-plane we can join the two points w_{2k-1} and w_{2k} by an arc γ_k of the circle $|w| = \varepsilon$, the smaller arc if there is any choice. Here γ_k is mapped on an arc Γ_k in the z-plane which joins z_{2k-1} with z_{2k} and

$$l(\Gamma_k) = \int_{\gamma_k} |z'(w)|\,|dw| \leq \tfrac{3}{2}|\zeta_{2k-1}|\,l(\gamma_k) \leq \tfrac{3}{4}\pi|\zeta_{2k-1}|\,|w_{2k} - w_{2k-1}|.$$

It follows that

$$l(\Gamma_k) \leq \tfrac{3}{2}\pi l(C_k).$$

The arcs Γ_k and C_k have only their end-points in common. They bound a portion of D_k in which $w(z)$ is holomorphic and has a single zero which is not on Γ_k. Hence, if for each large k we replace the arc C_k by the corresponding arc Γ_k, keeping the rest of C as it is, we obtain a new curve C' joining z_0 with a. Here C' is of finite length, does not pass through a zero or a pole of $w(z)$, and $\liminf |w(z)| = \varepsilon > 0$ if $z \to a$ along C'. This means that case V has been reduced to case IV and $z = a$ is a pole of $w(z)$.

After this laborious reduction process it is somewhat of an anticlimax to have to observe that the result shows that case V cannot arise at all. For, if the point $z = a$ is a pole of $w(z)$, then $\lim |w(z)| = \infty$ and $\liminf |w(z)|$ cannot be finite.

We have now proved Painlevé's theorem:

Theorem 12.4.1. *The solutions of Eq.* (12.4.10) *have no singularities other than poles in the finite plane.*

Our labors have given no information about the distribution of the poles of these meromorphic functions or of their global properties. This gap in the theory was filled by Pierre Boutroux in a memoir published in 1913–14, where he examined the function theoretical properties of the Painlevé transcendents, as well as the asymptotic integration of a class of second-order non-linear differential equations containing those of Painlevé.

For type (i), Boutroux took as his normal form the equation

$$w'' = 6w^2 - 6z \tag{12.4.26}$$

which is obtained from (12.4.10) by a simple change of variable ($z \to az$, $w \to bw$). Both equations are invariant under the rotation

$$z \to \alpha z, \qquad w \to \alpha^3 w, \qquad \alpha = e^{2\pi i/5}. \tag{12.4.27}$$

This implies that, if $w(z)$ is a solution, so is

$$\alpha^3 w(\alpha z).$$

It also indicates that the equation has five distinguished directions in the plane, the arguments of the fifth roots of unity, and that a study of the equation in one of these directions gives global information.

The substitution

$$Z = \tfrac{4}{5}z^{5/4}, \qquad w = z^{1/2}W$$

transforms the equation into

$$W'' - 6W^2 + 6 = -\frac{W'}{Z} + \frac{4}{25}\frac{W}{Z^2} \tag{12.4.28}$$

which is basic for the asymptotic integration. The situation is similar to but much more complicated than that encountered in Section 7.4, where we studied the asymptotic integration of the generalized Bessel equation. There the asymptotic sine equation

$$W_0'' + W_0 = 0$$

played a decisive role as well as its solutions

$$\sin(Z - Z_0), \qquad \exp(iZ) \qquad \text{and} \qquad \exp(-iZ).$$

Here it is the *asymptotic elliptic equation*

$$W_0'' - 6W_0^2 + 6 = 0 \tag{12.4.29}$$

which plays the corresponding role. Its first integral is

$$(W_0')^2 = 4W_0^3 - 12W_0 - g_3 \tag{12.4.30}$$

with the general solution

$$\wp(Z - Z_0 \mid 12, g_3) \tag{12.4.31}$$

where g_3 is any constant. This is normally a doubly-periodic function with periods $2\omega_1$, $2\omega_3$ which may be computed from the value of g_3, and an array of double poles at

$$Z_0 + 2m\omega_1 + 2n\omega_3.$$

Deviations from this pattern occur when $g_3 = \pm 8$, these being the values of g_3 for which the cubic in the right member of (12.4.30) has equal roots. Then one of the quantities ω_1 or ω_3 becomes infinite, the doubly-periodic functions degenerate into simply-periodic ones

$$1 + 3[\sinh\sqrt{3}(Z - Z_0)]^{-2} \qquad \text{or} \qquad -1 + 3[\sin\sqrt{3}(Z - Z_0)]^{-2} \tag{12.4.32}$$

and there is a single string of poles instead of the double array. These properties of $W_0(Z)$ are reflected as asymptotic properties of $W(Z)$.

Take a solution $W(Z)$ of (12.4.28) given by its initial values η and η' at $Z = Z_0$ where $|Z_0|$ is large. Set

$$D = (\eta')^2 - 4\eta^3 + 12\eta \neq \pm 8$$

and let $W_0(Z, D)$ be the solution of

$$(W_0')^2 = 4W_0^3 - 12W_0 + D \tag{12.4.33}$$

which has the same initial values as $W(Z)$ at $Z = Z_0$. It is an elliptic function of Z. Let a, b, c be the three distinct roots of the cubic

$$4s^3 - 12s + D = 0.$$

Boutroux is anxious to know what happens to $W(Z)$ when Z is replaced by $Z + 2\omega$ where 2ω is a period of $W_0(Z, D)$. Here it is more convenient to work with the inverse functions $Z(W)$ and $Z_0(W)$. Let W describe a simple closed curve Λ, beginning and ending at $W = \eta$, which surrounds two of the roots, say a and b, but not the third. At $W = \eta$ both inverses start with the value Z_0, at the endpoint of Λ we have

$$Z_0(W) = Z_0 + 2\omega_1, \qquad Z(W) = Z_{01},$$

where again

$$2\omega_1 = \int_\Lambda (4s^3 - 12s + D)^{-1/2}\, ds$$

is a period of $W_0(Z, D)$. Moreover,

$$|Z(W) - Z_0(W)| \tag{12.4.34}$$

is small for all W on Λ. In the same manner, one handles the case where W describes the loop Λ' surrounding b and c. Here the terminal values are, respectively,

$$Z_0 + 2\omega_3 \quad \text{and} \quad Z_{10}$$

where

$$2\omega_3 = \int_{\Lambda'} (4s^3 - 12s + D)^{-1/2}\, ds.$$

This operation can now be repeated at Z_{01} and Z_{10} where in each case initial values, the parameter D, the roots of the cubic and the loops are given their local values. It follows from (12.4.34) that all these quantities change by small amounts when we go from Z_0 to Z_{01} or Z_{10}. Suppose that at Z_{01} we use the Λ'-operation and at Z_{10} the Λ-operation. Normally, that is for the class of differential equations asymptotic to (12.4.29), these two operations would lead to distinct though nearby points. But in the case of (12.4.28) these points coincide and there is a unique point Z_{11} obtained in this manner. The four points

$$Z_0,\ Z_{01},\ Z_{11},\ \text{and}\ Z_{10}$$

form the vertices of a curvilinear quadrilateral Q_{11}, the sides of which are traced by the different determinations of $Z(W)$ when W describes the loops.

More generally, we can determine uniquely an array of lattice points $Z_{j,k}$ corresponding to j applications of Λ-operations and k applications of Λ'-operations. Here the four points

$$Z_{j,k},\ Z_{j+1,k},\ Z_{j+1,k+1},\ \text{and}\ Z_{j,k+1}$$

form the vertices of a quadrilateral $Q_{j,k}$. These quadrilaterals play the role of *approximate period parallelograms*. Each $Q_{j,k}$ contains a single double pole of $W(Z)$ and three zeros of $W'(Z)$. Further

$$|W(Z) - W_0(Z, D_{j,k})| \tag{12.4.35}$$

is small everywhere in $Q_{j,k}$ excepting small neighborhoods of the poles. Here

$$D_{jk} = [W'(Z_{j,k})]^2 - 4[W(Z_{j,k})]^3 + 12W(Z_{j,k}).$$

If the imaginary part of Z_0 is large, we can define $Z_{j,k}$ for negative values of j, if the real part is large, for negative values of k.

It should be noted that the approximation of $W(Z)$ by a solution of (12.4.29) is local and shifts from one quadrilateral to the next. It is true, however, that

$$\lim_{j\to\infty} D_{j,k} \quad \text{and} \quad \lim_{k\to\infty} D_{j,k}$$

exist. Further

$$\lim_{j\to\infty} (Z_{j+1,k} - Z_{j,k}) \quad \text{and} \quad \lim_{k\to\infty} (Z_{j,k+1} - Z_{j,k})$$

exist, the first being real the second purely imaginary.

Since in each quadrilateral $Q_{j,k}$ there is a single double pole, we see that the poles of $W(Z)$ form a net $\{Z_{j,k}\}$ which is approximately rectangular at a distance from the origin. This, however, holds only if the parameters $D_{j,k}$ keep away from the critical values ± 8. If this is not the case, Boutroux shows that there is an ultimate string of poles, approximately horizontal or approximately vertical, beyond which $W(Z)$ has no poles and tends to $+1$ or -1 in the pole-free half-plane. These solutions can be constructed by a method of successive approximations starting from one of the functions (12.4.32). Boutroux calls them *truncated solutions.*

Going back to the z-plane, we see that the solutions of (12.4.26) are meromorphic functions of order $\frac{5}{2}$ and normally have a curvilinear net of poles in each of the five sectors

$$k\tfrac{2}{5}\pi < \arg z < (k+1)\tfrac{2}{5}\pi, \qquad k = 0, 1, 2, 3, 4.$$

There are, however, infinitely many truncated solutions where there is an ultimate string of poles in one sector or such a string extending through two adjacent sectors. A truncated solution lacks roughly one fifth of the normal allotment of poles. There are *five triply-truncated solutions* obtainable from each other by the transformation (12.4.27). Such a solution has a net of poles in only one of the sectors; in the remaining sectors there is at most a finite number of poles and there

$$\lim_{z\to\infty} z^{-1/2}w(z) = +1.$$

Here the account of Boutroux's investigation ends and we add merely a few remarks on the applications of the Nevanlinna theory of value distribution to Eq. (12.4.26). Most of the results are due to Hans Wittich. Painlevé showed that a solution $w(z)$ of (12.4.26) omits no value. More precisely, Wittich proves that for each a the Nevanlinna defect $\delta(a) = 0$. This holds also for the truncated solutions. It is not merely the poles which occur with subnormal frequency; the same applies to all values a in view of the asymptotic behavior of the solution in the pole-free sector or sectors. As a consequence, the Nevanlinna characteristic function $T(r,f)$ for a simply (triply) truncated solution is about $\frac{4}{5}$ ($\frac{1}{5}$) of the $T(r,f)$ of a normal solution. The value infinity is *completely ramified* for all solutions, i.e. the equation $w(z) = \infty$ has only double roots. Wittich has shown that no other value can be completely ramified. He also showed that if it is assumed to be known that the solutions of (i) or of (ii) are single-valued then it follows from the form of the equations that the solutions are meromorphic function.

EXERCISE 12.4

1. Show that a solution of (12.4.10) can have a triple zero at $z = z_0$ iff $z_0 = 0$.
2. Transform $w'' = 6w^2 + z$ into $W'' = 6W^2 - 6Z$.
3. Justify Painlevé's α-method.
4. Let $z = x > 0$ and consider a solution of (12.4.10) with $w(0) = w_0 > 0$, $w'(0) = w_1$, $w_1^2 - 4w_0^3 > 0$. Show that $w(x)$ becomes infinite for some x with $0 < x < (w_0)^{-1/2}$.
5. Show that the $V(z)$ defined by (12.4.19) is holomorphic at a pole of $w(z)$ and find the constant term in its Taylor series.
6. Why is $w(z)$ of order $\frac{5}{2}$?
7. Prove (12.4.28).
8. Let $w(z)$ be a solution of (12.4.10), z_0 not a pole of $w(z)$ and set $\sigma(z) = \exp\left[-\int_{z_0}^{z}\int_{z_0}^{s} w(t)\,dt\,ds\right]$. Show that $\sigma(z)$ is an entire function and express $w(z)$ in terms of $\sigma(z)$ and its derivatives.
9. The equation
$$w'' = 2w^3 - 2zw + \tfrac{2}{3}a$$
is of type (ii). Transform it into type (ii). Show that the algebraic singularities of the solutions are movable simple poles and determine the first three non-vanishing terms of the Laurent expansion.

10. Show that $Z = \frac{2}{3}z^{3/2}$, $w = z^{1/2}W$ transforms the equation into

$$W'' = 2W^3 - 2W - \frac{W'}{Z} + \frac{1}{9}\frac{W}{Z^2} + \frac{a}{Z}$$

with the asymptotic elliptic equation

$$W_0'' = 2W_0^3 - 2W_0 \qquad \text{or} \qquad (W_0')^2 = W_0^4 - 2W_0^2 + D.$$

11. Assuming that $W(Z)$ can be locally approximated by a solution $W_0(Z, D)$ of the elliptic equation and that $w(z)$ is meromorphic, prove that $w(z)$ is of order 3.

COLLATERAL READING

The standard reference for Chapter 12 is

INCE, E. L., *Ordinary Differential Equations*, Dover reprint, New York (1944), Chapters 13 and 14.

See also the following monographs:

BIEBERBACH, L., *Theorie der gewöhnlichen Differentialgleichungen auf funktionentheoretischen Grundlage dargestellt*, Springer-Verlag, Berlin (1953), §§1, 2, 5, 12.

BOUTROUX, P., *Leçons sur les fonctions définies par les équations différentielles du premier ordre*, Gauthier-Villars, Paris (1908), Chapters 1, 2.

BRIOT, A. A., and J. C. BOUQUET, *Théorie des fonctions elliptiques*, 2nd ed., Paris (1875), Book 5, Chapter 4.

HORN, J., *Gewöhnliche Differentialgleichungen beliebiger Ordnung*, S. Schubert, Göschen, Leipzig (1905), Chapter 14.

PAINLEVÉ, P., *Leçons sur la théorie analytique des équations différentielles, professées à Stockholm* (1895). (Mimeographed only?)

SCHLESINGER, L., *Einführung in die Theorie der Differentialgleichungen mit einer unabhängigen Variabeln*, 2nd ed., S. Schubert, Göschen, Leipzig (1904), Chapters 7, 8.

WITTICH, H., *Neuere Untersuchungen über eindeutige analytische Funktionen*, Ergebnisse der Math. N.F. 8, Springer-Verlag, Berlin (1955), Chapter 5.

The last treatise gives an account of the Nevanlinna theory with applications to differential equations and an extensive bibliography. The following is an incomplete list of articles the results of which are mentioned in the text.

BOUTROUX, P., "Recherches sur les transcendantes de M. Painlevé et l'étude asymptotique des équations différentielles du second ordre," *Annales de l'Ecole Normale Supérieure*, (3) **30**, 255–375 (1913); *ibid.* **31**, 99–159 (1914).

BRIOT, A. A., and J. C. BOUQUET, "Intégration des équations différentielles au moyen des fonctions elliptiques," *J. de l'Ecole Polytechnique*, **21:36** (1856).

CHAZY, J., "Sur les équations différentielles du troisième ordre et d'ordre supérieur dont l'intégrale générale a ses points critiques fixes," *Acta Math.* **34**, 317–385 (1911).

FUCHS, L., "Über Differentialgleichungen deren Integrale feste Verzweigungspunkte besitzen," *Sitzungsberichte d. Akad.* 699–720, Berlin (1884).

GAMBIER, B., "Sur les équations différentielles du second ordre et du premier degré dont l'intégrale générale est à points critiques fixés," *Acta Math.* **33**, 1–55 (1910).

MALMQUIST, J., "Sur les fonctions à un nombre fini de branches définies par des équations différentielles du premier ordre," *Acta Math.* **36**, 297–343 (1913).

PAINLEVÉ, P., "Memoire sur les équations différentielles dont l'intégrale générale est uniforme," *Bull. Soc. Math. France*, **28**, 201–261 (1900).

PAINLEVÉ, P., "Sur les équations différentielles du second ordre et d'ordre supérieur dont l'intégrale générale est uniforme," *Acta Math.* **25**, 1–82 (1902).

PICARD, E., "Remarques sur les équations différentielles," *Acta Math.* **17**, 297–300 (1893).

POINCARÉ, H., "Sur un théorème de M. Fuchs," *Acta Math.* **7**, 1–32 (1885).

Reference (incomplete) is also made to

FUCHS, R., *C.R. Acad. Sci. Paris*, **141**, 555 (1905).

GARNIER, R., *Ann. École Norm Sup.*, (3) **27**, 1 (1912).

GARNIER, R., *C.R. Acad. Sci. Paris*, **162**, 937 (1916); **163**, 8, 118 (1916).

For the theory of elliptic and modular functions consult

HILLE, E., *Analytic Function Theory*, Vol. II, Ginn, Boston (1962), Chapter 13.

Chapter 14 deals with entire and meromorphic functions and contains an account of the Nevanlinna theory. For the latter see also

HAYMAN, W. K., *Meromorphic functions*, Clarendon, Oxford (1964).

BIBLIOGRAPHY

ACHIEZER, N. I., and I. M. GLAZMAN, *Theorie der linearen Operatoren im Hilbert Raum*, Akademie-Verlag, Berlin (1954).

ATKINSON, F. V., *Discrete and Continuous Boundary Problems*, Academic Press, New York (1964).

BELLMAN, Richard, *A Survey of the Theory of the Boundedness, Stability, and Asymptotic Behavior of Solutions of Linear and Non-Linear Differential and Difference Equations*, Office of Naval Research, NAVEXOS P-596, Washington, D.C. (1949).

BELLMAN, Richard, *Stability Theory of Differential Equations*, McGraw-Hill, New York (1953).

BIEBERBACH, Ludwig, *Differentialgleichungen*, Springer-Verlag, Berlin (1923).

BIEBERBACH, Ludwig, *Theorie der gewöhnlichen Differentialgleichungen auf funktionentheoretischen Grundlage dargestellt*, Springer-Verlag, Berlin (1953).

BIEBERBACH, Ludwig, *Einführung in die Theorie der Differentialgleichungen im reellen Gebiet*, Springer-Verlag, Berlin (1956).

BÔCHER, Maxime, *Leçons sur les méthodes de Sturm dans la théorie des équations différentielles linéaires et leurs dévelopments modernes*, Gauthier-Villars, Paris (1917).

BOCHNER, S., and K. CHANDRASEKHARAN, *Fourier transforms*, Princeton University Press, Princeton (1949).

BOURBAKI, N., *Elements de Mathématiques*, Livre IV, *Fonctions d'une variable réelle*, Chap. IV, "Équations différentielles. Actualités Scientifiques et Industrielles 1132," Hermann, Paris (1951).

BOUTROUX, P., *Leçons sur les fonctions définies par les équations différentielles du premier ordre*, Gauthier-Villars, Paris (1908).

BRIOT, A. A., and J. C. BOUQUET, *Théorie des fonctions elliptiques*, 2nd edition, Paris (1875).

CESARI, Lamberto, *Asymptotic Behavior and Stability Problems in Ordinary Differential Equations*, Ergebnisse der Mathematik, New Series 16, Springer-Verlag, Berlin (1959).

CODDINGTON, E. A., and Norman LEVINSON, *Theory of Ordinary Differential Equations*, McGraw-Hill, New York (1955).

COPPEL, W. A., *Stability and Asymptotic Behavior of Differential Equations*, Heath, Boston (1965).

DUNFORD, Nelson, and Jack SCHWARTZ, *Linear Operators.* II, *Spectral Theory*, Interscience, New York (1963).

ERDELYI, A., W. MAGNUS, F. OBERHETTINGER, and F. TRICOMI, *Higher Transcendental functions*, 3 vols, McGraw-Hill, New York (1953, 1955).

GANTMACHER, F. R., *The Theory of Matrices*, 2 vols, Chelsea, New York (1959).

HARTMAN, Philip, *Ordinary Differential Equations*, Wiley, New York (1964).

HAYMAN, W. K., *Meromorphic Functions*, Clarendon Press, Oxford (1964).

HILB, Emil, *Lineare Differentialgleichungen im komplexen Gebiet*, Encyklopädie der mathematischen Wissenschaften, Vol. II:2, B. G. Teubner, Leipzig (1915).

HILLE, Einar, *Analytic Function Theory*, Vol. 2, Ginn, Boston (1962).

HILLE, Einar, *Analysis*, Vol. 2, Blaisdell, Waltham (1966), Chapter 20.

HILLE, Einar, and R. S. PHILLIPS, *Functional Analysis and Semi-Groups*, American Mathematical Society Colloquium Publications, Vol. 31, Providence, R.I. (1957).

HORN, J., *Gewöhnliche Differentialgleichung beliebiger Ordnung*, Sammlung Schubert, Vol. 50, G. J. Göschen, Leipzig (1905).

INCE, R. L., *Ordinary Differential Equations*, Dover, New York (1944).

KAMKE, E., *Differentialgleichungen reeller Funktionen*, Akademische Verlagsgesellschaft, Leipzig (1930).

KAMKE, E., *Differentialgleichungen: Lösungen und Lösungsmethoden*, vol. I, 3rd edition, Chelsea, New York (1948).

KLEIN, Felix, *Vorlesungen über die hypergeometrische Funktion*, Springer-Verlag, Berlin (1933).

LAPPO-DANILEVSKY, J. A., *Théorie des systèmes des équations différentielles linéaires*, Chelsea, New York (1953).

LEFSCHETZ, Solomon, *Differential Equations. Geometric Theory*, Interscience, New York (1957).

MCLACHLAN, N. W., *Theory and Application of Mathieu Functions*, Oxford University Press, Oxford (1943).

MASSERA, J. L., and J. J. SCHÄFFER, *Linear Differential Equations and Function Spaces*, Academic Press, New York (1966).

MORSE, Marston, *Calculus of Variations in the Large*, American Mathematical Society Colloquium Publications, Vol. 18, New York (1934).

NAĬMARK, M. A., *Lineĭnye Differentsial'nye Operatory*, Gosudarstvennoe Izdatal'stvo Tehn.-Teor, Literatury, Moscow (1954).

PAINLEVÉ, P., *Leçons sur la théorie analytique des équations différentielles*, professées à Stockholm, 1895.

POINCARÉ, H., *Les méthodes nouvelles de la mécanique céleste*, 3 vols, Gauthier-Villars, Paris (1892, 1893, 1899).

PÓLYA, G., and G. SZEGÖ, *Aufgaben und Lehrsätze aus der Analysis*, Vol. II, 3rd edition, Springer-Verlag, Berlin (1964).

RICKART, C. E., *General Theory of Banach Algebras*, Van Nostrand, New York (1960).

SCHLESINGER, Ludwig, *Handbuch der Theorie der linearen Differentialgleichungen*, Vols. 1, 2:1, 2:2, B. C. Teubner, Leipzig (1895, 1897, 1898).

SCHLESINGER, Ludwig, *Einführung in die Theorie der Differentialgleichungen mit einer unabhängigen Variabeln*, 2nd edition, Sammlung Schubert, Vol. 13, G. J. Göschen, Leipzig (1904).

STONE, M. H., *Linear Transformations in Hilbert Space and Their Applications to Analysis*, American Mathematical Society Colloquium Publications, Vol. 15, New York (1932).

SZEGÖ, G., *Orthogonal Polynomials*, American Mathematical Society Colloquium Publications, Vol. 23, 2nd edition, Providence, R.I. (1948).

TITCHMARSH, E. C., *Eigenfunction Expansions Associated with Second-Order Differential Equations*, Clarendon Press, Oxford (1947).

TRICOMI, F. G., *Fonctions hypergéométriques confluentes*, Gauthier-Villars, Paris (1960).

TRICOMI, F. G., *Equazioni Differenziale*, Einaudi, Torino (1965).

WALTER, Wolfgang, *Differential- und Intergralungleichungen*, Springer-Verlag, Berlin (1964).

WATSON, G. N., *Theory of Bessel Functions*, 2nd edition, Cambridge University Press, London (1962).

WHITTAKER, E. T., and G. N. WATSON, *A Course in Modern Analysis*, 4th edition, Cambridge University Press, London (1952).

WITTICH, H., *Neuere Untersuchungen über eindeutige analytische Funktionen*, Ergebnisse der Mathematik, New Series, No. 8, Springer-Verlag, Berlin (1955).

YOSIDA, Kôsaku, *Lectures on Differential and Integral Equations*, Interscience, New York (1960).

INDEX

ABEL, N. H., 179, 690
  Abelian group, 1
  Abelian integral, 689
acceleration, 436
ACHIEZER, N. I. 566, 574, 711
adjoint
  differential expression, 391
  equation, 392
  self-adjoint operator, 392
AGMON, S., 272
algebra, 3
  Abelian, commutative, 105
  Banach, 105–111
  center of, 130
  quotient, 120
  simple, 119
  star, 110
amplitude
  cosine, delta, sine, 67
  of oscillations, 380
anticlinals, 577, 581
approach to singularity, 223–225
approximations, successive, 32–42
ARZELÀ, C., 21
ASCOLI, G., 21
asymptotic
  elliptic equation, 705
  integration, 330–344
  sine equation, 172, 330
ATKINSON, F. V., 425, 426, 566, 574, 711
axioms
  distance, 4
  norm, 4–5
  star algebra, 110
  triangle, 4
BANACH, S., 11
  algebra, 105–111
  fixed point theorem, 11
  space, 99
BARNES, E. W., 307, 326
BARRETT, J. H., 288, 481, 482, 483, 484, 493
  alternating method, 485
  cosines and sines, 481
  -Prüfer method, 481–486
BARTLE, R. G., 23
Bateman papers, 371
BEESACK, P., 576, 587, 588, 591, 593, 594, 598, 642, 657, 661
BELLMAN, R., 24, 168, 175, 492, 711
BENDIXSON, I., 80, 98
BERNOULLI
  Daniel, 319
  equation, 674
  Jakob, 319
BESSEL, F. W., 319, 322
  equation, 91, 257, 319–330, 611–613
  functions, 319, 320, 324
  hyper-Bessel equation, 97
Bestimmtheitstelle, 182
BIEBERBACH, L., 426, 672, 709, 711
BIRKHOFF, G. D., 32, 62, 189, 206, 208, 229, 251, 426, 566, 574, 576
  canonical form, 251
BLISS, G. A., 566, 574
BÔCHER, M., 425, 428, 492, 711
BOCHNER, S., 534, 574, 711
boundary conditions
  classical, 385
  lateral, 386
  of type (j, k), 404
  periodic, 391

boundary value problems
for Mathieu's equation, 361–366
regular, 384–394
Prüfer's method, 394–407
singular, 494–575
boundedness
of mapping, 6
total, 21
uniform, 21
BOUQUET, J. C., 674, 677, 691, 709, 711
equations of Briot-Bouquet, 684–693
BOURBAKI, N., 711
BOUTROUX, P., 277, 576, 638, 642, 662, 672, 673, 704, 709, 711
BRAUER, F., 566, 574
BRIOT, A. A., 674, 677, 691, 709, 711
equations of Briot-Bouquet, 684–693

CACCIOPOLI, R., 32, 62
calcul des limites, 48
calculus, operational, 125–129
CARATHÉODORY, C., 39
inequality, 16
uniqueness theorem, 40
CAUCHY, A. L., 42, 48, 62
-Lindelöf method, 48–57
-Lipschitz-Peano method, 42–48
convergence principle, 5
kernel, 125
majorant, 55
product series, 49
CAYLEY-HAMILTON theorem, 10
CESARI, L., 175, 492, 711
characteristic equation
of linear differential equation, 139
of matrix, 9
characteristic function, 385
of Nevanlinna, 510
characteristic, semi-, 625
characteristic value, 9, 385
CHANDRASEKHARAN, K., 574, 711
CHAZY, J., 693, 696, 709
closure relation, 315
CODDINGTON, E. A., 59, 208, 426, 502, 573, 711
commutants, 123
commutator operator, 129–138
compactness, 20–23, 514
conditional, 21
sequential, 21
comparison theorems
A. Kneser, 461, 462
Prüfer, 395
Sturm, 375–380, 384
sundry, 435, 440, 460, 462
concomitant, 391
condition, initial, 26
variation of, 76–90
cone, positive, 4, 110
conjugation, 110
constant coefficients, 139–147
constant solutions, 48, 81, 85, 277
continuation, analytic, 217–222
contraction fixed point theorem, 11
convexity
horizontal, vertical, 606
of zeros and extrema, 607
convolution, 124, 217
COPPEL, W. A., 98, 175, 213, 480, 492, 493, 566, 711
covering, 20
universal, surface, 634
cross-ratio, 274, 288
CUNNINGHAM, E., 204, 208
cylinder functions
circular, 354
elliptic, 358
parabolic, 355

DALETSKY, Yu. L., 132, 136, 138
defect, 618
dependence on parameters, 90–98, 638–642
determinant, 8
infinite, 202, 364
Vandermonde, 140
Wronskian, 179–181, 487
difference equation
for Bessel functions, 320
for Legendre functions, 317
mixed differential, 25, 27
difference set, 130
differential equations, 25–27
adjoint, 391

Bernoulli, 674
Bessel, 90, 319–330, 611–613
binomial, 674–684
Briot-Bouquet, 684–693
confluent hypergeometric, 90, 344–357, 619–620
diffusion, 384
Euler, 147
Halm, 357
Hermite-Weber, 354–357, 613–617
Hill, 364
hyper-Bessel, 97
hypergeometric, 91, 240–246, 291–307, 609–610
Kolmogoroff, 158
Legendre, 307–319, 610–611
Mathieu, 358–370, 620–622
self-adjoint, 340, 378
Thomas-Fermi, 42
Titchmarsh, 617–619
wave, 384
differential inequality, 20, 98
DIRICHLET, P. G. L.
-Mehler integral, 317
domain, 99, 102, 125
DOOB, J. L., 174
DUNFORD, N., 426, 573, 712

eigen-function, -value, 385
element, 3
divisor of zero, 108
Hermitian, 566
idempotent, 108
inverse, 106
lineal, 42
negative, 3, 110
neutral, 3
nilpotent, 108
positive, 4, 110, 486
quasi-nilpotent, 108
real symmetric, 110
regular, 106
singular, 106
unit, 106
unitary, 482
entire functions, 92
order, type, 92
equations
characteristic of
linear differential equation, 139
matrix, 9
differential—*see* Differential equations
discriminant, 678
integral
Fredholm-Schmidt, 413
Volterra, 14
equicontinuity, 21
ERDÉLYI, A., 371, 712
ETGEN, G. J., 491, 493
tangent function, 491, 493
EULER, L., 319, 435
equation, 147
transformation, 303
existence theorems, 26, 28, 31, 33, 40, 46, 50, 56
expansion problems, 407–425
extension of operator, 100

FABRY, E., 203, 208
subnormal series, 203
factors, determining, 203
FERMI, E.
Thomas-Fermi equation, 42
fixed point theorems, 10–15
Banach, 11
Volterra, 13
fixed point method, 27–32
FLOQUET, G., 360, 371
theorem, 360
fluxional equations, 48
focus, 627
FOGUEL, S. R., 134, 138
FOURIER, J., 33, 319
coefficients, expansion, 313
FRÉCHET, M.
analyticity, 128, 215
differentials, 128
FROBENIUS, G., 125, 182, 184, 208, 234
method of, 234–239
-Wedderburn norm, 482
FUCHS, L., 182, 208, 248, 677, 693, 710
Fuchsian class, 190, 191, 239–250
FUCHS, R., 697, 710

functions,
  algebroid, 203
  argument, 476–478, 480
  automorphic, 650
  Bessel, 90, 257, 319–330
  circular, 63–66
  contiguous, 306
  cylinder, 354, 355, 358
  elliptic, 66–75, 688–693
  Hermite-Weber, 354–357, 613–617
  hypergeometric, 70, 72, 91, 240–246, 291–307
  hyperlogarithm, 248
  Legendre, 307–319, 610–611
  Mathieu, 358–370, 620–622
  modular, 694
  Painlevé, 697–709
  spectral, 512
  Titchmarsh, 617–619
functional, 101–102
  analysis, 99–105
  inequalities, 15–20, 97, 98
  linear, 105
    multiplicative, 105, 122–123
  multiplicative, 215
fundamental
  solution matrix, 182
  system, 181

GAMBIER, B., 695, 697, 710
GAMLEN, J. L. B., 109
GANTMACHER, F. R., 175, 206, 712
GARNIER, R., 576, 696, 710
GAUSS, C. F., 291, 306
GELFAND, I. M., 574
  representation theorem, 119–124
  spectral mapping theorem, 128
    fine structure, 129
  spectral radius, 108
generating function
  of Bessel functions, 321
  of Legendre polynomials, 316
genus, 693
GLAZMAN, I. M., 566, 574, 711
grade, 199
GREEN, G., 409
  function, 409, 556
  transform, 365, 447, 495, 582
    Beesack's variant, 588
    Robertson's variant, 660
    use of, 598–609
GRONWALL, T. H., 19, 24, 80
  area theorem, 655
  lemma, 19
group
  Abelian, 3
  anharmonic, 243
  of differential equation, 219
  of monodromy, 217–222
  of regular elements, 106
  projective, 649
growth properties on the real line, 437–447
GUDERMANN, C., 67

HALANAY, 80, 98
HALM, J.
  equation, 357, 371
Hamiltonian, 480
HANKEL, H.
  Bessel functions of third kind, 324
  integral, 253
harmonics
  conical, spherical, zonal, 315
HARTMAN, P., 426, 492, 712
HAYMAN, W. K., 710, 712
HELLY, E., 514
  theorem, 514, 538
HELSON, H., 272
HERMITE, C., 354
  -Weber equation, 354
  Hermitian form, 533
HILB, E., 208, 712
HILL, G. W., 364, 372
HILLE, E., 23, 75, 174, 208, 272, 371, 372, 492, 576, 587, 620, 638, 642, 643, 644, 661, 710, 712
HORN, J., 206, 208, 209, 271, 710, 712
HOWE, A., 480, 493
HUKUHARA, M., 206, 209
HURWITZ, A., 576, 603, 643
hypergeometric functions, 240–246, 291–307, 609–610
hyperlogarithm, 248

ideals, 119
implicit function theorem, 14
INCE, E. L., 288, 371, 426, 642, 697, 710, 712
independence, linear, 3
indicatrices, 577, 581
asymptotic integration and, 624–638
inequalities, functional, 15–20, 97–98
absurd, determinative, restrictive, trivial, 15
inflection locus, 636
influence
domain of, 600
line of, 599
standard path, 602
initial conditions, 26
variation of, 76–85
initial parameter, 638
integral
curves, 43
equations, 14, 413
first, 705
Hankel, 253
representing hypergeometric functions, 303–305, 307
interlacing of zeros, 374
involution, 110
isomorphism, 9

JACOBI, C. G. J., 66, 690
elliptic functions, 66–75, 688–690
Jacobian matrix, 77
JACOBSON, N., 109
JAKUBOVIČ, V. A., 480, 493

KAMKE, E., 59, 371, 426, 712
KATO, T., 182
Kegelfunktion, 315
KELLOGG, O. D., 32, 62
KLEIN, F., 643, 650, 712
KNESER, A., 461
comparison theorems, 461, 462, 492
KNESER, H., 155, 175, 185, 192, 208
lemma, 198
method of, 192–198
KOCH, H. von, 200, 209, 364, 372
infinite determinants, 364
KOCH, R. M., 573
KODAIRA, K., 566, 574
KOLMOGOROFF, A. N.
equations, matrix, 158
Kugelfunktion, 315
KUMMER, E., 243, 291, 296, 345
principle, 292

LAGRANGE, J. L., 319
identity, 391
LAGUERRE, E.
polynomials, 352
LANGER, R. E., 566, 574
LAPLACE, P. S.
transformation, 204
LAPPO-DANILEVSKY, J. A., 138, 189, 208, 248, 250, 712
representation theorem, 249
LEFSCHETZ, S., 712
LEGENDRE, A. M.
equation, 181, 307–319, 610–611
functions 1st and 2nd kind, 315
polynomials, 311
generating function, 316
series, 313
LEVIN, J. J., 288
LEVINSON, N., 59, 168, 175, 208, 426, 502, 573, 711
LEVITAN, B. M., 574
limit-circle, limit point, 494–505
LINDELÖF, E., 48, 62
Cauchy-Lindelöf method, 48–57
majorant, 50
Phragmén-Lindelöf theorem, 511
LIOUVILLE, J., 373
transformation, 203, 340
371, 443–445, 624–636
LIPSCHITZ, R., 42, 62, 319
Cauchy-Lipschitz-Peano method, 42–48
condition, 6
inequality, 15, 16
LORCH, L., 380, 427
LOY, R., 109
LYAPUNOV, A., 209, 446, 492

MCLACHLAN, N. W., 371, 712
MAGNUS, W., 371, 712

MAHLER, K., 75
majorant, 48, 54
  Cauchy's, 55
  Lindelöf's, 50
MALMQUIST, J.
  theorem, 671, 710
Mappings, 6–10
  bounded, 6
  fixed points of, 10
  inverse, 7
  linear, 6
  onto, 6
  (1, 1), 6
MARČENKO, V. A., 574, 575
MASANI, P., 206, 209
MASSERA, J. L., 272, 712
MATELL, M., 204, 209
MATHIEU, E. L., 358
  equation, 358–370, 377, 620–622
  functions, 366
matrices, 8
  characteristic equation, 9
  infinite, 157–164, 364
  initial, 178
  inverse, 8
  Kolmogoroff, 158
  product, 9
  regular, 9
  Riccati equation, 283–288
  singular, 9
  sum, 8
  symplectic, 478–480
  trace, 180
  unitary, 10
measure (σ-), 532
Mehler-Dirichlet integral, 317
MELLIN, H., 306
methods of
  Cauchy-Lindelöf, 48–57
  Cauchy-Lipschitz-Peano, 42–48
  Courant-Hilbert, 425–426
  H. Kneser, 192–198
  H. Prüfer, 394–407
  Sturm, 375–384
  successive approximations, 32–42
  Titchmarsh, 425–426
MILLER, J. B., 257, 264, 272
  asymptotic representation theorem, 271
minimax problem, 199
MITTAG-LEFFLER, G.
  star, 211
  theorem, 512
modulus, 66
  complementary, 66
  of continuity, 23
monodromy group, 217–222
MORSE, M., 493, 712
motion
  almost uniform, 428–437
  equations of, 578–579
  Hamiltonian, 480
  of zeros and extrema, 615, 641
  rectilinear, 374
  spiral, 447–456, 477
multiplication
  of elements, 3
  scalar, 3

NAǏMARK, M. A., 426, 575, 712
NAGUMO, M., 16, 58, 62, 116
  inequality, 16
  uniqueness theorem, 58
natural boundaries, 694
NEHARI, Z., 576, 587, 590, 592, 593, 643, 655, 657, 661
NEUMANN, C., 319, 328
  series, 93
NEUMANN, F., 316
NEVANLINNA, R., 510
  characteristic, 510
  defect, 618
  Riemann surface theorem, 657, 661
NEWTON, Sir Isaac, 33
NIRENBERG, L., 272
node, 627
non-oscillation
  abstract, 486–491
  classical, 456–472
  necessary condition, 459
norm, 4–5
  Euclidean, 4
  Lebesgue, 104
  of linear operator, 100

norm—*continued*
of matrix, 9, 482
sup, 5

OBERHETTINGER, F., 371, 712
order of
differential equation, 25
elliptic function, 692
entire function, 92
ordering, partial, 4
of zeros and extrema, 606–608
orientation, 218
orthogonal system, 311
complete, 313
orthonormal expansion, 313
oscillation theory, 373–384, 472–479
oscillator, harmonic, 374
OSGOOD, W. F., 17, 59, 62
inequality, 17
uniqueness theorem, 59

PAINLEVÉ, P., 662, 664, 695, 710, 711, 712
α-method, 696
theorem, 664, 667
transcendents, 693–709
parameter
asymptotic, 638
expansion in powers of, 94
external, 638
initial, 599
internal, 638
Parseval's formula, 315
PEANO, G., 42, 62, 80, 98
Cauchy-Lipschitz-Peano method, 42–48
PERRON, O., 200, 209
PHILLIPS, R. S., 102, 138, 174, 712
PHRAGMÉN, E., 511
-Lindelöf theorem, 511
PICARD, E., 33, 61, 62, 695, 710
method of successive approximations, 32–42
theorem, 202
PICONE, M., 378
POCHHAMMER, L., 92, 326
POINCARÉ, H., 96, 98, 125, 168, 204, 206, 209, 248, 693, 710, 712
asymptotic series, 202, 326
automorphic functions, 650
point
focal, 627
irregular singular, 198–207
regular singular, 182–198
star, 626
point spectrum, 118, 520
POKORNY, V. V., 587, 593, 644, 657, 661
PÓLYA, G., 419, 427, 712
polynomials
Hermite, 355
Laguarre, 352
Legendre, 311
prime ring, 109
principle of
Kummer, 292
the maximum, 103
variation, 641
product
inner, 9, 412, 533
of elements, 105
projection, 109
PRÜFER, H., 373, 394, 427
Prüfer's method, 394–407, 472–486
Barrett's generalization, 481–486

radius, spectral, 108
rank, 199, 204
reciprocal gamma function, 253
Hankel's integral, 253
region
cuspidal, 627
of 1st kind, 631
of 2nd kind, 632
elliptical, 627
focal, 627
hyperbolic, 625
principal, 628
radial, 626, 634
vortical, 626, 635
REID, W. T., 288, 493
residue class, 119–120
resolution of identity, 119
resolvent, 112–118
equations, 113
of differential operator, 416, 556–565

set, 112
square root of, 288
summability, 407, 422, 426
REUTER, G. E. H., 161
RICCATI, J. F., 273
equation, 273–288
asymptotics of solutions, 464–472
classical, 273–277, 456–472, 670–672
matrix case, 283–288
star algebra case, 487–491
RICKART, C. E., 138, 493, 713
RIEMANN, B., 291
ROBERTSON, M. S., 659–661
modified Green's transform, 660
theorem, 660
ROUCHÉ, E.
theorem, 337

SAATY, T. L., 24
saddle point, 625–626
SAUVAGE, L., 185, 208
SCHÄFFER, J. J., 272, 712
SCHAFHEITLIN, P., 576, 638, 644
SCHLESINGER, L., 189, 208, 709, 713
SCHLÖMILCH, O., 319, 322, 328
SCHMIDT, E., 413
theorem on symmetric kernels, 413
SCHWARTZ, B., 576, 587, 595, 642, 644
SCHWARTZ, J., 426, 573, 712
SCHWARZ, H. A., 647, 650, 661
mapping of circular polygons, 650–654
principle of symmetry, 652
Schwarzian, 647–661
and univalency, 654–658
SEARS, D. R., 540, 561, 564, 574
sequence
Cauchy, 5
diagonal, 22
subadditive, 107
series
asymptotic, 202
factorial, 204, 207
hypergeometric, 92, 187
Neumann, 93
normal, 202
parametric, 94
subnormal, 203
SHATZ, S. S., 288
solution
constant, 48, 81, 85, 277, 680
dominant, 342
fundamental, 210–217
maximal, 46
minimal, 46
null, 161
singular, 680
subdominant, 342, 439
truncated, 707
spaces
abstract, 3, 99–138
adjoint, 101
B- (Banach), 13, 99
$BV[a, b]$, 104
characteristic, 153
$C[a, b]$, 5
Euclidean, 4
$\mathfrak{E}(\mathfrak{X})$, 7
$\mathfrak{E}(\mathfrak{X}, \mathfrak{Y})$, 6
(l), 30
$L(a, b)$, 103
L_p, 104
(m), 31
$\mathfrak{M}_n$, 8
metric, 4–6
complete, 5
null, 99
root, 153
vector, 3
normed linear, 4
spectrum
continuous, point, residual, 118
mapping theorem, 128
fine structure, 129
of differential operator, 385, 518–531
star
domain, 177
Mittag-Leffler, 211
point, 626
zero-free, 581
STERNBERG, W., 209
STOKES, G. G.
phenomenon, 203

STONE, M. H., 426, 573, 713
strong derivative, 30
STURM, C., 373, 375, 379, 384, 398, 427
  comparison theorem, 375
  -Liouville theory, 373–427
  monotonicity theorem, 379
SZEGÖ, G., 419, 427, 623, 643, 712, 713
SZEGO, P., 427
  Lorch-Szego monotonicity theorem, 380

TAAM, C. T., 576, 587, 588, 598, 644
TAMARKIN, J. D., 426, 427
tangent locus, 583, 637
THOMAS, L. H.
  -Fermi equation, 42
THOMÉ, L. W., 202, 209
  normal series, 202
TITCHMARSH, E. C., 425, 426, 527, 531, 553, 573, 713
  functions, 617–619
TRICOMI, F., 75, 371, 712, 713
TRJITZINSKY, W. J., 204, 209
transformation
  bounded, 6
  Euler, 303
  inverse, 7
  Laplace, 204, 251, 258
  linear, 6, 99–101
  Liouville, 340
  unitary, 532–540
TURRETTIN, H. L., 206, 209

uniqueness theorems, 27, 28, 31, 33, 40, 50, 56, 58–62
unitary transformations, 532–540
univalency, 587, 594, 595, 598
  of solution of $y'' + Py = 0$, 659–661
  Schwarzian, 654–659

VAN VLECK, E. B., 576, 644
variation
  bounded, total, 104
  of data, 76–98
  of equation, 85–90
  of initial point, 81–85
  of initial vector, 76–81
  of parameters, 147
    constants formula, 151
  variational system, 78
vector, 3
  characteristic, 9
  column, row, 10
  derivative of, 26
  differential equation, 26
  independence, 3
  initial, 27
  integral of, 28
  orthogonal, 9
  space, 3
VOLTERRA, V., 12
  equation, 13
  fixed point theorem, 13
vortex, 626

WALTER, W., 24, 713
WATSON, G. N., 319, 370, 371, 713
  transform, 539
WEBER, H., 354
  Hermite-Weber functions, 354
WEDDERBURN, J. H. M.
  Frobenius-Wedderburn norm, 482
WEIERSTRASS, K.
  approximation theorem, 315
  Bolzano-Weierstrass theorem, 5
  $\wp$-function, 688–691
    equiharmonic, 690
weight, 692
WEYL, H., 373, 428, 492, 525, 526, 527, 531, 567
WHITTAKER, E. T., 370, 713
WHYBURN, W. M., 288, 493
WIDDER, D. V., 514
WIMAN, A., 204, 472, 493
winding number, 218
WINTNER, A., 428, 492
WITTICH, H., 708, 709, 713
WRONSKI, H., 179
  Wronskian, 179, 487

YOSIDA, K., 426, 672, 713